Historical Map
Of The State Of
Washington

BUILDING
WASHINGTON

A History of Washington State Public Works

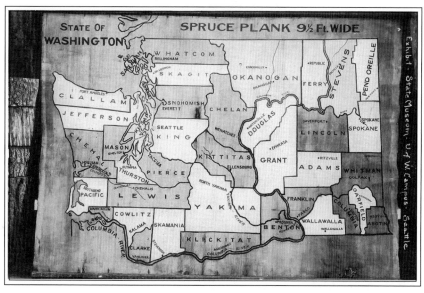

Paul Dorpat *and* Genevieve McCoy

Building Washington

is dedicated to

Richard Berner

———•———

Robert Burke

———•———

Murray Morgan

———•———

Rosa Morgan

———•———

Roy E. Morse

———•———

And the thousands of men and women who have helped build or maintain
public works projects and programs throughout Washington State.

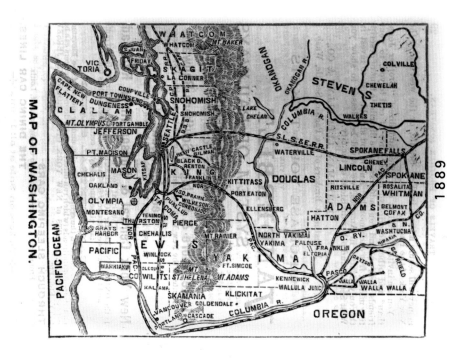

The Sponsors Edition of *Building Washington* was written and produced by its authors
with the support and encouragement of the Washington Chapter of the American Public Works Association.

It is hoped that readers will use the book to enrich their study of Washington State and public works history,
and will respond regarding the contents of the book directly to the authors at

Tartu Publications
P.O. Box 85208
Seattle Washington 98145

Reviews, corrections, and criticisms are welcome
on the chance that a second edition will be published.

CONTENTS

SPONSORS EDITION

INTRODUCTION

For its authors, *Building Washington* began in 1986 when we were asked by members of the Washington Chapter of the American Public Works Association (APWA) to write a history of the state's public works. The book was to be the chapter's contribution to the state 1989 centennial. Well into Washington's second century, memories of those intentions of 1986 and also of the missed ceremonies of 1989 faded like a canvas left in the sun. Instead, the feelings of 1998 were an alloy of relief and excitement as we prepared to deliver *Building Washington* to the presses. And here in place of ceremony you hold a book that was ten years in the making — a well-studied exploration of public works in Washington State and an unprecedented exhibition of many of the state's historical landmarks.

It was Jan Klippert, Community Relations Manager for King County Public Works and engineering consultant Dick Warren who shared the original vision. And it is they who have continued to both nurture and protect it. Their first "word of advice" to the authors was the example of another book, the *History of Public Works in the United States* published by the APWA for the 1976 U.S. bicentennial. The subjects and priorities of this federal history have helped us considerably in determining our own chapters. So has *Building Canada,* the book from which we effortlessly took our title.

Fancifully comparing the shelf space of our research to the dimensions of one of our subjects, the boxes and cabinets containing a decade's accumulation of notes, clippings, photocopies, and drafts could be stacked as high as the administration building at the Lake Washington Ship Canal's Chittenden Locks. Or these ephemera could be laid as wide as the small lock itself. That we also required three years more to conclude *Building Washington* than were needed by Col. Chittenden to build the canal sets in higher relief our rendering of the historian's conventional paradox: we did so much to do so little. This book is only a beginning exploration into the oversized subject of Washington public works and public workers. Many subjects are left out. Although it is larger than either of its models — the U.S. and Canadian histories – the book is yet much smaller even than the subjects that are included deserve.

The responsibility of choosing among the thousands of noteworthy public works undertaken in this "northwest corner" since its settlement has been a difficult one. Our first choices were guided in part by a series of meetings held around the state in 1987 and 1988. In Bellingham, Tacoma, Vancouver, Yakima, Spokane, Port Townsend, Port Angeles, Olympia, Grays Harbor, Tri-Cities, Walla Walla, Bremerton, Everett, Bellevue, and Anacortes public workers, consultants, and historians shared their opinions of what were the most important or representative public works in their counties and communities.

On the whole, we feel that we have chosen our subjects well. For their stories we have often had to search original sources because there existed either little or no secondary material. Now with *Building Washington* these subjects are, at last, recovered and still described in one accessible source, however, we have surely missed important subjects and made mistakes.

The authors, both of whom live in Wallingford, a Seattle neighborhood conveniently close to the University of Washington libraries, have attempted to transcend any Pugetopolis bias. Many of Washington's historic smaller communities like Pomeroy, Republic, and Index will be found here, usually represented by some landmark bridge, courthouse, or other notable work within or nearby their borders. The state's biggest public works were constructed beside its "River of the West," the Columbia; Grand Coulee Dam and the Hanford Reservation are oversized examples of obligatory subjects. So are Metro and the SeaTac Airport, with or without (still without at this writing) a third runway. Less well know but still keystones to Washington public works history are hundreds of other subjects including the mid-1950s diversion of U.S. Highway 99 from Vancouver's Main Street to a limited-access freeway ditch and Spokane's victorious 1890s courtroom struggle to fund the development of safe and abundant community water using revenue bonds.

Besides credits, this introduction like others will include its disclaimers. Although a score of authorities have read and corrected the drafts for *Building Washington*, the authors take responsibility for all errors, and we encourage all our readers to share their corrections and other suggestions with us. This, we hope, is only the first and limited edition of the book. If the demand for *Building Washington* is sufficient we may print it again, perhaps in a less expensive paperback edition, and will then make corrections and update many of the subjects.

Territorial Governor Isaac I. Stevens in Civil War uniform, ca. 1861.

Above: Washington Territory's seal depicted the Goddess of Hope, who symbolized the pioneers' hopes for "Al-Ki," the Chinook trade-talk term for "by and by." This image was officially recorded by Charles H. Mason, the territory's acting governor. The seal was designed by Lieutenant J.K. Duncan, a member of Territorial Governor Isaac Stevens' expedition to the new territory. Below: The April 23, 1853 issue of The Columbian, *Olympia's tabloid , joyfully announces (left column) the Senate's March 2 passage of the bill forming Washington Territory, but sadly reports (right column) the tardineess of funds appropriated by Congress for the construction of a military road through the Cascade Mountains. All photos this page courtesy, Washington State Archives, Olympia.*

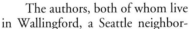

THE COLUMBIAN.

Olympia, Washington Territory.

"It is not always safe or wise
To judge of matters by their size."

Saturday, April 23, 1853.

Washington Territory.----"All's well that ends well."

What we confidently conjectured in our last issue, has been rendered "assurance doubly sure." The Territory of Washington is a fixed fact. The bill organizing the Territory, which passed the House of Representatives on the 10th of February, full details of which we have already published, passed the Senate on the 2d of March, without amendment. Henceforth Northern Oregon has an independent existence, and a destiny to achieve separate and distinct from that of her Southern neighbor. She has been baptised by the Congress of the United States, into a new name—a name glorious, and dear to every American heart. Everywhere, throughout the length and breadth of the Territory, the news will be received with joyful acclamations. At this place, the 25th of April, a day long to be remembered, was devoted to the general joy. Beneath the ample folds of our nations' flag, unfurled to the breeze, the deep mouthed tones of an hundred guns, awakening the echoes of our fair Pacific shores, proclaimed the welcome news.

We are only disposed at present to speed the full career of joyousness so befitting the

Road over the Cascade Mountains.

We regret that the twenty thousand dollars appropriated by Congress at its late session for the construction of a military road from Fort Steilacoom to Walla-walla, will not be expended during this season, and probably not even touched upon before July or August, so that we cannot look for any early benefit therefrom. But we should not despair. The road will be wanted late in the summer, and we can do much towards it if we will only try. What say you, fellow-citizens ? Let us all put our shoulders to the wheel, and amid a general hurrah, make one grand effort in this important matter. Late advices from the States say "an immense throng will cross the plains the present year"—and our word for it, many thousands will come to Washington, *if they can get here.* It is our duty to them to the country and to ourselves to open the way. Let us not by an unjustifiable, aye, criminal inertness, neglect to do everything in our power.

We can raise means enough to perform the heaviest labor necessary on the route, and admit a line of light between the two extremities. The advancing immigrants will do the remainder and make the road passable. To the work, men! Time flies : we have none to lose—all necessary preliminaries should be immediately arranged, and in less than thirty days the work be going on. It is proposed that contributions be made, and we learn that subscription papers are about being put in circulation, whereon our fellow-citizens may inscribe their names.

Editor

" Our table " has the week with a jar from Dr. JOHNSON ; cranberry jelly from with a splendid salm Gentlemen, call :

We return o various Expresses a latest files of Atlant Also to our old and for a profuse suppl: rial papers and mag

Mr. ANDRI cessful agent over a gentleman of ma lights us to perceiv acquaintance. Th favor of our paper, from the disinterest actuated. The NI sends us this week his other requests : tion. We quote fi

" We Vancouve the " belt " on you your agents on th line look out or we
We hope our ag low the example f

On our first Inaugural Message was delivered exte some 40,000 peop forward and sensit

ACKNOWLEDGEMENTS

The help given to this project deserves, besides our thanks, some explanation. We begin again with Dick Warren and Jan Klippert who shared the vision for this book and the confidence to get it started. King County Public Works and its director Paul Tanaka's encouragement of Jan Klippert's diplomatic go-between, helped the authors make connections with counties, municipalities and their public workers. A number of other members of the APWA's Washington Chapter should also be noted for participating in the project's earliest meetings, helping collect illustrations for this history, and reading its chapters. To name a few: Roy Peterson, Vic Sparling, Gene McMaster, Dave Hudson, Dennis Devries, Gordon Johnson, Larry Southwick, Frank Hansche, Ken Lowthian, John Mayo, Ray Einigel, and Roy Morse.

Jan Klippert and Dick Warren, American Public Works Association Washington Chapter members, stand beside Roy Morse, one of Building Washington's five dedicatees.

Many others have assisted us in a research project that was both complex and protracted. Early help came from Dave Osterberg, and Joan Specking. Later Mark Vacarro, John Hall, John Crawford, Laura Vanderpool, Clark Gilman, and Greg Lange helped with research on a variety of subjects. Laura Lewis helped with the book's earliest design including the sponsor section that concludes this first edition. More recently, Van Diep has helped fine-tune the book chapters as well as scan and place its hundreds of illustrations. No one but the authors, however, can be blamed for the packed quality of these pages. The urge to fill this vessel to the brim was ours.

Lane Morgan, the editor, improved the clarity of the writing and set the standards for the textural style of the book. Lane's father, Murray Morgan — certainly the dean of Northwest historians — was one of our many expert readers. Paul Spitzer, Ken Billington, Bob Burke, Keith Murray, Robert Hennes, Michael Green, P.C. Pitzer, and Ted Van Arsdol also examined various chapters. For all of their criticisms and corrections we are most grateful.

Many public works departments, libraries, and archives in municipalities of every size have helped build *Building Washington*. Michael Saunders and Phillipa Stairs at the Washington State Archives in Bellevue (formerly in Burien), and Dave Hastings, the Chief of Archival Services in Olympia, have been of great assistance with photographs, original documents, and other materials from state collections. It was Hastings who introduced us

to the decorated state map printed on the inside covers. Susan Karren and Joyce Justice at the National Archive and Records Administration Pacific Alaska Region guided us through their considerable store of photography and ephemera for federal projects in the state. Many of the illustrations for chapters on waterways, airways, public buildings, flood control, and irrigation appear with their imprimatur.

The libraries at practically all of the state institutions of higher learning assisted us. About a five-minute bike ride from the authors' desks, the University of Washington's several libraries and archives have been a recurring amenity — especially the Northwest Collection and the libraries for engineering and government publications. We give repeated thanks there to Richard Engeman, Carla Rickerson, Sandy Kroupa, Chris Kinsey, Gary Menges, Lisa Scharnhorst, and Andrew Johnson. Lawrence R. Stark and Carol Lichtenberg of Washington State University Archives and Special Collections opened their considerable collections to share sources and illustrations for this book. Thanks also to Bruce Harding who helped with this research in Pullman. A number of useful materials were also received from WSU's water research division. In Bellingham, our gratitude goes to Virginia Beck at Western Washington University library and in Cheney to Chas V. Mutschler at Eastern Washington State University.

Before he retired Harold Garrett, the state Department of Transportation's public relations director/historian, gave substantial and enthusiastic aid to the book. And many other DOT workers have also helped with the chapters on highways and bridges including Clariss Lundeen, Jennifer Marty, Elizabeth Robbins, Mazen Mahmoud, Mark Mason and Denton Vander Poel. Mason assumed Vander Poel's responsibilities as photographer for DOT's Northwest Region after the latter's untimely death in 1996. We will remember Denton's gracious help. Most of our historical ferry material came from Jim Faber, author of *Steamers Wake*, another friend of this public works project who has, unfortunately, passed on.

The Bonneville Power Administration, the Bureau of Reclamation, and the Army Corps of Engineers were the federal agencies of greatest relevance to this history. Representatives for each have given us generous assistance. For the parts played by the Army Corps of Engineers in the building of the state's public works we received help from Forest Brooks, Steve Johnson, and many others. We were also fortunate that historian Robert E. Ficken shared with us a manuscript copy of his history of the Corp's Seattle office. Francis Jensen, recently retired public relations officer for the Department of Reclamation's Ephrata headquar-

Right: Telegraph to the last territorial governor, Elisha P. Ferry, announcing the Washington State proclamation. Courtesy, Washington State Archives, Olympia.

ters, gave substantially of his time in searching for historical photographs of the Columbia Basin Irrigation Project. Nick Christmas III, photo archivist for the Bonneville Power Administration, was able to find nearly all of the illustrations we requested for our narrative of BPA history. For information and imagery on the history of Washington State's Public Utility Districts, we thank both Sarah Driggs and Ken Billington.

Many of the state's municipal libraries have departments dedicated to the study and preservation of community history. With only those few exceptions where slack funding curtailed the capacity to lend help with research, these institutions have come to our aid when asked. Naming only a few, our thanks go to Nancy Compau of the Spokane Public Library's Northwest room, and Janet Arkills of Spokane's South Hill Branch Library. Brian Kamens and Judith Kipp of the Tacoma Public Library found illustrations for many of the Pierce County subjects. We join our appreciation with many others who have been assisted by Margaret Riddle and David Dilgard, historians for the Everett Public Library. The effectiveness of their work is known well beyond the borders of Snohomish County.

With our earliest research we posted letters requesting advice from most of the state's many heritage groups. Both the percentage and quality of their response was high and they suggested several of the book's subjects. We borrowed some of the first illustrations chosen for the book from the Washington State Historical Society's Asahel Curtis collection in Tacoma. In Seattle, we thank librarians Carolyn Marr, Howard Giske, Ralph Lang, Mary Montgomery, and Rick Caldwell of the Museum of History and Industry. Of MOHAI resources, the *Post-Intelligencer* collection — named for Seattle's oldest daily newspaper — was often uncannily relevant to many of our rarer subjects. Many other heritage groups also gave us aid and comfort. A short list includes the Whatcom Museum, the Issaquah Historical Society, the Washington State Museum, the Renton Historical Society, the Anacortes Museum, the Mason

Above: While Aunt Columbia smells the flowers and Uncle Sam applauds, the cherubic Washington waves the banner of its "Chief City" in the Eshelman-Llewellyn Investment Company's imagined monument of their new state's donations to building America. Courtesy, University of Washington Libraries, Special Collections.

County Historical Society, the Snohomish County Museum, the Marymoor Museum, the Maryhill Museum, the Bellevue Historical Society, the North Central Washington Museum, the Museum of Flight, the Kitsap Museum and their historical society's prolific heritage activist and author, Fredi Perry.

The municipal archives in the public works departments of Seattle, Tacoma, Spokane and many other Washington cities also do important preservation work. We are especially thankful to Scott Kline and Ernie Dornfeld who in a few years have done much to make the Seattle Municipal Archives a valued resource for both city departments and historians. Nick Cirelli, Seattle Engineering Department photographer, has also given kind assistance to this production. Edwina Carlson, Brad Bogue and Barbara Werelius with Tacoma Utilities have been helpful, especially with photographs of that community's unique public works story. Duane Scroggins of Walla Walla, James Hudak of Pullman, Dave Mandyke of Spokane, Lloyd Berry of Chelan County, Ernest Geissler of the County Road Administration Board, Jack Pittis of Port Angeles, and Gerald Weed of Snohomish County are all public workers who helped with the making of *Building Washington*. Paul Chilcote, formerly with the Port of Seattle and now the Port of Tacoma, helped us with historical images of both ports and was a critical reader of our chapter on state waterways.

For its illustrations *Building Washington* has been dependent upon the interest and generosity of many collectors, antiquarians and dealers in historical photographs and ephemera. We will name a few: Dan

Left: Bothell students smoothing the streets of their community for "Good Roads Day," May 29, 1914. Courtesy, Bothell Historical Museum.

Kerlee, Michael Maslan, John Hanawalt, Michael Fairley, Bill Greer, John Cooper, William Mix, Warren Wing, and Lawton Gowey. Lawton Gowey died soon after his retirement as accountant for the Seattle Water Department, and a short time before work began on the book. This generous friend's sharing of his knowledge and considerable collection on Northwest transit history enlivens our chapter on Streets and Mass Transportation. Another employee of the Seattle Water Department, Nancy Ishii, identified and organized the thousands of negatives left in the estate of the author-photographer Hugh Paradise. Paradise's beat for *Sunset Magazine* was the back road destinations of the Northwest about which he often wrote poetically. Many of Paradise's images are used in *Building Washington* and we thank Byron Coney for introducing us to them. Thanks also to the memory of Galen Biery, for his own photography as well as his collection of historical photographs of Whatcom County. Since deceased, Galen's guidance, given through the pain of the illness that eventually took him, was a blend of graciousness and courage.

We also wish to make special note of the contemporary photographers who believed in the value of this project sufficiently to generously lend and often take original photographs for it. Included here are Dan Leen, Nancy Ishii, Ron Kesler, Abigail Harris, Miguel Edwards, George White, and Cathy Gilmer statewide; John Stamets and Frank Shaw in Seattle; Clark Gilman in Olympia, Mark Cutler in Bellingham, James Arrabito in Everett, Tom Heckler and Jack Arkills in Spokane, Holly Mayshark in Port Townsend, Ted Van Arsdol in Vancouver, Don Wilson with the Port of Seattle, and William Jones in Aberdeen. Jones Photography is a family firm that has been recording Grays Harbor subjects since pioneer days. William Jones shared with us many of this studio's historical images. Mary Randlett photographed a number of the works of public art that conclude the chapter on Public Buildings. In addition to her nature photography, Randlett's portraits of northwest authors and artists and their work is both well know and collected. We thank them all. (The contemporary photographs recorded by the authors are generally not credited. The few uncredited contemporary photographs that are the work of others are yet to be printed in the hope that their identity will come forth in time for the book's second edition.)

GOVERNOR ROSELLINI'S NEW FOUR-YEAR PROGRAM

SCHOOLS Increase education's share of the general fund. Expand community college, vocational and academic programs.

OUTDOOR RECREATION Enact Governor's program to buy and develop new public camping, hiking, boating, hunting, fishing areas.

JOBS Replace decreasing defense contracts by attracting and expanding diversified industries. Step up public works.

NUCLEAR INDUSTRY Provide further aggressive state efforts to develop nuclear industry and research by private business.

TAX CREDIT PLAN Encourage industry to expand and create more jobs through B. & O. tax credit on new construction.

BENEFIT BUILDING PLAN Enact Governor's Benefit District Plan to build cross-Sound bridges, Naches Tunnel, improve ferry system and reduce rates.

AGRICULTURE Push great Columbia Basin Project to completion. Assist farm groups to solve marketing and transportation problems so family farms can survive.

RIVER NAVIGATION Develop Federal-State plan to build Puget Sound-Columbia River Canal and make the Columbia navigable through Central Washington.

YOUTH Expand State Youth Corps and job training programs already begun by the Rosellini administration.

SENIOR CITIZENS Promote adequate medical care and housing, including limited property tax exemptions.

ELECTION REFORMS Push for law requiring compulsory disclosure of campaign contributions and expenditures.

SOCIAL PROGRESS Expand community level treatment of mental illness, retardation, alcoholism and juvenile delinquency.

Re-elect Albert D. ROSELLINI

Democrat

Committee to Re-elect Rosellini Governor
Stanly Donogh, Ed Weston, Joe Lux, Co-chairmen, 1110 Third Ave., Seattle

Above: From the evidence of his 1960 re-election campaign, Gov. Albert D. Rosellini emphasized public works. Included among those which have, so far, been too big to build were cross-Puget Sound bridges, a highway tunnel under the Cascade Mountains (the Naches Tunnel), and a canal connecting the Columbia River to Puget Sound through Willapa Bay and Grays Harbor. Some of the governor's other labors were lighter, like the ceremonial meeting each year of the new Miss Washington (below left). Photos courtesy Department of Transportation.

A number of other persons deserve specials thanks, including Maynard Eash, Roger James, Laura Arksey, and Mike Kobluk in Spokane, Ginny Butler in Dayton, Travis Skallman in Blaine, Bob Weatherly in Asotin, Bill Layman in Wenatchee, Larry Dodd and Robert Bennett in Walla Walla, JoAnn Hardee Collinge and Craig Garcia in Bellingham, Rufus Woods Jr. in Wenatchee, Noreen Robinson in Ilwaco, Rod Slemmons and Charles Peyton in Seattle, and Richard Slagle in Republic. Help about and from Anacortes perhaps inevitably goes through Wally Funk, that community's long-time journalist and historian. Sequim resident and community historian Harriet Fish plays a role for the north slopes of the Olympic Peninsula similar to that of Fredi Perry in Kitsap County. We also wish to make notice of the assistance given us by Otto Goldschmid and Billie Howard in Shelton, Barbara Collins in Pullman, Kari Black in Everett, Eunice Darvall in LaConner, Irma Gfeller in Lind, Margaret Wolf in Pomeroy, and Ted Van Arsdol. Historian-journalist Ted Van Arsdol has done a lot of reporting in both the Tri Cities area and Vancouver. From the start of this project, no community historian has been of greater aid than he. Again, we thank them all.

DEDICATION

The publishing of a new book offers the authors the pleasure of dedication. We have chosen a quintet of archivists and historians for our dedication.

Recently deceased, University of Washington History Professor Emeritus **Robert Burke** was both a preeminent historian and the inspiring teacher who mentored more Northwest historians than perhaps anyone in the history of the region. For twenty-eight years, Professor Burke was also editor for the scholarly *Pacific Northwest Quarterly.*

As the founder of the University of Washington Archives and Manuscripts Division, **Richard Berner**'s contribution to northwest history will continue to help scholars as long as the "University of A Thousand Years" survives. Since his retirement in 1984, Richard Berner has taken to authoring a history of the first half of the twentieth century in Seattle. At this writing, he has recently completed the third and last volume of this important addition to the canon of regional history.

Murray Morgan's contribution to Washington State history is well known and beloved with titles like *The Dam, The Northwest Corner, Skid Road, The Last Wilderness, Over Washington,* and *South on the Sound.* Although this last is the only one of these popular works which notes **Rosa Morgan** as co-author with her husband, she has been vitally involved with research and critical readings in their entire opera.

Roy W. Morse's influence on regional public works extends well beyond his time as Seattle City Engineer. Besides his role in the founding of the Washington Chapter of the American Public Works Association (APWA), Roy Morse has also served as president of both the APWA and the Public Works Historical Society. Morse is respected for a long career that includes his generous role as mentor to young engineers, many of whom became leaders in the engineering community and public works directors of state municipalities.

For these outstanding contributions, it is to Roy W. Morse, Rosa Morgan, Murray Morgan, Richard Berner, and Robert Burke that we dedicate *Building Washington.*

Finally, before listing alphabetically the roll call of persons who have helped build *Building Washington,* we need to thank the sponsors of this first edition. Without the substantial assistance of the persons, municipalities, businesses, and institutions for whom brief histories are included in the concluding section, a book of this size would have been difficult to undertake. Consequently, it is fair to call *Building Washington's* first edition its "Sponsors Edition." Further reason to hope for another edition is the opportunity to thank those whom we have neglected to include in these acknowledgments, as well as to correct the spelling of names we may have abused here.

Seattle Department of Public Works archive, ca. 1935. Courtesy, Seattle Municipal Archives.

ROLL CALL OF THANKS

Jon T. Aarstad	Dick Bakken	Owen Boe	Russell Cahill	Steve Cook
Ned Ahrens	Harold Balasz	Andriette Boersema-	David Cameron	Ann Cook
James Ajax	Byron Barber	Pieron	Mel Carlson	John Cooper
Jerry Alfendahl	Jim Baremore	Wes Bogard	Edwina Carlson	Jerry Copeland
Roy Allen	Robert Barr	Brad Bogue	Martin Carty	Patricia Cosgrove
Dennis Andersen	Virginia Beck	Tim Boles	LeRoy Chadwick	John Coyne
Dave Anderson	Frederick J. Becker	Rick Bollinger	Bernie Chaplan	Drew Crooks
Albert Anderson	Mark Behler	Gary Bourne	Paul Chilcote	Walter Crowley
Suzanne Anest	Frank Bennet	Mark Bozanich	Mary Christiansen	Frank Currie
Keith Angwin	Robert Bennett	Larry Bray	Nick Christmas III	D.W. Custer
Suzanne Annis	Rich Berner	Ken Brees	Nick Cirelli	Mark Cutler
James Arrabito	Lloyd Berry	Mary Joe Briggs	Dick Clifton	Eunice Darvill
Jack Arkills	Galen Biery	Bob Brittain	Jon Collier	Jeff Davis
Janet Arkills	Larry Biggs	Don Broadsword	JoAnn Hardee Collinge	Irene Davis
Laura Arksey	Ken Billington	Forest Brooks	Barbara Collins	Dwight Davis
Jim Arndt	Bob Bishop	Bill Bugge	Rodney Colvin	David Davis
Mel Avery	Kari Black	Bill Burden	Dennis R. Colvin	Alan Davis
Robert Baer	Lyle Bland	Ginny Butler	Nancy Compau	Dennis Davrees
Ann Bailer	Brad Blegen	Ben Butler	Denise Conner	Jack DeLay

Brewster Denny
Ernie Dornfeld
Claudia Devin
Helen Devine
Van Diep
David Dilgard
Jim Dilonardo
Helen Divine
Larry Dodd
Shirley Dodson
Glenn Dorsey
Lorin Doyle
Harry Drake
Sara Driggs
Edith Duttlinger
Carol Dyer
Gary Eagle
Clay Eals
Maynard Eash
Ray Einigel
Vivian Eldridge
Josie Emmons
Mildred Engels
Richard Engeman
Jean Engerman
Renee Estes
Doug Everhart
Lee Fagan
Michael Fairley
Mary Ferrel
Robert E. Ficken
Maria Fischer
Harriet Fish
Steve Fisher
Anita Fisher
Grace Fisk
Dave Fitzpatrick
James Fletcher
Dave Ford
Ray Fowler
Dave Free
David Freece
Dan Freise
Jack Frissel
Dennis Frommel
Wally Funk
Tim Galleger
Arnie Garborg
Craig Garcia
Sandy Gardner
John Garner
Harold Garrett
Ernest Geissler
Phil George
Betty George
Irma Gfeller
Warren Gilbert
Clark Gilman
Al Gilson
Inez Gingrich
Howard Giske
Otto Goldschmid
Joyce Gonzales
Marlene
    Gorrebeeck

Arvid Grant
Warren Gray
Michael N. Green
Stan Green
Bill Greer
Greg Griffith
Bob Hadlow
John Hall
Wayne Hampton
John Hanawalt
Karna Hanna
Mike Hansen
David Hansen
Frank Hanshe
David Hanson
Bruce Harding
Susan Harris
Dave Harris
Pat Hartle
Wayne Hartman
R.B. Hartman
David Hastings
Steve Hauff
Susan Hayton
Robert Hayton
Bret Heath
Tom Heckler
Peter Heffelfinger
Barry Heid
Jerry Hendricks
Robert G. Hennes
Jack Henry
Don Hertzog
Roy Hewson
Joyce Reed Holley
Paul Hooper
Ken Housden
Billie Howard
James Hudak
Dave Hudson
Dave Hughbanks
Darlene Hunting-
    ton
Nancy Ishii
Ken Jacob
Charles Jahren
Roger James
Francis Jensen
Bill Johnson
Gordon Johnson
Nada Johnson
Ralph W. Johnson
Steve Johnson
Steve Johnston
Pat Jollota
William Jones
Gloria Judd
Joyce Justice
Brian Kamens
Denice Keegan
Nancy Keith
Jerry Kemp
Dan Kerlee
Sue Kienast

Terry Kimpel
Paul King
Judith Kipp
Kenneth Kirkland
Scott Kline
Celeste Kline
Ted Knuth
M. Kobluk
John Komen
Jennifer
    Kuchenbecker
Lenore Lambert
Greg Lange
Stan Lattin
Bill Layman
Ken Leback
Dan Leen
Mark Leth
Ellen Levesque
Carol Lichtenberg
John Light
Louise Lindgren
Marie Little
Kristin Livingston
Jack Locke
Dennis Locke
Enzo Loop
Dennis Lovell
Ken Lowthian
Leon Luck
Clarissa Lundeen
Sue Lundiman
Mazen Mahmoud
Dave Mandyke
Ken Markel
Carolyn Marr
Susan Marshall
Jennifer Marty
Michael Maslan
Mark Mason
Glenn Mason
Susan Maxey
John Mayo
Holly Mayshark
Anne McBride
Marie McCaffrey
Teresa McCoy
John McClelland
Lawrence
    McCurdy
Melissa McGrew
Gene McManus
Tom Mercer
Barbara Mettler
Elaine Miller
William Mix
Carleen Montgom-
    ery
Pam Moore
Mary Moore
Jim Moore
Chuck Moore
Beverly Moore
Robert Moorhead

Murray Morgan
Rosa Morgan
Ed Morrow
Roy Morse
Elaine Moschilli
Marilyn Moses
Don Mosley
Dick Moultrie
Lyle Mumford
Keith A. Murray
Chas. V.
    Mutschler
Chris Nardine
Joy Neal
Don Nelson
Larry Nickel
Gary Nies
Ed Nobel
Don Noel
Ed Nolan
Bob Norton
Noreen O'Brien
Tim O'brian
Clair Oliver
Ron Olsen
Steve Olson
Craig Olson
Pat Osborne
Carol Osborne
Dave Osterberg
John Ostranski
John Ostrowski
Crystal Otoupalik
Phyllis Pack
Robert Paine
Maria Pasqual
Dan Patterson
Don Pauls
Cyndie Payne
Darlene Pearson
Judith Pearson
Joseph Peck
Don Peck
Christine Peck
Helen Perry
Fredi Perry
Brian Person
Teresa Peterson
Roy Peterson
Marion Peterson
Dick Peterson
Mary Pettus
Charles Payton
Shirley Phillips
Deborah Picket
Glenda Pierson
Chip Pierson
Elizabeth Pincha
Jack Pittis
Paul Pitzer
John Plimley
Mary Ellen Pyro
Jim Quiring

Dodie Quist-
    Markey
Mary Randlett
Marjorie
    Rechhardt
Gail Reed
Gary Reese
Tammy Reims
Kay Reinartz
Lee Reins
Jean Rettkowski
Bart Ripp
Margaret Riddle
Leonora Rines
Elizabeth Robbins
Noreen Robinson
Marshall Robinson
Albert Rosellini
Bob Roseth
Nadean Ross
Neena Rouseff
Gary Rowe
Phylis Royce
Ann Rutledge
Jack Sage
Bob Salmon
Bill Saraceno
Jack Sareault
Harold Sargent
Claire Saucier
Lewis Saum
Mike Saunders
Hugh Sazero
Colleen Schafroth
Mike Schultz
Duane Scroggins
Dick Selevold
George Shannafelt
Ehman Sheldon
Jack Shreault
Gerald Shrope Jr.
Dick Siegel
Eileen Simon
Trav Skallman
Richard Slagle
Rod Slemmons
Michelle Smith
Lyton Smith
Doreen Smith
Pat Soden
Lisa Soderberg
Larry Southwick
Vic Sparling
Joan Specking
Paul Spitzer
John Stamets
Lawrence Stark
Alan Stein
Barbara Stenson
Victoria Stepitova
Bill Stewart
Ted Stricklin
Celia Strong
Barbara Sullivan

Damon Taam
Paul Tanaka
Walter A.
    Taubeneck
Tia Tauscher
Eric Taylor
Tom Terrien
Berwyn B. Thomas
Fred Thompson
Harold Thompson
Inez Thompson
Virginia Thomson
Gordon Thorson
Jack Tipton
Marie Tolkins
Gene Tollefson
Jim Tolney
Bob Turner
Ted Van Arsdol
Roger VanOosten
Denton Vander
    Poel
Tim Varney
Wade Vaughn
Sue Veseth
Virginia Vincent
Arlene Wade
Milton Wagy
Jim Walker
Paul Waller
John Walter
Steve Wang
Patricia Wareen
Larry Water
Greg Watson
Bob Weatherly
Gerald Weed
Laura Weller
Barbara Werelius
Bob Wheeler
Netta Whipple
Dennis Whitcher
Kathlene White
Scott Wilburn
Carolyn S.
    Willberg
Keith Williams
Gerry Williams
Don Wilson
Warren Wing
Gary Wingert
John Wiseman
Lisa Woehle
Tim Wood
Wildred Woods
Rufus Woods, Jr.
Wayne Wright
Bill Yee

PUBLIC WORKS OF THE GREAT DEPRESSION

Members of Seattle's Unemployed Citizens League joyfully demand their rights. Courtesy, University of Washington Libraries, Special Collections.

For many, public works is synonymous with the great projects of the 1930s, and public works history, the story of how the PWA and the WPA put bread on the table by hiring the unemployed to rake leaves and build dams. Of the "alphabet soup" of depression-time agencies, the WPA is the best remembered because it was the largest and lasted the longest — long enough also to change names from Works Progress Administration to Work Projects Administration. There were, of course, many other full-cap acronyms — ERA, SERC, CWA, WERA/FERA, NYA, and CCC. But there were also projects neither sufficiently large nor lasting to reduce their names to monumental initials. One Washington State example of the latter, the Resettlement Administration, hired 85 men to clear 141 acres for 60 modest houses on lots big enough also for a cow and garden. The residents were provided with both seeds for their gardens and the tools and instructions to can and preserve the produce they grew. By WPA standards this was a small project but exemplary; for it wrapped the American dream of home ownership in a depression-time coat of self-help subsistence. The site chosen for the building of this pastoral experiment was Longview, a planned community of ambitious dimensions but with acres still vacant long after that company mill town was dedicated in 1923, (See Streets Chapter.)

Completed in 1935 the Longview homesteads could have been used much earlier in rural Washington where agricultural prices began slumping years before the 1929 stock market surprise. In spite of the optimism and opportunism of the 1920s,

This new home welcomes one of sixty families that were part of the Resettlement Administration Project's housing experiment in Longview, Washington. Courtesy, Washington State Archives, Olympia.

Washington's larger communities were increasingly visited by migrant farmers looking for work, while their families camped in car parks or on side streets. For these the Great Depression came early. But for most Washingtonians it fell later, even than the crash on Wall Street, partly because projects begun in the late 1920s building boom continued writing pay checks into 1930. By 1931, however, matters were generally dismal.

Statewide unemployment increased from an estimated seven percent in 1930 to twent-five percent in 1932, and employment in factories declined fifty-five percent between 1929 and 1932. By the fall of 1931 charities, which had traditionally given food and temporary shelter to the unemployed, were overwhelmed by the vast numbers of destitute. The realization that things would not improve came first, of course, to those who most needed relief. Only rarely did it come to politicians or boomers who were more likely to believe the then-popular bromide "good times are just around the corner." Some towns and counties hired a few

unemployed for road and park maintenance, but funds quickly ran out. The unemployed then did the obvious. They organized.

In the summer of 1931 a group of about thirty Seattle men joined to pool work and resources in what is claimed to be the first self-help organization of the Great Depression and thereby a national model. By New Years Day 1932 the swelling membership of the Seattle Unemployed Citizens League (UCL) had cut over 10,000 cords of firewood, harvested eight railroad carloads of surplus potatoes, pears, and apples in Eastern Washington, borrowed fishing boats to catch and preserve 120,000 barrels of fish, and opened eighteen commissaries throughout King County to distribute fuel and food. These new community centers for the "republic of the penniless" also became clearing houses for work exchange and bartering. Nearby the UCL commissaries, tailors, barbers, shoe repairers, and mechanics often established shops where they mainly bartered with members of the League. The League also negotiated with landlords to exchange home and apartment repairs for free rent. In the spring of that year Seattle officials gave permission to grow vegetable gardens on public lands (a practice which was revived in the 1970s with the city's P-Patch-Program). Nearly all of the self-help programs started by the Unemployment Citizens League were continued as government-sponsored programs. Some services were transitional. For instance, former Seattle Mayor Bertha Landes, with some assistance from the city, ran two sewing rooms that repaired and produced clothes for needy children. The cooption of most of these "good works" by government agencies was done at least in part to deflect the UCL's increasingly progressive influence on local politics.

President Herbert Hoover, in the last days of a term made generally dismal by the depression, established the Reconstruction Finance Corporation to assist financial, industrial, and agricultural institutions with loans. However, it was Franklin D. Roosevelt through the famous "100 days" following his 1933 inaugural who steered government's radical turn to battling the Great Depression. The PWA (Public Works Administration, 1933-1941) was one of the first federal agencies

The first Tacoma Narrows Bridge under construction in 1939. Courtesy, Washington State Archives, Olympia.

established to put the unemployed to work. It generally funded larger construction projects. In Washington some of these were the Montesano Post Office, the Colfax sewage treatment plant, the Tacoma Narrows Bridge, the Lake Washington Floating Bridge, the Keyport Naval Torpedo Station Quarters, and the largest public works project in the nation, the Grand Coulee Dam. Consequently, PWA projects often involved considerable engineering by skilled workers and the delivery of construction materials to remote sites. With these larger projects quick relief for the unskilled unemployed was either not intended or slow to arrive.

WERA sewing center in Auburn, Feb. 17, 1934. Courtesy, Washington State Archives, Olympia.

In 1933 the Washington state solons made their first serious commitment of state funds for relief — $10 million worth. The size and scope of the projects funded through the State Emergency Relief Commission (SERC) ranged from the administration building at Western State Hospital to the Timber Damage Survey, sponsored by the State Land Department. The larger works were usually also sponsored by the PWA and the Civil Works Administration (CWA). Some examples of the hundreds of SERC projects are the Eastern State Hospital's administration building, the Washington State Penitentiary power house; the Felts Field hangar; natural resource and mineral surveys; the Deception Pass Bridge; the White Bluffs-to-Othello Road; and the Seattle Armory (now Center House at Seattle Center, recently remodeled for the third time since the structure's 1962 conversion for the Century 21 Worlds Fair).

By November 1933, the state's unemployment rate, swelled by the seasonal drop in lumber, fishing, and farming, approached 30 percent. The newly-created Civil Works Administration began to implement a relief program with "speed, speed, and yet more speed." That the CWA projects proposed by towns, counties, and school districts would use few materials and mostly hand labor was more or less insured by the federal prescription that only ten percent of

Seattle Armory. Courtesy, Lawton Gowey.

the funding could be used for tools. By Christmas Eve, 54,000 able-bodied unemployed were at work in every county on thousands of projects that required little more than a hammer, paint brush, shovel, or broom. In San Juan Country over 10 percent of the population 21 or older was employed repairing old county roads and grading new ones, reclaiming waterfront, painting county buildings — including the county court house — and schools, providing nursing service, making and repairing clothing for the Red Cross to distribute to those on relief, clearing land for the Friday Harbor airport, and offering regularly scheduled classes in art and metal work.

After Congress discontinued the CWA in March of 1934 both the WERA and FERA (Washington and Federal Emergency Relief Administrations, respectively) were organized and ran through the spring of 1935. Some incomplete CWA projects were continued like: improvements at Burton School on Vashon Island, the Port Angeles airport, and the Sand Point Naval Station in Seattle where 220,000 man-hours were spent mostly clearing,

grading, and eliminating the site's lake descriptively called "Mud." Among its many projects the new relief programs also built rustic bus stop shelters on Vashon Island, removed a log jam on the Elwha River, ran three miles of watermain to the Coast Guard base at the end of Ediz Hook, and installed 2,000 feet of sewers in Bremerton. FERA even released funds to grub-stake gold miners in 1934.

The hardships commonplace in the depth of the depression are revealed in the March, 1935 monograph prepared by the Transient and Homeless Department of WERA. Ten lodges and eight rural camps were built around the state in part by those who would use them, the "transient and the homeless." Seattle's four lodges with a bed capacity of 1,400 fed more than they lodged, on average 6,300 meals a day. The lodges also housed health services, vocational classes, and recreational space. The variety of work performed by the residents was Whitmanesque in its breadth — building the lodges, gardening, cleaning brick, planting and cutting trees, building roads and repairing them, painting signs, installing pipelines, razing buildings, blazing trails, landscaping, and clearing beaches. Although much of the WERA work was of the shovel sort, its goal, the 1935 report makes clear, was to "revive self-confidence and initiative, restore lost work habits,

WERA workers apply a new layer of cedar shingles to the Tukwila School, District No. 144. Courtesy, Washington State Archives, Olympia.

remove depression-produced handicaps, and, most importantly, to provide food and shelter and thus retain public spiritedness and social sanity." It also created landmarks that endure. For instance, the seventy men lodged at the Dry Falls Camp at the Grand Coulee developed the state park there. (See Floods Chapter.)

Summer was the season for reorganizing the nation's relief, and in June 1935 a new relief administration was launched which survived deep into the war years, 1943. The WPA was rife with projects from dams to paintings. In the spotlight of mere efficiency, many were not "cost effective." The King County Engineer estimated that the North Beach sewer line, which cost $5.25 per foot as a WPA project, could have been done at half that price by a private contractor paying low depression-time wages. In one Vancouver project, it was determined that the shovel work of

The title Washington State Made New Through WPA Improvements *appears on the flip side (not printed) of this brochure above WPA State Administrator Don*

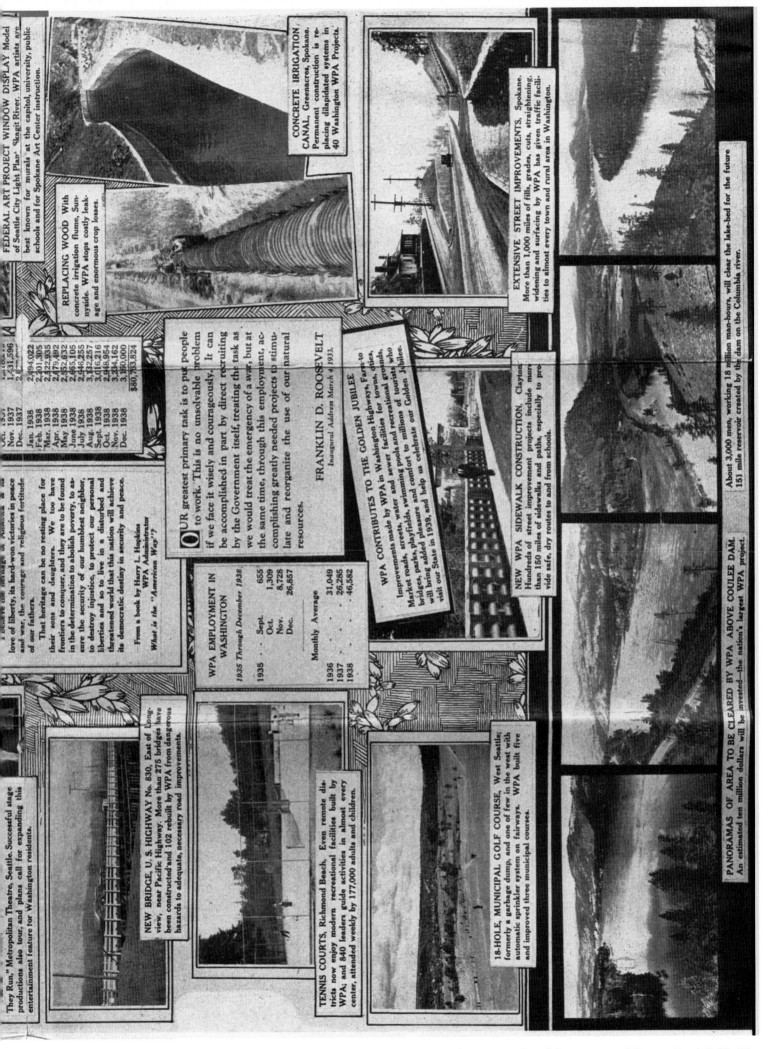

FEDERAL ART PROJECT WINDOW DISPLAY Model of Seattle City Light Plan" Skagit River. WPA artists are best known for murals at the capitol, university, public schools and for Spokane Art Center instruction.

REPLACING WOOD With concrete irrigation flume, Sunnyside. WPA stops costly leakage and enormous crop losses.

CONCRETE IRRIGATION CANAL, Greenacres, Spokane. Permanent construction is replacing dilapidated systems in 40 Washington WPA Projects.

EXTENSIVE STREET IMPROVEMENTS, Spokane. More than 1,000 miles of fills, grades, cuts, straightening, widening and surfacing by WPA has given traffic facilities to almost every town and rural area in Washington.

Nov. 1937	1,131,596
Jan. 1938	2,494,022
Feb. 1938	2,201,305
Mar. 1938	2,522,935
Apr. 1938	2,479,492
May 1938	2,552,632
June 1938	2,665,105
July 1938	2,946,255
Aug. 1938	3,132,257
Sept. 1938	3,016,216
Oct. 1938	2,948,954
Nov. 1938	3,234,162
Dec. 1938	3,150,000
	$80,753,824

OUR greatest primary task is to put people to work. This is no unsolvable problem if we face it wisely and courageously. It can be accomplished in part by direct recruiting by the Government itself, treating the task as we would treat the emergency of a war, but at the same time, through this employment, accomplishing greatly needed projects to stimulate and reorganize the use of our natural resources.

FRANKLIN D. ROOSEVELT
Inaugural Address March 4, 1933.

...love of liberty, its hard-won victories in peace and war, the courage and religious fortitude of our fathers.

That heritage can be no resting place for their sons and daughters. We too have frontiers to conquer, and they are to be found in the determination to abolish poverty, to assure the security of our humblest neighbor, to destroy injustice, to protect our personal liberties and so to live in a disturbed and threatened world that this nation will achieve its democratic destiny in security and peace.

From a book by Harry L. Hopkins
WPA Administrator
What is the "American Way"?

WPA EMPLOYMENT IN WASHINGTON
1935 Through December 1938

1935	Sept.	655
	Oct.	1,309
	Nov.	8,728
	Dec.	26,857

Monthly Average

1936	31,049
1937	26,285
1938	46,582

WPA CONTRIBUTES TO THE GOLDEN JUBILEE. Farm to Market roads, streets, water and sewer facilities for towns, cities, and recreational grounds. Improvements made by WPA in Washington Highway, bridges, parks, playfields, swimming pools and comfort to millions of tourists who will visit our State in 1939, and will bring added pleasure and help us celebrate our Golden Jubilee.

NEW WPA SIDEWALK CONSTRUCTION. Clayton. Hundreds of street improvement projects include more than 150 miles of sidewalks and path, especially to provide safe, dry routes to and from schools.

PANORAMAS OF AREA TO BE CLEARED BY WPA ABOVE COULEE DAM. An estimated ten million dollars will be invested—the nation's largest WPA project.

About 3,000 men, working 18 million man-hours, will clear the lake-bed for the future 151 mile reservoir created by the dam on the Columbia river.

They Run," Metropolitan Theatre, Seattle. Successful stage productions also tour, and plans call for expanding this entertainment feature for Washington residents.

NEW BRIDGE, U. S. HIGHWAY No. 830, East of Longview, near Pacific Highway. More than 275 bridges have been constructed and 102 rebuilt by WPA from dangerous hazards to adequate, necessary road improvements.

TENNIS COURTS, Richmond Beach. Even remote districts now enjoy modern recreational facilities built by WPA; and 840 leaders guide activities in almost every center, attended weekly by 177,000 adults and children.

18-HOLE, MUNICIPAL GOLF COURSE, West Seattle; formerly a garbage dump, and one of few in the west with automatic sprinkler system on fairways. WPA built five and improved three municipal courses.

Abel's claim that his workers are "the pioneers who rebuilt our state and advanced by a quarter of a century much needed improvements." Courtesy, Seattle Public Library.

13

eighty-five men could have been duplicated by one power shovel. And it was this image of the man-and-shovel that was most often parodied by a press unfriendly to "make-work" projects. However clever these recurring lampoons, they were cumulatively not as effective as the widespread feeling that the WPA was getting much done — from putting bread on tables to saving the world for democracy. In the floodlight of public spiritedness, the work of the WPA was insurance for "social sanity." And when calculated, its constructions were also substantial. By the end of 1941, 28,000 miles of streets, roads, and alleys, 1,000 bridges, 6,000 miles of road drainage ditches, 135 miles of guard rails, 1,100 street lights, 553 schools, 26 libraries, 400 recreational buildings, 90 stadiums, grandstands, and bleachers, 193 parks, 16 golf courses, 760 miles of watermains, 380 miles of sewers, 32 miles of telephone lines, 16 fish hatcheries, 900 miles of river banks, 275 miles of irrigation canals and 15,500 traffic signs had been put in place or improved by the WPA.

A small sampler of WPA projects in Washington includes a public dock at Kalama, schools at Bay Center and Electric City, parks at Lind and Wenatchee, waterlines at Mansfield and Tekoa, community recreation buildings at Cashmere and Opportunity, a livestock pavilion at Sunnyside, a state soldiers home and cemetery at Retsil, fish hatcheries at Underwood and Carson, dikes on the Cowlitz River, sewer lines at Chewelah and PeEll, sidewalks at Clarkston, a swimming pool at Oakesdale, tennis courts at Roslyn, fairground improvements at Deer Park, and waterfowl refuge improvements near Dungeness. The monthly WPA state payrolls ranged from 19,612 in September 1937 to 58,967 in November 1938. The average worker stayed with WPA for about one year, suggesting that either their time allotment had run out or the stated goal of graduating workers into the forces of private enterprise had succeeded.

The National Youth Administration (NYA) which ran from June 1935 into 1942 was designed to help the high percentage of unemployed young adults — many of them hoboing about the country — work while they continued their school and/or lived with their parents. Students in the state's high schools and twenty-four of its public and private colleges were paid to work on campus assisting librarians, conducting research, maintaining buildings and grounds, and working in school cafeterias. The NYA's many off-campus projects for drop-outs and graduates were sometimes menial — raking leaves, filing documents — and other times formidable. The remodeling of both the Ruston Community Center and the conversion of the old Port Townsend High School into a community center were both NYA projects generally involving crews of no more than fifteen. Other NYA projects included the carving of a totem pole under supervision of Tulalip tribal elders, the repair of an estimated 100,000 library books

DON'T BE SO CONSCIENTIOUS, MR. ICKES -:- By Carlisle

Above: Political cartoonist Carlisle's parody of FDR's reelection shovel-work printed on the Seattle Times editorial page August 23, 1936.
Left: State citizens employed to do WPA shovel work were not discriminated against because of size. These "poster boys" are unidentified.
Bottom left: WPA workers laying Goldendale sewage lines. Courtesy, Washington State Historical Society, Tacoma.

throughout the state, AND assistance for the Eastern Washington Historical Society in the Grand Coulee Archaeological Project. The division of these labors in 1940 involved about 4,200 high school youth, 1,900 college students and 3,900 in the out-of-school programs.

The inventiveness of many WPA projects is still remembered by many former participants, especially, by those in the arts. In theater, plays were performed in hospitals, retirement homes, and CCC camps. In Seattle between 1935 and 1939, the Negro Repertory Theater performed fifteen plays. The WPA commissioned murals for many state walls, and gave employment to artists, like Mark Toby and Morris Graves, who have since become widely known. The Federal Music Project formed symphonic bands in both Seattle and Tacoma, and the Federal Writers Project hired authors statewide for contributions to *Washington A Guide to The Evergreen State*. (See Buildings Chapter.)

WPA projects also produced: a Seattle juvenile crime survey; a Spokane Negro worker survey; ten playground leaders for Wenatchee parks; a fruit, nut, and berry farm census for twenty-seven counties; readers for the old and blind; a survey of Yakima Valley farm labor; office help for the Whitman Centennial Celebration; sewing projects in Ritzville and Prosser; housekeeping visits to families suffering from illness, desertion, and death; and thousands of other projects combining ingenuity with common sense.

The Civilian Conservation Corps (CCC) that ran from March 1933 to July 1942 was the first and probably the most popular work program created by Roosevelt and his activist cabinet. The CCC was established to assist an estimated 250,000 young men then drifting about the nation. By the summer of 1933 about 8,000 eighteen-to twenty-five year-olds from Washington, New York, New Jersey, Delaware, Michigan, Wisconsin, and Illinois found new homes in thirty-seven, mostly western Washington, camps to restore public lands. Mimicking military life, CCC

The Quinault Camp for the Civilian Conservation Corps (CCC). Below left: Fourth Anniversary cartoon celebrating the CCC's role as a "builder of men," printed on the front page the Ft. Lewis District Herald, April 1937. Bottom: Front cover to the Washington Pioneer Project's first of three volumes of pioneer reminisces. Courtesy, University of Washington Libraries, Special Collections.

camps paid its enlistees for six-to twenty-four-month stints $30 per month, $25 of which had to be sent home to dependents. The clothing and equipment issued the enrollees were World War I surplus. The camps were run by US Army Reserve officers and located in national forests, state parks, military reservations, and soil conservation lands. The "CCC boys" improved Olympic and Mt. Rainier National Parks and seventeen state parks, controlled erosion and fires, protected wildlife, constructed roads, trails, bridges, lookout towers, and dams, and planted thousands of Douglas firs. By 1935 the number of camps increased to fifty-four, and two years later the age requirements were extended to between seventeen and twenty-eight. On average the camps — like those at Longmire, Darrington, Icicle, Humptulips, and Elwha — housed more than two hundred men. Camp North Bend, since renamed Camp Waskowitz, is the best preserved of these.

CCC accomplishments, to name a few, included: the development of Ginkgo Petrified Forest State Park above Vantage; improvement of the 4,500-foot-long trail up Beacon Rock near Skamania; installation of twenty stone and timber structures by

residents of Camp Deception Pass; construction of a ninety-foot-long steel bridge over the Tieton River, east of White Pass; building of campgrounds in the Chinnok Pass and White Pass region; completion of one of the CCC's largest hydroelectric projects with the 185-foot-long Trout Creek Dam and fishladder; construction of many forest roads, trails, campgrounds, and lookout stations; control of the pine beetle infestations on the Yakima and Spokane Indian reservations; constructed of Vita House at the summit of Mount Spokane; and the cutting down of dead trees — remnants of the 239,000 acre Yacolt Burn of 1902 in Clark County. Before the "boys" of the CCC arrived, most of the state parks were little more than wilderness.

Ultimately the most enduring effects of the agencies — especially the WPA — will be the work they did in exploring and preserving the state's past. The WPA's Historical Records Survey began in February 1936 with an inventory and classification of all records to be found in the county courthouses. Eventually this work was broadened to include community, state, and church archives. The interest in church records was understandable for many of the details of personal history, especially in its passages like marriage and death, are often best preserved there. Attempts to also inventory the records of existing businesses were so frequently frustrated by the reluctance of holders to open them that this part of the survey, regrettably, was dropped. By 1939 the archival inventory of fifty-one towns and cities was completed. The *American Imprints*, another WPA project made an inventory of known publications printed in Washington Territory before 1876. Yet another, the Pioneer Project, was certainly the most evocative. Hundreds of the state's long-time residents were interviewed in their homes for their oldest reminiscences. The results were compiled in the always touching and sometimes revealing three-volume publication, *Told By The Pioneers*, which has long since been a collector's item.

Many other public works accomplishments from the Great Depression are described below in the chapters treating waterways, highways, streets, waste management, public buildings, and other subjects. Many of those that survive are public works landmarks for the heritage of Washington State.

Hood Canal Bridge, May 31, 1996.
Courtesy, Department of Transportation (DOT).

The Port of Seattle's Fishermen's Terminal on Salmon Bay. The Ballard Bridge is on the right and the Ballard waterfront across the bay, ca. 1917.

Celilo Falls on the Columbia River, ca. 1938. Photo by Dell W. Thomas. Courtesy, Sara Hueston Culver.

WATERWAYS

Water has shaped Washington in ways that are generous and diverse. On both the dry and wet sides of the Cascade Mountains erosion has sculpted waterways that have shaped the history of the state. The Columbia River, whether remembered as the wild cataract rolling 800 miles out of Canada to tidewater or exploited as a slackwater public work, is the "River of the West." On the west side, the off-shore waterways are generally deep and require no dredging, except where channels penetrate the upland across bars and estuaries. There the public work of keeping the way safe and clear is an eternally recurring one. The diversity of the state's 2,337 miles of marine shoreline favors beaches — 1,847 miles of beach. The rest consists of rocky headlands, marsh areas, bulkheads, and revetments. Only about a quarter of Washington's shoreland above extreme high tide is publicly owned. The state has sold about 60 percent of its shoreland to private interests. The story of how these shorelands and waterways were divided, dammed and diverted by private and public works is, of course, a very recent one.

The tribal production of digging a canoe out of an aromatic cedar log was, perhaps, the first public work done on the waterways of Washington. The natives' tools and techniques also artfully shaped a generously pliant nature into duck nets, baskets, and longhouses. For millennia this small technology was thoroughly appropriate to the generous dynamics of the tides and seasons. Then in the rush of a few decades this ancient culture was wracked and its land divided by men carrying Gunther chains and/or pistols.

THE UNEXPLORED CORNER OF THE WORLD

In the moment that Capt. Vancouver claimed and named his discovery New Georgia, its namesake King George III was celebrating his fifty-fourth birthday in the splendid circumstances of St. James Castle. Vancouver was charmed by Puget Sound. In his oft-quoted lines, "To describe the beauties of this region, will on some future occasion, be a very grateful task to the pen of a skillful panegyrist...the abundant fertility that unassisted nature puts forth, require only to be enriched by the industry of man...to render it the most lovely country that can be imagined..." Natives, of course, had been assisting nature here for many millennium before Vancouver's appearance, but the exploitive reshaping of this New Georgia began in earnest about a half century later, first by the English Hudson Bay Company at Fort Nisqually and soon after by a trickle of American settlers which in less than a century after Vancouver's visit swelled to a flood.

May 1792 was the month for discoveries on Washington waterways — Puget Sound and the Columbia River. On the 11th, while Vancouver was charting Hood Canal, the American trader Capt. Robert Gray tested his *Columbia* at the bar to the river he would soon name for his ship. Gray's willingness to risk the breakers and cross into the unknown was not for what Capt. Vancouver called "that noble science of discovery" but for a Yankee trader's true delight, profits. As first on the river, Gray was also its "possessor,' although apparently unwittingly. The fragment of the Columbia's log copied for the archives makes no mention of taking the land. The international significance of trader Gray's enterprise was added as an afterthought to the journal of John Boit, a crewman on the *Columbia*. Boit writes at the time that "I landed abreast the Ship with Capt. Gray to view the Country." Sometime later an unidentified hand has added in a different ink "and take possession."

The influence of winds, currents, and tides on the lower Columbia were made less important in 1836 when the Beaver was first fitted at Fort Vancouver with the machinery she carried with her under sail from England. With the first steam engine on the West Coast she could at seven knots perform her dogged service to the arts and enterprise of the Hudson's Bay Company.

The Oregon Territory census of 1849 could locate only 304 non-natives living north of the Columbia. These early pioneers, living on land to which they had no title, were rewarded in 1850 with the Donation Land Law that gave every adult, husband and wife alike, 320 acres of realty they laid claim to. The act's generosity with aboriginal property resulted in the great migrations of the 1850s. The Northwest had already become a national preoccupation and the summer migration of wagons bound for the Pacific Coast etched parts of the Oregon Trail with permanent ruts. But the migrants dreams for their promised land were not so indelible. The prodigious work of actually taking a hold on the land was often a great eraser of hopes. The land was neither like Kansas nor the European landscape developed through hundreds of years of picturesque pruning. Understandably, most of those who arrived early chose to live beside a waterway, in part, to stay out of the forest.

Another census, hurriedly canvassed in the summer of 1853, counted 3,965 non-natives living within a Washington which then included Idaho and Western Montana. This three-year gain was impressive, especially considering the competing lure of California's goldfields. Washington's great attraction was above ground — timber. On Puget Sound and the Strait of Georgia, the opportunities to clear the best firs and cedars from the shoreline extended for 1,784 miles along a deep waterway that, except for tideflats and estuaries, needed no dredging — a logger's heaven. And with little interest in platting, planting, or penetrating the forest any deeper than was necessary to easily drag to tideline the best timber, the lumbermen's vision of this evergreen land was considerably less nervous than the settler's.

Hudson Bay Company side-wheeler The Beaver, *the first steam vessel on the West Coast.*

COAST WATERWAYS

The United States first construction — its first public work — was the light house at Cape Henry, Virginia. The application for this construction issued from the 1787 Constitutional Convention at Philadelphia (which itself had grown out of a 1785 meeting at Mount Vernon where representatives from Maryland and Virginia concurred on duty-free passage through the mouth of the Chesapeake Bay and bi-lateral navigation on the Potomac River, the two waterways they shared as a border.) This precedent for the constitution's "commerce clause" is still the basic authority for federal waterways improvements.

Capt. Robert Gray's 1792 crossing of the bar was done without the aid of buoys or a beacon to show the way. In the years between his success and first ignition of the sperm oil atop the Cape Disappointment lighthouse on Oct. 15, 1856, many other captains were not so fortunate. Approaches to the Columbia River bar

The loss in 1841 of the Peacock *at the Columbia River bar was later illustrated in the U.S. Navy's Wilkes Expedition's published reports. Courtesy Jack Henry. Inset left: After a gale drove her ashore near Ocean Park on Jan. 15, 1909, the crew of the square-rigged French ship* Alice *was rescued but not the 3,000 tons of cement she carried in her holds. Inset right: Up until 1930, one of the* Alice's *masts held upright by the hardened cement remained a popular North Beach Peninsula landmark. Photos courtesy Daniel Kerlee.*

Above: North Head Lighthouse by Hugh Paradise. Top left: The Willapa Bay Light Station moments before her crash to the beach in 1940. Left: Willapa Light Station after the crash. Courtesy WA State Corps of Engineers. Bottom left: Dredger Tacoma's *early-century work on the Willapa River channel at Raymond. Courtesy Michael Maslan.*

were accompanied by a profound ambivalence — the joy of having safely arrived at the harbor's door was sobered by the remaining task of having to pass through it. The loss of the *Peacock*, one of a squadron of vessels in the United State's 1841 Wilkes Expedition, inspired its leader, Lt. Charles Wilkes, to exclaim that "mere description can give little idea of the terrors of the bar. All who have seen it have spoken of the wildness of the scene and the incessant roar of the waters, representing it as one of the most fearful sights that can possibly meet the eye."

Wilkes' worries, while real, were also rhetorical — designed to bring relief. Seven years after the Lieutenant's "fearful" experience, the U.S. Coast Survey finally recommended a light at the mouth of the Columbia. Another five years passed before the government began to build it or attempted to. The bark *Oriole*, carrying construction supplies for the lighthouse, came to an ironic end directly below the Cape. All the supplies were lost and the crew was saved only after being tossed about offshore in lifeboats through a cold night. With this sinking, the Cape Disappointment sentinel, 192 feet above mean tide, was first lit only in the fall of 1856. And once operating, the government lighthouse service's pockets were steadily tapped by the light's monthly consumption of 170 gallons of costly sperm oil.

The boom in coast construction during the period of the

Spanish-American War included a second lighthouse on the Cape at North Head. Commissioned in 1898, its classic sixty-five-foot tower was built of several courses of brick masonry set upon a sandstone base and overlaid with a cement plaster painted a brilliant white. Only two miles from the beacon at Cape Disappointment, its public work was to mark the southern end of the twenty-two-mile North Beach peninsula, a ships graveyard.

WILLAPA BAY

Twenty-four miles north of the Columbia Bar, at the end of a beach so far-flung that it is named simply 'Long,' is another bar. Although the mouth to Willapa Bay has an appetite for ships historically less voracious than the Columbia's, it has devoured a few. Some captains in a frontal fog — meteorological or mental — have mistaken the Willapa's entrance for the Columbia's. It was an error not ordinarily disastrous, for this harbor built an early reputation as the safest between San Francisco and Puget Sound. Yet, because it is so shallow strangers can easily get stuck in Willapa Bay, making the harbor inhospitable to most pleasure boaters but also making it the most pristine harbor in the continental United States. Oysters, the bay's original export, are still its most famous and abundant crop.

Before 1962, when the last section of the north-shore highway (S.R. 105) was completed east of Tokeland, it was not possible to drive directly from Raymond to Cape Shoalwater. Sometimes it still isn't. West of Tokeland, where the older road to the Willapa Lighthouse passes close to Graveyard Spit and Washaway Beach, the highway is periodically broken by the surf which pounds against the north shore. But it is the Willapa Lighthouse at Cape Shoalwater which has put on the biggest disappearing act.

When the original Willapa Bay Light Station was constructed in 1858, it was prudently sited on a firm promontory two-thirds of a mile inside the ocean beach. It took eighty-two years of pounding for the sea to reach and consume the light on December 22, 1940. A new light was raised atop a steel tower 380 yards inland. It took twelve years for the bay to reach it, when the tower was moved

DREDGER TACOMA
RAYMOND, WASH.

again to firmer ground, 148 feet above the water. Eroding forces took but six years to reach this new siting. On March 12, 1959 the light was moved yet again, 1,100 yards from its original charted position. As of this writing its survives.

Most of the 30,000 tons of primarily woodchips and oysters shipped annually from the bay come from industry on the Willapa River. The Army Corps of Engineers' work began on this estuary in the mid-1890s and by 1908 they had dredged a twelve-foot channel between the towns of South Bend and Raymond. Obliging the local lumbermen's desires for schooners and steamers with deeper drafts, the Corps and the Port increased these dimensions in 1913 to an 18-foot deep by 200-foot wide channel to Raymond which they deepened to 24 feet by 1924. Now, ocean barges of only 18-feet draft are the preferred carriers out of Raymond, and the Corps is committed to maintaining the river channel to suit their needs.

GRAYS HARBOR

A dozen miles up the coast from the homely Willapa Lighthouse is its beautiful younger sister, the Grays Harbor Lighthouse. This statuesque pile of whitewashed concrete was the 1898 creation of C.W. Leick, who also designed the lights at North Head, Burrows Island in the San Juans, and Mukilteo. According to Jim Gibbs, the author of Lighthouses of the Pacific, the Grays Harbor light is Leick's "greatest achievement — a masterpiece in every respect. It contains an iron spiral staircase with 135 steps. Set on a sandstone base the four-foot-thick lower section tapers gently to the top of the tower. For many years it was the tallest building of any kind in the county." At 107 feet it is still the second tallest lighthouse on the coast, the tallest being the 127-foot Estevan lighthouse on the west side of Vancouver Island.

The Grays Harbor light was built about 200 yards from the shoreline. Unlike the Willapa light, however, Leick's light is now a half-mile from the beach. These added sands of time are the deposits of jetties built first south and then north of the harbor entrance at Point Chehalis and Point Brown.

An 1882 Coast and Geodetic Survey of Grays Harbor confirmed the expected — the fluid dynamics at the bar made the accuracy of any published chart very temporary. The survey's findings and the public work that followed helped encourage the boom on the harbor which quickly created two arche-typal lumber towns side-by-side, Hoquiam and Aberdeen.

In the early 1890s, the Army Corps of Engineers created a second office in Portland for its work north of the Columbia River. Captain Thomas Symons, the same Corps officer who in 1881 had led a survey party down the middle Columbia, examined Grays Harbor. He recommended deepening the north channel between the Chehalis River and the harbor's mouth, and closing

Above: Grays Harbor Light, second tallest on the West Coast. Below: Aerial of Point Brown and jetties at entrance to Grays Harbor. May 6, 1942. Courtesy National Archives, Alaska-Pacific NW Region.

South Jetty

Entrance

North Jetty

POINT BROWN

Old Jetty

S HARBOR

Ferry slip

Barge "Mastodon"

NORTH BAY

Left: 1924 ceremony attending the Port of Grays Harbor crane loading timber marked "The Billionth Foot" bound for the Orient. Courtesy, Jones Photo Company, Aberdeen. Below: Celilo Falls. Courtesy Old Seattle Paperworks.

sloughs along the river. Symons' intent was to create flushing hydraulics that would clear both the river and the north channel to a depth acceptable to the sixteen-foot draft of the standard lumber carriers of the time. Begun in April 1893 the work was completed in the summer of 1894. After a year of monitoring its effects, Supervising Engineer J.M. Clapp concluded, "The velocity of both the ebb and flood tide in the north channel has wonderfully increased."

A year later in 1896 construction began on the south jetty at Point Chehalis. The projected three-and-one-half-mile finger of rubble on a mattress of woven brush was the first big public work of the Army Corps' then-new Seattle District. After four years project money ran out and the jetty was stopped 400 feet short of its planned length. The effects were disappointing. As it wore away, the jetty was itself a navigational hazard submerged at extreme high tide. The shifting harbor floor had also filled in the channel at the bar to a shallow twelve feet at extreme low tide.

By a consensus of nervous mill owners and Corps engineers, work began on the north jetty in October 1907. With its completion in 1916, effects at the bar were at last improved. The main channel maintained a nineteen-foot depth, still five feet less than the desired twenty-four feet.

Following the First World War the public Port of Grays

Harbor became an important player on this waterway, effectively lobbying the Army Corps to eliminate the shoal off Cow Point where the Port's public facilities were dedicated in 1922. Set as the border between Aberdeen and Hoquiam this sixty-eight-acre gift from the state allied the competing communities in a variation of the theme "good fences make good neighbors." The Corps' work was completed in 1923, creating a channel twenty-six feet deep off Cow Point. Some of the material sucked and scooped from the channel was used to reclaim more port-owned land, and to also help elevate the previously soggy town of South Aberdeen. Since the Corps' and Port's early cooperation in these projects, the two public agencies have continued to work together. In 1945 the channel leading from the bar to Aberdeen was deepened to thirty feet and by the mid-1950s extended at this depth to Cosmopolis.

Conditions at the bar in the mid-1950s were mixed. The ends of both jetties were lost to erosion, and a good percentage of both structures had slipped below grade. Still, the agreeably steady depth of thirty-seven feet was maintained at the bar and District Engineer Col. Robert Young concluded in 1960 that "there is, therefore, no bar channel condition that requires rebuilding of either entrance jetty." Sen. Warren Magnuson, however, disagreed, and technical acumen bowed to political opportunity. Four thousand feet of the south jetty was repaired in 1966 and a similar rehabilitation was undertaken again in 1975.

THE COLUMBIA RIVER

Visions of the Columbia as a great waterway, as a "Mississippi of the West," precede those of it as a great irrigation ditch or power generator. However, once the technique of pulling electricity from a head of water was invented, the Columbia's predisposition for power — not primarily navigation — was obvious throughout the 745 miles it courses from the Canadian border to its bar. The Columbia River's watershed is modest when compared to the Mississippi's but not its fall — 1,284 feet south of the 49th parallel. Even after eons of erosion two drops, at Kettle and Celilo Falls, were obstructions to craft of all descriptions until they were flooded behind dam pools. Still, most of the river's drops were not sudden. And by the time explorers and trappers followed its course, the navigation of its many rapids was already an ancient skill. Explorers Lewis and Clark had confidently described the Indian paddlers on the Columbia as the "finest in the world." Pioneer literature is also replete with praise for the natives' knowledge of the river and their mastery of its navigation.

JAMES PATRICK'S EXAMPLE

In 1934 James Patrick and a friend put their canoe in the water at Trail, B.C. and proceeded to paddle the 750 miles to the mouth of the Columbia, a reach then still very much like that known to the natives. There was only one artificial barrier they portaged, Rock Island Dam, twelve miles below Wenatchee. Forty-two years and ten dams later, a seventy-two-year-old James Patrick once again dropped his canoe (now fiberglass) in at Trail, B.C., and with his son, James Jr., headed for the river mouth. In 1976, they took an outboard motor; paddling the slack-water lakes behind the dams was less risky than running rapids but more dreary. Seven times they had to arrange with dam employees to truck their canoe around dams without locks: first Grand Coulee, then Chief Joseph, and so on through Wells, Rocky Reach, Rock Island, Wanapum and Priest Rapids.

Below Priest Rapids the Patricks were trucked through the Hanford reservation away from the only stretch of the Columbia preserved as the river the elder Patrick knew in 1934. Below Hanford, the father and son navigators were reunited with a warmer river, first heated by nuclear fission and then by the McNary's pool, Lake Wallula. As the Patricks' canoe moved through the last big bend in the river, their outboard strained against the headwind blowing up from the Gorge, slopping waves over their sides. At McNary's lock they joined a grain barge for the ninety-two-foot drop, and then set out across Lake Umatilla for their next descent at John Day Dam. They never made it. The elder James concluded, "In a lot of ways the river was better for canoeing the first time. With the current we made better time. And we didn't have to get permission to go around dams." The Patricks pulled out at Arlington.

In 1930 the Columbia Valley Association organized to promote a truly navigable river upstream from the government lock at Celilo Falls. "We want boats, that is swift water boats, on the river at once," the association's secretary R.H. Kipp exhorted, "...as the government engineers' reports are to be made in July 1931, and will say that the river is navigable. But unless we get action it also will say that the river is not used. Such a report will admit a weakness on our part and make it difficult to get appropriations for the improvement of the river."

Above: On July 9, 1938, The Charles L. Wheeler Jr., was the first ocean-going vessel to pass through the Bonneville Locks, then the highest single shelf sea-lock in the world, and continue along the Columbia's passage through the Cascade Mountains to reach The Dalles, 182 miles from the ocean. Courtesy Bonneville Power Association.

Above: Opened in 1896, the Cascade Locks permitted navigation around the Cascade Rapids until the rapids were inundated behind Bonneville Dam. Courtesy Michael Fairley. Below: Whitman County celebrants ride the river steamer J.N. Teal for the 1915 opening of the Celilo Canal. Courtesy Columbia River Maritime Museum; Astoria, Oregon.

308 REPORT

Secretary Kipp was uneasy about what he might find in the Army Corps' 1931 report. For power and reclamation, the "308" — named for the number assigned it in the U.S. House of Representatives — was a watershed, but not for boating. In line with the report's explanation that hydroelectricity, not navigation, should determine the height and location of dams on the Columbia, it concluded that a high dam at The Dalles with a head of 275 feet would produce the most power. Fortunately, for the hopes of navigators like Kipp, the Corps' conservative Board of Engineers for Rivers and Harbors substituted four low dams for this big one in its first review of the "308." Still it was power, not grain barges, that inspired the substitution of four wind-swept but navigable lakes between The Dalles and Pasco for the single oversized super-pool. Four dams would allow for the progressive development of the river's potential as the power — not navigation — was needed.

GOVERNMENT CANALS

For many of the pioneers who usually first reached the river near Celilo Falls, the "Upper" Columbia drained an unknown region. Below the falls the waterway to Portland was interrupted by the Cascade Rapids. Working this river and its portage soon became a paying proposition and the captain who made the most was the transplanted Mississippi navigator, Capt. J.C. Ainsworth. In 1860 Ainsworth incorporated the Oregon Steam Navigation Co. not in Oregon but in Washington Territory where the laws were lax and soon encircled his competitors with a growing monopoly. This included a six-mile portage railroad on the Washington side of the Cascades. In 1863, for $50,000 per mile,

Above: Celilo Canal on Oregon side. Courtesy, U.W. Special Collections. Both right: Work in progress on locks at Dalles Dam. Courtesy National Archives, Alaska-Pacific NW Region.

Ainsworth added a fifteen-mile railroad around Celilo Falls. This was hurriedly built in response to the discovery of gold in Idaho on the Clearwater and Salmon River tributaries to the Snake. The ensuing rush upriver was such that a sternwheeler could pay for itself in one trip.

The agitation for navigational aids on the Columbia above the Cascades began in the 1870s with the rise of the Grange. To lower the fees charged by Ainsworth and others, the Patrons of Husbandry lobbied for government canals at the Cascades and Celilo Falls. The Army Corps, instructed by Congress in 1874 to survey sites and determine costs, concluded that while the Dalles-Celilo barriers were "almost insurmountable," the Cascades were not. Work began on locks and a 3000-foot canal in 1878. But the work dragged on to 1896. Next, in 1902, the federal government began construction on its eight-mile-long and eight-foot-deep canal around Celilo Falls. Completed in 1915, the canal was a white elephant. The competition of the Seattle Portland and Spokane Railroad's new north shore track and the development of new highways drove the sternwheelers out of the business of moving freight through the Columbia Gorge. No navigation aids of consequence were constructed on the river in the years between the Corps' completion of the Celilo Canal in 1915, the North Jetty at the bar in 1917, and the construction of Bonneville Dam in the 1930s. The Army Corps' 308 Report of 1931 concluded simply, "It would appear that the principal cause of the failure of attempts to establish boat service on the river above Portland has been the lack of patronage."

Deal president's proposal and completion of McNary Dam, freight service on the Columbia had been revolutionized. Replacement of sternwheelers by powerful diesel tugs and cargo barges was aided by the Corps' periodic attempts, beginning in 1935, to clear obstructions between Celilo Falls and Pasco.

The 1947 Bureau of Reclamation's "Comprehensive Report on the Development of the Water Resources of the Columbia River Basin" could claim that "traffic on inland waterways on the basin has recently increased significantly after declining to a position of very minor importance following the advent of well-developed rail facilities." In December of the following year, the Bureau announced "complete agreement" with the Army Corps' most recent revision of its 308 Report. Together they would persuade Congress to build seven more dams on the mainstem of the Columbia, including the final three of the four planned

DAMS WITH LOCKS

President Franklin D. Roosevelt visited the Bonneville Dam site in 1934 and talked about people's power. Earlier that year FDR had announced in a special dispatch to the *Walla Walla Union* his preference for a lock at Bonneville large enough to admit ocean-going vessels. And when it opened it was the highest single-lift sealock in the world, raising the *Charles L. Wheeler* Jr., the first ocean-going vessel to steam the 182 miles from the Columbia bar to The Dalles. Roosevelt also expressed his preference for the eventual development of a waterway as far east as Pasco. In the nineteen years that separated the New

Right: The 1953 opening of the locks at McNary Dam to sixty-one miles of slack water made freight service to the Tri-Cities area considerably smoother. Barges enter Lake Wallula at 340 feet above tidewater.

1) Sternwheeler Lewiston *on the Snake River. Courtesy Garfield County Historical Society. 2) Ice Harbor Dam, Aug. 1960. Courtesy Corps of Engineers. 3) Port of Pasco, ca. 1960. Courtesy Ted Van Arsdol. 4) Lower Monumental Dam, Aug. 1981. Courtesy Corps. 5) Washington Gov. Albert Rosellini (left) speaks at 1962 dedication of Ice Harbor Dam. Sharing stage are Sen. Warren Magnuson (middle) and then Vice President Lyndon Johnson (far right). Courtesy Corps of Engineers, Walla Walla.*

between tidewater and Pasco.

On the Washington side of the river, McNary Dam's single 675-foot-long navigation lock was four feet wider than the seventy-two feet at Bonneville and gave a ninety-two-foot lift that was twenty-two feet higher than Bonneville's. The Dalles Dam followed in 1957, flooding the natives' ancient fishing platform at Tum Tum (Celilo) Falls and the government canal. The lock there was also 675 feet long, although six feet wider than McNary and its lift was five feet less. In the seventy-seven miles of fast water that remained below McNary Dam a 2,000-horsepower tug could handle only one 1,500-ton barge. With the completion of the John Day Dam in 1968 — exactly a century after the Corps first set charges to obstructing rocks at John Day Rapids — the same tug could handle six barges through the slack-water Lake Umatilla behind the new dam which featured the system's highest lift at 113 feet. (For a brief moment John Day was the nation's largest producer of hydroelectricity, 2.16 million kilowatts; a distinction that lasted only until the completion of the work then in progress on the Grand Coulee Dam's new powerhouse. (See Power Chapter.)

In 1986, 6,250,000 tons of cargo went through the McNary locks — nearly all of it from either the wheat ports on the Snake River or from the Port of Pasco. Formed in 1940 to transfer the region's grain, the Port of Pasco added the first container service on the upper river to its usual business of barging commodities in 1976. Through the mid-1980s its thirty-six-ton whirley crane handled an average of over 2,000 containers each year, most of them used to export local products. A sizable percentage of this business had formerly been directed to Puget Sound ports by rail. Earlier, in 1959, the Port had added 600 acres and 1.7 million square feet of buildings to its facilities when it bought the World War II Army depot just downriver from the Port's barge terminal. Appropriately renamed the Big Pasco Industrial Park, its eastern border lies beside Sacajawea State Park which covers the promontory at the confluence of the Snake and Columbia Rivers.

IDAHO SEAPORT

The vision of giving Idaho its own "picture window to the sea" began with the gold rush in the 1860s. The federal government made its first report on Snake River navigation in 1866, investigating yet another of the many gold rushes that propelled grubby men to wander about the West. The Army Corps' interest continued when grain replaced gold as the area's preoccupation. In November 1871, the year the Corps opened its Portland office, Capt. Ainsworth of the Oregon Steam Navigation Company noted that "every available house in Wallula is now filled with wheat." In 1877 Major John Wilson of the Corps predicted that the fertile lands bordering the Snake would be fully settled if the farmers could get the grain to market by the fall. Too often the river would not cooperate, especially during the winter when the stream flow was often too low to carry grain-laden steamers over the rapids. The Corps responded with an attack on the Lower Snake's worst rock obstructions, including those at Pine Tree, Monumental, Fish Hook, and Texas Rapids. By the mid-1880s the Snake was easily navigable for the seventy miles between Lewiston and Riparia, roughly halfway to the Columbia. At Riparia grain and passengers were transferred to cars of the Oregon Railway and Navigation Company for the final train ride to Portland.

Aside from these few but effective channel improvements, no dramatic public works were planned for the 150-mile section of the Washington Snake until the 1930s. The Army Corps' 308 Report for developing the basin with multipurpose dams included some hope for a slack-water Snake. When Ice Harbor Dam was first authorized in 1945, a general plan for a series of four low-level navigation dams was in place. A 330-foot-high dam was rejected as an obstruction to both navigation and salmon. Nonetheless, the Snake system of four low dams still proved to be profoundly disastrous for the fish.

Ice Harbor Dam

On a site chosen in 1948 ten miles up the Snake from the Columbia, construction of the Ice Harbor Dam was assigned to the Corps' then new Walla Walla District. Until the construction of the 118-foot lift lock at John Day, the Ice Harbor's 103-foot lock was the highest single-lift lock in the world, a distinction it wrested from McNary Dam. The monumental symmetry of the lock's vertical lift gate with its two counterweight towers is striking. After many delays the dam was at last dedicated on May 9, 1962 with a marine parade. It was the first time since sternwheeler days that the river had been used as a waterway. There remained 118 miles to be opened to traffic.

Lower Monumental Dam

After Ice Harbor came Lower Monumental Dam, forty-one miles above the Columbia. The two dams are almost mirror images. The navigation lock is nearly identical with the Ice Harbor lock. Because the Corps' Walla Walla office was building the John Day Dam on the Columbia's mainstem, the Corps' Seattle office took over the Lower Monumental project.

Construction, however, was delayed four months by discovery at the dam site of the then-oldest known human remains in the Western Hemisphere, the 10 to 13,000-year old Marmes Man. When the 2,000-foot levee built to protect this archaeological discovery leaked the site was wrapped in plastic and buried behind fill. There the Marmes Man must wait until either silt from the Palouse River or political will can reseal the levee and allow the unwatering of this rare find.

Little Goose Dam

The Little Goose Dam was completed one year after Lower Monumental and looks strikingly similar to it and Ice Harbor. At Little Goose, however, older style universal miter gate leaves were installed at the lock's lower gate rather than the vertical lift lock gates used at the Lower Snake's first two dams.

Lower Granite Dam

Construction on the cofferdam for the Lower Granite Dam, the last link in Lewiston's 114-year effort to become the "upstream anchor of today's Northwest Passage," was begun in 1965, two years after work was underway at Little Goose. Lower Granite was completed five years later than its downstream neighbor when work was put on hold in 1967 due to the budget drain incurred by the war in Vietnam. Completed in 1975, Lower Granite shares a family resemblance with the first three dams on the Snake.

The last three of the four Lower Snake dams were dedicated together in June 1975. As Idaho's Senator Frank Church put it to the celebrants at Lewiston, once the capital of Idaho Territory, "This part of Idaho is now a coastal state." The Lower Snake system cost nearly $900 million. And the environmental price, besides the loss of orchards alongside the old wild river, included exchanging a vital and ever-moving channel of cataracts for a pool where migrating fish were depleted through confusion and trauma. In the first full three-year period after the "Inland Passage" was completed, barge traffic increased through Lower Granite from 559,000 to 1,422,000 tons. Most of this was wheat which the railroads had formerly hauled, some of it to Puget Sound ports.

COLUMBIA RIVER ABOVE THE SNAKE

The Columbia of the Big Bend has a waterway history which is, with a few heroic exceptions, a frustrating story of effort without effect. And for public works it is a cautionary tale replete with abandoned projects. In the Army Corps of Engineers "308" Report of 1931, Major Butler gives it this flat description.

The Columbia above the Snake has a very stable channel, being generally confined by rock banks and having a bed composed of material not easily transported by even the high-current velocities obtaining in this river. It is a river with a steep slope, high velocities, numerous rapids, and is navigable with great difficulty... In that portion of the river between the mouth of the Snake River and the international boundary line the fall is about 980 feet, the distance being 425.3 miles... The slope, however, is not uniform.

City of Ellensburg *steamer, the first on the upper Columbia River.* Courtesy *The Wenatchee World*

Not uniform, indeed! At Priest Rapids seven separate cataracts fell in nine miles a total of seventy-two feet. At Grand Rapids, seven miles below Kettle Falls, the river descended twenty feet in one thousand yards. At Kettle Falls the river dropped thirty-three feet. Priest Rapids merited mention in an early executive report of Washington Territory's first governor, Isaac Stevens. Stretching the truth for the sake of his new territory, Stevens declared that construction of a canal around the nine-mile cataract would make the river "continuously navigable from its mouth to Kettle Falls, a distance of 735 miles."

One half-century before the 1931 308 Report, Army Corps Lt. Thomas W. Symons had surveyed the Columbia above the Snake. In the late summer of 1881, Symons' party of engineers and instruments took to their flat-bottom bateau with a hard-of-sight Iroquois navigator, Old Pierre, who felt more than saw the channel after years of working in the fur trade for the Hudson's Bay Company. What Symons found was a difficult waterway gouged through a landscape where "complete silence and lifelessness...makes it almost unearthly." For many years the lieutenant would return to the river in repeated attempts to pound a path through the obstructions in its "very stable channel."

The first captain and steamer to surmount the river as far as Wenatchee was Capt. William Polk Gray in the *City of Ellensburg*. In 1888 Gray pulled his sternwheeler through both the Priest Rapids and the Rock Island Rapids with lines tied to the shore. Two years later when Lt. Symons returned to the river to try to clear Priest Rapids of its most inhibiting obstructions, he was guided by the knowledge Gray had gained while dragging and pushing the *Ellensburg* up to Wenatchee. After a year spent trying to improve the Columbia at Priest Rapids, "with a bed of the hardest and roughest basaltic rock," a frustrated Symons declared, "it is not possible for me to believe that it can be successful." In mid-1891 Symons moved his drilling scow fifty miles upriver to the Cabinet Rapids, just below Rock Island, where he removed rocks and imbedded ringbolts in boulders along the channel's east side. Using these, steamers could repeat the Ellensburg's technique of running a line through the rings and reeling themselves up the rapids on their own capstans. Yet in the midst of his daring industry, the realist Symons would conclude, "It is not probable that this river for its whole length...will ever be used as a through highway of commerce."

Above Wenatchee

Symons began his survey of the Columbia north of Wenatchee in 1895. River traffic there was the monopoly of the Columbia and Okanogan Steamboat Company. Practically tied to the Great Northern Railroad most of the COSC's freight either wound up on the railroad or came from it. In its twenty-two years on the river above Wenatchee, the company had relied on the Corps' public works to clear the way for its generally profitable enterprise. Symons' 1895 survey discovered that parts of the river, such as the mouth of the Methow, were dangerous in high water. Other sections, like the Entiat Rapids, were treacherous at low water. Symons recommended work on both. In 1907 the Corps returned again to the upper river — this time without Symons — to resume its attack on the basalt. However, work stopped when commerce on the river did not warrant it. (In this instance, the expanding service of the railroad up river quieted traffic on the Columbia and virtually silenced the Corps' own movement there.)

Between Bridgeport and Kettle Falls the Corps' endeavors were encouraged by an absence of both railroads and any plans for them. The difficult current in this section was demonstrated during the Corps 1908 survey which required one week to cover the 168 miles upstream but only a day for the steamer *Enterprise* to return. In 1910 Congress appropriated $99,600 for the work of pacifying this channel on the condition that the state steamer *Yakima* help haul drill scows to the scattered work sites. She had the power to do it. As one pioneer captain W. P. Gray reminisced, "Especial [sic] mention should be made of the Yakima that went as far up the river as Rocky Rapids, near Kettle Falls. She made the trip from Pasco to Bridgeport without using a line at any rapids, as she had plenty of power." The fitful work proceeded until 1917 when once more the Corps withdrew from the Upper Columbia. The Corps' Major Cavanaugh concluded, "All fair-minded men must recognize that the very large expenditures required...cannot be justified as sound business of the United States."

After 1917 no further attempts were made to tame the upper river for traffic. Throughout the 1920s, a decade the railroads dominated, the Columbia above the Cascades was rarely used as a waterway. In a 1930 report to Congress, the Corps' General Lytle Brown confessed that for the $9.4 million spent on Columbia River navigation, including the canals at the Cascades and Celilo Falls, the commercial results had been "very disappointing."

DAMS WITHOUT LOCKS

In 1910 Army Corps Major Charles Kutz studied the Columbia as a resource for power as much as for navigation. Traditionally, power generation had been the concern of neither the Corps nor those who used and promoted the river. Yet Kutz concluded that damming the river for hydroelectricity would do "far more to develop the country and increase its prosperity than...providing a navigable channel." He even advised — radically for the time — that the federal government might build the dams, with the electricity generated helping pay for navigation, the government's

Above: Steamer Enterprise *at the Upper Long Rapids during the Corps of Engineers's survey of the Columbia River between Bridgeport and Kettle Falls, January 1908. Below: Construction work along the upstream face of the Rock Island Dam powerhouse, March 4, 1931. Courtesy National Archives, Alaska-Pacific NW Region.*

traditional point of entry in river and harbor public works. In this, Kutz's report did offer some hope for the Upper Columbia's determined navigators. The proposed dams would be multipurpose and include locks behind which navigable pools would create a waterway at much less the cost than the Corps' repeated attempts to blast — or "regularize" — the river into navigable submission. Unfortunately for waterborne traffic the creation of locks was an opportunity which would be ignored eight times on the river above the Snake — first at Rock Island which was developed by Puget Power and Light Company for power and with no provisions for irrigation, flood control, or navigation. Navigational aids were never a serious concern at Grand Coulee, especially following the eleventh-hour decision to build a high dam. The 200-foot-high intrusion of Chief Joseph Dam at Bridgeport in the early 1950s was not designed with a lift. However, neither of these obstructions was a great disappointment; the sustained interest in an Upper Columbia waterway was applied to the river between Pasco and the Okanogan River. As for the lockless Rock Island Dam, it was understood that when the time came for adding a lift there it could be easily, albeit dearly, engineered. These hopes, however, were seriously deflated when construction on the dam at Priest Rapids was begun in 1956 without locks, although it was built to later accept them if needed.

Above: Chief Joseph Dam near Bridgeport, May 15, 1979. Courtesy, Seattle District USCE. Below: Early-century scene of steamers on the Upper Columbia near Wenatchee. Courtesy The Wenatchee World. Bottom: Pasco Commercial Club on a turn-of-the-century excursion on the Columbia River aboard the sternwheeler Inland Empire.

STRANDED BARGES ON THE COLUMBIA

Shallow draft barges like the one shown here were typical on the Columbia before its rapids were inundated with the slack water pools formed behind the many dams with locks built along the main stem of the river below Pasco. The precarious condition of this barge is, however, not typical. Normally it would have been towed by its owner, the Inland Navigation Company, through the Celilo Canal. Here, after breaking its moorings it is stuck on the falls themselves in the summer of 1945 when the river was low. The unusual rescue took three days to materialize: the time required for the head of water released from Coulee Dam to reach the falls and release the barge. *Photo courtesy, National Archives, Alaska-Pacific NW Region.*

On March 17, 1963, Washington Senator Henry Jackson titillated the 150 delegates attending the Upper Columbia Navigational Conference in Wenatchee by advising them that prospects for navigation to Rock Island would be considerably brightened when the Corps revised its criteria for determining worthy projects to include considerations both of an area's industrial potential as well as its rate of unemployment. Yet while Jackson was rallying the delegates, Wanapum Dam was already under construction, Priest Rapids and Rocky Reach dams completed, and Wells Dam planned — all without locks.

In 1964 and again in 1967 the Army Corps conducted new studies on the feasibility of extending the head of navigation to Wenatchee and subsequently proposed in its 1970 report the dredging of a navigable channel through the last stretch of wild river from McNary Pool to Priest Rapids Dam and the installation of locks there and at Wanapum and Rock Island dams. The idea was rejected by the Washington State Department of Ecology. The multipurpose river had a new assignment — actually, its oldest — nature. The environmental impact statement, the then recent creation of the National Environmental Policy Act of 1969, gave fish, nature lovers, and archaeologists a tool they hadn't previously enjoyed.

The Ben Franklin Dam, the eighth and last on the Columbia above Pasco (and below Canada), also has no lift lock, but neither has it a spillway, powerhouse, or fish ladder. Long proposed but never disposed, the Ben Franklin would have completed the stretch of slack-water Columbia between tidewater and the Canadian Border. Its pool would have extended 57 miles between Priest Rapids Dam and the Ben Franklin's site a few miles north of Richland. The Ben Franklin was initially plotted in 1957 by the Washington Public Power Supply System (WPPSS) as its first power producer. Navigation was included in the plans from the start. A quarter-century later the project was abandoned when the Corps concluded in 1981 that the clout of objecting environmen-

Top right: Mud and debris released with the 1980 eruption of Mount St. Helens darken and clutter the Cowlitz River in this early scene of the Corps of Engineers work in dredging and clearing the channel. Courtesy Corps of Engineers. Right: Dredger Wahkiakum *at Vancouver site of aluminum plant, Sept. 9, 1949. Below: Dredger* Multnomah *and its floating pontoon discharge line on the Columbia River, August 1949. Courtesy National Archives, Alaska-Pacific NW Region.*

talists was sufficient to make the engineerable Ben Franklin politically impossible. This decision came one hundred years after Lt. Symons first surveyed this part of the river. The proliferation of lockless dams that had begun at Rock Island in 1932 ended here at Ben Franklin, sending the warriors for an Upper Columbia waterway home to their orchards, warehouses, and associations. For many it is satisfying to reflect that with Ben Franklin's demise there survives a Columbia just north of Richland where if Lt. Symons had taken Rip Van Winkle's nap he could still awaken to a river instantly recognizable. Ironically, this is also the "secret river" closed in 1976 to the return of the James Patricks, Senior and Junior (see above).

RETURN TO TIDEWATER

When the new Reagan Administration adopted one of the railroads' persistent arguments against tax-supported public works on waterways — that its users were getting a free ride — the river's ports and traffickers were understandably alarmed. The bell tolled loudest on the lower Columbia where profitable transshipment between barges, trains, trucks, and ocean-going vessels was elaborately dependent on tax-paid lightships, jetties, buoys, pilots, dredges, the Coast Guard, and the Army Corps. Through public works the mercurial Columbia bar had been made predictable and the channel dredged to a depth that permitted all but the largest ships to call on Astoria, Longview, Kalama, Vancouver, and Portland — especially Portland. In 1978 the Port of Portland had the highest dollar increase in cargo of any U.S. port, from $1.9 billion in 1977 to $2.7 billion, a rise of 44 percent.

But two years later Portland's success was threatened by both Reagan's platform and an act of God: the May 21, 1980 eruption of Mount St. Helens. Eighteen-and-a-half hours after St. Helens blew its side, at 8:30 Sunday morning, a large container ship ran into the mountain. For two miles the normally forty-foot low-tide channel off Longview had filled to a depth of only fifteen feet with St. Helens mud and debris. In the first week as much as fifteen million cubic yards of silt passed down the Toutle and Cowlitz Rivers to shoal the channel for nine miles below the Cowlitz. More than fifty ships were stalled, about half of them at the bar wanting to go upstream with the rest at Vancouver and Portland waiting to get out. The Corps predicted that restoration of the original channel might take as long as five months. Working seven dredges at the site, ships with drafts shallow enough to make it through in the first days were piloted together during a one-to-two-hour "window" twice a day during high tides. By June 28 a channel deep enough for many container ships was ready, and on July 31 the waterway was opened to regular shipping with a depth only two feet less than the standard forty-foot channel first guaranteed in 1976 after a decade of dredging.

The Corps had, in fact, been working on the lower Columbia for many years prior to the St. Helens eruption. In 1959 the new forty-eight-foot channel across the bar was completed by the 525-foot *Essayone*, the world's largest sea-going hopper dredge. Five years later the 265-foot pipeline dredges *Multnomah* and *Wahkiakum*, painted a brilliant red and yellow, began "walking" the channel to Portland, vacuuming it to a new and still-maintained depth of forty feet. In 1977, one year after the forty feet was reached and 100 years since the government engineers first proposed improving the waterway, the Army Corps estimated that they had applied $60 million towards regularizing the bar and another $116 million for working the river as far inland as Portland.

Above: Dumping rock at the double track turnout on the south jetty of the Columbia Bar, Nov. 14, 1933. Left: Dredge activity on the Columbia River near Vancouver, ca. 1965. Courtesy Ted Van Arsdol.

The north and south jetties at the Columbia bar are other important devices for maintaining a navigable channel. The often heroic work of building them began on the Oregon side in 1885. A stretch of quarried rock 4.25 miles long was strung out from Clatsop Spit in an attempt to train the river currents to flush the channel. Construction on the second jetty began at Cape Disappointment in 1912. In five-and-one-half years, three million tons of rock were barged in and transferred to gondolas atop a railroad trestle which was continuously extended a short distance ahead of the jetty it was helping to build. At the bar anything constructed must eventually be reconstructed. Beginning in 1932 two million more tons of rock blasted from a quarry a few miles up the river were applied in reconstructing 3.75 miles of the sinking south jetty. The north jetty was repaired in the late 1930s and by 1947 the combined action of the two jetties had at last greatly improved the bar. The once treacherous Peacock Spit, named for the ship in Lt. Wilkes' fleet that struck it and sank in 1841, had shifted from the middle of the channel to a position safely behind and outside the north jetty.

Top left: Columbia River ferry from Maryhill. Top right: Ferry James A *takes on vehicles at West Roosevelt, Washington for its run to Arlington, Oregon, ca. 1965. Photo by Hugh Paradise.*

With the improvements in piloting, rescue operations, dredging, and jetty construction, the souls of fewer mariners have been surrendered to the "Pacific Graveyard" at the bar. The Army Corps 1947 statistics indicated that about one half-million deep-sea vessels had crossed the bar since the turn of the century, with only a dozen serious wrecks and a total loss of life of about 100. Another installment was added to the north jetty saga when further repair was completed there in 1965. At its outer end 2,200 feet were corrected surgically by a crawler-type crane placing stones one at a time at the weakened sides. A walkway was added along the top of the jetty leading hikers far out to an exhilarating prospect exposed twenty-four feet above the pounding Pacific.

Above: A variety of Columbia River navigation aids. Courtesy National Archives, Seattle.
Bottom: Looking east across the Columbia River bar, ca. 1930, the view shows both the north (left) and south jetties. Courtesy National Archives, Alaska-Pacific NW Region.

PUGET SOUND

There has been and, perhaps ever will be, confusion about Puget Sound, the waterway which British captain George Vancouver named for his lieutenant, Peter Puget. Puget Sound has crept north far beyond Restoration Point on Bainbridge Island where in 1792 Puget set south on his exploration. For many of those to whom maps are a puzzle, the waters of Puget Sound mingle with Canadian waters somewhere off the northern shores of the San Juan Islands. However its borders are drawn, Puget Sound is an inordinately fecund deep-water harbor protected between two mountain ranges below an ordinarily temperate gray sky.

Nearly all the waterways east of Tatoosh Island and south of Point Roberts are unusually kind. In most areas the bottom slopes precipitously to average depths of 300 to 600 feet, plunging 930 feet to its lowest point off the shore of Richmond Beach. Submerged shelves are rare and well-charted. At the few locations where dredging is a necessity for traffic, such as at the Sound's estuaries, a redistribution has followed the scooping, resulting in the reclamation of hundreds of acres of tidelands. For instance, around Elliott and Commencement Bays the sediment dredged from the Duwamish and Puyallup River waterways has added hundreds of acres to the Ports of Seattle and Tacoma. In Seattle, Harbor Island was once the world's largest man-made sandbar, and as such one of the

Above: Variations on the theme of "Twilight of the Natives" were popular subjects for pioneer photographers like Asahel Curtis who photographed this silhouette of Puget Sound Indians beaching their dugout canoe beneath a sky at once revealing and threatening. Courtesy U.W. Library, Special Collections.

public works victories of this reclamation. Although the Army Corps was an early promoter of grand works like the Lake Washington Ship Canal, it was towards the clearing of rivers like the Skagit, Nooksack, Snohomish, and White rivers that the Corps' first work was directed.

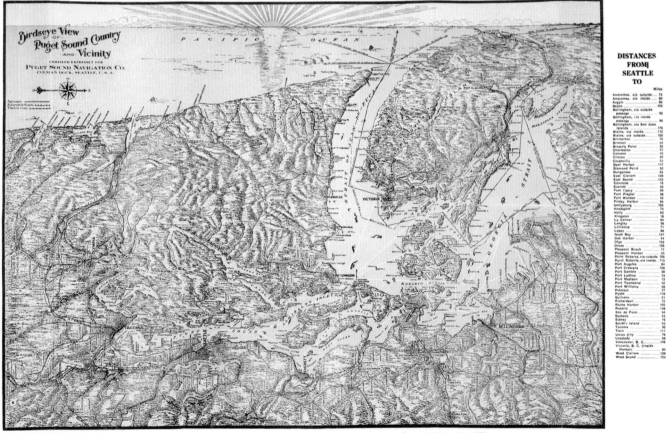

SHORT, INEXPENSIVE STEAMER TRIPS ON PUGET SOUND—FULL INFORMATION AT COLMAN DOCK, SEATTLE, WASH.

PUGET SOUND NAVIGATION COMPANY, COLMAN DOCK, SEATTLE, WASH.

Besides depicting the waterways of Puget Sound, the Strait of Juan De Fuca, Georgia Strait, and British Columbia's inside passage and identifying most communities between the mouth of the Columbia and the north end of Vancouver Island, the Puget Sound Navigation Company's ambitious topographic birdseye also marks routes for railroads, electric interurbans, and highways and provides a sidebar listing the distances between Seattle and major destinations serviced by P.S.N.C.. Courtesy Waterfront Awareness.

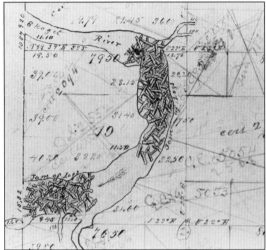

Top: Snag boat Skagit *corralling logs on the Skagit River. Above: Federal Land Bureau map, ca. 1870, of log jam near the mouth of the Skagit River. Below: Engine room of the snag boat* Swinomish, *Feb. 15, 1915. Bottom: Stern-wheeler W.T. Preston. Courtesy National Archives, Alaska-Pacific NW Region.*

The Tributaries

Settlement along Puget Sound's largest tributary, the Skagit River, was inhibited by two ancient log jams. The first of these, ten miles upstream from the river mouth, was first attacked in 1874 by seven loggers, who sustained by donations of $4,000 and whatever logs they could salvage, chipped and sawed at the obstruction for three years. In 1877 a five-acre section broke free and scattered downstream. The success of this publicly subscribed work encouraged the founding of Mount Vernon near the site of the lower jam. By the late 1870s shallow-draft steamers could race up the Skagit as far as Goodell Creek, carrying miners to the Skagit Valley gold rush of 1879-80.

Gold, of course, got the government's attention. In 1880 Congress appropriated $2,500 for removal of snags on the Skagit. A log raft with derrick and capstan was assembled thirty miles upstream. Consuming snags, it ate its way to the river mouth. Next, Major Gillespie of the Army Corps' Portland office advised that "one snag-boat, well equipped, will be able to clean out all these rivers and keep them in a good navigable state...for the small steamers which carry out the commerce of the valleys." In 1882 Congress allowed $20,000 to build the snag boat *Skagit* which became the most popular and dogged symbol of government work improving and maintaining Puget Sound waterways and Skagit River tributaries.

In 1896, the *Skagit* received a thorough renovation. The timing was fortunate. In November 1897 a hundred-year flood closed the Skagit River to navigation with two new jams. The largest, at the river's mouth, filled the stream from bank to bank for about 800 yards. Unlike the primeval jams sawed away twenty years earlier, these were constructed not only of virgin giants swept from the river banks but the loose edges of civilization, including whole sections of barns and houses, bridge piers, barbed-wire fences, and the refuse of logging, principally immense stumps. The improved *Skagit* required only a month to break this jam. In his annual report for 1898, E. H. Jefferson, the sternwheeler's master, related to Capt. Taylor, the first director of the Army Corps Seattle office, that "if it had not been for the snag boat, navigation in the Skagit River would be closed yet and thousands of acres of tillable farm lands overflowed and ruined." Jefferson's report noted other benefits. "The towing of logs from upriver points has never been so easy and safe... The regular steamer from Seattle has recently been extending her trips to Sedro for the first time in years, and I understand has brought the railroad rates to that point down a few pegs." Jefferson claimed to have removed 8,445 snags in the twelve months following June 1897, 7,838 of them from the Skagit.

In 1905 the Nooksack River had been newly reopened after the recalcitrant logjam at its mouth was removed by the Corps. Under good conditions, light-draft boats could make it as far as Lynden, nineteen miles above the mouth. On the Duwamish, small steamers plied as far as the junction of the White and Black rivers, or about twelve miles from the mouth. If the flow was sufficient they could continue several miles up the White (now the Green) River or, if their cargo was light and their draft shallow, through the Black River's short course to the southern end of Lake Washington. (The Black River was later dried up with the lowering of Lake Washington nine feet for the 1916 opening of the ship canal.)

In 1909 the worn *Skagit* was pronounced "not sufficiently seaworthy to be safe in ordinary rough weather in the Sound." Congress responded with the *Swinomish*. The name change was telling. The Corps' Skagit Valley attentions were slowly but steadily turning from the river towards the eleven-mile Swinomish Slough that connected Saratoga Passage with the flats of Padilla Bay giving La Conner, one of Skagit County's oldest communities, its water-link. It was, the Corps claimed, "a waterway of great importance…, giving an inside passage for small craft in rough weather." The Corps' first project of dredging and diking the channel was completed in 1937 and it is still a busy waterway. Not so the river.

In 1929 the Corps snagboat *Swinomish*, much worse for wear, was rebuilt as the *W.T. Preston*. As a combined snagboat and small suction dredge, the steel-hulled *Preston* and its Capt. George Murch labored hardest on the Skagit River. By the time of the captain's retirement in 1962 the priorities of the last sternwheeler operating on Puget Sound had shifted. In 1960 the *W.T. Preston* pulled 395 snags from the Skagit; however, most of its efforts were spent on Lake Washington where it removed 4,708 snags. In 1983 she was retired to Anacortes as the main attraction at its maritime museum.

Mosquito Fleet

The modern era of steaming on Puget Sound began not in 1837 when the Hudson's Bay Company sent the side-wheeler *Beaver* up from the Columbia River, but in 1852 when she was seized at Port Townsend by a United States customs collector, Simpson P. Moses. With this lock-up of a ship which had hitherto been free to do as she pleased, Puget Sound was demonstrably regulated. Ultimately, the government's readiness to take taxes and license fees from this waterway meant that it would have to return it in the form of services and public works. Ultimately, but not immediately.

The first steamers on Puget Sound had little trouble with the waterway itself which was both protected and deep. It was with the increments of success that those vessels struggled — the bursting boilers, the winning and losing of mail contracts, the rate wars with competing vessels, the weeks of unbroken work and its opposite, the utter lack of it, especially in the beginning when there were few settlers and little cash.

The doldrums following the war with the natives in the late 1850s were extended by the Civil War. Activity on Puget Sound was restrained until 1869, when the successful completion of the transcontinental railroad to Sacramento opened all of the West to a second wave of hope and immigration. There was but one steamer on Puget Sound that prospered in the decade before the '69 boom. Like those times, the *Eliza Anderson* was also trudging, although it was said of her that "no steamer went so slow or made money faster." Launched in Portland in 1858, she was brought around to Puget Sound the following year where for a decade she perfected her monopoly. Her fares between Olympia and Victoria could swing between 50 cents and twenty dollars depending upon the competitors, all of whom were either driven off or paid off to leave the route.

The *North Pacific* was the Sound steamer of the 1870s. Like the *Anderson*, she held sway over the Olympia-Victoria run for years, although her owners, the Starr brothers, were prudent enough to set generally affordable fares. This practice discouraged competition by companies of similar and smaller means, but not by the Northwest's transportation giant, the Oregon Railway and Navigation Company, which in 1881 entered the Puget Sound field. The smart Starrs stayed so and sold out to the Oregon company, which ran the *North Pacific* as its flagship.

By 1889, the last territorial year, the steam-parade on Puget Sound had developed into an armada of tooting packets and freelancers reflecting a shoreside explosion. Between 1881, the year the *North Pacific*'s original owners sold her to the Portland corporation, and 1898, the year she joined the gold rush, three transcontinental railroads to the Northwest were completed, and Seattle's population increased almost twenty-fold, from about 5,000 to over 90,000. Although spectacular, Seattle's growth was not peculiar. Tacoma eclipsed Olympia and mainland Vancouver, B.C. eclipsed the insular Victoria. The North Pacific's last route before her 1903 demise on the rocks off Marrowstone Point was between Tacoma, Seattle, and Vancouver, the region's new cities where transcontinental rails met transpacific sails. This "Where Rails Meet Sails" rhyme encapsulated a popular pioneer expectation, which by the turn of the century was made increasingly routine not by sails but by steam. The public part in these new opportunities and abuses was, at first, minimal, but ultimately a variety of public ports and public works including new waterways, canals, connecting channels, boat basins, and public ferries resulted.

By 1917, the year the Lake Washington Ship Canal was dedicated, the war-time Emergency Fleet Corporation had five yards for steel ships and a dozen more for wooden ones working on Elliott Bay. The following year Puget Sound handled more cargo than any American port except New York. Puget Sound had been busy within itself as well. Most of the intra-Sound cargo was carried not by truck or train but aboard "Mosquito Fleet" steamers or barges. Well into the 20th Century it was still more economical to haul all but the finest lumber on ships, and even as late as the close of the First World War it was not peculiar to see schooners

Top: Turn-of-the-century steamers on the Skagit River at Mount Vernon. Courtesy Skagit County Historical Society. Above: Eliza Anderson *on the Seattle waterfront, ca. 1885. Courtesy Jim Faber. Below: "Mosquito Fleet" steamers (left to right)* Verona, Nisqually, *and* Flyer *maneuvering in Tacoma Waterway on Feb. 15, 1913 in connection with the dedication of the Eleventh Street Bridge from which the scene was recorded. Courtesy Oregon Historical Society. Bottom: Captain H.N. Wallen presents E Flag to gold star workers representing all Todd Pacific employees at the destroyer yard on Harbor Island, Seattle; March 29, 1944. (Left to right) Capt. Wallen, Stanley Toothman, rigger; Cliff Beahre, electrician; Bill Borlen, sheet metal; Peggy Morris, electrician; Wanda Fink, welders helper. Courtesy National Archives, Alaska-Pacific NW Region.*

On the Ways

PUBLISHED BY THE LAKE WASHINGTON SHIPYARDS ★ HOUGHTON, WASHINGTON

Volume 4 — FEBRUARY 23, 1945 — Number 4

WAR WEARY SHIPS FIND HAVEN AT LWS

Top: A montage of the "endless armada of ships" worked on during World War II at Houghton, the "haven of the Lake Washington Shipyards." Courtesy National Archives. Above and below: Ferries Leschi *and* Lincoln *for many years mainstays of Lake Washington transportation. The Lincoln, below, receiving a new wheel house at the Lake Washington Shipyards. Courtesy, Museum of History and Industry, Seattle.*

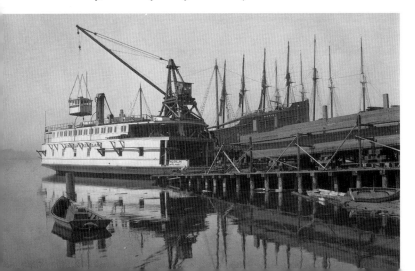

stacked with logs or finished lumber heading for the straits under tow. Puget Sound was the last waterway in the U.S. where sailing ships were still used in that work.

All these fleets — for fish, lumber, recreation, passengers, and other cargo — heated a waterway that nearly boiled with the ignition of World War I, a heavy-industry alchemy which was repeated a quarter-century later with World War II. The estimated value of the shipbuilding industry on Puget Sound was $6.5 million in 1939, the year of the state's fiftieth anniversary. Four years later all seventeen of Puget Sounds' shipyards, commercial and military, were contracted for 200 ships worth $700 million. And this prodigious public work was more than doubled by a related effort in the camouflaged factory beside the Duwamish Waterway. First the Boeing B-17 and then the B-29 were convincing evidence that a region blessed with a waterway like Puget Sound could ascend to the world's airways. Earlier, the successful June 8, 1938 liftoff from Elliott Bay of the Boeing Clipper, the *314*, became the enduring symbol of their union. Clearing West Point she headed north towards the white cliffs of Whidbey Island's Possession Point. There, 2,000 feet above the harbor where 146 years and 4 days earlier the English explorer Capt. George Vancouver had claimed possession of Puget Sound, the Boeing *314* turned to the south. Thirty-eight minutes later she set down to a fresh water harbor at Mathews Beach on Lake Washington.

WASHINGTON FERRIES

The first vessel built on Puget Sound specifically for cars was the *Leschi*. Constructed on the East Waterway for the Port of Seattle, she was disassembled and carted to Lake Washington and there reassembled in 1914 for a long career on the lake. The new car ferry was sent down her way by Eleanor Chittenden, the daughter of the Port Commission's president, General Hiram Chittenden. As the administrative genius behind the Lake Washington Ship Canal, another public work then in progress, the Army Corps' Chittenden was identified with the future of the lake.

The *Leschi* was preceded fourteen years earlier by the ferry *King County of Kent*. The first double-ender built in the Puget Sound region, the side-wheeler *Kent* was King County's public works response to the pleading of Eastside residents for a regular connection with the city. The county's 1900 entrance onto that field was authorized five years earlier when the state legislature first allowed counties to build and operate ferries. In competition with private steamers on the lake, the *Kent* halved the fare between Kirkland and Madison Park. Consequently, she lost money consistently. And her career was a brief one; continuously springing leaks and lawsuits, she was condemned in 1908. In 1914, months after the *Leschi* was launched by the Port of Seattle, King County introduced the double-ender car ferry *Lincoln* on the lake. With roadwork on the Sunset Highway heroically approaching Snoqualmie Pass, 1914 was a promising year for eastside transportation.

In February 1919, Capt. John Anderson, the ferry system's principal private competitor on the lake, was appointed King County Superintendent of Transportation, a stewardship that included the ferries. The county had first sued Anderson for some of his competitive practices and then settled by hiring him. In 1920 a King County representative complained to the press that the city had not done its part towards preparing adequate street access to the county ferry docks at Madison Park and Leschi. "We landed and took on 1,000,000 persons at Leschi last year and everyone needed a flying machine to get over and down the hills of the city." The county ferry system cost $433,000 over revenues earned from fares in 1921. When the county council that year allotted only $116,000 for the entire system in 1922,

Daily Time Card

PUGET SOUND NAVY YARD AND BATTLESHIPS

U.S. BATTLESHIP "NEBRASKA" on Trial Run "MADE IN SEATTLE"
copyright 1906 by W.P.Romans

NAVY YARD ROUTE
COLMAN DOCK
SEATTLE

for **information** regarding Puget Sound
STEAMER TRIPS · SUMMER RESORTS
AUTOMOBILE TOURS *call or phone*
Tourist Information Bureau
MAIN 2222 · COLMAN DOCK

EFFECTIVE JAN. 20, 1926

Below: The Chippewa *was one of many Mosquito Fleet passenger steamers (left) whose bows were opened and whose decks were widened to carry automobiles (right).*

the Department of Transportation recommended the inevitable, that the county get out of the ferry business. Captain Anderson then replaced his public hat with a private one, and took on a ten-year franchise and lease on county vessels and routes to Vashon Island, West Seattle, and on Lake Washington.

Anderson's fortunes soon flourished. In his hands the county ferries, formerly consistent losers, turned a profit. In 1925 the Captain bought controlling interest in the Kitsap Transportation Company and entered the field of Puget Sound. Of the scores of companies that through the years had some success in the competition for runs on Puget Sound, the Kitsap Transportation Company grew to be the second largest. Called the "White Collar Line," it and its larger competitor, the Puget Sound Navigation Company, or the "Black Ball Line" as it was eventually called, were both formed in the mid-1890s. The auto-conveying came later, primarily on the "Navy Yard Route" to Bremerton. Beyond the battleships on display at the Puget Sound Ship Yard, the wild Olympics were being increasingly penetrated by roads. The peninsula developed into a popular retreat from the urban congestion on the east shore of Puget Sound. The most obvious effect of this growing influence of highways on the public's waterway habits was the shift in routes. As highways increasingly linked communities on Puget Sound's eastshore, the role of water transportation shifted to carrying passengers and automobiles across the Sound.

By the mid-1920s the conversion of passenger steamers into car ferries was commonplace. Not even the finest of the Sound's passenger steamers were exempt. In 1926 the PSNC's Chippewa's bow and stern were cut away and its beam widened to accept 2,000 passengers and 90 cars. With the 1937 opening of the Golden Gate Bridge the car ferries of San Francisco Bay were suddenly available and cheap. Between 1937 and 1942, Puget Sound Navigation's Capt. Alexander Peabody Californiated his Puget Sound fleet with seventeen used ferries, rechristening them with Northwest names like the *Kehloken, Klahanie, Elwha, Willapa, Enetai, Quinault, Illahee, Klickitat,* and *Malahat.* When the *Shasta, San Mateo,* and *City of Sacramento* were brought north during World War II, the apparently preoccupied Peabody allowed them to keep their California names.

In 1935, after selling his Puget Sound fleet to Peabody's Black Ball, John Anderson returned to the lake, his county franchise, and a new problem. In 1938

Anderson presented the Washington Toll Bridge Authority with a bill in excess of $200,000 for the losses he expected to suffer with the construction of the concrete pontoon toll bridge then proposed. Ultimately, Anderson was compensated $35,000 for the promise that he would continue to operate all the lake routes until the bridge was completed. When the floating bridge's ribbon was cut on July 2, 1940 (see Bridges Chapter), the ferry routes to Medina and Roanoke on Mercer Island were wrapped up. Within a year, Captain John Anderson was dead. The county ferries *Lincoln* and *Washington* were idled, but the *Leschi* continued with the Kirkland connection through the 1940s. In the first year its revenue actually increased, but near the end of the decade the city of Kirkland was forced to appoint and pay for its operators to keep the route active. After the *Leschi's* last cross-lake steam to Kirkland in January, 1950 — the end of car-ferries on Lake Washington — she was transferred to the Vashon-Fauntleroy Ferry District, formed earlier to guarantee the island's mainland connection during the stormy and uncertain last days of the Puget Sound Navigation Company.

The Black Ball's "last days" ran about fifteen years. The forces that would lead ultimately to the 1950 sale of its fleet to the state began in 1935, the first year of its monopoly. With the purchase of Capt. Anderson's strike-injured Kitsap Transportation Company, the PSNC became the largest inland fleet in the world and in 1935 its art deco *Kalakala* was launched as a ferry to Bremerton and symbol of modernity to the world. But the strike of 1935 was the first of many contests between labor, the company, the riding public, landlubber taxpayers, and the state. And only the patriotic and imposed peace of the Second World War could interrupt this steady slide through strikes, rate hikes, and withdrawal of routes.

The idea that the public should control its own ferries is an old one. There is an economy to the logic that describes waterways as a continuation of the highways. Public ownership was politically prefigured in the growing influence of state and county agencies in the operation of private ferries. In 1854 Washington Territory's second legislature empowered counties to license ferryboats operating over the "lakes and streams in their respective counties." The 1869 amendment of this law to include waters "bordering" the

FELLOW COMMUTER

Be sure and sign the petition being circulated regarding ferry service. Your signature will help to get yourself a seat and a life preserver every time you ride. Let's prevent a catastrophe before it's too late. Let's all unite against being treated like cattle.

—This handbill paid for by Ferry Riders.

counties — an attempt to extend an individual county's right to regulate ferries to salt water as well — was successfully challenged in the mid-1920s by the state Department of Public Works, then a growing player in transportation, including ferries. The decision of first King County in 1900, with the *King County of Kent*, and then Seattle in 1913 with the *Leschi*, to take physical control of ferrying on Lake Washington (see above) was the stroking of a bottle which required a half-century more to finally release the genie. The materializing of this public spirit was helped considerably by public resentment over rate hikes and strikes.

In 1940 the argument that ferries were an extension of the state's highways was given a kind of concrete confirmation when the Tacoma Narrows Bridge shook to pieces. The State Highway Commission "bridged" the broken highway with the ferry Crossline. That summer the Black Ball bought six more California ferries after the military encouraged the sale as a service necessary for the Navy shipyard at Bremerton. By 1942 the round-trips to Bremerton had almost doubled to twenty-eight. With twenty-three ferries the Black Ball claimed it could evacuate the entire population of its Seattle district in two days, although the Navy would allow no cameras or binoculars. With nowhere to take them the company's boast was as odd as the military's precautions against spying. Better and more readily understood was the PSNC's decision to lower ferry rates an average of 25 percent during the war.

Right: The burning of the Black Ball Lines original flagship, the Willapa *(a.k.a.* Bellingham*) for the 1950 Seafair was the first instance of a Seafair Pirates tradition long since abandoned for environmental reasons. Courtesy* Seattle Times.
Below: The Kalakala, "the world's first streamlined ferry," was long the symbol of a modern Puget Sound. Courtesy Puget Sound Maritime Historical Society.

At the war's end peacetime strife returned and came to a head on February 29, 1948 when Peabody tied up his fleet in protest against the state's unwillingness to allow Black Ball to keep its 30 percent rate hike. On March 6th, Washington Governor Mon C. Walgren at last announced firmly, "The state definitely is going into the ferry business" The state but not this governor. Walgren's perceived fumbling of the ferry issue lost him that year's gubernatorial election to Seattle Mayor Arthur Langlie, who was perceived as a more ardent supporter of state ownership. When the state Supreme Court decided that the state had no right to sell bonds for the purchase of the Black Ball Line, Langlie steamed around the legal blockade by writing a new law that allowed it. Next, as the new governor was preparing to overwhelm the natty Peabody's puckish resistance to state purchase with an outright condemnation of the Black Ball, the line's president reluctantly withdrew after bankers advised Peabody to take the $4,944,499 offered and pay back his loans. At the time most parties expected that much of Puget Sound's ferry system would soon be superannuated by cross-Sound bridges; a possibility which no doubt also encouraged the anxious bankers to push Peabody into lowering his Black Ball flags and selling his fleet to the state.

At the 1950 Seafair, Seattle's summer festival, Captain Peabody allowed the hull of the *Bellingham* to be torched by the Seafair Pirates, the festival's official thugs, in a bit of sensational performance art. The gaudy destruction was grandly described as the sacrificial burning of Neptune's barge. The *Bellingham* was the last name given the oft-rebuilt hull of the *Willapa*, the PSNC's original steamer and Peabody might have seen in its destruction by fire a different ritual: the funeral pyre of his company's ferry fleet. On December 30, 1950, Puget Sound Navigation Company's stockholders agreed to sell. Alexander Peabody did not vote. The state took control at midnight June 1, 1951. Earlier at sundown the fleet of Black Ball ferries paused mid-course for one minute and lowered their flags for the last time. Included in the transfer were sixteen ferries (all but four from California), twenty terminals, one destroyer escort, and some odds and ends. When the new flags, emblazoned with the green silhouette of an evergreen, were hoisted at sunrise, those pulling the ropes still belonged to the union; the ferry workers did not surrender advantages won earlier battling the Black Ball. On occasion the ferry workers' powerful status would become a sore point, especially for the riders who, with public ownership, were still not free of the threat of strikes, and slow-downs. Gov. Langlie predicted that someday cross-Sound ferry rides would be free.

The cross-sound bridge visionaries were generally encouraged by the state's control of the ferries. New state bridge work began with the 1950 construction of the bridge at Agate Pass at the north end of Bainbridge Island. The new open gate to the peninsula through Bainbridge Island made the Seattle-Winslow route the system's busiest, a popularity which was increased with the ambitious 1961 addition of the Hood Canal Bridge. By then, however, the romance for the ultimate bridge, one crossing the Sound, had slipped. Both of its proposed routes, to Bainbridge and Vashon Islands, threatened those rural communities with gentrification. The islander's political instincts were developing in

Featured on the front cover of the May 1959 issue of Pacific Work Boat, *Washington State Ferries' newest vessel,* Tillicum, *approaches Colman Dock, the system's Seattle headquarters. Courtesy National Archives.*

environmental directions, and some of the them who earlier had threatened to pirate a ferry to preserve their vital connection to the mainland were now in favor of keeping it difficult to make any link that didn't require a paddle or propeller.

Gov. Langlie's fantasy about free ferries was quickly dissipated by the realities of operating the system. The original act allowing the purchase of the system was an example of hopeful legislation, stating that the enterprise should be both revenue-producing and self-liquidating. In its second year, the system hit red and while its service improved and the fleet enlarged, so did the debt. Taxpayers from Seattle and Poulsbo, more than those of Selah and Wapato, were inclined to support the necessity of using gas taxes to support ferry rides. In 1961, ten years after the acquisition, the legislature raised motor-fuel taxes to pull in an additional $2.6 million subsidy for the ferry system. The new money was also for maintenance, and the existing fleet that was savable was well-serviced considering the constraints. However, the legislature's new subsidies promised no relief for the fleet's obvious but pricey need: new and larger ferries.

In a 1962 report on the status of its twenty-one vessels management was gloomy. The condition of the *Kalakala* was typical. As the Californian *Peraltra*, she had been originally very lightly constructed, and in her 1935 streamlined *Kalakala* redesign, function was often sacrificed for style. Now in the year of the Space Needle — a showtime silhouette soon to replace the streamlined ferry as the region's international symbol — the *Kalakala* needed a complete overhaul. The world's first streamlined ferry held on until 1967 when she was sold for $100,000 to American Freezerships Company and towed to Kodiak where she was landlocked and put to the unromantic work of processing crab. (And ever since the *Kalakala's* nostalgic activists have been trying to bring her back.)

In 1954 Washington State Ferries built its first commissioned ferry, the *Evergreen State*. The *Klahowya* followed in 1958 and the *Tillicum* in 1959. The 1962 report on the fleet concluded that only twelve of the state's twenty-one ferries had future value for the system and one of this dozen, the venerable *Leschi*, the first car ferry built in the Puget Sound area, was doubtful. The state would sell the *Leschi* in 1968. She was converted to a floating cannery and sent north to Alaska.

The answer to the anxieties of 1962 was $24 million worth of "superferries" in 1967, made half-affordable by an $11.4 million grant from the federal government. At 382 feet each, the *Hyak*, *Kaleetan*, *Yakima*, and *Elwha* were certainly super, but ultimately not super enough. In 1972 the "jumbo ferries" *Spokane* and *Walla Walla* joined the fleet. Designed locally by Philip Spaulding & Associates and built at Todd Pacific Shipyards on Elliott Bay, they were at the time the biggest ferries in the world, with room for 206 automobiles and 2,000 passengers. Named for the tribes, rather than the cities, the jumbos might nonetheless help a visitor from Eastern Washington feel more at home on Puget Sound. The fleet's next additions, "The Issaquah Class," inspired comfort in very few. Authorized in 1977 through a $135 million general obligation bond, the *Issaquah*, *Kittitas*, *Kitsap*, *Cathlamet*, *Chelan*, and *Sealth* were built by Marine Power and Equipment Company in Seattle at about half

Clockwise: The Issaquah *at Seattle's Colman Dock, flagship for the* Issaquah *class of ferries;* Superferry Hyak; Evergreen State *and* Klahowya, *the first commissioned vessels for the state's "Evergreen Fleet" in 1954 and 1958, respectively;* Superferry Yakima.

Clockwise: The Tyee catamaran passenger ferry with Seattle skyline, ca. 1995; The Issaquah-class Kittitas in the slip beside Colman Dock; launching of the Tacoma, flagship of the department's new Jumbo Mark II class of ferries, at Todd Shipyards in Seattle; jumbo ferries Spokane and Walla Walla; the Illahee, signed for the 1962 Century 21 World's Fair, was built for San Francisco Bay in 1927 and then transferred to Puget Sound in 1937 after completion of the Golden Gate Bridge.

the capacity of the jumbos. Although designed to feature the leading edge in computer controls, their high-tech parts performed fitfully.

With the completion of the *Chelan*, Washington State Ferries had increased its car capacity to nearly 2,500, almost twice the number it could handle in 1966, the year construction began on the "superferries" and the last year of a serious cross-Sound bridge proposal.

In August of 1996 Washington State Ferries launched at the Todd shipyards the longest double-ended car passenger ferry in North America. The *Tacoma* was the first of three Jumbo Mark II ferries due to be put in service before the turn of the century. With a capacity of 218 vehicles and 2,500 passengers the trio was designed primarily for the crowded run between Seattle and Bremerton. The *Tacoma* began this packet in the fall of 1997, not in time, however, to relieve that summer's record-setting delays or to subdue rider protests. The traffic of 1997 indicated a need for a fourth (and more) Jumbo Mark IIs with the ferry system expecting 70 percent growth by the year 2015.

The revival of Puget Sound's "Mosquito Fleet" with passenger-only ferries has proven a popular strategy for dealing with the system's growing congestion. Nearly twice as fast as auto ferries, the *Kalama, Skagit,* and the catamaran *Tyee* began zipping from Seattle to both Vashon Island and Bremerton in the spring of 1990. (At this writing, February 1998, passenger-only ferries also run regularly to Bainbridge Island and are being studied for service to Kingston.) This was a delayed inauguration, postponed by lack of funds to operate the vessels when they were first delivered. Soon, however, the waiting ferries were sent south for emergency service to commuters on San Francisco Bay following that area's October 1989 earthquake that damaged the Bay Bridge.

PUBLIC PORTS

The Port on Elliott Bay

In Puget Sound harbors, such as Elliott Bay, where rivers have deposited a few millennia of sediment onto wide tideflats that are alternately flooded and exposed, the first settlers recognized that many of these shallows could be reclaimed from the shellfish and shore birds that used them. In Seattle these reclaimable acres extended south from King Street to the islands at the mouth of the Duwamish River and east to the foot of Beacon Hill. Seattle pioneer Henry Yesler had made a small beginning at filling these flats with sawdust from his lumber mill, the first steam-powered mill on Puget Sound.

All the land below the line of high tide was claimed by the federal government and kept in trust for the territory until it became a state, which it was about to do in 1888. Understandably, the federal government's tidelands trust inspired a good deal of distrust on the part of both those who owned the upland shores — the squatters — and those who had made improvements in territorial tidelands and waterways — the jumpers. Yesler was both: a squatter, with his spreading wharf at the foot of Yesler Way, and then a jumper, on the tidelands south of King Street. In 1888, after his mill on the central waterfront burned down for the second time, Yesler resumed his pioneer initiative by moving a few hundred yards to the tideflats and driving piles there for a new mill. He was one of a crowd. Piles driven by one party during the day might be pulled up by another during the night. In a letter to a friend, Seattle lawyer and judge Thomas Burke described this tidelands free-for-all in the spring of 1888.

A swarm of salt water lunatics of high and low degrees has alighted, like so many cawing crows on the mud flats in the Southern part of town, and have made the place a veritable sight with piles stuck all over it. And herein is where there was a great

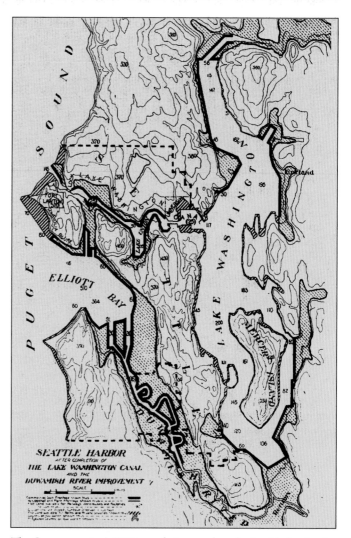

The Coast *magazine's 1909 speculations on the reshaping (darker lines) of Seattle, Elliott Bay, amd Lake Washington after the completion of the Lake Washington Ship Canal and the Duwamish River Improvement. Courtesy, University of Washington Libraries, Special Collections.*

abuse of charity by the sea — it should have drowned the whole of them but so far I am sorry to say, not a single man of them has ever got wet.

Actually, Burke was the raven among crows, although most of the judge's piles were driven along the central, not southern, tide flats first with the 1887 construction of his Seattle Lake Shore and Eastern Railroad and later with the extension of Railroad Avenue far out from the city's original waterfront. Burke was good at describing his own motives as guided by the "Seattle Spirit," but by 1889, the year of both Seattle's Great Fire and Washington Territory's statehood, it was not so easy to rationalize the forces competing for space on the waterfront as guided by a civic spirit. They had created an economy of large private profits at both public and environmental costs. And every shoreline ambiguity in this tidal maze of industry and reclamation was attended by a legal one: whose shoreline and tideland was it? Henry Yesler was pretty sure it was his — certainly that part beneath his sprawling wharf.

The Constitutional Convention

It was with two hands that the state Constitutional Convention's Committee on Tidelands wrote its Article XVII — Tidelands. Its public hand wrote "the state of Washington asserts its ownership to the beds and shores of all navigable waters in the state up to and including the line of ordinary high tide, in waters where the tide ebbs and flows, and up to and including the line of ordinary high

Above: Birdseye of Seattle in 1884. For only three years Seattle had been the largest city in Washington Territory (surpassing Walla Walla) when it extended its waterfront with timber trestles (far right), south of King Street. Courtesy University of Washington Library. Below: Seattle, 1996. The Kingdome and the Port's container yard south of King Street were constructed on reclaimed tidelands. The difficulties of this yard's railroad connections made questionable its long term usefulness for containers. Photo by Wilson, Port of Seattle.

water within the banks of all navigable rivers and lakes..." But its private hand added, "provided, that this section shall not be construed so as to debar any person from asserting his claim to vested rights in the courts of the state."

The state Harbor Line Commission made its first report public in the fall of 1890 and unanimously recommended that the Elliott Bay harbor line "include the space known as Railroad Avenue for about two miles, and also more or less of the space occupied by about thirty-five wharves..." Thomas Burke bubbled. The judge responded for the *Seattle Post-Intelligencer*, "A monstrous outrage has been attempted to be perpetuated upon those whom the state should honor and protect, those who came to this country when it was a howling wilderness, the home of the savage and the lair of the wild beast."

Appropriately, the first pioneer to test the commission's intent was Yesler, and Burke used the resultant *Henry Yesler v. Harbor Line Commission* to request from the state Superior Court an injunction temporarily prohibiting the commission from publishing its prescriptive maps. The covenous word here is "temporary," for Burke was bluffing to take time. After months of plotted delays, his last appeal reached the United States Supreme Court which quickly agreed with the state's attorney general that *Henry Yesler v. Harbor Line Commission* was an unmerited ruse to buy time. However, as Nesbit explains in his biography of Burke, *He Built Seattle*, "Burke won only the preliminary skirmishes and lost all of the major battles in his struggle with the harbor line commission. But he won the war." With Burke's delays, the Harbor Line Commission's term expired before it could complete work on Grays Harbor, and Commencement and Elliott bays. As Nesbit summarizes it, "Burke had triumphed over the clear intent of the state constitution and the enactments of the first legislature, the legal decisions of the first Harbor Line Commission, and the clear mandates of the state and federal supreme courts."

With a new state land board assuming the unfinished work of the commission and a new governor — John McGraw, Burke's old Seattle crony — harbor lines on Elliott and Commencement bays were soon drawn clear of the wharves and Railroad Avenue. These new lines were in harmony with the desires of the railroads and pioneer squatters like Henry Yesler, although Yesler did not survive to gloat in this victory. With the surrender of the public's part in its waterfront, Burke and his fellow nabobs could do their will on the waterfront. While professing civic concern and, as Nesbit calls it, playing the "pioneer pedal,' the waterfront was exploited by the few at the expense of the many. Soon, however, the tides would change.

The Port of Seattle

Virgil Bogue, the engineer who had established his reputation bringing the Northern Pacific Railroad through Stampede Pass in 1887, was the first progressive to attempt to make Seattle's waterfront public. In 1895 describing conditions on Burke's Railroad Avenue as "a blot on the city and a menace to the lives of its citizens," the cosmopolitan Bogue cited European ports as evidence that "the greatest commercial success has resulted where there has been, either in part or in whole, municipal or other public ownership and control of dock frontage." His proposal that a shared terminal company be organized to relieve the blight and unravel the chaos on the waterfront was rejected outright by the Great Northern Railroad, one of Judge Burke's clients.

While Bogue was proposing, ex-territorial governor Eugene Semple was disposing the glacial till of Beacon Hill onto the tidelands south of King Street. Beginning in 1896, Semple dug into three Herculean tasks at once: cutting a "South Canal" to Lake Washington through Beacon Hill, dredging the Duwamish, and spreading the combined gravel and muck from both onto the tidelands. Semple's enthusiasm was suddenly gilded in 1897 with the discovery of gold in the Klondike. A happy chaos was brought to the sidewalks and waterfront of Seattle.

In 1897 Populists were more popular than railroads and Seattle City Engineer R.H. Thomson and his assistant George Cotterill were populists with white collars — that is, progressives. In 1897 they began the work of plating the tidelands and regularizing construction on the waterfront. By the early century the city's waterfront had been schematized with new and longer piers set at a uniform angle to eliminate right turns for ships and railroad spurs to the pier's aprons. (See Streets and Mass Transportation Chapter).

Ten years later, in 1907, Cotterill was a state senator and chairman of the Senate Committee on Harbors and Waterways. His Tideland Improvement Bill of that year provided for "public facilities for shippers and others." Significantly, his proposals no longer seemed radical; Senate Bill 190 passed in both houses. However, for the veto of the bill Gov. Meade came dressed in the conventional cloak of "property rights" — the Great Northern had asked him to wear it.

Army Corps Col. Hiram Chittenden arrived in Seattle in 1906. He brought with him a confidence that the long-desired Lake Washington Ship Canal would be built, but along a northern route through Ballard and away from Elliott Bay. Eugene Semple's South Canal was abandoned to cave-ins, although two of his ambitious trio of projects were continued — the dredging of Elliott Bay and the Duwamish estuary and the reclamation of the tideflats below Beacon Hill.

In the 1910 King County voters approved bonds to both further straighten the Duwamish River and build the canal to Lake Washington through Lake Union. This time the railroads interceded with an injunction arguing that the state constitution specifically forbade the formation of special improvement districts. At last the railroads were isolated and vulnerable, and a short-lived alliance between capitalists, newspapers, populists, and progressives supported the drafting of yet another piece of waterways legislation by Senator George Cotterill. House Bill 426 circumvented the state constitution's inhibitions and enabled citizens to vote themselves a municipal corporation with powers to tax and condemn for the purpose of operating a harbor. This Port District Act passed through the legislature in June of 1911 and that September 5th, the voters of King County approved their public port. Two days later in a moment of futuristic euphoria the city's Municipal Plans Commission passed the Bogue Plan. (See Streets Chapter.) Although the Bogue Plan was defeated in the March 1912 election — its remake of the city was, perhaps, both too profoundly elegant and

Bell Street Terminal and Port of Seattle Administration Building, 1915. When this photo was taken, the tides still swept through the pilings of Railroad Avenue (now Alaskan Way). Later, in the mid-1930s, a seawall was completed as far north as Broad Street. Since the mid-1990s this Pier 66 site of the Port's old headquarters has been thoroughly made over for diverse maritime activities including a maritime museum, recreational vessel marina, restaurants, and the Bell Harbor International Conference Center. Courtesy Seattle Municipal Archives.

costly — still, many of the plan's waterways features became a continued source of inspiration and reference for the Port of Seattle.

By comparison with Bogue's vision, Col. Chittenden's initial proposals for his public port were politically prudent. Chittenden circumvented the dangers of cooption and redefinition by starting small. He persuaded the Port Commission to first ask the voters for one public pier only, with the rest — facilities at Smith Cove, development of the East Waterway, acquisition of land at Salmon Bay and expansion of the Lake Washington ferry service — to follow in later requests.

The Port of Seattle's facilities took shape with its philosophy of setting wharfage rates that would encourage use more than profits. The Port's fees were consistently less than half those of private piers. And the size of the Port's construction once it began in late 1912 worried the private powers on the harbor. On the East Waterway a 1,000-foot slip long enough to allow the biggest cargo ships to transfer all their cargo at one anchorage was planned. The superlatives continued at Smith Cove where work began on the Pacific Coast's largest pier on land purchased from the Great Northern. And on the central waterfront at the foot of Bell Street, the Port constructed the public dock and warehouse that until 1993 was used for its administration offices. In 1996, the Port offices moved north to their remodeled Pier 69.

Colonel Hiram Chittenden, Army Corps of Engineers

Irritated by the Port's speedy successes, the Seattle Chamber of Commerce tried stacking its commission from three to five seats elected county-wide. By a margin of two to one, the voters rejected this ruse in the election of June 1913. Many of the Port's strongest allies were among the smaller businesses — members of organizations like the Seattle Municipal League and the Seattle Commercial Club — who were understandably supportive of any efforts to make the waterways less costly.

Out of town in 1914 for a convention in Baltimore, Chittenden was candid on the subject of Seattle's port in his speech before the American Association of Port Authorities.

Almost at the outset of [the Port's] existence it ran into difficulties which for a time seriously threatened the ship-wreck of its purpose. In no port of the United States have private

Paving East Marginal Way in front of the Port of Seattle's Hanford Street Wharf and Grain Terminal; May 9, 1932. The Hanford Wharf, Pier 25, was separated from the Port's Spokane Street Wharf on Pier 24 by the turning basin (left) in which the freighter Steel Inventor *is here berthed. Courtesy Seattle Municipal Archives.*

interests become more thoroughly entrenched on the waterfront. Practically every foot was privately owned, the tide flats, now worth millions, had been sold for a song, and even the so-called harbor area — the phantom relic of a once priceless possession — though still belonging to the state, was so tied up by preferential rights to the abutting lands as to give the upland owner full control for 30 years at a rate so low as to be simply farcical. Local business sentiment was thoroughly imbued with the doctrine of private ownership and objected to public control... but there was a large progressive element among our citizens, who realized the evils of the existing system and undertook to remedy them... the principle of its organization was thus established on a firm basis, and while its work does not yet command the support of those who so strenuously oppose it, the district as a whole is solidly with the commission.

Commissioner Chittenden's popularity was tested in the year of this oratory — in his bid for reelection to the Port Commission, he overwhelmed his opposition 7,342 votes to 417.

The Port's steady assumption of services often in competition with private interests continued at pace, building cold storage and grain storage facilities, cutting rates, and, in the 1916 November election, handily beating a second attempt to stack the commission with more members. The year 1916 was a spectacular one on Elliott Bay. King County's was the only port in the nation that not only owned facilities but operated them as well, and the combination of favorable rates and new business generated by World War I pushed the volume of imports and exports on Elliott Bay to three times what they had been the year before. In this, Seattle surpassed San Francisco. Besides being the cheapest big port on the coast, Seattle was closer to the Orient than the Golden Gate and because of the Port's aggressive building projects, she had the facilities to surpass San Francisco's shipments to Asiatic ports by more than 154 percent in 1916. Only two years later, Seattle was the second busiest harbor in terms of the value of the cargo handled in the nation, surpassed only by New York.

Inspired in part by the exemplary success of the Port of Seattle, the public ports movement flourished through the 1920s, with the result that they competed among themselves. For instance, in the mid-1920s the Port of Tacoma initiated a wharfage rate war in an attempt to pull shipping from Elliott to Commencement Bay. In 1929, on the eve of the Great Depression, the Port Authorities Association instituted a policy designed to fix uniform rates for all West Coast ports.

In its plush parchment-bound yearbook for 1927, the Seattle Port confidently explains its prudent stewardship, "Over $10,000,000 of public money (is) being appropriated to expend in broad, well-thought-out plans to serve a shipping, manufacturing and commercial city of one million people, which will soon be here." The 1927 yearbook is a testament of pride; the 1934 yearbook is one of faith. In his *History of the Port of Seattle* Padraic

Burke quotes from the latter report. "In 1932 we prayed for something to happen. In 1933 we just prayed." The Great Depression had come and stayed. Its ruinous effects on the Port's economy were mildly ameliorated by the diversity of its capacities, a flexibility the public ports of Tacoma and Portland with their dependence on grains did not share. However, all West Coast shipping was double-punched when the International Longshoremen's Association struck for eighty-three days in 1934.

The artificial economy of the World War II interrupted the depression — the tonnage of ships launched on Elliott Bay during the second war was three times that sent down its ways during the first — but was quickly followed by a post-war maritime slump which lasted well into the 1950s. By then the port which was one of the great ones during the early 1920s lagged behind Tacoma in the business of exports. Padraic Burke summarizes the Port's contradictions in the twenty years between 1940 and 1960:

The 1940s and 1950's were a period of its greatest expansion and acquisition in its history: building a mammoth airport south of the city; expanding and modernizing its Fishermen's Terminal (on Salmon Bay), erecting one of the most modern small-boat marinas on the West Coast (Shilshole Bay) and laying plans for a very ambitious industrial development program along the Duwamish Waterway... The Port would embark in the late 1940's on a building program costing millions of dollars that would find it owning the vast majority of the docks and wharves in Seattle by 1959. But throughout the period the Port's non-defense-related commerce continued a steady and almost inexorable decline that had begun in the 1930s.

The maritime slump that followed WWII was worsened by labor troubles and the success of the trucking and rail services developed during the war. In peace many manufacturers did not return to the marine highway they had been booted off of during the war. The Port's first postwar public works included a $1 million enlargement of the Salmon Bay Fishermen's Terminal, a $5 million modernization of the East Waterway dock it had acquired during the hostilities, and the purchase of Piers 43 through 49 between Dearborn and Washington streets at the southern end of the central waterfront. A decade later, in 1958, the Port would direct $3.25 million to their modernization. In the early 1950s the Port again added to the capacity of its Hanford Street grain terminal and in 1955 began work on its Shilshole Bay small boat harbor — but not without objections. Some argued that those who could afford sailboats and yachts should build their own dock.

In 1954 the Port registered its first profit in several years, but it was a deceptive advance, for relative to most other Pacific coast ports King County's continued to slide. The reversal of this decline in the 1960s was cushioned by the Port's extensive land acquisitions and public works of the preceding two decades. But it was the Port's ultimate response to the "box" that turned things around.

Introduced in the mid-1950s, containers revolutionized shipping and transshipment. By efficiently moving freight across the waterfront in uniform-sized receptacles it took less than a day to do what before took four or five. By 1964 more than $60 million was directed in a modernization plan to the purchase and reclamation of new sites, many of which were along the Duwamish Waterway. The next year the Port for the first time surpassed its tonnage record during 1918. By the early 1970s its annual budget had surpassed $100 million. A good portion of this was the result of innovative efforts to establish a public cargo consolidation program. An arrangement called overland common points (O.C.P.s)

allowed for efficient break-down of containers and redistribution into trucks of expensive general cargo. Between 1963 and 1972, the Port's O.C.P. volume increased fifteen times to 759,000 tons and became a major factor in the Port's growth, much like that of low tariffs in the 1920s.

In 1970 the Port's new Pier 86 grain terminal, at the foot of Queen Anne Hill, introduced fast service to ships with a draft up to seventy-three feet, thirty-six feet deeper than what the Northwest's premier grain port in Portland could handle. Also in 1970, the Port successfully coaxed a consortium of six Japanese containership lines to call first on Seattle, an agreement that the Port of Portland

attempted to upset by appeal to the Federal Maritime Commission. The Port of Seattle's successes as it entered the 1970s were a heartening contrast to the generally recessed state of Puget Sound's economy. The flop of Boeing's SST project and its unexpected loss of subsonic orders had much to do with the area doldrums. Still, in 1969 the Port inaugurated its $150-million construction project at Sea-Tac Airport.

Sea-Land Corporation, the largest carrier in the Transpacific, moved from Seattle to Tacoma in 1985. Soon both K-Line and Evergreen followed, propelling the port on Commencement Bay to equal the business on Elliott Bay in the early 1990s. In 1993, only Los Angeles/Long Beach exceeded Seattle/Tacoma in container volume.

Seattle and Tacoma became exceedingly successful in capturing cargo, with a volume that far surpassed what would be expected by population alone. Quick service and good rail connections between Asia and eastern U.S. markets were largely responsible. As a measure of that success, in 1996 Seattle and Tacoma handled more of New York's Asian traffic than the New York harbor. Together the two ports that year handled a volume of containers approaching that of the entire North American trade with Europe, excluding only countries bordering the Mediterranean.

On Elliott Bay harbor space is limited and urban pressures continually raise costs at selected terminals. Non-containerized cargo such as petroleum, ores, and grain have long since sought less urbanized areas along the lower Columbia River and in northern Puget Sound. Terminal 86, built for grain in 1968, was the last bulk terminal in Seattle. Yet Seattle stayed competitive into the mid-1990s. The West Seattle terminal, Terminal 5, was expanded to retain American President Lines, one of the top container lines in the transpacific. Doubled in size the terminal also features an on-dock rail yard eliminating the dray to existing yards several miles away. In 1996, for the fifth consecutive year, King County residents saw no increase in the Port-levied property tax. Port taxes on a $150,000 house dropped from $66 in 1990 to $43.41 in 1996. That year, $118 million of the Port's total $177 million in capital investments went for maritime projects, including the expansion of Terminal 5, noted above, Terminal 18 on Harbor Island, and repairs at the Shilshole Bay Marina. And the Port was also busy on Seattle's central waterfront, developing at Pier 66, the site of its original headquarters, a center for diverse maritime activities including cruise ships, a maritime museum, the Bell Harbor International Conference Center, a recreational vessel marina, restaurants, and retail shops including a fish market.

Top: East Waterway with Hanford Grain Terminal (far right), ca. 1965. Photo by Hugh Paradise. Above: Cranes at Terminal 18, work with the Golden Arrow moored beside the Port's container facility at East Waterway and Harbor Island. Courtesy Port of Seattle. Right: The Port of Seattle moved into its new headquarters on Pier 69 in 1996. This northern anchor to the Port's Central Waterfront Project was designed by Seattle architects Hewitt-Isley. Photo by Don Wilson, Port of Seattle.

The steamer Flyer *at Tacoma Municipal Dock with Hotel Tacoma on horizon. Photo taken from the 11th Street Bridge. (See p. 173). Courtesy Dan Kerlee.*

Port of Tacoma

When the Northern Pacific announced its intent in 1873 to locate its terminus at Tacoma, they chose a harbor wide and deep enough to dock a large fleet in any weather. And Commencement Bay's miles of tideland waterfront had a wide shallows across the Puyallup River's estuary ready to be dredged for deep draft steamers and reclaimed for sprawling warehouses and factories. So when in 1883 the transcontinental reached New Tacoma (the opportunistic Northern Pacific prudently located its new town a mile from old Tacoma and closer to the tideflats of the bay) the twin communities joined and boomed so well that its citizens declared it a "City of Destiny." However, like other company towns, the Northern Pacific's was predisposed to difficulties.

In 1890 when its population of 36,000 was only 7,000 behind Seattle's, Tacoma might have hoped to catch and pass its neighbor. However, Tacoma's economy lacked the resilience of Seattle's older and more diversified wealth and the international economic crash of 1893 was exceptionally hard on it. By 1900 Tacoma's population had increased by less than 2,000 while Seattle's had doubled to 80,000, and by 1910 the size of Seattle was three times that of Tacoma.

In 1911, the year the Port of Seattle was founded, the first public dock on the West Coast was ceremonially opened on the Tacoma waterfront by its mayor Angelo Fawcett. The progressive politician reminded those present that "the opening is taken to signal a new industrial epoch in Tacoma. Tacoma now leads many cities in a variety of ways. She owns her own electric light plant and now she owns her own dock." Soon the city joined a second municipal dock to the first, creating the 1,440-foot landmark that for years was port-of-call for Puget Sound's "Mosquito Fleet." And next to the Municipal Dock the new Eleventh Street Bridge across the city waterway to the tideflats was dedicated in 1913.

Also in 1911, Tacoma hired Virgil Bogue, fresh from the formulation of his monumental Seattle Plan, to design a master scheme for the development of Commencement Bay. As in Seattle, Bogue's vision was too grand and expensive for the pensive taxpayer and both communities rejected his proposals in 1912 elections, although the tally was much closer in Tacoma than in Seattle. Had the decision been left to the citizens of Tacoma proper, without the participation of Pierce County's farmers who were not convinced that a public port would help them, the port proposal and Bogue's master plan would have succeeded. (Eventually, the last of the reluctant farmers embraced the Port in 1931 when it completed its low-rent cold storage facility.)

One of the first activists for public ports on Puget Sound was the Tacoma politician, Ralph Metcalf. Although his 1907 bill for public port districts made it through the state legislature, it was vetoed by Gov. Albert Meade who bowed to the Great Northern Railroad's description of public ports as socialistic intrusions on private initiative. As with Elliott Bay before the Port of Seattle began to systematically buy large portions of it back, most of the Tacoma waterfront was owned by the railroads.

The heated economy of WWI strengthened commerce on Commencement Bay and left Tacoma with her familiar industries, principally ship-building, flour-milling and wood-processing. On November 5th, 1918, six days before the armistice was signed with Germany, the citizens of Pierce County overcame their earlier reluctance and voted by an resounding 5-to-1 margin to form a port district. Frank Walsh, a consulting engineer who had assisted in the construction of Camp Lewis, was hired to revise the Bogue Plan and in 1919 the Walsh Plan, with a bond issue to fund it, was passed by another landslide. About 340 acres were purchased between what are now the Blair and Sitcum waterways, and the new Port contracted the Tacoma Dredging Company to prepare an 800-foot-long and 166-foot-wide Pier 1. On March 25, 1921, exactly one year from the day the first pile was driven, the Admiral Line's ocean steamer *Edmore* accepted the first cargo from the new pier: timber bound for Yokohama. Next and nearby, the Port's Pier 2 was ready in 1923. This speedy work was the result, in part, of "The perfection of the suction dredge." This reclamation technique is effectively described and its future prophesied in the 1925 promotional chapbook, *Tacoma, A World Port.* "It is only necessary to erect a bulk head and to pump the sand from a waterway of a width and depth which might be desired using this same sand to fill in behind the bulk head and then erect a face to which ships may tie, and you have created an ideal type of water terminal… This development of our Tide Flat is still in its infancy and… will easily be increased ten-fold when our industrial development demands it."

By 1925, the year the Port of Tacoma (or "Portacoma," as Tacoma's dailies sometimes called it) lowered its charges to entice customers from Seattle. Tacoma partisans claimed that there were more people engaged in manufacturing on Commencement Bay than anywhere west of Minneapolis and north of San Francisco: 20,000 persons worked in 600 mills and factories. Tacoma led the world in the production of veneer panels, porch columns, and doors — twelve plants turning out 16,000 of them a day. The "City of Destiny" was becoming the "Grand Rapids of the West" with the largest output of furniture west of Chicago. Tacoma was also home to the largest railroad car shops in the West. And on Piers 1 and 2, the Port had its own switch engine with tracks connecting it with the city Belt Line railway.

Portacoma was sufficiently confident in the lure of its facilities that the onslaught of the depression did not prevent it from completing its first grain terminal in 1930 and a cold storage facility the following year. With the help of the Public Works Administration, the Port extended its Pier 2 during the depression and also constructed a sizable fruit and vegetable processing plant. In a move to stimulate recovery, the state legislature in 1939 empowered public ports to develop new industrial areas. The Port of Tacoma responded with the Industrial Development District, off East 11th Street between the Hylebos and Milwaukee waterways. There, before World War II interrupted its plans, the Port was busy constructing streets, utilities, and rail connections as well

The core of the Port of Tacoma's original installations, Piers One and Two, were reclaimed by suction dredge in the 1920s along the south side of Blair Waterway. This depression-time aerial also shows the port's grain terminal, added in 1930. Courtesy National Archives, Alaska-Pacific NW Region.

into the Port's main area for handling the transshipment of automobiles — Chrysler joining in 1976 and General Motors two years later. The availability of accessible but then unused Port land was an inviting alternative to the relatively land-poor Port of Seattle struggling to acquire rights along the environmentally-sensitive Duwamish Waterway and Smith Cove. In 1975 the Port also significantly increased its grain capacity with the construction of the Continental Grain Terminal below Tacoma's landmark Stadium High School on the west shore of the City Waterway. Throughout the 1970s the flow of cargo through the Port more than

as recruiting tenants. After the war, land acquisition continued and although the general post-war recession dulled the Port's economy, it continued to attract manufacturers to its industrial district.

During the war the Navy took over Piers 1 and 2. By mid-1942 military cargo required the commandeering of private docks. Between the Hylebos and Blair waterways, Todd Shipyards built seventy-four warships, many of them escort carriers. At the peak of production 30,000 workers were involved. In 1955 the Navy declared the site surplus property and in 1959, agreed to sell it to the Port of Tacoma for $2,125,000 on the condition that the military could retrieve the site if war broke out within ten years. By 1964 most of the usable space in the old Tacoma Navy Yard was under lease to private industries including the Tacoma Boat Company which worked a site of the old World War II shipways. In 1969 the Navy relinquished its retrieval rights. The yard was the Port's.

The Navy's 1955 announcement coincided with the Tibbets-Abbert-McCarty-Stratton plan for the Port's development. TAMS recommended that the Port reach deeper into its industrial district by extending both the Hylebos and Industrial waterways. Voters approved bonds to dredge four additional miles of deep water frontage. Fill sucked from the waterways created 1,200 acres of industrial land. Throughout the 1960s the Port of Tacoma continued to improve its waterways, purchasing property and building new facilities, including the dome (the first "Tacoma Dome") for storing alumina and more piers and warehouses for handling container cargo.

In 1976 the Totem Ocean Trailer Express shipping line moved from Seattle to Tacoma. When TOTE could not persuade Seattle Local 19 of the International Longshoremen and Warehousemen Union to agree to its terms for determining who was qualified to drive the company's semi-trailers and containers on and off their vessels, the company asked Tacoma's Local 23 if it would allow the shippers to train union members at company expense and also guarantee trained drivers. Local 23's agreement with the TOTE proposal was not a great surprise. TOTE made its move and in 1979 dedicated its Alaska Terminal, built on what had been a part of the Port's Navy Yard beside Blair Waterway.

Earlier in 1969 the Blair Waterway had been extended another 2.4 miles. Construction of the Blair terminal followed in 1972 and one year later the Pierce County Terminal was dedicated, also on Blair Waterway. The county terminal developed

doubled to over seven million tons.

By 1991 the Port of Tacoma's status was world class — the sixth largest port in the U.S. – twenty-first largest in the world. Tacoma handled more cargo than Seattle, was the nation's second largest rubber importer, and the West Coast's third largest dry-bulk operator. It was also the principal port of entry for Washington State's imported automobiles. The 1982 decision by Sea-Land to break its two decades of service at the Port of Seattle and move to Tacoma was the most dramatic evidence of the Port's land-rich advantages. At that time Sea-Land accounted for more than a third of all the container cargo on Elliott Bay, and occupied eighty acres. But faced with a 290 percent rent increase in Seattle and an offer of 130 acres in Tacoma, the company chose to move south.

The linkage of East and West which the Great Northern's "Empire Builder" James Hill envisioned when his railroad reached Puget Sound in 1893 was, a century later, stronger than ever. The United States' steady shift of trade from Europe to Asia propelled the twin ports of Seattle and Tacoma ahead of the Port of New York/New Jersey — a development that might have surprised even Virgil Bogue. Tacoma, especially, was able to offer new cargo handling devices to the large transpacific container lines by placing Port-constructed rail yards directly on marine terminals. This time-saving technology, referred to as on-dock rail, has been copied throughout North America.

In 1993 Tacoma and Seattle were effectively identical in size, both handling approximately 1.1 million teu (twenty foot equivalent units, or containers to a twenty-foot common denominator in length). The two ports have become the tenth largest container complex in the world and second largest in North America, behind that of Los Angeles/Long Beach, but well ahead of all other west coast rivals, including the pioneer leader, San Francisco Bay. Tacoma and Seattle's destinies have become intertwined. Cooperation between the two ports has evolved from name-calling to serious attempts to capitalize on the mutual advantages of common efforts, ranging from basic planning to marketing and emphasis on improving rail access into and out of Puget Sound.

The Port of Tacoma's container services had been limited to the area outside of the Blair Bridge where it crosses that waterway on 11th Street. There the older terminals developed in the first half of the century were rebuilt for modern container shipping. In 1997 the Blair Bridge was removed with completion of a new bypass free around the end of Tacoma's waterways. The dismantling of the bridge along with the deepening of the Blair Waterway, begun in

Top left: The Northern Pacific Railroad pier at Tacoma, ca. 1885. Top right: Early-century waterfront row of Northern Pacific Railroad warehouses below Tacoma's central business district photographed from the Eleventh Street Bridge. Right: Port of Tacoma's Terminal 7C alumina domes, one completed and the other in the early stages of its 1969 construction. Photo by Bud Kimball Aerial Photography. Courtesy Tacoma Utilities. Above: Container gantry cranes at Sea-Land Terminal on south side of the Sitcum Waterway. Courtesy Port of Tacoma. Below: A 1993 aerial of the reclaimed Tacoma waterfront at the Puyallup estuary from Hybelos Waterway, far left, to Foss Waterway and the central business district, far right. Also showing is Tacoma's namesake mountain, Mount Tahoma (now called Mount Rainier), center, and Mount Adams, right. Photo by George White Location Photography. Below insert: Plan for Tacoma's Terminal 2, ca. 1919. Courtesy WA State Archives, Bellevue Branch.

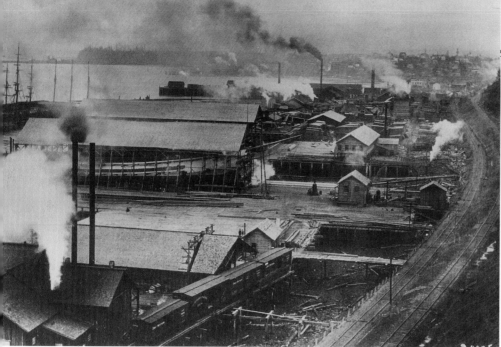

Top left: A portion of the early Everett waterfront when it was dominated by lumber mills and ship builders. Courtesy, Everett Public Library. Above right: Looking north into Port Gardner Channel and the mouth of the Snohomish River with Jetty Island left of center, July 19, 1940. Courtesy National Archives, Alaska-Pacific NW Region. Bottom: 1997 aerial of Everett Harbor with the Navy homeport piers in the foreground, Port of Everett Hewitt Terminal on the right, and marinas on the left. Photo by and courtesy of James Arrabito.

late 1993, will ultimately open new land one and a half times that of the existing acreage Tacoma has in containers and equal to that of Seattle's entire harbor. Container forecasts into the next century warranted this expansion. In 1997, the Port of Tacoma handled a record 1.16 million container units, an increase of 8 percent from 1996. Automobile imports increased by 37 percent, and the Port contracted a new line, Hyundai Merchant Marine, to its stable of container transporters.

The Port of Everett

A century of changes on the Everett waterfront has resulted in a shorescape with landfills and concrete pile piers supporting a diverse working, recreational, and military economy.

The boom town promoted by the Everett Land Company and its eastern investors began construction on the Port Gardner Channel with the 14th Street Wharf in 1892. (This was exactly one century since the English explorer Capt. George Vancouver named the harbor, facing the future Everett, Possession Sound for his act of discovery and, by European convention, possession of all these inland waters in the name of his king, George III.) By 1920, twenty-two of the city's ninety-five manufacturing plants were located on the wharf.

The public Port of Everett was formed in 1918. The Port's presence on the Everett waterfront advanced considerably in 1930 when it took the opportunity of depression-time low prices to purchase the 14th Street Wharf. Beginning in 1944 this already

sprawling pier was considerably enlarged with the reclamation of forty acres of tide flats adjacent and north of it. After the last lumber mill left the wharf in 1962 the waterfront extending far to both sides of it was transformed into a marina for pleasure and fishing vessels. By 1996 the 2,200 moorages of the combined north and south marinas made Everett's waterfront marina the second largest on the West Coast.

The Port's transhipment services are grouped at the southern end of Port Gardner where features of the Hewitt Terminal and South Terminal include: thirty acres of paved storage used primarily for sorting and storing logs; 22,000 square feet of dry storage; Pier 1, a new cement pile pier with four on dock rail spurs for moving produce, logs, and general cargo; a thirty-five-ton mobile track crane for containers and specialized shipments for the Boeing Everett plant; a 36,000-square-foot multi-purpose warehouse with rail sidings and refrigeration; and the Port's landmark 55,000-ton dome for the storage of alumina.

The U.S. Navy's carrier-homeport in Everett began to take shape in the mid-1990s. The two Navy piers extend from the Port's Marina Village to the southwest like a colossal tuning fork. The carrier *U.S.S. Abraham Lincoln* and its battle group are stationed there. Everett is also homeport for the *M/V Washington Responder*. Like the Navy the Marine Spill Response Corporation chose the Everett harbor for its easy access and central location allowing the MSRC to respond to emergencies quickly anywhere on Puget Sound.

The Port of Port Angeles

By the time the idea of a public port in Port Angeles became commonplace (an idea largely drawn from Seattle's success), Port Angeles' waterfront was dominated by mills, and the ships sheltered in the embrace of Ediz Hook were filled with either their raw materials or their end-products.

Ediz Hook, Port Angeles' natural breakwater, is a finger of land deposited by the erosion of the Elwha River delta. The gently curving shape of this three-mile spit was formed about 5,000 years ago, when the slowly melting ice-age glaciers at last raised the ocean to a level sufficient to inundate the river delta and retard erosion. The harbor behind the hook was used by natives long before the Spanish captain Francisco Eliza visited in 1791 and named it Porto de Nuestra Senora de Los Angeles. One year later the Englishman Capt. George Vancouver contracted the Spanish name to the simple Port Angeles.

In 1862 treasury agent Victor Smith, a Lincoln appointee, persuaded the President to reserve 3,520 acres on the bay, which included the hook, for federal purposes. Smith then promptly removed the custom house from Port Townsend to Port Angeles, platted its upland, and ambitiously called it "The Second National City." He was ready should the Civil War force the first national city far west. And the prospects of mid-1800s Port Angeles did seem boundless. Somewhat like San Francisco, it is set at the top of a peninsula that protects an inland sea. Its harbor was undoubtedly one of the best anywhere; the problems began at the shore.

Little industrial space could be surrendered by the business district which clung to a narrow beach inhibited by the steep upland behind it. There the citizens looked down from their homes onto the squeezed economy below. The county-wide public port was formed in the fall of 1922. Three years later work began on the Port's pier between Valley and Tumwater streets. Nineteen acres were reclaimed behind a rip-rap, constructed piece-by-piece of stone carried on scows to the site from a quarry near Bremerton. The first unit of Pier 1 was completed August 1,

Artist's impression of Port Angeles' ideal setting, ca. 1890.
Courtesy, University of Washington Libraries, Special Collections.

1926 and measured 150 by 500 feet. It included a hammerhead crane with a 5-ton capacity and a 95-foot reach.

In 1930 the Port hired a past secretary to the Port of Seattle. The first project under Henry Davis' watch was the construction of the small boat basin the following year. The popularity of this public work was registered in 1944 when voters approved in wartime a bond issue to enlarge its mooring basin to 550 by 1,200 feet. In the 1950s the Port built a second marina at Sequim Bay and named it for a patron with whom many of the local individualists could identify, John Wayne.

Public works activity in Port Angeles during World War II included an oversized ship building project which was cut off before completion. Eleanor Roosevelt was the honored guest at the launching of the first wooden cargo ship completed there in 1943. However, the First Lady's influence was not as great as that of

Below: Army Corps aerial view of Ediz Hook photographed in 1978 for documenting the perennial problem of beach erosion, also shows the U.S. Coast Guard Air Station. Inset right: The Air Station, commissioned in 1935 for sea planes only, got its first hard surface runway in 1938. Courtesy National Archives, Alaska-Pacific NW Region. Inset left: Port of Port Angeles Municipal Pier with the Coast Guard cutter Active. Photo by Abigail Harris.

radar. With the increasing effectiveness of aircraft carriers and radar, more steel-hulled ships were escaping submarine attack and the need for wooden boats diminished. Only six ships were completed when government orders were canceled.

The most enduring of Port Angeles' waterways public works is the Ediz Hook Lighthouse. The original thirty-five-foot Ediz light was approved by Abraham Lincoln — then still under the spell of Victor Smith — in 1863 and built two years later. In 1885 a large fogbell was mounted nearby in a pyramid-shaped bell tower. In 1908 the light was moved to a larger frame tower, where it remained until its postwar move to the Navy airport. The light was moved again in 1945 to the seventy-eight-foot top of the Port Angeles Air Station's control tower where it worked doubletime as a marine and air beacon.

The deposits from the Elwha River which helped replenish the Hook's natural breakwater were severely retarded with construction of the Lower Elwha Dam in 1910-13. The Army Corps had already battled the Hook's erosion with tons of rip-rap on its outer shore. The dam increased the need. By 1950 major repairs were required on Ediz Hook and again in 1970 this work was resumed with the creation of the Hook Erosion Control Program. Damage from the storms of 1973-74 was extensive. (Considerable attention was given to undamming the Elwha during the early 1990s. This ecological activism was motivated not by the need to replenish the river deposits along Ediz Hook but by the desire to return wild salmon to the river.)

By 1970 the Port of Port Angeles had accumulated nearly 300 acres of industrial land and that year constructed a warehouse just south of Port Dock for the storage of pulp and newsprint. By 1986 the Port had grown to handle 70 percent of all the cargo entering and leaving the harbor behind the Hook — this only sixty years

Above: Early century "Union Wharf Scene" in Port Townsend. Courtesy Jim Faber. Below: Port Townsend, U.S. Coast Survey, ca. 1856. Courtesy, U.W. Library, Special Collections.

after the construction of its first dock.

While the Port of Port Angeles is the big public worker on the waterfront, the city has done something to encourage public play there as well. In 1980 the Municipal Pier at the foot of Lincoln Street introduced Port Angeleans to new facilities for public fishing, seaplane docking and moorage, transient small boat docking, spaces for exhibits and public meetings, an observation tower near the pier end, and an adjoining waterfront park.

Port of Port Townsend

Port Townsend's career as the front door to Puget Sound opened in 1854 when federal customs collector Col. Isaac Ebey had the district headquarters moved there from Olympia, where it had first been established in 1851. Ebey reasoned that Port Townsend was closer to the smugglers who typically dropped down from Canada.

The Treasury Department agreed and Port Townsend was quickly turned into a sailor town with its attendant vices. The key virtue to the "Key City," as it was called, was cash. All vessels entering Puget Sound were first required to clear customs at Port Townsend. Frequently, ships crews would be paid off and put ashore with predictable results.

Moving customs did not please Olympians but they were powerless to stop it. Later, they enjoyed a kind of revenge when Victor Smith's description of Port Townsend as "a rotten borough whose people fared so sumptuously on the spoils of government that their eyes stuck out with fat" was published in the February 8, 1862 issue of Olympia's newspaper, *The Standard*. Smith's diatribe, of course, was his prelude to removing the Customs House to Port Angeles where he had plans for his own spoils. Soon, however, Smith drowned at sea and could not prevent the return of customs to Port Townsend in 1866, the year a tidal wave flooded the port to its bluff. Soon a second wave of boozers, gamblers, and prostitutes attached themselves to the town's renewed success. In 1889, Port Townsend was described by an upstate New York newspaper as ranking "only second to New York in the number of marine craft reported and cleared, in the whole U.S." The port was home to consulates for Peru, Chile, Great Britain, Germany, the Hawaiian Islands, and France. However, with the national economic crash of 1893 Port Townsend's boom time population of 7,000 quickly crashed to a depressing 2,000. The custom district's official port was filled with ships, but they were anchored and idle.

The coup de gras to community hopes came in 1911 when the Treasury Department transferred the Puget Sound Port of Entry to Seattle, leaving Port Townsend a sub-port. The crowding of waterways with steamships at the expense of many-masted brigs and barkentines

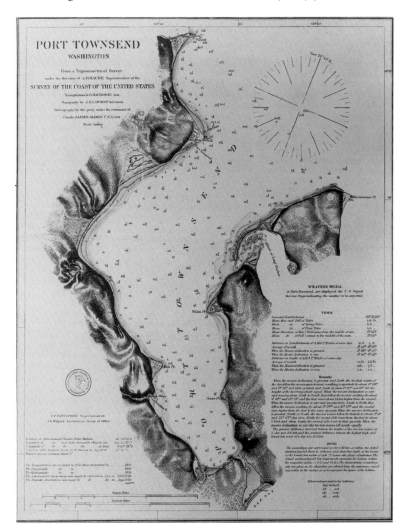

made Port Townsend's advantage of being almost constantly air-conditioned by westerly winds increasingly irrelevant. The steel-hulled ocean-going steamships didn't need the breeze and preferred combining their customs work with the lucrative labors of trans-shipment — usually in Seattle.

The industry that is now best identified with this historical maritime community is the building of wooden boats. In 1977 Port Townsend produced its first Wooden Boats Festival. By 1986 there were more than a dozen firms engaged in the fulltime construction of wooden boats.

In 1979 Port Townsend's maritime spirit was temporarily quickened with the destruction of the Hood Canal Bridge, and the renewal of the old Mosquito Fleet packet of direct ferry service from Seattle to the Quincy Street ferry terminal. (See Bridges Chapter.)

Above: Testing "Disappearing Gun" at Fort Worden. Courtesy, Daniel Kerlee. Left: Fort Ward dormitory used as a state Department of Public Works children's recreation camp, 1935. Courtesy, U.W. Library, Special Collections.

COAST DEFENSES

Congress approved construction of the triangle of forts at Admiralty Inlet in 1896. Although proposed by the military as early as 1850, it was not until the 1880s that cannons were developed that could effectively fire the width of the Inlet — at whom was a matter of opinion. In the early 1850s settlers were understandably nervous about marauding North Coast Indians, and if the Haidas were a proven threat, the English remained no less of one in jingoistic imaginations. What finally built the coast defenses was the creation of something to defend, the Puget Sound Naval Shipyard at Bremerton. Conveniently, when construction began, an enemy materialized to assure full funding for the batteries at Admiralty Head, Point Wilson and Marrowstone Point, Fort Casey on Whidbey Island, Fort Worden by Port Townsend, and Fort Flagler on Marrowstone Island respectively. Although there wasn't the remote possibility that the Spanish fleet would hazard an attack on Bremerton, Washington, the military enthusiasm that accompanied the Spanish-American War spread a mantle of money over the rough promontories of the proposed defenses.

Building the forts was not easy, especially at Marrowstone where the matted underbrush was higher then the heads of the surveyors. At Point Wilson the tangle was legal. Parts of the old military reserve lay within Port Townsend and had been developed as town lots. And construction had its secret side, with contractors making bids only after looking at the plans under the watch of an officer. All laborers were required to be nationals — no Chinese cooks allowed. Concrete work on the batteries at Fort Worden was completed early in 1900. The monumental sculpture was hardened with 424,000 pounds of cement shipped from Belgium. The first guns were installed in 1901. Once practice firing commenced, sections of the fort began to crack. The mixers had been too stingy with the cement.

In 1903 the triangular forts failed in their first war game. Imperfectly positioned, they were unable to synchronize their fire. Lack of telephone or wireless connections and a haze from forest fires allowed the enemy flotilla — actually conscripted merchant marine captains — to run the gauntlet intact steaming to their targets at Bremerton and/or Seattle. Fortunately, the forts never fired on an enemy.

After World War I anti-aircraft guns were installed in the forts — a sign of their obsolescence — but the defenses were soon placed on inactive status and remained so until World War II when they were used as training sites for the Army and the National Guard. The military presence that swelled during World War II continued after it. In 1950 nearly half of the 6,888 residents of Port Townsend were either military personnel or their dependents, and the fort payroll was twice that of the town's principal industry, Crown Zellerbach. But a 1953 telegram from a politician whose reputation was ordinarily built on giving, not taking, changed that. Senator Warren Magnuson wired, "Sorry to advise you that the Army is today announcing the closing June 1." The chamber of commerce's attempts to raise $5,000 for yet another dose of Port Townsend hope could only raise $2,000, and the Army slipped out the back door without thanks or fanfare. The old fort was then used as a state diagnostic and treatment center for juveniles until 1973 when it was dedicated as a state park. Fort Worden soon developed into the state's most popular park. In 1983 more than a million guests explored its batteries and attended its concerts and seminars. Forts Flagler and Casey were also transformed into state parks and, ultimately, the playful uses of these coast defenses proved more stimulating to the local culture and economy than had the work for which they were originally designed.

Fort Ward, Puget Sound's fourth coast defense, met a similar recreational fate. Established in 1898 at the south end of Bainbridge Island, its first battery was in place in early 1900. Originally intended to watch over the Rich Passage route to the Navy Yard, it served primarily as a mine sweeping station. During the depression, the fort was used as a recreation camp for children of families on the dole until it was loaned to the Navy in 1938 as a recreational area for servicemen stationed at Bremerton. With World War II the site was converted into a Naval radio station that was instrumental in helping break the Japanese code. For the duration of the war a submarine net was also strung across Rich Passage. Fort Ward was deactivated in 1958 and two years later it was purchased by the Washington State Parks and Recreation Commission.

Above: First drydock of the Puget Sound Navy Yard, ca. 1905. Courtesy Museum of History and Industry, Seattle.

Puget Sound Naval Shipyard

A Kitsap County legend has it that when William Bremer sculled his rowboat across Puget Sound from Seattle in the winter of 1891, he was carrying "insider information." Preferring the southern shore of Sinclair Inlet but knowing that the Navy planned to purchase land on the north side at Point Turner, Bremer bought some of the latter. His reward for this moment of real estate opportunism was a profitable nineteen years of selling lots in a Navy town that would have his name attached to it.

It is, however, a different name that is linked with the creation of Bremerton's shipyard. In 1877 Ambrose Barkley Wyckoff, a lieutenant in the United States Navy, conducted a hydraulic survey of Puget Sound aboard the survey schooner *Yukon*. In the more than two years required to complete the study, Wyckoff was transformed into a "Puget Sounder" and subsequently a campaigner in Washington, D.C. for a shipyard on that waterway. In fact, Wyckoff would later claim that had the Navy not sent him off to China in 1881 he would have brought the yard to Sinclair Inlet ten years sooner.

The first federal commission sent in 1890 to examine Wyckoff's preferred site returned with a report recommending purchase. Despite the objections of Oregon senators who were planning their own Navy yard on the Columbia, Congress eventually approved the Puget Sound choice and sent Wyckoff back to Port Orchard with $10,000, most of which wound up in Bremer's pocket. On September 16, 1891 Wyckoff took possession, raising the flag over the 191 acres he had bought from Bremer at Turner Point. Three months later William Bremer platted Bremerton on his remaining acres, and forever after the two — town and shipyard — were joined in a sometimes uneasy marriage.

Ground was broken for the dry-dock on December 10, 1892, with Wyckoff's daughter, Stella, pressing the first shovel. Not feeling well, Wyckoff left Puget Sound soon after the ground breaking and did not return for seven years. In between, the 650-foot dry-dock was completed, ceremonially tested by the *U.S.S. Monterey*, and pumped dry to the injury of hundreds of trapped salmon floundering on the exposed floor. The *U.S.S. Oregon* was the first battleship docked within and the first consistent tourist attraction at the yard. From there she was called to Cuba and the Battle of Santiago.

From the start, Wyckoff and other officers who favored the site plotted for a "building and repairing yard of the first class." However, not until Wyckoff returned in 1899 was the generally moribund yard enlivened with new appropriations and within three years its rank was raised and its name changed to Navy Yard Puget Sound. Bremerton was also aroused, incorporating and installing its first electric light system in 1901, adding telephones, a volunteer fire department, and its first piped water system the following year. A.L. Croxton, Bremerton's first mayor, later reminisced that "there

Left (from top to bottom): Olympic Mountains , Dabob Bay, Hood Canal, Kitsap Peninsula, Dyes Inlet, Bremerton, Navy Yard, Sinclair Inlet (attached to Dyes Inlet by Port Washington Narrows). Aerial looks to the northwest. Courtesy Navy Yard Museum.

were seventeen saloons in Bremerton when I took office... The county was overrun by gamblers." An ordinance passed in the first year of Croxton's charge made it a misdemeanor to "sell or roast peanuts, loaf, tell stories, whittle, or scatter litter" near the entrance to the Navy Yard.

Pre-WWI additions to the Navy presence at Port Orchard included an ammunition depot on Ostrich Bay in 1904, a second dry-dock at the Naval Yard in 1913, and the following year a torpedo station at Keyport on Liberty Bay. During World War I the yard plunged into shipbuilding. The 2,000 men employed there in 1916 doubled the following year when the Navy decided to start laying keels at Bremerton. It was during this wartime rush that the first dry-dock in the nation designed for building ships was constructed at the yard. At 927 feet it could work on four destroyers at a time. By the end of WWI, forty-one ships and 1,700 small boats had either been launched at the yard or were nearing completion. PSNS had reached first class. In 1935 one of the world's largest machine and electric shops was added. Up to 1,000 workers at a shift labored within a well-lit 805-foot by 251-foot steel and concrete shed constructed with walls made almost entirely of a special light transmitting glass. The Navy Yard's World War II work began with the $33 million rehabilitation of five of the eight ships bombed at Pearl Harbor. By 1953, sixty-one years after work began on its first dry-dock, the Navy had five of them at Point Turner.

In both 1991 and 1995, Bremerton's Puget Sound Naval Shipyard won the Commander-in-Chief's Installation Excellence Award for its combined service as a shipyard, home port, and support base. In 1995 the naval shipyard, in the midst of a $100 million construction program, was the second largest home port on the West Coast (after San Francisco). It had nearly as many buildings as acres (not counting submerged land and remote housing areas), 335 and 344 respectively, as well as nine permanent piers totaling 12,310 feet of deep water space. Bremerton's newspaper, *The Sun*, then estimated that the base had brought 40,000 people to the area, including 10,000 military personnel, 10,000 civilian workers, and another 20,000 dependents. Included then among its approximately twenty-four tenant activities, was PSNS's pioneer work in devising environmentally safe methods of deactivating and recycling nuclear-powered submarines.

Bangor

Bangor on Hood Canal received its first public work in 1890 when Joseph Thurston was appointed postmaster. The post office was named Charleston for the pioneer from whom Thurston bought his land, but the name was changed to Bangor when mail for Charleston kept making it to Charleston and vice versa. The reason Bangor was chosen is now lost, but it is speculated that the name may have been read from a cancellation stamp sent from the post office in Bangor, Maine. The community was also platted in 1890, a dock was built and its first public school opened in 1892. A half-century later, about 350 families lived in the area, busy with farming, lumbering, fishing and recreation. In the summer of 1944 they were ordered to move out. The Navy purchased 6,000 acres for the Bangor Naval Magazine.

When it was opened in 1945, the Bangor Naval Magazine included forty-three miles of railroad track constructed from Shelton and another twenty-two miles on the huge encampment laid to connect its magazines and warehouses. After the war, the site was sometimes used to unload and store ammunition from ships enroute to Bremerton either for inactivation or overhaul. The Polaris Missile Facility Pacific was commission at NAD (Naval Artillery Depot) Bangor in 1964, but it was the conventional weapons used in Vietnam that created a

Top: Navy Yard machine and electric shops, 1935. Above: Portion of the sprawling Bangor Naval Magazine. Below: Marginal Pier on Hood Canal, looking north, for Naval Magazine at Bangor, 1945. All courtesy National Archive, Alaska-Pacific NW Region.

swell in employment at Bangor in the late 1960s, reaching 1,729 workers in 1968. The base was responsible for about one-third of all the ammunition shipped to Vietnam at that time, but the work suddenly stopped with the last shipment on June 4, 1970. For transshipment Bangor's position was not ideal. Larger steamers had to wait for the tide and all ships had to contend with the Hood Canal Bridge. Pres. Nixon's 1972 acceleration of bombing temporarily resumed the station's Vietnam shipments, although not without resistance from the "People's Blockade," protesters who attempted to stop or slow ammunition shipments with an obstructing armada of small boats. (Submarines have little difficulty passing through — or under — the Hood Canal Floating Bridge.) Construction began in 1974 and the "sub-base" was officially activated in 1977. In 1989 Bangor also won the Commander-in-Chief's Installation Excellence Award, aka "Best Base in the Navy" award. Between 1995 and 1997 six new commands with 500 additional personnel were relocated to Bangor resulting in approximately $26 million in new construction.

Above: Development at Bangor site for the nation's first Trident submarine base. Courtesy Seattle Post-Intelligencer. *Below: Sentinel architect Carl Lieck's comely lighthouse at Fort Casey on Whidbey Island's Admiralty Head, 1909. Courtesy Fairlook Antiques, Seattle.*

LIGHTHOUSES

Of Washington's twenty-nine historical lighthouses a few — the coast lights at Destruction Point, North Head, Willapa Bay, and Grays Harbor, and the beacon at Ediz Hook, — are treated briefly above. The remaining sentinels are sited at Admiralty Inlet, Tatoosh and Destruction islands, Dungeness Spit, Slip Point, Smith Island, Lime Kiln, Stuart Island, Cattle Point, Patos Island, Semiahmoo Harbor, Burrows Island, Dofflemyer Point, Mukilteo, Point Robinson, Point Roberts, Browns Point, Alki Point, West Point, and Point No Point. Here we will make only a few points regarding a selection of them.

Lighthouses and their well-manicured grounds were often attended for years by the same civil servant, who raised a family on the site and sometimes passed on the keep to offspring. When the Lighthouse Service was absorbed into the Coast Guard in 1939, the death of this domestic romance was assured. Even the short-hitch attentions of young Coast Guardsmen were withdrawn when one by one the lights were automated, many of them in the 1960s. Often, but not always, the grounds then also went to seed.

Admiralty Inlet Lighthouses

The triangulated coast defenses at Admiralty Inlet were only fired in practice and their need was questioned from the start. There were, however, three structures built besides the forts whose public work was obvious most nights.

The lighthouse at Whidbey Island's Admiralty Head was the first of the three constructed. Ignited in 1861 it was not architecturally distinguished. A second light designed by celebrated sentinel architect Carl Leick featured a striking masonry tower lifting its lens 127 feet above sea level. Built in 1903, it was turned-off in the 1920s when steamships, which by then dominated the waterways and stayed close to the west side of Admiralty Inlet, required no directions from Whidbey Island. In 1927 Leick's comely tower was even decapitated, its lantern house removed and used in the reconstruction of the New Dungeness Lighthouse. During World War II the truncated tower was painted olive-drab and used temporarily as officers quarters. When Washington State Parks purchased the fort in 1956, the lighthouse was renovated and recapped with a restored lantern tower. It is presently used as an interpretive center.

The light at Point Wilson — the right-turn signal for vessels heading into Puget Sound — was constructed in 1879. For foggy conditions a steam whistle was also installed. In 1913 the old frame sentinel was replaced by an octagonal concrete one and the whistle traded for a chime diaphragm. Eventually, a radio beacon was added to the site. Unlike the light at Admiralty Head, Point Wilson signals still function.

The last of the triangle of lights was constructed at Marrowstone Point in 1888. The present structure was built in 1918 and equipped with three large trumpets replacing the original fog bell that was often hard to hear.

Destruction Island

On a thirty-acre patch first reserved for the purpose in 1866, the Destruction Island sentinel was built between 1889-91. Three miles offshore and 147 feet above the sea, the post was the loneliest off the Washington coast. Braced against the elements, the ninety-four-foot masonry tower was encased in iron plates. The diaphragm horn, which replaced the station's first sounding device, a steam siren, created one of the island's few non-meteorological tempests when the lighthouse keeper's bull imagined it a rival's battle cry and tore up the station grounds looking for a fight. A noise of a different sort — one both nostalgic and political — followed the Coast Guard's 1963 attempt to close down the lighthouse. The USCG's decision was a technical one, based on the efficiency of modern navigation devices. The public outcry that stopped the closure was motivated by aesthetic and sentimental instincts as much as by an interest in waterways safety. Nonetheless, a good measure of the Destruction light's lonely romance was withdrawn when the light was automated in 1968.

Cape Flattery Lighthouse on Tatoosh Island

For obvious reasons, a light at Tatoosh Island, only four-tenths of a mile northwest of Cape Flattery at the entrance to the Strait of Juan de Fuca, was recommended by the U.S. Coast Survey in 1850 and was one of the five Washington Territory lights approved by Congress two years later. The choice,

however, was not popular with the Makah Indians. This heroic whale-hunting culture, more like Canada's North Coast tribes than the natives of Puget Sound, used the island for whale spearing and growing potatoes. When the construction crew arrived, 150 Makahs were on the island. Their mood was not improved by the memory of the smallpox that two years earlier had reduced half their number. Before the invaders began construction on the lighthouse in 1855, they raised a blockhouse loaded with twenty muskets. Three months after work began the crew abandoned the island, frightened and lonely. A second crew also fled the scene. But the third crew stayed and the light was completed on December 28, 1857.

Through its first years the Tatoosh light had trouble keeping a keeper, until Capt. William W. Winsor arrived in 1865. Winsor developed a trading economy with the natives that pleased them both. Some of his successors were neither so handy nor so hardy. A turn-of-the-century light keeper threw himself from the rocks in a failed attempt to do himself in. He was sent off the island.

Dungeness Spit

Dungeness Spit lies so low that ships have often felt it before seeing it. Appropriately, this five-mile-long finger of sand is also known as "Shipwreck Spit." Construction of the lights at Tatoosh Island and Dungeness Spit were supervised together by Isaac Smith who used the situation to have his crews compete. The winners were at the spit, finishing their light fourteen days before the island crew completed theirs. First a fogbell and then, after 1874, a steam fog signal added warning noises to the tower's Fresnel signals. In 1927, sixty years after Smith's winning crew completed it, the Dungeness beacon's 100-foot tower was reduced to sixty-three feet and reappointed with a light borrowed from the then abandoned beacon at Admiralty Head.

Top: Destruction Island Lighthouse. Above left: Lighthouse on Dungeness Spit. Above right: View of Cape Flattery from Tatoosh Island's sentinel lantern house. Below left: Tatoosh light with Makah Indian camp on beach. Below right: Keepers of Tatoosh light, Sept. 25, 1943. Photos courtesy National Archives.

San Juan Lights

Of the lights that direct traffic around the San Juans, either through Rosario or Haro Straits we will describe only the oldest — the lonely sentinel on Smith Island. About six miles west of Joseph Whidbey Park on Whidbey Island, it was one of the original five sentinels approved by Congress in 1852. The lamp atop its forty-foot tower was first lit on October 18, 1858. A blockhouse which was prudently built next to the tower was used soon after its construction. A group of Haida Indians who may have been making a merely curious investigation were fired upon by the light's assistant keeper who assumed the worst. More recently, visitors have been warned away by the presence of an air-to-surface weapons range west of Smith Island. Erosion was the light's ultimate enemy. In 1949 the tower was forty feet from the island's cliff on its west side. Traveling an average of two feet a year, the retreating cliff took the tower with it in 1969. Earlier, a replacement light atop a skeleton tower had been built well inland from the advancing shore.

Puget Sound Lights

The solid little sentinel at Point No Point was the first light built south of Admiralty Inlet. The 27-foot masonry tower is set on a sandspit and was first lit in 1880. The next sentinel south was a late construction. Designed by lighthouse architect C.W. Leick the Mukilteo Lighthouse was constructed in 1906 on the beach where Washington Territory's first governor Isaac I. Stevens signed the treaty with the local natives in 1855.

The West Point Lighthouse at the northern entrance to Elliott Bay was commissioned in 1881. Jim Gibbs, in his book *Lighthouses of the Pacific*, recorded the West Point light's service statistics at the year of its centennial, 1981. Gibbs learned from a former warden of the light "that after a century of service the French-made...Fresnel with its 12 bulls-eyes had given out better than 35,000 nights or about 395,000 hours of light over those decades. The fog signal...logged an annual average of 344 hours."

The next station south, Point Robinson, on the extreme eastern shore of Maury Island, was fitted with a fog signal first in

1885. A light followed in 1887. The addition of a forty-foot tower in 1894 was evidence of the increasingly crowded conditions on Puget Sound's busiest "Mosquito Fleet" route between Seattle and Tacoma. In 1915 a new tower and fog signal building were added. The beacon at Brown Point, the next signal south of Point Robinson, at the north entrance to Tacoma's harbor, was not fitted with its thirty-one-foot tower until 1933, nearly a half-century after the light was first placed there in 1887. Similarly, the southern-most light on Puget Sound, on Dofflemyer Point at the entrance to Budd Inlet, was introduced in 1887 but was not elevated to its thirty-foot pyramidal tower until 1936.

Also in 1887, the U.S. Lighthouse Service mounted a lens-lantern on a scaffold at Alki Point on the beach where Seattle's first settlers landed in 1851. For years the family which owned the point was paid $15 a month to tend the government's new light. Finally, in 1911 Alki Point was bought outright and the thirty-seven-foot octagonal tower that still marks the site was completed in 1913. Five years later it was converted to electricity. In October

Lightships

Stationed at the entrance of the Columbia River in 1892, *Lightship No. 50* (above) was the first vessel placed on the Pacific Coast by the U.S. Lighthouse Service. The circular screens on the masts were daymarks. At night three oil lanterns were run up each auxiliary mast, aft of the masts bearing the daymarks. *Number 50* served at the bar until 1908 when the wooden sailship was replaced by a new class of steel-hulled and steam-powered vessels of which both the *Columbia* and *Swiftsure* (below) were members. The *Columbia* was the mainstay of guarding the Columbia bar and, for a time during World War II when the *Swiftsure* was sent to Alaskan waters, this responsibility was hers alone. Both vessels —as well as their sisters, the *Umatilla Reef* and the *Relief* lightships— were equipped with a bright beacon light, sound signals, radio, radio-telephone, and radio beacons.

1984 its operation was made fully automatic. The lighthouse is open for weekend tours, and visitors are invited to sign the lighthouse log. There, in 1984, H. Nelms wrote, "Looked on by ye landlubbers with but a passing glance, looked on by ye seafarers as a beacon of hope, ye light must not fail."

LAKE WASHINGTON SHIP CANAL

Of the five potential canal routes connecting Lake Washington with Elliott Bay studied by Army engineers in 1898 the one preferred began at Shilshole Bay. In the years following, the Corps periodically appropriated funds for the dredging of Shilshole and Salmon Bays always disclaiming that this indicated any final commitment to a canal. Still, Seattle secured the canal's right-of-way in 1900 for $250,000 and deeded it to the federal government.

Colonel Hiram Chittenden arrived in 1906 as the Corps' chief engineer for the Seattle office. Chittenden later recalled that "when I examined the list of public works in the district I had no hesitation in estimating this as the most important of any. I was then bitterly disappointed when I discovered... our people had been carried away with a glittering project supported by a few daring promoters." The colonel's reference was to the victory of Seattle's can-do developer James A. Moore in the 1906 fall elections. By a nearly unanimous vote Moore won the right to build a narrow timber lock at Fremont. However, with a deft engineering of politics and opinion Hiram Chittenden renewed the public's faith in the full-sized canal with its large masonry lock at Ballard (in 1954 it would be named for him) and wide cut at Montlake as significantly superior to Moore's smaller timber lift. The federal government's $2.275 million appropriation to the project eliminated any need for anxious canal boosters to again turn to private developers.

Ground was broken November 10, 1911, and the first concrete poured February 26, 1913. On February 2, 1916, in the emergency of the "Big Snow" of that year, the first vessels to pass through the still-open gates carried commuters, who would have normally used the currently snowbound trolleys, from Ballard to downtown. On July 12, of that year, the lock gates were closed, and the filling of Salmon Bay followed. The *Seattle Times* reported that this "marked the beginning of a new era of prosperity for Seattle, an indication that the dream of the fathers... to make Seattle the 'New York of the Pacific' is about to be realized." It took thirteen days for the water behind the dam to reach the level of Lake Union, and another three months to lower Lake Washington nine feet, to the level of Thomas Mercer's joining lake.

Construction of Lake Washington Ship Canal; Dec. 11, 1913. Looking west along the south wall of the Large Lock with a portion of the cofferdam in the background. Courtesy Army Corps of Engineers.

On July 4th, 1917, the Lake Washington Ship Canal was dedicated. Confined by stroke to a wheelchair the partially paralyzed Chittenden watched what he could of the naval parade from the prospect of his Capitol Hill home. He died 97 days later.

The canal's 825-foot-long, 80-foot-wide main lock was big enough to accept the largest ship in the Pacific. The lock was deeper than any in the United States and as deep as those of the Panama Canal. Comparisons with New York's harbor were also popular. With the canal completed Seattle possessed 130 miles of waterfront to Manhattan's 43. Lake Union alone could provide berthing space for 40 ocean-going vessels. Once inside the lock they had neither tides nor the current of the Hudson River to contend with.

The ditch dug to open a fresh water harbor to safely clean and service America's dreadnoughts and the big ships of the working world has developed primarily into a passage for pleasure craft. The big lock can handle about 100 small boats at a time. More than 78,000 vessels went through "the busiest locks in the world" in 1986; 60,000 of the total png through were recreational boats ten years later in 1996. From the rim of the big lock, more than one million visitors each year look down on the rising and falling of the yachts.

Right: Repairs on the drained Large Lock. Below: Seattle District Corps' post-WWII pamphlet with statistics of the Lake Washington Ship Canal. Courtesy Corps of Engineers.

1 – FISHWAY
2 – SPILLWAY DAM
3 – SMALL LOCK
4 – LARGE LOCK
5 – CENTER GUIDE PIER
6 – WEST GUIDE PIER
7 – EAST GUIDE PIER
8 – ADMINISTRATION BUILDING
9 – SUPERINTENDENT'S RESIDENCE

LAKE WASHINGTON SHIP CANAL
Seattle, Washington

Constructed by
**SEATTLE DISTRICT
CORPS OF ENGINEERS
WAR DEPARTMENT**

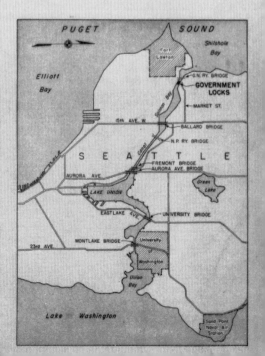

PRINCIPAL FEATURES	LARGE LOCK	SMALL LOCK
Construction commenced	Aug. 6, 1911	Aug. 6, 1911
Opened to traffic	Aug. 3, 1916	July 30, 1916
Extreme length of masonry walls	1,425 feet	690 feet
Length of chamber between upper & lower miter sills	825 "	150 "
Width of chamber	80 "	30 "
Useable length of chamber	760 "	123 "
Lift	6 to 26 "	6 to 26 "
Depth on upper miter sill	36 to 38 "	16 to 18 "
Depth on lower miter sill	25 to 43 "	12 to 30 "
Lock walls, height above floor	55 "	42 "
Lock walls, height above foundation	64 "	49 "
Quantity of concrete in both locks and dam	227,000 cubic yards	

The locks are operated 24 hours daily by three shifts working 8 hours each.
The canal was opened to navigation into Lake Union in October 1916 and into Lake Washington in June 1917.

Statistics on large locks of North America:	USEABLE LENGTH	WIDTH
Panama Canal Locks	1,000 feet	110 feet
Lake Washington Ship Canal Lock	760 "	80 "
Bonneville Ship Lock	500 "	76 "
Welland Ship Canal Lock	820 "	60 "
Saulte Ste. Marie Canal:		
Davis and Sabin Locks	1,350 "	80 "
Mac Arthur Lock	800 "	80 "

The existing project provides for a channel 34 feet deep, 300 ft. wide from Puget Sound to the G.N.Ry. Bridge; thence 34 feet deep, 150 ft. to 200 ft. wide to the locks; from the locks to Lake Union 100 ft. wide, 30 ft. deep; and from Lake Union to Lake Washington 200 ft. wide, 30 ft. deep, except through Portage Cut where the width is reduced to 100 feet.

Right: Large Lock in 1914. Bottom left: First flooding of Large Lock on Feb. 2, 1916 during the regional "Big Snow" of that year. Bottom right: Leak in the west gate of Large Lock, Sept. 19, 1944. Courtesy Corps of Engineers.

Salt water intrusion into the lakes increased with the number of recreational craft using the locks. The opening of the Shilshole Marina outside the locks in 1958 only temporarily relieved this problem. On busy summer days the salinity in the canal could reach as far as the Montlake Cut. In 1966 a huge salt water barrier was installed on the floor of the large lock at its east, or fresh water, end. Since salt water is heavier than fresh water it collects at the bottom of the lock. The device is hinged and so can be lowered for vessels with drafts too deep to clear it in its working position. While not stopping the intruding "salt water wedge," the mechanical barrier has significantly lessened its size.

At the July 4, 1967 ceremonies for the lock's fiftieth anniversary, Senator Henry Jackson, principal speaker, noted the canal's historical irony. "Those who had the keen foresight 100 years ago to press for this canal never fully appreciated its future in pleasure-boating," he said. "Early sponsors promoted the locks and the canal as a passageway for ships."

The recreational features of the Lake Washington Ship Canal extend throughout its seven miles between Shilshole Bay and Lake Washington. In 1958 the Seattle Garden Club began its campaign to beautify the banks of the ship canal, and has produced results. The work of landscaping between the Fremont Bridge and the locks progressed sufficiently that a new "Canal Parkway" was dedicated on Oct. 11, 1960. Ten years later the University of Washington nature trail was extended along the Montlake Cut, again with the cooperation of the Army Corps of Engineers and the Seattle Garden Club. This Montlake Waterside Trail was eventually recognized as a

Top: On Oct. 5, 1975 the 81-foot-wide dry dock White Sands *made it through the 80-foot-wide large lock by being tilted 40 degrees under steel and concrete ballast while riding pontoon barges. The tugs* Dorothy Foss *and* Josie Foss *then successfully delivered her to the Seattle Ship Yard. Above: A nearly intact B-29 is barged through the locks for its destination at the Renton Boeing Plant.*

National Recreation Trail. In 1976 the educational side of canal recreations was again extended when the new fish ladder dedicated that year at the south side of the locks included public viewing facilities. Three years later a visitors interpretive center was added on the lock's north side. After the Seattle Center, Chittenden Locks is the community's second most popular recreational destination.

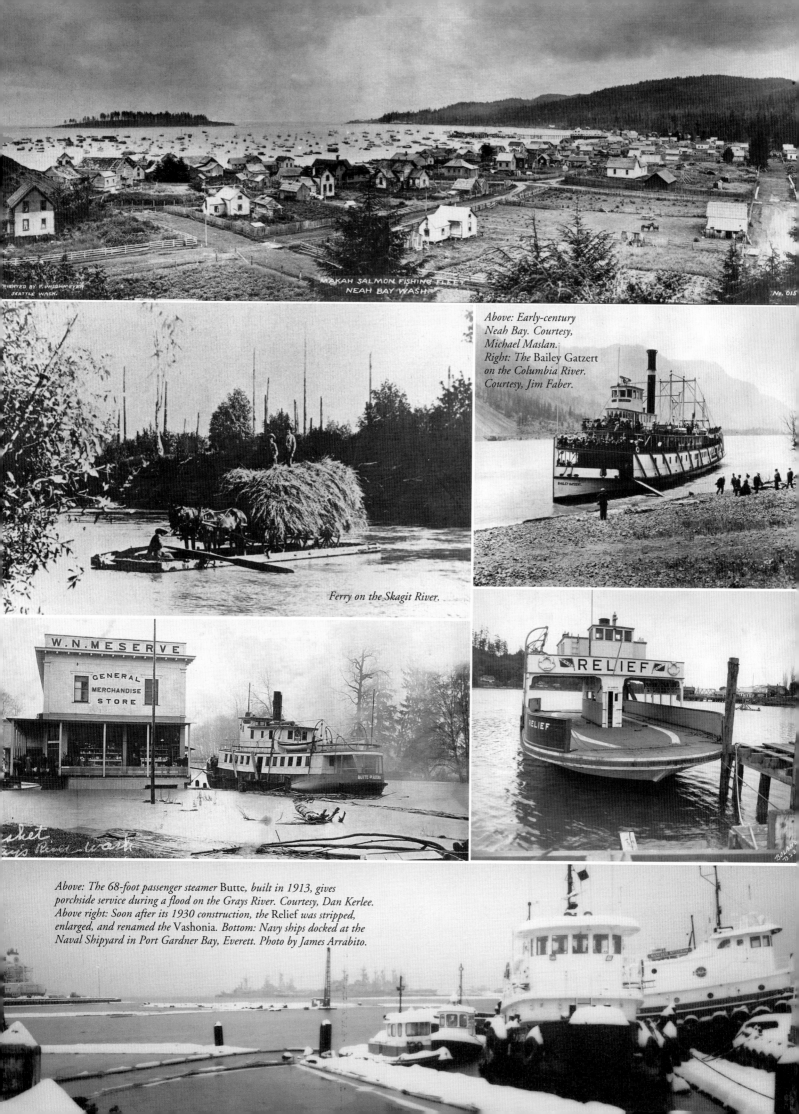

MAKAH SALMON FISHING FLEET
NEAH BAY WASH.

*Above: Early-century
Neah Bay. Courtesy,
Michael Maslan.
Right: The Bailey Gatzert
on the Columbia River.
Courtesy, Jim Faber.*

Ferry on the Skagit River.

W.N. MESERVE

GENERAL
MERCHANDISE
STORE

RELIEF

Above: The 68-foot passenger steamer Butte, *built in 1913, gives
porchside service during a flood on the Grays River. Courtesy, Dan Kerlee.
Above right: Soon after its 1930 construction, the Relief was stripped,
enlarged, and renamed the Vashonia. Bottom: Navy ships docked at the
Naval Shipyard in Port Gardner Bay, Everett. Photo by James Arrabito.*

Above: Lake Union and the Aurora Bridge seen from the deck of the Fremont Bridge, Seattle. Courtesy, Jim Faber. Bottom: The double-ender Gig Harbor *was built in 1925 for a short-lived service to Pierce County destinations on Puget Sound. She was destroyed by fire June 10, 1929.*

View looking north at Mount Rainier with part of Gibraltar Rock showing (far right). The road curve shown here is at Ricksecker Point, which was named for Tacoma resident Eugene Ricksecker, the civilian employee of the Army Corps of Engineers, who began surveying park roads in 1903. This view had been taken before a shortcut through the point was constructed. Photo by Will Hudson. Courtesy, Jean Lunser. Facing page: Snow clearing on Chinook Pass, May 3, 1947. Photo by Simmer. Courtesy, Department of Transportation (DOT).

ROADS AND HIGHWAYS

The first Euro-American highways into the northern part of Oregon Territory were neither surveyed, nor graded, nor even trod down. They were floated and paddled. When the first American settlers came from the Midwest, there were no wagon roads into the territory north of the Columbia River. Streams provided the primary transportation lines. Settling into Indian canoes in 1845, the Michael T. Simmons and George Bush party paddled north up the Cowlitz River, a tributary of the Columbia, to the point where the river turns east. There they stepped ashore at what would later become known as the Cowlitz Landing (present-day Toledo). As they headed overland to Puget Sound, they hacked out a makeshift road, part of the way through virgin timber. Dragging their belongings on sleds, it took them fifteen days to blaze the trail from the landing to the Sound — a distance of sixty miles.

At the mouth of the Deschutes River, the group established the first American town north of the Columbia River. They called it New Market, later changed to Tumwater. The few hardy overlanders who followed them to settle at points along the Sound typically made their way north from Portland on a small steamer to Monticello (present-day Longview). At that time Monticello, according to one early pioneer, was "more a name than a town." From there the settlers either struck out on an old Indian and fur trapper trail or squeezed themselves into a overloaded canoe for an all-day trip up the Cowlitz. At Cowlitz Landing the canoe passengers continued north on the road cut by the Simmons and Bush party, which was negotiable only by foot or with difficulty on horseback.

In 1852 the only newspaper in northern Oregon Territory was the Olympia *Columbian*, and it was zealously promoting a movement to create a new territory north of the Columbia. Any communication improvements in the area were enthusiastically supported. One of them was a "practicable wagon road" up the Cowlitz from Monticello to the landing where it would intersect with the road to Puget Sound. The road was not simply a matter of convenience. It would provide the only link between the northern part of the territory and the capital in Salem. Although the Cowlitz River was the easier route in good weather, between fall and spring it was often flooded, choked with drift, and sometimes even frozen over — making passage difficult if not impossible.

That year a number of men assembled at Monticello and drew up a memorial to Congress requesting the division of the Oregon Territory. All of their reasons for creating the new territory of Columbia stressed either geographic isolation or the difficulty of travel to the southern capital. One claimed that "it costs more for a citizen in the North of Oregon Territory to travel to a clerk's office or to reach a District Judge than it does for a man to travel from S. Lewis (sic), Missouri to Boston, Massachusetts and back." The alleged "three thousand Souls North of the Columbia" feared that the hundreds of miles separating them from the main population and meeting place of the territorial legislature would deprive them of political representation and congressional appropriations. Road building and road improvements were "an absolute and indispensable necessity," the *Columbian* exhorted. It was the only way to attract more settlers, and thus more labor and capital, into the sparsely settled region.

TERRITORIAL AND COUNTY ROADS

As it turned out, the creation of a new U.S. territory was much easier than the creation of new roads. In early 1854 when the Washington Territorial Legislature met for the first time, there were only three roads in the new territory: the Cowlitz-Olympia, a Nisqually-Olympia connection negotiable only by horseback, and the Naches Pass Road. All of them were decidedly deficient. In his opening message to the legislature, Gov. Isaac I. Stevens stressed the urgent need for more and better roads. The legislature agreed, and along with the enormous task of compiling all of the territory's first laws, they created ten territorial roads. According to Puyallup Valley pioneer Ezra Meeker, "the mania was for Territorial roads; everybody wanted a Territorial road."

Most of the roads approved by the legislature during its first six sessions were located around Puget Sound where the largest communities were developing — at Steilacoom and Olympia. But it was one thing to say where territorial roads were to be and another to get them built. No territorial money was appropriated, and construction and maintenance was left up to the counties — which meant county residents had to build and pay for the roads. Defined as roads that passed through two or more counties, the territorial roads were, in effect, county roads under the supervision of the county commissioners.

Area residents who wanted a county road to connect with their property went to their board of three county commissioners with a petition signed by at least twelve "householders." The commissioners then appointed three disinterested county residents as "viewers" to mark the proposed route and recommend whether they thought the road was feasible. If at least two of the three viewers favored building the road and there were no objections to it, the commissioners were required by state law to see that it was built. Following centuries-old common law principles, county commissioners directed all able-bodied male citizens be-

tween the ages of eighteen and fifty, except ministers, to labor on the roads three days out of the year. Those who did not want to work could pay the county instead. Usually, the commissioners divided the county into road districts and appointed a supervisor of roads in each district who was responsible for keeping the roads in good repair. The post was not a popular one. Appointees served under penalty of fine, although no one could be forced to serve more than one term.

In 1857 the legislature inaugurated a regular fund for road purposes by authorizing county commissioners to assess an annual tax of $9 on every person liable for road labor. A property tax of $.25 on each $100 dollars of assessed value was also allowed. Along with the property tax, the commissioners financed roads with a $2 poll tax and bond issues approved by the voters. Most county residents preferred to work off their property taxes instead of paying them. Years later, Bill Nye, a popular humorist recalled that "no taxpayer would pay a dollar, when he could come and make mud pies on the road all day and visit and gossip with the neighbors and save his dollar too."

Although eventually county residents were relieved of the personal responsibility for building roads, the policy of county jurisdiction over road building remained in effect for the next fifty years and had a significant impact on state highway development. County commissioners and engineers built an extensive system of roads within their individual counties, but there was no integration among them to form a coordinated statewide system.

Even under the best conditions the territorial and county roads were little better than abominable. Loaded vehicles could seldom travel more than fifteen or twenty miles a day because of the gullies, stumps, mud pits, and boulders in the roadway. Bridges regularly washed away, trees fell across the route, and corduroy eventually sank in the marshes. Corduroy or puncheon sections of road were laid across swampy areas. They were made of slabs of cedar set (but not fastened) like railroad ties across long poles, with heavier poles laid on top. Travelers had to bring along tools to remove obstacles and repair their wagons.

Sometimes conditions were so bad that the only way to get around was "hoofing it." A Clark County resident in 1869 wrote the editor of the *Vancouver Register* about the wagon road from Vancouver to the eastern part of the county along the Columbia River bank. After the first ten or twelve miles, the river road was "almost impassable for a Cayuse Horse; — It is one continued series of ravines, gulches, hills, and rocks." In 1904 Ezra Meeker reminisced about the state of the Cowlitz road in 1853 when he first attempted to travel north from the Willamette Valley. Another road had emerged a few years after the Simmons-Bush road. The later route went along the east bank of the Cowlitz River to the mouth of the Toutle where the Cowlitz looped to the West. From there the trail proceeded more directly north until rejoining the river where the Cowlitz makes its wide turn to the east. After crossing the Cowlitz the trail continued north, a few miles west of the original Simmons-Bush trail, which it joined at the Chehalis River near the present city of Chehalis. "The facts are," Meeker wrote, "this road, like Topsy, 'just growed,'. . . one could scarcely say when the trail ceased to be simply a trail and the road actually could be called a road." The mud holes were so deep that it became a standing joke "that a team would stall with an empty wagon going down hill."

An early road ordinance dated March 27, 1854 and printed by the new territory's Olympia printer instructs a committee of mostly Seattle citizens to "locate and mark" a road leading southeast from Seattle to the "Emigrant Trail" over Naches Pass. The worst of the hardships accompanying these road ordinances was the lack of funds to actually build the roads surveyed, and nothing much became of them, including Bill No. 16. Courtesy, Washington State Archives, Olympia.

Lithograph published as Plate 44 in the U.S. Pacific R/R Exploration and Surveys, *ca. 1855. The Old Hudson's Bay Company in Fort Vancouver is on the right, while above it, on the left, is U.S. Fort Vancouver, first called Columbia Barracks when it was established in 1849. Courtesy, Library of Congress.*

MILITARY ROADS

For all their vaunted individualism, Western pioneers relied heavily on the federal government to help them solve their transportation problems. The enormous task of planning and building wagon roads west of the Mississippi River to the Pacific Ocean was too great for any other organization. For many years Congress debated the constitutionality of federal road building within state boundaries. However, few objections were raised to construction in the territories, particularly if a military justification could be demonstrated. The term "military road" was used to classify the construction works involving exploratory expeditions, reconnaissance of trails, surveying, and supervision of road workers performed by the Army Corps of Topographical Engineers. National defense, the need to facilitate the movement of men and supplies between army forts, was the avowed purpose of the improvements. But, even early on, the Army recognized that the primary importance of the routes was to prepare the way for the covered wagons and livestock of the pioneer settlers.

Naches Pass Road

General George McClellan

Appropriations for the first military road in the future state of Washington were won through the efforts of Oregon's territorial delegate Joseph Lane. At the same time, Lane lobbied for the passage of the Washington territorial bill. Both bills were approved in 1853 by the thirty-second Congress — Washington became a territory and $20,000, a fraction of what was actually needed, was appropriated for a road from Fort Steilacoom to Fort Walla Walla (at Wallula). The road was intended partly to expedite the movement of troops. But its primary purpose was to give Oregon Trail overlanders a more direct route to Puget Sound.

Capt. George B. McClellan was put in charge of the road by Secretary of War Jefferson Davis. Like his superior officer in the far western field, Gov. Isaac I. Stevens, McClellan had graduated from West Point and served with distinction in the Mexican War.

(Unlike Stevens, McClellan would survive the Civil War and even go on to run for president in 1864 against Abraham Lincoln.) McClellan's work in Washington Territory actually had a dual purpose. He had orders to prepare the military road from Fort Steilacoom in time for the emigrants arriving at Fort Walla Walla in the late summer. He was also assigned to Stevens' railroad survey party and directed to search for a pass through the mountains for a transcontinental railroad.

Proceeding with the extreme cautiousness that would later characterize his Civil War career, McClellan and his party set out late from Fort Vancouver, and in the first ten days they traveled an average of only three-and-one-half miles per day. At that speed the emigrants journeying west from Missouri to the Pacific would have taken six years instead of the average five to six months to cross the continent. McClellan was aided by local Indians who directed him to their trails. Yet the captain missed every one of the several passes through the mountains when he retreated at the first sign of snowfall.

A party traveling to the summit of Mount St. Helens in September 1853 was clearly unimpressed with McClellan's surveying and the work of his road crew, who sometimes got sidetracked panning for gold. "After four days hard traveling," one of the group reported,

we have made 40 miles toward Mount St. Helens, upon a trail (by some called a "military road") which we care not to travel again. This trail was recently cut by a party under the command of Capt. McClelland [sic], who is engaged in exploring . . . for the Pacific railroad. It would seem that they had taken extra pains to cut and mark their way in the shape of a ram's horn, for the purpose of crossing every fallen tree in sight.

Meanwhile, Washington settlers, eager to bring as many of the 1853 Oregon Trail party as possible to Puget Sound, had also grown impatient with McClellan's circumspect construction. The *Columbian* had been urging Thurston and Pierce County settlers to build the road from the Oregon Trail stopping point at Fort Walla Walla themselves. If finished in time, the road would offer the overlanders another destination than the Willamette Valley or California and a much shorter route for those already headed for the Sound. Assuring them that Congress would probably reimburse them for their labor and expenses, the paper called on all male settlers of northern Oregon to demonstrate their commitment to the region — and volunteer. The editors held out a prospect even more alluring than financial reimbursement. In mid-May of 1853 the paper's Cowlitz Landing correspondent wrote that among the families that had arrived in the last three weeks, many brought

a handsome representation of female youth, of fine intelligence, well adapted to grace the parlor or the school room; . . . This addition to our population, lovely as the opening rose, are calculated to produce quite a fluttering among a certain class of bachelors — I mean of course that class of whom there is yet hope — whose sap has not been wholly dried up from the roots, and like dry and barren sticks are only fit for their own place — the land of owls and bats!

Two weeks later the paper reported:

The girls are Coming. — Our latest accounts from the States, inform us that with the immigration of the present year, we shall have a large number of young and beautiful ladies. Glorious good news! Where is the bachelor who will not share in the labor of making the road to Walla-Walla to enable the dear creatures to come to the happy homes of their future consorts?

Whether it was from civic pride or the promise of a young wife, local response was good. Led by Edward J. Allen, a twenty-two-year-old New York-born engineer and Olympia resident, Thurston and Pierce County citizens held public meetings, organized committees, and canvassed for funds, laborers, and supplies. At the beginning of the summer after $1,200 was pledged, two groups, one starting from the Puyallup Valley and the other starting later from the Yakima end of the road, began work on the route over Naches Pass.

Allen, leader of the western-end party, reported to the *Columbian* in August that the men were "going to it like fire, making good time." The next month he wrote the paper that the Steilacoom-Walla Walla wagon road, which followed an old Indian trail, was a good one. It crossed few hills, its greatest elevation was 5,000 feet, and it had plenty of water and grass along it. By the middle of October the Puget Sound emigrant road was reported to be finished from Walla Walla, down through the Green and White River valleys, across the Puyallup River and onto the plains of Pierce County. However, unknown to Allen and the paper, the party at the eastern end had not completed its portion. Having received a false report that there was no wagon train on the way to use it, they had gotten discouraged and quit.

It was a dismal surprise for the Oregon trail emigrants who arrived at Fort Walla-Walla in August. The party was led by James Longmire who would homestead in Yelm Prairie. Looking forward to the end of their 2,000-mile trek, they had been persuaded to take the so-called "People's Road." It would save them the wearisome trip through the mountains over the Barlow route to Portland, then down the Columbia, up the Cowlitz and north over the miserable road to Puget Sound.

George Himes, a boy in the party who would later found the Oregon Historical Society, told of that experience many years later. After crossing the Columbia on a flatboat which they improvised by whipsawing lumber out of driftwood, the party of thirty-six wagons went up the Yakima River, crossing it eight times. Next, following the Naches River, the wagon train passed through sage brush "frequently as high as a covered wagon, which had to be cut down before we could pass through it." On

Westward view from the Pyramid Peak Forest Service lookout station into the Greenwater and White River Valley and the route taken by the Longmire party from Naches Pass to Puget Sound. Courtesy, Claire Raaum.

September 15 they reached the mountains, but to their chagrin "found that there was no road, nothing but an Indian trail to follow." By the time they got to the summit on October 8, cutting the road as they went, they had crossed the Naches River sixty-eight times. Everyone, according to Himes, lent a hand — even himself, ten years old and "barefooted to boot, but not much, if any, worse off than many others."

When they came to the edge of a near-perpendicular bluff surrounded by heavy timber, they were forced to lower the wagons down the thirty-foot cliff. Since their longest rope wouldn't reach, the men slaughtered three cattle to turn their hides into a rope and lowered the wagons "to a point where they would stand up." It took "the best part of two days to make this descent," Himes recalled. In mid-October the weary group, short on rations, finally staggered into Steilacoom where they got "some good, fat beef and plenty of potatoes." It was a meal they would long remember and a road they would sooner forget.

The hand-hewn road over Naches Pass through densely timbered virgin forest was cut partly by McClellan's party, partly by Allen and the volunteers, and partly by the unfortunate emigrants. With grades nearly impossible for wagons and over sixty river crossings on the eastern slope, it never became a popular route. However, after the volunteer road crew returned to Olympia, the thirty-six wagons in the Longmire party having "inaugurated" the trail, the laborers were lionized for their great contribution to the future growth of the territory. Steilacoom's founder, Lafayette Balch, even presented each road worker with a town lot. In January 1854, Captain McClellan's replacement, Lt. Abiel Tinkham, reported to Governor Stevens on the feasibility of a road over Snoqualmie Pass. But by that time the settlers west of the mountains were preoccupied with the fear of Indian attacks, and nothing was done. The Snoqualmie Pass wagon road (discussed below) would take many years and many attempts to complete.

Fort to Fort

During 1856 and 1857 the Army worked on two military roads originating from Columbia Barracks, or Fort Vancouver. Lt. George H. Derby, who was also a humorist and cartoonist, had been put in charge of the Army's Northwest road construction. Derby figured that a connection with Fort Dalles was vital in the aftermath of the outbreak of Indian warfare in the fall of 1855. Supervising a party of Irishmen, who grumbled about having to do guard duty and took every opportunity to desert, Derby eventually had to get a contingent of soldiers to guard the workmen while they planked, corduroyed, and graveled the roadway. The completed five-mile stretch between the upper and lower steamer landings at the mighty Cascade rapids could accommodate a six-mule team hauling two tons. And it saved the public the high fees charged by the portage companies.

The road to Fort Steilacoom, which was in part contracted out to an association of residents along the route, was completed in stages between 1857 and 1861. Where it passed through flood plains of Chehalis River tributaries, corduroyed road connected with causeways and bridges. The completed Fort Vancouver-Fort Steilacoom road provided the first passable route, at least in dry weather with careful driving, for wagons and stage coaches going from Cowlitz Plains to Puget Sound. Traveling from Olympia to Portland was expensive, however — $30 per passenger by stage coach — and took three to five days. Lt. Derby's portage road to Fort Dalles was soon superseded by a railway. But the Columbia-Puget Sound connection, described by one traveler as little more than a "path through the dense forest," remained in use until the building of a railroad spur in 1873.

Fort Steilacoom to Fort Bellingham— "The Old Military Road"

Hostilities between the settlers and natives on Puget Sound erupted into war in 1855, a situation that was soon complicated by the contest between Great Britain and the United States over the ownership of the San Juan Islands. In 1856 the War Department built Fort Bellingham on the bay of the same name as a border watch on both the British and the north coast tribes. The sum of these concerns also stimulated the war office to build a road between Fort Steilacoom and Fort Bellingham. Intended to move troops between the forts and communities on the east side of the Sound, the road was designed to follow a path inland and out of

reach of the British Navy's cannons.

In the summer of 1857 Capt. W.W. DeLacy, assisted by a crew of six Indians and three whites and a pocket compass, set out to survey a trail from White River Bottom on the Puyallup River to Fort Bellingham. Marking trees as he went, DeLacy headed north on the high ground west of the White (Green) River. (See Flood Control Chapter for route of White-Puyallup-Green River.) Much of his route, which now crosses and recrosses the I-5 freeway, is still called the Old Military Road. Near the present site of Georgetown in south Seattle, the crew crossed the Duwamish valley to Beacon Hill, staying near the top of that ridge until they dropped into the rough little milltown of Seattle on Elliott Bay.

Continuing into the wilderness north of Seattle, they marked the trail first to Salmon Bay, near the present community of Ballard. They then turned northeast for a cross-country trek to the north end of Lake Washington. Skirting the swamps beside Sammamish Slough, the party moved north by northwest roughly in line with the present State Highway 9 to the Snohomish River at the present town of Snohomish. From there they continued north, still along the future Highway 9 route, and passed near the meeting of the north and south forks of the Stillaguamish River at Arlington. After skirting the east shore of Big Lake, the survey party descended into the Skagit Valley. The final section of the trail to Bellingham Bay was marked along the present routes of U.S. Highway 99 and Interstate 5 through the Chuckanut Mountains and along Lake Samish.

After DeLacy finished his survey, Lt. George H. Mendell was directed to build the road. Mendell decided to start with the sections of road connecting the more populated areas — between the Puyallup Valley and Seattle and between Fort Bellingham and Whatcom. By the time the lieutenant had let contracts for this work in mid-1858, the little milltown of Whatcom (future Bellingham) had exploded into the largest town in the territory —

Below: Pioneer Bellingham photographer E.A. Hegg's portrait of the bridge over Whatcom Creek, a remnant of the northernmost section of the military road surveyed but only partially built between Forts Bellingham and Steilacoom in the late 1850s. Courtesy, U.W. Libraries, Special Collections.

KING COUNTY ROAD BOOK, No. 4.
(FOR PLATS.)

Plat of
White River & Stuck Valley
Road.

for field notes see Road Book
No 3 page 14
M.S. Booth
Auditor

Filed for Record January 6th 1879 M.S. Booth Auditor   Scale 40 che to inch

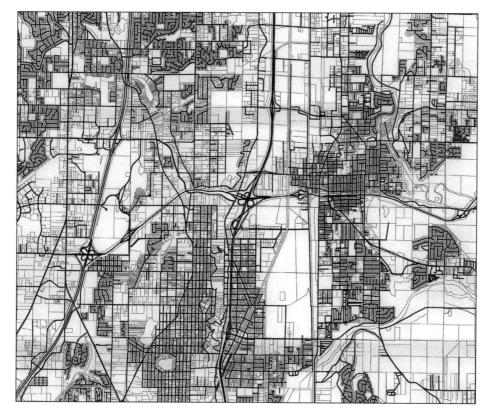

A comparison of 1879 (right) and 1997 (below) maps for the same Auburn and Kent vicinity of South King County reveals only the outline of lakes and the Military Road on the left, and parts of the Green, Stuck, and White Rivers on the right. In 1915, the White River, center-right in the map at right, was diverted into the Stuck (now Puyallup) River, bottom right. (See Floods Chapter.) Courtesy, King County Public Works.

a tent city of miners camped on the shores of Bellingham Bay, waiting to join the gold rush to the Fraser River.

Despite the labor shortage and wage inflation created by the stampede to British Columbia, Mendell proceeded with his scaled-down plans and completed much of the work. But when his army superiors learned that he had, in effect, abandoned the longest stretch of the route between Seattle and Fort Bellingham, he was relieved of his duty. In 1859 a small congressional appropriation made it possible to advertise for bids on the road north of Seattle, and Steilacoom resident Phillip Keach was awarded the contract.

Another Steilacoom citizen (and disappointed California and Fraser River miner) heard of the road plans and hurried north. Hoping to cash in on the prosperity he expected the road to bring, Emory Ferguson hired a steamer to take him to the point where the military road was to cross the Snohomish River. Here he unloaded a portable shack with which to make a homestead claim and prepared to build a store and eventually a town which he called Snohomish. Equally eager to collect proceeds from the road, contractor Keach asked Ferguson to help him expedite the work. Ferguson and Keach and his crew took apart a small wagon and carried it by horseback over their newly cut "wagon road" to Ferguson's backyard in Snohomish. There they reassembled it so that when the Army road inspector arrived, he could verify that a wagon had made it all the way through to Snohomish.

Keach got paid, but the road between Seattle and Bellingham never amounted to much more than a horse trail. Nevertheless, the "Old Military Road" for the first time opened a land connection along the entire eastern shore of Puget Sound. Portions that survived in Thurston, Pierce, King, and Snohomish counties were later developed as parts of county roads.

In 1859 another military road was planned from the mouth of the Columbia River by way of Olympia to Port Townsend. But it soon became a casualty of the government's preoccupation with the impending war between the states. By this time most of the territory's military roads had either never been completed or had fallen into disrepair. In 1858 the territorial legislature had attempted to solve the repair problem by declaring all the military roads to be territorial roads. That way the counties would be responsible for their upkeep.

Ruts and the occasional historical pylon mark the Mullan Trail at points along its route through Eastern Washington. Photo by Hugh Paradise.

Mullan Road

The most ambitious military road in the Northwest also enjoyed the longest existence, even though that was still quite brief. As part of Gov. Isaac Stevens' railroad survey, a young West Point graduate, John Mullan, came to the Pacific Northwest in 1853. He spent that winter crossing and recrossing the Continental Divide, searching for a practical route through the mountains for a railroad or a wagon train. The outbreak of Indian hostilities in the Northwest during 1855-6, followed by bureaucratic inertia, postponed the work until 1858. Then Lt. Mullan received his special assignment to begin work on a road across the northern Rockies. While he was organizing his crew of road laborers and a military escort for defense against the Indians, Mullan received news that Col. Edward J. Steptoe had been routed by a large party of Spokanes, Palouses, and Coeur d'Alenes along the line of the proposed route. The lieutenant got himself attached to the retaliatory expedition of Col. George Wright as a topographical engineer so that he could familiarize himself with the regional geography. After Wright successfully concluded a bloody campaign, Mullan was confident that the road building could go ahead. In the spring of 1859 he set out with an expedition of 230 civilian and enlisted men.

The road was to run from Fort Benton in Montana, at the head of steamboat navigation on the Missouri River, to Fort Walla Walla, in a similar position on the Columbia. The 624-mile-long road was to provide steamboat travelers with a well-built wagon road to travel overland between docking points. The War Department hoped that in addition to serving as a highway for emigrants migrating to the Columbia River region, the road would facilitate the quick deployment of troops in case of emergency and serve as an avenue over which supplies for a future transcontinental railroad could be moved.

Starting at the site of the Hudson's Bay Company's Fort Walla Walla, the Mullan party proceeded up the valley of the Walla Walla River to near the present city of Walla Walla, then known as Steptoe City. There it left the valley and ascended north to the benchlands, directly through the site of the present Washington State Penitentiary, to the confluence of the Snake and Palouse rivers where it proceeded northeast to the Spokane River. Up to this point no major construction was needed. However, in the area around Lake Coeur d'Alene the ground was so marshy that trees had to be felled for corduroyed strips. One crew of laborers, teamsters, and twenty soldiers worked for a week cutting through three miles of timber, building bridges, and excavating side hills.

East of the Coeur d'Alene Mission, in the vicinity of present-day Kingston, Idaho crews of axmen worked during every hour of daylight to hack a twenty-five-foot-wide passage through 100 miles of almost impenetrable forest up to the St. Regis-Borgia River. Mullan later admitted that "the amount of work required was immense, and very much underestimated by myself and others." By the time the party had made its way down the Clark Fork River, past modern-day Missoula and Helena, Montana to the termination point at Fort Benton on August 1, 1860, many in the crew were suffering from frostbite and scurvy.

And yet the road was far from complete. Improvements were made as Mullan returned over the route from east to west. But since no federal funds had been made available for maintenance, portions of the road deteriorated even while it was being built. Like all the military roads in the area, the Mullan Road fell far short of the Army's original plans — its military function was limited to a single occurrence; its use as a passage for immigrant groups was only partly realized during the 1860s; and its utility for supplying railroad builders was minimal. It took the discovery of gold in the northern Rocky Mountains in the early 1860s to give the Mullan Road its greatest, although fleeting, importance.

Once Walla Walla merchants discovered that the road provided a route for supplying the several mining districts north and east of them, Walla Walla, located at the junction of the Oregon Trail and the Mullan Road, underwent a dramatic change. Gold fever was catching for miners, merchants, and farmers alike. From a seven-house outpost in 1860, Walla Walla grew to become the largest city in Washington Territory in 1870 with a population of 1,394. Catering to the miners, and packers who hauled supplies to the mines, Walla Walla merchants imported goods from Portland and San Francisco by steamboat to Wallula. Packers liked Walla Walla, which they called "a considerable city" where they could have "a good time."

Ferry operators on the Snake River also got into the act. Each claimed to have the best location for the quickest route to the mining areas. The proprietors of McWhirk's (later Lyons) Ferry, on the main Mullan Road crossing, promised a $1,000 reward to anyone who could find as direct a wagon road to the Colville or Kootenay mines as the route crossing the Snake River at McWhirk's Ferry. Even Mullan, by then a captain, was not immune to the lure of potential riches. In October 1863 the *Walla Walla Statesman* announced that, along with a party of twenty others, he had just left Walla Walla on a prospecting trip to the Kootenay region.

EASTERN WASHINGTON WAGON ROADS

Mullan's road, although the most frequently remembered by historians, was only one of several wagon roads in the Inland Empire. The Colville Road, the oldest of the pioneer trails, was followed by Indians, miners, traders, and stockmen going from the Snake and Columbia rivers north to the Colville Valley and Canada. Like the Mullan Road, it began at Wallula, now submerged beneath the backwaters of McNary Dam. It crossed the Snake River at Lyon's Ferry and ended at old Pinckney City on Mill Creek, about two miles from present-day Colville. In 1858 and 1859 the route was developed as a military route because of the Indian wars. Until it was replaced by the Northern Pacific Railroad which reached Spokane Falls in 1881, the Colville Road carried the bulk of the freight going north from Walla Walla.

The Cariboo Trail, also called the Wallula-Okanogan Road, was used by miners going to the mines in British Columbia. The road started at Wallula, crossed the Quincy Basin near Moses Lake, and continued east of the lower Grand Coulee, which it crossed at Coulee City. After reaching the Waterville Plateau, the trail went north to a point near the site of Fort Okanogan, at the junction of the Columbia and Okanogan rivers, and followed the valley of the latter across the border into Canada. A number of other north-south roads originated at Walla Walla, which in the 1860s and 1870s operated as the major supply center for all of eastern Washington. The Texas Road, the Old Territorial Road, and the Kentuck Trail, and the ferries that operated along them over the Snake River were responsible for bringing thousands of people into Spokane and Whitman counties, increasing the population from 147 in 1870 to 11,276 ten years later.

SNAKE RIVER CABLE FERRIES

In a stretch of fifteen miles along the lower Snake River in eastern Washington, five cable ferries offered their services for travelers going north from Walla Walla. The ferries, attached to a cable anchored on either side of the river, were powered by controlling the angle of the boat against the river current. Starting on the west were the Lyons Ferry for the Colville and Mullan roads; the shortlived Kellogg's Ferry at the mouth of the Tucannon River; the Texas, where steamboats to Lewiston loaded fuel; Tormy's, nearby and later also known as the Texas Ferry, on the Texas Road (one of the longest lived); and the Blackfoot Ferry, used mainly by miners going to Montana. In June 1960 the Lyons Ferry, previously known as the Palouse Ferry, celebrated its centennial. As both the first and last ferry to operate on the river, it had supplied the longest continuous cable ferry service west of the Rockies. In 1969 the ferry was finally put to rest as waters backed up behind the newly completed Lower Monumental Dam. Today motorized traffic crosses the river at this site near Starbuck on a steel girder bridge assembled from parts of the old Vantage Bridge.

SNOQUALMIE PASS WAGON ROAD

As soon as Americans established their tiny communities on Puget Sound, they began to compete among themselves for the settlers following them in ever-greater numbers. The Naches Pass road had been a failure. In 1859 emigrants headed for Puget Sound were still compelled to go first to Portland, then down the Columbia to Monticello, up the Cowlitz to the landing and overland sixty miles to the Sound. In August of that year a group of Seattle men, including pioneer-founders Arthur Denny and Henry Yesler, subscribed $1,000 for the opening of a road through Snoqualmie Pass. At their request the territorial legislature that winter memorialized Congress for appropriations for a wagon road from Fort Colville to Puget Sound. A bill appropriating $75,000 was passed but later waylaid by the Civil War, which

Above: Fort Colville remnant. Courtesy, U.W. Library, Special Collections. Below and bottom: The Lyons Ferry, ca. 1965, last of the cable ferries on the Snake River. Photos by Hugh Paradise.

Above: Wagon road east of Snoqualmie Pass along the north shore of Lake Keechelus in 1911. Photo by Asahel Curtis. Courtesy, WA State Historcal Society.

ended all possibility of federal help for many years to come.

In 1863 Territorial Gov. William Pickering, a personal friend and political ally of President Lincoln, appealed to the state legislature for a good mountain pass road "to mutually bind together the various and diversified interests of our widely spread population." But the legislature followed its short but firm tradition of assuming no financial responsibility for roads and declined.

Disgusted with the legislature's intransigence, Seattle men in 1865 again pledged their dollars and backs for a wagon road from Ranger's Prairie (now North Bend) over the summit to the Yakima Valley. Two years later when the rough-hewn, fifty-five-mile-long road was about half-finished, King County representatives and Gov. Pickering again applied to the legislature for help. They were not proposing a well-graded road, they stressed, but one only good enough for the emigrants to get through. This time the legislature complied and appropriated a total of $4,500 over two sessions. With this and other funds they scraped together, the road builders finished the route in 1868. That year the new governor, Marshall F. Moore, a great advocate of improved territorial communications, proudly crossed the pass on horseback. The next year cattle from eastern Washington ranges were being driven over Snoqualmie Pass to coast markets. However, like the other inadequately funded wagon roads, the Snoqualmie Pass road succumbed to washouts and fallen trees even as it was being completed. (Yet some parts of the old puncheon road, built over bogs with cedar planks, survived 100 years.)

In 1873 the Northern Pacific Railroad chose the barely formed village of Tacoma, still engulfed by forest, as its Puget Sound terminus. After recovering from their surprise, Seattleites decided that they could get along without the N.P. and deter-

mined to build their own railroad over the pass to connect with the transcontinental mainline at Walla Walla. Although the Seattle and Walla Walla Railway took off with a rousing start, the line never made it past the coal mines on the east side of Lake Washington. Twice-disappointed Seattleites turned again to the wagon road as a way to bring more traffic to their city. As long as it didn't cost any money, the legislature agreed to help, figuring that the increased traffic would benefit the whole territory.

Henry Yesler's Grand Lottery ticket, 1876. Courtesy, Seattle Public Library.

In 1875, lawmakers passed an act that allowed anyone living in King and Yakima counties to put up property in a lottery, provided that 10 percent of the net proceeds was set aside for the Snoqualmie Pass wagon road. Henry L. Yesler, a Seattle founder and owner of the sawmill that became the economic center of the community, was the lottery bill's instigator and chief proponent.

The cash-poor Yesler hoped that the "Grand Lottery of Washington Territory," which offered his sawmill as first prize, would help him pay his bills. He hoped to sell 60,000 tickets — no small feat when 3,000 or 4,000 people lived in King County. When ticket sales faltered, Yesler postponed the raffle. Before he could reschedule it, a district court found the lottery illegal. In the 1880s, when Seattle's population and property values soared, the still land-rich Henry Yesler would be grateful for the failed experiment in road funding. His property made him a very rich man.

In the mid-1880s the Snoqualmie Pass road was operated as a toll road by the Ellensburg-based Seattle and Walla Walla Trail and Wagon Road Co. The company promoted the road, which was completed from Taneum Bridge, southwest of Ellensburg, to Ranger's Prairie, as an efficient route for stage and mail lines. They even advertised ambitious but never-realized plans for "cabins and stables constructed not more than five miles apart along the snowy portion of the road." Tolls were steep: a horse and buggy was charged $2; a man on horseback, $1; three cattle for $1; and sheep and pigs cost ranchers ten cents each. The company collected tolls from 1884 at least until 1888, when the N.P.'s completed line over Stampede Pass radically cut into their business.

With the coming of the railroad the problem of establishing communication between the western and eastern sides of the mountains was solved. For years afterwards the Snoqualmie Pass wagon road was neglected. In 1899 the state legislature made a half-hearted attempt to revive the usefulness of the "almost forgotten Snoqualmie Pass wagon road" with a grant of $1,000 for repairs. David Denny of Seattle, who supervised the work, found that the tiny allocation was inadequate for making even the minimum number of necessary restorations. Effective improvements to the Snoqualmie wagon road would have had to wait until the twentieth century and the coming of the motor car.

CASCADE WAGON ROAD TO NORTH CASCADES HIGHWAY

Another wagon road with an even longer history of interrupted development was the Cascade Wagon Road. Established by the legislature with the first state highway appropriation in 1893, the road was originally intended to access the Ruby Creek placer

Above: North Bend below Mount Si, 1909. Courtesy, Michael Maslan.

deposits in eastern Whatcom County and also serve as a cattle trail from the Okanogan Valley to markets on Puget Sound. The original project was soon abandoned, however, because of the difficulty of the proposed route and the shortage of funds. The legislature had presumed that engineers could survey a route, blast out tunnels, grade hillsides, and build bridges all for $100 a mile.

In 1896 state road commissioners decided on a route over the Cascade, or Skagit Pass, but, because of another small appropriation, little surveying was done. To further cut costs, the roadbed was graded to only four feet where heavy excavation was needed, and portions of the road were not widened even to wagon width. In one place the route crossed a rock slide at a 20 percent grade. By 1897 because of slides and washouts, most of the Cascade Wagon Road had become all but impassable.

In 1906 a disgruntled highway commissioner, Joseph Snow, made his first report to the legislature. He said that although $85,200 had been spent on the road, most of the money had been wasted. At least, there was little to show for it except a thirty-mile horse trail from Marblemount to the summit of the Methow Range, twelve miles of wagon trail between the head of the Twisp River and the town of Twisp, and fourteen miles of trail on the

Left: The note on the back of this postcard reads, "Four miles from summit of Cascades. Snoqualmie Pass road. Taken by Order of North Bend Commercial Club, May 12, 1913." Courtesy Department of Transportation. Above: Good Roads boosters meet at the top of Stevens Pass, June 1928. Courtesy, U.W. Library, Special Collections.

Stehekin River between the mouth of Bridge Creek and Lake Chelan. Most of the road along this line had been built without engineering assistance and without any regard to grades or stability. A few friends had agreed to accompany Commissioner Snow over the road to Republic, but they "flatly refused to return over the same road owing to its excessive grades and dangerous condition. This was the first and last wagon to pass over the road," Snow grumbled.

In 1907 and 1909 the legislature made appropriations for the three — western, mountain, and eastern — sections of the road. A survey was made, contracts were let, and the state tried its first experiment in convict road building on the Okanogan County mountain section. But little work was finished. Another discouraged highway commissioner, Henry Bowlby, recommended that the road be abandoned in Whatcom County. The highway department rationalized that a road wouldn't be of much use anyway because there were so few residents in the area. The department was eager to get one cross-state highway completed, and assuming, like the legislature, that there would be no demand for more than one, they pushed for the Snoqualmie Pass route instead.

Later, in the 1910s and 1920s, the legislature allocated small amounts for the grading and repair of portions of the road between Marblemount and Republic, as did Whatcom, Skagit, Okanogan, Ferry, and Stevens counties. As its many designations — among them the Methow-Barron Road, the Skagit River Road, the Marcus-Marble Mount Road, and the Roosevelt Highway — indicate, the route of the highway was redefined with each new reconnaissance trip and survey. Construction work started and stopped more often than the name changed. Either initial allocations were not adequate or natural catastrophes intervened and pushed construction schedules back and costs up.

The boom in automobile ownership in the late 1920s and early 1930s prompted the legislature to open highways over both Stevens and Chinook passes. But once again the northern Cascade route was passed over — partly because a feasible route had not yet been decided upon. Then, in 1932, Ivan ("Ike") Munson, a highway department location engineer, was sent to the North Cascades to survey for a highway that followed a trail across Washington Pass, went down Bridge Creek, up the Stehekin River, and across Cascade Pass to Marblemount. This was the first time Washington Pass was identified as a possible route. Along with the crew of surveyors, packers, and cooks, Munson took his wife and two children on a working summer vacation. For three and a half months the survey party, draped with towels over their heads and under their hats for protection against the persistent mosquitoes, packed over the territory on horseback, establishing base camps every ten miles.

For the rest of the decade and during World War II, the northern pass remained a low priority. In fact, it was not until 1957, twenty-five years after Munson's party implanted their cedar survey stakes, that the final assault to complete the highway project was mounted. Then Ike Munson led highway commissioners on another horseback reconnaissance through the mountains and they decided to route the highway over Rainy and Washington passes, following Munson's 1932 survey almost exactly. Construction began on the North Cascades Highway in 1959. At long last in the fall of 1972 the state's first legislated highway, now considered to be its most beautiful mountain road, was finished.

Top: With Liberty Bell Mountain in the background, surveyors scout a cross-Cascades route, 1957. Center: Crews construct highway near Washington Pass, 1965. Above: North Cascades Highway, 1966. Photo courtesy, MOHAI, Seattle P-I Collection.

Washington State Good Roads Association

1914 Convention at Spokane, November 18, 19 and 20

WITHOUT MAINTENANCE   WITH MAINTENANCE

Above: A Good Roads letterhead promoting road maintenance using a split log illustrated by before and after photos.

Good Roads Day
Has been Proclaimed by Gov. Lister for
May 24, 1913
NEXT SATURDAY
Get your people out and do some Good Work
for Your Community on That Day
Spokane County Good Roads Association

Above: In Sam Hill's "backyard," Good Roads inspectors ascending from the Columbia Gorge enjoy a smooth section on the Maryhill Road.

GOOD ROADS MOVEMENT

Before motor vehicles, railroads provided the long distance hauling and roads between towns could largely be ignored. However, since farmers needed roads to connect their widely scattered farms to the railroad siding or directly to the market, Washington's campaign for road improvements aimed first at better farm-to-market wagon roads. In the 1890s a crude road network across eastern Washington, intended to get the farmer to the nearest town, was built by farmers pulling half logs behind teams of horses.

The first coordinated lobbying for public support of better surfaced roads did not originate with the farmers, however. It began with a small segment of well-to-do urban residents — the bicyclists. These fitness and racing enthusiasts loved to stream out into the countryside, crouched low over their handlebars. But too often for their liking the racers were hurled out of the running by the muddy quagmires and many obstacles in the unmarked country roads.

At the beginning of the twentieth century probably many people in the state had never seen a hard-surfaced road. In 1904 a federal road survey showed that of the 2,151,570 miles of highway in the country, 93 percent were unimproved, that is, plain dirt. In Washington in 1908 there were 1,081 miles of officially designated state roads of which only 125 were improved. Most of these improvements were main streets in towns that had tried to achieve some semblance of urban refinement by putting down a few yards of plank, brick, or wood-block paving. The norm was the all-too-common dirt road — dusty in dry weather and usually impassable in wet.

Until the 1930s, the movement for good roads, supported by the bicyclists, the National Grange, and America's motorcar drivers, remained exclusively concerned with rural roads. Even so, many farmers initially opposed improvements designed for fancy motor vehicles owned by city folk. The unnatural machines frightened the work horses, and farmers were not about to pay higher county road assessments to accommodate a few hobby-riders. Sometimes they plowed deep ruts in the road or strewed broken bottles across the path of the motor cars. Besides, some farmers reasoned, with poor roads they could earn extra money pulling stuck vehicles out of the mud.

Whether they realized it or not, the farmers had an advocate in the state's earliest and greatest hobby-rider, Sam Hill. Son-in-law of the railroad magnate, James J. Hill, Sam Hill pioneered thousands of miles of Northwest roads in his first car, a Locomobile bought at the dawn of the auto industry. Hill would not have been happy with the hobbyist tag, however. "Good roads are more than my hobby; they are my religion," he once claimed. In 1900 when Hill lobbied before a Senate committee for a federal highway act, one of his aims was to secure funds for the states to improve county roads for rural mail delivery. Hill advocated better roads for the farmer, not only to help them transport their produce to market, but also for reasons of morality. Referring to the widely-accepted belief in the corrupting influences of the city, he said, "We cannot keep the ambitious boy or girl on the farm unless we make life attractive and comfortable."

Hill invited 100 of the state's important business and civic leaders to attend a meeting in Spokane on September 14, 1899, about forming a state good roads organization. Only fourteen showed up, but those that did liked the idea and voted to form the Washington Good Roads Association. At first many solid citizens, bankers, merchants, and farmers alike, considered the group unbalanced and argued that they didn't need better roads, and, even if they did, they wouldn't pay for them. Gradually the association developed more support and political influence, particularly as automobile ownership grew.

Due to Hill's remarkable campaigning efforts, which took him around the state and the region, to the nation's capital, and even to Europe for international road congresses, Washington became one of the leading states in the nationwide good roads

GOOD ROADS!
★ ★ ★
BUILD THEM NOW AND SEE HOW QUICKLY
GOOD TIMES
WILL ROLL DOWN THE ROADS

Above: The Blaine Juvenile Band at the International Boundary during the dedication of the Peace Arch at Blaine, 1921. Courtesy, Maryhill Museum of Art. Inset left: A Good Roads broadside. Inset right: Good Roads promoter Sam Hill. Below: Construction scene along Chuckanut Drive. Courtesy, DOT.

movement. One of the Washington group's first objectives was to convince state legislators of the advantages of building a statewide highway system administered by a state highway department. Centralized administration and regulation, they argued, would eliminate the customary wasteful and uncoordinated road-building of the counties.

A DEPARTMENT FOR HIGHWAYS

The establishment of a state highway department in 1905 when only thirteen other states in the country had them, was in good part the result of the lobbying efforts of the Washington Good Roads Association. In fact, Sam Hill, who loved to boast about the state's progressive highway legislation, bragged in 1907 that the legislature had "passed all the measures we asked for." Under the legislation a highway fund was established to subsidize work on ten designated state roads in mountainous and sparsely settled districts.

Hill's achievement was notable since before 1910 there was no groundswell of public support for hard-surfaced roads in Washington. Few people owned the expensive and problem-ridden horseless carriages. The inconvenience of the new inventions was at first compounded by conflicting local laws which required motorists to stop at city or county limits to purchase special licenses in order to go on. Many were not happy with the new state road-making authority either. The detractors included Governor Albert E. Mead, whose veto of the bill establishing the office of State Highway Commissioner was overridden.

County commissioners were even more displeased. Accustomed to being in charge of all road building in their districts, they had tried to block the proposed highway department legislation. For several years afterwards county employees continued to resist the highway department's prerogative. They refused to cooperate with state officials and engineers and sometimes attempted to sabotage their efforts.

In 1907 the state agreed to pay all the costs of building twelve designated state roads, and 50 percent of state aid roads. The latter were roads requested by the counties that had been approved by

Text continues page 77

CONVICT LABOR

One of the proposals Sam Hill urged on the newly formed highway department was to use state convicts as construction laborers on macadam roads. Highway Commissioner Joseph Snow was apparently convinced by Hill's arguments that it would save taxpayers money, and he, in turn, proposed the idea to the Whitman County commissioners. But the commissioners turned thumbs down on the suggestion. One of them wrote Snow that it wouldn't be right to bring in state convicts to work on county roads when the county had its own prisoners sitting idle in their cells. Spokane County turned down a similar offer the next year. But Commissioner Snow remained convinced, mostly from the results of a Lewis County experiment that employed fifteen convicts to crush rock for macadam, that prisoners could be employed profitably both for the state and for themselves — for their "mental and physical improvement."

Snow was eventually able to test his convictions on the Methow-Barron Road, part of the elusive highway through the North Cascades. Here the state's first experiment in convict road building was made in 1907-08. Not surprisingly, Commissioner Snow reported that "the experiment was a success," and it set the precedent for using unskilled prison inmates on the most difficult kind of rock excavation. The convicts worked entirely by hand, with picks, shovels, and wheelbarrows, sometimes even pushing and pulling the ore car themselves. A second convict camp was established in Kittitas County in 1909 to do heavy rock work and clearing on the Snoqualmie Pass Road.

A third crew was employed near Lyle in Klickitat County for "the heaviest kind of rock excavation along the bluffs of the Columbia River" for the Columbia River Road. At the latter site, where prisoners were housed in wooden buildings surrounded by a portable stockade of heavy timbers, a convict who had been jailed for dynamiting was put in charge of the explosives. Since armed guards were on hand, escape attempts were rare. Also, inmates nearing the end of their term were reluctant to risk a return to the pen. On the Columbia River Road, the highway department figured they saved taxpayers $1.87 per day per man over what it would have cost for regular contract labor. By 1910 Washington's experiment in convict

Convict shovel work on construction of the Olympic Highway. Courtesy, Department of Transportation.

labor was receiving national attention.

That year the Waterfront Road, the future Chuckanut Drive, which overlooks Samish Bay in Skagit County north of Blanchard, became the site of another convict road camp. Problems with the project came not so much from the occasional convict who disappeared in the dust stirred up by the road work as from an inexperienced superintendent and the clifftop route itself. The men had to cut the stone from the face of a ledge and try to keep it from falling on and damaging the Great Northern railroad tracks below. It was 1916 before the road was completed and became part of the Pacific Highway and "one of the most scenic drives in the state." Meanwhile, the railroad sued the department for damages. Today, Chuckanut Drive, which is still subject to mudslides and washouts, remains one of Washington's favorite tourist routes.

The state legislature had adopted another plan to save taxpayers road assessments in 1909 when it approved $124,000 for five

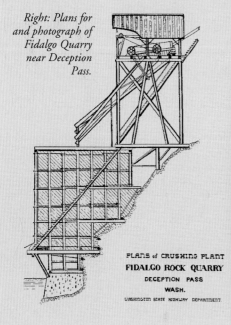

Right: Plans for and photograph of Fidalgo Quarry near Deception Pass.

PLANS of CRUSHING PLANT
FIDALGO ROCK QUARRY
DECEPTION PASS
WASH.
WASHINGTON STATE HIGHWAY DEPARTMENT

Above: Bunkers at Selah Quarry. Courtesy, Department of Transportation (DOT). Right: Gravel crusher and hauling train on Selah Road, Yakima County. Courtesy DOT.

quarries and crusher plants to be manned by state convicts. By using the captive labor, the highway department reckoned it could produce the crushed rock that counties needed for macadam roads at a fraction of the current price. Within three years the five "modern crushing plants" with "comfortable housing [for] officers and convicts" were all operating and self-supporting, the pride of the department. However, even as the plants became fully operational, orders for crushed rock began to sag. Counties had found that the rates charged by the Northern Pacific for transporting the rock made it more expensive than developing their own quarries. Moreover, the trend to concrete surfaces that could use the cheaper gravel as a bottom course was quickly causing the crushed rock macadam surface to become obsolete. In 1917 the legislature voted to dismantle the quarries due to lack of sales.

Gov. Ernest Lister, a Democrat who believed in expanding governmental activities as long as it was economical, continued the practice of convict road building. In fact, during Lister's first term beginning in 1913 the "honor system" was begun. Under this program, prisoners became eligible to work out of an unsecured camp after signing a pledge of honor to perform the work and not leave camp without permission. Some of the initial construction work on the Olympic and Pacific highways was performed in 1913 by honor camp prisoners from the Walla Walla state penitentiary. The first honor camp was established on the west shore of Hood Canal, one mile north of Hoodsport, and the second, on the Pacific Highway, was located two miles south of Kalama.

Conditions on the Olympic Highway project were particularly bad — described by the highway commissioner as those "which no contractor would have ventured to face." The excavation was entirely in earth and performed during the winter when it rained nearly every day. The men sank halfway to their knees in mud. As they attempted to scoop up the mortar-like earth, stumps and brush continually slid down embankments onto the roadway. Yet, the department reported that there was "comparatively little ill feeling." In the first four honor camps, where most of the men had not previously worked as common laborers, only three out of 100 "failed to uphold their honor and deserted the camps." Nevertheless, convict labor was discontinued shortly afterwards.

the highway commissioner. Under the traditional system, where county property taxes financed the roads, county commissioners were naturally more concerned about meeting the transportation needs of local residents than with coordinating their system of roads with those of other counties. This could mean that a road passing through more than one county might be graded or paved with gravel or crushed rock in one county only to turn into a muddy, chuck-hole-ridden mess in the next. Or the road might end altogether at the county line. The 1907 state aid law was supposed to encourage coordination among the counties, but it fared little better with county officials than the original highway legislation. Farmers, accustomed to bearing a heavy share of road costs, were also suspicious, fearing that the new laws would only bring them higher taxes.

By 1910 the highway department was clearly on the defensive. The governor even appointed a commission to investigate charges that the costs of engineering on state roads had been excessive. One example given of the department's "bungling" was the Chuckanut Mountain Road, a sore point for many Whatcom County residents. Twenty-five thousand dollars had been appropriated to build a 5.5-mile stretch of road. Before the construction crews had completed one mile, the funds were depleted. The gravel road was often blocked by slides or portions of the roadway itself would slide away, leaving impassable gaps. Sometimes frightened motorists were assisted by an enterprising young daredevil who drove their cars across any gap that could be spanned by two timbers. After a lengthy investigation, the special commission found that the department had been operating efficiently. The criticism about high road building costs, they determined, was more a consequence of faulty construction cost estimates and inadequate appropriations than of incompetent road work.

Below: Construction scene along Chuckanut Drive. Bottom: The completed highway with the Mount Vernon-Bellingham Interurban trestle below. Both courtesy, DOT.

Above: Finishing surface on early State Highway 10 (now U.S. 97) near Omak. Below: Building concrete road sixteen feet wide near Centralia, July 19, 1912. Bottom: Concrete base and curb with sand cushion ready for brick paving on Pacific Highway in King County. Courtesy DOT.

In an attempt to improve the condition of the road fund as well as relations with county authorities, legislators approved the Permanent Highway Act in 1911. This law allowed the state to levy a one mill tax on all real property in the state and assured the delighted highway department an unprecedented $1 million year — enough to finance over 100 miles of highway annually. After the plans for the state-funded roads were approved by the state highway commissioner, the county commissioners were to be in charge of construction. The legislation required the roads to be hard-surfaced with macadam, stone, gravel, or some durable material for a width of not less than twelve feet. They also had to be located along main lines of travel, primarily for commercial transport. Grades were generally not to exceed five percent and in no case to exceed ten percent. For many counties, the money that became available under the law gave them the means to build their first hard-surfaced roads.

While it set new standards and collected more revenue, the Permanent Highway Act failed to resolve the administrative problems that had hindered the earlier legislation. The legislature continued to make individual appropriations for specific roads. This type of pork barreling caused funds to be spent on small sections of road that, according to critics, began nowhere and ended nowhere, or were built in the mountains where neither present nor prospective traffic seemed to warrant their construction. Not only was the highway commissioner unable to determine where funds would be spent, but the legislature ordered that any unused appropriated funds were to be returned to the general fund. In the counties this resulted either in the uneconomical practice of building very small sections of road, sometimes only a fraction of a mile long, or the loss of the funds altogether.

EARLY ROAD SURFACES

By 1910 there were enough automobiles in the state to cause highway engineers to reevaluate their road surface technology. Originally, highway officials anticipated that the automobile's weight and rubber tires would cause little or no road wear. It was expected, in fact, to help compact the stones of the water-bound macadam that had by then become the latest thing in road surfacing. However, it was soon discovered that this was not the case. In the early days of the auto industry when cars ran at low speeds, Highway Commissioner Henry Bowlby wrote in 1910, they were hailed as great road preservers.

But with the present small locomotive running at high speed and seldom requiring the services of the plow team to get back to town, it has been found that the water-bound macadam will not stand the strain. . . . in a short time the road has gone to pieces.

The year before Bowlby's predecessor, Commissioner Snow, had recommended that "to assist in the maintenance of the expensive roads which they invariably use for speeding purposes," drivers of the road-destroying automobile should pay an annual license fee. The roads that the state and counties had designed were already outmoded. Road surface technology would have to be revised and soon, for the motor car was beginning to catch on.

By 1912 the availability of state funds from the Permanent Highway Act allowed several counties to begin experimenting with hard surface materials that could withstand the punishment inflicted by automobiles. Kittitas County tried out a patented surface known as "Dollarway" over a concrete pavement, while Pierce County experimented with a two-course concrete known as "Granocrete." King County began building with two types of hard surfacing: Warrenite, a bituminous wearing surface laid upon a concrete or crushed rock base; and brick on a concrete base. Franklin County tested a concrete roadway with a top course of "one-third of a gallon of asphaltic oil per square yard with screenings to take up the oil." Snohomish County laid its first mile of hard

Sign marks beginning of Warrenite surface on King County road. Courtesy Department of Transportation (DOT).

Road work near Walla Walla. Courtesy DOT

Macadam surface on Redmond-Kirkland highway. Courtesy DOT.

Above: Typical Highway Department construction camp, ca. 1912. Below: Road work near Raymond. Courtesy DOT.

Top to bottom: Portion of Maryhill Highway between Columbia River and Goldendale. Courtesy, Ted Van Arsdol; Split log drag in use on unidentified state road; DOT dump trucks for the maintenance division; Work on the Sunset Highway east of Ellensburg, 1926; Surface trestle above wetlands in Pacific County. Courtesy DOT.

Ford cars on the road to Chelan, May 15, 1910. All photos this page courtesy Department of Transportation.

First crossing of Sanpoil River on early State Highway 4 (now S.R. 1).

Early State Highway 10 (now U.S. 97) overlooking the Columbia upstream from Wenatchee.

Portion of highway near Tonasket that was built with donated labor.

A portion of completed highway on State Road 10 (now U.S. 97).

Section of Central Washington Highway (now U.S. 395) in Adams County.

Touring car on State Highway 2 leaving Waterville, Aug. 17, 1912.

A heavy load—5,600 pounds—testing the new Apple Way east of Spokane.

80

pavement between Stanwood and East Stanwood using vitrified brick. That same year Lewis County became the second locality in the country and the first in the state to build a reinforced concrete highway. Three miles long, with concrete six inches thick and expansion joints every fifty feet, the roadway was laid at a cost of $1.30 per square yard.

FEDERAL ASSISTANCE FOR HIGHWAYS

What finally changed the minds of rural Washingtonians was the realization that they too could benefit from good hard-surfaced roads *and* that they would have help paying for them. The federal government stuck to its policy of denying rural free mail delivery to communities where the roads were impassable. But even more important for the farmer's future was the federal commitment of funds in 1916 and 1921 to improve farm-to-market and rural post roads. The Federal Aid Road Act of 1916, better known as the Good Roads Act because it was brought about through the efforts of the good roads movement, began the practice of granting federal funds to states on a matching basis. Washington used its first appropriation on 3.5 miles of one-course concrete paving on the Pacific Highway one mile east of Olympia. Originally, the federal funds were available for state roads only, since the allocations were supposed to encourage states to develop interstate highway systems. After county authorities expressed disappointment about this arrangement, the state legislature of 1919 amended the state's assenting act so that counties could also be eligible for the federal funds.

Like the 1916 legislation the Federal Highway Act of 1921 also limited the use of federal funds to rural roads and was meant, in part, to help with the improvement of farm-to-market roads primarily for the isolated farmer. But by the end of World War I, the second objective of expediting the completion of a connecting system of interstate highways had become more urgent. The number of motor vehicles in the country had jumped from 2 million in 1915 to nearly 10 million in 1920 — and they were all trying to use an inadequate road system.

During the war the country's railroad system had been brought to a near standstill by monumental congestion, revealing the need for a coherent network of truck highways. The first truck convoys, used during the war years to relieve some of the strain on the railroads, had impressively demonstrated their potential for long-distance commercial hauling. In Eastern Washington farmers got around the railroad traffic jam by buying trucks and motoring their produce to market. In the immediate postwar years, heavier vehicles and higher speeds posed new problems for highway designers who also had to consider the needs of an expanded and diverse group of road users. The 1921 Federal Aid Highway System designers hoped to create a coherent highway network by requiring states to concentrate federal aid on projects that would become part of an interstate system.

64TH CONGRESS, 1ST SESSION.

H. R. 3715.

IN THE HOUSE OF REPRESENTATIVES.

DECEMBER 10, 1915.

Mr. HUMPHREY of Washington introduced the following bill; which was referred to the Committee on the Public Lands and ordered to be printed.

A BILL

Authorizing the setting aside of certain lands for highway purposes through the public domain, forests, and other reserves of the United States.

1   Be it enacted by the Senate and House of Representa-
2   tives of the United States of America in Congress assembled,
3   That where any permanent hard-surfaced highway has been
4   or shall hereafter be built, in whole or in part, by State aid,
5   through any forests or other reserves or public lands of the
6   United States not reserved for governmental purposes, the
7   Secretary of the Interior, upon the written request of the
8   governor of the State which has granted such aid, shall set
9   aside out of such lands the land upon which the highway is
10 located and such additional land along or in proximity to
11 such highway as may add materially to its scenic effects and
12 its utility to the public, and reserve the same from sale or
13 other disposition.

State Representative Humphrey's 1915 bill for the national government to set aside federal lands for highway purposes was one of the legislative precursors that prepared the way for the following year's Federal Aid Road Act. Courtesy, WA State Archives, Olympia.

MORE CARS, MORE ROADS, AND A NEW SYSTEM OF FINANCING

Once the American automobile, specifically the Ford Model T, became inexpensive enough during the 1920s for nearly every middle-class Washington family to afford, opposition to improved roads became a thing of the past. Particularly with the federal appropriations, and after the legislature's enactment of a Motor Vehicle Fund in 1919 was followed by an excise tax of one cent per gallon of gasoline in 1921, the tax burden began to shift from the property owner to the road user. This new source of highway funding, relating highway revenue to highway use through gasoline taxes, was first adopted in Oregon in 1919 and represented a breakthrough for the auto industry and highway builders alike. Under the former system of highway funding, financed by a portion of property taxes, special levies, and individual assessments, county and state authorities had difficulty raising adequate funds for road improvements, even with matching state and federal appropriations. For example, the public highway levy of 1922 credited to the state motor vehicle fund amounted to $1,124,680. Following the repeal of the one-mill highway levy in 1923, all state funds for primary and secondary state highway construction were to be derived from automobile license fees and the gasoline tax. In the 1923-24 biennium this amounted to more than $12 million.

Affordable cars, reasonable auto license fees ($2 per year in 1912), and road taxes borne by an ever-increasing number of motorists caused the demand for better roads — and for getting people and their cars out of the mud — to grow ever more insistent. By 1920 the number of motor vehicles registered in the state had risen to 186,827. This was up from 70,000 vehicles in 1916 and from 763 in 1906. In 1921 the state began requiring the licensing of drivers, charging $1 "except in the case of children driving automobiles for the purpose of attending school, in which case one-half of the regular license fee is charged."

Between 1910 and 1920 the number of completed miles of primary and secondary state highway expanded from 159 to 2,976, of which 1,945 were improved. Roads had proliferated despite the World War I biennium of 1917-19 when all construction was restricted only to routes considered to be essential to the war effort. Construction that was performed during the conflict cost the highway department twice as much as usual due to the excessive cost of materials, inadequate transportation facilities, and labor shortage. Quite out of keeping with "woman's work" at the time but indicative of the dearth of skilled road workers, Verona Morgan, 19-year-old daughter of an Everett contractor, worked as superintendent on two road projects in the area during these war years.

After the war, with a steady source of revenue in the Motor Vehicle Fund and the resumption of federal funding, the state began its largest building program yet. Road construction and

repairs were so extensive that the highway department had difficulty finding enough workers. The wages of common laborers rose from a prewar level of $2 a day to an unprecedented $6 for an eight-hour shift. Unfortunately, Highway Commissioner James Allen complained, "production has seemingly been inversely proportional to the increased wage."

In 1922 in Washington there were 45,640 miles of rural roadway outside of incorporated cities and towns. Of this total approximately half were improved with surfaces including macadam, sheet asphalt, concrete, brick, plank, gravel, crushed rock and "improved earth." The road improvements were not equally distributed among counties, however. Only 11 miles of the 1,828 miles of rural road in King County remained unimproved, while in Douglas County only 165 miles of the 2,000-mile total were improved. Several counties, including Ferry, Clallam, Island, Jefferson, Kitsap, Okanogan, Pend Oreille, San Juan, Stevens, and Wahkiakum, had no improved road surfaces outside of incorporated areas at this time.

During the 1920s the state concentrated its efforts and funds on extending and improving its system of primary roads: the North Central, Inland Empire, Sunset, Navy Yard, Tonasket-San Poil, Olympic, National Park, Pend Oreille, Ocean Beach, Central Washington, North Bank, and Pacific highways. By June 1929 the state had spent over $12 million of federal allocations on these and other major transportation routes approved by the Federal Aid Project.

PRIMARY STATE HIGHWAYS

In 1913 the economy-minded legislature surprised everyone when they finally responded to the continued needling of the Good Roads Association with a $2 million road appropriation. At the same time they agreed to the highway proposals favored by residents of the state's major cities. City and rural residents had disagreed over the routes for state highways. Seattle and Spokane citizens favored an east-west highway across the state that would enlarge their trade with each other and points in between. They also wanted a north-south highway on both sides of the Cascades that would, naturally, converge on Seattle and Spokane. Rural residents considered such routes mere "peacock allies" (as they called the Lincoln Highway connecting New York and San Francisco) for rich tourists. The farmers wanted good roads between their fields and the nearest town or railway siding. However, the lawmakers approved the proposal of the Good Roads Association, basically that of the cities, for building three state trunk highways —the Sunset Highway, Pacific Highway, and Inland Empire Highway.

Sunset Highway

The Sunset Highway was intended to be the state's primary east-west trunk highway. According to the route developed by 1924, it began at the Pacific Highway at Redmond, went through Issaquah and North Bend, proceeded over Snoqualmie Pass and through Easton and Cle Elum. East of Cle Elum the route took a sharp northerly turn, went over Blewett Pass and looped southeasterly to Wenatchee where it turned north again to Waterville, and proceeded easterly through Wilbur and Davenport to Spokane and the state border.

In 1915 enough of the road was considered finished to warrant a dedication by Gov. Ernest Lister. Lister, who motored to the pass in a seventeen-car caravan from Seattle to meet groups from Yakima and

Scenes on the Sunset Highway. Above: A section on the western side of Snoqualmie Pass, 1915. Below: June snow near the pass in 1916, the year of the Big Snow. Bottom: Switchback on western slope. Bottom right: The atmospheric profile of Mount Si appears above the 1914 construction scene on Sunset Highway. All courtesy, Department of Transportation.

Ellensburg, declared it Washington's first passable route between the east and west sides of the mountains. However, "passable" was all the Sunset Highway would be for several more years. It took until 1922 before gravel surfacing was finished as far east as Ellensburg, and throughout the twenties the only paved portions were found in Spokane County, in and around Wenatchee, and west of North Bend. It was not entirely paved west of the pass until nineteen miles between Redmond and Fall City were completed in 1932. However, two years before, after the "ski mania" came to the Cascades, the highway department began plowing Snoqualmie Pass and kept the highway open to traffic all winter.

The Inland Empire Highway was a cross-state route that ran south from Spokane through Colfax, Dodge, and Dayton to Walla Walla where it turned west to go through Pasco and Kennewick, then northwest through Yakima to Ellensburg. Midway between Ellensburg and Cle Elum, it joined the Sunset Highway at Blewett Pass. The Inland Empire Highway formed a part of the original route through Washington of the Yellowstone Trail. One of the first transcontinental highways built for automobiles, the Yellowstone Trail was hailed as a "good road from Plymouth Rock to Puget Sound."

Pacific Highway and Early Motoring

Washington motorists who tried to drive from Seattle to California before the completion of the Pacific Highway had to be both courageous and hardy. In 1907 Seattle resident Judge James T. Ronald made what he believed was only the second motor trip undertaken from Seattle to San Francisco. It took twenty-one days in his new White Steamer, most of the time spent making repairs to the car enroute.

Like Judge Ronald, all pioneer motorists had to be their own mechanics and know how to compensate for the deficiencies of their pioneer cars. Until the development of the hardtop, the roofless or canvas-canopied touring cars, with windshields an extra, were designed for fair-weather driving only. When tires were worn down to the canvas fabric, the well-prepared motorist might pump the tire with a sticky mixture of chopped-up feathers and heated molasses in order to seal it. Oatmeal flakes or dried horse manure usually could fix a leaky radiator. And to boost braking power when going down an especially steep grade, a small tree could be tied to the back fender—a practice the Forest Service did not appreciate.

It was not unusual in the twenties to see passengers pushing the family Model T up the steep grades. Sometimes the old gray mare was hitched in front, with the reins stuck through the divided windshield held by the driver in the front seat. When the low gear transmission band was worn or the gas tank, in the back, was low, drivers sometimes backed up the hill. One eastern Washington mailman recalled how on cold winter nights he drained the oil from his 1916 Model T and put it on the stove to warm up in the morning. For years many Ford owners believed that if the car wouldn't run, all they had to do was rest it a few days and it would start up again.

For the most part, the 310 miles of Pacific Highway in Washington followed already established county roads. The original route in Washington began at the international border at Blaine and went south through Bellingham, Mount Vernon, Everett, Seattle, Kent, Auburn, Tacoma, Olympia, Chehalis, Kelso, Kalama, and Vancouver to the interstate bridge over the Columbia River. Even so, it took the nine counties through which it passed nearly ten years to complete the concrete paving. In some cities on its route, such as Marysville, the Pacific Highway was one of the first streets in town to be paved.

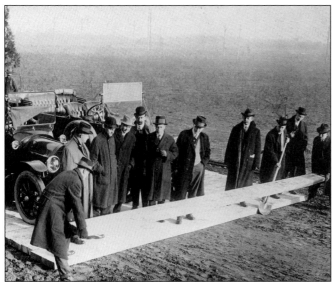

Pacific Highway. Top: The 1915 dedication of a section of the Pacific Highway near Olympia. Courtesy, DOT. Above: Quagmire near south Park on old Highway 1 (now U.S. 99). Courtesy, South Park Historical Society. Below: Section of Pacific Highway south of Olympia, Oct. 10, 1923. Photo by Asahel Curtis. Courtesy, WA State Historical Society. Bottom: West Valley Highway, a part of the Pacific Highway's original route near Auburn. Courtesy, DOT.

When the final stretches of paving between Vancouver, B.C. and Oregon were undertaken in late 1922, Washington journalists gushed about the highway's importance for the convenience of state residents and for the stimulation of commercial truck transport and the new auto tour industry. The road going north from Olympia to Tacoma, according to a *Seattle Times* reporter, went through "typical Western Washington country, every mile of which is a delight." It also took the motorist past "one of the sublimest things in America. . . . If there was nothing else in Washington but Mount Rainier the Pacific Highway would be worth every cent it cost for it helps the motorist to get to 'The Mountain That Was God.'" A miles-long procession of cars streamed over the border to Cloverdale, B.C. in early September 1923 to celebrate the completion of the stretch north from Seattle to Vancouver. A banquet prepared by the women of Cloverdale was followed by Scottish pipers strutting the pavement "in gaudy array." Later others danced on the pavement "strewn with flaxseed and borax."

That same year in the fall after 700 miles of highway from Vancouver to the Oregon-California border had been smoothed and widened to two lanes, a dedication caravan of 500 cars formally inaugurated the stretch between the Washington and Oregon capitals. The *Times* reported:

This great cavalcade of cars, bearing state and city officials of Washington, Oregon, California and British Columbia wound its way around the perfectly banked curves, up the grades which at no place on the highway are greater than five per cent, down the slopes and across picturesque and artistic bridges much as a huge and exceptionally agile worm would do.

Below: For this quagmire near Queets, the shovel operating a dragline was supported on a sixteen-foot-wide log mat while workers waded knee deep for the difficult construction of the Olympic Highway. Courtesy, DOT. Bottom: Ceremony at the Aug. 26, 1931 dedication of the Olympic Loop Highway bridge over the Hoh River. Courtesy North Olympic Library System.

The dedication of Willapa Bay-Grays Harbor section of U.S. Highway 101 on Oct. 8, 1930. Courtesy, Jones Photo Company, Aberdeen.

Olympic Loop Highway and Highways for Tourists

The construction of good roads transformed many rural areas. Along the state's primary and even secondary highways, roadside restaurants and camping grounds sprang up. "Tourists Lodged" signs began to appear in the late teens in front of farmhouses, followed by a proliferation of autocamps in the twenties and thirties, and motels in the forties. By the mid-twenties a vacationing motorist had a choice among many auto campgrounds along the Sunset Highway, both near the pass and in towns and cities on either side of the mountains. The auto and improved roads had set off a major revolution in recreational habits. For the first time the majority of middle-class city dwellers could get out of town for an affordable family vacation. For Washingtonians living on both sides of the Cascades, the mountains, ocean beaches, and nearby lakes and parks became more accessible than ever.

The transformation in the countryside was not always for the better, as far as some were concerned. Good roads and affordable passenger cars also spelled the end of most small-town trading centers when rural people began driving to the larger towns and cities to shop. Between 1920 and 1930 nearly three-quarters of the small towns in eastern Washington wheat counties declined in population and business. Others complained about the unsightly bill boards along the major routes that marred the beauty of the countryside.

Even before it opened in the summer of 1931, the 330-mile-long Olympic Loop Highway (U.S. Highway 101) became one of the most advertised portions of the state highway system. After an extremely difficult excavation through heavy underbrush and unstable soil, it encircled the Olympic Peninsula. Starting from the Pacific Highway at Olympia, it went through Shelton, Hoodsport, Duckabush, Quilcene, Port Angeles, Forks, Hoquiam, Montesano, Elma, and McCleary, and reunited with the Pacific Highway again at Olympia. The "Loop," according to one travel reporter, would open up areas of the Olympic Peninsula that had been seen only by Indians and a few white settlers "still found hewing bathtubs out of logs." Another promoter rhapsodized about "Washington's marvelous highway system" which had conquered "the last frontier of the northwesternmost part of the northwesternmost state."

At the two-day Olympic Loop opening celebration in late August, "the world's largest outdoor picnic" was held. Gov. Roland Hartley, who had earlier decried the money wasted on roads for "joyriders," British Columbia Premier Simon F. Tolmie, youngest son of Hudson's Bay Company physician and trader Dr. William Tolmie, and Mark Reed, millionaire lumberman of Shelton, were all on hand to make speeches, dedicate bridges, and view the games, dances, and contests held by five peninsula Indian tribes.

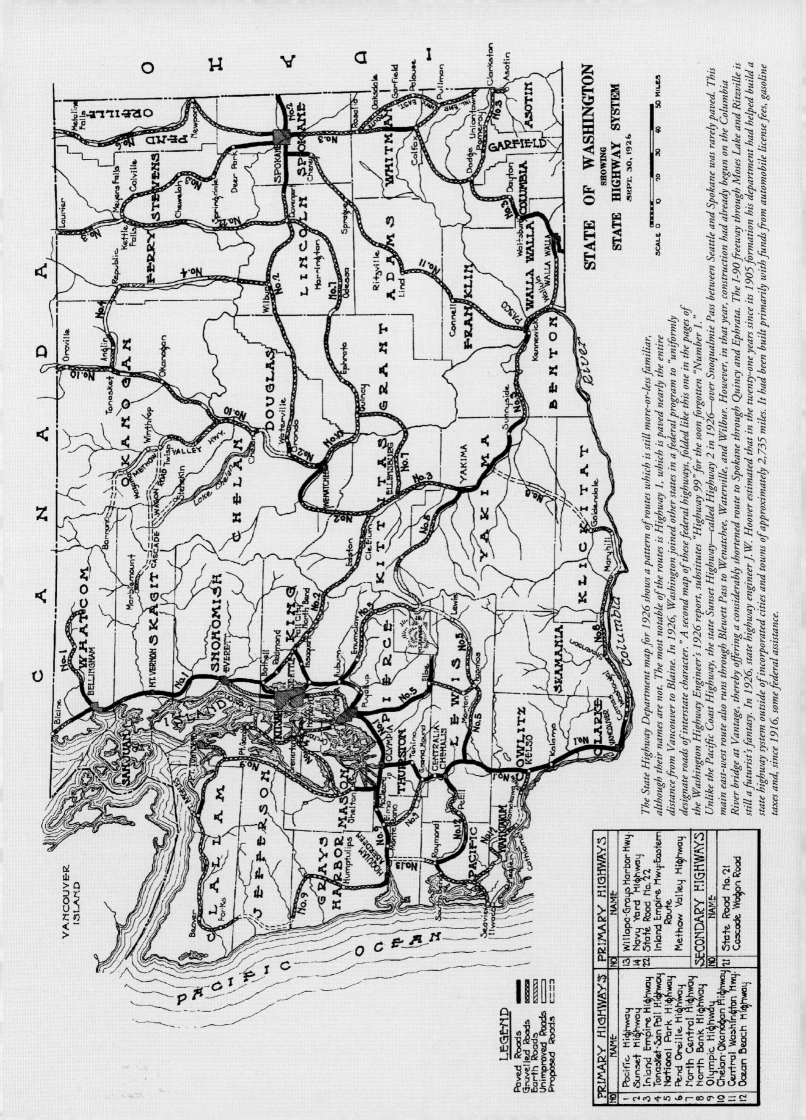

STATE OF WASHINGTON
SHOWING
STATE HIGHWAY SYSTEM
SEPT. 30, 1926

SCALE 0 | 0 | 10 | 20 | 30 | 40 | 50 MILES

LEGEND
Paved Roads
Gravelled Roads
Earth Roads
Unimproved Roads
Proposed Roads

PRIMARY HIGHWAYS		PRIMARY HIGHWAYS	
NO	NAME	NO	NAME
1	Pacific Highway	13	Willapa-Grays Harbor Hwy.
2	Sunset Highway	14	Navy Yard Highway
3	Inland Empire Highway	22	State Road No. 22
4	Tonasket-San Poil Highway		Inland Empire Hwy-Eastern
5	National Park Highway		Route
6	Pend Oreille Highway		Methow Valley Highway
7	North Central Highway		
8	North Bank Highway	**SECONDARY HIGHWAYS**	
9	Olympic Highway	NO	NAME
10	Chelan-Okanogan Highway	21	State Road No. 21
11	Central Washington Hwy.		Cascade Wagon Road
12	Ocean Beach Highway		

The State Highway Department map for 1926 shows a pattern of routes which is still more-or-less familiar,
although their names are not. The most notable of the routes is Highway 1, which is paved nearly the entire
distance from Vancouver to Blaine. In 1926, Washington joined other states in a federal program to "uniformly
designate roads of interstate character." A second map of these federal highways, folded like this one in the pages of
the Washington Highway Engineer's 1926 report, substitutes "Highway 99" for the soon forgotten "Number 1."
Unlike the Pacific Coast Highway, the state Sunset Highway—called Highway 2 in 1926—over Snoqualmie Pass between Seattle and Spokane was rarely paved. This
main east-west route also runs through Blewett Pass to Wenatchee, Waterville, and Wilbur. However, in that year, construction had already begun on the Columbia
River bridge at Vantage, thereby offering a considerably shortened route to Spokane through Quincy and Ephrata. The I-90 freeway through Moses Lake and Ritzville is
still a futurist's fantasy. In 1926, state highway engineer J.W. Hoover estimated that in the twenty-one years since its 1905 formation his department had helped build a
state highway system outside of incorporated cities and towns of approximately 2,735 miles. It had been built primarily with funds from automobile license fees, gasoline
taxes and, since 1916, some federal assistance.

One of the biggest gatherings ever held in the harbor districts celebrated the opening of a twenty-five-mile stretch of U.S. Highway 101 between Willapa Bay and Grays Harbor on October 8, 1930. The old sign at Aberdeen's south gateway which read "Willapa-Harbor 119 miles" was pulled down and replaced by another reading "Willapa Harbor 28 Miles." The Grays Harbor-Willapa Harbor Road, which took five years to build because of conditions similar to those on the Olympic Peninsula, saved motorists eighty-six miles of the long drive around by way of Centralia and Chehalis. The new road from Aberdeen, which went south through Cosmopolis to connect with a Grays Harbor County road, made two communities that had been virtual strangers, Raymond and South Bend, neighbors for the first time.

DEPRESSION-ERA ROAD BUILDING

With the onset of the depression in the early 1930s, the basic purpose of federal road aid shifted from building a system of national arterial highways to providing economic relief. As far as the Civil Works Administration (CWA) program was concerned, road work offered one of the best opportunities for absorbing large numbers of workers on relief. Consequently, highway improvements were reoriented to meet local needs. Most of the state's share of federal funds was diverted to the counties so they could hire the unemployed in the area and determine their own priorities. From December 1933 through March 1934,

Left: Motorcade for the two-day, Aug. 26-27, 1931, inaugural of the Olympic Loop Highway. Courtesy, North Olympic Library System.
Below: Scene on the Yakima River Canyon highway between Ellensburg and Yakima, Aug. 28, 1932. By Asahel Curtis. Courtesy WA State Historical Society, Tacoma.

approximately 7,000 men were employed between twenty-four and thirty hours per week on 151 separate projects in the state, mostly involving road maintenance, repairs, and landscaping.

The federal funds that became available through the Works Progress Administration (WPA) and other federal programs supported a number of projects that otherwise would not have been undertaken so early. Some of these were the First Avenue viaduct in Seattle, the Sixth Street overpass in Centralia, the Mount Spokane Highway leading to Mount Spokane State Park, the scenic drive encircling Lake Stevens in central Snohomish County, a reinforced concrete bridge on Eldridge Avenue in Bellingham, and a railroad overpass on State Road No. 3 near Wallula. Projects using Public Works Administration (PWA) funds allocated for 1938 included the Hylebos Waterway Bridge in Tacoma, the Tacoma Narrows Bridge, and the first Lake Washington floating bridge. For all the improvements they brought, the New Deal public works programs were not without critics who had trouble adjusting to the government's new involvement in work relief. To some, the federally funded road projects seemed to be mere make-work jobs. Workers, they claimed, were required to do little more than sweep leaves from one side of the road to the other.

In 1933 federal aid at last became available for urban segments of primary roads. Until then cities and towns had for the most part been excluded from the federal aid program. This was a problem for municipalities located on the route of primary state highways. Usually traffic was routed directly through the center of town on city streets that had not been designed to handle such levels. The National Industrial Recovery Act (NIRA) of 1933 replaced the usual federal highway grants and specified that at least 25 percent of funds allocated to the states should be used on extensions of the federal aid system into and through municipalities. An equal percentage was designated for secondary or feeder roads, which included state roads not on the federal aid system and main-traveled county roads. The remaining 50 percent went to the customary projects on the federal aid system outside of municipal corporate limits. Under the 1934 Hayden-Cartwright Bill, the state received the federal allotments without the provisions requiring matching amounts of state and local funds.

The allocations of the federal relief agencies were crucial to the highway department's depression decade construction program — particularly as the tax revenues of cities and counties dwindled. In 1933 the legislature responded to the appeals of the hard-pressed counties and municipalities and raised their share of the five-cent state gasoline tax, allowing them to collect 47 percent of gross receipts of the motor vehicle fund, while the highway department got only 38 percent. Although the funds were supposed to be spent only on county highways and maintenance of city streets on state highways, they often were used for badly needed utilities, especially sewers. Washington highway department officials, who prided themselves on being one of the few states that had never had any bonded highway indebtedness, bristled when the legislature passed a $10 million emergency relief bond. Very little of this bond was to be used for state highway purposes, the commissioner complained, yet the bond was supposed to be repaid with highway revenues.

TRAFFIC SAFETY

Ever since the motor car proved itself to be the transportation mode of the future, Washington highway department administrators kept up what they called a "constant struggle to adapt highways to the ever expanding growth of auto use and to the accelerating evolution of the auto itself." Between 1906 when there were 763 registered automobiles in the state and 1937 when there were 548,479, there were over 8,300 reported traffic fatalities. In 1921 the highway patrol division was established within the Department of Efficiency to help reduce traffic accidents and

Above: Highway Department's radio headquarters in Olympia, ca. 1947. Photo by Simmer. Courtesy DOT. Below: Portrait of WA State Highway Patrol forces, May 23, 1963. Courtesy Museum of Industry and History (MOHAI), Seattle Post-Intelligencer *Collection, Seattle.*

the damage caused to state highways by overloading. At a time when there were few automobile and highway safety standards, the highway patrol had to be efficient. During the first year of the division's operation, the director reported, a total of 31 men around the state "patrolled 257,741 miles, made 3,203 arrests [and] 123 investigations; weighed 365 loads; recovered 27 stolen cars… and procured the cancellation of 1,009 operators' licenses and the forfeiture of 74." All this was on top of the five weeks during July and August when the eleven motorcycle men and two loadometer crews helped fire wardens fight forest fires.

In 1922, highway patrol director L. D. McArdle claimed that "highway safety must be a religion with anyone who expects to accomplish even a moderate betterment" of highway traffic conditions. McArdle was proud of the results he attributed to his force — a one-third reduction in traffic fatalities over the previous year. But his men could do better, he advised, if motorists and lawmakers would only cooperate. The director recommended "compulsory inspection of equipment, especially brakes and lights," and stiffer penalties for "flagrant violations." Qualifying examinations for drivers should be required and "character should be one of the primary investigations." In 1921 the state required of would-be drivers only an application for a license and the word of two reputable citizens that the applicant could drive. McArdle blamed most of the traffic fatalities and injuries on operators who forget to "take their brains with them upon the road instead of leaving them in the garage."

Fifteen years later, in 1937, the legislature approved some of McArdle's safety recommendations when it adopted the state's first comprehensive highway code. When the highway depart-

ment began conducting the annual vehicle safety inspections required by the code in mid-1938, its suspicions that large numbers of vehicles were defective were confirmed. Even with tolerances considered by highway officials to be so low that only a bare minimum of safe operating equipment was required, about 65 percent of the first 85,000 vehicles examined were rejected on the initial inspection. Incorrectly aimed, glaring, or insufficiently bright headlights were the main offenders at 73 percent of the cases, with defective brakes following at 45 percent. In other words, three out of every five vehicles on the road were unsafe and potentially dangerous. Adjustments were quickly made, however. Before the end of 1939, 97 percent of all vehicles inspected were passed. That year the department, which had also begun conducting examinations of vehicle operators, happily reported that accidents had dropped by 25 percent over the previous two years.

During the late 1930s the state's newly established traffic engineering division began studies to correlate safety and traffic flow considerations with highway construction and maintenance. Highway designs were examined to determine whether there was provision for sufficient sight distance on curves and for safe stopping distances within posted speed limits. Accident spot maps were used to determine the hazardous sections of existing roadways. The department completely re-signed the primary highways with reflecting signs that indicated maximum speeds, curves, and potential roadway dangers. Overhead flashing signals were installed at busy intersections, and sodium vapor fog lights were installed in high fog areas along the coast.

In 1928 the Richfield and Standard oil companies had proposed an ambitious "safety" plan that called for a chain of powerful beacons mounted on 125-foot-high steel towers along the Pacific Highway. The idea was to space the beacons so that motorists would always have one within sight, either behind or ahead of them. The companies, however, were less concerned with safety than with profit. At the foot of each beacon they planned to install not only gas pumps but a whole "model village layout of hotel, cafe and stores" for the motorist's convenience. Needless to say, the system was never built.

Seattle experimented with a number of safety measures during the depression decade. Studies had identified the major causes of accidents as defective equipment, compounded by speeding and the failure to signal, yield the right of way, or stop at stop signs. One-bell signal lights replaced the two-bell system that had been used from 1924 through 1934 because accidents occurred when drivers started in anticipation of the second bell. Danger flags were hoisted atop poles to mark dangerous intersections. A forty-five-foot flag pole was erected in Times Square on which the flag of the National Traffic and Safety Council was lowered to half-mast whenever a traffic fatality occurred in the city. Nine-foot-square "death crosses" were painted on the road to mark traffic fatality spots. WPA "traffic safety observers," whose first duty was "to keep on the job," were hired as official snitches to report minor traffic violations. During Christmas 1937 the University of Washington Campus Radio Players began broadcasting a dramatized radio program based on actual incidents and produced from the city morgue. The purpose of "The House of the Dead" was to "depict the heartbreaking incidents" of traffic fatalities in the hope it would convince listeners to become "careful, sane drivers."

WORLD WAR II — ROADS FOR DEFENSE

With the bombing of Pearl Harbor in December 1941, the government's public works priorities shifted radically. All unobligated federal aid road funds were frozen, and regulations were issued that no work was to be done except upon those roads considered essential to the national defense. This was followed by increasingly stringent regulations for obtaining critical roadway

and bridge construction and repair materials. Iron, steel, and reinforced concrete became more and more difficult to obtain in the state, even for the building of high-priority access roads to military establishments and war-related industrial plants. The highway department abandoned the use of steel and reinforced concrete in their bridge designs. The more permanent spans were replaced with temporary timber bridges, that is, until the sale of construction lumber was also limited to military uses in May 1942. In an effort to complete the work in progress before wartime restrictions accelerated, highway department employees tried to help their contractors locate bridge hardware wherever they could find it. Often they had to buy bolts, rods, and spikes for the timber structures in small quantities at retail hardware stores. They also searched junkyards for any usable material.

Meanwhile, the war added to the kind of traffic that produced the bulk of road maintenance expenses. Heavy truck traffic increased considerably, particularly in logging areas and on the coast where military installations were concentrated. The building of access roads to accommodate the abnormally heavy loads and traffic generated by the military bases and war-related industries in Seattle, Bremerton, Tacoma, and Vancouver nearly equaled prewar construction programs. Some sections of the Olympic Loop Highway, which was designed for passenger-car travel, as well as a great number of the many timber highway bridges, needed complete replacement after being subjected to the log hauling and heavy munitions loads. Traffic engineers also had their work cut out for them. New roadway channels had to be designed and signals installed so that especially large loads, such as the midsection of a B-29, could be carried over the Pacific Highway and other busy roads to the Boeing assembly plant at Renton.

Western Asphalt Company packs a portion of the highway between Bremerton and Tidewater Creek, Oct. 9, 1946. Photo by Simmer. Courtesy DOT.

PLANNING FOR POSTWAR HIGHWAYS

While couples danced in the streets of Seattle and San Franciscans pulled trolleys off their lines to celebrate the surrender of the Japanese in early September 1945, government planners at all levels prepared to help Americans make the transition from an economy held back by fifteen years of depression and wartime shortages. As hundreds of thousands of GIs returned home to find jobs and settle down, the housing industry and local governments strained to keep up with the demand for homes and public services. By the end of the decade tens of thousands of new residents had come to Washington. For normal mobility, most were dependent on automobile transportation. Traffic volumes in the state practically doubled within a month of the lifting of the 35-miles-per-hour speed limit and gasoline rationing imposed during the conflict. The accident rate rose along with the traffic

The earliest Highway Department efforts to keep the lowest passes through the Cascade Mountains open for winter traffic were frequently snowed-under. The practice of tying a steady team of horses to the front bumper of a stranded automobile offered motorists the best chance of beating the snow. The ultimate solution, tunnels beneath the passes, has been often proposed and even rendered, as with this drawing for a 1930s entrance to Snoqualmie Pass, but never built.

congestion, and alarmed citizens besieged city hall with requests for more traffic signals, speed zones, signs, and other safety measures.

By the time the troops returned, state and federal highway planners had mapped out a long-range, coordinated federal highway system. The network was designed in response to concerns about higher safety standards and the need for more federal aid to improve urban portions of the national interstate system. City leaders, commercial truckers, and auto industry spokesmen had long complained about the concentration of federal and state highway allocations on rural areas. By the early 1940s urban expressways began to appear to some city planners as the only way to revitalize their deteriorating city centers. The Federal-Aid Highway Act of 1944 was passed by Congress to fund a national system of interstate highways that would link the principal metropolitan areas and industrial centers and serve the national defense. The legislation specified minimum design standards that were much higher than those of prewar days and expected to safely accommodate traffic levels for the next twenty years. Congressional appropriations of $1.5 billion for the program for the three years following the war were not adequate, however. And construction was left up to the states, where rural and urban interests continued to battle over where the funds should be spent. Washington received an allotment totaling approximately $15 million for 1946 and 1947, of which $3 million was designated for urban portions of the state's primary highways.

LIMITED ACCESS HIGHWAYS

Even outside city limits the two-lane highways built in the 1920s and 1930s had become obsolete by 1940. And they could not easily be brought up to modern standards because the earlier engineers had generally failed to allow right-of-way for future expansion. The wheels of eight-foot-wide buses and trucks were forced to the edge of the narrow pavements designed for smaller vehicles. The state's first stage of highway building was tourist-oriented, fostering the "ribbon development" of roadside restaurants, motels, and gas stations. As traffic speeds and volume grew, vehicles entering or leaving the traffic stream for roadside service turned the high-speed highways into accident traps. In 1951 when the state legislature passed the first effective limited access law and raised the maximum speed limit to 60 MPH, the highway department could not find a single highway in the

western part of the state that was safe to drive at that speed.

Making the transition to limited access highways was neither simple nor popular with local property owners, who wanted to be able to keep turning off the highway into their driveways. In the 1940s state traffic engineers began working on the conversion of the Pacific Highway, the most heavily traveled highway in the state, to a four-lane, limited access roadway. However, business establishments along the highway between Tacoma and Everett fought legislation that they believed would make it difficult for their customers to get to them. In 1947 the legislature balked at the destruction of that age-old right of access enjoyed by property

Below: Postcard artist, Ellis' early view of an unidentified section of the Pacific Highway, which although four-lane, is not yet limited access. Note the Shell station (center-right). Courtesy, John Cooper.

Left: View north on U.S. Highway 99, where it begins its climb up Riverton Hill to Highline after crossing the bridge (center right) over the Duwamish River. Before the mid-1960s construction of the I-5 freeway, this was the direct route to both the SeaTac Airport and Tacoma.

owners fronting the road. They stipulated that access could be limited only on new routes, not on existing highways.

Despite the legislature's ruling, the highway department was committed to reducing the accidents that resulted from unrestricted access, and highway engineers went ahead with their original plans to modernize the Pacific Highway. Maurice Veys, a Kelso man who planned to build a motel on his property along the highway, was all for a smoothed and widened roadway. But Veys didn't like the convoluted access route that highway engineers told him his potential customers would have to take. When he took his complaint to court, the state Supreme Court upheld the legislature's qualification about restricting access on existing highways. Veys was able to keep a driveway on Highway 99, forcing the highway department to buy new right-of-way and build an entirely new section of road. The court's decision also obliged the engineers to plan a new limited access route between Everett and Seattle and Seattle and Tacoma. To avoid further costly rerouting where existing roadway could be updated, the 1951 legislature amended the 1947 limited access law so that property along existing highways could be acquired, provided public hearings were held beforehand.

Acquiring the necessary right-of-way without jeopardizing the economic health of local communities or of the state motor vehicle fund slowed the transition to limited access. So did the time-consuming condemnation proceedings that had to be approved by the courts before construction could begin. By the middle of 1952 the state had completed only 208 miles of limited access highway. Two years later they had only doubled that number. To speed highway construction, the legislature was persuaded to break away from its thirty-year reliance on the pay-as-you-go type financing in the motor vehicle fund. In the early 1950s the lawmakers authorized bond issues totaling $85 million, more than half of which went to upgrade the Pacific Highway into the four-lane and limited access roadway of U.S. Highway 99.

Highways during the 1950s enjoyed strong political support from such leaders as Democratic Gov. Albert Rosellini; State Rep. Julia Butler Hansen, a Cathlamet Democrat and leader of the highway forces in the legislature; and Daniel J. Evans, assistant manager of the regional chapter of Associated General Contractors and future three-term state governor. Probably few citizens or lawmakers at that time would have questioned the belief of Highway Director, W. A. Bugge that "every page of our history tells us that Washington never really intensified its development beyond any point where adequate transportation halted. Our ability to advance goes only as far and as rapidly as our transportation facilities permit."

In some cases, such as when the Pacific Highway became limited access and bypassed Marysville to eliminate one of the highway's worst bottlenecks, local residents complained about the longer roundabout routes they had to take to get to town. Still, for those going long distances the limited access, straightened, widened, and in some places divided U.S. 99, which took a good part of the decade to build, meant a considerable time savings — such as an hour off the drive from Seattle to Portland. For those traveling even short distances, restricted access and grade separations did what they were supposed to do. They reduced accidents and saved lives.

MID-CENTURY HIGHWAY CRISIS

Each extension and improvement in the highway system contributed to higher traffic volume and changing traffic patterns. Highway planners and engineers scrambled to keep up with the suburban growth fueled by their previous projects. Ever since the 1920s, when the automobile established itself as the preferred means of transportation, it was no longer good enough to build highways primarily for recreational traffic and farmers going to market. As the metropolitan population grew, it continued to shift from the city to suburban areas. Automobiles and the new and improved roads that the state and counties built to keep up with them dramatically expanded land use outside the cities. Less than two years after the Pacific Highway in Washington was completely paved in 1923, the state legislature approved the relocation of its route between Seattle and Tacoma in order to straighten and shorten it.

In the decade of the 1940s, after the Lake Washington floating bridge cut driving time for Mercer Island residents going to downtown Seattle by more than half, the island's population grew 230 percent — more than twice the rate of growth in King County

A regular Highway Commission meeting, April 17, 1952. Members (left to right): O.E. Stone, George B. Simpson, Secretary H.C. Higgins, Chairman Fred G. Redman, Director of Highways L.B. Wallace, and R.A. Mosio. Photo by Simmer. Courtesy, DOT.

during the same period, and almost ten times that of Seattle. The early twentieth-century challenge of accommodating horses and buggies, electric trolleys, pedestrians, and motor cars on the same crowded city streets had been replaced by the need to move growing numbers of suburban commuters and commercial truckers crowding onto the too few two-lane highways and arterials to get to the city center. By the early 1950s new industrial and commercial developments had sprung up outside the state's major cities, and 75 percent of all freight was being transported by truck. By 1953 the state had invested more money in highways during the previous five years than in the prior forty-two years of the highway department's operation. Yet it was still not keeping up with the demand. Improved roads bred traffic that in turn bred the need for more roads and improvements.

Along with the peace and prosperity of the Eisenhower era came a major highway crisis in America. Newspapers around the country and the state printed story after story about congested streets and jammed arterials. For the most part, they attributed the growing number of traffic accidents to an outmoded highway system. By then the call of the nation's good roads associations was to "get our people out of the mess." Traffic violations and tempers rose steadily. When a Skamania County newspaper editor came to Seattle, hoping his observations could deflect some of King County's portion of the state gas tax revenue to his area, he became convinced that Seattle and King County might need their arterial and highway projects after all. He found cars "parked" in both lanes on streets in the University District and so tightly packed on Aurora Avenue that he figured he "could run out of gasoline and not find out about it for five miles." An earnest *Seattle Times* columnist warned in 1953 that "within five years, the bridges across the canals in Seattle will be loaded beyond their capacity at peak hours."

The highway program adopted by the legislature in 1953 was the state's most comprehensive and ambitious ever. Among the projects approved were a Tacoma-Seattle-Everett "toll superhighway," a bridge across Puget Sound at an undetermined point, a second floating bridge across Lake Washington, completion of Highway 99 into a four-lane thoroughfare, widening of the Snoqualmie Pass Highway, and access roads for the Columbia Basin region. The parts of the program that were actually undertaken then, such as the widening of U.S. 99 and the Sunset Highway over Snoqualmie Pass, a new four-lane bridge across the Chehalis River in Aberdeen, and a new stretch of highway between Wenatchee and Rock Island, were a boon to smaller cities and unincorporated areas and to the long-distance traveler. But they didn't offer much relief to the traffic-clogged cities — like Seattle, Tacoma, and Spokane — that the highways still ran through. The only way to further upgrade the highways in metropolitan areas to safely handle more vehicles at greater speeds was to design and build an entirely new system. While the state made its greatest-ever road effort to finish its second stage of highway building, highway officials began plans for a third level, incorporating urban expressways.

Top: Two-lane blacktop along the Columbia River, ca. 1965. Photo by Hugh Paradise.
Above: Snow shed at "Alpine Curve" on western slope of Snoqualmie Pass. Photo by J. Boyd Ellis. Courtesy John Cooper.

This March 31, 1955 aerial of downtown Vancouver shows how the nearly-new Interstate 5 freeway diverts, through a limited access ditch, traffic which previously was routed onto Main Street from the Interstate Bridge. The new freeway also separates the Vancouver Barracks, on the right, from downtown. The Interstate Bridge's second span was added in 1958. Courtesy The Vancouver Columbian.

FREEWAYS

The cost of urban expressways was something to ponder. Typical right-of-way was 200 to 300 feet wide and consumed about 20 to 40 acres of land per mile. This was two to four times greater than the prewar highways required, and four to eight times greater than was ordinarily needed for city streets. The largest land requirements were near the city center for access ramps and interchanges, and there land costs could run into millions of dollars per mile. A section of expressway passing through downtown Seattle, according to estimates in 1955, would cost $10 million per mile. This was far beyond the taxing capacity of the state, even with 50 percent federal matching funds. The cities certainly did not have the means to raise such enormous sums. And it was not politically possible to raise the statewide gas tax to pay for an intracity expressway that was expected to be used primarily by metropolitan area residents. However, the argument that urban expressways would relieve the traffic congestion that kept business away from the central core, would raise suburban land values, and, above all, save motorists time, money, and possibly even their lives convinced the majority of state residents and government officials that they had to have them.

Because of the costs, toll roads seemed to be the only answer. In July 1951 a newly reorganized highway commission at its first meeting recommended that a toll road authority be established. That way the state could finance construction of the proposed Tacoma-Seattle-Everett Tollway with revenue bonds to be redeemed through tolls. Figuring that motorists would be willing to pay one cent per mile to escape the congested city arterials, the legislature in 1955 passed three toll road acts. But before any construction could begin, the state Supreme Court found them all

unconstitutional. However, six months after the court's decision, the federal government passed highway legislation that would make further discussion of toll roads unnecessary. Massive public support throughout the country for safer and faster highways had finally gotten through to Congress and President Dwight D. Eisenhower. Normally opposed to federal participation in large public works projects, Eisenhower, in this case, believed that more autos and more highways meant "greater convenience . . . greater happiness, and greater standards of living." He decided that the government should commit substantial funds to boost road spending around the country in order to accommodate the upsurge in traffic volumes (and ensure quick evacuation in case of nuclear attack).

According to enthusiastic news accounts of the time, the National System of Interstate and Defense Highways Act passed by Congress in mid-1956 would undertake the largest and most expensive public works project anywhere in history. "The construction of the Panama Canal . . . could be fitted into the highway program with ease," the *Seattle P-I* exclaimed. The program was designed to lace the country with 41,000 miles of freeways, connecting nearly all cities with a population of more than 50,000. To finance it the government would raise the federal gas tax from two to four cents per gallon and pay a whopping 90 percent of the states' interstate expenses. The system was to be built to the highest engineering and safety standards with no crossings at grade, no stoplights or stop signs, and no commercial establishments fronting the right-of-way. At an estimated cost of $750 million, 740 miles of the 41,000 total were designated for Washington. That included an allocation of $168 million for the sixty-six-mile-long Tacoma-Seattle-Everett freeway (part of the future Interstate 5). While "motorists will have to cope with higher speeds," Ross

The Spokane Freeway advances from the west (above) and from the east (far left) in 1965. In the above view, which looks west along the freeway's future route, a portion of its construction can be seen at the top of the scene in the rough swath between the newly-completed but unopened Latah Creek (Hangman Creek) Bridge and Walnut Street. On the far left, the new freeway ends near Hamilton Street where it connects to Second and Third Avenue. Courtesy, DOT. Left: Governor Rosellini uses real scissors in ceremonial opening of the Tacoma Freeway. Courtesy, MOHAI. Below: Looking west through Tacoma's I-5 and 705 interchange and the Pacific Avenue overpass. Courtesy, DOT.

Many of the ramps built below Seattle's Beacon Hill in the late 1960s for the interchange of I-5 and I-90 were left stranded in space when the completion of I-90 was forestalled by protests over the freeway's disruption of established neighborhoods. Top: Seattle freeway construction looking over Dearborn Street to city skyline from Beacon Hill, August 1965. Courtesy, MOHAI, Seattle P-I Collection. Above: The completed Interstate 5–Interstate 90 interchange, 1997.

Cunningham, highway reporter for the *Seattle Times* wrote, "the vexing problem of city traffic will be eased, if not eliminated." The section of freeway crossing the bridge over the Lake Washington ship canal, traffic studies projected, would relieve Seattle's five congested ship canal bridges of 70,000 vehicles a day.

Soon after word of the huge highway program was released, a fierce competition began in the state for a piece of the federal pie to finance favorite projects. In 1957 the Stevens Pass Highway Association conducted an ambitious drive to have U.S. 2 modernized to four lanes from Everett to the Washington-Idaho border. Another group of local residents agitated for the Chinook Pass highway to be made into a year-round roadway, while others lobbied for another cross-mountain highway to link Skagit and Okanogan counties (the North Cascades Highway). However, top priority projects for the legislature and the highway commission were to finish upgrading Highway 99 and the Sunset Highway (U.S. 10) over Snoqualmie Pass to four-lane, limited-access standards, and to build new bridges over the Columbia River at Vancouver and Vantage. The highest wish on their list was not difficult to determine, however. In 1957 the legislature passed a $75 million bond issue so that right-of-way acquisition could begin immediately on the Tacoma-Seattle-Everett freeway and hopefully reduce the construction period from eight to five years. A seventh state highway district was also created. It included only the route of the planned Seattle freeway.

Seattle Freeway

In 1952, four years before the government agreed to build the country's present interstate system, the state highway commission announced its plans for the route of the Seattle freeway. There was little reaction from the general public. A few local government officials and civic leaders were skeptical about the wisdom of cutting a wide swath through the downtown area where right-of-way costs would be especially high and parking space lost. Most of

the city council members, however, claimed that they had received few complaints from the public or business interests against the downtown route. They accepted the conclusions of Seattle City Engineer R. W. Finke and Director of Highways W. A. Bugge that if the tollway was to pay for itself it must be routed where the greatest number of motorists would use it. Since origin-and-destination surveys conducted by the department showed that 75 to 80 percent of those who would use the Seattle tollway would be commuting to the central business district, Bugge told the press, it wouldn't make sense to bypass the area.

About the time that the 1956 federal highway program set aside the prospect of toll-funded expressways, Seattle city leaders and downtown business operators, as well as a few state legislators, began to question the urgency of running the freeway through downtown. King County Engineer D. L. Evans and former Seattle mayor and engineer George F. Cotterill both opposed the route that cut through the east side of the downtown core. Not only would the cost of right-of-way be excessive, they argued, but the corridor went through at least two hillside slide areas. (When the freeway was later being built, the slides that developed were even worse than soil experts had originally predicted. The highway department hired research specialists who discovered that glacial ice had compacted the clay and locked in stresses that were released, along with the hillside, when excavation began. To stabilize the path of the freeway, the contractor sunk hollow steel cylinders up to 120 feet into the earth and then filled them with concrete.)

The Seattle Chamber of Commerce tollway committee and a group of downtown business owners that had formed specifically to oppose the downtown route clung to their predictions that it would bring more congestion to the central core, where parking space was already inadequate. Members of the city arts commission criticized state and city officials for failing to consider aesthetic and planning factors in laying out the "multimillion-dollar ditch." William C. Goodloe, a state senator and 1956 Seattle mayoralty candidate, also campaigned against the route. Goodloe claimed that the downtown itinerary was selected more for its ability to market the tollway-revenue bonds than to meet the city's needs. Several of these critics argued that the state had not made adequate studies of other possible routes east of downtown, such as an extension of Twelfth Avenue or Empire (now Martin Luther King Way).

However, by 1957 the highway commission's proposed downtown corridor had been in the works for nearly ten years. Public pressure on political leaders to do something about the appalling traffic congestion and the heavy toll of lives extracted on the outdated highways and arterials had become relentless. The primary problem with other proposed routes was the number of

Interstate 5 freeway at its interchange with Spokane Street and Columbia Way, Seattle. Courtesy, Seattle Post-Intelligencer.

connecting arterials that would have to be built. To many it seemed that their development would result in unnecessary and costly delay. The downtown path had become acceptable to the governor, Albert Rosellini; the mayor, Gordon Clinton; the city council; the city planning commission; and apparently the majority of Seattle residents. Merlin Brown, Seattle Planning Commission chairman, reported to the mayor that "no route suggested approaches the goals of city planning as closely as the state-proposed route through Central Seattle." He urged only that the freeway be "attractively landscaped" and "lend beauty and grandeur to the city as well as handle traffic efficiently."

The freeway route, which bisected the hourglass-shaped city, did not arouse much public controversy until after construction began. Even then, most homeowners located on the right-of-way, whose houses had to be moved or razed, expressed resignation to what seemed the inevitable forces of progress. The Tacoma-Seattle-Everett freeway required the taking of 6,600 parcels of land, 4,500 of them in Seattle. From 1958-59 when the state auctioned houses whose owners had been cashed out by the highway department, final bids ranged from $20 to $1,250 for

residences in the North Broadway, University District, and Greenlake areas. Since moving costs were great, most bought the houses for salvage — the more ambitious hoping to reassemble them elsewhere, that is, if they could get them disassembled before the thieves did. A house once owned by former Seattle mayor and two-term Washington governor Arthur B. Langlie was one of the few that was spared the crowbar when its new owner moved it to Magnolia. Several of the city's historic buildings, including the 1881 Hotel Kalmar and the 1890 Seventh Avenue Fire Hall, the oldest public building in the city, could not be saved despite the eloquent pleading of architect, preservationist, and U.W. professor Victor Steinbrueck.

The opponents of the "ugly open ditch" were few in number but determined in their objections to the downtown freeway which they said would restrict local traffic, spew suffocating exhaust fumes, and divide the heart of the city. The First Hill Improvement Club, which represented hospitals and doctors in the area, the Washington Chapter of the American Institute of Architects, and the city Art Commission proposed an alternative to mitigate the aesthetic and social damage caused by the sunken

Construction work on the Seattle-Tacoma Freeway and the Tukwila Interchange. This mid-1960s aerial looks north toward the Duwamish Waterway, Elliott Bay and most of Seattle. Lake Washington (right) and Metro's Renton Wastewater Treatment Plant (bottom right). Kitsap Peninsula, Hood Canal, and the northeast corner of the Olympic Mountains (upper left). Vancouver Island and part of the San Juan Islands on the horizon (upper left and right, respectively). Courtesy, Port of Seattle.

roadway. In 1961 they waged a public campaign for a landscaped park over the freeway between Madison and University streets and between Pike and Olive streets. The issue pitted the engineers against proponents for citizen participation in highway planning. It resulted in wildly different cost estimates for the cover — the highway engineers' as much as eleven times that of the architects'— and a six-month delay while local, state, and federal officials considered the proposal. Seattle architect Paul Thiry argued that the seven-block cover would lure first-class apartments and office buildings. Otherwise, "Nobody wants to build next to a ditch with lights, exhaust fumes, and acres of concrete alongside." A Los Angeles city councilman visiting Seattle at the time commented that covering portions of the freeway for purely aesthetic reason made no sense at all. L.A. had no lidded freeways.

Initially Mayor Clinton favored the cover, but that support dissipated when both federal and state authorities refused to pay for the new design. To salvage the proposal, some suggested that the covered freeway section could double as a fallout shelter. But by the end of the year, both the mayor and Governor Rosellini declared that no further delays on the downtown freeway would be tolerated. The project went ahead as originally planned. Not until 1970 did highway department officials exhibit the influence that a larger group of concerned Seattle citizens had had on them. Financing provided by an unusual consortium of federal, state, and city agencies also contributed to the state highway planners' change of heart about a four-and-a-half acre park over the freeway lanes between Seneca and University streets. Freeway Park, a highway department spokesman proudly announced, was a "balanced use of the vital urban environment" of downtown Seattle. By the mid-1980s attitudes toward proximity to the freeway had changed considerably. When the strongly-contested Seattle site of the Washington State Convention and Trade Center was finally resolved, the project's chief business backers got their preferred location. The convention center was built over the lanes of the downtown freeway.

Anti-Freeway Movement

When the hundred "Walk the Ditch" marchers hiked behind a police escort along the proposed Seattle freeway route in June 1961 to demonstrate their support for a lid and park, the state got only a glimpse of what was to become a formidable nationwide phenomenon by the end of the decade — the anti-freeway movement. In the early 1960s those few Washington residents who objected to the state's massive highway building were usually living in or near the planned right-of-way. Naturally, many were reluctant to be relocated. Those who didn't have to move often feared the unknown consequences that the projects might have on their property values and on the integrity of their neighborhoods. But to the great majority of freeway supporters, whose property would not be directly affected and even some whose would, social, aesthetic, and environmental factors, if even considered, were generally thought to be worth sacrificing for the greater good of improved traffic flow and safety. In 1961 Highway Director William A. Bugge announced that in the five-and-a-half years since the $8 million Vancouver freeway was opened, savings from reductions in accidents, traveling time, and vehicle-operating costs totaled more than $4 million. A Seattle traffic engineer, Ken Cottingham, referring to national studies on existing freeways, predicted that the Seattle freeway would bring a five-fold drop in the city's accident rate.

Evidently, the Seattle electorate had been convinced of the benefits freeways would bring, for in 1960 they easily passed an $11 million bond issue to finance the Empire Expressway. The expressway was designed as a north-south, limited-access arterial which would skirt Lake Washington and run through the Central District, the University of Washington Arboretum, under Union Bay via a tunnel and north to about 145th Street. As in the case of the downtown freeway route, the opponents of the Empire Expressway came mostly from communities along the proposed route and were not against urban freeways per se. But they believed strongly that residents should have a hand in their design so that they could be made more compatible with their physical and social surroundings. Their convictions were so strong, in fact, that work on the Empire Expressway, which was renamed the R. H. Thomson Expressway in 1961, was brought to a halt by litigation over the route.

Meanwhile, Puget Sound transportation experts had begun planning a whole gridwork of freeways for the Queen City. While hundreds of thousands of 1962 Seattle World's Fair visitors to the General Motors exhibit marveled at visions of space-age, missile-

Top left: Gov. Dan Evans cuts the dedicatory ribbon for the Seattle Freeway, Jan. 3, 1967. Above left: Seattle Freeway work in progress on the Ravenna overpass, May 5, 1960. Below: "Stop the Ditch" freeway protest in downtown Seattle, June 5, 1961. All courtesy, MOHAI, Seattle P-I Collection.

shaped cars guided automatically along electronic highways, the region's highway planners laid out more immediate solutions to the city's traffic problems. Their conclusions, published in the 1967 Puget Sound Regional Transportation Study, proposed three parallel north-south freeways within the city, located only a few miles apart — from the west the Aurora Expressway, the central I-5 freeway, and the R. H. Thomson Expressway. (The Northwest Expressway, an extension of Alaskan Way to run through Interbay and Ballard and ultimately connect with the Aurora Expressway, was dropped from the original plans.) Planning on at least a doubling of the population in the metropolitan area by 1990, the group recommended up to ten bridges to connect the city with suburban areas, five east over Lake Washington and five west across Puget Sound. Maynard Arsove, a Montlake community activist and University of Washington mathematics professor, wryly responded in a publication entitled "Puget Sound Battles the Concrete Dragons." "From 'All-American City' in 1967," he wrote, "we thus advance to 'All-Freeway City' by 1987."

R. H. Thomson Expressway

Designed to deflect some of the traffic from the central I-5 freeway, the eight-lane R. H. Thomson Expressway became the target of a new kind of anti-freeway sentiment welling up in a larger population. By the late 1960s Seattle residents were no longer so willing to acquiesce to the "inevitable" forces of progress and had begun to challenge the desirability of growth and the highway building planned to accommodate it. Residents of the Montlake community and other north Seattle neighborhoods turned out in large numbers to form neighborhood coalitions that took their objections to City Hall. They were encouraged by Mayor Dorm Braman to provide input regarding the design of the Thomson expressway. Consequently, the highway department and Seattle planning commission were obliged to hold a number of public hearings. The community residents were not satisfied until the planners went back to the drawing board several times and were made to defend their plans in court.

Mayor Braman agreed with community council representatives that the city should not be converted into a "vast network of superhighways which split and divide the neighborhood." In 1968 he announced that the proposed expressway would be trimmed to a four-mile, 35 MPH parkway through the Central Area and become a "greenway" as part of the Model Cities Program. That was still not good enough for the 2,000 project opponents who met in the arboretum in May 1969 to protest the "Jack the Ripper Freeway." Finally, in 1970 after $4.2 million had been spent on the design and right-of-way acquisitions, the city council bowed to community sentiment and voted to abandon the Thomson project.

When the expressway toppled, it took with it plans for new crossings of the ship canal at Montlake and the Duwamish River near First Avenue South. City Engineer Roy W. Morse commented that it was hard to know what the public wanted. Morse told about a man who came to his office to complain about why the city didn't do anything about the congestion on the Montlake Bridge. The man had stopped by on his way to a hearing to protest the Thomson Expressway.

In 1972 the proposed Bay Freeway, to run from I-5 to the Seattle Center and intended to relieve the bottleneck on Mercer Street, was defeated along with the Thomson Expressway by a decisive majority of Seattle voters.

Interstate 90

The anti-freeway revolt of the late 1960s and early 1970s became part of the larger dissatisfaction with government leadership and policies in general. As the civil rights movement heated up, racial issues entered the debate. Black activists questioned the redevelopment that the routing of highways through low-income residential neighborhoods was supposed to achieve. In Seattle most of this kind of protest activity was directed against the last

R.H. Thomson Expressway. Top: Construction beside Lake Washington's Union Bay, 1969. Above: Unused piers at the Washington Park Arboretum. Courtesy, Department of Transportation (DOT).

seven miles of I-90. The original plan for this final section of highway, originating in Boston, called for a new ten-lane bridge across Lake Washington, a "cut and cover" trench for five tunnels through the Mount Baker ridge, and a swath of highway wide enough to allow 70-MPH speeds through Rainier Valley.

In January 1970 when an overflow crowd of 900 people attended a city council hearing about the I-90 project, a group of young black militants attempted to take over the meeting. Like other minority spokesmen, they denounced plans for "white highways through black bedrooms" — projects that would displace the poorer black families and result in a "full-fledged urban slum." The day before the hearing, a group of about twenty young people, calling themselves the Seattle Liberation Collective, marched into the highway department's Seattle district office to stage a guerrilla theater. Shouting "Off the bridge," they enacted a symbolic uprising of the people against the "destructive, inhuman" forces of the freeway and the automobile.

The view that automobiles, highway engineers, and freeways were seriously endangering the environment and the quality of human life was not widely shared. At least, few were yet willing to leave the car in the garage and hop on a bike or take the bus to work in order to help reduce air and noise pollution and the displacement of people from their homes. However, by 1969 organized environmental groups in the state and the country had gained political ground. A national public outcry that citizens had been excluded from the planning phases of projects financed by their taxes and that these public works drastically altered or harmed the environment resulted in the passage of the National Environmental Policy Act (NEPA). The act required federal planners to analyze the environmental costs of developing major projects. Before going ahead with any construction, they were to draw up a formal statement called an environmental impact statement (EIS) that identified and assessed possible environmental consequences. In 1971 the state legislature passed the State Environmental Policy

Interstate 90. Above: Work on I-90 near Ellensburg, June 7, 1968. Photo by Forest and Whitmire Photography, Yakima. Below: Mercer Island lid over Interstate 90. Lake Washington, the I-90 floating bridges, and the Seattle skyline are in the distance, ca. 1996. Photos courtesy, DOT. Bottom right: Venting towers on Mercer Island lid, 1997.

Act (SEPA) that closely resembled the federal act. Both the NEPA, authored in part by Sen. Henry Jackson of Washington, and the SEPA gave Washington citizens and interested government agencies an opportunity to debate publicly the potentially damaging impact of projects and to suggest alternatives that might lessen the harm.

Soon after the NEPA was implemented in 1970, seven Seattle Central Area residents filed a suit against the I-90 project. It was the first time in the country that the NEPA had been invoked against highways. Although they lost the first round in the local courts, the plaintiffs won their appeal the next year. The appeals court issued an injunction against all construction on I-90. It would remain in effect until the highway department prepared a relocation assistance plan for those forced from their homes and an environmental impact statement acceptable to the court.

And Interstate 90's problems had barely begun. Over the decade it would become a warning sign of the new kinds of road obstacles that highway builders could expect to encounter. While the highway department conducted new corridor hearings following the court's rejection of its first EIS in 1972, Seattle and Eastside municipal leaders and Metro Transit officials wrangled over the highway and bridge design. The highway department and Eastside planners wanted as many general use lanes as possible, while Seattle officials, concerned about the impact of a massive traffic surge onto I-5 and city arterials, wanted at most eight lanes for automobiles and at least two lanes reserved for transit. The 1973 gasoline shortage reinforced Seattle's position when it reawakened calls for an effective mass transit and a scaled-down bridge design.

Many months of negotiations later, in 1976, the state, local governments and METRO sat down with representatives from the University of Washington's Office of Environmental Mediation and essentially redesigned the project. After reaching an uneasy consensus about the number of auto and special designation lanes for transit and carpools, they also had to respond to a new public consciousness about noise and air pollution in highway corridors. Groups on both sides of the lake had demanded expensive landscaped lids. By then blame for the delay of construction was being hurled back and forth between the cities, the state, the anti-freeway "obstructionists," and Gov. Dixy Lee Ray. Governor Ray didn't help matters when she blamed the accidents and deaths that had recently occurred on the original Lake Washington floating bridge on "those few [anti-freeway] individuals," whom she said had held up I-90's construction.

In August 1979 when the court approved the state's second, 1,300-page EIS for I-90 and finally lifted the injunction against it, the need for equity among the affected communities had been resolved. Lids to become parks of trails and trees were approved to shield communities on both sides of the bridge. The highway plan accepted by the court called for eight lanes of traffic across the new and existing bridge. Then, when it seemed that everyone was ready to proceed, 27,000 I-90 foes signed an initiative that would prohibit the city from approving permits for the project. That potential blockade was soon put to rest by the state Supreme Court, which ruled that the initiative violated state law.

However, neither foes nor favoritism could do anything about the condition of the state motor vehicle fund, then close to broke, nor about the Carter administration's cuts in federal highway spending in 1980. Action on I-90 was deferred until 1981. At that time state lawmakers, gambling that the Reagan administration would follow through on its commitment to complete the remaining five percent of the 1956 federal highway program, approved $325 million in bonding authority so that work could resume as soon as possible. Work began on the pontoons of the floating bridge in December 1982, and excavation of the new Mount Baker tunnel began the next year. (See Bridges Chapter.)

Top: Surveying for Interstate 82 between Ellensburg and Yakima. Above: West end of the Denny Creek bridge near the conclusion of construction, 1980. Left: View towards Snoqualmie Pass during construction work on new southbound lanes and Denny Creek Bridge (left), Nov. 11, 1979. All courtesy, DOT.

In 1989 when the last 6.9 transcontinental miles of I-90 were opened to traffic on June 4, its costs had risen from the original mid-1960s estimate of $75 million to $1.4 billion — a price tag of over $200 million per mile. It had become one of the most expensive pieces of roadway ever built. Perhaps that was one of the reasons why, along with the project's advanced safety and convenience features, the highway department boasted in announcing the forthcoming opening, "Drivers of the new I-90 might well presume themselves elevated to royalty."

ENVIRONMENTAL LEGISLATION

For highway boosters of the 1950s and 1960s who equated economic growth and potential with the state of the region's transportation facilities, the 1970s must have seemed an ominous step backwards. Both the NEPA and SEPA required planners at all levels of government to write detailed environmental impact statements, often on subjects in which they had no expertise and for which they could see no purpose. Both laws were plagued with ambiguities. Basic terms were not defined, and directions were not given about how the environmental review process should work — leaving their interpretation and implementation, at least initially, up to the courts. The highway department was required to hold at least three costly public hearings for each major project proposal to allow citizens to respond to the EIS. It was also directed by the new rules to replace the park land it used for right-of-way, build bicycle trails and pedestrian paths, take down billboards, hand-clear brush, and plant tress and shrubs along the roadway.

As was often the case in other parts of the country, the federal Environmental Protection Agency (EPA) found the Washington highway department's early environmental impact statements far from satisfactory. For example, in 1973 the EIS for the proposed Interstate 82 extension from Yakima to Prosser failed to supply the required information on the effects the freeway would have on air and water quality, noise, flood hazards, solid waste, and wildlife. According to the EPA, the route chosen on the Yakima River flood plain violated a host of federal regulations and would result in adverse impacts to the environment and public welfare. The department's report, they charged, seemed "to argue around the crucial environment issues, rather than trying to openly and objectively discuss them."

About the same time, environmental groups, charging the highway department with another case of circumvention of the law, halted construction of new lanes and bridges through a stand of old growth timber on I-90 about two miles west of Snoqualmie summit. The Alpine Lakes Protection Society and the North Cascades Conservation Council filed suit, accusing the highway department of deliberate violation of the NEPA. Although the route which crossed scenic Franklin Falls had been determined and contracts were made prior to the passage of the federal law, the appeals court ruled that the highway department had to prepare an acceptable EIS before the project could continue. Following the injunction the contractor, Peter Kiewit Sons, successfully sued the department for $2.4 million for abrogating their contract.

Once the legal problems were resolved and an environmentally acceptable design was approved, the 3,620-foot-long Denny Creek Bridge was built over Franklin Falls in 1980. So that environmental disturbance could be kept to a minimum, the concrete viaduct, which carries westbound lanes from the summit, was built high above the originally proposed ground level. For the first time in North America, the bridge designers used an unusual cast-in-place method of construction. With the help of a moving scaffold, the bridge girders were erected on top of the piers without falsework, thus also reducing environmental disruption.

The quest for preservation of the environment became a political football game. Disputed cases usually ended up in skirmishes in court where opposing groups debated the harmful effects of development on man and nature. In the name of the environment, planners proposed that Interstate 90 bypass North Bend, and in the name of the environment a lawsuit was filed to keep it in town. Washington Automobile Club representatives publicly deplored the "wide-eyed zealots who persist[ed] in stymieing all highway progress," and who would have the state "return to the 19th century." In 1971 state Highway Director George Andrews complained that if environmental pressures had existed in 1958 as they did then, Interstate 5 would never have been built. "The people would not have stood for the increased costs." Although admitting that some of the environmental protection measures for the redesigned I-90 were worthwhile, in 1973 Andrews blamed "flaws" in the federal and state environmental laws for delaying $700 million worth of state road projects.

RAID ON THE ROAD FUNDS

The state's slide into the economic dumps in 1970 brought new recruits to the anti-freeway revolt. Environmentalists and community activists were joined by others concerned about unemployment and the effects of the downturn on social, health, and public services. Record-high rates of unemployment and depleted tax revenues led county administrators to lobby the legislature to allow them to use a portion of their allotted state road funds for other purposes. In the House chambers a group of mostly freshmen lawmakers from King County decried the plight of human resource programs in the state budget. Urging their colleagues to give more consideration to "people needs," they argued that a transfer of some of the gas tax revenue would do little damage to the highway budget but would pump needed funds into education, health, and welfare programs. The Washington Federation of Teachers also lobbied for a "complete reallocation of the highway budget to moving people, not automobiles, to education, to institutions, [and] to welfare."

It was not the first time that a raid upon the motor vehicle fund had been attempted. During the depression and afterwards it became so common that in 1944 voters, convinced by such groups as the Good Roads Association and the Automobile Club of Washington of the threat to highway construction and maintenance, passed the 18th Amendment to the state constitution. The amendment specified that all gasoline tax revenue must be used exclusively for highway purposes. In 1971 the counties were able to convince lawmakers to allow them to spend the ten mills of property tax earmarked for county roads on other services. But neither the King County representatives, the teachers, nor the anti-freeway activists could crack the 18th Amendment.

FROM HIGHWAYS TO TRANSPORTATION

Although they could not bust the highway trust, the "freeway revolt block" in the House had clearly put the old highway forces in the legislature on the defensive. The public outcry for major traffic improvements in the 1950s had, for the most part, been quieted by the state's great highway building and upgrading program of the 1960s. But to the mostly Seattle-area lawmakers

Old (below) and new (above) DOT logos. Courtesy, DOT.

and to such groups as the Washington Environmental Council, the adverse impact of the multilaned freeways and "concrete canyons through the city" were all too evident. So by the late 1960s the highway committees of the Senate and the House, which lawmakers used to fight to get on so that they could better deliver the goods to their constituents, had become *transportation* committees. Committee leadership shifted from the strongly pro-highway legislators to those favoring a more comprehensive system that included provisions for mass transit as well.

In a major political upset in 1970, fourteen-year veteran Republican Al Leland of Redmond, the House highway committee chairman, was defeated for reelection. Leland, who called freeway opponents "those bird watchers" and was in turn labeled "Concrete" or "Asphalt Al," had long championed a freeway to move traffic around the Seattle metropolitan area, east of Interstate 405 in the vicinity of Lake Sammamish. However, many Eastside residents were not at all pleased with the prospect. Bellevue homeowners in Lake Hills formed an opposition group and turned out in large numbers at meetings in late 1968 to protest the plan. When Leland reached the end of his legislative road and returned to his Eastside real estate business, he was replaced as Chairman of the House Transportation Committee by the more moderate Duane Berentson.

Environmental legislation and the diversion of tax revenues earmarked for roads were not the only monkey wrenches that got thrown into the 1970s road building program. No sooner had the new environmental laws steered state and county road officials into the courts, when the 1973 energy crisis threw up major road blocks around the state. The long lines and high prices at the gas stations translated into sharply decreased gas tax receipts and steep cutbacks for road and bridge construction. The Arab oil embargo set off inflationary pressures that persisted into the next decade and sent the price of asphalt and other road building materials soaring an average of 12 percent a year. Even transportation experts began predicting that the reign of the automobile, which was portrayed as inefficient, costly, polluting, and contributing to sprawl, was coming to an end. In 1976 the accumulated drop in revenues, which had forced the state and counties to cut back even on maintenance, caused highway officials to request the first gas tax increase since 1967.

The hard economics lesson did more than any environmental argument to convince legislators and state and county officials that the period of extensive, uninterrupted road building in the 1950s and 1960s had come to an end. In 1977 the highway department became the Department of Transportation with a new emphasis on public transportation and the need to move *people* as well as vehicles. The new department was mandated by the legislature to develop a comprehensive and balanced multimodal transportation system that provided for mass transit along with the building and upkeep of state highways. By then the department had already become active in the development of park-and-ride lots, freeway flyer stops, and exclusive transit and carpool lanes. In 1976 Highway Director William Bulley asked the legislature to extend toll collection on the Evergreen Point Floating Bridge over Lake Washington so that the money could be used to build a high-occupancy-vehicle lane for transit and carpool use.

But neither designating lanes for high-occupancy vehicles nor building new ones would come easily with the depleted condition of the state motor vehicle fund. In 1980 Bulley predicted that with

Above left: A common problem on early-century Washington highways. Courtesy DOT. Above right: Normal traffic on the Seattle freeway portion of Interstate 5, 1998. Below: FLOW control center, Seattle, ca. 1996. Courtesy DOT.

inflation continuing and gas tax revenues declining at both the state and federal level, "we will soon be out of business unless something is done quickly to increase revenues or reduce costs." Three years later a federal study showed that of the 7,000 miles of state highways, only half were in good condition. A large percentage of the 42,137 miles of county roads and the 10,812 miles of city streets had deteriorated more than at any time since World War II. And, partly because many localities were still diverting their portion of state taxes allocated to roads to other services, local governments were spending less on roads and bridges than at any time in the last twenty years. High interest rates, inflation, inadequate tax revenues, and the cutbacks in federal grants made it impossible to repair all the worn and potholed pavements and the rusting and cracked bridge supports, or to update the rural two-lane highways of the 1930s, now crushed by huge semi trucks and antiquated by suburban sprawl.

Partial relief came in April 1983 when the hike in the federal gasoline tax, passed by Congress the previous December, went into effect. It was the first boost in the gas tax the government had made since the Eisenhower administration's National Highway Act of 1956. The nickel-per-gallon increase, one cent of which was to go to mass transit projects, was expected to bring to Washington over $300 million in additional federal aid funds for the period of 1983 through 1986. It meant that the state's freeway construction could increase by over 50 percent. Money would finally be available to widen a section of I-5 at Olympia and complete I-90, I-82, and I-182 in the Tri-Cities area, the I-5 Tacoma spur to the Tacoma Narrows Bridge, and the I-205 bridge between Vancouver and Portland, as well as scores of smaller projects. The following spring, after the state transportation commission convinced the legislature that still more money was needed for the state, counties, and cities to catch up with the backlog of reconstruction and repairs, the lawmakers approved a six-cents-per-gallon increase in the state fuel tax, to a total of 18 cents per gallon by 1985. Yet even this major fill-up was not enough to keep up with the cost of upgrading and maintaining all the state, county, and city roads that needed attention. To generate the type of funding and purchasing power that the highway department possessed in 1959, the state gas tax in 1980 would have had to have been about 42 cents per gallon.

By the late 1980s congested metropolitan stretches of state highways and county arterials, some claimed, had begun to rival the infamous freeways of Southern California. In the Puget Sound counties, experiencing a robust economy and large influx of new residents, traffic backups became an everyday experience, not only between the suburbs and the central city, but between and within the suburbs themselves. Yet earlier in 1982 the Puget Sound Council of Governments, a planning group composed of representatives of the region's counties and Indian tribes, had recommended against adding more highway lanes for general use, at least until the year 2000. While recognizing that motor vehicles would continue to be the dominant mode of transportation for the foreseeable future, the group concluded that both the cost of new freeways and their impact on communities and the environment was too great. If there was to be any relief to traffic congestion during rush hour along heavily traveled corridors, mass transit systems would have to carry a greater share of peak-period travelers. As alternatives to highway building, the group and other state transportation experts proposed that local governments and employers more actively encourage their employees to use bus transit, ridesharing, flextime, or even try telecommuting. The state was encouraged to continue its development of high-occupancy-vehicle lanes, and traffic management systems such as the FLOW system of on-ramp metering in use on I-5 in Seattle. While plans were being studied for a light-rail rapid transit system, the area's transit agencies were also urged to improve their service and facilities to promote greater ridership. (See Streets and Mass Transportation Chapter).

Unfortunately, most experts acknowledge that no one solution or combination of solutions to the state's transportation problems will come easily or as soon as we would like. In a society and a region where personal freedom of movement and the choice of where one lives and works largely depends upon the availability of the automobile and the freeway, weaning even a small percentage of Washington drivers from their cars will be a formidable challenge. Local government and transportation officials may not have much success until freeways are no longer free and tolls are charged during peak driving periods, or until the cost of operating and parking an automobile becomes much less affordable. At least, past experience offers little encouragement for the harried Washington motorist of the 1990s. For as long as there have been urban roads, even long before the birth of the automobile, there has been traffic congestion. Perhaps one can find some consolation in trying to imagine what it would be like traveling to work or across the state *without* the freeway.

1) Scene on McClellan Pass Highway, April 29, 1918. 2) Olympic Highway, six miles from Humptulips. Courtesy, Jones Photo Co., Aberdeen. 3) Scene on Chinook Pass Highway beside the Naches River, Oct. 3, 1931. 4) Switchback on Blewett Pass. 5) Highway along the Skykomish River, May 1915. 6) Opening of the Sunset Highway (Snoqualmie Pass) for traffic, April 25, 1921. Photos 1,3,4,5,6 by Asahel Curtis. Courtesy, WA State Historical Society. 7) Concrete roadmaking machine on Seattle-Everett freeway stretch of I-5 at 155th Street North; Aug, 30, 1964. Photo by Bob Miller. Courtesy, MOHAI, Seattle P-I Collection. 8) Early concrete paving scene on an unidentified road in King County, 1915. Courtesy, King County Public Works Department. 9) Construction of Seattle-Tacoma freeway stretch of I-5 at border of SeaTac and Tukwila. Orilla Road passes beneath freeway overpass. Serpentine loop in Green River, now site of Brisco Meander Park. Photo by Lavanaway.

Timber and Steel: Bridges over the Washougal and Nisqually rivers.

BRIDGES

BRIDGES IN TERRITORIAL AND EARLY STATEHOOD DAYS

Timber Pile-and-Beam

Settlers arriving in Washington Territory in the 1850s must have sighed in weary resignation when they came upon yet another stream crossing. Since the area's few wagon roads wound around the natural features of the terrain, and their route was dictated by the supply of water, wood, and grass, overlanders might have to cross the same river many times. And whether they waded, rode, paddled, or were ferried across, they usually got wet.

Once settlements were established in the territory, county residents worked off their road taxes by hacking, shoveling, and smoothing out more permanent roads to connect their properties with the local market. Those who wanted the convenience of a bridge presented a petition to their county commissioners who would decide if it was necessary and who would pay for it. If enough potential users willing to help pay for the span could be found, a contractor was hired. The contractor had to agree not only to build the structure but to keep it in good repair for a minimum of two years.

Because manpower and county road funds were generally insufficient, individuals were also authorized to build roads and bridges — and put tolls on them. An act passed at the first session of the territorial legislature in 1854 allowed any person owning land, or having permission of the affected landowners, to build a bridge or a plank or turnpike road at his own expense and receive compensation in "reasonable" tolls. The legislature reserved the right to regulate toll rates, and it granted dispensations from tolls to anyone going to or returning from church, a funeral, or an election. The lawmakers also authorized county commissioners to collect fines for speeding over public and private bridges and for causing willful damage to the structures. The fines were to be deposited in the school fund to help support the territory's yet nearly nonexistent schools. As late as 1893 the first bridge over the Skagit River, a wooden truss with a draw span, bore a large sign at either end that read "$25 Fine for Riding or Driving over this Bridge Faster than a Walk."

Sometimes settlers wishing for a bridge could get help from soldiers stationed at the local U.S. Army fort, since the early wagon roads often overlapped with the territory's military roads. Along the Mullan Road, three miles from its western starting point at the site of old Fort Walla Walla, Lt. John Mullan's crew built the first bridge across Mud Slough. About four miles further on another was erected across Dry Creek. The third went up across the

Workers and their loaded wagon demonstrate the sturdiness of the log bridge over Thirty Mile Creek, a tributary of the Sanpoil River in Ferry County. Courtesy, Department of Transportation (DOT).

Touchet River, just below the site of the present town of Prescott. Because Mullan lacked the time and the powder needed to blast a road through the most rugged mountain areas, heavy construction work had to be avoided. This forced his company to make numerous river crossings. In a 100-mile section of road in the northern Bitterroot Mountains, they made 146 crossings of the Coeur d' Alene and Saint Regis-Borgia rivers. Like the settlers' spans, many of the soldiers' timber bridges were soon washed away by flood waters.

For the most part, the pioneers' bridges were simple functional affairs, built quickly with little expense and little concern for durability or for other stream uses. Usually two trees were felled across the narrowest part of the stream and a deck of smaller logs or whipsawed plank was laid across them. When pile driving equipment became available, pile trestles were used for the wider crossings. The limitations of the timber pile-and-beam bridges became immediately apparent, particularly as more people arrived in the region. The low height of the support pilings for the relatively short spans made the bridges virtual barriers across the streams. They restricted navigation and were especially vulnerable to logs, drift, and high flood waters. Apparently, many builders ignored or were unaware of the territorial law that made it a crime, carrying up to a $500 fine, to obstruct any watercourse generally used for navigation or for floating logs downstream.

Even with all their limitations, the timber beam bridges were a welcome improvement compared to the alternatives — expen-

Early wagon bridges on the Yakima River at Granger (below left) and over the Skagit River at Mount Vernon (below right) are examples of the popular Howe Truss construction. The Skagit bridge was opened in 1893, the first to cross the river at Mount Vernon. Courtesy, Dan Kerlee and the Skagit County Historical Society, respectively.

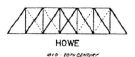

1) Example of the simple Queen Post Truss on the Sunset Highway. 2) Example of the Parker Truss over the Skookum Chuck River, June 1912. 3) Local ranchers pose on the Pratt Truss bridge they had helped build over the Okanogan River at Tonasket. The sign over the bridge reads "$25.00 REWARD for information leading to the conviction of anyone driving more than 15 head of horses or cattle, 30 head of sheep or hogs, or riding or driving faster than a walk across this bridge. County Commissioners." 4) The bridge at Monte Cristo over the south fork of the Sauk River is an early example of a partial Howe Truss structure. Photos courtesy, DOT. Below: Profiles for a few typical truss types.

HOWE
1840 - 20TH CENTURY
(WOOD, VERTICALS OF METAL)
DIAGONALS IN COMPRESSION, VERTICALS IN TENSION
LENGTH: 30 - 150 FEET
9 - 45 METERS

PRATT
1844 - 20TH CENTURY
DIAGONALS IN TENSION, VERTICALS IN COMPRESSION. (EXCEPT FOR HIP VERTICALS ADJACENT TO INCLINED END POSTS)
LENGTH: 25 - 150 FEET
8 - 45 METERS

PARKER
MID-LATE 19TH - 20 CENTURY
A PRATT WITH A POLYGONAL TOP CHORD
LENGTH: 40 - 200 FEET
12 - 60 METERS

LENTICULAR (PARABOLIC)
1870 - EARLY 20TH CENTURY
A PRATT WITH BOTH TOP AND BOTTOM CHORDS PARABOLICLY CURVED OVER THEIR ENTIRE LENGTH.
LENGTH: 150 - 400 FEET
45 - 120 METERS

PENNSYLVANIA (PETIT)
1875 - EARLY 20TH CENTURY
A A PARKER WITH SUB - STRUTS.
B A PARKER WITH SUB - TIES.
LENGTH: 250 - 600 FEET
75 - 180 METERS

sive ferries or nothing at all. In October 1854 the Olympia *Pioneer* and *Democrat* reported that county commissioners had awarded to Mr. J. L. Perkins a $1,550 contract to build a bridge across the east fork of Budd Inlet, which separated the fledgling community of Olympia from those homesteading across the water. The county pledged $500 and counted on a private subscription "which had been set afloat" to make up the deficiency. The bridge was to be 360-feet-long and sixteen-feet-wide, "about one-third of which will be constructed over piles, and the remainder over substantial bents, with secure mud sills." According to the paper, the bridge would be a "great public convenience" for people living on the east side of the bay, who had "long suffered materially for want of means of communication with Olympia."

In October 1866 the Vancouver *Register* announced a similar happy development — the building of a 220-foot-long bridge over the Washougal River. Promising to be "one of the best public improvements in Clarke [sic] County," it would allow farmers living on the other side of the river to go to Vancouver during all seasons.

Timber Trusses

In order to build a span of sufficient height and length that would not impede river traffic or be damaged by it, more sophisticated bridges than timber beams were needed. Since Washington Territory was not settled to any degree until well after the period

of experimentation in iron and steel bridge design, Washington bridge engineers were able to import an already developed technology. But what the structural design engineers in the East built using iron and steel was usually constructed in Washington with lumber. Timber was abundant and much less expensive. Beginning around 1880, the timber truss became the most common bridge form in Washington for railroad and highway structures.

The full potential of lumber as a bridge material was realized when the truss form began to be used in the mid-nineteenth century. By using a triangulated arrangement of short timber elements, the truss allowed longer spans to be erected than could be achieved with the pile-and-beam. It is the rigidity of the triangle in tension or compression that make trusses work. The Howe truss was probably the first truss form bridge to be built in Washington. In this design the vertical members of steel or iron resist the load in tension, while the diagonal members of wood resist the load in compression. Another early truss form used for timber structures in the state was the Pratt truss. Here the function of vertical and diagonal members is reversed so that the vertical components are timber and the diagonal components are steel. For bridge builders in Washington and in the country, the Howe form was usually preferred for timber construction over the Pratt. The oldest surviving Howe truss in Washington is the Little Sheep Creek railroad bridge built in 1896 in the vicinity of Northport, Stevens County, just south of the international border.

The oldest of the state's few surviving covered bridges, the Wahkiakum County span across the Grays River, has also become one of Washington's favorite picturesque subjects. This distant view, which includes the bridge's pastoral setting, was photographed for Sunset Magazine *by Hugh Paradise.*

Covered Bridges

In the best of conditions, bridges built from untreated lumber might last fifteen years. In order to extend the life of the timber components, builders sometimes constructed a housing around them to protect them from the elements. At one time there were several of these stark utilitarian structures, usually built by railroad companies, spanning Washington waterways. Of the four covered bridges remaining in the state, the oldest is the Grays River Bridge, a two-span, Howe truss highway structure. Known by locals as "Sorenson's Covered Bridge," it was built in 1905 in Wahkiakum County to improve access for dairy farmers going to market on State Route 830. The 188-foot-long span, 1.5 miles east of the town of Grays River just south of Highway 4 on Covered Bridge Road, has a fourteen-foot-wide roadway and was probably originally roofed with corrugated iron. An unusual covered Howe pony truss in Lewis County is still in use. The Pe Ell Bridge was built in 1934 by the Pe Ell water department to transport a water main, as well as pedestrians, across the Chehalis River.

Timber truss bridges continued to be built by logging and railroad companies and by counties and the state highway department throughout the 1930s. Because of wartime restrictions on steel and concrete, many were erected even into the 1940s. Aiming to hold down costs, the highway department during the middle of the depression decade touted a new method of timber construction that called for less steel than was generally required for timber spans. They cited the Bear Canyon Bridge on a Lewis County road near Morton as an example of an inexpensive and fully adequate timber truss. The 140-foot truss spans with their supporting towers were constructed "almost entirely" of lumber treated with creosote. Like their steel counterparts, the wooden trusses were preassembled before transport to the bridge site, which, according to the highway commissioner's 1936 report, ensured better workmanship and made the span less expensive.

Steel Trusses

By the time most Washington bridge-building projects got underway in the nineteenth century, steel and iron truss technology was fairly standardized. Bridge engineers did not have much opportunity for major innovations. But the established technol-

ogy also saved them the costly mistakes and potentially dangerous errors that were a necessary part of arriving at an efficient design. The superiority of the simple system of verticals and diagonals of the Pratt truss, and the single system of triangles of the Warren truss configuration, had been confirmed by the time most of the early steel truss bridges were being built within the state. There were few of the early double- and triple- intersection truss forms, whose complex systems of triangulation, according to a later expert, created an "unavoidable ambiguity in stress distribution."

One of these complicated forms was recently offered free by Grays Harbor County to anyone willing to maintain it according to the regulations of the National Historic Preservation Act. The West Wishkah River Bridge on West Wishkah Road just north of Greenwood was built in 1915 as a riveted double intersection Warren truss. The last highway bridge of its kind in the state, the 120-foot span carried a one-lane roadway until it was replaced in 1989.

In Washington, as well as in the rest of the country, most of the steel bridges for spans under 250 feet built during the early twentieth century were Pratt trusses. One of the earliest and least altered remaining examples of this type of truss in Washington is the West Monitor Bridge, one mile northwest of

When it became clear that the Grays Harbor County would have to replace its old single lane Wishkah River Bridge (top) with a modern structure of reinforced concrete (above) public works officials attempted to save the old bridge by selling it. Although the initial response to this marketing-for-preservation was encouraging, the steel truss bridge ultimately went to the scrap heap. Courtesy Grays Harbor County.

Above: The West Monitor Bridge as it appeared in 1937, after thirty years of service over the Wenatchee River. The 320-foot long span is one of the oldest pin-connected Pratt truss bridges in the state. Courtesy, DOT.
Bottom: Crossing the Kettle River on State Route 21, the Curlew Bridge (1908) is typical of many small bridges constructed statewide in the early 1900s.

Monitor in Chelan County. The bridge over the Wenatchee River was built in 1907 by the Puget Sound Bridge and Dredging Company and consists of two 140-foot steel trusses and two twenty-foot timber trestle approach spans. Built before the improvement of riveting techniques, particularly the development of the pneumatic riveter, the trusses were pinconnected, making them less rigid than the riveted truss.

Attempting to construct ever longer spans, nineteenth-century bridge engineers modified the Pratt truss by subdividing the configuration's panels with additional substruts and subties. The resulting Petit truss developed during the 1870s represented a major advance in strengthening the standard Pratt truss form. An existing, modified example of this design is the Middle Fork Nooksack River Bridge on Mosquito Lake Road, about a mile and a half north of Mosquito Lake in Whatcom County. Referred to as a Pennsylvania Petit truss because of its polygonal top chord, it was built in 1915 by the Weymouth Construction Company who moved the pin-connected through truss of an existing bridge and laid it across the middle fork of the Nooksak. Two panels of the 380-foot structure were removed in order to adapt the bridge to its new location. Even at a diminished 338 feet, the Middle Fork Nooksack River Bridge remains the longest pinconnected highway bridge in the state.

The Curlew Bridge over the Kettle River at Curlew in Ferry County is another extant pin-connected steel bridge. Built in 1908 at the former cable ferry crossing, it replaced the first bridge, which had been washed out by a flood. Its builder William Oliver of Spokane, used what was by then another common truss type. The Parker truss design employed an arched top chord that increased the rigidity of the structure. It enabled the bridge to be thirty feet longer than the maximum length generally used for the basic Pratt truss. However, Curlewites probably didn't appreciate this extra technological capacity so much as the convenience of once again being able to make the weekly trip to the general store.

On February 6, 1947, the meeting of the westbound wide-load hay truck with two gas trucks going east on the Evergreen Highway bridge over the Washougal River caused one of the stranger mishaps in Washington State's bridge history. Sideswiped by the hay truck, which escaped, the lead gas truck stalled and caught fire from a leaking gas can dislodged in the accident. Although both drivers fled to safety, the bridge quickly buckled under the extreme heat of a fire fed by 9,000 gallons of gasoline and fanned by a brisk breeze. About a half hour after the accident, the twenty-one-year-old structure crashed with what the next day's Portland Oregonian *described as a "thunderous splash" into the river. Photos courtesy Ted Van Arsdol.*

Above: The Elwha River Bridge, the oldest deck highway truss span in the state, was constructed in 1913. Courtesy, DOT.

Like the Pratt truss, the Warren truss is still used by engineers. This simple design is composed of diagonals placed alternately in tension and compression. The Elwha River Bridge, a two-span, riveted carbon steel deck truss, is the oldest existing Warren truss, as well as the oldest deck highway truss, in the state. It is located on State Highway Route 112 one mile west of the junction with U.S. 101, three miles west of Port Angeles. As part of their effort to connect the Olympic Peninsula with the rest of the state with wagon roads that would "serve the tourist as well as the agricultural and lumbering interests," Clallam County road commissioners built the bridge over the Elwha in 1913.

During the decade beginning in 1925, bridge building accelerated as the state stepped up its highway program to meet the swelling demands of automobile traffic. As bridges for municipal street railways and for the railroads became rarer, roadway spans multiplied at an astonishing rate. Although the monumental and graceful suspension bridges of New York and San Francisco provided the major spectacles of the time, the common truss became the workhorse of the road and highway system.

STATE HIGHWAY BRIDGES, 1906-1930

Before the relatively lightweight automobile appeared, the heavy load capacities required by railroad traffic determined the development of bridge design. Railroad bridges that were not made of wood were usually built of, characterized by the heavy riveted steel truss. Automobile traffic eventually changed the direction of American bridge building. By 1910 it was apparent to federal and state highway planners that the automobile was here to stay. Not only were new standards of roadway construction needed, but the bridges that accompanied highways presented engineers a new and complex range of structural requirements. The lower maximum load requirements for highway use enabled engineers to use a greater range of bridge designs and materials. For reasons of economy they chose, for the most part, to use concrete, but the steel truss remained an essential component of roadway bridge building. Steel is still the most suitable material for the longer spans over navigable waterways.

Above photos: Scenes from the early life of the old Lewis River cantilevered bridge at Woodland. Several pages in the earliest Highway Department photo album are dedicated to its 1912 construction. Bottom right: One of two bridges built for U.S. Highway 99 in the 1940s about one mile downstream from the 1912 bridge. Bottom left: The Washougal River Bridge between Camus and Washougal, was one of the Highway Department's earliest steel spans, on old State Road 8 (now S.R. 14). Photos courtesy, DOT.

Top left: Wenatchee River Bridge, west of Dryden, 1928. Top right: The Howe truss North Fork (Snoqualmie River) Bridge near North Bend. Above left: Tolt River Bridge at Tolt (now Carnation). Above right: Motorcyclists on unidentified state bridge. Below left: Early-century bridge on the Yakima River with variation on Pratt truss. Below right: White River Bridge with sign reading: "Ten Dollars Fine for driving over this bridge faster than a walk." Photos courtesy, DOT.

Top and above: Skagit river Bridge at Mount Vernon, opening day, 1913. Below: Bridge at Sedro Wooley over the Skagit River. Courtesy, DOT.

Above left: Pratt truss bridge over Yakima River at Cle Elum. Above right: Chehalis River Bridge at Dryad. Below: Unidentified Whatcom County Bridge by Bellingham pioneer photographer E.A. Hegg. Photos courtesy, DOT.

Steel Cantilever Trusses

Rivaling the suspension bridges, at least in length, the largest steel truss bridges were cantilever structures that used a combination of cantilevers and anchors and suspended spans. The pinconnected highway bridge across the Columbia River at Wenatchee, built in 1906-8, is the oldest cantilever truss in the state. The Pasco-Kennewick Bridge, the Longview Bridge, and the Vantage or Lyons Ferry Bridge, all built during the 1920s, are representative of the cantilever construction of that decade. By the 1930s, when the Grand Coulee Bridge, the Deception Pass Bridge and the George Washington Memorial (Aurora Avenue) Bridge were built, the design of the cantilever truss had been refined and simplified. Because all these bridges are equally notable for their use as well as their structure, they are discussed in more detail below.

Construction work on the Fairfax Bridge over the Carbon River. Courtesy, DOT.

Wenatchee Columbia River Bridge

At the beginning of the 1890s Wenatchee had little going for it. It was not on a main highway, and the ferry, which provided the only means of crossing the river, docked several miles north of town. But Wenatchee boomers had great hopes that the Great Northern Railroad would soon turn the settlement into "a good, substantial, prosperous town, well supported by an excellent country of varied resources." They were not disappointed. The completion of the railroad line into the town in 1892 and the inauguration of regular steamboat service to upriver points in 1893 soon made Wenatchee a major trading center for the Okanogan and Big Bend areas.

The plan to build the first highway bridge across the Columbia River was another sign of Wenatchee boosters' confidence that their town was destined to go places. And this bridge would carry not only people, horses, wagons, and a very occasional motor car, but also water. The bridge was the brainchild of W. T. Clark, builder of the Highline Canal, a major irrigation project in the valley. (See Irrigation Chapter). Clark's ambition was to extend his gravity system to the east side of the river and open up another 5,000 acres for the expanding apple industry. While carrying the growing road traffic from the Douglas County side of the river, the bridge was to be financed by charges for the irrigation water which it would transport in two pipelines along its sides.

A few days after the first wagon bridge across the Columbia opened in 1908, Clark's paper, the Wenatchee *Republic*, proudly

The bridge at Wenatchee, the first to span the Columbia River in Washington State. Although constructed in 1907-08 with private funds, it soon was purchased by the state. Courtesy, DOT.

proclaimed that the project, financed in part by "J. J. Hill [the Empire Builder] and his railroad associates," was "one of the largest undertakings ever attempted by private parties." The self-congratulations did not last long, however. The next year Clark's canal company announced that it could not stay in business unless it began collecting bridge tolls. To prevent this development, town leaders proposed to the legislature that the state take over the bridge and make it part of the state highway system. A consultant who examined the bridge for the state reported that there were defects in the timber floor and concrete piers and leaks in the two pipelines, and that "the ugliness of the structure is very apparent." Nonetheless, the heavy wagon traffic the bridge had experienced in the year since it was completed convinced the highway commission that it would soon be of even greater value to state residents as the orchards east of the river began bearing fruit. The highway board purchased the 1,060-foot bridge for what it cost the company to build it — $177,000.

The pinconnected steel cantilever bridge remained in service on the Sunset Highway until a new structure was built in 1950. Today the old bridge carries only pedestrians, but it still sends water — through a much larger pipe — to the apple ranches of East Wenatchee. The bridge that replaced it is a graceful, three-span steel cantilever and tied arch. Designed by George Stevens of the highway department bridge division, the Wenatchee bridge was judged to be the most beautiful span of its type in the nation in a 1951 competition sponsored by the American Institute of Steel Construction.

Columbia River Interstate Bridge — Vancouver to Portland

Two months before the United States declared war against Germany in April 1917, the second bridge to span the Columbia River was completed. As thousands crowded onto the bridge deck cheering, the Portland-Vancouver ferry tooted a mournful salute.

Left: The "new" Wenatchee Bridge. Courtesy, DOT. Below: The grand opening of the Interstate Bridge at Vancouver. Courtesy, Ted Van Arsdol.

Above: Interstate Bridge with the 1958 addition photographed in 1996 by Nancy Ishii. Right: Original photo postcard caption reads, "Pacific Highway Interstate Bridge length which approaches four miles, making it one of the longest steel bridges in the world. Vancouver Wn-Portland Ore." Courtesy, Dan Kerlee.

"With brilliant formality," the Portland *Oregonian* reported, "the Columbia River Interstate bridge yesterday swung into its niche in the great scheme of commercial and industrial development of the Northwest." Built by the people of Clark and Multnomah counties, the toll bridge was expected to unite the two communities, both socially and commercially. The bridge was a critical link on the not-quite-completed Pacific Highway. It also marked the beginning of a new era in transportation, one in which the motor vehicle would become the most common means of traveling between Portland and Puget Sound.

This vertical lift bridge was enormous. Consisting of a series of through riveted truss spans with polygonal top chords, it was 23,000 feet long, including the approaches. The draw span provided a clearance of 150 feet above ordinary high water and allowed a channel 250 feet wide. Because of the bridge's tremendous length and the difficulty of building falsework in the river, all but one span was erected on falsework on shore. The Parker truss spans were then lifted onto barges which floated them to the proper piers. The piers were constructed to rest on exceptionally long piles sunk to a depth of 110 feet below low water. The Kansas City, Missouri engineering firm of Harrington, Howard and Ash were the designers. John L. Harrington worked with J. A. L. Waddell to design and build Tacoma's two vertical lift bridges during the early teens.

In 1929 the states of Washington and Oregon jointly purchased the bridge from the two counties and subsequently removed the tolls. In 1958 the bridge was rebuilt and another vertical lift bridge was erected alongside it.

Pasco-Kennewick Bridges — 1920s – 1970s

When the highway bridge across the Columbia between Pasco and Kennewick was completed in 1922, it became the first of five steel structures and the first of four cantilever trusses to be erected across the river during the 1920s. The steel span was built by the Union Bridge Company, which put up a number of bridges throughout Washington when the state embarked on a major highway and bridge-building program in the twenties and thirties. The Pasco-Kennewick Bridge was on the route of the Inland Empire Highway, one of the state's three

original trunk highways. (See Highways Chapter.)

By replacing an outmoded ferry system that could carry at most six cars per trip, the bridge facilitated cross-river traffic enormously and transformed the old adage of "twin cities" into a reality. In October 1922 the Kennewick *Courier-Reporter* claimed that "although Pasco and Kennewick [had] grown up side by side on the banks of the Columbia," they had not yet "been close together in the lives of the people." When the bridge opened, "a new era dawned for each community. Pasco awoke in possession of thousands of acres of fields and orchards and Kennewick annexed a railroad payroll." For some the cantilever truss was expected to do far more than unite two communities. The idea of the bridge was first seriously discussed during the postwar agricultural recession. Despite the hard times, prominent businessmen and farmers in the area were willing to gamble that the span would become an integral part of the economic development of the state — both east and west of the mountains. In less than eighteen months over 1,400 "public-spirited citizens" from seventeen communities in Washington and Idaho responded to a public subscription drive and subsidized the bridge through the formation of the Benton-Franklin Intercounty Bridge Company.

Opening day ceremonies were attended by "a happy, singing, rollicking, yet orderly crowd," liable to break into song whenever

The Pasco-Kennewick "Yellowstone Trail" Bridge over the Columbia River, ca. 1922. Courtesy, Ted Van Arsdol.

the spirit moved them. At an evening banquet, Frank Waterhouse, president of the Seattle Chamber of Commerce, proudly compared the bridge to the golden rivet driven at the junction of the eastern and western ends of the Union Pacific transcontinental railroad. Like the rivet, the new bridge would bind together the two sections of the state. Even more important, it demonstrated "the wonderful possibilities of statewide cooperative effort." The press apparently agreed. The Seattle *Times* called the subscription effort the "greatest community undertaking in the history of the Northwest." The Portland *Oregonian* described the project as the "first undertaking in which the extreme east and west sides of the State cooperated to the fullest extent." Before the year was over, about 200 motorists a day were paying the steep 75-cent toll to cross the bridge.

Above: Cable stay Intercity Bridge between Pasco and Kennewick. Courtesy, Arvid Grant.
Bottom: The "Blue Bridge" opened in 1954 upstream from the Intercity Bridge. Courtesy, DOT.

Nine years later, in 1931, the highway department purchased the bridge and removed the tolls. According to one former toll taker, "it touched off a celebration that rivaled the Fourth of July." In 1954, when a new span was completed upstream, the state transferred the bridge to the Franklin and Benton county road systems.

The new state highway bridge, dubbed by locals the "blue bridge," is one of the few nameless spans across the Columbia. Need for another bridge became all too apparent soon after World War II ended. The old two-lane structure could not stand up to the heavy postwar traffic generated by the many Hanford war workers who had decided to remain in the Tri-Cities area. Congestion got worse when construction workers for McNary Dam arrived in the late 1940s. One major traffic tie-up occurred in April 1948 when a farmer lost a load of hay on the bridge during an Army Day parade. The spill resulted in an investigation by the army, which confirmed what the Tri-City residents had been complaining about — the old bridge was inadequate. But relief was not forthcoming until state lawmakers passed a statewide highway bond issue in 1951 that included money for the new span. It took another three years to build the 2,250-foot, four-lane "blue bridge."

Fifty-four years after the first Pasco-Kennewick bridge was heralded as one of the area's most progressive achievements, a new and extraordinary bridge stood alongside it. Superlatives again seemed in order for the Intercity Bridge, which was credited with inaugurating a new era in American bridge building. This cable stay concrete span introduced into U.S. bridge technology two unprecedented achievements — the use of concrete as a girder in a suspended bridge and a cable-supported girder length of 1,794 feet. (Prestressed concrete rather than the usual steel was used in the girder because in the Northwest concrete was more readily available, less expensive, and of high quality.) The cable stay design was structurally more efficient and economical than a cantilever truss for spans between 600 and 1,800 feet long.

The cable stay bridge resembles a suspension bridge in its use of twin towers from which cables fan out and down in either direction. But unlike a suspension bridge, the cable networks of the two towers are not joined together. Instead, they independently support equal halves of the bridge. In the suspension bridge large cables are anchored at each end and buried underground to support the weight of the bridge. The cable stay bridge uses the bridge girder itself for anchoring, making it a more technically advanced system according to Arvid Grant, whose Olympia firm designed the bridge and oversaw construction.

To learn as much as possible about steel cable stay technology, Grant consulted with Fritz Leonhardt, a noted German bridge designer from Stuttgart. Leonhardt, whom Grant in 1978 called the "most eminent bridge technician living today," developed the cable stay method as an inexpensive way of rebuilding bridges destroyed in Germany during World War II.

Part of the construction work involved using a 200-ton crane to lift six eighteen-ton pieces of steel weldments, designed to hold the ends of the stay cables, from a barge in the river. Each of the 12 x 25 x 2.5-foot pieces had to be set within an eighth of an inch of its final position — at the top of the two 250-foot concrete towers. Engineers believed that it was the first time such an undertaking had been tried in North America, at least on a bridge. At the time of its erection from 1975-78, the Intercity Bridge was one of the few and the largest of the cable stay spans in the country. It quickly became a model for bridge builders around the world.

The Intercity Bridge was intended to replace the first Pasco-Kennewick bridge, which by 1967 was restricted to passenger cars and light trucks only. But ten years after the cable stay bridge opened, the old "green bridge" still stood alongside, protected by local advocates of historic preservation. Pasco Mayor Ed Hendler had long vowed to see it torn down because he and others considered it unsafe and a hazard to navigation. The supporters of the bridge argued that it could be refurbished for less than the cost of demolition and would enhance riverfront improvements as a pedestrian and bicycle path. After a small turnout of Pasco and Kennewick residents voted to raze the "big white elephant" in 1980, a save-the-bridge campaign took the issue to court. However, their legal battle was unsuccessful, and the old green bridge that long ago inspired Washingtonians as a symbol of intrastate unity was torn down.

Above: The new Columbia River Bridge at Vantage, ca. 1970. Photo by Hugh Paradise. Right: The original Vantage Bridge under construction in 1927. Bottom: The original Vantage Bridge under reconstruction in 1968 at Lyons Ferry on the Snake River. Courtesy DOT.

Vantage Bridge

In 1927 when the highway department began building a 1,640-foot cantilever truss on the Sunset Highway across the river at Vantage, locals predicted that the volume of traffic on "one of the finest stretches of graveled road in the state," between Quincy and Odessa, would grow tremendously. The new bridge, they anticipated, would also "lure many tourists from other cross-state highways."

How many tourists the Vantage Ferry Bridge lured is not known, but we do know that its construction attracted attention. In order to build the bridge's main piers, engineers sunk caissons, which were imbedded seventy feet under the river bed. It was the first such project in the state. The air pressure in the caissons, supplied by 350-pound compressors, was heavy. Although workers entered the caissons through airlocks and worked only in two-hour shifts, three suffered serious cases of "caisson fever," or the bends, and had to be hospitalized.

The Vantage span, the seventh bridge to cross the Columbia, consisted of one 200-foot suspended span, two 160-foot cantilever spans, two 220-foot anchor spans, and four 170-foot Warren deck spans, with a twenty-foot roadway and concrete deck. Including

approaches, it was nearly half a mile long. The center span was designed to rise ninety feet above the water to allow for navigation and high waters. The minimum height of all the Columbia River bridges was set above the river's largest recorded flood stage of 1894, when sections of the river rose eighteen feet above the banks.

One of the four large cantilever highway bridges built across the river during the 1920s, the Vantage Ferry Bridge continued to be an important link for local and cross-state traffic until late 1962. At that time it was replaced by another bridge at a higher elevation because the pool backing up behind the new Wanapum Dam would soon overwhelm it. The span was saved from a watery

burial, however, when its steel trusses were carefully dismantled and stored by the highway department at a railroad siding in Beverly. In 1968 the original 1,640 feet of cantilever truss was resurrected and reerected on newly constructed piers over the Snake River at Lyons Ferry on State Highway 261. The Lyons Ferry Bridge is actually a rather late example of the once common practice of reusing a truss at a different location. The new 2,040-foot bridge put the last cable ferry on the Snake River permanently out of service after more than 108 years of river crossings. (See Waterways Chapter.)

Today the steel tied-arch truss of the second Vantage Ferry Bridge crosses the reservoir created by the dam. On the route of Interstate 90, it was built by the highway department in cooperation with the Grant County Public Utility District.

Columbia River Longview Bridge
ON THE DIRECT ROUTE FROM CANADA TO OLD MEXICO
Connecting Lower Columbia River Highway With Pacific Highway
Between Rainier, Oregon and Longview, Washington

LENGTH OF BRIDGE—1 6/10 miles.
HEIGHT ABOVE WATER—Roadway, 210 feet; top steel, 340 feet.
CENTER SPAN, 1200 FEET—Longest cantilever span in United States.
LOAD CAPACITY—Continuous line of two 20-ton trucks abreast.
Open for Traffic Day and Night—Toll Schedule Reverse Side.

Another Get-Together Movement —:— By Stuart Morris

Lewsiton-Clarkston Bridge, Snake River. Courtesy Ted Van Arsdol.

Verita Bridge, Columbia River. Courtesy, DOT.

Bridges at Kettle Falls. Courtesy, National Archives.

Bridge at Chief Joseph Dam, Columbia River. Courtesy, DOT.

Longview Bridge

The Longview Bridge, built in 1927-30, was a long-awaited connection on the Pacific Highway. The last of the four steel cantilevers constructed across the Columbia in the 1920s, it was also the most controversial. Originally, people in Oregon had welcomed the idea of a bridge across the Columbia downstream from Portland because they figured it would encourage Washington residents to patronize Oregon businesses. However, when the Oregon Highway Commission recommended that the steel structure be located at the newly founded town of Longview, the Portland Chamber of Commerce and other Oregonians became worried that the bridge might aid economic interests in Washington at the expense of the Portland area. Longview boosters did not allay their fears when they boasted that the new Washington city would overshadow Portland, just as Portland had bested Oregon City and Seattle had Tacoma and for the same reason — they were closer to the sea lanes. Having second thoughts, the Oregonians decided to drop the plan altogether.

After the failure of the joint state initiative, the Columbia River-Longview Company was formed by Seattle and Longview investors. However, their franchise required that both states approve the bridge plans. Washington approved the plans but Oregon would not, and the franchise expired before the design problems were resolved. The company obtained a second franchise in January 1927 that did not require approval by the two state highway departments. But under the new requirements, the design had to be approved not only by the Secretary of War, which was the usual procedure, but also by the Secretaries of Agriculture and Commerce.

When a bill authorizing the bridge construction was finally passed by Congress, the company's permit stipulated that there be a clear channel of 1,000 feet and a clearance of 195 feet at the channel center, forty feet more than in the original plans. The designers, Strauss Engineering Corporation of Chicago, met the requirement that there should be only one pier between the channel and the Longview pier-head line by building a main channel span of 1,200 feet and two unusually long anchor spans of 760 feet. At the time of its erection the Longview Bridge had the longest cantilever span in the country. The designers claimed that any vessel then in existence, including full-rigged clipper ships, could pass under the bridge. Workers erected the deck truss spans and the anchor arms on falsework, while the two cantilever arms of the main span were erected by a traveler operating on the top chords. The suspended span was cantilevered out from both arms and closed in the center by eight 500-ton hydraulic jacks.

When President Herbert Hoover pressed a golden telegraph key in the East Room of the White House on March 29, 1930, a guillotine dropped to cut a cord of yellow daffodils strung across the roadway, and the bridge was officially opened to traffic. As was customary for the opening of sections of interstate highway, the governors of both Washington and Oregon and the premier of British Columbia officiated at the well-attended ceremony. The Longview Bridge got off to a rocky start since the toll was higher than most depression-era people could afford, forcing several reorganizations of the company. And although it never made Longview the commercial trade rival that Oregonians had feared, it was instrumental in the burgeoning commercial development of the state's first "planned city." The Washington State Toll Bridge Authority purchased the structure in 1947, and in 1965, with the revenue bonds repaid, the tolls were removed. In 1980 the span was rededicated and renamed the Lewis and Clark Bridge.

CONCRETE ARCHES

O riginally built by the highway department along the Inland Empire Highway in 1923, the Indian Timothy Memorial Bridge today stands alongside State Route No. 12, which replaced the old highway. While this stretch of roadway in Asotin County, just west of the Alpowai Interpretive Center at Chief Timothy State Park, was abandoned, the bridge was preserved as "a lasting tribute to a true friend of the early settlers of Washington, Oregon and Idaho." The two-span was named in honor of Chief Timothy, a Nez Perce Indian who had remained a helpful friend of missionaries Marcus Whitman and Henry Spalding.

The reinforced concrete bridge consists of two 100-foot arches that have a twenty-foot rise. Like the Goldsborough Creek Bridge in Shelton, it has no horizontal struts connecting the two arches above the roadway. This allows the simple ribbed through arches to reflect the undulating contours of the surrounding hills.

In 1924 the Colonial Building Company built for the highway department two identical single-spanned through arches over

Hamma Hamma Bridge on U.S. Highway 101. Courtesy, DOT.

the Hamma Hamma River. Located at Eldon in Mason County on the Olympic Loop Highway (U.S. 101), the North Hamma Hamma and South Hamma Hamma River bridges are situated only a few hundred feet apart and illustrate how techniques commonly used in steel arch construction were adapted to the concrete. Because the spans are so close to saltwater, the highway department decided to use concrete instead of steel. The two 150-foot-long, three-hinged arches with a thirty-foot rise were the longest through hinged arches the state had yet built.

Highway 101 travelers can also find the first reinforced-concrete tied arch in the state over the Duckabush River near Duckabush in Jefferson County. As bridge expert, Robert W. Hadlow explains, the tied arch, developed in the early century and perfected in the 1930s, was an economical alternative to the

Top: Walla Walla Bridge at Wallula. Above: Bridge at Fall City. Photo by Juleen. Below: Baker River Bridge at Concrete during construction and completed. Courtesy, DOT.

traditional through or deck arch. Because the opposite ends of each rib are tied together by the road deck itself, the tied arch does not require rock ledges or other heavy abutments to hold the ribs in compression. Thus as a self-contained unit, it can rest on lightly constructed piers in sandy streambeds. Although there were steel arches built in the state during the 1920s and 1930s, the Duckabush River bridge was unusual for its concrete composition.

The Mononegehela, *one of the tall ships harbored in Lake Union, makes her escape before the 1931 closure of the Aurora Bridge in Seattle. Courtesy, Museum of History and Industry (MOHAI). Below: Twilight lights on the new Aurora Bridge, ca. 1932. Courtesy, Seattle Engineering Department.*

AURORA AVENUE (GEORGE WASHINGTON MEMORIAL) BRIDGE

Proof of the emerging dominance of the automobile in the transportation system of both state and city could be found in Seattle's first major bridge to be built without streetcar tracks. Completed at the onset of the depression in 1932, the Aurora Avenue Bridge was not sponsored by federal public works programs, which had yet to be initiated, but was jointly funded by the city, King County, and the state. Officially designated the George Washington Memorial Bridge, the span was an important connection on the Pacific Highway. More important for Seattleites, its high clearance over the Lake Washington Ship Canal eliminated the opening of bridge spans for boat traffic. This considerably eased the traffic congestion caused at the city's four bascule drawbridges over the canal. Unusual for its fifty-seven-foot-wide, four-lane deck, the bridge also linked Seattle's business center with the expanding residential districts to the north.

This 800-foot cantilever structure offers a good example of the progressive refinement of the cantilever form, in which functional and aesthetic elements were merged. It also marks a departure from the cantilever structures built in the state during the previous decade. The Aurora Bridge's deck type cantilever consists of two 325-foot cantilever arms and one 150-foot Warren truss suspended span. The main span is flanked by two anchor arms and two Warren deck truss spans. The two main piers, which support a load of 8,000 tons, actually rest on timber piles — over 800 piles in the south pier and nearly 700 piles in the north pier. A specially designed pile driver was used to drive the 110-foot piles to a depth of fifty feet below the water's surface (See Streets & Mass Transportation Chapter).

DEPRESSION ERA BRIDGE BUILDING

Steel Cantilevers

In the midst of the Great Depression, Washington undertook its largest-ever bridge-building program. The economic downturn brought with it the financial aid and work relief programs of the New Deal that made big expensive state projects like bridges possible. Moreover, the automobile industry continued to produce and sell cars throughout the decade. Somehow, many of those without steady work found the resources to buy gasoline and keep the car running. By the 1930s a family car, especially in the West, was no longer a luxury — it had become a necessity. During this great public works period some of the state's most notable — and notorious — bridges were erected.

Grand Coulee Bridge, ca. 1994. Photo by Jet Lowe.

Grand Coulee Bridge

The Grand Coulee Bridge cannot match the monumental impact of the dam whose name it shares. But it made a big contribution in helping the contractors complete the dam ahead of schedule so that the giant powerhouses could begin sending kilowatts to the region's war-related industries. Built in 1934-35 to handle extra-heavy loadings, the cantilever steel truss was needed to transport heavy equipment and materials across the Columbia River. In 1937, during the height of construction activity on the dam, the bridge gave more than 7,000 men employed on the project easy access to and from their living quarters in Mason City. (See Power Chapter.) It was also designed to be used after the dam's completion as a permanent highway structure on State Route 155.

The bridge consists of two 200-foot anchor arms with a Warren through truss suspended span of 550 feet. It is supported by monolithic 150-foot high concrete piers resting securely on bedrock. Shortly before the span was completed, however, it was discovered that its underpinnings were not yet so secure. Due to the shifting of fine glacial material underneath the 20 to 30-foot surface layer of gravel, the east pier tilted nine inches from its original position. Emergency measures prevented the collapse of the steel framing until the piers could be taken down to a firmer foundation.

Deception Pass and Canoe Pass Bridges

As early as 1908, the highway department had conducted surveys to determine the feasibility of building two steel arches over the Deception and Canoe Pass channels that separated Whidbey and Fidalgo islands. A model of the proposed bridge was displayed at the Alaska-Yukon-Pacific Exposition in 1909.

The Deception Pass Bridge under construction. Courtesy, DOT. Below: The completed Deception Pass Bridge. Photo by J. Boyd Ellis. Courtesy, John Cooper.

But when Highway Commissioner Henry Bowlby discovered that the bridges would cost about half a million dollars, the project was dropped. Not until August 1934 did the Puget Construction Company of Seattle, assisted by a camp of Civilian Conservation Corps (CCC) workers, begin work on excavation of the piers. The Emergency Relief Administration allocated $245,000 for the project, which was matched by county and other federal funds.

The smaller Canoe Pass Bridge spanning the passageway between Fidalgo and Pass islands was built first. It is a 511-foot steel bridge composed of a 350-foot arch and three concrete T-beam approach spans. The department next erected the Deception Pass Bridge between Pass and Whidbey islands. The 976-foot steel Warren deck truss consists of a 200-foot suspended span, two 175-foot cantilever and two 175-foot anchor spans, and four concrete T-beam approach spans.

Since both bridges rise to 180 feet over the channels, providing navigable passageway, it was not possible to construct falsework. As a result, both spans were erected by the cantilever method. The spandrel-braced arch across Canoe Pass was completed with the help of a cableway system strung from Pass to Fidalgo Island to transport cement, aggregate, and the structural steel. When the Canoe Pass Bridge was finished, a light railroad was built across it to haul materials for the erection of the Pass Island end of the Deception Pass Bridge. Materials and supplies for the Whidbey Island end of the bridge were shipped by barge and transported three miles overland to the building site.

The bridges opened to traffic in July 1935 and immediately began attracting sightseers from around the region. The structurally simple and aesthetically pleasing contours of the steel arches are accentuated by the steep rocky bluffs they connect. They remain today a breathtaking sight. Lacey V. Murrow, Director of Highways, supervised the design and construction of the bridges, and O. R. Elwell was chief bridge engineer.

Concrete Beams

Most of the highway bridges built with federal assistance during the depression decade were clearly not in the same class as the Aurora Avenue and Deception Pass bridges. In attempting to upgrade their highway and arterial systems while they provided jobs for the unemployed, the state and counties generally opted for the most economical spans. This usually involved the use of concrete in simple or continuous beams.

For instance, when the Pacific Highway between Olympia and Fort Lewis was relocated in the mid-1930s, a series of bridges was built across the Nisqually River and its delta. In one case, a bridge with an aggregate length of 4,497 feet with a 48-foot-wide roadway was needed. The highway department decided to construct "a series of three-span continuous reinforced concrete T-beam units, supported by four-column reinforced concrete bents." The uniformity of the concrete design standardized the construction process and kept costs down. For the final unit in the crossing, which was too long for a concrete beam, the department decided upon a 322-foot simple steel truss. At that time, it was the longest and heaviest simple truss on the state highway system.

Capitol Boulevard Crossing

The concrete girder has become a familiar feature in the landscape of the American highway. Yet not all of these kinds of structures, erected by the state and counties in the 1930s and 1940s, were carbon copies of each other. Some were notable for their pleasing design, which incorporated aspects of the Art Deco style. This is true of the still-standing Capitol Boulevard Bridge that spans the Deschutes River, once on the route of the Pacific Highway and now in the city of Tumwater.

What appears from a distance to be a simple and commonplace eighteen-span concrete girder reveals on closer inspection an array of chevrons, zigzags and rectangular forms. These designs are molded in low relief in a series of setbacks on the bridge railings and columns. The lamp posts and the four polychromed totem poles were also typical of Art Deco ornamentation. This concrete viaduct, constructed in 1936-37, exemplifies the way decoration was used during the period to transform an ordinary structure into a city entranceway.

Above: Auto caravan at the 1935 opening of the Deception Pass Bridge. Courtesy DOT.

Johnson Bridge

Another unusual concrete beam structure is still in use in Walla Walla County, a dozen miles west of Walla Walla in the vicinity of Lowden. The Johnson Bridge may have a common name, but the design of this three-span, concrete T-beam across the Touchet River strays off the beaten highway track. The engineers used simple geometric shapes to transform a straightforward, commonplace bridge type into a structure with a compelling visual impact. Both sides of the twenty-foot-wide roadway and railings are cantilevered from the deck. The lower portion of the two short beam approach spans has been shaped into an arch that is repeated in the curving lower edge of the three green geometric forms painted on the spans. The Johnson Bridge, erected in 1929, is the most striking of several spans in Walla Walla County designed by E. R. Smith during the twenties and thirties.

Above: Purdy Bridge over Henderson Bay. Below: Ebey Slough Bridge entering Marysville on U.S. Highway 99. Photos courtesy, DOT.

Purdy Bridge

The Purdy Bridge over Henderson Bay west of Tacoma is another unusual reinforced concrete beam bridge designed by Homer Hadley. Built in 1936, it was a rare American example of concrete hollow-box construction. Its 190-foot central span was at the time the longest single span among concrete girder forms.

In the Purdy Bridge, concrete was poured around a hollowed steel box girder of which the roadway slab forms the top flange. The central span was designed as a simple suspended beam, completely separated from the rest of the structure. At both ends the suspended span is seated on shelves that are continuous with the deck structure of two 140-foot girders and two 40-foot cantilever spans. Here the ends are locked in laterally with 15-inch solid concrete sections. The pier shafts also used a hollow or cellular construction.

Cost factors largely dictated the form of the bridge. Due to the navigational use of the upper portion of the bay, the War Department required an eighteen-foot clearance at high tide. Since piers had to be taken down to a depth of twenty feet because of the scouring potential of strong tidal currents, the highway department wanted to keep their number to an absolute minimum — two. The economy measures did not detract from the visual result, however. The hollow-box concrete girder with only two piers created what Lisa Soderberg, state historic preservation officer, called "a distilled concrete form that is powerful in its organic structural simplicity." Neither was the highway department disappointed with the total cost of the bridge, which at $62,000 broke down to a mere $5.64 per square foot of net roadway width.

Hadley suggested the major design features and layout of the Purdy Bridge, which was built under the supervision of Forest Easterday.

McMillin Bridge. Photo by Jet Lowe. Courtesy, DOT.

McMillin Bridge

When the McMillin Bridge, on Route 162 five miles south of Puyallup, was completed in 1934, its 170-foot main span was claimed to be the longest reinforced concrete truss or beam span in the country. This unusual concrete through truss replaced a steel structure that was washed out by flood waters in the winter of 1933. The highway department chose the concrete design over the usual steel truss design because it came in as the lowest bid.

The McMillin Bridge is unusual not only in its use of concrete for a truss design that conventionally uses steel or timber, but also for its hollow-box construction. At the time, this method of cellular construction was widely practiced in Europe, but it was not common in the United States. The system of pouring concrete around hollowed wooden pier shafts to reduce the amount of concrete in the truss allowed the wide concrete truss to be more economical than the conventional steel span. It also reduced the dead weight of the bridge with corresponding decreases in total stresses, reinforcement, and column and footing loads. The unusual length of the span made it necessary to keep the dead load to a minimum. Two twenty-foot concrete T-beam approach spans flank the 170-foot truss.

The bridge was built by Pierce County under the direction of county engineers W. E. Berry and Forest Easterday. Its major design features were suggested by Homer M. Hadley of the Portland Cement Association. Hadley was responsible for several unique concrete designs adopted by Washington bridge engineers during the 1930s and 1940s.

FLOATING CONCRETE BRIDGES

First Lake Washington
or Lacey V. Murrow Bridge

Probably the most unusual use of con crete in box-girder bridges are the state's three, formerly four, floating concrete pontoon bridges — three over Lake Washington and one across Hood Canal. Pontoon bridges have been built since antiquity. But in the late 1930s, when the first of Washington's was built, a reinforced concrete floating structure 8,583 feet long was the most ambitious pontoon span yet attempted in the world.

A bridge between Mercer Island and Seattle had become a common topic of discussion at island community club meetings by the late 1910s. In 1922 a group of island residents proposed recycling fifteen of the government's surplus World War I wooden vessels stored on Lake Union by stringing them together into a floating bridge. The South Mercer Island Improvement Club raised $1,500 to pay for the hulls, but the King County Commissioners refused to turn their check over to the government's shipping board. The commissioners insisted that the county would get stuck for hundreds of thousands of dollars to put the hulls in place and maintain the bridge.

Another idea was conceived by Homer M. Hadley. The young Seattle engineer had worked as a designer in a Philadelphia shipyard where concrete vessels were produced for the government during the steel-short World War I years. Confident that such a huge concrete structure could float, Hadley proposed a bridge consisting of a series of hollow, attached barge-like forms. But, as Hadley recalled later in 1964, when he went to Seattle financier James D. Hogue to ask about financing, Hogue "thought it pretty wild and looked on me as a screwball." In 1926 at least three companies filed for a franchise with the Seattle City Council for toll pontoon bridges at various locations across the lake. One councilman called such proposals "freak" projects. Secretary of the Navy Curtis D. Wilbur wrote Seattle Mayor Bertha Landes protesting that any bridge on the lake would interfere with the takeoffs by the Navy's heavily-laden seaplanes based at Sand Point on the lake.

But by 1928 Mercer Islanders were determined to get a bridge no matter where or of what it was built. They persuaded the Seattle City Council to consider plans for a toll bridge from Seward Park to the southern tip of the island, the narrowest crossing on the west side of the lake. But since the plan involved a 1,700-foot earth fill across the park, the Seattle Park Board vigorously objected, calling the proposal a "sacrifice of the people's playgrounds for private gain." Nevertheless, on February 1, 1930 the city council granted a franchise to the Seattle Toll Bridge Company for the Seward Park span.

Eastside resident and Seattle *Times* publisher Gen. C. B. Blethen, who had been devoting many column-inches to bridge stories in his zealous campaign against a Lake Washington span of any kind, exploded when he heard of the council's decision. Under a huge-type headline, he roared about the council's plans to destroy Lake Washington "by constructing a bridge that is wanted only by certain contractors and dealers in securities. To the sanity of the county commissioners," he appealed, "to save the Lake. In the name of common sense — PREVENT THIS WANTON

A decade of adversarial politics and alternate plans preceded the 1939 construction of the Lacey V. Murrow Bridge to Mercer Island. The Seattle Times *was especially active in opposing early proposals that the bridge touch the western shore of Lake Washington at Seward Park. This report dates from the Feb. 7, 1930 issue of Seattle's afternoon daily. Courtesy* The Seattle Times.

DESTRUCTION!" of "one of Seattle's greatest assets."

Meanwhile, Eastside bridge promoters, among whom the greatest was Mercer Island resident Gordon Lightfoot, continued to argue that a link across Lake Washington not only would be good for development east of the lake but would benefit Seattle and the communities east of the mountains even more by opening up a faster, safer, and more direct route to the Seattle waterfront and business district. "The growth of Seattle, the necessity for bringing the orchards and farms of Eastern Washington nearer to the state's metropolis, the development of the state's finest residential property and the need of quicker and safer travel, all demand it," the *Bellevue American* editorialized. The floating bridge would amplify what the Snoqualmie Pass Highway had done. It would connect the two sides of the state and give Seattle "a strategic position among Pacific Northwest cities."

Despite Blethen's long stories lamenting the "wanton destruction" of virgin timber in Seward Park, the King County commissioners followed the city council's actions and granted a franchise to the Seattle Toll Bridge Company. Over the next five years the plans for the proposed steel cantilever, soaring high above the water on concrete piers from the south side of Seward Park to the foot of Baker Street on Mercer Island, became ever more ornate. There was plenty of time to refine the design into the misty, mythological aura of the never-built, because before the plans could be transferred from paper to steel and concrete, the company had to secure financing. And finding investors in a busted bond market, the company learned, was like trying to convince General Blethen that the bridge would not forever scar the natural beauty of Lake Washington.

By 1935 everyone — Seattle and Eastside citizens and civic leaders alike — had grown impatient with the company. An ever-increasing number of motorists was getting weary of poking along the meandering two-lane roads they had to take to get around the twenty-mile-long lake. The county decided to take over and build the toll bridge itself. By spring 1937 county engineers had nearly completed their plans for a 3,400-foot steel truss cantilever from Seward Park to the southwest shore of Mercer Island. But still, the prospect of financing the $3.5 million project did not look good. A Public Works Administration (PWA) grant of $1.5 million had been approved but had not yet received the president's signature. In March, the state legislature was able to break through the administrative stalemate by creating the Washington Toll Bridge Authority (WTBA), a state agency specifically designed to meet PWA requirements. The toll bridge authority was given sole power to finance, locate, build, and operate all state toll bridges. It would help to settle disputes over the bridges' design and location and would facilitate funding since it could market revenue bonds more easily than the county. The King County commissioners willingly turned over the long-drawn-out project to WTBA and the state highway department. Meanwhile, Congressman Warren Magnuson kept after PWA administrators, telling the Seattle press that he was "moving heaven and earth" to get the grant released so that construction could begin.

The PWA grant had been awarded for the Seward Park steel cantilever. But Lacey V. Murrow, a member of the toll authority and director of the highway department, wasn't satisfied with the proposed site. On June 10, 1937 Murrow had lunch with Homer Hadley, who described the bridge plan and location he had so long envisioned. According to Hadley, "Murrow clicked," agreeing that a pontoon bridge from Seattle's Mount Baker area seemed to be the most direct, practical, and economical proposal. A bridge at Day Street would line up more directly with the route of the cross-state highway on the east shore of Lake Washington than the Seward Park site. It would shorten the distance between Seattle and North Bend by fourteen miles and cut out, on average, an hour's driving time. It would also, as Hadley had discovered years before, be on a straighter route into Seattle's downtown.

The route may have been right, but the price was wrong for any conventional bridge over the nearly one-and-a-half mile crossing. A suspension bridge would cost from $20 million to $50 million dollars and require tolls so high that most motorists would presumably be unwilling to pay them. A long-spanned concrete girder bridge was not feasible either because of the great depth of the lake. The 150 to 200 feet of water underlain by another 100 feet of soft clay made it too expensive to sink piers. However, pontoons would eliminate the need for piers, and concrete would bring down material and construction costs. The great weight of the reinforced concrete pontoons and their deep, seven-foot immersion ensured the bridge's stability in rough water. In fact, the conditions in Lake Washington were ideal for a pontoon structure — there was no tide and minimal currents, and the level of the water was closely regulated to a three-foot maximum annual variation.

In August Murrow announced the floating bridge plan. The highway director wanted to hire Hadley as a consultant on the project, but Hadley's association with the cement industry, as regional structural engineer for the Portland Cement Association, created a conflict of interest that prevented it.

Public reaction to the proposal resembled that to the earlier Lake Washington bridge plans. Most of Mercer Island's 2,500 residents favored a bridge of any kind. But residents on the island's northwest shore and self-professed lake preservationists objected to "a monstrosity of floating pontoons" that would forever "fence off" the lake, bring heavy traffic through their peaceful communities, and ruin their views and property values. They preferred a steel structure from Seward Park to a bridge floating on "ungainly pontoons" of concrete. Protests also came from the Navy, which again argued that the long span would hamper navigation and jeopardize the seaplane approach to the Sand Point air base. While the highway department conducted test borings and surveys at

The tug Wanderer *dragging Pontoon A-1 of Unit 4 for the Lake Washington Floating Bridge through Chittenden Locks, Oct. 13, 1939. In 1995, the many original pontoons which survived the sinking of the "Mercer Island" floating bridge were carried out through this same large lock in Ballard. Courtesy, DOT.*

both sites, Rep. Magnuson warned that unless an agreement was soon reached on the bridge's design and location, there was little chance of getting federal money to support it.

But Murrow was satisfied that the site and design of the pontoon bridge were the best possible choice. Hoping to get professional support for his opinion, he formed a board of four consulting engineers, chaired by Charles E. Andrews of San Francisco, a former Washington highway department bridge engineer and the designer and builder of the San Francisco-Oakland bridge. In early December the board concluded its four-month study and approved the floating span. Although it clearly had more engineering problems than the conventional steel truss bridge, the pontoon plan was forwarded to the WTBA for its approval.

Immediately a cry went up from a number of Seattle community clubs, who claimed the bridge would injure property values, spoil the lake for recreational purposes, and benefit trucks and other commercial users more than the general public. The Lake Washington Protective Association, an organization formed expressly to oppose the proposal, sent 25,000 letters of protest to Gov. Clarence Martin. They described the bridge as "a financial folly, an unnecessary tax burden, and a desecration of the lake." Seattle City Council president David Levine complained that the city was never even consulted about the effect the bridge would have on the city's traffic problems and residential property.

General Blethen, who ran in the *Times* large drawings of partially sunken pontoons washed up along a desolate shore, drew epithets such as "Seattle's No. 1 Obstructionist" from the Eastside community, which generally supported the pontoon bridge. Still convinced that such a span would destroy the lake's beauty, Blethen was also skeptical that a concrete floating structure could hold up in a bad storm. "Wouldn't the lake look pretty with these gargantuan concrete bathtubs floating from Kirkland to Renton and scattered along Seattle shores from Laurelhurst to Rainier Beach!" Seattle would become "the laughing stock of the nation." Blethen was not alone in his concerns about the stability of the bridge. In fact, it was an engineer, C. F. Sanborn of Seattle, who led the forces of the Lake Washington Protective Association. Sanborn predicted that "within five years the scows strung across the water will sink to the bottom of the lake."

Responding to these concerns, Gov. Martin promised that the toll bridge authority would hold public hearings and would not sponsor the project unless it was structurally and financially sound. But Martin himself favored the plan and recognized the urgency of submitting the pontoon design as soon as possible in order to obtain PWA funding.

To win the interest of the bond brokers, and thus the approval of the government, Murrow concentrated on working out the details of a financing plan. In June 1938, the highway department hired 130 unemployed men and trained them in "disarming politeness." The men were instructed to stop all cars on the highways around Lake Washington and question their drivers about their destinations and usual driving patterns. Some motorists were not happy with the survey and complained about the delay and the "high-handed use of police power smacking of Prussianism." But the results satisfied Murrow, the toll bridge authority, and investment houses that enough motorists would use the bridge, at 25 cents per car and driver, to repay the revenue bonds that would fund 55 percent of the $8 million price tag. In November the PWA approved a $3.7 million grant for the remaining 45 percent.

With the financing approved, the highway department rushed to get bids and award contracts for the project before the end-of-the-year deadline for the PWA grant expired. The department also had to win the consent of the restive Seattle City Council. The PWA had informed Seattle

Above: Mercer Island's first span opened the Eastside to the mainland in 1923. This 1,200-foot span was replaced in 1940 when Mercer Island's new floating bridge west to Seattle required a new concrete East Channel Bridge to Bellevue as well. The "fingerprints" of the treeline can be readily matched in the two East channel scenes (above and below). The bottom view was shot Oct. 10, 1940 from the Seattle side of the Lacey V. Murrow Brisge. Courtesy, DOT.

Mayor Arthur Langlie that the council had to endorse the project or the grant would be canceled. Murrow hastened to soothe and inform the council about the project. Then on December 20 he met with the mayor and Councilman William Norton, the most likely swing vote. When Norton switched sides, the council approved the project by a one-vote majority. Members of the Lake Washington Protective Association immediately sent angry telegrams to PWA Administrator and Secretary of the Interior Harold Ickes demanding that he cancel the grant.

But with only minutes remaining in their eleventh-hour drive, the bridge builders were not about to be waylaid by citizen protests. On Christmas Eve the toll bridge authority accepted an offer for $5.5 million worth of revenue bonds to be retired over a thirty-year period. On December 30, while state officials rushed to award the final contracts so that work could begin the next day, Gov. Martin broke ground. Following the ceremony at a banquet in a Bellevue clubhouse, Martin delivered a "time to bury the hatchet" speech and praised the work of the bridge's supporters. As far as Murrow, Martin, and the toll bridge authority were concerned, the drive for the pontoon bridge, begun only seventeen months earlier, was over.

For the next eighteen months the project, which included the floating bridge, twin 1,445-foot-long tunnels, the East Channel Bridge connecting Mercer Island to the eastern mainland, and a reinforced concrete span over the Mercer Slough, employed more than 3,000 men. When the bridge was formally opened to traffic on July 2, 1940, Gen. Blethen publicly "ate crow." In a front-page editorial he admitted that he now believed that the bridge was "an unqualified success." Its beauty was "utterly amazing," and it was going "to stay right where the engineers and builders put it." The dedication ceremony, which was broadcast on nationwide radio

Top: Pouring concrete to pave the Twenty-third Avenue South crossing, west of the Mount Baker tunnel. Courtesy, DOT. Above: Drawspan half open, Oct. 3, 1940.

Above: Celebrants look down on preparations for eastbound motorcade on opening day, July 2, 1940. Courtesy, DOT. Right: Gov. Clarence Martin in lead convertible begins return trip from toll booth on Mercer Island side. Courtesy, Seattle Post-Intelligencer.

and attended by about 2,000 people who filled the tunnel plaza area, was officiated by Gov. Martin, Director Murrow, and Mayor Langlie. Mrs. Kate Stevens Bates, daughter of Washington Territory's first governor, Isaac I. Stevens, cut a red ribbon and sent crashing against a pylon a huge yellow urn which held the waters of fifty-eight of the state's lakes, bays, and rivers. Officials had decided that since the 100,000-ton bridge would be the largest floating structure in the world, "relegating the Queen Elizabeth to second place," it should be "christened just like any other maritime work." Minutes later the governor crossed the bridge and paid the first fare at the Mercer Island-end toll plaza.

Up to that time pontoon structures had been simply boat-shaped sections, as Hadley had contemplated, bridged together with ordinary spans. But in the words of one engineer, the Lake Washington Floating Bridge was "a 4-lane concrete highway formed out of the top slab of a concrete monolithic box floating on the surface of the lake." Not only did the structure have the world's longest floating span at 6,620 feet and the world's first floating draw span, but it also represented the first use of reinforced concrete in a pontoon structure. The roadway was supported directly on twenty-five concrete pontoons bolted together end-to-end and attached to fixed approaches at either end. The standard pontoon was 350 feet long, 60 feet wide, and 14.5 feet deep. Their cellular construction made them resemble a honey-comb — each was divided into twelve watertight cells that were in turn divided into eight smaller cells, fourteen inches square. The cellular design enabled the bridge to withstand penetration: one or two compartments could be flooded without danger of sinking the pontoon. The concrete sections were built in specially constructed graving docks on Harbor Island and towed through the locks and Lake Washington Ship Canal to the bridge site.

One of the eight Lake Washington floating bridge pontoons that sank in the late November 1990 storm before the plunge. Photo by Denton Vander Poel, DOT.

In order to resist the horizontal forces of wind and waves upon the span, the massive concrete pontoons were anchored transversely and horizontally by steel cables to three types of anchorage systems built for the varying conditions of lake bottom. The most common were the forty-one soft-bottom mushroom anchors of concrete and steel, each weighing sixty-five tons. To allow for the rise and fall of the lake level, the cable ends were racked back and forth by means of portable hydraulic jacks to let out or take up slack. Cells in the pontoons next to the fixed approaches held bilge water. An automatic system pumped water into or out of them every time there was a six-inch change in the lake's water level.

The 200-foot central sliding draw span pontoon could be pulled back inside a well formed by two side-arm pontoons to permit the passage of larger vessels. The retractable draw pontoon was powered by two 75-horsepower motors and could be opened and closed in a record 90 seconds. But what was efficient for barges and other large vessels turned out to be dangerous for motor vehicles. The circuitous roadway around the well became a dangerous obstacle. Too frequently cars ran into and sometimes even leapt over the low wall surrounding the well. Because of this hazard, the "bulge" was removed and replaced by fixed pontoon sections in 1981.

On July 2, 1949, exactly nine years after the bridge's ceremonial opening, some of the same officiates and onlookers attended a second ceremony that celebrated the lifting of the tolls. The $5.5 million bond issue for the bridge had been repaid in less than half the time predicted, even with defense industry workers doubling up in carpools because of the wartime tire shortage. In 1967 the Lake Washington Floating Bridge was renamed in honor of Lacey V. Murrow, who guided the once-controversial project to completion — in record time.

The Lake Washington floating bridge was such a success that state bridge engineers, using it as a model, became world experts in concrete pontoon design and technology. But its success also lulled them into an incautious overconfidence. On November 25, 1990 in a winter storm that brought record rainfall to the area, the 50-year-old bridge ripped apart. Astonished bridge inspectors and onlookers watched as eight pontoons in the center of the span sank beneath the waves. The breaking up of the bridge also forced the closure of the year-old floating span alongside it (see below), when a dozen of the new bridge's anchor cables were severed by the pontoon debris. Highway department officials scrambled for solutions to preserve the newer structure. They decided to hire tugboats and tether them with cables to pull against the bridge's south side in order to keep it stable and open to traffic until temporary ship anchors could be sunk and new cables attached to the permanent anchors.

Immediately parties began debating the cause of the sinking of the old bridge and who was responsible. The span had been closed and undergoing renovation. To expedite the work of removing the concrete sidewalks, Traylor Brothers, Inc., the contractor, had used high-pressure water streams. Some of the water along with rainwater entered the pontoon cells through holes in the bridge deck. The problem of water accumulation was compounded when the state Department of Ecology forbade Traylor Bros. from dumping the demolition water into the lake, forcing them to store it in the pontoons before transporting it to a disposal site. State bridge inspectors several times ordered the contractor to pump out the pontoons. But some pontoons became so heavy with water and sank so low that lake water also entered them through construction access holes cut in their sides. The day before the bridge sank, state inspectors found seven feet of water in one pontoon.

State Transportation Secretary Duane Berentson blamed the sinking on the contractor. However, the state had not heeded the warnings nor taken the precautions during renovation recommended four years earlier by consultant Arvid Grant and Associates. In May 1991 a blue ribbon panel appointed by Gov. Booth Gardner concluded that although they could not pinpoint a single cause, both the state and the contractor had failed to take seriously the possibility that the bridge could sink. Consequently, they did not observe the signs of its vulnerability to the stresses caused by the renovation and excess water accumulation. Fortunately for state tax payers U.S. Transportation Secretary Samuel Skinner assured the state transportation department that up to $100 million in federal emergency highway funds would be available to replace the sunken bridge. But for area residents who remember the Art Deco lampposts and their soft lights strung "like pearls" across the darkness of the lake, only a copy of the "old bridge" could duplicate their effects.

Work on the design for the replacement bridge began within two weeks of the sinking. The new Lacey V. Murrow bridge takes advantage of fifty years of improvements in reinforced concrete construction, including a concrete strength of 6,500 pounds per square inch (more than twice that of the old bridge), and more reinforcing steel and post-tensioning of concrete.

Mount Baker Ridge Tunnel

While work began on the floating bridge immediately after the contractors signed their contracts on the last day of 1938, right-of-way proceedings delayed construction on the Mount Baker Ridge tunnels for two months. After more delays were caused by earth slides, the contractors had to work four shifts around the clock to complete the structures on time.

The Bates and Rogers Construction Company of Oakland, California drove the twin 1,466-foot-long tunnels through the Mount Baker Ridge. The route went through heavy blue clay, an uncommon material in the history of western tunnel driving. Because no rock was encountered, there was no need for drilling or for explosives. First, seven small tunnels called plump-post drifts were excavated using pneumatic shovels or "air-spades." Then the drifts were braced with heavy timbers. The main core section surrounded by the drifts was then driven through the

Above: Entrances to first Mt. Baker tunnels with relief sculpture "Portal of the Pacific" by James FitzGerald, Oct. 22, 1940. Below left: Cross-section of the first Mt. Baker tunnel. Courtesy, DOT.

hardpan at a rate of six to nine feet a day. After the core material was removed by electric rail cars, the temporary wooden braces were replaced by a permanent twenty-four-inch-thick concrete lining, heavily reinforced with steel.

By penetrating the 260-foot high Mount Baker Ridge, the tunnels provided a direct link between the pontoon bridge and the city business center. Spaced sixty feet apart on centers, each was designed to carry two lanes of one-way traffic. The tunnels also provided Seattle with a new and monumental eastern entrance. The tunnel facade is tiered in a series of setbacks that echo and emphasize the arch form of the tunnel opening. Three pictorial scenes of swirling geometric shapes and figures in the Art Deco style, created by sculptor James Fitzgerald, project from the smooth surface of the portal and portray Seattle as the nation's gateway to Alaska and the Orient.

Second Lake Washington or Evergreen Point Bridge

At four o'clock in the afternoon of August 29, 1963, Gov. Albert Rosellini snapped the ribbon at the center draw span and formally opened the Evergreen Point Floating Bridge. The ceremony climaxed a fifteen-year fight to get a second bridge across Lake Washington. Study after study had been performed to satisfy citizen groups on both sides of the lake who questioned whether the span was needed and where it should be located. Residents of Seattle's Montlake community had been especially active, but they were unsuccessful in their opposition to the final location — from Evergreen Point on the Eastside to Union Bay on the Seattle side — at the north end of their neighborhood. Gov. Rosellini, for whom the span would be renamed twenty-five years later, had been one of the bridge's greatest advocates. In 1988 he recalled that he had been "pushing so hard for the bridge that some of the opponents said that I must own a lot of land on the Eastside."

The second Lake Washington bridge had been designed to link the greater Seattle area's two main north-south traffic corridors — Interstate 405 east of the lake with the Seattle Freeway, part of future Interstate 5. In the decade before the bridge's completion, the Eastside suburbs had experienced an 88 percent population growth, more than any other section within the metropolitan area. City and county planners and transportation experts pre-

dicted that the trend would continue. Yet none of them anticipated the numbers of motorists who would rather pay the 35-cent car-and-driver toll and save an average of ten minutes of driving time than use the "old" and then-tollfree Mercer Island floating bridge. So many commuters took the new route, in fact, that the revenue bonds which financed the 5.8-mile, $35 million project were repaid twenty years ahead of schedule. In June 1979 Kemper Freeman Sr., a Bellevue businessman and leader in the effort to build the bridge, paid the last toll. By then more than four times as many cars and trucks were crossing the bridge as when it first opened. By 1988 when that number had jumped to seven times the original figure, the Albert D. Rosellini Evergreen Point Bridge had become one of the state's worst traffic bottlenecks. At 7,578 feet, the second Lake Washington floating bridge has the longest floating span in the world.

At each end it connects to elevated steel truss structures supported by fixed piers and designed to accommodate large pleasure craft. In the center the floating draw span provides a 200-foot clearance for large ships. Of the twenty-nine pontoons, the typical one is 360 feet long, sixty feet wide, and almost fifteen feet deep and floats seven feet above the water. Like the first Lake Washington floating bridge, the entire structure is anchored in position transversely and longitudinally by steel cables and concrete and steel anchors.

Third Lake Washington or Homer M. Hadley Bridge and Second Mount Baker Tunnel

At 8,567 feet from abutment to abutment, the third Lake Washington floating bridge is sixteen feet shorter than the original pontoon span that used to float alongside it. But with a roadway deck of 105 feet, it is more than twice as wide. The bridge was formally opened to traffic on June 4, 1989, following a ceremonial

Aerial of Seattle end of the Evergreen Point Floating Bridge where it passes beside the U.W. Arboretum and the Montlake neighborhood. The scene includes several of the "ramps to nowhere" constructed for connection to the cancelled R.H. Thompson Expressway. Courtesy, DOT.

procession led by four covered wagons and a stagecoach. To some the horse-powered transportation might have seemed an appropriate symbol of the long construction delay caused by the controversy over the I-90 project. (See Highways Chapter). But it was, of course, the state's centennial that was being celebrated along with the long-awaited bridge opening. Four years later the bridge in another July dedication ceremony was named after Homer M. Hadley.

The floating part of the span is 5,800 feet long and composed of ten standard pontoons, 354 feet long, sixteen feet deep, and seventy-five feet wide with cantilever slabs extending the roadway to 105 feet. Eight additional pontoons are of the same length and width but much deeper and without cantilever slabs. They support an elevated concrete superstructure on crossbeams and columns and raise the roadway to meet the level of the fixed approaches at either end. The pontoons are joined together by high-strength bolts or wire-cables and are held in place by fifty-two anchors each weighing ninety tons.

With an interior diameter of sixty-three feet, the second Mount Baker Tunnel is the world's largest diameter tunnel through soft earth. The design won the Howard, Needles, Tammen, & Bergendoff firm of Bellevue top prize for engineering excellence from the American Consulting Engineers Council in 1987. The bore was performed by the Guy F. Atkinson Construction Com-

Construction beside the wide deck of the Homer M. Hadley Floating Bridge proceeds while light traffic uses the original Lacey V. Murrow span. Courtesy, DOT.

pany of San Francisco from 1983-86, using the stacked drift method of excavation. To avoid the slides that delayed the original tunnels, the state transportation department ordered a concrete wall design that would protect workers as they drove the 1,332-foot tunnel. The tunnel shaft is surrounded by a ring of twenty-four smaller interlocking drifts. The drifts were dug first using a specially designed, laser beam-guided boring machine. After each of the drifts was bored, it was filled with concrete. When the drift lining was completed, the soil center of this concrete doughnut, the tunnel itself, was excavated.

The tunnel carries three levels of traffic — two levels for motorists and a top level for pedestrians and bicyclists.

Hood Canal Floating Bridge

On August 12, 1961 thousands sat in their cars backed up for miles waiting to get to the west end of the brand-new Hood Canal Bridge. Residents of Port Angeles, Port Townsend, Sequim, and Bainbridge Island had had a long wait, not only that day, for a bridge across the canal. By the time it opened the bridge already had a long and controversial history. When the legislature first appropriated funds for feasibility studies in the early 1950s, it was conceived as one of a series of five spans across Puget Sound. Since then it had been hampered by a number of delays caused by political maneuvering, problems securing bond financing, construction mishaps, and just plain bad luck.

Some engineers were still skeptical about its design and location. The floating pontoon structure was the first of its type to be built over saltwater subject to tides. At the selected site, the north end of the fifty-five-mile-long canal, the water level rose and fell as much as eighteen feet and was subject to heavy currents and sizable waves. A suspension bridge had not been out of the question. But because of the depth of the channel — ranging from seventy feet near the shore to a maximum of 340 feet — the installation of the supports would have been complicated and expensive. Having experienced the financial and engineering success of the first Lake Washington Floating Bridge, the state toll bridge authority decided instead to build another floating bridge. Conditions at the site, however, were far removed from the ideal lake situation. Some engineers wondered how permanent a floating structure would be in the canal, which acted as a natural funnel for both wind and tides.

The final design for the world's largest floating bridge consisted of twenty-three pontoons, each composed of ninety-six cells, 360 feet long by fifty feet wide, and weighing nearly 5,000 tons. Bolted together to form two continuous rigid piers, they met in the middle of the canal at the retractable pontoon draw span, which allowed a 600-foot clearance. The twenty-eight-foot-wide, two-

Above: Interior of the new Mt. Baker tunnel. Photo by Jet Lowe. Courtesy, DOT. Below: Brownie Elissa Rosenberg assists state Transportation Commissioner Aubrey Davis in opening the new Lacey V. Murrow Memorial Bridge. The Sept. 12, 1993 ceremony also marked the completion of Interstate 90, the transcontinental link from Seattle to Boston, and one of the last monumental freeway projects. Photo by Mark Mason. Courtesy, DOT.

lane roadway stood on concrete pillars descending from the shore to a minimum of fourteen feet above the deck of the pontoons. The 6,520-foot floating portion of the bridge was held in place with braided steel cable attached to forty-two concrete block anchors each about the size of a two-story house and weighing 530 tons.

Problems began during construction. In December 1958 two pontoons sank in the graving yard on the Duwamish Waterway in Seattle. Then the bolted joints between several pontoons in place at the site were damaged during winter storms, convincing consulting marine architects and the contractor, Morrison-Kaiser-Puget Sound-General, that the bridge design was faulty. A second engineering firm had to be called in to modify the plans and a new contractor was hired. After the bridge finally opened, fifteen months behind schedule, maintenance was a continuous worry. The joints tended to open when the bridge arched with the waves, the draw span machinery was easily damaged during storms, and hairline cracks appeared in the pontoon concrete.

In 1961 an engineer observing the construction was not particularly reassuring when he spoke about the strains that winds, tides, and waves would exert on the structure. If the bridge could stay together through the winter months, he told a Seattle newspaper reporter, "it should be safe." Eighteen years later the bridge failed the test of one winter storm. On February 13, 1979, what was later termed "a storm within a storm" — an 80-MPH storm with gusts as high as 120 MPH — battered the bridge for several hours. The southwest winds aligned precisely with the direction of the fifty-five-mile-long canal over which they sped without impedence — except the bridge. Just after 2 a.m., waves estimated to be from ten to fifteen feet high began crashing into the bridge. Five hours later the entire western section of the structure sank, leaving three-quarters of a mile of open water.

In the wake of the disaster Washingtonians offered a number of reasons why the bridge went down. Some claimed that it had been sabotaged by peninsula residents who believed it jeopardized their rural existence. Others speculated that the U.S. Navy had cut some of the anchor cables to accommodate the new Trident submarines. The last man on the bridge before it went under claimed that he saw at least three open maintenance-access hatches through which water poured to swamp the pontoons. After a three-month study, an independent consulting firm hired by the state determined that the sinking began with the movement of three anchors tied to the first pontoon just west of the draw span section. This caused weaving and bucking movements along the entire 3,500-foot western section. The high seas and steady winds caused the next pontoon sections to sink in sequence. The 470-foot retractable draw span floated free of its control tower wishbone section, moved 3,000 feet north, capsized, and sank. The consultants concluded that the bridge never had a chance in the storm. It was overwhelmed by forces far greater than its designers had foreseen.

A shocked and embarrassed state transportation commission immediately began assessing alternative means of cross-channel transportation for the 200,000 residents in the area. A high-level fixed bridge — of the suspension, cable-stayed girder, truss, and tied-arch type — a submerged tube or a tunnel under the canal, and permanent ferry service were all considered. The bridges and underwater tunnels were abandoned as too costly and the no-bridge alternative was rejected for the economic hardship it would create for peninsula residents. Since half the bridge was left intact, design consultants and the state agreed that the most economical solution would be to rebuild the sunken west half and replace the east section later.

Soon after the disaster Sen. Warren Magnuson, chairman of the Senate Appropriations Committee, pledged to promptly begin lobbying for federal funds. However, after having wrangled emergency funds to repair the recently rammed West Seattle Bridge, and recalling a similar request he made years ago for the Tacoma

Top: A portion of the Hood Canal Floating Bridge begins its long trip from the Duwamish Waterway to the bridge site. Below: A portion of the floating bridge's center section is maneuvered into place. Courtesy, DOT.

Narrows Bridge, he sighed, "They must think we don't know how to build bridges out here at all. Every time I come around, it's for some bridge money."

The new $200 million west section was eventually funded, however, and designed to withstand three to four times the stress of the old one. In the twenty years since the original design had been drawn, the science of marine engineering had made considerable advances, learned mostly from the building of offshore oil drilling platforms. The new pontoons are bigger, heavier, and pretensioned in three directions instead of one. Post-tensioned

Below: The west end of the Hood Canal Floating Bridge, Tuesday morning, Feb. 13, 1979. After winds gusting more than 100 mph pulled the bridge's west movable span and tower loose, the thirteen west end pontoons supporting the two-lane highway sank. Courtesy, DOT.

Top: A suspension bridge near Ruby Creek before the site was inundated by the Skagit River power project of Seattle City Light. Above: Pioneers' makeshift suspension bridge over the Skykomish River north of Index. Photos courtesy, U.W. Library, Special Collections.

Above: Yale Bridge over the Lewis River. Photo by Jet Lowe. Right: Tacoma Narrows Bridge deck supports showing stresses after the bridge's failure. Courtesy, DOT.

cables grouted into place make the joints between the pontoons as strong as the rest of the pontoon and reduce the risk of a chain reaction sinking. The new anchors, forty-six feet in diameter and twenty-nine feet high and filled with slag from the ASARCO copper smelter in Tacoma, weigh more than three times as much as the old ones.

By 1987 the state had invested $131 million in rebuilding and repairing the Hood Canal Bridge, which reopened to traffic in October 1982. Yet according to a 1987 engineering study, the bridge was still vulnerable to a major storm. Although the state transportation department has taken several measures to strengthen the old eastern part of the span, plans to completely rebuild it have been put aside until federal funds become available.

SUSPENSION BRIDGES

It was not until motor vehicles became the dominant form of transportation that most American engineers accepted the suspension bridge as a workable and safe alternative to trusses, cantilevers, and arches. Suspension designs had not been suitable for the weight requirements of railroad bridges, and railroad technology continued to affect bridge engineering principles until highways proliferated in the 1920s and 1930s.

At Devil's Corner in the North Cascades near Newhalem, you can still find a number of timber suspension bridges slung across the steep-walled Skagit River Canyon by miners in the 1890s. And a few steel suspension bridges remain from the early twentieth century, but since they were more expensive to construct than simpler designs, they were not often built. Once the suspension bridge caught on, however, it captured the imagination of the times. The composition formed by the high supporting towers and slender horizontal deck, united by the graceful sweeping curve of the suspension cable, possessed a dramatic beauty that no other bridge design could approach. Suspension bridges became the choice for spans of 1,500 feet or more.

Yale Bridge

In 1932 Clark and Cowlitz counties jointly erected the Yale bridge to replace a steel truss across the Lewis River on State Route 502 that was demolished as a result of the building of Ariel Dam. The backwater from the dam created a depth of ninety feet at the bridge site. Falsework, the temporary support structure required for constructing the typical highway bridge, would have been unusually difficult to put in place, so it was necessary to turn to less conventional solutions for bridging the river.

The structure, originally 532 feet long, consists of a 300-foot steel truss span supported by three-inch galvanized steel cables suspended from two 332-foot steel towers. The 17-foot-wide roadway is carried 50 feet above high water. To simplify erection, the highway department incorporated a number of innovative details. Four rope cables were prestressed to 75 tons, and the discontinuous main and back stay cables were attached to castings at the tops of the towers with links and pins to approximate the function of a swivel joint. This simplified erection and avoided wear on the main cables, allowing the use of smaller, less expensive cables.

The Clark County bridge, which is the only short-span steel suspension bridge in the state, was designed by Harold H. Gilbert and built by the Gilpin Construction Company of Portland.

Tacoma Narrows Bridge

If there ever was a bridge that can be said to have gone down in history, it is the Tacoma Narrows suspension bridge. Nicknamed "Galloping Gertie" for a rolling deck that could induce seasickness, the bridge achieved worldwide notoriety November 7, 1940, when it plunged 190 feet into the swift, cold waters below. The sensational motion picture of that collapse is one of the two

great disaster clips Washington State has given the world through newsreels and low-budget sci-fi motion pictures. The other, of course, is the eruption of Mount St. Helens.

The bridge was designed to span the shortest possible route between the mainland area and the Kitsap Peninsula. In its planning and promotional stages, its advocates called it a "public necessity." Not only would it eradicate "the formidable barrier of the Narrows which separated Tacoma from the large undeveloped area to the west," but it would also provide vital direct transportation between the Puget Sound Navy Yard at Bremerton and the military reservations at Fort Lewis and McChord Field. However, the location was an inordinately difficult one. Since the last receding of the glacial ice, the tidal rush through this narrow channel — only one mile wide — had washed away loose bottom soil to a depth of 120 feet. To reach a firm foundation it was necessary to sink false bottom caissons twice the depth of any previous pier construction.

When the Tacoma span was formally opened on July 1, 1940, it was the third longest suspension bridge in the country — 5,939 feet, including approaches and anchorages. It was exceeded only by the George Washington Bridge in New York and the Golden Gate Bridge in San Francisco. The two supporting towers were 425 feet high and, although fully anchored at the base, were designed to allow movement at the top up to five feet in either direction of the longitudinal axis of the bridge. Because of the extreme lightness of the structure, design engineers tried to create more stability by adding weight with a concrete slab deck and concrete curbs and sidewalks.

The Narrows Bridge represented a culmination of the trend to increase the span length, reduce the width of the deck, and minimize the depth of the stiffening components, all of which simplified and distilled the bridge form. Following this mainline of development, the Tacoma suspension bridge was the epitome of a move towards a suspension bridge of slender proportions that placed a premium on flexible design. With its graceful draping cables and spare design attached to high bluffs to the east and west, it was an extraordinarily beautiful sight.

It had been designed by engineers of proven experience, including Leon S. Moisseiff of New York City, who had participated in the design of the New York and California bridges and who was then considered the authority on suspension bridges. The project's head engineer was Highway Department Director Lacey V. Murrow.

The original plans for the bridge were not as innovative as the final design. Submitted in May 1938 to the Public Works Administration for funding, the first design called for a traditional twenty-five-foot deep, open stiffening truss for the bridge's sidewalls. When the PWA awarded the grant it also required a review of the design. The resulting revisions adopted for greater economy used solid, shallow sideplate girders as stiffening members in the place of the usual deep open trusses. This worried some of the highway department's bridge engineers.

With hindsight, their anxieties seem warranted. A short history of recommended ratios between truss depth and bridge length is revealing. Only a generation earlier experts prescribed for the stiffening trusses of suspension spans a minimum depth of one-fortieth of the span's length. This ratio was later reduced to one-fiftieth, and then further to one-ninetieth for spans between 2,000 and 3,000 feet long. The stiffening girders of the Tacoma bridge were only eight feet deep for a center span of 2,800 feet — a ratio of 1 to 350!

Top: Construction scene on Tacoma Narrows Bridge. Roadway forms in place on east side span, May 7, 1940. Photo by Simmer. Above: Moment of structural failure, late morning of Nov. 7, 1940. Left: After the fall. Photos courtesy, DOT.

A ghost of forces unknown began haunting the bridge even during its construction. Vertical waves moving from tower to tower through the deck reinforced each other on reflection and then developed into a harmonic twisting motion. The movement of the deck was at times so violent that men working on it became seasick. After the bridge opened to traffic, motorists were no less uncomfortable with Galloping Gertie's rolling and rippling roadway. To some the bridge was an amusement. When the wind was

Late construction scene on the second Tacoma Narrows Bridge. Note the Tacoma City Light twin towers (upper right) for the Cushman transmission line (See Power Chapter). Photo by Harry R. Boersig. Courtesy, DOT.

up, college students headed for the Narrows to ride the "roller coaster." While University of Washington and highway department engineers worked with scale models of the bridge to find a way to reduce the movement, the *Seattle Post-Intelligencer* described the bridge's peculiar activity:

> *At times of extreme agitation automobiles passing over the bridge when viewed from other cars appear to be rolling over a moving washboard, now rising, now falling out of sight behind folds of concrete pavement. The bridge, engineers say, is perfectly safe at such times, but they desire to overcome the psychological hazard which the movement sets up.*

The engineers were perplexed especially when they could find no correlation between the prolonged intervals of vertical wave motion and the velocity of the wind. However, cables attached beneath the deck of the bridge (first tried successfully on the model and then installed on the real thing) and anchored at either end, reduced "the vertical motion in the bridge's center by 50 percent, all other conditions being equal." The problem was that all other conditions were not equal.

On the morning of November 7, the deck started moving in a steady vertical oscillation which it kept up for about three hours. Designed, it was thought, to withstand winds never before re-

corded on Puget Sound — gusts up to 122 MPH — the Narrows Bridge started galloping when gusts of only 35 MPH hit it from the side. At 10 a.m. the highway department became concerned and closed the bridge to traffic. And none too soon for Tacoma newspaperman Leonard Coatsworth, who was almost too intrepid in his reporting. Abandoning his car — and dog — on the bridge, Coatsworth had to crawl to safety over a rippling roadway amidst yawning cracks in the bridge deck.

With a gale building to a steady 40-plus MPH, the vertical oscillation of the bridge suddenly turned into a rhythmic twisting motion which reached an amplitude of twenty-eight feet an hour later. As one eyewitness described it, the "span was swaying wildly, it being possible first to see the entire bottom side as it swung into a semi-vertical position and then the entire roadway." The cables were moving in opposite directions, tilting the deck from side to side. The center of the span appeared to remain horizontal while both ends twisted about it in opposite directions like a corkscrew. At 11 a.m., a 600-foot length of the center span tore loose from the suspenders and fell into the water.

Local people as well as bridge engineers throughout the country were stunned. It was particularly hard on Tacoma area residents for whom the bridge had been a source of civic pride. Several years later one Tacoma loyalist recalled his incredulous reaction to the catastrophe that put the "City of Destiny" on the

LAKE WASHINGTON SHIP CANAL BRIDGE

Although it was not unique in its steel truss design or method of erection, the Lake Washington Ship Canal Bridge when it went up in the early 1960s was certainly the largest of its kind ever built in the Northwest. The six-spanned double deck steel truss portion alone is 2,294 feet long and carries eight lanes of traffic on the upper deck with four reversible lanes below. It was designed to bridge the long gap between North Capitol Hill and the University District and allow uninhibited traffic flow over the busy Lake Washington ship canal. The first contract made for the Seattle Freeway (part of future Interstate 5), awarded in August 1958, was for construction of the bridge's piers. The approaches are concrete box girder and flat slab. The three simple Warren truss spans, and the flanking spans of the three-span continuous unit sitting directly over the canal, were erected on falsework. The longer central span of the continuous unit was built as a cantilever. Twelve painters, with nerves that matched the truss material, applied 10,000 gallons of undercoat and green linseed oil topcoat with brushes so that nearby houses and cars would not be inadvertently decorated.

Late construction scene of the Lake Washington Ship Canal Bridge, 1962. Courtesy, Seattle Post-Intelligencer.

The giant 4,429-foot-long bridge was completed by the fall of 1961 — more than a year before the one-and-a-half mile stretch of freeway that it partly carried was first opened to traffic in December 1962. Delays caused by labor strikes, the time-consuming process of relocating utility lines, the controversy over a downtown lid, and the location of the second Lake Washington bridge had put the Seattle freeway far behind schedule. Consequently, the bridge stood silently towering above the channel and the neighborhoods, all finished and freshly painted but with nothing to do. It could not even double as a fallout shelter, a proposal commonly made to justify expensive design features such as freeway lids.

But it wasn't long before someone suggested a way to put the bridge to work. It could be a parking lot. After the Seattle World's Fair opened on April 21, 1962, the World's Fair Commission and the highway department rushed to put together plans to meet the expected flood of end-of-the-school-year tourists in June. Although the bridge was more than two miles from the fairgrounds, optimistic planners figured it could hold 2,500 cars. A shuttle operating between the "lot" and the grounds would draw curious fairgoers to the unusual "high level" parking. However, an unexpected expansion in private parking facilities around the fairgrounds scuttled the plan, and the bridge's parking-lot signs came down.

Today frustrated motorists crawling across the span could surely advise future fair planners that you don't need a world's fair to turn a bridge into a parking lot.

---

international map of disasters. "When anyone showed pictures," Arthur N. Gunderson told a reporter on the silver anniversary of the collapse in 1965, "I wouldn't look. I just said: They can't do this to us!"

After several comprehensive investigations, experts concluded that the bridge's failure occurred when "forces heretofore not considered became dominant." The unconsidered force was the aerodynamic instability that had earlier perplexed the University of Washington experimenters. The bridge's combination of solid plate girders and a solid floor prevented even low-velocity winds from passing through it, as would normally be the case in a truss design. Together with the lightness and high flexibility of the bridge, this made the span susceptible to vortex shedding. This aerodynamic phenomenon occurred when the wind, even one of low velocity, was interrupted by the solid plate girders and the displaced air formed eddies like the swirls of water created by a drawn oar. These vortices of air produced the vertical undulations of the deck which tended to change into twisting motions.

The plunge of the Tacoma Narrows Bridge alerted bridge engineers around the world to the aerodynamic dangers of its design. In New York noted bridge engineer Ottmar H. Amman returned to his recently completed Bronx-Whitestone Bridge and replaced its Tacoma-type stiffening girders with open trusses.

To meet PWA funding schedules, the first Tacoma Narrows Bridge had been put up in a remarkable rush: from study to service in 26 months. Prudently, the second Narrows Bridge did not open until 1950. The lessons of bridge number one (combined with the preoccupations of World War II) were given a decade to sink in. Number two was thicker and wider. It also used deeper, truss-type girders that allowed the winds to pass through.

Nearly twenty-five years later the state highway department could look back on the time Galloping Gertie "galloped itself to pieces" with equanimity and even pride. In the December 1964 edition of the highway department's *Highway News*, the lessons of the first Tacoma Narrows suspension bridge were reviewed and illustrated with photographs, many of which were taken from the familiar footage University of Washington professor F. B. Farquharson filmed on the day of the bridge's destruction. Much credit was due to the "spectacular but heart-breaking collapse," the department figured, for it had "sparked the most comprehensive probe ever conducted into the numerous forces acting upon suspension bridges." Given the impressive technological results of that research, the department might be excused for giving an ironic twist to its greatest moment of disaster, Beneath a photo of the fallen bridge the department inscribed the caption, "Dawn of New Knowledge."

Above: Satsop River Bridges on the Olympic Loop highway. Courtesy, DOT. Above right: Swinomish Slough Bridge at La Conner. Photo by Hugh Paradise.

AWARD-WINNING BRIDGES

A number of steel and concrete Washington bridges built in the past forty years have been recognized as outstanding in their design and use of materials. Two graceful one-span steel tied arches over the Satsop River on U.S. 101 (Olympic Loop Highway) five miles east Montesano won international attention soon after they were built in 1965. The weight of the structures is borne by extra-strong girders and eliminates the need for the more familiar steel truss superstructure. The Satsop River bridges were designed by the state highway department bridge division and built by the Troy T. Burnham Company.

Cicero Bridge at the North Fork of the Stillaguamish River. Photo by Hugh N. Stratford. Courtesy, DOT.

A 279-foot-long steel tied arch on the North Fork of the Stillaguamish River, called the "Cicero Bridge," won the most beautiful short span steel bridge award for 1967 from the American Institute of Steel Construction. The bridge, designed by the state and built by the Dale M. Madden Construction Company, is on S.R. 530 seven miles east of Arlington.

The Parker Bridge in Union Gap, south of Yakima, is an unusual steel girder bridge. Designed by Homer M. Hadley of Seattle and built by Yakima County, it won the top award in its division from the American Institute of Steel Construction in 1963. Taking advantage of the higher-strength steels of the day, Hadley used a Y-shaped, delta-girder configuration. Beautiful as well as strong, the flowing design also cost considerably less to build than a truss of the same length.

Another award-winning Seattle engineer who, like Hadley, believed that beauty, strength, and economy did not have to be mutually exclusive was Harry R. Powell. The graceful arch across the Swinomish Slough at La Conner was designed by Powell and won first prize in its class in 1958. It was also recognized as having the lowest dollar cost of any winning bridge in that class since the competition began thirty years earlier. The 550-foot, orange-painted arch, which allows a seventy-foot clearance, has been one of the state's most photographed bridges. At least Powell continued to receive snapshots from admiring amateur photographers for several years after it was completed. Although Powell considered himself to be more of a specialist in timber and concrete construction, the five steel bridges he had designed by 1963 all won prizes. According to a contemporary trade journal such a record was extraordinary for "most engineers would be happy to win one such contest in a lifetime of bridge designing."

Two concrete arch designs built in the late 1960s not only won awards but set new records. The Cowlitz River Bridge east of Mossyrock on U.S. 12 (White Pass Highway) won two awards for excellence in the use of prestressed concrete. At the time it was finished in 1968, the 520-foot arch was the longest concrete arch on the continent. Paul Jarvis Inc. of Seattle was the prime contractor and the designers were Howard, Needles, Tammen and Bergendoff, also of Seattle. Because it was built to replace an existing highway which was inundated when Tacoma City Light built the Mossyrock Dam on the river, the project was largely financed by the utility.

Yakima County's Parker Road Bridge, No. 809, showing designer Homer M. Hadley's Y-shaped delta-girder construction. Courtesy, Yakima county Public Works Department.

The record set by the Cowlitz River span was broken within a year by another Washington concrete arch. On S.R. 82 a few miles north of Yakima, the twin arches crossing the Selah Creek Gorge were 550 feet long. At 325 feet above the canyon floor, the Selah Creek bridges also set a new record as the highest bridges in the state. The structures, erected by Peter Kiewit & Sons, were honored as the Grand Award winner for excellence in the use of concrete by the Washington Aggregates and Concrete Association in 1971.

Above right: Cowlitz River span.
Above left and below: Selah Creek Bridge.

From top left, descending, are three bridges that use concrete girders designed by Washington State innovative bridge builder Arvid Grant: Okanogan River Bridge at Riverside, 1971; Okanogan River Bridge at Monse, 1965; Toutle River Bridge below Mount St. Helens, 1981. All courtesy, Arvid Grant. Four bridge details photographed by Jet Lowe. Three, from upper right: Top of the Tacoma Narrows Bridge; trusses of the Grand Coulee; the approach to Ft. Spokane Bridge on the Spokane River. Below: Another detail of the Ft. Spokane Bridge. Bottom right: Columbia River Bridge between Maryhill and Biggs from Washington side. All courtesy, Department of Transportation.

Clockwise from top left: Stone Bridge in Rainier National Park. Photo by Hugh Paradise; Lacey V. Murrow (wearing light-colored overcoat and standing on step of steam shovel) poses with the shovel crew and others, including R.H. Thomson (front row-center with cane), at the start of Mount Baker Tunnel excavation, April 24, 1939; members of the tunnel crew pose beside the entrance to the second Mount Baker Tunnel; sprayers' cocoon above the north shore of Lake Union's Portage Bay during the 1998 repainting of the Lake Washington Ship Canal Bridge; toll gate guards at the Lacey V. Murrows Bridge's Mercer Island end. Courtesy, DOT; parents and students protest unsafe condition of old bridge on Cedar Falls Road near North Bend, Oct. 16, 1963. Courtesy, MOHAI, Seattle P-I Collection.

STREETS AND MASS TRANSPORTATION

The Great Northern Railroad's transcontinental "Empire Builder" first hairpinned through Index in 1893, the year this combination railroad, milling and mining town on the North Fork of the Skykomish River was also both platted and burned down. The late-century view, above, of a rebuilt Index looking west on Avenue A towards Mount Persis was photographed by Anders Wilse, former surveyor of Stevens Pass for the Great Northern. According to David Cameron, the town's resident historian, Index is the only extant incorporated town in Snohomish County which has lost population in the last century—although its streets are now paved with an aggregate smoother than the rough-hewn timbers showing in the older view. Historical photo courtesy, Museum of History and Industry (MOHAI), Seattle. Contemporary repeat by Louise Lindgren, curator of the Pickett Historical Museum in Index.

Pomeroy, the ultimate victor over Pataha City in the protracted fight between them for the seat of Garfield County government, retains much of the winner's distinction in the businesses along its well-preserved Main Street. In the older view, below left, the business district is getting the modern appointment of a freshly paved street and sidewalks. The contemporary "repeat," below right, was photographed in 1994. Courtesy, Margaret Wolf and the Garfield County Historical Association.

Above: Illustration of Pataha City, ca. 1888, from West Shore
Magazine. *Courtesy U.W. Libraries, Special Collections.*
*Right: 1890s Pataha City. Courtesy, Margaret Wolf and the
Garfield County Historical Association.*

PATAHA CITY

Getting represented in *Western Shore Magazine*, the
popular periodical of travel and industry in the
American West, was an accomplishment many small
communities hoped for but few could realize. But
already in 1888, when this charming birdseye of Pataha
was shared with the magazine's far-flung readership,
Pataha was a shadow of its founder's hopes, the loser of
a drawn-out battle with Pomeroy to take and keep the
seat for Garfield County. When the county was formed in 1881
and named for the president assassinated that year, Pataha was
designated its temporary seat. Like a medieval fief, Garfield
County was divided from Columbia County when the residents of
Dayton decided that the twin towns on Pataha Creek, Pomeroy,
and Pataha City, could be prevented from grabbing Dayton's seat
away by getting their own county to fight over. And fight they did,
with a struggle so byzantine that the winner was finally decreed not
in Olympia but in Washington, D.C., by a special act of Congress.
In 1886, two years after its victory, Pomeroy was reached by the
Starbuck branch of the Union Pacific Railroad, and there the rails
stopped, further stranding poor Pataha.

Throughout Washington there are communities like Pataha,
Ruby, Newcastle — a host of ghost towns, abandoned mill towns,
towns reduced to remnants — whose streets now make impressions fainter than cave drawings. Many other of Washington's
pioneer streets were graded only by the imagination. Drawn on
plat maps by either developers or opportunists (or both), they
represented dream topographies that exhibited little sympathy for
the actual lay of the land. Like the streets, a plat map's other urbane
appointments, its parks, school lots, and municipal squares, were

wish fulfillments for a community with seemingly unrestricted
opportunities and also, at the beginning, without taxes.

CASCADE CITY

In late 1893 the Adams County clerk in Ritzville began receiving
inquiries from a few conscientious Midwesterners about taxes
owed on lots they had recently purchased off plat maps for Cascade
City. The artist's birdseye, which was attached to the plat map in
its Midwest marketing, revealed a busy metropolis where three
railroad lines converged at the Columbia River. The rendered
community was also liberally appointed with schools, churches,
and public parks, a main street named Park Avenue, and cross
streets whose numbers began not at one but at ten, thus leaving
room for the town to grow either forwards or backwards. It was
backwards progress that Midwesterners discovered when they
arrived to view the actual townsite. Actually contiguous to only
one railroad, the Northern Pacific, it also lay sixty miles short of its
meeting with the "Great River of the West." Not long after,
Cascade City was remembered in the *History of The Big Bend
County*: "It is probable that in the early days bands of cattle and

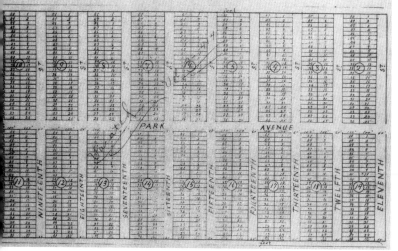

Portion of Cascade City plat. Courtesy Adams County Clerk.

horses may have grazed there. Possibly a cowboy may have driven over it. And that was as close as it ever came to being anything resembling a town."

Some of the Nebraskans who purchased land in Cascade City paid more than $100 for a lot, even with the premium of a $2.50 bottle of patent medicine. But this kind of profiteering was the extreme case. Washington Territory was more often set upon by would-be city-builders for whom drawing a plat map was an inspired act of faith and hope. And the territory did have plenty of natural city sites, especially alongside its generous waterways.

REPUBLIC

In many pioneer towns the efforts required to mark and lay streets were extraordinary. In Republic what was most important lay below the street. After gold was discovered there in 1896, the daily stages from Marcus arrived, as a contemporary described it, "with loads of mining men seeking investments, business men seeking locations, workmen seeking employment and 'rounders' seeking graft." By 1900, the year of its incorporation, Republic was sixth in population among eastern Washington cities. The rush to dig into the chalky white quartz that laced the hills beside the Sanpoil River created a booming community whose most important map was not that of blocks, lots, and street, but rather a crazy-quilt of miners claims. Clark Avenue, Republic's main street, was marked, cleared, and dragged in such haste that an ancient Ponderosa pine was left standing near its centerline, requiring traffic to swerve in order to avoid it.

Of course, swerving was guaranteed anyway. After the mines, Republic's principal feature was its twenty-eight saloons and two dance halls. The boomtown quickly got a telegraph line, two telephone networks, a water system, and in 1902 even a railroad

connection with Grand Forks, British Columbia. Republic's criterion for choosing public works was necessity, not civic pride. Consequently, the earliest street improvement was not in its cramped commercial district but a more-than-mile-long boardwalk to Eureka Gulch that allowed miners a relatively clean and dry commute. Clark Avenue remained little improved until its paving in the early 1960s, although two blocks of concrete sidewalks were laid along it in the mid-1920s.

Above: Walla Walla's Main Street looking west from the bridge at First Avenue. The street is decorated and spanned by a tempoary ceremonial arch for the 1880 visit of President Rutherford B. Hayes. Courtesy Penrose Library, Whitman College. Below left: Republic's Clark Avenue, ca. 1902. Below right: Republic and a portion of the boardwalk to the gold mines of Eureka Gulch. Courtesy, Ferry County Museum.

COMMUNITY AND CONTINUITY ON WALLA WALLA'S MAIN STREET

Walla Walla's Main Street is older than Walla Walla. The Nez Perce Trail which it follows preceded Euro-American settlement by centuries. The trail and then the street were located for their easy portage of Mill Creek, which still runs through the center of town. In 1856 the army built Fort Walla Walla on the north side of the creek. Soon after the town of Steptoeville was founded on the creek's south bank and its name was changed to Walla Walla in 1859. When the fort was moved a year earlier, it allowed Main Street to follow the Indian trail north of the portage, which by then was bridged, and into the old military compound.

In 1859 all the businesses of Walla Walla, including two general stores, two saloons, a tin shop, a meat market, and a boarding house were owned by squatters. The land was not legally opened to homesteading until 1861. Then the town was quickly platted along Main, or Nez Perce Street as it was sometimes called, and the buildings which sat in the platted cross streets were either moved or razed. A year later when the Idaho gold rush began, bringing thousands of miners through town, Walla Walla became

Wheat farmer and Walla Walla mayor, Dr. N.G. Blalock hooks twenty-four wagons filled with 800 kids to his steam tractor for a ride to the 1890 Walla Walla Fair. This view looks west on Main Street from First Avenue. Courtesy Penrose Library, Whitman College.

the principal supply depot for the region. In the summer of 1862 about fifty buildings went up and another thirty were under construction. They were quickly filled, day and night.

Over the next eighteen years Walla Walla became the largest town in Washington Territory and its Main Street showed it. In the mid-1870s it was widened from 80 to 100 feet and lighted with gas lanterns, which were replaced by electric lights in 1888. The pioneer street would also have its share of fires, about one every ten years — in 1865, 1875, and 1887.

The paving of Walla Walla streets began in 1904. Prior to that, sprinkling wagons covered about two miles of streets twice a day between April 15 and November 1 to subdue the dust. In 1911 telephone poles were moved to the alleys and the following year Main Street's hitching posts were, at last, removed. Walla Walla's ancient Nez Perce trail had entered modernity.

In 1922 Walla Wallans formed the Walla Walla Pageant Association to reenact the community's early history on the seventy-fifth anniversary of the Whitman massacre. The summer event was titled "How The West Was Won," and many of the Walla Walla pioneer parts were played by their descendants or, in a few cases, by the pioneers themselves. For its direction the pageant committee imported Percy Burrell, a professional from Boston, who described the prepared field at the Walla Walla fairgrounds as "the largest expanse visible to all spectators ever employed in a pageant in this country, if not in the world." The stage was more than 800 feet wide, the backdrop nearly half that, and the mountain scenery reached a height of 48 feet. The third of the pageant's four movements reenacted the pioneer history of the town before a faithful replica of the original buildings on old Main Street. Today, even without the original clapboards or their canvas recreation, the historical continuity of Walla Walla's Main Street remains palpable for those who wish to feel it.

The Main Street set for Walla Walla's Pioneer Pageant, 1923. Courtesy, Penrose Library, Whitman College.

VANCOUVER

Walla Walla's Main Street began from a trail; Vancouver's from a tree. In 1847 Henry Williamson started a survey from the "Balm of Gilead Tree" for what he called Vancouver City. Three years later Amos Short also used the tree as the surveying anchor for the town he temporarily called Columbia City. The tree sat at the waterfront foot of Short's designated main street. Urban expectations for the site were reasonable for it was known worldwide as the North Pacific home for the Hudson's Bay Company (HBC), which had traded there since 1825. After England agreed by treaty in 1846 to move the southern border of its dominion from the Columbia River north to the present Canadian border, the United States built its own encampment at Vancouver, the first federal army base in the Northwest. The Vancouver Barracks looked down to the river over the rooftops of the Hudson's Bay encampment. Since the United States did not purchase the remaining HBC properties in Washington Territory until the 1860s, English presence continued at Vancouver for some time after the treaty was signed.

HBC and other company vessels would often tie onto the "Balm of Gilead Tree," sometimes called the "Old Witness Tree," which was thought to have been used originally by Lewis and Clark as a shoreside anchor. Just to the west of the two forts, Amos Short's first town plat extended about eight blocks back from the river. A mix of Americans and English attended when Main Street's first two retailers, a saloon and a hotel, opened their doors with an 1854 Independence Day celebration. When the wharf at the foot of Main was completed in 1856 the street developed quickly, and Vancouver was incorporated the following year. However, as elsewhere in the American West, the town's development was somewhat retarded by the Civil War. It was not until 1872 that the city constructed a combination fire house and town hall on Main Street, and seven more years before the street's first six blocks north of the river were graded. However, Vancouver's citizens were just across the river from sophisticated Portland, the Northwest's premier community.

For Washington communities on or near the railroad, the growth that followed the 1883 completion of the transcontinental Northern Pacific to Portland continued with varying intensity until the 1893 market crash. Vancouver's reluctance to show off its share of this prosperity inspired the weekly *Clark County Register* to criticize conditions on Main Street in 1888. "Twenty-five hundred in the treasury, and a city hall and council chambers that are hardly fit for a barn and hayloft. The streets dark as Egypt, except where certain citizens have erected lamps that cast a sickly light from coal oil burners, and not a sewer yet laid through the principal street of the city." Only four years later, after electric lights and trolleys were introduced on Main Street, another publication, the Vancouver *Independent,* found the changes confusing, vexatious and even dangerous. "Electric light wires, electric car wires, are strung over our streets in great profusion... necessitating the presence of a large number of unsightly poles on streets and corners." The muckraking *Independent* might have but did not compliment the city for the new sewer system laid below Main Street, nor for the few blocks of wood block paving installed on it. Soon enough the blocks became a sore point. In 1898 the mayor reported to the city council that they had become "very badly decayed" would soon have to be repaired. The blocks were later abandoned and by 1909 Vancouver streets were being regularly oiled. The opening that year of the Carnegie Library at Fifteenth Street and four years later the high school at Twenty-sixth Street extended the civic reach of Main Street.

Most importantly for Vancouver, the Interstate Bridge to Portland was completed in 1917, delivering the touring traffic of the Pacific Highway directly onto Vancouver's Main Street. (See Bridges Chapter). Following the flow, businesses built north along Main through the twenties. When a new electric lighting system was installed between Third and Tenth streets in 1928, its ignition was coordinated with the opening of the Evergreen Hotel at Fifth and Main. For the evening ceremonies of March 17 the street lights were briefly extinguished to create a dark stage upon which the lights of the new hotel and its grounds could be viewed. This was not a mere light show but a leaping of centuries and hemispheres. For in London, 103 years after his company chose the site for its fort, the president of the HBC turned on the lights with the press of a telegraph key.

Vancouver's Old Apple Tree is surrounded by roads and rails set at higher grades. Although it was saved from the I-5 freeway, the historic apple tree must be visited through a railroad underpass. Inset: An earlier view of the Old Apple Tree. Contemporary photo by Nancy Ishii. Historical view courtesy, Ted Van Arsdol.

The dark side of Main Street commerce was the increasing congestion and high octane dangers that U.S. Highway 99 brought to it. Relief, of sorts, began with the highway department's 1948 plans to replace the Pacific Highway through Vancouver with a limited access freeway along the western border of the Vancouver Barracks. In more than thirty years of construction and reconstruction, the Vancouver Freeway had profound effects on the business district and its Main Street. (See Highways Chapters). In 1984, when the section through downtown was redesigned and enlarged to six lanes, Main Street was cut off at Fifth Avenue. The rebuilding of this part of Interstate-5 forced either the destruction or removal of forty commercial buildings and apartment houses south of Sixth Street, nineteen buildings at the Vancouver Barracks, and about 250 residences along the roughly three-mile cut through the city. The improved freeway was considerably safer, cutting accidents more than in half. The 1982 opening of the Interstate Highway 205 bridge helped with these safety statistics. But it also funneled more of the growth and commercial activity into the suburbs and malls, resulting in the closing of many of the old businesses along Main Street.

The city responded to this partial abandonment with heritage — architectural and natural. Vancouver preservationists restored and saved a number of historic structures including: the Barracks Officers Row, Providence Academy, Hadley's Department Store, the Ford Building, the County Museum in the old Carnegie Library and the pioneer Hidden home — the last four all on Main Street. The city also helped revive its central business district botanically with street plantings. The project of landscaping downtown streets can be seen as a rebirth of the tree from which Main Street was first platted. Undermined by a flood in 1909, the "Old Witness Tree" eventually slipped away into the river but not before several cuttings were saved and eventually planted about town at sites which included, in 1913, the grounds of the Clark County Courthouse.

The most famous Vancouver tree to become entwined with the city's past and its streets is not the Old Witness, but the Old Apple Tree. Reputedly planted from a seed brought west to Fort Vancouver in 1826 by British Lt. Emilius Simpson, the apple tree was saved from a concrete internment when freeway plans at the south entrance to the Interstate Bridge were redrawn to avoid it. In its three-sided plot at the north end of Waterfront Park, the Old Apple Tree is surrounded by two freeway off-ramps and an embankment of the Burlington Northern Railroad. The tree is reached by walking beneath a concrete railroad overpass. (See photo top of page.)

Curvilinear Tacoma

The preference for straight streets was an industrial age orthodoxy increasingly challenged by late nineteenth-century reformers who sought to romance the cityscape with curvilinear and irregular forms. The new taste was generally late in coming to the Northwest; the best examples date from the early twentieth century in the systems of parks and boulevards developed in Seattle and Spokane. (See below) However, the advance guard for such

Above: Westward view along Walla Walla's Fifth Avenue and its intersection with Main Street, Aug. 21, 1942. Courtesy, DOT. Below: The same intersection in 1986 with the addition of brick arches which mark the permanent closure of Main Street south of Fifth Avenue. Courtesy, Ted Van Arsdol.

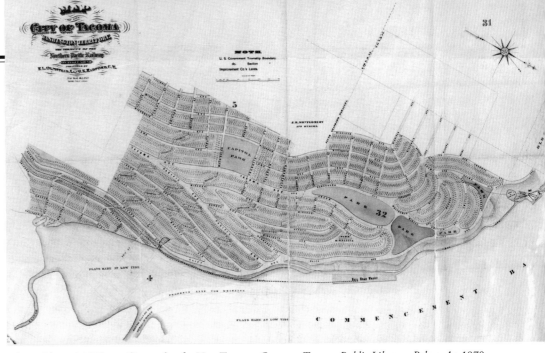

poetic platting came with the founding of Tacoma, or New Tacoma, in 1873.

Soon after, the officers of the Northern Pacific Railroad chose Tacoma over Seattle for their Puget Sound terminus, and they hired Frederick Law Olmsted (the famous landscape architect who designed New York's Central Park) to plan their new city. Because the townsite was both steep and dappled with springs, the Olmsted firm sent a hydrographic engineer to survey and design the Tacoma Plan. By following the contours of the land, the Olmsted plan solved the site's drainage problem and created a varied system of winding wide streets and alleys expressive of the natural topography.

The problems with the plan were its timing and good sense. While the maps were being drawn, the boomtown swelled with opportunists anxious to invest in the marvelous future predicted for Commencement Bay. Herbert Hunt, Tacoma's pioneer historian, described the effects:

Above: Olmsted 1873 curvilinear plan for New Tacoma. Courtesy, Tacoma Public Library. Below: An 1878 birdseye of New Tacoma and the mountain whose Indian name it was named for, as rendered from First Hill. Tacoma was then still a company town for the Northern Pacific Railroad whose wharves (far left) and car works (far right) are the young community's real landmarks. Courtesy, U.W. Libraries, Special Collections.

> *Prospective buyers were here in numbers and looking for rectangles of ground, easy of description and readily found… [Instead] the streets followed the contour of the hills, and while all the lots had a frontage of 25 feet, they had varying depths and diverse shapes. The sarcastic settlers vowed that everything that ever had been exhibited in an agricultural show had its counterpart in the shape of lots in this townsite, from calabashes to ice-boxes. And that came near being the fact. The designer was seeking easy grades and a marvelous beauty. Had the plat been adopted and followed it would have produced perhaps the most picturesque city on American soil. Some of our steep and expensive hill streets would have been avoided and the community would have been saved thousands of dollars in street paving costs.*

So much for organic design. The common rectilinear plan that replaced the Olmsted's vision also fulfilled the traffic and hydraulic effects predicted. Its grades were cruel to horses and pedestrians, and periodic floods exploded manhole covers on the streets with the steepest inclines from Pacific Avenue to the top of First Hill.

During its boom years, between the 1887 completion of the Northern Pacific's Cascade line over Stampede Pass and the economic Panic of 1893, Tacoma's population rivaled Seattle's. It was a wild time for city additions when parades of buyers were led to new plats by brass bands and sleepless agents. In 1891 Tacoma annexed the Oakes Addition, Ridgedale, Fernhill, and South Tacoma. Without the curvilinear ease of the Olmsted plan, the burgeoning Tacoma of new plats and additions came to resemble a collision of crystals. The variously sized blocks and blocks of blocks consistently jarred with their neighbors. Consequently, hardly anything quite lines up in Tacoma, but rarely are these incongruities guided by nature as did the Olmsted plan.

VIEW OF

NEW TACOMA AND MOUNT TACOMA,

Right: Snohomish birdseye, ca. 1889, includes view of the cable ferry at Avenue D (bottom center) and the Seattle Lake Shore and Eastern Railroad trestle (far right).

Below: Early century panorama of Snohomish before the 1910 arrival of the Milwaukee Railroad and the intrusion of its waterfront trestle east of the Avenue D swing bridge (right) to Avenue A. Both views courtesy, U.W. Library, Special Collections.

SNOHOMISH PANORAMA

Like a number of other state communities which faced waterways, Snohomish pioneers gave the descriptive name "Front" to their main street, which ran somewhat precariously above the Snohomish River. The original structures on the fledgling street were built on its far side, safely away from the river bank. The south or wet side of Front was eventually developed with structures raised high on pilings between the street and the river. When the town was platted in 1871 "First" was substituted for "Front," and the depressions in grade were smoothed with a supporting architecture of small bridges. Some of First Avenue's wooden sidewalks reached the riverside structures over short trestles. An 1889 birdseye of Snohomish shows the pile-supported row of structures which lined up between the river and First Avenue from Avenue B to Avenue D. Also shown in line with Avenue D is the   that crossed the river there beginning in 1884. Two years later the cable ferry connected with the road to King County and Seattle, which was built that year across a marsh south of town. The artist's panorama also reveals, far-right, a glimpse of the Seattle Lake Shore and Eastern Railroad (S.L.S.E.) and its bridge at State Street.

In a pattern repeated many times among waterfront communities, the arrival of the railroad upset the old arrangements. When the S.L.S.E. from Seattle appeared in 1888, Snohomish business interests shifted from First Avenue to the railroad depot between Lincoln and Maple avenues. In 1910 the Milwaukee line effec-

tively separated First from the river — the town's original source of commerce and connection — when the railroad laid its main track into town over a 1,100-foot-long pile trestle along the north side of the river between Avenue A and Avenue D. Remarkably, this arrangement held until 1927. In its remodeling of the waterfront, the railroad acquired most of the buildings located between the river and First Avenue. It also explored Snohomish with a number of spurs, many of them servicing the retail and manufacturing firms on First. The beginning of passenger service was celebrated on April 21, 1912, with an excursion train filled with members of the Everett and Snohomish commercial clubs. The latter wore white ribbons captioned "You can't miss Snohomish if you come over the Milwaukee." In 1930 the Milwaukee's rail passenger service was replaced by buses, and in 1936 the railroad left the waterfront to share tracks with the Great Northern Railroad on the south side of the river. Its big trestle was eventually dismantled.

OYSTERVILLE AND SOUTH BEND

Oysterville created its Front Street on pilings. Its waterfront faced shallows of oyster beds, requiring a quarter-mile-long wharf to reach water deep enough to service vessels. Unlike Ilwaco's, its Front Street was trackless, for the narrow-gauged railroad that ran up the Long Beach Peninsula to Ocean Park but

NARROW STREETS BESIDE THE SKAGIT RIVER

With many of the buildings on its waterside supported by piles punched into the Swinomish Slough, LaConner's narrow Main Street clings to the slim strip of land left between the slough and the town on the hill. LaConner arose as the principal outlet for the produce and materials brought down the Skagit. Its position, however, was precarious. When the tides were sufficiently high or the valley flooded, LaConner became an island. The systematic diking and reclamation of these floodplains, beginning in the 1870s, improved the hydraulics of LaConner's farm milieu and allowed its commercial and cultural appetites to flourish — briefly. In preparation for the 1883 separation of Skagit County from Whatcom County, LaConner was platted, incorporated, and named county seat, a status it was required to prove the following year with a countywide election. Surprised, it lost its seat to its upstart and upriver neighbor Mount Vernon.

Top: Reclamation work along South Bend's waterfront. Courtesy, U.W. Libraries, Special Collections. Above: Water Street in South Bend in its early century heyday. Courtesy, Dan Kerlee. Below left: Long Beach terminus for the railroad that ran north along the peninsula from Ilwaco. Courtesy, Dan Kerlee.

refused to go the final four miles required to reach the original Pacific County seat. In 1893, only five years after it was isolated by the railroad rejection, a gang of young Turks from South Bend raided Oysterville and kidnapped the Pacific County courthouse records they had won the year before by election. Another railroad figured in their seat victory. Temporary crews of the Northern Pacific, which was then approaching the Willapa River Valley, were charged by Oystervillians with creating a South Bend voting majority. Although South Bend got both its county seat and railroad, the lingering effects of the panic of 1893 considerably subdued developers' hopes, suggested by the names they chose for residential neighborhoods — such as Nob Hill, Quality Hill, and Alta Vista. South Bend's commercial strip, Water Street, was crowded between the waterway in front of it and the hills behind.

Mount Vernon's real boom began with the joyful arrival of the Seattle and Northern Railroad (Great Northern) on August 12, 1891 when every noise-making device in town — church bells, steam whistles, fire alarms, trumpets — was sounded. Mount Vernon also had its Front Street for river trade. At first, Front Street was Mount Vernon's chief business strip as well, but the "Great Fire" there in 1891 destroyed most of the stores and hotels along the waterfront. Afterwards the business center was moved two blocks east, jumping over Main Street to First Street. It was a prudent leap, for eventually all of Front, as well as the west side of Main Street, was lost to Skagit River floods. The eroding river was in time restrained with the construction of a sturdy revetment. The move to First also symbolized Mount Vernon's growing separation from its dependence on the river. As in Snohomish, this community turned to its tracks and later to its highways.

Above: Narrow-gauge peninsula train dominating Ilwaco's Main Street. Courtesy, Dan Kerlee. Below right: La Conner's narrow Main Street. Courtesy, Mike Maslan.

Above left: Panorama of Port Townsend taken in the late 1860s after construction of the embankment (upper left). Above right: Mid-1990s repeat of historical scene. Photo by Holly Mayshark.

PORT TOWNSEND: DOWNTOWN UPTOWN

The earliest panorama of downtown Port Townsend from its "uptown" bluff shows its primeval situation, a sandspit beside a salt marsh at the windswept entrance to Puget Sound. The plan for the Port Townsend townsite was drawn in 1852, two years after the first settler's arrival at Point Wilson. The primitive streets developed from the plat map required relatively little work for their foundation had been prepared by a few thousand years of winds and waves. But the risk in this setting was exposed in 1866 by a tidal wave which broke over the salt marsh and into town. Port Townsend's 1868 panorama also reveals the citizens' response to the deluge, their first big public work.

Two resident contractors named McNear and Fortman were paid the large sum of $3,425 to raise an embankment across the entrance to the salt marsh. The line of that dike is apparent top-left in the panorama, lower-left, as is the trapped lagoon. A year later the contractors returned to widen the bulkhead by four feet. The penultimate step to reclamation was made in 1871 when the water captured behind the bulkhead was drained away. The work was soon concluded by a horse and scraper, improving the embankment and filling and grading the dewatered acres behind it.

Port Townsend's bluff was precipitous and initial efforts to surmount it were with zig-zagging steps. On Taylor Street the contractors measured — and wagered between them — the height of the bluff by tying a wood block to the line of one of the community's highest flag poles. Then they sighted the block as it was raised along the pole with a spirit level from the bluff. With an elevation of a little more than eighty feet, considerably more than the wagered seventy feet, the contractor on the ground won the dollar bet.

Plans for a second stairway at Quincy Street were blocked by Dr. T. T. Minor, director of the landmark Marine Hospital. Minor's claim that the Quincy Street course, which ran into hospital property on the bluff, had never been dedicated for public use was at least not contradicted by municipal records, for neither the official plat map nor any record of its filing could be found in Jefferson County records. Luck intervened when, after months of searching, city councilman A. H. Tucker, at the last moment before tackling the city's claim, spied a dust-covered roll, half-hidden in the mayor's office. Opening it Tucker discovered the town's original plat map inscribed with the legend "put on file for record the 2nd day of August 1856 A. A. Plummer, county auditor." This resurrection created such a sensation in court that Minor not only agreed to settle but prudently drew a deed transferring to the city his claim to the disputed street. Soon after, in 1878, the second steps to Uptown were constructed on Quincy Street.

Actually, many citizens of Port Townsend believed that it should not be easy to either leave Uptown or approach it, because "sin flourished at sea level." Saloons, serving single wayfarers visiting the port of entry, were the rule on Water Street. Above them the old families, living along Franklin, Clay, and Lawrence streets, went to uptown schools, churches, and markets, rarely having to descend to the sandspit. It was a separation with hidden ties, for uptown Victorian rectitude and splendor were more often than not paid for by downtown doings.

The optimism accompanying the 1883 arrival of the Northern Pacific to Puget Sound quickly spread to Jefferson County, its seat began to prepare for what this "Key City" to Puget Sound considered its destiny — rail connection with the world beyond the Quimper Peninsula. At this time Port Townsend's downtown rose about five feet closer to its uptown at an elevation safely above

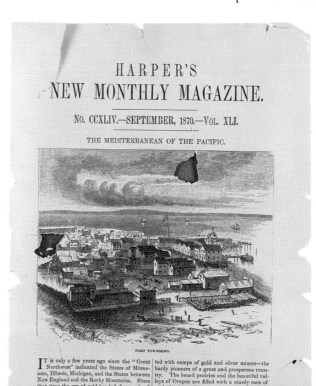

Above: Blasting the bluff with water cannons for fill to extend Water Street. Courtesy Jefferson County Historical Society.
Left: Port Townsend birdseye on torn cover of Harper's New Monthly Magazine, *Sept. 1870, can be compared with the photos at the top of the page.*

those who are not familiar with Port Townsend this view of Water Street will seem quite imposing, but you who have seen it will not be deceived thereby.

I believe I have no more that will interest you that you have not already.

Yours truly
O.H. Gardner

Above: Whether O.G. Gardner was a Port Townsend resident or merely an acerbic visitor, his or her message of disappointment is a sign for the general depression that befell the "Key City" when its boom-time hopes could not be sustained. Ironically the town's protracted depression was a good preservative for many of the distinctive structures siding Water Street, landmarks that are a part of Port Townsend's considerable charm. Courtesy, Mark Maslan.

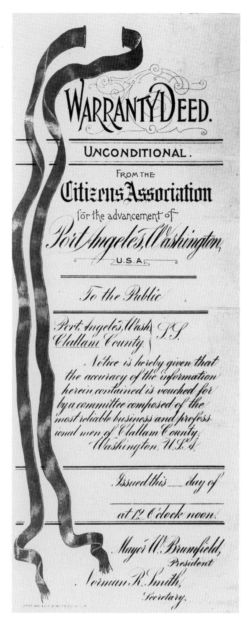

With warranty deeds, the self-styled Citizens Association formalized the procedure, that turned jumpers on the Port Angeles federal reserve first into squatters and then preferred buyers. Courtesy, U.W. Libraries, Special Collections.

any odd disaster that might roll in from the sea. Owners of substantial buildings downtown had to make adjustments to the regrade by either raising their structures or cutting sidewalk wells to their original front doors. Through these boom years and into 1891, Water Street was lined with distinguished multistory business blocks. The town was also at last united, when Washington Street (paralleling Water Street) was graded up the hill to the west of downtown.

Expanding the business district west along the waterfront was another important work of the 1880s. Eventually, Water Street was extended along the waterfront through to Kah Tai Lagoon, west of downtown. As in Tacoma, Olympia, Seattle, and many other Puget Sound communities, the placer mining technique of blasting glacial till with high-powered water jets was used to pare away Port Townsend's bluff for use as fill in reclaiming the north end of downtown.

Ultimately the regrade and reclamation necessities for downtown Port Townsend were fairly self-evident — diking and draining the salt marsh, raising the streets, building a seawall, subduing the bluff, and opening a direct route to and across the Kah Tai lagoon. For years a variety of timber trestles were used to cross the wetland. It was not until the arrival of the Crown Zellerbache Paper Mill at the lagoon in 1928 that it was sealed off from the tides with the construction of Sims Way. After the Chamber of Commerce planted rows of poplar trees along Sims Way in 1930, a depression-time WPA project removed the vestiges of the old bridge, diverted freshwater overflows from the city reservoir into the lagoon, and planted wild rice throughout to attract waterfowl. The effect was the growth of a new freshwater habitat and a poplar-lined promenade that created a grand entrance to Port Townsend. This picturesque effect suddenly wilted in the early 1960s when the Army Corps of Engineers used the lagoon as a dumping ground for the salty fill it dredged from the bay to produce a new boat haven. The poplars died within days, and for years their lifeless skeletons lent the hitherto picturesque city portal a macabre quality. But slowly the idle lagoon revived, and after rebuffing plans to use the site for a supermarket the Kah Tai citizens' alliance won the right — and funding — to develop the fill and surrounding acres as a park. In 1985, twenty-one years after the Army Corps had moved it there, this regenerated ground was "broken" again for Kah Tai Lagoon Point Park.

Left: Taylor Street Steps frame the Haller Fountain, Port Townsend's Venetian monument to its pioneers. Photo by Abigail Harris.

PORT ANGELES: TWO BOOMS

In 1890 the old order in Port Angeles either surrendered to the new or skipped town. As the socialist experiment at the Puget Sound Cooperative Colony on the east waterfront fell apart, some of the colonists stayed to join a horde of newcomers. On Independence Day this crew of rowdy reformers and opportunists jumped onto the federal reserve lands at the west waterfront — the shoulder for the long arm of Ediz Hook. The statistics of the Port Angeles land boom of 1890, when the town's population ballooned from 500 to 3,000, were aided significantly by those jumpers who stayed to squat. Most were careful to mark the borders of their claims in line with the lots originally platted for this "Federal City" in the early 1860s by Victor Smith. The squatters

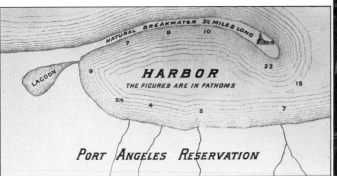

Above left: Early federal map of the site chosen for the "second federal city." Courtesy, U.W. Libraries, Special Collections. Above right: Releasing the superficial liquids from the sediments captured to elevate Laurel Street. Courtesy, Old Seattle Paperworks (OSP).

eventually won the right to purchase the land at assessed value from a federal government pragmatic enough to know nothing good would come from punishing the participants of such a popular invasion.

Soon after Port Angeles incorporated in 1890 and under the spell of the boomers' "do it now" attitude, its mayor and city council got busy fixing up the business district. Like its pioneer

Pouring concrete retaining walls for 1914 reclamation. Courtesy, OSP.

rival Port Townsend, Port Angeles squatted upon a narrow waterfront. Barely two blocks wide at the base of a bluff, it was periodically flooded from the north by winds and high tides and regularly irrigated from the south by Peabody Creek which ran down the middle of Front Street. In the beginning this work of constructing sidewalks, filling and grading streets, and building steps up the bluff was financed with stiff "sin taxes" — expensive

licenses extracted from the young town's many saloons. Both Front and First streets were extended west over the tideflats, the former on piles and the latter on fill. The dirt was handshoveled from the bluff, loaded to narrow-gauged mining cars, and hauled by rail to the work with the feeding line extended step-by-step over the new grades. The width of the sidewalks on Front and First were set at ten and twelve feet respectively, but only after months of councilmanic wrangling through the summer of 1890 did its members agree on a width of eighty feet for Front Street itself. The decision required owners on the north side of Front street to set their pile-supported structures back ten feet and to do it in ten days. It was a prosperous autumn for Port Angeles house movers.

The booming optimism of both Port Townsend and Port Angeles in 1890 could not, of course, be sustained. The open doors of both the "Key City" and the "Gate City" took a hammering with the financial Panic of 1893. However, Port Townsend still had its official duties as Port of Entry for Puget Sound, a role it had earlier in the 1860s lost briefly to Port Angeles. Port Angeles had only its spit and whatever polish the Clallam County Immigration Association could give to the promotional literature it circulated in the Midwest promoting what the association variously called "The Cherbourg of America," "The New York of the Pacific," "The Port of Angels," and most often "The Gate City."

A quarter century later hopes harbored by Port Angeles' faithful that their strategic location would someday be fully appreciated and exploited seemed suddenly realized with the second boom of 1914. Also that year, its rival Port Townsend lost to Seattle its official distinction as the federal port of entry. And in 1914 the railroad arrived — in a way. Using a portion of the relatively useless Port Townsend and Southern rails, the Milwaukee Railroad constructed a line to Port Angeles and a few miles beyond to the forest reserves west of town. That the Milwaukee line was

Below right: With concrete walls in place, Front Street awaits its fill while buildings on the south side of the street (left foreground) have been raised to a new level. View looks west. Left: Looking east on the Front Street a block after plank paving has been laid on the elevated street. Structures on the south (right) side of the street have all been raised while most of those on the north side are still on the level of the old grade. Courtesy, OSP.

connected to the "main land" not by rails but by railroad barges on Puget Sound did not dilute the excitement of Port Angeleans who enjoyed their first passenger excursion on July 21, 1914.

The developments of this banner year also included: a dam on the Elwha, which generated enough power to electrify all of Port Angeles; a major new waterfront lumber mill; and the start of construction on a Georgian Revival Courthouse. One of the more daring street improvements undertaken in the history of the state raised downtown Port Angeles one story during the summer of 1914.

"The Curse of Port Angeles" was high tide, which would return raw sewage to the business district and carry away street planks and wooden sidewalks. It was exorcised by a baptism of water cannons blasting the bluff onto the streets. Water was drawn from both the bay and Peabody Creek which was, at last, diverted away from Front Street through a tunnel beneath the "hog back," a hump of land near the waterfront, to enter the bay near what is now the site of the modern City Pier. The top of the hog back was also a target, as was the steep Front Street Hill. Both were subdued by jets shot from the water cannons and channeled through pipelines and flumes to the streets below. There, on the street side of the wooden sidewalks, concrete slabs were installed to contain the fill. "Dirt bins," usually a block long, were created behind temporary dams erected across the streets and between the slabs. After a bin was filled and drained, the dams were moved along to the next block and the reclamation process began again. Following the fill the new grades were leveled by horse-drawn drags and then paved with locally milled planks, four inches thick, fourteen inches wide and eighteen feet long. This planking was temporary. After five years the fill had settled sufficiently to allow replacing the wood with composite pavement.

OLYMPIA: EARLY STREETS AND BRIDGES

Waterpower and waterfront were Budd Inlet's attractions for Michael Simmons and Levi Smith, the first American settlers on Puget Sound. In 1845 Michael T. Simmons chose the falls of the Deschutes River for his grist and lumber mills. The future Tumwater he called New Market. One year later, less than a mile north of Simmons, Smith chose the waterfront promontory of the future Olympia. With a south Sound tidal range that could run twenty feet, Olympia's waterfront advantages were intermittent. An extremely high tide could flood the townsite as far inland as Second Avenue. Regardless, it was Olympia that the federal government originally chose for its port of entry in 1851. More imprimaturs followed.

First, in 1852, Thurston County was created from a part of Pacific County, and Olympia became its seat and thus a center for taxation and the management of, among other civic necessities,

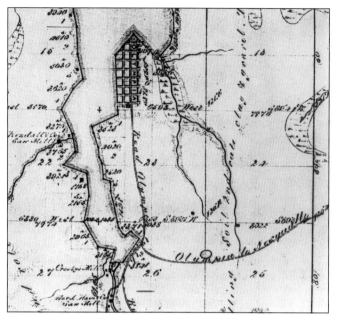

Early mid-1850s map of Budd Inlet; Olympia, the territorial capitol; and the road south to New Market (now Tumwater). Courtesy, U.W. Libraries, Special Collections.

road districts. The only trail that was at all passable then was the rough wagon road from the Cowlitz River. (By 1853 a stage line advertised in the *Columbian*, Olympia's first newspaper, twelve-hour service between Puget Sound and Cowlitz Landing.) Olympia's political-bureaucratic future was set in 1853 with the separation of Washington Territory from Oregon. Although challenged several times afterwards, the new territorial capital was never successfully kidnapped by Vancouver, Walla Walla, Yakima, Ellensburg, or Seattle. With the arrival of Territorial Gov. Isaac Stevens late in the year, two one-story structures on the west side of Olympia's Main Street became the first home of Washington government.

Although built in line with Fourth Street, Olympia's first large public work had little to do directly with streets. The rumors of war following Steven's harried treaty-making with the Indians spurred the small settlements around Puget Sound to build local defenses. In Olympia a stockade was quickly constructed from the east inlet to the west down Fourth Street. This high wall, made of four-inch-thick, twenty-foot-long planks cut continuously day and night at the Crosby (grandfather of Bing) mill at Tumwater Falls, connected with a blockhouse. (In 1868 the blockhouse, which after the Indian War served as a city jail, was disassembled and the lumber recycled for planks on Main Street just above

Left: 1884 birdseye of Olympia looking southwest. Right: Olympia's Main Street (Capitol Way), ca. 1875. Photo by Huntington. Courtesy, Michael Maslan.

Thirteenth Avenue.) With the stockade behind it and Budd Inlet on all other sides (there were as yet no bridges across the arms of the Inlet), the community awaited attack while it also constructed a 300-foot-long pier at the end of Main Street for commerce and/ or escape. Olympia, however, was never besieged.

Among the lessons learned from the 1855-56 Indian War was the old one that the connections between the few settlements on Puget Sound (roads) were more pressing than those within them (streets). So soon after the Olympians returned to their homes they joined to improve their attachment to Tumwater with a planked road. The county survey committee concluded that an eight-foot-wide road, 3,350 feet long, would require about 80,400 board feet of three-inch planks for a surface and an additional 15,075 feet for stringers. The planks were again manufactured at the Tumwater mill. The com-

mittee estimated the cost for the lumber, grading, and building of the Tumwater connection at $2,583. After the 297 days of "tax labor" owed by citizens was figured in (at an inflated $3 a day), the total cost was reduced to $1,962. Promptly, a second committee was assigned to raise subscription pledges.

Planked roads were a great improvement over the old puncheon or corduroy roads of split lumber, and they required only as much grading as was needed to lay the stringers and eliminate the bumps between them. However, as noted earlier, along the waterfronts of most Puget Sound settlements, planking was laid on piles, and these streets like their sidewalks were sometimes carried to sea or burned. Fire was always a hazard for any wooden street or road. Much of Whatcom County's elaborate system of planked roads was consumed in an 1897 forest fire. On the Guide Meridian Road, which runs north from Bellingham, 80,000 board feet of lumber were required to repair destroyed stretches. Unless shortened by fire or flood, a planked road might make it

Top left: Drawspan over the west arm of Budd Inlet between Olympia and the suburb of Marshville, ca. 1895. Courtesy, U.W. Libraries, Special Collections. Top right: Reclaiming Olympia's tidelands. Courtesy, Old Seattle Paperworks. Above: Aerial of Capitol Campus above Budd Inlet before the formation of Capitol Lake. Courtesy, Michael Fairley.

through five years of service before requiring fresh boards.

Upon incorporation in 1859, Olympia's first elected officers prepared to expand the town south of Fourth Street by directing the removal of stumps on Main Street (Capitol Way). Underground water tanks on Main at Third and Fourth streets were also installed, along with a community water pump. The pump created an open-air community center where, one contemporary recollected, "the federal official joshed with the day laborer and probably his beautiful daughter flirted with the dusky Siwash." The waterworks laid below Olympia streets in 1865 eliminated both the pump and this democratic mingling.

Swantown, to the east, and Marshville, to the west were pioneer suburbs separated from Olympia by, respectively, the east and west arms of Budd Inlet. The narrower east arm was first spanned in 1860 with a $300 appropriation from the county. This first structure was certainly flimsy, for in 1867 the street committee returned to the county with a request for a new bridge. After the county offered them instead a low-interest loan, the bridge work in line with Fourth Avenue went ahead, slowly and poorly. Within a year of its completion yet another bridge was needed. The ultimate solution for this impediment was fill, so the east bay served as a city dump until it was reclaimed from the tides in the mid-1920s.

The first bridge to Edmund Marsh's Marshville (West Olympia) was not constructed until 1869. Its drawspan failed within a year. Years of patching and other piecemeal repairs followed. The construction of a new eighty-foot-wide lift-span in 1891 was designed, in part, to allow the West Side Railway to reach its new franchise. In 1894 the Army Corps deposited about the bridge's Olympia side the dredgings drawn from the waterway. This work extended the business district along Fourth Avenue, crowding the east approach of the bridge with some of the commercial vitality asso-

ciated with the medieval London Bridge.

Olympia's size was considerably increased through the reclamation of tidelands. After the Army Corps' work on the West Waterway, the town's first large reclamation was the work of local promoter, P. H. Carlyon. The fill, which added some twenty-nine blocks to the city's north end between 1909 and 1911, is named for him. Most of this new land was made from two million cubic yards of mud removed from the harbor. This work was considerably extended in the 1920s when the long finger of tidelands north of the Carlyon Fill was reclaimed for the Port of Olympia.

When the Army Corps announced that a new drawbridge to West Olympia was required, Carlyon proposed building a dam instead and creating behind it a freshwater lake. The realtor imagined the new capitol campus reflecting in a quiet lake bordered on its west side by a boulevard with an "auto hotel" seated in the greenbelt above it. Although this vision was proposed by the State Land Commission and supported by the Capitol Commission, it was rejected by the state attorney general who ruled that the state land commissioner had no authority to vacate the Deschutes Waterway for a lake. Also, the Olympia Brewery wanted to continue to ship its popular drink Apellju by water. The community was stuck with the Corps' new lift bridge, tended at first by the city hall janitor and later by the Olympia police department. The present concrete span, built in 1921, was the first step in the ultimate transformation of the West Waterway into the reflecting pond of Capitol Lake. Construction of the dam and spillway began in 1948, and soon after a fish ladder and parkway along the lake's west shore were added. In the early 1980s this expansion of Olympia onto its tidelands moved again to the East Bay, where 543 new and well-landscaped acres were developed with shoreline slips for 500 boats.

BELLINGHAM

More nagging promise than prosperity was mined from the coal seam William Pattle discovered in the fall of 1852 near the foot of Bellingham's present-day Taylor Avenue. He called the spot Unionville, as it developed an ironic name for the first of several competing settlements on Bellingham Bay — Whatcom, Sehome, New Whatcom, Fairhaven — which would fuse only a half-century later as Bellingham. Ultimately, it was streets and streetcars that would give Bellingham's parts the political will to unite. The network of trolleys and planked throughways rapidly developed in the early 1890s to effectively knit as one what was previously merely contiguous.

Two months after Pattle's discovery, partners Henry Roeder and Russell Peabody went out hunting for a site to mill lumber and also stumbled upon a vein of coal richer than Pattle's. They named the Whatcom Creek mill site, Whatcom and the site of the coal mine, Sehome. The two points look at each other across a corner of Bellingham Bay. Although close enough to shout across the water, people either rowed between the towns, walked the beach, or risked getting lost in the forest.

Sehome was developed around the opening to the coal mine, about a block in from shore, near what is now State Street between Ivy and Laurel streets. At Whatcom a row of quarters, constructed of finished lumber milled in town, lined up comfortably above high tide on the "Basin," the triangle of beachfront north of the creek outlet. In the beginning Whatcom's only street on the beach was the width of an alley. Drawn between two wider streets on the plat map filed in 1858, it was named Division and remained Whatcom's main commercial street until the fire of 1885 destroyed seventeen buildings on the Basin, most of them on Division.

Designated seat in 1854 for its new namesake county,

Above: The earliest photo of Whatcom County dates from the mid-1870s. This view looks west into Bellingham Bay across a portion of the Whatcom Creek Waterway. Most of the buildings on Division Street, in midground, were destroyed in the fire of 1885. Below: Looking east across Whatcom's original business district. The land here is mostly reclaimed tidelands, including Holly Street, which crosses near the bottom of the scene. Aerial photo by Galen Biery. Photos courtesy, Galen Biery.

Whatcom had government added to its responsibilities. As in Olympia this meant, primarily, county roads. Commissioners Roeder and Pattle were appointed part of a committee of "viewers" to mark a trail back from the beach. The blazing of this forest path was largely the labor of locals working off their poll taxes by clearing, ditching, and, rarely, grading. The county's work was soon improved by Capt. George Pickett in 1857-58 — six years before he led at the Battle of Gettysburg what would become known as "Pickett's charge." Here "Pickett's Road" was the northern end of the Military Road originally planned to run between Fort Steilacoom and Fort Bellingham.

In response to the hostilities between settlers and natives that followed Governor Stevens's speedy treatymaking, Fort Bellingham was constructed above the bay, about three-and-a-half miles north of Whatcom. From there Pickett's Road traveled south above the beach to Whatcom where it crossed the creek behind the mill. This span survived long enough for Bellingham photographer E. A. Hegg to preserve a record of it in the 1890s. From the south side of the creek the Military Road headed southeast for the Sehome coal mine, passing enroute near the future intersection of Holly and State streets. This more than four miles of wagon road was, in effect, Bellingham's second street, and the first above the beach.

The bridgework at Whatcom Creek was done during the summer of 1858 when thousands of argonauts arrived, expecting to make a shortcut across the country's "Northwest Corner" to the Canadian Fraser River gold fields. This flood took only a few months to dry up. But while the miners were still pouring through, both Whatcom and Sehome were platted into salable blocks and lots facing streets sketched on vellum. Cut from the familiar rectangular grid, Sehome's thirty-three blocks were positioned in

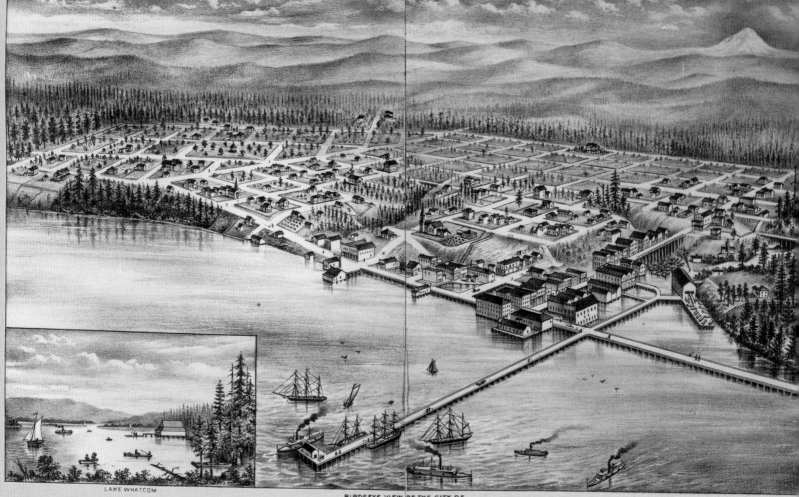

LAKE WHATCOM

BIRDSEYE VIEW OF THE CITY OF
WHATCOM, WASHINGTON TERRITORY.
1888.

Top: Bird's-eye view of Whatcom in 1888 includes the Holly Street trestle which was completed the following year across the Whatcom Creek Waterway. Above: View northeast along Sehome's main commercial arterial, State Street, in 1885. Below left: Looking southwest on the same portion of State Street from the opposite end in 1889. Courtesy, University of Washington Libraries, Special Collections. Below right: A 1997 repeat of the 1889 view of State Street. Photo by Mark Cutler.

four rows parallel to the waterfront and out of line with the national township/range survey, which was then being completed in the Northwest. Again, the street closest the water was called Front. And, again typically, it would later be renamed Railroad. Behind it was Main Street (now State Street), followed by Washington and Jackson streets.

When the rush collapsed a few of the disappointed horde retreating through Whatcom were desperate enough to become highwaymen on Pickett's new road. For safety the settlers returned to walking the beach. But once it was cleared of ruffians, the citizens of Whatcom and Sehome regularly used Pickett's throughway and regularly squabbled over the cost of maintaining it. Bellingham's first street above the beach was used well into the 1880s.

Before George Pickett left the abandoned Fort Bellingham to join the Confederate forces in his native Virginia, the captain and his regulars stood up to the English on San Juan Island. However, more important

than the "Pig War" for the story of Bellingham, Pickett also made a sketch of Sehome's Main Street. He dated it April 10, 1859. Whatcom's first extant recording comes much later, in the early 1870s. The photograph shows a dozen or so buildings, including the brick courthouse (the Richards Building on E Street), strung along the waterfront. It just missed including the mill site at Whatcom Creek, perhaps because the mill burned down in 1873, the photo's conventional date. In the early 1870s the bay communities were briefly enlivened by the presence of Northern Pacific representatives examining their waterfront as a potential transcontinental terminus. This was a scene enacted also in Seattle, Olympia and elsewhere but fulfilled only in Tacoma. With the crash of its prospects for a railroad, the destruction of its lumber mill, and in 1878 the flooding and abandonment of its coal mine, the future Bellingham was left with a total population of about a dozen families scattered about the bay.

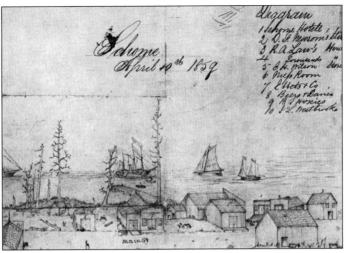

George Pickett's sketch of Sehome, dated April 10, 1859. Courtesy, Galen Biery. Below: Interurban trolleys helped prepare the way for Bellingham's 1903 unification of the once separate towns of Whatcom, Sehome, and Fairhaven. Courtesy, Galen Biery.

Soon the arrival of the transcontinental to Tacoma in 1883 reopened the spigot of immigration and flooded the streets of Puget Sound towns with consuming strangers, the liquor of growth. That year Sehome and Whatcom were replatted, now with streets drawn hopefully beyond the shoreline onto the tideflats. The acres between them reserved for railroads, the no man's land on the south side of Whatcom Creek, which is now the civic center, was also platted appropriately as Central Whatcom. There the streets were drawn in conformity with the compass, creating curiously shaped corners where they met the plats of Whatcom and Sehome.

The 1885 panorama of Sehome, which looks northeast along the line of Elks Street (now State Street, see facing page), reveals it as a wide path irregularly defined by the habits of its users. Another view of State Street (see facing page), photographed five years later and looking in the opposite direction from Chestnut Street, shows a parking strip still littered with rocks, weeds, refuse, and even stumps, but the

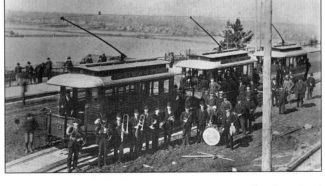

loose planks which span it now connect elevated wood sidewalks with a pavement of planks laid along the centerline of the street. Although the older photo includes a bit of the bay, the town of Whatcom is to the left of the picture frame.

In Whatcom there was throughout the 1880s an offshore push against the tides with piles and planks. Along C Street this wooden reclamation was extended along a trestle to the top of the low bluff above the sandy beach. The 1885 destruction of Division Street by fire added opportunities to this expansion, especially along Thirteenth Street (Holly Street). The opening of Holly is one of the amusing incidents in the development of the Whatcom-Sehome connection. When pile drivers began punching posts for a trestle connecting Whatcom's Thirteenth Street with Sehome's Holly Street, Nelson Bennett, owner of the new lumber mill built at the creek mouth in 1883, sent his millhands

to prevent the closing of this waterway by blocking the work with log booms. But Bennett was rebuffed within two hours by fifty deputized citizens whose interests were aligned more with throughways than waterways.

An 1889 birdseye sketch of Whatcom reveals the latest features of the burgeoning community. This includes the mill wharf which reaches beyond the tidelands to deep water, the Holly and C street trestles — the former marking a new waterfront and the other climbing the bluff to Whatcom's still sparsely settled residential neighborhood. Most of the larger buildings of the town's new business district are constructed on pilings just off shore of the basin. The 1889 sketch, which like many other city lithographs of the time incorporated planned structures as well as extant ones, would be obsolete within the year. For as the new state harbor commission began the long deliberations and litigation over who should use and own state tidelands, the latter were being "jumped and squatted" by speculators in hip boots.

One example. Illinois immigrant George Bacon joined a friend who "looked like a fighter" and staked out a tideland rectangle off Holly Street, 100 by 85 feet. The next day Bacon and his heavyweight friend let a contract for piling the flats they'd staked the night before, and within weeks had added their frame shack to the "miniature Venice" that they and other opportunists had assembled off of Holly Street. Camped in their shack, or "office" as they called it, Bacon and his Illinois friends defended it against the claims of shore owners. Their tactics were ultimately successful after the state gave title to squatters who had lived on or worked the tidelands they had jumped. Years later George Bacon and his pals sold their lot to the Great Northern railway for a small fortune. The 1889 creation of a continuous Holly Street through Sehome and Whatcom hastened their union the following year. When Fairhaven and its neighbor Bellingham (the original Uniontown) were united in 1891, the four contiguous communities on Bellingham Bay became two. The Fairhaven promotion which began in earnest in 1888 was propelled, again, by hope for a railroad, this time the Great Northern. Before the Empire Builder settled on Seattle, Fairhaven had raised distinguished buildings, graded and planked streets, and built sidewalks in anticipation of becoming the terminus. Soon the Great Northern — and the Canadian Pacific, the Northern Pacific and the Seattle Lake Shore and Eastern — did come to Bellingham Bay, but as spurs rather than main lines. By 1901 the cities of Fairhaven and New Whatcom are described in their combined city directory as "practically one, being joined by streets, thoroughfares, and a street railway system operating fourteen miles of tracks in common." Two years later these twin cities were joined politically and with its first election in 1904 the name New Whatcom was dropped for Bellingham.

Above: Looking south across the grain of First Street's sodden planking in Raymond, ca. 1910. Courtesy, Dan Kerlee. Right: Raymond's First Street during the 1936 flooding of the Willapa River. Courtesy, National Archives, Alaska-Pacific NW Region.

RAYMOND: TRESTLE TOWN

The creation of Raymond, Washington has been a process of give and take. It is one of the state's best examples of a community built by deepening waterways to raise land. About eight miles above the bay, the Willapa River divides into two forks. The several sloughs and islands there were settled first by farmers and later by a variety of small mills. This floodplain was not a hospitable foundation for street construction, and the first plat filed for the site in 1904 featured streets and sidewalks constructed on pile trestles, five or six feet above the tidelands. The effect was musical. Or at least as Raymond "old-timer" C. S. Beall recounted in Ruth Kirk's and Carmela Alexander's *Exploring Washington's Past*, "It took a little learning, but ultimately the roar and rumble of cars over planked streets… became a soothing lullaby."

By the time the Bealls moved to their piling-supported home, this trestle timpani had quieted some, for a good portion of Raymond's downtown had already been reclaimed with mud dredged from the bottom of the river's south fork. Work began in 1911 and by 1923 the business district had been filled and its streets paved. Bridges across the main (north) and south forks were constructed in 1911 and 1912, respectively, stimulating the development of bedroom neighborhoods for the mill workers. The reign of lumber in Raymond was predisposed not only by the forests that surrounded it by also by its developers, who offered free waterfront sites to mills and manufacturers. The arrival of the Northern Pacific spur in 1893 and later the Chicago, Milwaukee, and St. Paul Railroad in 1915 helped make the town a manufacturing center for wood products.

EVERETT: WIDE STREETS AND GRAND PLANS

When hundreds from Seattle and Snohomish accepted the Everett Land Company's invitation to celebrate Independence Day, 1891 on the stump fields of Everett, there was no Fourth of July parade to entertain them. There were no improved streets down which to parade. Everett was preoccupied with industry, of all sorts, and with promoting the future townsite as a mecca of opportunity. Henry Hewitt, company president and a principal developer, was a Tacoman, but he had the necessary eastern contacts, including John D. Rockefeller.

Organized in 1890, the Everett Land Company did not file a townsite plat until 1892. Understanding that the appeal and value of its holdings would swell considerably when embraced by a circle of industries along its shores, the company was only faintly interested in streets. While gangs of hundreds were sent to clear the land and open the streets, only a very few were graded or improved. The more important throughway was the grade of the Great Northern, then approaching from the east.

Hewitt Avenue, one of the first pre-plat street developed by the company, was graded and planked through its first half-

View of Chestnut Street North From Hewitt Ave - July 14 1892 Everett Historical Series Nº 5 Courtesy · BERGMAN & FOLLESTAD

Above: A stump-strewn Chestnut Street north of Hewitt during Everett's boom year of 1892. Courtesy, Everett Public Library. Right: View of the same intersection in 1997 revealing Interstate-5's intrusion on the scene. Photo by James Arrabito.

mile west from the river. Although the work was contracted in late November 1891, it was not completed until the following June. One settler later claimed that the avaricious contractor removed by night the planks he laid by day. Even before the paving Hewitt Avenue was described "as busy as Broadway in New York City." Everett's developers were fond of these Gotham comparisons, even imagining that the shape of the fledgling town, squeezed between Possession Sound and the Snohomish River, resembled Manhattan — albeit upside down. The ambitious 100-foot width of Hewitt Avenue set the pattern for Everett's main streets, including its Broadway.

When the Everett plat was at last filed on February 6, 1892, its grid generally stuck to the compass directions. Quickly the longed-for lots were purchased, and a community sprouted. While the citizens wished to incorporate, the company, with its eye on state tidelands off Port Gardner, did not. Tidelands next to incorporated communities were more expensive. The Everett Land Company had consolidated its control by incorporating four utility companies to monopolize water, trolleys, telephone, and light and power. Without political organization and the power to tax for the construction of streets, sewers, and fire protection, the residents — most of them previously strangers — formed the Committee of 21 to act as a town council. When it came in the spring of 1893, the enthusiasm that rode Everett's incorporation was soon bucked off by the market crash of that year. The trauma was compounded when the Great Northern chose Seattle for its transcontinental terminus and not Everett.

The intentions of Great Northern president James J. Hill had seemed promising the previous year when he addressed Everett movers at a banquet in his honor at the land company's Bayview Hotel. Norman Clark in his Everett history, *Mill Town*, writes how Hill's humor was also ambiguous. He commented about "how everyone in the Puget Sound country seemed to have founded a townsite since he arrived; in his week here, he said, he had 'found only four stumps without a name.'" However, Hill assured them, with its lumber resources all Everett needed was "a cheap railroad connection. You will find that we will treat you well. . . . You have no reason to fear any city south of you."

While in 1892 the happy banqueters responded to the

Above: Early 1890s view east on Everett's Hewitt Avenue from Colby Street. The planking on Hewitt is still nearly new as is the young mill town's electric trolley. Courtesy, Everett Public Library. Left: A 1992 wintertime repeat from two blocks east at Rockefeller Street shows Hewitt's new centerline of street trees. In the distance is the bridge over the Snohomish River. Photo by James Arrabito.

Empire Builder's words with "an unchoked roar of approval," in 1894 they rejected the depression-injured Henry Hewitt's offer to sell them their own empire. After Everett voters defeated the land company's proposal to sell them the water works, electric works, and street railway, Hewitt, the "father of Everett," was incrementally cut down. In the end Rockefeller assumed Hewitt's debt but he also unloaded on the town, withdrawing from the company hotel, the street railway, nail factory, and papermill, effectively retreating from Everett's raison d'être, its industrial vision. The following year the Everett City Council turned off the street lights.

In 1899, seven years after his "stump speech," Jim Hill returned to fulfill, and exploit, his prophecy about lumber for Everett. Hill's enormous sale of railroad forest lands to the Minnesotan Frederick Weyerhaeuser directed through Everett a good percentage of the cuttings from the Great Western Tree Farm well into the twentieth century. The original Everett vision of a halo of industry, a Rockefeller ring of smokestacks crowding the shores materialized in lumber mills — ultimately, giant ones. An excursion along Everett's Norton Avenue (now Marine View Drive) became an elaborate inspection of the community's pulp on parade. Marine View Drive follows a shoreline which was first reclaimed for the railroad. Its importance as a throughway for the Great Northern was diminished when Hill built a railroad tunnel beneath Everett in 1905. The tunnel entered the bayside bank beneath Marine View Drive and ran west for seven blocks, one half-block north of and paralleling Hewitt Avenue.

In the century following the railroad's tampering with the Everett waterfront, the shoreline has been elaborately extended with fills into the protected waters behind the Port Gardner seawall. The most recent reclamation here was for the U.S. Navy's home port. Crisscrossing the peninsula behind the destroyers and earth-fill piers, the wide streets of Everett still recall — for those who know how to read them — the big-deal dreams of city

Before this late 1920s application of concrete, Everett's Broadway was paved with creosoted wood blocks which, while cheap, were also slippery and inclined to swell into mounds. Courtesy, Snohomish County Museum.

founders. That these streets are often lined with the small affordable lots Hewitt's company sold to working families is also a sign of the capitalist's dependence on a community of labor.

ANACORTES: CITY OF NECESSITY

Washington Magazine pushed its promotional pedal to the floor when its April 1890 issue concluded that "it is apparent to all who have given the map careful study and reflection that Anacortes sometimes called 'The City of Necessity' will one day be the Key City of the Sound." The new town's advantages were revealed partly in its streets. "The careful and scientific manner in which the town is planned is at once apparent to all who have visited it. The streets, which run north and south, are designated by the letters of the alphabet and those which run east and west by numerical figures." Only four months earlier there were no street improvements and the population was listed at forty. By the Ides of March the figure had swelled to 3,000 and within the year an estimated $250,000 was spent on street improvements, including three miles of graded streets. Through 1890 there were sixty-three regularly platted additions to Anacortes, and the number of real estate houses — twenty-seven of them were counted at year's end — about equaled the sum of saloons. *Washington Magazine* went on to predict "that in one year there will be four railroads with terminal depots on Fidalgo Island, centering in Anacortes." Years later a nostalgic *Anacortes American* editor reflected that "This was the heroic age of Anacortes. Those beautiful solitudes… became

suddenly transformed into one of the most typical of all typical western boom towns, where the boomer boomed, the promoter promoted, the gambler gambled, the grafter grafted, and the sucker sucked." This reflection also recalled the chief oratory at Anacortes's boom year Independence Day celebration. Encouraged by both the real estate about him and the spirits within him, the orator concluded by waving his hand in the direction of Guemes Channel, commenting "There are whales in the straits, blackfish in the channel, and suckers on every corner."

Soon signs appeared to indicate that the Anacortes boom was fading. In March 1891 the heavily financed but underpowered Anacortes-Fidalgo City Electric Railway failed to complete its first and only interurban run. For Anacortes's true believers, the failure signaled that their future as the "shortest route to the Orient" may have been abandoned by the railroads. This turn of events was peculiarly wrenching for Amos Bowman, the town founder who had named it with an exotic variation of his wife's name, Anna Curtis. Bowman, a civil engineer, bought his part of the future Anacortes in 1877. He soon published a map, which he circulated widely, pointing out the strategic advantages of Fidalgo Island's protected deep-water port. Bowman worked with railroads, or at least their revival, in mind. For, as he was fond of explaining, it was only by way of the "purest accident" that in 1873 Tacoma was chosen as the Northern Pacific's Puget Sound terminus and not Ships Harbor (Anacortes). Bowman claimed that by 1872 Northern Pacific officials "had already secured the entire waterfront and… but for the panic [of 1873] would undoubtedly

Top left: On Puget Sound the availability of inexpensive lumber allowed streets to be raised to assigned grades with elaborate timber trestle work. Here, planking proceeds on P Street (now Commercial Street) near Fourth Avenue during Anacortes' 1890 boom. Top right: A collection of Anacortesians pose for the July 4, 1997 annual community portrait on Commercial Street, near Fourth Avenue. Photo by Jon Bauer. Courtesy The Anacortes American. Center page: Early-century promotional birdseye of a new addition to Anacortes. Right: A portion of Anacortes stump-strewn business district in its boom year of 1890. Courtesy, Wallie Funk.

Above: The work of paving Anacortes streets was not made easier by the generous widths drawn for them in the original plats. Two-lane strip paving was a common solution. For other unpaved streets, maintenance was reduced to periodic applications of raw oil. In 1957 Anacortes still had fifty-two miles of unpaved streets. That year, however, was also a turning point for street-paving when the ultimately successful campaign began to persuade property owners facing Ninth Street to pave it with a local improvement district. Other citizens and their streets followed. Here paving, ca. 1912, progresses on Commercial Street between Seventeenth and Twentieth Streets. Courtesy Wallie Funk. Right: The short-lived Fidalgo City-Anacortes interurban. Courtesy Wallie Funk.

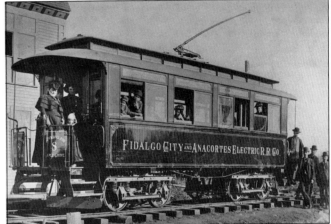

have built their terminal works at Anacortes." However, never in the course of Northwest historian Murray Morgan's research at the Northern Pacific Railroad archives in St. Paul, Minnesota, did he find any indication that Anacortes was ever a serious contender for the Northern Pacific's ultimate favors.

By the time the Great Northern arrived on Puget Sound in 1893, practically all of Washington's city sites had been chosen, most of them in line with the railroads or their spurs — Spokane, Pasco-Kennewick, Walla Walla, Wenatchee, Yakima, Vancouver, Olympia, Aberdeen-Hoquiam, Tacoma, Seattle, Everett, Bellingham, as well as Anacortes. By then the state's city trinity of Spokane, Tacoma, and Seattle was identified. After the effects of the market crash of that year had dwindled, this urbanization resumed at a quickened pace so that by 1910 these pioneer towns were cosmopolitan cities with complex economies attended by public works professionals with responsibilities that included the by-then elaborate engineering of a city street.

In 1910 paved streets in Anacortes were in a state of such disrepair that the locals began campaigning for modern surfaces. Within two years the program of replacing the planks with asphalt was in process. By then the Anacortes waterfront was crowded not with tracks but with lumber mills and fish processing plants including, since 1905, the largest codfish operation on the West Coast — hence the town's new moniker, "Liverpool of the West." The shipyards which opened on Guemes Island heated the economy during World War I. Anacortes' most emblematic addition, the ferry to Victoria, arrived in 1926, as did the public Port of Anacortes. One year later the construction of a gas distribution plant on the Anacortes waterfront prefaced— by 28 years — the 1955 arrival of the Shell and Texaco refineries. In 1962 Anacortes was named among the eleven communities chosen for that year's All-America City Awards. The award recognized the community's new city charter, renewed schools, and paved and repaired streets.

YAKIMA: RAILROADED AND RESTORED

The land-grant Northern Pacific was notorious for its manipulations of the communities along its line. Rarely was it refused what it wanted. As it western terminus Tacoma was more

kidnapped than chosen. The mill town of Tacoma City, which Gen. Morton Matthew McCarver laid out in 1869 as an alluring townsite waiting for the railroad, was missed by the rails. Instead, a mile and a half away a "New Tacoma" was cleared and grubbed on land that Hazard Stevens, son of Isaac, purchased for Northern Pacific, a site whose contours inspired the Olmsted firm to design their imaginative city plan.

When the Northern Pacific arrived in Yakima City in 1884, it repeated its Tacoma performance. After residents would not freely unroll their property before the railroad's cowcatcher (they wanted to be paid), the company extended the rails four miles further north and laid out a new town there. The railroad's offer of free town lots to any Yakimanian who would follow created one of the great sensations of western migration. Most of Yakima City went along, dragging their homes and businesses with them. At sunset, the patrons of the town's largest hotel, the Guilland House, which lumbered north to North Yakima on log rollers, were able

Above: Yakima's restored Northern Pacific Railroad Depot on North Front Street. Photo by Mary Randlett.

155

to survey from their windows a subtly different scenery than that which they had opened their shades to in the morning. According to one of the new town's three weeklies, "There appears to be a regular stampede of buildings from old Yakima northward. Some large business blocks 50 by 80 have now joined the procession." Within a month about 100 buildings in all were moved. Within four months of the platting of North Yakima, there was a post office, government land office, five real estate agencies, five Chinese laundries, an ice cream parlor, fifteen saloons, one church and, of course, a railroad station.

The station was set near the middle of Yakima Avenue, the new town's main street, at its intersection with Front Street. Yakima Avenue was built 100 feet wide and Natches Avenue, a boulevard, 140 feet wide. The railroad even planted 2,000 trees to create what Robert Harris, its president, predicted would be a community "equal in beauty to any in the territory and one that may possibly become the capital of the future state of Washington." Less than a year after it was platted, North Yakima was chartered and soon after made seat for the state's second largest county. The last building to be moved from the old Yakima to the new was the county courthouse.

Yakima's civic center complete with opera house was then along North Front Street, and city hall was to the west of the Northern Pacific depot with the warehouses of "fruit row" across the tracks. Set with the luxuries of concrete sidewalks and a long landscaped park extending north from the Northern Pacific station, North Front Street remained a civic keystone through the youth and adolescence of the "Jewel City of Central Washington." By 1900 North Yakima was the seventh largest town in the state. Its population of only 3,156 was deceptive, for the community was quickly becoming the commercial center for the valley. By then North Yakima's commercial tide was moving off North Front Street, its railroad avenue, and east along Yakima Avenue to Third and Fourth streets. In 1910 Yakima Avenue and a number of other downtown streets were paved with four-inch bricks. Some of this pavement survives — on North Front Street, for instance, beneath a layer of asphalt.

In 1917 North Yakima became the only city called Yakima, and Yakima City had to settle for the old name of Union Gap. By the following year, with 8,000 cars registered in Yakima County alone, Yakima Police Chief J. M. Gilmore interrupted the old pioneer habit of driving down the middle of the street. However, this swelling volume of motorcars and prepared roads considerably increased the city's market influence in the valley. Many valley towns suffered from the new freedom their citizens enjoyed in taking their business to Yakima in the family's own flivver. In the 1920s the city organized summertime autocamps for tourists,

stationed traffic cops at Yakima Avenue's busiest intersections, and, at the end of the decade, installed its first traffic lights.

The city also tried to keep its streets clean of horse flies, opium dens, and Wobblies. In 1910 there was still no regular garbage collection in North Yakima, and the dilapidated sewage system installed in the early 1890s was so inadequate that outhouses were common throughout the city. Typhoid epidemics were frighteningly recurrent and inspired a citywide contest for exterminating horse flies. Some of Yakima's opium consumption took place in workers' tenements beside North Front Street or even, perhaps, beneath the streets in Yakima's mostly legendary "underground." While dope was ordinarily off the street, the Wobblies — Interna-

Bricked Yakima Avenue, ca. 1910. Courtesy, U.W. Libraries, Special Collections.

tional Workers of the World — were above it, either parading on Yakima Street or broadcasting from soap and apple boxes their disturbing notions of class conflict and workers' rights. Regularly breaking the local ordinance that made public speeches illegal within 100 feet of Yakima Avenue, the Wobblies were repeatedly thrown in jail where they typically continued to make speeches.

Almost half a century later, the mostly dilapidated Front Street was largely abandoned, resulting in a kind of preservation by neglect. In the early 1980s a combination of users and owners formed their own North Front Street Improvement Association, intending to restore the street's historic character and revive its commerce. The members themselves did much to repair the street and sidewalks and to revive the historic district, including the original grand opera house, the city hall, which held municipal offices until the late 1940s, and other old, distinguished, and structurally sound commercial buildings. Today, North Front Street's original bricks still hide beneath a patchy cover of asphalt, and the old tree-lined railroad park has been long since clear-cut and paved over for parking. However, the Spanish Mission-style Northern Pacific depot and most of the street's other historic structures have been revived and are being used once again.

ELLENSBURG: AT THE CROSSROADS

It is more than a point of state trivia that the first steamer to make it up the Columbia River as far as Wenatchee was named the *Ellensburg* (See Waterways Chapter). Beginning in 1870 with a trading post named "Robber's Roost," the future Ellensburg became the hub for roads which led north over Colockum Pass to the Okanogan mines, east to the Columbia Basin, west over Snoqualmie Pass to Seattle, and south to the Yakima Valley and beyond that to The Dalles on the Columbia. At first, most of the Roost's supplies came from The Dalles, carried on freight wagons pulled by four- or six-horse teams often driven by teenagers who could best survive the trip. (One stagecoach driver concluded that "there is no hell in the hereafter; it lies between The Dalles and Ellensburg.")

John Shoudy, an early proprietor of the Robber's Roost, was a booster for improving the road over Snoqualmie Pass. His brother-in-law, Dexter Horton, was one of Seattle's principal capitalists and the founder of SeaFirst Bank. Shoudy platted the land surrounding his trading post and named it for his wife, Ellen: Ellen's Burgh. At the request of the postal service, the name was contracted to Ellensburg when the town became county seat of the newly created Kittitas County in 1883.

One of the first acts of the new county commissioners was to improve the old wagon road to the Yakima Valley, beginning at the south end of Ellensburg's Pearl Street. The incipient coming of the Northern Pacific aroused street works in town as well. In 1884 more than a mile of sidewalks were improved, Fifth Street was graded, and Third Street was opened to the depot site. Earlier, merchants on Third had resisted spending tax money to fill the "lake" which had formed on nearby Pine Street. "Let folks drive around it," they advised. Nevertheless, the pond was filled and the road graded.

After the 1886 arrival of the railroad, the biggest event in the early growth of Ellensburg was its "Great Fire" of 1889. Nine blocks, ten commercial structures, and about 200 houses were consumed that summer. After the fire the merchants on Third Street returned to the city council with an offer to give up land for a ten-foot widening of the street from 90 to 100 feet. Refused, one of the petitioners offered "some day that idiot council will wish the streets were a lot wider." Asked what the widened streets would be used for, the merchant responded, "How would I know, but somebody will think of something." As with Seattle and Spokane

Ellensburg, Pearl Street, ca. 1920. Courtesy, Michael Fairley.

after their 1889 fires, Ellensburg rebuilt its central business district with substantial structures, many of which survive.

Other key events in the life of Ellensburg involved the creation of Central Washington College in 1890, the completion in 1909 of the electrified Milwaukee Road (the second railroad through town and the first through Snoqualmie Pass), and the opening of the pass highway in 1915. From its beginning in the 1870s with John Shoudy's blood and cash connections to Puget Sound, the Snoqualmie Pass (See Roads and Highways Chapter) became an object of considerable interest in Ellensburg. Beginning in 1917 the Ellensburg Chamber of Commerce organized volunteer crews to clear snow from the pass. Ellensburg representatives were also active in the Snoqualmie Cross State Highway Association, founded in the 1930s to promote building a paved highway across the state by way of Snoqualmie Pass.

SHELTON: STREETS AND RAILS

On land that he had been farming for thirty years, David Shelton and his sons surveyed a town site on Oakland Bay and called it Sheltonville. Making candid the influence of the rails, he named the community's main street, Railroad Avenue. Other than saws, steam engines were the most important machinery for mill men who built on the Shelton waterfront, for their and Shelton's prosperity depended on penetrating the Olympia Peninsula forests. Until April 7, 1948, when the last logging train pulled away from the business district, the north side of Railroad

Left: A rebuilt Pearl Street in 1890, after Ellensburg's "Great Fire of 1889." Courtesy, Tacoma Public Library. Above: Same scene, 1989. Photo by Bill Burden.

Avenue had been busy with this rolling stock since the mid-1880s.

Shelton grew with, effectively, only rail and steamer connection to the world. The first motorcar did not appear on Railroad Avenue until 1906. Eight years later the construction of the highway to Olympia and the presence of vehicles of all sorts in Shelton motivated Mayor Charles Pritchard to campaign for getting loose livestock off the streets. Also in 1914 surveyors established a new benchmark at the corner of the new town hall and the library, and with this grounding new elevations were set at most downtown streets. The quickest changes of 1914 came suddenly on August 27 when seventeen downtown buildings were destroyed by fire, many of them on Railroad Avenue. In the late 1920s a number of Shelton's central streets were paved, including Railroad Avenue. The slew of accidents at intersections motivated the city council to introduce an arterial system. The new program temporarily stalled when the first man assigned to paint "stop" on the cross streets was run over. The last train to leave Railroad Avenue to its own devices in 1948 left town only far enough to reenter it along a new grade. The removal of the old tracks allowed the widening of Railroad Avenue between Front and Ninth streets, and the razing of the railroad shops allowed the "other side" of the avenue to be eventually developed into a new shopping center. In his *History of Shelton* Berwyn B. Thomas notes that "Perhaps more than any other single change, this opening of the town center made it possible for Shelton to move easily into the automobile age. Many other small logging towns built years ago have remained cramped and have seen their business cores neglected in favor of outlying expansion areas."

SEATTLE THROUGHWAY — WATERFRONT LINKS

In the spring of 1866, a freelance surveyor named H. J. Stevenson was hired by the town's board of trustees to survey Seattle's rough roads and draw a uniform system of street grades. The

primary business strip, First Avenue South (called Commercial Street then), rose so gently in its four blocks from Mill Street (Yesler Way) to King Street that its regrading could wait. Rather, Front Street (First Avenue), the waterfront link to the wild land north of Yesler Way, became the city's first major public work. Even so, the city council did not pass the necessary ordinance to begin the project until a full ten years after Stevenson did his work.

The earliest "profiles" of Front Street photographed from the end of Yesler's Wharf reveal its slippery ups and downs. With First Hill lifting behind its shoulder and the tides lapping at its ankles, Front Street was an ambiguous border for a townsite. In the six blocks north from Mill Street, Front dipped and rose four times. The fourth depression at Seneca Street was actually a ravine over which the locals built a bridge. The regrade eliminated all these ups and downs with the construction of a timber cribbing behind which Front Street was filled and scraped to a coherent grade and comfortable ascent to Pike Street. Except for some modest changes following the "Great Fire" of 1889, Front's Street's 1876 profile to Pike Street is the same as First Avenue's more than a century later.

Front Street's new log embankment served as the anchor from which pile-supported wharves were built out into the bay. By the time of the 1889 fire, squatters and city-franchised railroads had created a territorial tangle along the waterfront. Although south of University Street the fire destroyed everything off-shore, much of the scorched piling was reusable when mended with new caps. The reconstruction went quickly. In a matter of weeks both the offshore streets, Post and Western, were set atop piles while beyond them the several railroads quarreled over the size and position of their places on the new Railroad Avenue (now Alaskan Way).

Although not the first railroad to land on Railroad Avenue,

The same section of Seattle's Front Street (First Avenue) between Madison and Columbia streets (far left and right, respectively), as seen from Yesler's Wharf, in 1869 (left) and 1878 (right) revealing the effects of Seattle's first major public street work, the 1876 grading of the street between Mill Street (Yesler Way) and Pike Street. Much of this improvement involved raising the street behind the timber seawall showing in the 1878 Peterson Brothers' view. Both scenes include the Territorial University on the horizon. Photos courtesy, Old Seattle Paperworks.

the Great Northern shaped its use during the two decades of Seattle's explosive expansion following the fire. Two months before its arrival in 1893, the Great Northern asked the city council for a franchise to operate across city streets in the tideflats south of Pioneer Square, acres about to be reclaimed for industry. City Engineer Reginald H. Thomson recommended that the railroad proposal be rejected. It was a courageous stand in the face of the common attitude that James J. Hill, the "Empire Builder," could have what he wanted in Seattle. But Thomson held firm, noting the network of bridges and grade separations that would be required to accommodate the Great Northern on projected elevations too low for the gravity sewage system. Biting his tongue the city engineer quietly endured the barrage of criticism that his resistance would push the railroad, its yards, and elegant depot into the willing embrace of Everett and/or Fairhaven (Bellingham). Rather, Thomson's resistance insured a rational cooperation between streets and rails (and sewers) in the city's industrial neighborhood.

Above: Work on the north portal of Seattle's railroad tunnel, ca. 1904. Courtesy, Bill Greer. Below: Seattle's Railroad Avenue, spanning nine tracks wide, looking north from Yesler Way, ca. 1905, . Courtesy, Lawton Gowey.

The Great Northern arrived in June 1893 to a shack-like depot at the foot of Marion Street, only one block north of the Northern Pacific depot. Shoulder to shoulder these rivals performed their daily ballet of hazardous switching along Railroad Avenue's rows of tracks. The partial solution to this acrimonious congestion, Thomson decided, existed not on or over the city streets but under them. The city engineer convinced Hill to bore beneath the city; however the tunnel would not be completed for another decade.

In 1899 James Hill returned to Seattle to repeat as his own the warnings Thomson had first directed against him. Hill cautioned the city council that the Northern Pacific's plans to construct a grand depot on Railroad Avenue would shut off the city from its waterfront. The increasing volume of Puget Sound "Mosquito Fleet" steamers, gold rush traffic, and coastal and ocean commerce meant more teamsters and hotel hacks bumping across the barriers of Railroad Avenue's nine tracks to reach the piers. Hill's quarrels with the Northern Pacific were resolved when he controlled it. In January 1903, the two transcontinentals signed a joint proposal to build the tunnel and a new depot on the tidelands, the King Street depot. The boring began in May at the north beneath Virginia Street and at the south below Washington. The 5,141.5-foot-long tunnel's deepest displacement was 110 feet beneath street grade at Fourth and Spring, where passing trains still lightly shake the basement stacks of the public library.

Before, during, and after scenes of 1934-36 seawall construction on Railroad Avenue. The Seattle Engineering Department photographer was looking south from the Bell Street viaduct. The Port of Seattle headquarters is on the right. Photos courtesy, Lawton Growey.

The diversion of passenger and through trains below the city did not, at first, dramatically relieve the confusion on Railroad Avenue. The avenue was a hole-ridden hell to cross, inspiring progressive muckrakers to see in the decaying timber quays a sign of the scabby morals on the waterfront. Switching freight from wharf to wharf or trucking it across the 150-foot-wide timber trestle from the pier sheds to the wholesalers along Western Avenue could be an elaborate undertaking. Built upon a soft bottom, battered below by a sixteen-foot tide range, and above by row upon row of rolling freight, Railroad Avenue was deteriorating. Between 1911 and 1916 the western limit of the central business district was set in concrete with a seawall from Washington to Madison streets. A 1920 levy of $200,000 for waterfront improvements north of Madison street was diverted to the general fund and never used on Railroad Avenue. Some relief came in 1929 when railroad franchises were renewed, restricting them to the east side of the street and allowing only spurs from there to the piers. Episodic fills north of Madison, although frustrated for want of a seawall, did manage to create a partial foundation for a dewatered Railroad Avenue. At last, in 1934 the seawall was continued north from Madison and by 1936 the avenue was protected, filled, and paved as far as Broad Street.

Finally inviting to motorcars, the Seattle waterfront became part of the city's larger scheme for moving north-south traffic through its hourglass shape. The actual construction of the Seattle part of the Pacific Coast Highway began north of downtown with the Aurora Bridge. Not even the intelligent enthusiasm of Bertha Landes, Seattle's first (and still only) woman mayor, could sway conservative state Gov. Roland Hartley into supporting the construction of the Stone Way High Bridge, as it was first called. Hartley had once remarked that paved roads were "hard surface joy rides." Landes was more successful with state legislators, many of whom joined a convoy of state patrol-led buses to inspect the proposed bridge site and witness first-hand rush time traffic conditions at the inadequate Fremont Bridge. With perfect timing the bascule's wings opened for a tug-escorted pile driver. The parade of solons and commuters was stopped for a full twenty minutes, and the jam of an estimated 500 autos and 30 streetcars persuaded the representatives of the 1926 legislature to grant the city $50,000 for a feasibility study. Briefly during his 1928 re-election bid Hartley courted the Wallingford Commercial Club and its Stone Way bridge advocates after the highway department recommended either an Aurora or Whitman Avenue location. But once safely reelected Hartley lost interest in the bridge route and within days the highway commission unanimously chose the Aurora Avenue site. Threatening injunctions, the Stone Way advocates dreamt of building a subway under Lake Union.

The two cantilever arms of the George Washington Bridge first touched on June 1, 1931. Less than nine months later the span was dedicated on February 22, 1932, the bicentennial of Washington's birthday. But from the beginning the founding father's link with the bridge was dropped in favor of its ties with Aurora Avenue.

Work on constructing an Aurora Speedway from Broad Street to the northern city limits continued apace. By the summer of 1931 a widened and freshly paved Aurora Avenue was extended from Woodland Park to the city boundary. The stretch was illuminated by decorative standards designed by Carl Gould, the architect responsible for much of Seattle's civic architecture. North of Eighty-fifth Street the concrete Aurora turned to bricks, a surface so slippery that the county coroner branded it a "death trap." Prodded by Gov.

Hardly more than a dozen cars can be counted on the top, northbound lanes of the Alaskan Way Viaduct, about two years old in this aerial, ca. 1955, of Seattle's central business district. Photo by Fred Milkie. Courtesy, Port of Seattle. Right: Pedestrian safety islands in the middle of Aurora Avenue, Seattle's first speedway, proved hazardous for both motorists and pedestrians. Courtesy, Seattle Engineering Department.

Arthur B. Langlie, the highway department in December 1941 agreed to resurface Aurora with blacktop to the Snohomish County line. South of the bridge Aurora was similarly transformed from a narrow residential street into a wide speedway with limited access. When it finally opened in the spring of 1933, motorists were invited to throttle to a liberal 30-mph speed limit from their last restriction, the traffic lights at Mercer and Broad streets. A visiting highway expert from Chicago described this portion as "the best express highway in the U.S." However, the new expressway quickly became one of the most deadly as motorists regularly raced along it despite monthly arrests that mounted into the hundreds.

With a speedway opened north from Broad Street, Seattle traffic planners turned their attention to unraveling the more difficult problem of moving traffic through the central business district. Again they looked to the waterfront. Included in the mix of 1930s ideas was a renewed proposal for a viaduct for cars and trucks along a scenic waterfront route; yet this was too expensive for depression era funding. Following World War II, the practical and political ascendancy of the automobile renewed this vision, and designs for an elevated expressway were begun in 1948. Intended as a city bypass to ultimately connect Aurora Avenue with East Marginal Way, the Alaskan Way Viaduct would transport northend residents to industries south of downtown.

The first unit of the elevated highway from Battery Street to Dearborn Street was opened on April 4, 1953. The extension south to West Hanford Street opened in 1959. Because it was designed as a means of avoiding the central business district, it was not until 1961 that an off-ramp at Seneca Street was added,

followed in 1966 by the Columbia Street on-ramp. Constructed before requirements for environmental impact statements, the Alaskan Way Viaduct was, by the late 1960s, increasingly criticized with complaints that repeated somewhat the early-century attacks against the waterfront's dangerous and obstructing railroads. Although the two-tier concrete ribbon did not restrict street traffic, it stretched a permanent cataract over the eye of the city. In 1973 Seattle City Councilman John Miller proposed (demanded actually) that the eyesore viaduct be torn down. As of this writing in 1998, after more than twenty years of similar calls, the viaduct endures.

BIKES AND STREETS

Especially after the pneumatic tire was introduced in 1893, bicycling developed into a nationwide craze. Bicycle clubs were commonplace in communities by the mid-1890s, and many of these early cyclists were also activists in the improvement of city

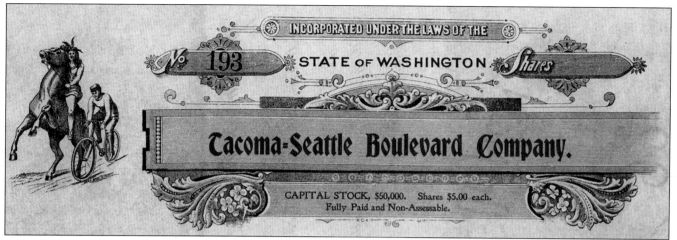

Above: Masthead of a certificate for the Seattle-Tacoma Boulevard. Right: In a basket decorated with stuffed pheasants and owls, a young woman holds the ribboned reigns for the Columbia Cycle float in a Spokane parade, ca. 1890. Behind her is a swan, while below, fit cyclists carry her forward. Courtesy, Thomas Heckler. Bottom: The claims of Tacoma wheelmen that their bridge was the "only exclusive bicycle bridge in the world" made it also the lowest and shortest of its type. Courtesy, Tacoma Public Library.

streets. Wheelmen and wheelwomen gave the Good Roads Movement both its technical and political kick start, testing surfaces and promoting them.

Spokane's first brick pavement, laid in 1897 on a six-inch concrete foundation for two blocks on Howard Street between Riverside and Trent, was not the first hard surface applied for local travelers. Construction of cinder bike paths, paid for largely through license fees, began four years earlier. At about five feet the paths were wide enough to allow approaching cyclists to pass one another safely. Spokane's bicycle "rage" and activism were given sudden impetus in 1891 when about nine miles of city streets were graded, although not surfaced.

Bicycling on Yakima streets was not as safe as in Spokane, at least by the satiric account of the *Yakima Herald* in the summer of 1893: "The deadly bicycle appears to be getting in its work. Elgin Baxter is walking around on a crutch, the result of a knee cut; some wheelman fell over on Mrs. W. W. Atherton's baby boy, knocking out one of his eight prized teeth; and F. M. Spain has lost his mustache, the supposition being that it is due to this destroying rage." Along Grays Harbor local cyclists quickly adopted the new planked road built between Aberdeen and Hoquiam as a speed-way.

In the early 1890s cycling was already a tradition in Tacoma where a bike club had been formed by 1885. Perhaps the most ambitious of the regional promotions for the bicycle age was the Seattle-Tacoma Boulevard, an improved bicycle toll road between

the two cities which was to be constructed through the sale of stock. About eight miles were completed — including a two-and-a-half-mile trestle across the tidelands south of the Seattle business district — before the company went bankrupt. It was difficult to connect the two cities' cyclists politically as well. The Tacoma bikers were so active in the League of American Wheelmen that they controlled its promotion and fund-raising in Washington. Seattle cyclists eventually fled the organization. The strength of Tacoma's wheelmen was also demonstrated on its streets. In 1896 the bike club built what was then the only bridge in the country exclusively for bicycle traffic. The 127-foot-high timber span reached 440 feet across Galliher Gulch. The city also added a $1 bicycle tax, leveraged with fines, to help build its system of wide cinder bike paths.

The Queen City Cycle Club, later renamed the Queen City Good Roads Club, became a significant local mover in Seattle street work. In 1895, future Seattle mayor George Cotterill, a club leader, described Seattle streets as "strewn with wrecks of old planking which had survived from five to ten years of traffic. Spikes, splinters, and holes were the principal features which distinguished the remains." Then the only hard surfaced streets were a 240-foot section on First Avenue south from Yesler Way, which was bricked as an experiment in 1893, and a block of brick paving laid in 1894 on Union Street between First and Second avenues. After the club's prompting, in 1896 the city paved Second Avenue with brick from Yesler Way to Pike Street, although not by using convict labor as the bike club had recommended.

The lasting testament of this activism are the city boulevards, many of which began as an elaborate system of bike trails offering picturesque prospects by way of grades not too difficult to peddle with single-gear bikes. The Lake Washington bike path along the route of Lakeview and Interlaken boulevards opened June 19, 1897. Sporting mileage markers, lunch houses, scenic vistas, and guard rails at exposed prospects, the trails were extended to Leschi,

ing thefts, writing tickets, and fixing the trails. In 1897 he was one of four "bike cops" in the state who together that year reported 183 bicycles stolen, and 1,402 violations of which 1,041 were for speeding or "scorching." Seattle's speed limit was set at 10mph.

For the dozen or so years that it was thrust forward by the pounding hearts and feet of its many enthusiasts, the statewide bicycle craze profoundly democratized the politics of streets. And when the influence of bikes and bike clubs quickly waned in the first years of the twentieth century the automobile, its replacement, followed directly. However, for a few years following the turn of the century, bikes and motorcars, as well as horses, trolleys, and pedestrians, shared the right-of-way together.

Ralph Hopkins, Seatttle's first car owner. Courtesy, Seattle Public Library.

THE ASCENDANCY OF THE AUTOMOBILE

In 1900 automobiles were still extremely rare in Washington. The appearance that July of the first horseless carriage on Seattle streets inspired more satire than auto sales. A reporter for the *Argus* suggested that Ralph Hopkins, the first car owner, might want to give the next "distinguished visitor from the East" a sight-seers' tour of the city and that "when the machine falls to pieces they might take the remnants on their shoulders and trudge over most any sidewalk in the city back to the starting point, falling through an occasional hole, stubbing their toes over spikes that stick up an inch or two, gazing at the beautiful and sightly telegraph and telephone poles which adorn the city." Later that summer Hopkins took his auto south aboard the Mosquito Fleet steamer *Flyer* for another first on Tacoma streets that earlier had been described in the *Tacoma Ledger* as "better for the machines than the streets of either Seattle or Spokane." The *Argus* responded snidely, "There would certainly be very little chance of running into anyone in Tacoma."

In 1904 a one-day count of traffic at Second Avenue and Pike Street in Seattle recorded only 14 automobiles out of the 3,959 vehicles that crossed the intersection. The remainder, of course, were horse-drawn wagons and buggies. However, soon the popularity of the motorcar grew as rapidly as the enthusiasm attending bicycle purchases fifteen to twenty years earlier. In 1915 roughly 9,300 licenses were issued for automobiles and trucks in Seattle. Only five years later the number increased to 44,000.

The marks made by motorcars, it was soon learned, were deep. The accelerating wheel acted like a grinder, and the

Top left: Built in the mid-1890s the first bridge over Juanita Bay became in 1922 Juanita's link in the system of roads and boulevards that first encircled Lake Washington. Six years earlier the bridge was lowered when the lake was dropped nine feet with the opening of the Lake Washington Ship Canal. With the 1916 drop, this portion of Juanita Bay was transformed into a wetland. Above: Although wider than its predecessor, the Juanita Bay Park Causeway is built on some of the same pilings that support the old bridge. For pedestrians only, the causeway and the wetlands on both sides are cared for by a committee of volunteer rangers. Bottom: A fork in the Seattle bike trail to Lake Washington, ca. 1900. Courtesy, Michael Maslan.

Green Lake, Ballard, and Magnolia Bluff. They were financed through a combination of license fees and club promotions, like bicycle raffles and races, and subscriptions from bike dealers or businesses along the paths. Increasingly, cycling was a partner to romance. In 1896 the Comos Cycle Club, a branch of Seattle's Comos Dancing Club, ventured on a two-wheeled expedition to West Seattle and, as it was locally reported, "every gentlemen was accompanied by a lady."

Bike thefts considerably inflated the incidence of street crime through the years of the cycling craze. Seattle's first bike patrolman, A. C. Deuel, was responsible for selling licenses, investigat-

163

emphasis on road maintenance turned from dust prevention to surface preservation. The entire street and road picture was rethought, and silent prayers of thanks were repeated that no large national effort had been directed to building roads before understanding the motorcar's revolutionary demands. (See Highways Chapter.)

Seattle's 1908 purchase of a used asphalt plant increased its paving capacities significantly. City Engineer Reginald Thomson estimated that the amount of street construction achieved the following year amounted to one-quarter of the total work performed in the previous nineteen years. Excluding planking, which the city was abandoning as too costly to maintain, by 1913 asphalt accounted for nearly two-thirds of all the hard surfaces, including brick, wood block, sandstone block, granite block, and concrete, on Seattle streets. By then it was possible to drive the ten miles from Pioneer Square to the city limits at Eighty-fifth Street and Greenwood Avenue all on hard surfaces, most of it asphalt. The city continued to manufacture asphalt until 1964.

Bellevue Style

Few Washington communities have been as shaped by the automobile as Bellevue. Kemper Freeman, the developer of Bellevue Square, the community's mall-temple for well-parked shoppers, was a patriot for automobile mobility and often shared his firm opinion that a driver's license was a motorist's "special declaration of independence." Particularly with Bellevue Square, Freeman helped create out of the strawberry fields of old Bellevue a new retail Bellevue that was easy to get to, park at, and shop in.

Bellevue was largely a creation of the Lacey V. Murrow

(Mercer Island) Floating Bridge. Fifty years before the bridge, Old Bellevue's Main Street was a "natural" county road. Linked to Meydenbauer Bay, it wasn't included in a townsite plat until 1904. In 1913 the auto-ferry *Leschi* began its packet between Leschi Park and Meydenbauer Bay, and the following year the first few street lights were installed on Main Street. A direct route between Bellevue and Redmond was still years away. One teacher's commute between her Redmond home and Bellevue classroom took her through Seattle, riding two ferries, two trolleys, and two auto-stages. In 1918 it was still much more common for Bellevue residents to take a horse and buggy to the ferry and park them in a nearby barn than to get there by motorcar or auto-stage. Two years later Lake Washington Boulevard reached Bellevue from the south, crossing Mercer Slough on a timber quay. By 1922 it was possible to drive the entire distance around the lake, although the going was much rougher and longer than today. A year after the lake loop was opened it sprouted a spur to Mercer Island across a 1,200-foot-long wooden span with a manually operated 245-foot swing truss. In 1922 the present Bellevue Way, the community's future north-south throughway, was

Below: In 1928, Lake Washington Boulevard's route through Bellevue avoided the mess of Peach Street by turning west on Main Street for a more circuitous but smoother path to Kirkland. Soon Peach Street was graded through for a direct connection with Kirkland and was renamed, first Lincoln Avenue and, later, Bellevue Way. Courtesy, Bellevue Historical Society. Left: The intersection of Main Street and Bellevue Way repeated in 1997.

Opposite: A 1946 aerial of Bellevue Square. Above: When still healthy and standing, Bellevue Square's Madrona tree, seen in this postwar scene, was a community symbol. Bottom: Part of Bellevue's modern skyline seen above the cascading waters and promenade of Downtown Park, 1997. Historical photos courtesy, Bellevue Square.

still a cow trail named Peach Street. The creek that flowed beside it drained Clyde Hill into Meydenbauer Bay and once washed away a portion of Main Street.

Bellevue had entrepreneurial optimism. Declining to incorporate, the merchants on Main Street instead launched a 1924 joint-stock operation, the Lakeside Development Company, to support the work of a municipal government with investments (and anticipated profits) rather than taxes. When this enterprise fizzled the Bellevue Business Men's Association returned to ringing doorbells for donations to turn the street lights back on. In 1928, two years after the businessmen relit the streets, another of Bellevue's early big boomers, James Ditty, published a master plan for the Eastside which included widening the rutted bucolic Peach Street into a commercial thoroughfare and thereby shortening by two miles the Lake Washington Boulevard between Bellevue and Houghton-Kirkland. By 1930 this work was finished and Peach renamed, for the moment, Lincoln Avenue. In 1929 Ditty had opened (at the site of the future corner of NE 8th Street and Bellevue Way) his Lakeside Supermarket, a kind of precursor of Freeman's Bellevue Square. Also that year the base of Ditty's customers was considerably widened with the completion of the first mile of concrete paving on the new Bellevue-Redmond highway.

Soon after the floating bridge opened in 1940 (when the combined Eastside population of Bellevue, Kirkland, Redmond, and Issaquah was about 5,000), Ditty's supermarket was joined kitty-corner by a lumber and hardware store with, fittingly, a large asphalt-paved parking area for shoppers. Northeast Eighth Street

and Bellevue Way also marked the northeast corner of Freeman's Bellevue Square. Excavation for Freeman's project began unexpectedly early in mid-June 1945, when the War Manpower Commission learned that an attractive movie theater was part of his design and might keep many war workers in Bellevue. The crowd attending the August 1946 opening of Frederick and Nelson's Bellevue Square store spilled over to the businesses along old Bellevue's Main Street, breaking best business-day records there as well. Also in 1946, just to the northeast of Bellevue Square, Vuecrest, the area's first planned residential community, was laid out with cirques, curving streets, and a gated entrance. The new Bellevue was taking shape with both bedrooms and businesses, and Overlake Transit was running twenty-six trips a day over the bridge to and from Seattle.

Bellevue was finally incorporated in 1953 with 5,940 citizens. Its northwest corner — the large-lot districts of "gold coast" Medina and Clyde Hill where many of those resisting incorporation lived — was not included. With incorporation the city council quickly appointed a planning commission and hired Seattle planner Fred Herman as director, and Irving Rodley as city engineer. The "Bellevue Style" of planning — with off-street parking and loading, restrained signage, greenbelt separation of residential from industrial zones, street plantings, and low building height limits — was an aesthetic nurtured by Herman, Rodley, and the commission. Within two years of their first labors, Bellevue won an award in the All American City competition sponsored by the National Municipal League and *Look Magazine*. The periodical's editor, Pete Dailey, explained "Your comprehensive plan for traffic diversion, a controlled business district and an industrial park has gained national recognition. You have grappled with phenomenal growth and won."

And the growth continued. In less than thirty years following incorporation, Bellevue added more than sixty separate annexations, including Newport Hills, Lake Lanes, Sherwood Forest, Woodridge, Crossroads, Wilburton, Lake Hills, and some of the Lake Sammamish shore. The 1969 annexation of the Eastlake District propelled Bellevue past Everett in the 1970 census to the status of fourth-largest community in the state with a population of 61,000. By 1980 it had reached nearly 74,000 and more than 90,000 by 1995. Over the years, Bellevue's public works department has made heroic attempts to keep up with this explosive growth. The 1963 opening of the Evergreen Point Bridge and plans for the I-405 freeway required considerable retuning of streets associated with those throughways. Toward the end of the decade the department undertook the widening of the Bellevue-Redmond Road and the creation of the Lake Hills Connector through the mostly undeveloped land between SE 8th Street and 140th Avenue SE.

In 1977, old enough to reflect on its past, Bellevue returned to Main Street and named it a "special design district." Plans for the street included new landscaping with siding trees, new lights, and brick-covered sidewalks. Except for the street paving all the improvements were financed by Main Street merchants. It was an eleventh-hour attempt to preserve the remnants of heritage in Bellevue, which regional architect-preservationist Art Skolnick described then as "the best example in a metropolitan area where unrestricted growth has obliterated any evidence of historical beginnings." Earlier, in 1961 the city's symbol, a 100-plus-year-old madrona tree preserved in Bellevue Square, was cut down after two leafless

Above: North Bend Way before and after it was widened to accommodate the increased stream of traffic which followed the 1940 Lake Washington Floating Bridge opening. The widened street was photographed in 1942, and the more conventional street scene some months earlier. Courtesy MOHAI, Seattle P-I Collections.

years. Citizens carried away its branches as keepsakes.

But Bellevue was rarely ever about the past, and while reflecting on Main Street it was also planning a business district that would allow more intensive, including high-rise, development. For a moment in the mid-1970s Bellevue's shopping core was threatened by plans of the nation's largest developer of malls and shopping centers, the Edward J. DeBartolo Corp. of Youngstown, Ohio, to build Evergreen East: another downtown Bellevue a few miles east of the original. Although ultimately defeated, the prospect of this competition spurred Kemper Freeman to go ahead with his expansion of Bellevue Square. It also convinced city managers to adjust zoning requirements. From 40 feet in 1954, part of the downtown was rezoned in 1981 to allow buildings to reach 200 feet or 20 floors, creating the modern Bellevue skyline.

North Bend's Redoubtable Traffic Light

With its neighbor Snoqualmie, North Bend sits at the base of Mount Si, where the Snoqualmie River takes a right turn to the north and the broad Puget Sound basin extends an arm into the Cascade Mountains to Snoqualmie Pass. Sited along the Indian path that used that low pass, North Bend became a combination trading post for persons settling along the Snoqualmie River and a way station for pass travelers. There at the intersection of North Bend Boulevard and North Bend Way one of the West's most notorious traffic lights was installed in 1965.

An early — perhaps the first — automobile to pass through North Bend was the Model T Ford driven by James Scott and H. B. Smith, winners of $2,000 and a handshake from Henry Ford. Scott and Smith won the transcontinental race over Snoqualmie Pass to Seattle's 1909 Alaska Yukon and Pacific Exposition. With the dedication six years later of the Sunset Highway the volume of traffic headed for the pass increased substantially. North Bend was then only one of many small towns whose interests and services might have been attached to the new highway. However, following the 1940 opening of the Mercer Island floating bridge, Redmond, Snoqualmie, Kirkland and the others were left behind as the Sunset Highway made its way directly from Bellevue to the pass through North Bend.

North Bend traffic became so heavy that highway department officials issued the town an ultimatum: either agree to some alterations or the highway would be rerouted around it. So the city widened North Bend Way, describd by *Seattle Times* writer Doug Welch as "a cluttered little thoroughfare jammed with trucks and passenger cars from curb to curb." Nearly thirty structures on its north side were moved back thirty feet.

During World War II, gas-rationing inhibited cross-state travel and so, also, visits to North Bend. But after the lifting of rationing motorists once again headed for the "Evergreen Playground" and the highway town soon returned to form — filling up cars with gas and oil and skiers with breakfast eggs and hash. By 1949 there were twelve gas stations in North Bend — and one

church. Nearby, but off the beaten track, in Snoqualmie there were more churches, seven, than service stations. In 1956 the highway department predicted that within three years or so, they would need to build a Sunset Highway bypass. But the threat to reroute the highway was forestalled. Not three but twenty-three years passed before the North Bend bypass opened.

In the interim the swelling North Bend bottleneck, while good for business, was dangerous and in 1965 the locals petitioned the highway department for relief. The answer was the notorious North Bend traffic light. Highway officials allowed it only on condition that it be manually operated and used at hours limited to safely moving children to and from school and for the annual jamboree parade. Such restraints, however, will not be remembered by motorists who seemed to regularly find the light red. North Bend's weekend traffic jams behind the light are now legendary.

The highway department's goal of having a four-lane bypass ready for the 1971 ski season stretched on to 1978. The delay was largely due to North Bend factions who could not agree on whether the freeway should pass through town or beside it. The courts decided in 1974 that it would be the latter, a bypass one-and-one-half miles south of town. On October 13, 1978 the citizens of North Bend staged a mock funeral for their redoubtable traffic light — the last on I-90 this side of Wallace, Idaho.

With the traffic light gone, the last of the old Sunset Highway visits to familiar towns, each with its own unique pie cafes, truck haunts, and service stations, was lost. North Bend joined Issaquah, Cle Elum, Ellensburg, Moses Lake, Ritzville, Sprague, Cheney, and other towns which for years had served as friendly speed bumps that were once such a welcome part of highway travel.

Richland: Atomic City

In 1941 the *Washington Writers Project* guide book to Washington described Richland as "one of the irrigation boom towns that has settled into a farming community." By 1944 the village of approximately 250 would balloon to 11,000 residents. Of course, it wasn't irrigation alone that caused this boom but rather the government's decision to locate the "Hanford Engineering Works" twenty-five miles to the north that caused Richland to explode. During and immediately after the war, Richland was a government issue town — made of 6,000 prefabricated clapboard houses in several standard models, painted in regulation pastels, and furnished with bland but sturdy government-selected furniture. For fifteen years Richland enjoyed steady growth, all the time owned by the federal government and managed by General Electric, the government contractor at Hanford. People occupied homes owned by the government; they could not have bought them if they wanted to. But rent was cheap — $57.50 for a four-bedroom house — a bargain even by 1950 standards.

The flat-roofed houses were constructed well and with high quality materials. But nothing could enliven their generally

166

*Above: Early reclamation and road work in the building of Richland.
Below: Typical early Richland homes for Hanford workers. Bottom:
Temporary trailer housing for Hanford workers in Kennewick. Photos
courtesy, MOHAI, Seattle P-I Collection.*

monotonous rectangular layout on the floodplain at the confluence of the Yakima and Columbia rivers. It was a deluge that initiated Richland's slow path to privatization. In early June 1948 when the Columbia rose to its second-highest recorded level in state history, Richland citizens speedily erected a "Miracle Mile"-long dike against the coming flood, saving a city that was still not their own. Within a week the first meeting of a temporary community council was held. An elected council and town charter followed, although the government and its contractor, retained ultimate control and supervision over the running of the community. Together the government and the community council developed a "Master Plan" that designated a second business district (Uptown Richland), a mile north of the existing commercial area. The town council was primarily an advisory body, which was fine with most Richlanders. The prospect of having to pay for the fire, police, water, sewer, garbage, and electrical services, as well as streets, persuaded a substantial majority — 2,414 to 1,914 — to vote against incorporation in 1955.

Only three years later the numbers were more than reversed when locals voted 4-to-1 for incorporation of the "Atomic City." (As a sign of the community's attachment to its work, a simulated atomic attack was part of the incorporation celebration. Later, the high school, a state leader scholastically and athletically, adopted "Bombers" as its nickname and the mushroom cloud as its emblem.) The town's attitude toward self-rule had turned around when Congress agreed to help subsidize city services. Richland adopted a council-manager form of government that is considered a model charter for a first-class city. One of its prudent features requires two ballots for every town ordinance — with at least one week intervening between votes. On occasion this arrangement has proved itself an effective remedy against a rush to judgment.

In 1958, the year it incorporated, Richland built a new city hall, annexed 836 additional acres from the Columbia Point floodplain, and took ove the managing of water and sewer services from General Electric. However, the government still had to pay for about half of the municipal budget that year. By then most of Richland's white, well-educated, and highly paid residents had purchased their homes. During the 1960s new companies arrived, including subsidiaries of Douglass Aircraft and ITT and a Battelle Institute "think tank." Local entrepreneurs, many of them former Hanford employees, also came.

In 1970 the Tri-Cities area welcomed the construction of three WPPSS plants. Subsequent growth throughout the area during the decade brought tract houses, fast food franchises, and strip malls with the attendant traffic snarls and displacements — especially in the downtowns of Pasco and Kennewick. These older communities responded with "beautification" and renewal projects in their retail districts. The shift to the malls was especially painful for Kennewick, where years earlier a portion of downtown had been transformed with potted plants and curving streets into a parkade but with little economic effect. Unification of the Tri-Cities for political clout was a popular subject during the mid-1980s, but not compelling enough to effect a merger.

Although Richland was the fastest growing of the Tri-Cities, it was still dominated by nontaxable governmental agencies. Yet it continued to expand with several more annexations, and in 1983 a small part of the Horn Rapids annexation was developed into a 190-acre industrial park. Here the city invested $2 million for streets and utilities, successfully expanding its tax base. (Richland's fortunes were, of course, negatively affected by the WPPSS debacle of the early 1980s. However, even with the diversification of its economy, the city cannot seem to escape its historic ties to Hanford, whether as a future and major nuclear waste facility or as one of the country's primary waste sites to be cleaned. The government may no longer own their homes and furniture, but its decisions still determine whether many Richlanders can pay the rent.

Longview: Progressive Plans

In 1921 after purchasing a large tract of timber in the hills about the confluence of the Cowlitz and Columbia rivers, lumber baron R. A. Long decided to build there one of the great lumber centers of the world. This was the site of the Monticello Convention in 1852, when citizens living north of the Columbia River proposed that they be separated from Oregon into a new territory. Nearby the mills and shipping facilities of his Long-Bell Lumber Company, Long intended to construct residences for his employees. Longview was, in effect, the first thoroughly planned community in the Pacific Northwest: a model "industrial city."

The old Monticello site had been virtually swept away in the big floods of 1866-67, and most of the surrounding farms had reverted to wetlands. To build a city upon this swamp the Long-Bell Company constructed dikes and an elaborate drainage system that converted sloughs and swamps into sunken gardens and a chain of lakes in the heart of the city. The company spent over $9

167

million for draining, diking, grading and graveling of streets, paving sidewalks and curbs, installing sanitary and storm sewers, and light and water systems. Teams of horses pulling scrapers were the "power equipment" used for much of the work. Long further materialized his civic spirit by spending an estimated $1 million on a public library, railroad depot, and city high school.

Long employed nationally recognized city planners to design a city where all "industrious," family oriented workers and entrepreneurs could prosper and live together safely and comfortably. Using state-of-the-art urban design, the planners divided the city into distinct districts. The zoning of land for particular uses was a recent innovation intended to maximize profitable real estate development and control and stabilize the pattern of land uses. According to the central plan, if the city were to grow as an organized unit, rather than in the typical haphazard manner from the inside out, then more land had to be set aside than was immediately needed for industrial, commercial, and residential districts. The open land between the seven distinct districts — retail, industrial, railroad, and the four neighborhoods, St. Helens, West Side, Olympic, and Columbia Valley Gardens — was expected to gradually fill in. By 1930, it was predicted, the city plan would be completed with a population of 50,000.

In its hurry to realize Long's dream, his company also constructed the community's first business buildings and residences. But most Long-Bell Company workers could not afford the latter. It was cheaper to live in nearby Kelso, which was growing at Longview's expense. To counter this flight the company reluctantly built and rented to workers inexpensive houses, including temporary trailer-like shacks on skids in an area just one block off the civic center. This violation of their own building codes remained an anomaly in a model city built for the middle class. However, by 1930 the temporary skid houses were mostly gone as more and more workers purchased homes. Still, by the advent of the Great Depression, Longview's districts had not yet filled in, and through the hard times which followed pedestrians habitually complained about the distance required to travel between the business and residential districts. These criticisms dissipated after the war when the gaps were soon closed.

Longview's classic European pattern is as old as the Roman empire. It was, however, also laid out with the future in mind, specifically the automobile. In this scheme long tree-lined through-streets or parkways, intended to move cars quickly through the city, radiate like spokes of a wheel from the city center. These handsomely landscaped thoroughfares received an exceptionally generous 120-foot right-of-way with 60-foot roadways. Between the radials are city blocks with streets providing access to adjacent areas. Bypasses around town were built to keep industrial and through traffic out of the city center. Finally, buses replaced streetcars whose tracks would have interfered with the flow of the Model-Ts. Although Longview never became the large city its founder envisioned, its design determined that it would grow as its planners intended.

SEATTLE STREETS

Increasingly politicians and planners have turned to restoring historic neighborhoods rather than renovating them. This new politics of preservation was learned from the failures of urban renewal during the 1950s and early 1960s. In Seattle the victories which followed in the 1970s include the many officially designated and protected "landmark" neighborhoods — the Pike Place Market, Ballard's Market Street, Pioneer Square, and others. In every case it was the sensitive handling of the street itself that helped create a binding for the neighborhoods alongside them. This has involved decorative paving, sidewalk plantings, vacating streets for parks, dividing others with landscaped strips, and introducing historic light standards.

Within a few years of its reconstruction following the 1889 fire, the area today called Pioneer Square was increasingly deserted by the city's commercial interests as they moved north. In the late 1950s the city, focusing on "urban renewal," proposed turning the old, architecturally coherent neighborhood into a kind of interstitial service and parking area between the "new" business district to the north and the industrial area to the south. Instead, a nostalgia for Pioneer Square's heritage, encouraged in part by architect Victor Steinbrueck who won a mid-1950s design contest for the

Top: The model landscape of a young Longview city center. Courtesy, UW Libraries, Special Collections. Below left: Seattle's Pioneer Place (Square), ca. 1917. Courtesy, WA State Historical Society, Tacoma. Right: Birdseye for a new civic center drawn for Seattle's 1911 Bogue Plan.

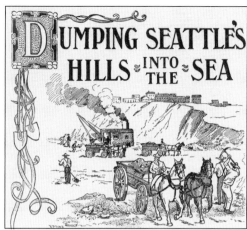

Left: The Denny Hill regrades of Second Avenue (left) and Pine Street (center) encroach upon a doomed Denny (Washington) Hotel, ca. 1905. Courtesy, WA State Historical Society, Tacoma.

square, advocated preservation of the old buildings. Many of Steinbreuck's proposals — notably preservation of the totem, and the Pergola and enlarging the square with the closing of First Avenue in front of the Pioneer Building — were later adopted.

The Seattle Bogue Plan

The revival of Pioneer Square has been decidedly piecemeal compared to the city's first grand urban design, the Bogue Plan. The 1912 scheme of Virgil Bogue reworked the city, from subways to sky-scaling monuments, into a Beaux Arts metropolis that was a cross between Antwerp and Paris, two of its models. The centerpiece of this creation was a grand civic space surrounded by distinguished Neo-Classical structures and tied by a boulevard (Dexter Avenue) to a great railroad depot on the south shore of Lake Union. Located on the freshly smoothed land of the largest of Seattle's many regrade projects, the Denny Regrade, the heart of the civic center would have been near the present intersection of Fourth Avenue and Blanchard Street. However, some of those who had earlier abandoned Pioneer Square feared becoming similarly superannuated by a grand tax-supported enterprise to the north. The objectors with the most at stake were the partners in the Metropolitan Building Company, which had plans to create, although on a lesser scale than Bogue's, a "city within a city" on the original University of Washington campus. First applauded, the Bogue Plan was ultimately defeated by arguments that it was too remote from the central business core.

Looking north from the five-star corner of Pike Street and Fourth Avenue up Seattle's new Westlake Avenue soon after its early-century creation. Fourth Avenue still climbs to Denny Hill (far left). Courtesy, MOHAI.

Westlake Mall

Ascending south from Lake Union through a draw, the route of Westlake Avenue is ancient. In 1872 this natural way was made industrial with the construction of the narrow gauged railroad that carried coal cars from the scows on the lake to the Pike Street coal wharf. Later a boardwalk was added, making a mud-free promenade to Lake Union a popular recreation. But although long proposed as a street Westlake was not cut through the city grid until 1905, creating a scattering of odd-shaped blocks which offered opportunities for open public spaces in the heart of the retail core. Times Square and Westlake Mall are the obvious examples.

With approach of the 1962 World's Fair, Westlake's five-star corner at Fourth and Pike was again examined as a unique civic pivot. The monorail terminated there, echoing the areawide rapid transit system proposed prior to World War I whose elevated monorails also converged there in artist's renderings. The modern monorail invited visions of a pedestrian park, and the eventual vacation of Westlake's last block between Pine and Pike made its further enlargement palpable. By the mid-1970s a local consensus had grown to create there a uniquely shaped reserve for the relaxation and reflection of workers and shoppers. But the proposals that followed were hounded by anxieties over the costs of condemnation and congestion. The open space activists, many of whom had learned their politics in the successful struggle to save the Pike Place Market, had to settle for much of their proposed park being developed into a shopping arcade. The 1992 failure of Frederick and Nelson's Department Store, the mainstay of the retail neighborhood surrounding the mall, also helped create a new concern for the survival of the downtown core. When the Nordstrom Company made the reopening of Pine Street a requirement for their purchase and renovation of Frederick and Nelson's distinguished terra cotta block at Fifth and Pine, Seattle voters showed their prudent consistency and approved it.

Seattle Regrades

Overall, the story of Seattle streets is more about digging — and filling — than about planning. Every downtown street was at some point regraded with cuts or fills altering the street level, in some locations by ninety or more feet. When they recycled the old university campus, the Metropolitan Building Company razed Denny Knoll, the modest promontory from which the Territorial University looked down on the developing central business district. The city's deepest cut — 112 feet — was on Denny Hill (not Knoll), near Fourth Avenue and Blanchard Street where Virgil Bogue envisioned his grand civic center.

LEVELING STREETS IN SEATTLE   O.T.FRASCH SEATTLE 611

The years of great upheaval on Seattle streets began on First Avenue north of Pike Street in 1898. This completed the regularization of First Avenue from Pioneer Square to Belltown which, as noted above, was begun south of Pike Street in 1876. However, the modern regrade era really began the Sunday morning of September 26, 1881, when R. H. Thomson first stepped ashore, looked about, and remarked to his host that Seattle was built in a hole and that he meant to dig it out. Appointed city engineer in the early 1890s, Thomson first turned towards improving the city sewerage and water services. In 1898 he began his attack on the city streets beginning with Denny Hill at First Avenue where the cut further deepened the cliff first made in 1882 along the east side of the street. In 1903 the regrading moved east and up the hill for a deeper incision on Second Avenue, leaving a higher precipice along its eastern border.

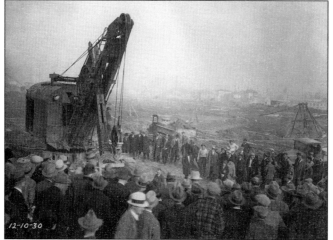

12-10-30

Above: Erosion of the "spikes" or mounds of Denny Hill, ca. 1909. Left: Ceremony for the last shovel full of Denny Hill, taken Dec. 10, 1930. Bottom: The last of the blocks regraded from Denny Hill show improved streets, but no structures, as yet. Lake Union is on the right, and Queen Anne Hill is at center and left. Photo taken Sept. 22, 1931. Photos courtesy, Lawton Gowey and Seattle Municpal Archives.

While the Second Avenue regrade was being completed, work also began on lowering the front hump of Denny Hill, south of Virginia Street, above which the gothic pile of the Washington Hotel rose high above the city. Although apparently doomed, the Victorian landmark had its defenders, including Judge Thomas Burke who proposed saving it and the hill with a tunnel bored directly beneath it and in line with Third Avenue. The tunneling, however, could not undermine the agreement Thomson finally struck with the hotel's owner (and the city's most important developer), James Moore, to shift his affections from the "scenic hotel of the west" to a modern hotel. Moore's new Washington Hotel at the freshly regraded corner of Second Avenue and Stewart Street was ready for guests by late 1908, while behind it the rest of Denny Hill west of Fifth Avenue was being liquefied and run into the bay along the timber trestle flume between Bell and Battery Street. This phase was completed by 1911, and the submission of what was left of Denny Hill did not resume until 1929. Then, in place of spouting hoses, giant steam shovels chewed to the north and east, dumping the hill by the mouthful onto conveyor belts which could be moved to follow the digging.

Even before its completion many believed that the entire Denny Hill Regrade was a form of human hubris more than an urban necessity, for the former grades could have been readily climbed by the automobile. Today's critics, which include neighborhood condominium owners, describe Denny Hill as a lost natural resource. Had it survived it would have allowed their highrises to be stacked up the hillside, offering better views all around.

Seattle's other big hill removal, the Jackson Street Regrade, began in 1907. Here 3.5 million cubic yards of hosed earth was run onto the tidelands south of King Street helping raise 678 muddy acres two feet above high tide. The steepest grade on Jackson Street between Sixth and Seventh avenues was reduced from 15 to 5 percent. Hoping to make the Rainier Valley as accessible to the business district as Capitol Hill was by way of Pike Street, the project's promoters advertised Jackson as the "Pike Street of the South."

On November 1, 1909, politicians and promoters gathered to celebrate the conclusion of the Jackson Street Regrade. One month earlier work had begun on the deeper Dearborn Cut, four blocks south of Jackson Street. For almost three years a daily deluge of 6 million gallons of water was shot at the ridge with ultimately 1.25 million cubic yards of hardpan removed to reclaim 77 more acres below Beacon Hill. Even more than Jackson Street, the Dearborn Cut connected the developing tidelands with Rainier Valley and the neighborhoods east to Lake Washington. Its namesake developer, Ralph W. Dearborn, dealt exclusively in

Left: Scaffolding and flume from failed South Canal excavations into Beacon Hill. Seattle's business district is on the horizon. Courtesy, UW Libraries, Special Collections. Right: Releasing mud from a Jackson Street Regrade pipeline to raise Seattle tidelands south of King Street.

tidelands. "Get the Tidelands Habit and Make Money While You Sleep" was the formula Dearborn trumpeted in banner-sized headlines over full-page advertisements in the Seattle dailies.

Seattle Tideland Reclamation

The first filling of Seattle's great tideland bay began with wheelbarrows. The salt marsh between Beacon Hill and Piners Point (U.S. Navy Lt. Wilkes's 1841 attribution for the peninsula which twelve years later became the first Euro-American settlement on the east shore of Elliott Bay) was the pioneers' dump and the greatest contribution was sawdust from Henry Yesler's sawmill. The earnest filling of Seattle's tideflats began only when the pressures of the expanding city in the early 1890s made its systematic reclamation appealing to developers like Ralph Dearborn and Eugene Semple.

In 1895 ex-governor Semple proposed filling the tideflats, straightening the Duwamish River into a deep draft waterway, and cutting through Beacon Hill to Lake Washington, all at once. Semple announced to the crowd assembled for the July inauguration of his Herculean intentions that in about five years they would all return for a second celebration "to witness the opening of the locks that will admit a great warship into Lake Washington." Semple was a poor prophet. After five years of sporadic dredging in Elliott Bay only 175 acres had been reclaimed from the tides. When, at last, he began his attack in 1901 to sunder Beacon Hill with four-inch thick jets of water for a canal to Seattle's "inland sea," the operation failed because of cave-ins. The flume which carried the run-off over a high timber trestle to fill the tideflats was dismantled, and the work of building a canal shifted for good to Salmon Bay and Lake Union.

Although Semple abandoned the project, both the dredging of the harbor and the filling of tidelands including the creation of Harbor Island continued into the 1930s. In the end Seattle's regraders were so successful in humbling hills and exalting tidelands and valleys that serious consideration was given to even such drastic proposals as filling in Lake Union with Queen Anne Hill. Thankfully, other forces and feelings prevailed.

TACOMA STREETS AND BRIDGES

Broadway Plaza

When the Broadway Plaza was in the last month of its construction in 1973, Gary Sullivan, Tacoma's irrepressible urban renewal director, joyfully revived Tacoma's old rivalry with Seattle. "There's nothing else like it in the state," he announced while inspecting his project. "Cities across the state and nation, even Vancouver, B.C., have written us asking how we did it!... [But in Seattle] they still haven't figured out what to do with Westlake Mall or how to spend millions on the Pike Place Market. We've suggested they move them to Tacoma. It drives them crazy."

Three decades earlier planning experts had proposed a pedestrian mall as an "uplift for Tacoma's often dilapidated business district." The pedestrian reserve was widely supported by downtown retailers, who already in 1944 feared the development of suburban shopping centers. In 1948 the city adopted a master plan that called for landscaping and removing poles and wires from the streets, and a fourteen-block civic center on the hillside behind Union Station that included a new city hall, county administration buildings, art museum, auditorium, library, and other public buildings. It was Tacoma's first glimmer of postwar urban renewal. However, the $2.5 million bond issue to fund it was turned down by the voters.

A variation of this theme was revived in 1963 for Broadway. Here the plan was to turn six blocks of the avenue into a pedestrian plaza with marquees, benches, and decorative lights, making it

Below left: A 1952 aerial of the future site of Tacoma's Broadway Mall, the five-star corner where South Ninth Street (right), St. Helens Avenue (below) and South Broadway (left) meet. Right: An island of public sculpture, center, and the restored Pantages Theater are surviving elements from Tacoma's 1970s pedestrian plaza experiment on Broadway Avenue. Part of the Art Deco Medical Arts Building (now the City Hall) appears on the left. Photo by Mary Randlett.

essentially an urban park. Tacomans waited a decade, however, before the three-acre Broadway Plaza was ready to open. Closed off to traffic, the state's first downtown pedestrian park was resurfaced with an exposed aggregate cement and brick paving, landscaped with 600 trees and shrubs, illuminated by new standards, and sheltered by several large and small canopies.

Besides the commercial boost it gave the shops that faced it, the plaza provided a market for farmers and craftspersons during its first summer. Soon, however, it became apparent that too few pedestrians were enlivening the place. Old traffic concerns returned with proposals for eliminating meters and opening one-way streets. Even so, in 1977 Broadway Plaza was extended south from Thirteenth to Fifteenth Street. The new section, however, included one important departure—it reserved single lanes, north and south, for drive-through traffic. The widened pedestrian areas were again given the amenities of benches, planters, and new lighting, and the traffic lanes were built with a gentle curve, reminiscent of the Olmsteds' original dreams for a curvilinear Tacoma street plan. But with this extension the pedestrian-only door was pried open for a return of the automobile. By 1986 the Broadway Plaza was most commonly referred to as Tacoma's white elephant, and on the advice of a retail consultant two-way traffic was restored to most of Broadway Avenue.

Pacific Avenue

When asked to fashion a predictable and practical street plan in place of the Olmsted Brother's romantic vision for New Tacoma, Col. Isaac Smith drew a conventional grid. He claimed to have been inspired by Melbourne, Australia, which had a major show street, impressive in all dimensions. Smith's show street, however, did not get far past the typical stump and mudhole strewn path until it was graded in 1882. The busy part of Pacific Avenue was then still beside the Northern Pacific railway station at Seventeenth Street. With the population booming in the late 1880s, Tacoma commerce began to expand north up Pacific towards Eleventh Street where impressive two- and three-story brick blocks had been built after the city's big fire of 1885.

Tacoma's sometimes delirious prosperity continued until 1893, when the city's overinvestment in the railroad made it considerably less resilient to the blows of the economic panic of that year than the more economically diverse Seattle. Improvements on Pacific Avenue continued, however, when its boom-years planking was replaced in the mid-1890s with a concrete-based bituminous surface. The city also tried out wood blocks on parts of Pacific but with little success. The blocks were soon replaced by brick which remained in use until the early 1920s when an asphaltic-concrete material was spread over them. In places the 1939 repaving of the street was an archeological revelation of several strata of surfaces, but the immediate objective was removal of the trolley tracks as Tacoma joined the movement "from rails to rubber." The surface applied then, in part with the help of PWA funds, was concrete covered with a solution of pink paraffin to prevent the exposed skin of the new pavement from drying too quickly. Pacific "in the pink" was a temporary condition as the paraffin soon wore away.

Eleventh Street Bridge

Aside from the railroad trestle, no span reached the Tacoma tideflats until the 1893 tide of populist enthusiasm, which empowered the city to control both its own water and electricity, also directed it to raise a span between the business district and the St. Paul and Tacoma Company mill on the sandbar island called "The Boot." The swing bridge carrying lumber wagons and workers was also expected to open the tideflats to more development. But it lasted barely twenty years before it was replaced by the lift bridge that is still the principal route to the tidelands. The new bridge's statistics were impressive — it was one of the largest lift bridges ever built. Two hundred piles up to 125 feet long were driven into the two central piers and 150 piles into the end piers. At its dedication on February 15, 1913, celebrants crossed the new span

Left: Pacific Avenue, ca. 1890. Below: View up Pacific towards City Hall. Bottom left: Paving Pacific, 1939. Courtesy, Tacoma Public Library.

over a pavement of creosoted wood blocks manufactured by the St. Paul and Tacoma Lumber Mill.

Eventually, with further development of the tidelands, the lift bridge was required to do little lifting, for most big barges and ships were directed east of the river mouth to the many new waterways penetrating an industrial district that rivaled Seattle's. This new quietude on the old city waterway also had unexpected consequences for Seattle. Tacoma author Murray Morgan, the bridge's night tender in 1949-50, had plenty of time to write while waiting for orders. Never in the months he was perched above Tacoma's harbor completing *Skid Road*, the most popular history of Seattle yet published, was his writing interrupted by a request to lift the Eleventh Street Bridge.

In 1997, Tacoma's lift bridge to its tideflats was renamed for Murray Morgan. The local author's name was first chosen for the city's new cable stay bridge, now popularly and descriptively known as "Web Bridge," but was switched to the venerable old lift bridge when it was pointed out that the historian had not only once cared for the Eleventh Street Bridge as its tender, but that the local landmark was only three years older than the "local treasure," Morgan. Since its 1997 opening, the Web Bridge handles most of the Port of Tacoma's tidelands traffic, as well as traffic between northeast Tacoma and the business district. Also at its west end, the bridge is a distinguished addition to the city's new cultural center, where the Tacoma Branch of the University of Washington; federal offices and courtrooms, housed in the restored Northern Pacific Depot; and the new Washington State Museum are grouped together on each side of Pacific Avenue.

Top: A mid-1890s view of the Eleventh Street Bridge taken from the Tacoma Hotel. Courtesy, Fairlook Antiques, Seattle. Above: Old swing bridge is turned towards new temporary approaches while pier construction proceeds on the new Eleventh Street Bridge. Courtesy, Old Seattle Paperworks. Below left: Tacoma's Eleventh Street Bridge, renamed the Murray Morgan Bridge in 1997. Courtesy, Michael Maslan. Below right: The "Web Bridge" spanning the Thea Foss Waterway (City Waterway) in 1997. Photo by Mary Randlett.

Top: Birdseye of Spokane in 1884 looking south over the falls. Courtesy, WSU Library. Above: Ruins of the 1889 fire on Riverside Avenue. Courtesy, Spokane Public Library. Right: Trolleys, bikes, horseless carriages, jaywalkers, a single "pooper-scooper" and a "wrongway-team" make an irregular tableau on early-century Riverside Avenue. Courtesy, U.W. Libraries, Special Collections.

SPOKANE STREETS

Spokane's "Main Street": Riverside Avenue

The rebuilding following the fire of 1889 brought alterations to Spokane streets. However, the townsite which "city father" James Glover platted in 1878 was not changed and it still displayed wide streets and sidewalks. Their alignment with the compass conformed with the general east-west direction of both the Spokane River and the city bluffs north and south of the river. It was Glover's plan that Trent and Main streets, between the river and Riverside, would handle the business of his city. However, before the fire it was Howard Street that felt more like the city

center. After the fire the commercial energy moved steadily to Riverside where the first brick block and three-story structure, both at the corner of Riverside and Mill (Wall) Street, were built in 1880.

Riverside Avenue, which soon developed into the principal business street, had been laid out as the widest street in Glover's first plat. He envisioned it as a promenade, "a boulevard or drive along the river bank" as far as Hangman (Latah) Creek gulch. The name "Riverside" is descriptive of the avenue only west of its five-star corner at Monroe Street. Equestrians used this section, which curved along the bluff above Peaceful Valley, for their races. The backdrop included a view of Spokane Falls, which was quite spectacular before construction of the distinguished Masonic

Lodge and Spokane Club between the avenue and the bluff blocked the prospect.

The work of cutting Riverside's lava foundation to grade began in the fall of 1882. When completed a few months later a number of pioneer structures were left exposed several feet above the new street. In 1886 Riverside was distinguished by a new opera house and a horse-drawn trolley line. The line started at the City Park Transit Company stables at Division Street, proceeded west on Riverside to Browne's addition, where it looped around Coeur d'Alene Park (the city's first) for its return to the city center. Tracks were a fixture on Riverside until they were removed for the 1935 conversion to gas-powered buses.

Eastward view on Riverside Avenue from the Spokesman Review *Building, ca. 1939. Courtesy, Jack Arkills.*

The fire in the summer of 1889 started near the old Northern Pacific depot on Railroad Avenue. From there it ate its way north to the river, destroying thirty-two city blocks in about four hours. Reconstruction was surprisingly fast. Within a year a showstrip of six- and seven-story brick blocks stood along the south side of Riverside. But for all its architectural distinction, Riverside after the fire was a roost for the rougher pleasures enjoyed by miners, loggers, and gandydancers. By 1904 most of this seamy Riverside had moved on — much of it near the Great Northern and Union Pacific stations off Trent Avenue.

Before it was paved in 1898 from Division to Monroe, Riverside alternated between ankle-deep mud and thick clouds of dust. Local tobacconier and Riverside merchant Frank W. Smith resorted to parody by operating a minature "ferry" across the street in 1891. The tobacconist's protest pried permission from the city council to span Riverside with a crosswalk. The 1898 surfacing of the street was part of a districtwide project in which concrete was poured as a foundation for an asphalt surface, first on Howard Street, then Riverside, Monroe, Lincoln, Post, Wall, and Stevens streets. Riverside, however, was distinguished by an experiment in which stone blocks were used in portions of the avenue between Monroe and Stevens streets.

Beyond its commercial status Riverside's ascendancy was also symbolic. It became Spokane's parade route. In fact, by 1910, when Spokane's population was reaching well beyond one hundred thousand, Riverside was described as "plagued by parades." Through World War I, parades of one sort or another were an almost weekly occurrence. There were even parades protesting parades, especially as found in the serpentine lines of rambunctious student rallies and the many self-promoting processions for products and services. In the spring of 1926 seventy-six-year-old Thomas O'Brien, described as an "old Indian fighter," got his own parade, and brief national celebrity, simply because he wanted it. Not until 1960 did the city finally restrict parades on Riverside to events described as "beneficial to the entire community."

By the 1920s all the space along Riverside was in use, as well as the space beneath its sidewalks, which was illuminated by glass prisms imbedded in the pavement. Many buildings encroached on the sidewalk with projecting stairs and window wells, and basement stairs off the sidewalk were commonplace. Add the newsstands and the many jewelers' two- and four-faced clocks and Riverside's street scene was a stimulating confusion. The minimalist taste of the 1950s removed much of this vital clutter.

The 1974 Spokane Expo was the catalyst for much of the recent revitalization of Riverside and the downtown. With the merger of the Great Northern and the Northern Pacific in 1969, the railroad depots, which had spread along the south shore of the Spokane River and over its islands, became expendable. The development first of the fair and then of Riverside Park in this area became the bounty of that abandonment. The effects rippled through the downtown with tree plantings, decorative paving, benches, fountains, and a system of pedestrian street crossing bridges— skywalks — which helped humanize the business district, creating between its parts a new sense of physical continuity and community.

Sprague Avenue

The story of Spokane's Sprague Avenue can be compared with the arterial histories of Tacoma's South Tacoma Way and Seattle's Aurora Avenue. Sprague was James Glover's connector running east into the valley where it eventually met the old Mullan Road east of Dishman. Glover platted his arterial on a section line and, with perhaps equal measures of gratitude and flattery, named it for Gen. J. W. Sprague, superintendent of the Northern Pacific's western division. If Glover's community was to be favored with the patronage of his railroad, Sprague insisted that its streets be platted and named. The enlightened Glover acted quickly, naming Sprague Avenue first.

Paralleling Riverside one block to the south, the downtown portion of the much longer Sprague was first graded in 1887 and paved in 1901. In 1900 a cinder path for bicycles was built along the avenue a short distance into the valley. As the city followed its cyclists Sprague was improved to the east with regrades, including in 1909 the filling of a gulch near the interstate fairgrounds. The following year J. A. Perry, secretary of the Spokane County Good Roads Association, announced the imminent construction of the "great Apple Way" between Coeur d'Alene and Spokane. Built through the cooperation of the Good Roads group and the Coeur d'Alene commercial club, the road described by the Spokane *Spokesman Review* was to be "sixty feet wide and lined on both sides with apple and other fruit trees interspersed with English elm and a fountain for man and beast at intervals of a mile."

The actual Sprague Avenue extension was less ambitious — thirty feet wide from ditch to ditch. Still, its boosters noted, that was six feet wider than the standard roadway of the time. By 1917 the paved Apple Way reached ten miles east of the city, within another year it reached Liberty Lake Road, and by 1920 the

Top: View of downtown Spokane across the south channel from Havermale Island and in line with the Howard Street Bridge. Photo by Northern Pacific photographer F. Jay Haynes, ca. 1888. Courtesy, Montana Historical Society. Right: A contemporary repeat of Haynes' view by Jack Arkills. Bottom: North approach to the Post Street Bridge. Courtesy, Michael Maslan.

pavement was completed to the state line. One consulting expert — no doubt, expected to compose hyperboles — described it as the "most remarkable roadway in America." Ten years later the process was repeated when Sprague was widened to four lanes reaching a half mile east of Dishman in 1931 and concluding in 1938 with a four-lane bridge over the Spokane River near State Line.

SPOKANE BRIDGES

When James Glover carried his 1878 plat for Spokane Falls to the county seat in Colville, he probably crossed the river aboard one of the frayed cable ferries installed upstream from the falls. The Spokane River had only two bridges then, one near the Washington-Idaho state line and the other thirty miles downstream near the present site of Long Lake Dam. Yet from the moment of its 1881 incorporation, Spokane began to earn its title, the "City of Bridges." Counting the variety of spans leaping from island to island above the falls and the several bridges upriver and down within its city limits, Spokane in 1915 had, by one reckoning, twenty-nine bridges. That was on average slightly less than one bridge built for every year since its incorporation.

Howard Street Bridge

Spokane Fall's first public work, in 1881 when city residents numbered 525, was a 700-foot-long timber truss across the river at the Howard Street site of Papa Glover's store. The city continued to build wooden truss and deck spans at the south channel Howard Street crossing through the 1920s, unlike the original timber bridges at Monroe and Post streets, which were immediately replaced by steel and concrete. The concrete Howard Street bridge still stands. However, since it became part of Riverfront Park and its seventy-five-foot-wide roadway and sidewalks were covered with blacktop, it bears little resemblance to the continuous beam structure built in 1929. The city spanned the middle channel of the river with a unique steel through truss in 1892, followed by a classic six-panel Petite Baltimore steel truss in 1916. On the north channel a steel through bowstring truss built in 1892 was replaced by a two-arch concrete span in 1907. The latter was the first concrete bridge in downtown Spokane. (For details on truss designs see Bridges Chapter.)

Post Street Bridge

The original Post Street bridge was built by private subscription in 1883 to serve the immediate north side of the river, which was booming as a result of the completion that year of the Northern Pacific's transcontinental line through Spokane Falls.

Five years later the bridge was declared unsafe and the city reinforced the three-span double Warren truss with timber "knee braces" which were themselves soon determined to be inadequate. In 1893 the city was persuaded to replace the wooden structure with a steel crescent-shaped, two-hinge through truss. Since the new bridge spanned the channel from rock abutments, the piers in the stream could be removed. This Post Street span and the steel Monroe Street bridge were the only Spokane wagon bridges to withstand the river's 1894 flood.

The proliferation of automobiles and hard surfaced highways convinced the city in 1917 to replace the second Post Street structure and the streetcar bridge that ran alongside it with a single, wide concrete bridge. The new Post Street span was one of several reinforced concrete arches built in the city during the first two decades of the century. Constructed in 1908, the three ribbed-arch Washington Street Bridge is the oldest surviving concrete arch highway bridge in the state. Although nearly inundated, both of these concrete spans withstood the battering of the great flood of 1931.

Monroe Street Bridge

The concrete arch which crosses the river at the lower end of the falls where the water rushes through a 140-foot gorge is, for many witnesses, the city's most satisfying structure. It is the third bridge to span the Spokane River in line with Monroe Street.

The first Monroe Street Bridge was a 1,240-foot-long timber trestle, completed in 1888. Besides its pedestrian and equestrian uses, it was also designed to carry cable cars. However, the two spans over the water were supported only by a single small masonry pier in the river. Even after it was reinforced, the bridge continued to shake and sway so much that some workmen refused to labor on it while the cable car was in use. Few bridge workers or citizens were displeased when the timber span burned in July 1890.

The three-span cantilever steel bridge that replaced it in 1891 was a great improvement. At first the straightened deck eliminated the roller coaster thrills of crossing the falls. Later, however, by 1907, when elephants in a Ringling Brothers Circus parade refused to cross it, the structure vibrated even with light pedestrian use. Designed for maximum economy, the bridge was too light to carry the increasing loads of streetcar traffic.

The 1912 concrete Monroe Street Bridge was designed with a fifty-foot-wide roadway to carry a double-track electric trolley line, a highway, and two nine-foot sidewalks cantilevered from the deck. The

The three Monroe Street Bridges. Top to bottom: the 1888 timber span; the 1891 steel cantilever; and the 1912 concrete arch. Courtesy, UW Libraries, Special Collecions.

massive 281-foot-long center arch is flanked by two 120-foot side arches with the main piers located on the rock cliff at the north shore and on the south shore at the edge of the water. Because the ribbed arches exert such a tremendous horizontal thrust on the piers, the latter are twenty-four feet wide. When it was completed the Monroe Street Bridge was the largest monolithic arch in the country. The graceful architecture of the concrete arches have made it the city's favorite artistic subject, and it eventually replaced the old city hall on the seal of the City of Spokane.

BOULEVARDS AND PARKWAYS

Spokane

Above: Aubrey Lee White. Courtesy, Spokane Public Library. Right: One of the three rock-faced pillars which distinguish Spokane's Rockwood Boulevard. Photo by Jack Arkills. Far right: A portion of the brick retaining wall designed in 1913 by W.R.B. Wilcox for Seattle's Queen Anne Boulevard. Courtesy, Lawton Gowey.

Much of Spokane's early-century Progressive interest was directed toward developing parks and the boulevards and parkways that connected them. One of the leaders in this movement was Aubrey Lee White, for many years the president of the Spokane Board of Park Commissioners. As a young man in the 1890s, White began exploring Spokane's natural setting, touring it by buggy and recording its features, especially the views. After a stint in New York City selling mining stock for one of Spokane's pioneer capitalists, White returned to Spokane imbued with the values of City Beautiful planning— most famously represented by the Boston-area landscaping firm, the Olmsted brothers.

Under White's direction the newly formed park commission hired the Olmsted firm in 1907 to draft a general plan for Spokane's parks and boulevards (work they also performed for Seattle, Portland, and scores of other communities nationwide). The streets part of the Olmsted's plan described "eight boulevards or parkways, diagonal avenues for architectural variety, decorated squares and ornamental trees along the streets." Typically, the Olmsteds made imaginative use of the city's canyons, bluffs, and basalt ridges, as well as the gently curving path of the Spokane River. Their work was both the trigger for increasing the city's commitment to funding parks and boulevards and a guide to several real estate developers who either conformed to their visions or did variations on them. Rockwood Boulevard in particular with

Below: The Lake Washington Boulevard curve between Colman and Mount Baker parks. This scene was taken before the nine-foot lowering of the lake for the ship canal. The view looks south towrds Mt. Rainier, which in this case is more obligatory than real—the mountain has been stripped into the photo.

its wide sweeping curves, the verdure of its center parking strip, and the wealth of its neighbors resembled the kind of idyllic patrician parkway that much older affluent neighborhoods in eastern cities gained only after years of investment and grooming.

Looking down on the city center from the rim of its southern bluff, Cliff Drive was another of the Olmsted's desiderata. It is still Spokane's classic postcard prospect and so also its lovers' lane. Cliff Drive, however, was not developed until the early 1930s. Then the combination of a *Spokesman Review* campaign, city council activism, and the need for employment overwhelmed a quarter-century of resistance from property owners on the bluff. In 1931 a gang of out-of-work married men graded the drive from Wall Street to Grand Boulevard. Two years later it was paved. Other White-Olmsted inspired boulevards and parkways include Manito Boulevard, Highdrive Parkway, Upriver and Downriver drives, Rimrock Drive, and Elliott Drive.

Aubrey White was, of course, an energetic promoter of trees. In 1915 when the parks department cut back its subsidy for street plantings, White appealed to homeowners to plant street trees at their own expense. As Spokane historian John Fahey notes, the generous citizen "response turned Spokane from a city of pines to one of elms, locusts, maples, and oaks." When White retired from the Board of Park Commissioners in 1921, he left Spokane with one of the largest park systems in the country and a network of drives, boulevards and parkways, including the Aubrey L. White Parkway Drive in Riverside State Park.

Seattle

In 1903, when the Olmsted firm came to Seattle, they proposed adding enough new parks and playgrounds that no home would be more than one-half mile from one, and that the city and its parks be linked by a system of boulevards and parkways. During his stay in Seattle John Olmsted spent much of his time trekking about Seattle hills, making notes and taking photographs. Five years later the Olmsteds returned for a retuning and amplification of their plan to include the large areas annexed to Seattle the year before. By 1909 the Olmsted proposals had materialized to such a degree that the park department could boast, with some justification, that "Seattle, though a young city, today stands

Above: Early-century view from Beacon Hill across Seattle's tidelands and along line with the Spokane Street viaduct to West Seattle. The trestle in the foreground is in line with what is today Airport Way. Below: Lake Washington Boulevard at Colman Park. Photos courtesy, MOHAI.

foremost of the cities on the Pacific Coast in the matter of parks… and with the development of its system as outlined by the Olmsted Bros., it will take rank with the leading cities of the U.S."

For parkways and boulevards the Olmsted plan concentrated in the beginning on the west shore of Lake Washington, ultimately linking Seward Park on the south with Washington Park and the University of Washington Arboretum on the north with the Lake Washington Boulevard. The Olmsted recommendation that the city purchase the entire "Yesler Slide" — the ridge above the lake between Mount Baker Park and Denny Blaine Park — for a Rainier Crest Drive, was declined as too expensive. Instead, the city supported the construction of a lower serpentine parkway in time for the multitudes of touring motorists expected for the 1909 AYP. The new parkway ran through the string of parks — Colman, Frink, and Leschi — that extended from the shoreline up the lower reaches of ridge's eastern slope. The nine-foot drop of Lake Washington in 1916 for the building of the Lake Washington Ship Canal considerably widened the park strip between the boulevard and the lake.

In one form or another the Olmsted boulevards and parkways reached most of Seattle's hills, parks, and promontories. The old Lake Washington bike trail that wound about the north end of Capitol Hill was eventually included in the system as Interlaken Boulevard. Although originally rebuffed by the park board, a citizen campaign to include a scenic circle atop Queen Anne Hill was also incorporated into the plan. Although many of the existing streets were too narrow for the Olmsted's expansive taste, one feature of the Queen Anne drive, the ornamental Wilcox Wall where Highland Drive curves into Eighth Avenue West, is among the city's finest street works.

By their own description the Olmsted landscapes were meant in part to pacify a city of "unsympathetic strangers." The father of the firm, Frederick Law Olmsted, concluded that "parks tend to weaken the dangerous inclinations." However, the Olmsted boulevards were, frankly, meant for the few who could afford to run their horses and carriages through the many picturesque delights prepared for them along the way. The masses were expected to take trolleys directly to the often kitschy attractions of waterfront parks or visit neighborhood parks or playgrounds, usually on foot. Nevertheless, today by any accounting the Olmsted heritage is one of the foundation stones of Seattle's periodically vaunted "livability."

SEATTLE BRIDGES

Seattle's early boosters were fond of describing it as a city with seven hills. This Roman allusion is still a commonplace in the Queen City—or Emerald City, as the latest promotion would have it. The allusion is, of course, an illusion. As any Seattle map with topographic lines will reveal the city has not seven hills but seventeen or seventy. The number depends on what one counts as a summit. Add all these hills with Seattle's many waterways and you get more than 160 city bridges. Include the spans within city limits that are controlled by the state and the number noticeably inflates.

Seattle settlers built their first village bridge on Commercial Street (First Avenue South) one half block or so south of Mill Street (Yesler Way). The rudimentary span kept Piner's Point, the four-block-long peninsula on which the original business district was developed, connected with the rest of the community when the combination of extremely high tide and stiff breeze briefly made the point an island. The first municipally funded bridge was probably the improved span built across the Seneca Street ravine during the 1876 regrade of Front Street (First Avenue) between Mill and Pike streets.

When steel was first used on Seattle bridges, the city already had a population of 240,000. In 1911 the city built three steel spans: the Twelfth Avenue South Bridge (Jose Rizal Bridge) with timber approaches over the freshly dug Dearborn Cut (see pg. 168); a shorter steel bridge on Yesler Way spanning Fifth Avenue South; and on First Avenue South near Michigan Street the first steel swing bridge across the Duwamish River.

The rapid expansion of the city following the 1889 fire was facilitated by the construction of lengthy timber trestles south along the base of Beacon Hill and north across the tidelands at the base of Queen Anne Hill. Both the Grant Street plank road to South Seattle and the West Street and North End Electric Railway trestle to Ballard were built by trolley companies, as was the timber trestle completed to Fremont along the west shore of Lake Union in 1890. When the Fremont trestle opened for trolleys in the fall of that year, the little lake steamers, which earlier had relieved

Above: Fremont Bridge construction. Courtesy, Lawton Gowey and Seattle City Archives.

north end settlers from the drudgery of having to travel the old military and wagon roads, were quickly abandoned. Eventually these privately constructed trestles were filled for streets: Grant Street for Airport Way, the Ballard route for Elliott Avenue and Fifteenth Avenue NW and the trestle to Fremont for Westlake Avenue.

Before the Lake Washington Ship Canal required the construction of Seattle's necklace of bascule bridges, the old log canal at Montlake and the Lake Union outlet at Fremont were crossed by primitive wooden spans. The Fremont Mill Company's bridge at the outlet was built beside a dam meant to control the level of Lake Union for protection of the mill and its pond. The spillway there was a favorite place for snagging salmon with makeshift hooks tied to broom handles or longer pieces of wood salvaged from the mill debris. In 1914 the center section of the span, which connected to Fremont's business district at Thirty-fourth Street, was swept away when the dam between it and the lake broke. Although repaired a year later the bridge was again cleaved, this

Below: Completed Fremont Bridge with the temporary Stone Way Bridge beyond, 1917. Courtesy, Lawton Gowey and Seattle City Archives. Insert: Campaign literature for construction of the University Bridge. Courtesy, Dan Kerlee.

Above left: A new University Bridge with wooden trestle approaches, 1920. Right: Construction on Ballard's 15th Avenue Bridge, 1917.

time intentionally for the construction of the bascule bridge. Built only thirty feet above the water the Fremont bascule opens so frequently to passing masts that motorists are inclined to believe local claims that it is "the busiest drawbridge on the planet earth."

Like the Fremont "teeter-totter," the Ballard bascule was opened for use in 1917, the year the ship canal was dedicated. Built in line with Fifteenth Avenue NE, the bridge was one block west of its predecessor, the low timber trestle that touched at Fourteenth Avenue, Ballard's only boulevard. In the University District as well, the new bascule was constructed alongside of the bridge it replaced. The old Latona Bridge was dedicated on July 1, 1891, precisely twenty-eight years to the day before the 1919 dedication of the University bascule. (The Latona Bridge was in line with the present Interstate-5 Lake Washington Ship Canal Bridge across Portage Bay.) In 1932 the wooden approaches to the University Bridge were rebuilt

Above: The North Bridge over the west waterway to Pigeon Point and West Seattle, 1928. Bottom: Montlake Bridge construction, 1925. All photos on this page courtesy, Lawton Gowey and Seattle Municipal Archives.

in steel supported on concrete piers (Franklin D. Roosevelt pressed the dedicatory golden key at the White House), a conversion also given the Ballard Bridge eight years later.

The last of the canal's simple trunnion bascules was completed in 1925 across the Montlake Cut. The architectural distinction of this short span is its "Academic Gothic" style designed to complement the architecture of the nearby University of Washington campus. Three of the Montlake Bridge piers were incorporated into the construction of the canal. The fourth pier and the rest of the bridge had to wait the persistent activism of its neighbors, notably the University of Washington Athletic Department. For the 1920 dedication of Husky Stadium, Graduate Manager Dar Meisnest tied together a row of barges to let fans from the south side of the Montlake cut reach the UW-Dartmouth football game. Thereafter, the inventive Meisnest became a leading promoter for the bridge. (See Highways Chapter for descriptions of Seattle's Aurora and Lake Washington Ship Canal bridges.)

The Duwamish Waterway also has its string of bascules — although today

depleted. A year before the UW Athletic Department got its bridge at Montlake, West Seattle's first bascule over the West Waterway of the Duwamish was christened by Miss Sylvia Tell's interpretive dancers from Cornish Arts School. Although called "Bridge No. 1," it was actually the fourth span connecting West Seattle with Seattle along Spokane Street. The first, built about 1900, was merely a swing gate in the long timber trestle that extended across the tideflats. A second bridge designed in 1910 and another in 1917 were both termed "temporary." Doubling as the carrier of West Seattle's source of fresh water, the earlier of these two swing bridges had the habit of turning off neighborhood baths and sprinklers as often as it opened to let ships enter and leave the waterway.

After Bridge No. 2, the North Bridge, was added to No. 1 in 1930 and the east and west traffic divided between them, the old complaints from West Seattle commuters were quieted for a number of years. The addition of the Spokane Street viaduct in 1944 reinforced this temporary peace. However, the noise reported when Capt. Rolf Neslund plowed his gypsum carrier ship the *Chavez* into the North Bridge on June 11, 1978, was merely antiphonal to West Seattle's trumpeting for a high bridge. And in five years they got it through the combined clout of Senators Jackson and Magnuson, Jimmy Carter's transportation secretary Brock Adams, and Seattle Mayor Charles Royer. Below the new span the remaining bascule on Spokane Street was dismantled and in its place was built the only concrete swing span in the world. At

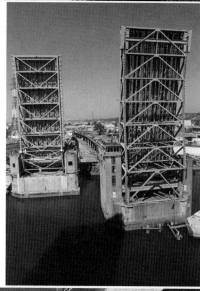

Above: The Boeing "Red Barn" being transported through the First Avenue South Bridge enroute to its new home at the Museum of Flight, 1975. Right: New and old First Avenue South bascules, left and right, respectively. Photo by Nick Cirelli. Below: Construction on the West Seattle High Bridge, 1983. Courtesy, Seattle Engineering Dept.

7,500 tons, it is the planet's heaviest movable structure, opening and closing on average six or seven times a day.

The First Avenue South Bridge across the waterway floats — or nearly does. Its semi-floating cellular piers of reinforced concrete were the solution for the generally unstable soil conditions on the Duwamish flood plain. The piers connect to the river bottom by two reinforced concrete struts. The First Avenue South Bridge has been one of Seattle's most notorious spans, generating, since its opening in 1956, more casualties than any other. Built parallel to and east of the original bridge, a second span was designed to reverse this perilous record. Paved with a concrete which reduces skidding, when the bridge was completed in 1997, the new bascule became the third longest in the country with a span of 294 feet between pivot points.

Above: Aberdeen Fire Department rigs amid the ruins left by the city's Great Fire of 1903. Bottom left: Many Aberdeen residences, including these at D and First Streets, were built on pilings, and the way to the front door was by timber trestle. Bottom right: The participants in Aberdeen's 1908 Independence Day celebration still paraded on Heron Street, which was planked above a foundation of piles and rubble. Courtesy, U.W. Libraries, Special Collections.

ABERDEEN HOQUIAM: FROM PLANKS TO BRIDGES

Set on aromatic tideflats at the confluence of the Wishkah and Chehalis rivers, Aberdeen was nicknamed Plank Town. By the first impression of Mrs. A. D. Woods who arrived there in 1885, the year after it was platted, Aberdeen was a labyrinth of vegetation and deep sloughs. "The only semblance of a street was the elevated one-plank sidewalk." A contemporary told of a Methodist minister who arrived with saddles, explaining that his wife was "very

fond of horseback riding." He was quickly told, "Mister, the only animal you'll ride in these parts is a sturgeon." Although not suitable for horses or wagons, Aberdeen's elevated walkways quickly proliferated above the flood plain. As a rule they were two planks wide in the business district and one plank everywhere else.

While Woods was recording her impressions, the town mills began to dump their wastes, causing real streets to slowly rise. Once the sawdust streets were piled high enough, 4 by 12-foot timbers, which would generally last about four years, were laid over them. The busiest streets, like Heron, required more frequent resurfacing. Following the big fire of 1903 that consumed 140 buildings on fourteen city blocks, several buildings on Heron were rebuilt on friction piles supported entirely by the friction of the earth surrounding them. Like piles, planking was so plentiful in Aberdeen that non-wood paving wasn't introduced until 1908, and then it caused an upheaval. Before Heron Street could be paved with brick, all its rotting sawdust had to be replaced with 17,000 yards of earth (by modern calculation, about 1,700 dump trucks full). As late as 1919 planks were still covering twenty-six of Aberdeen's fifty-six miles of streets. This pattern was repeated in South and East Aberdeen, Hoquiam, and Cosmopolis as well.

In 1890 a bridge was finally built to connect the "twin cities" of Aberdeen and Hoquiam. Although it was really just another planked trestle, it was big enough to handle the sudden loads of sawmill workers rushing to and from work. The following year spans were constructed across the Chehalis and Wishkah rivers. The former was a toll bridge connecting Aberdeen with the homes of mill workers in South Aberdeen. Named for its developer, Aberdeen mill owner, A. J. West, the West Bridge also carried the trolley line that ran through South Aberdeen to Cosmopolis. It held together until the early 1920s when its southern span collapsed into the river and a nearby railroad bridge was quickly planked for one lane of automobile traffic until the old bridge could be returned to service. The West Bridge served until the new bascule state highway bridge over the Chehalis River opened in January 1956. The 1891 Wishkah River Bridge entered Aberdeen at Heron Street. Ultimately, this was Aberdeen's connection to the world — through Olympia by State Route No. 9.

Since they were first surmounted, the three rivers have seen a variety of bridges come and go. At the Hoquiam River, a wooden swing bridge replaced a pedestrian trestle and by 1906 electric trolleys were crossing it with regular service to and from Aberdeen. Briefly, in 1911, an autobus company competed with the trolley service between Aberdeen and Hoquiam. The planked road, however, was so slick that within a week the bus slipped into a slough and the unhappy promoter abandoned it (See following page). In 1928 the Puget Sound Bridge and Dredging Co. erected a 1,980-foot-long bridge with a 200-foot bascule span at the Hoquiam crossing. Most recently, in 1971, a second large span, the Riverside Bridge, completed a four-lane widening of the Olympic Loop Highway between

Top: Enroute to a second life over the Chehalis River near Satsop, part of the dismantled Humptulips Bridge is barged through the opening of Hoquiam's Simpson Street Bridge. The bascule bridge over the Hoquiam River dates from 1928, the year it replaced Hoquiam's old swing bridge at Eighth Street, seen below. Above: The old West Bridge to South Aberdeen and its planked roadway in their latter days, December 1955. Photos courtesy, Jones Photo Company, Aberdeen.

Montesano and Hoquiam. In 1926 a bascule bridge also replaced the old Heron Street Bridge over the Wishkah River. Bridge traffic counts there between 1921 and 1931 revealed that daily vehicular crossings had more than doubled from 2,800 to 6,000, accompanied by a free fall in pedestrian counts from nearly 3,800 a day to a number the tabulators considered too insignificant to record. The daily crossing over the Wishkah in 1980 revealed the effects of a half-century of growth and consumer spending. The count had risen to over 24,000.

Right: This Jones Photo Company aerial is a panoramic record of the Chehalis River estuary, its communities and bridges, the Port of Grays Harbor facilities (above, center), as well as Bowerman Basin and the Port airport (top center).

The Grays Harbor Automobile Omnibus Company's interurban bus service between Aberdeen and Hoquiam was an effort distinguished by both its entrepeneurial optimism and its speedy demise. Described as a "monster automobile" by the local press, it was delivered from San Francisco by steamer July 16, 1901. In a tongue-in-cheek report, the Aberdeen Daily World *concluded, "Thus the Grays Harbor leads the country in all things, and innovations multiply with us. The next improvement will be a line of airships between Aberdeen and Westport." Two weeks later the steam-powered Omnibus' steering failed while returning from Hoquiam on the planked road which connected the "twin cities." The common carrier quickly turned from the trestle and dropped to the tidelands, severely injuring two passengers. Although the service was not revived, the planked road continued to be a favorite speedway for local cyclists. Note the resting bike on the right of the crash scene. Photos courtesy, Jones Photo Company, Aberdeen.*

URBAN MASS TRANSPORTATION

Municipally owned mass transportation arrived piecemeal and late. Seattle did not tentatively enter this field until 1914, thirty years after horse cars were first pulled along their tracks on Second Avenue. It required five years more before the arguments about "natural monopolies" convinced Seattle Mayor Ole Hanson to purchase the city's many private transit systems. Tacoma and Spokane did not control their transit systems until 1961 and 1968, respectively.

Not counting the few stage lines, urban mass transportation began with horse cars in the mid-to late-1880s. Municipalities had some control over the companies, which were often the target of complaints and even an occasional boycott. The city could stipulate rates, demand schedules, inspect for safety, and require the trolley companies to care for areas of the street between and contiguous to their tracks. A city's power, however, began with the awarding of franchises and requests could be refused. In 1885 the city council rejected the first petition it received for a horse car that would have tied together old and new Tacoma, explaining simply that the city was not ready for it. Three years later it was, and Nelson Bennett, the first of a slew of Tacoma "trolley tycoons," inaugurated his horse line on Pacific Avenue. Because it was the first, Bennett's franchise controlled the best streets. With their introduction in 1884, Seattle's "bob tail" horsecars were shunted to Second

Above: The turntable at the Elliott Bay end of Seattle's Madison Street Cable Railway, ca. 1900. Both top and above right: Horse-cars on Olympia and Spokane streets, respectively. Bottom: One of Port Townsend's short-lived electric trolleys. Photos courtesy, Lawton Gowey.

Avenue from Front Street by merchants who did not want their street cluttered with tracks. In a few places, notably Seattle and Spokane, the horse cars were removed for both cable and electric lines. In Seattle three cable lines held on well into the next century, but the rest of the city's pioneer lines switched to electricity. By 1890 in Spokane there were already thirty-four miles of street railways in operation, involving one horse, one electric, and three cable companies.

Ordinarily, several franchises in a community were united under the control of the wealthiest among them. Spokane's 1892 merger was first and Tacoma's next in 1898, when the Tacoma Railway & Power Company united what was left of the trolley companies after the 1893 financial panic. In Seattle the Boston-based power and traction enterprise, Stone and Webster, applied its considerable financial clout in a spending spree that began in 1900 and ended in 1907 with the control of all but one of Seattle's trolley companies. Rather then merge during the 1893 depression Port Townsend's three lines failed together.

Through these early years urban transportation was a kind of egalitarian monopoly in which the affluent and the indigent sat side by side for a ride to the office or mill. The trolleys were also the route to weekend recreation and romance. Many lines reached from downtown through the forest to special retreats in picturesque spots like Natatorium Park in Spokane, Point Defiance Park in Tacoma, and Ravenna Park in Seattle.

Seattle's swim into municipal control began with a cautious dip but quickly kicked itself into a reckless freestyle. In 1911 Seattle voters approved the purchase of the one line not controlled by Stone and Webster. Even though nothing actually came of the acquisition, the city did cautiously purchase and improve lines to Burien and Ballard. These prudent immersions were followed by the plunge of 1919 when Seattle Mayor Ole Hanson, buoyed by his success that winter in ending the city's general strike, paid, or

promised to pay, Stone and Webster the imprudent price of $15 million for their rundown conglomerate of electric and cable lines — about three times its value. From its appropriate April 1 inaugural the municipal system competed with the automobile. The new utility became increasingly irrelevant and unfashionable to commuters and its income woefully inadequate. By 1929, when the utility stopped making its annual purchase payments to Stone and Webster, it could hardly repair its rolling stock or pay its conductors.

Public withdrawal was a national phenomenon and touched private carriers as well. Throughout the 1920s Spokane's system declined with its service. Although streetcars were predictable, so long as they did not derail, they were still dangerous, particularly for passengers required to step far into the street in order to reach them. These perils plus the costs connected with maintaining and improving lines led Spokane to become one of the first communities to replace its rails with rubber. On August 23, 1936 a fleet of gasoline-powered buses took over. This passing of the streetcars was an event worthy of a spectacle. After a million miles of running

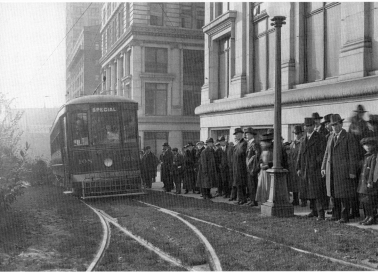

Top: A trolley at Tacoma's Point Defiance Park Station. Above: The formal opening of Seattle's first publicly-built trolley line. The Jan. 28, 1918 celebration began here on the City Hall Park siding to the City-County Building and continued to Ballard, the line's northern terminus, with a caravan. Below: Following the 1940-41 scrapping of the city street cars Seattle Municipal Transit pulled up the rails but kept some of the overhead wiring for its new fleet of trackless trolleys, seen here resting beside the Jefferson Street car barn. Courtesy, Lawton Gowey.

between Hillyard and the business district, Spokane Trolley Car No. 202 was packed with bales of hay and ignited before thousands at Natatorium Park to the accompaniment of a single fiddler playing "Auld Lang Syne." A few of the cars were sold for diners or other roadside attractions, but most were scrapped.

After thirty-one years of service the electric trolleys in Everett were withdrawn in 1934. Buses began appearing on Olympia streets in 1923 and the last of the capital's electric streetcars were retired in the late 1930s. In Yakima trolleys held on until the fall of 1946, and then in the mid-1970s were revived over electrified Union Pacific rails as a weekend attraction. Seattle's trolleys, which were scuttled in 1940, were also recovered for tourists and nostalgic rail fans along a short waterfront line in 1982. In 1990 this new old service was expanded through two historic neighborhoods, Pioneer Square and the International District.

During World War II with the government's rationing of gasoline and rubber, common carriers enjoyed a brief moment of prosperity. By the war's end Spokane had reached a peak of more than 25 million passenger rides per year. But after the conflict, the general downward spiral returned. The decline followed the flight to the suburbs and the rise of the shopping mall. By 1955 the city's general fund was subsidizing the busses, and inadequately. Seattle Transit accumulated an operating deficit of more than $5 million by 1970.

Given its precocious example for municipal control of water and, especially, power with Tacoma City Light, the City of Destiny's 1961 takeover of its transit seems late. Yet it was unique. For the buses it purchased belonged to the system workers, who six years earlier had bought the $2 million worth of stock in the Tacoma Transit Company. Unfortunately, worker control did not reverse the problems of commuter delays and mechanical dilapidation. The city acquisition was an act of necessity and ultimately Tacoma City Light's charity. Beginning in 1965, residential light bills went up 75 cents a month as a subsidy for the vehicles. Meaning, perhaps, to sweeten the subsidy, the city transit director, Doug Hendry, laced the buses with the additive PR-105, which turned the smell of diesel exhaust into a fragrance resembling lavender cologne. However, not a single unsolicited comment was received from the public about the new bouquet. Later that year the director put his best construction on a second disappointment. After Hendry learned that only ten of the thirty-

Enroute to its ceremonial immolation at Natatorium Park, Spokane Trolley car No. 202 makes its last hurrah through the business district, leading a parade of buses which replaced it and the rest of the city streetcars in the summer of 1936. Courtesy, Spokane Public Library, Northwest Room.

five new diesel buses ordered from the General Motors Corporation would arrive before Christmas, plans to spell out "NOEL" with the conveyances were dropped for a New Year's spelling of "1966." The director might have spelled "FEDS," for two-thirds of the cost of the new equipment was paid for under the Federal Mass Transit Act of 1964.

The 1964 act was a milestone for urban mass transportation in the country. In the twenty years since the close of World War II nationwide transit use had dropped 64 percent. Whether public or private, the common carrier had become dilapidated and obsolete and in desperate need of funds and new ideas.

Above: New GM busses for Tacoma. Courtesy, Tom J. Terrien. Below: Seattle waterfront street trolley at its Bell Street station in 1997. Below right: Seattle Monorail leaves the Century 21 World's Fair grounds. Courtesy, Metro.

Four times, in 1958, 1962, 1968 and 1970, proposals for improving Seattle area metropolitan transportation were put to the voters and each time defeated. The 1962 effort, which hoped to capitalize on the year's Century 21 World's Fair with its symbol for modern movement, the monorail, was defeated, in part, by the lobbying of the American Automobile Association. The 1968 transportation proposal was the keystone in the "Forward Thrust" program, the coordinated plan to accommodate area growth with new infrastructure in fire stations, parks, community centers, low-income housing, sewers, a domed stadium, eight miles of new roads (to appease the AAA), and a 47-mile transit system radiating from downtown Seattle north to Ballard, south to Renton, and east to Bellevue. The proposal also expanded bus service over ninety miles of express freeway lanes for which the federal government was expected to pay two-thirds the cost. Opponents of this plan advised voters "Don't be railroaded," but seven historic Forward Thrust bond proposals passed. Unfortunately, transit was not one of them. Two years later, the 1970 effort was done in by a combination of doldrums attending the "Boeing Depression" and "Overtaxed, Inc.," a group of light-rail opponents organized by King County's rogue assessor, Harley Hoppe.

After its 1970 defeat regional mass transit waited a quarter-

One of the fleet of city buses assigned to the World's Fair airport service poses beneath the landmark Space Needle. Built for the 1962 Exposition, the Space Needle then looked down on everything in Seattle, including the Municipal Transit bus yards on Fifth Avenue, across the street from the fair grounds.

century before its revival with the proposed Regional Transit Authority (RTA). In 1993 newly-elected governor Mike Lowry chose Sid Morrison to lead the state's Department of Transportation (DOT). Morrison's advocacy of regional solutions to the growing traffic gridlock through the Pugetopolis corridor was one of the reasons the Democratic governor chose the progressive Repbulican to direct the DOT. However, in its March 1995 test vote the tri-county (Pierce, King, Snohomish), sixteen-year, and $6.7-billion proposal was defeated by a slim margin. The plan was a modest proposal meant to only slow the rate of regional traffic congestion, not reverse it. Most important, the RTA plan was designed to handle up to 46 percent of all rush-hour travel projected for the year 2010. By then the system would have completed its package including sixty-nine miles of new electric light rail linking Seattle, Lynnwood, Bellevue, and Tacoma, eighty-one miles of commuter rail on existing tracks between Everett and Lakewood, and new suburb-to-suburb express bus service. The planners predicted that this alternative to traffic jams would cost the "typical household" from $100 to $125 a year.

RTA's friends included most of the region's biggest commercial players including Boeing, Weyerhaeuser, and SeaFirst. As with the earlier mass transit proposals, most of RTA's opponents were suburban residents. And most of them lived in Snohomish County, which would not have been reached by major RTA improvements until late in the project, and on the Eastside, where Kemper Freeman, Jr. created FACT, Families Against Congestion and Taxation, RTA's principal organized obstructionist. However sensible and restrained, the RTA proposal could not overcome the fact that only about 3 percent of central Puget Sound residents used public transit for all trips. To most voters, including those who in the past had voted for the several mass transit proposal, buses, light-rail, and commuter trains were meant for other people.

RTA and its several predecessors were all tools in regional land-use planning. In *Routes, A Brief History of Transportation in Metropolitan Seattle*, Walter Crowley notes that "The subtext of land use versus transit use continues to shape the politics of public transportation and governmental reform in metropolitan Seattle.

The argument is often couched in euphemisms of technology, economy, jurisdictional scale, professionalism and accountability, but the adequacy — and courage — for political institutions in controlling regional growth remains the real issue." Writing in 1993, Crowley was reflecting on the earlier election failure of the Forward Thrust transit bonds. His points remain current.

In its "mere" alternative to freeway congestion, RTA offered the region an important tool for guiding its development while protecting natural resources. It was, however, the growing congestion of the streets and highways of Pugetopolis that finally brought RTA victory in the November 1996 election. With voter approval ranging from 51 percent in Pierce County to 60 percent in King County, a tri-county $3.9 billion rail-bus network called Sound Transit was envisioned connecting Everett with Tacoma through the congestion of Seattle's hourglass shape. The expectation that engineering for the project would continue into the year 2000 with construction to follow was prudent, given the politics of choosing routes and the area's often recalcitrant geology and difficult topography. RTA's favored alternative of a light-rail tunnel with stations burrowed 50 to 100 feet beneath Seattle's First Hill and Capitol Hill seemed to be in some trouble in early 1998 when new Seattle mayor Paul Schell urged that more study be given to a surface route along the Eastlake/I-5 corridor. Tukwila interests were also insistent then that the light-rail service into South King County be routed from old Pacific Highway 99 to Interurban Avenue with direct service to its Southcenter Shopping Mall.

In the 1997 fall election, the RTA selection of Seattle routes was complicated further when voters approved by a slight majority the formation of a public development authority for extending (although not funding) the rubber-tired Monorail, first introduced as a space age ride between Seattle's business district and its 1962 Century 21 World's Fair, to the four corners of the city.

Regional consciousness long predates these late-twentieth century transportation efforts. In Washington laying rails to

An artist's mock-up of an RTA carrier in the Seattle Metro bus tunnel, with a portion of Roger Shimomura's untitled 10 x 35-foot vitreous enamel tile mural behind it. Courtesy, Metro.

suburbia is nearly as old as the trolleys. The ultimate destination of most of Seattle's earliest electric lines was the suburbs — Ballard, Fremont, Ravenna, South Seattle, and the west shore of Lake Washington. Many portions of Stone and Webster's right-of-way for the Seattle-Everett Interurban (1910-1939) remain open today, coveted by light-rail revivalists. The Anacortes-Fidalgo City Electric railway company found its ambitions were more powerful than the company generators, which in 1891 failed to move the VIP-loaded inaugural car more than a mile beyond its ceremonial start. In 1888 the Spokane Cable Railway's three-mile track to a real estate speculation called Twickenham was the first of the suburban spokes growing from the hub of downtown Spokane. Others later reached South Hill, Coure d'Alene, Medical Lake, and Cheney.

The 1981 voter approval of a Public Transit Benefit Area (PTBA) made regional control of Spokane's transit system official. Two years earlier PTBA's predecessor, the Spokane Transit Authority, prepared the way with the adoption of a multicenter design for public transportation. Departing from the traditional hub-spokes model in which all transportation routes radiated from the central business district, the STA proposed transfer sites at selected outlying centers, allowing passengers to bypass downtown with cross-town service. In 1982 and 1983 PTBA instituted this service and added feeder service to outlying areas in the Spokane Valley.

Above: Beginning in 1902 the Seattle-Tacoma Interurban offered speedy competition for the "Mosquito Fleet" steamers that had previously held a monopoly on convenient transportation between the two cities. Here passengers board Interurban cars at the line's terminus on Occidental Avenue at Yesler Way. In 1928 this regular rail service to Tacoma was closed, the victim of a further convenience, the automobile. Courtesy, Lawton Gowey.

Above: Interior and exterior views of The Plaza, Spokane's public transportation center on Riverside Avenue, built in 1995. The Plaza, designed by architect Ron Tan, also hosts concerts and the Winter Spokane Market. Life-sized mountain lions by sculptor Ken Spiering are installed as part of the waterfall fountain which cascades between The Plaza escalators.

Since then PTBA has added new buses and routes, acquired vans specially equipped for the elderly and handicapped, instituted new van and car pool services, and by 1991 had its buses traveling about twice as many miles as ten years earlier. Economic performance was also noteworthy with the agency keeping annual operating costs during the 1980s to one-sixth the national average. Efforts to attract new riders were not, however, rewarded. Traffic congestion and the cost of parking were still not the irritants they had become in the central Puget Sound region. In Snohomish

County, another Public Benefit Transit Authority created Sno-Met in 1969, and in 1974 Olympia's PTA was given a portion of the state sales tax for its expansion into unprofitable areas.

In 1972, fourteen years after its first attempt to include public transportation in its service, Metro Transit and the sales tax to support it was approved by King County voters. In its efforts to rescue the dilapidated system it inherited, the new Metro, like Spokane's PTBA, built a multicenter system featuring twenty-five new routes and twenty-five park-and-ride lots, a regional network of bus bases, 1,200 passenger shelters, 100 miles of high-occupancy "Freeway Flyers" lanes on state freeways, free "Magic Carpet" service in downtown Seattle, and 550 new buses. The 1973 OPEC oil embargo increased ridership and the federal government's $86 million grant, the largest sum ever provided for an all-bus mass transit system, increased liquidity. After four years federal officials praised the utility for its efforts which they found so creative that they denied Metro a grant for rail planning which instead went to Portland for its MAX rail system.

The combination of improved facilities and an energetic promotional campaign (along with the long lines at the gas stations) resulted in a doubling of ridership between 1973 and 1979. The fifty-eight million passenger rides in 1979 surpassed the goal set for 1980, and beginning in August many busriders were using the new articulated buses. Ridership soared to 66.1 million in 1980 when, in his last state pork barrel, Sen. Warren

Left: A Seattle-Everett Interurban car sits beside its trackless competitor at the Interurban terminus on Stewart Street and Eighth Avenue, which was later the site of the Greyhound bus depot. Courtesy, Warren Wing. Below: Thurston County's Intercity Transit Customer Center in Olympia, 1997. Photo by Clark Gilman.

Above: Inspection of Metro tunnel during construction. Right: Construction work on tunnel. Below: One of Metro's double-length buses entering the north entrance to the bus tunnel at Convention Place Station. Photos by Metro photographer Ned Ahrens. Courtesy, King County Transportation and Natural Resources Library.

Magnuson, loser to Slade Gorton in the Reagan election landslide, directed $38 million to Metro for the purchase of an additional 202 articulated buses.

In 1983 Metro Transit was chosen by the American Public Transit Association as the best major system in the nation. However, that year the new system also witnessed its first decline in ridership. The obvious need for greater intra-suburban service, as well as cooperation with its neighbors north and south, eventually led to sharing with Pierce Transit and Snohomish County's Community Transit downtown bus stops and park-and-ride lots for interurban shuttles originating in Tacoma and Everett. Also in 1983 the Metro Council approved both the downtown Seattle transit tunnel and the use of the dual-propulsion diesel/electric buses needed to keep the tunnel's confined atmosphere breathable and the decorative tiles of its five stations gleaming. The versatile buses meant that suburban riders could pass between the heart of the city and their communities without transfer. The boring began March 6, 1987 and the tunnel opened on September 15, 1990.

From its southern depot between the International District and the old Union Depot at Fifth Avenue and Jackson Street the bus tunnel proceeds north to Third Avenue, following it to Pine Street before turning east for the short leg to its northern opening at Ninth Avenue. Along the way the high-speed buses stop at only three stations: Pioneer Square, University Street and Westlake Mall. Thanks to a $1.5 million government grant for the installation of original art, the ornamentation of the tunnel's public spaces is among the most elegant examples of Washington public art programs.

Tacoma Belt Line

Long before it took over the buses, the City of Tacoma entered the field of municipal transportation with a short line across the Eleventh Avenue Bridge and onto the industrial tideflats.

It was understood that Tacoma's destiny would materialize on its reclaimed tidelands. In 1912 Tacoma voters, as they generally did at the start of municipal projects, liked the idea of this rail connection but refused to pay for it. The city then made a deal with the Tacoma Railway and Power Company to build the line if the private transit company would operate it. The inaugural run on January 10, 1915, included a VIP-laden trip over the full mile and a quarter of tracks to the car shops of the Chicago, Milwaukee, and St. Paul Railroad. Soon it became clear that the Belt Line was a money loser, and the company abandoned the city. However, the cars kept running, carrying workers back and forth between the tideflats and Pacific Avenue. With all the hubbub of World War I, the city extended the line to the new Todd Shipyards.

In the beginning the line was considered primarily a device for moving workers, yet during the war its eighteen cars could never handle more than a third of those employed on the tideflats. Paying the fare was still on the "honor system," but most of those riding the line to their wartime work treated it as a kind of patriotic perk and did not pay. Most importantly, the war revealed that of the Belt Line's two services, to workers and for freight, it was the latter which was more profitable. In 1924 this primacy became official when the city signed contracts with the three transcontinental railroads using the tidelands. Passenger service continued to be a loser, and by the early thirties it was reduced to nine streetcars and two buses. In May 1938 the utility stopped carrying passengers over its tracks and went with buses alone. By then the system's freight service between ships and the transcontinental railroads was making a profit. The enormous activity on the Tacoma waterfront during World War II overwhelmed the system's few buses, and in 1947 the Tacoma City Council eliminated the passenger service. The Belt Line's freight switching operation, however, continued to prosper modestly.

Throughout the 1960s logs and grain remained the Belt Line's staples. When the Toyota Company moved to Tacoma in 1971, automobiles were added to the diet. By 1970 the line had thirty-three miles of track, but most of it was wearing out. Derailments were a daily event. In its 1984 diagnosis the Federal

Railroad Administration found more than 400 defects in the line, from missing bolts to cracked tracks. As an antidote, the Tacoma Public Utility Board and City Council directed the utility to cancel its contracts with the port's several carriers and instead file a tariff with the Interstate Commerce Commission for a charge of $77.45 for each car served. With the promise of this increased income the Belt Line was allowed to borrow from the city's general fund the $1.5 million needed to repair its tracks and purchase new locomotives. Although the Belt Line continues to occasionally entertain the idea of offering itself to the Port of Tacoma, in 1995 it was still an independent utility and in the eightieth year of binding Tacoma to its tidelands.

In 1998, the eighty-third year of binding Tacoma and its tidelands, Tacoma Utilities changed the name of its Belt Line to Tacoma Rail. Although this utility remains independent, a formal agreement signed between it and the Port of Tacoma in the early 1990 effectively makes their relationship a partnership.

Above: At the time that the public art project for the Metro Transit Tunnel was completed in the early 1990s, it was the largest such project ever undertaken in Northwest history and featured the work of twenty-one artists. Laura Sindell's untitled ceramic tile mural at the Pioneer Square Station entrance on Third Avenue features variations on North Coast Native American motifs and artifacts like the dugout canoe. Photo by Mary Randlett. Below: The rolling stock of the Tacoma Belt Line in its prime. Courtesy, Tacoma Utilities.

Above left: Cedar River Falls on the river which since 1900 has supplied Seattle's principle source of community water. Above right: To compliment its sublime setting, Seattle's 1907 Volunteer Park standpipe was given a distinguished brick casing with interior stairwells to an observatory at the top. Below: Mrs. Elizabeth Morrice rests upon a seat borrowed, most likely, from a car for her comfort, for the Oct. 4, 1933 groundbreaking of the $350,000 Everett-Alderwood Manor water project. Neither Mrs. Morrice, Peter Tutmark, with the ceremonial shovel (far left), nor anyone else attending the event could have known that their new community's suburban retreat would eventually be best known for a shopping mall with scores of shops and acres of parking lots constructed beside the convergence of two freeways, I-5 and I-405. Photos courtesy, Everett Public Library.

The Seattle Water Department's Lake Youngs Supply Lines No. 4 and No. 5 (left and right, respectively) on May 27, 1930. Here the two parallel wood stave pipes carrying Cedar River waters reach their intersection with the steel riveted Lake Youngs Bypass No. 4 (left), a dished head for the future Lake Youngs Bypass No. 5 (center-right), and the steel riveted connectors for No. 4 and No. 5 with the Lake Youngs spillway (bottom-right). Lake Youngs is directly behind the photographer who sites his camera east along the twin 78-inch pipelines where they cross the since-drained Robertson's Pond.

PUBLIC WATER

PIONEER WATER

A source of clean, accessible water was often the first thing would-be town builders in Washington Territory looked for once they found an appealing site. West of the Cascades they were seldom far from a spring or stream. East of the mountains and on the coast, they more often had to dig a well. Once found, the water had to be hauled and the first settlers in each area had to do the job themselves. Later an enterprising local might invest in a horse and cart and begin delivering water to whoever would pay. In Wenatchee, U. F. Lake and his sons delivered a barrel full of water to the back door for a quarter. That supply was supposed to last a family a week, obviously making bathing a luxury. Other early "waterpreneurs," like D. C. Hannah in Tacoma in 1873, built flumes tapping the larger streams and piped water downhill to a storage tank for the benefit of a few customers. Later as neighborhoods ascended the slopes, small companies like the Mount Vernon City Waterworks pumped it uphill, in this case Lincoln Hill, to storage in tanks or reservoirs. Simple gravity systems or wells that served the immediate neighborhood could be found in nearly every nineteenth-century Washington town.

Since they usually had little capital and were often counting on the inflation of land values to turn a profit, the early water companies built systems that were crude, unreliable, and apt to quickly deteriorate. Often a humble timber diversion dam was built on the closest stream, presumably above any communities using the stream for sewage disposal. From the intake the water flowed by gravity through pipes made of bored logs or wooden staves. If they did not rot out within a decade or two, the wooden pipes almost always leaked. Timber flumes and earthen or concrete reservoirs were open and accessible to any human or animal (and thus any infectious microbe) who cared to bathe, drink, or just cool off. Typhoid, as early Tacomans found, often came with the water service, no extra charge.

As populations rose, town and city councils awarded franchises for designated areas to the water company or companies deemed to be the more reliable. In 1901, the Fourth of July brought water along with the usual Independence Day celebrations to the newly incorporated Bremerton. One of Bremerton's first franchised companies, the Bremerton Water and Power Company, built a crib dam on Charleston Creek, a small stream three-and-a-half miles out of town. The supply line from the intake consisted of 8- to 12-inch wooden mains; the wooden distribution mains were half their size. Because the water supply in Charleston Creek was so meager, the company had to raise the dam several times to increase storage — until they added two more crib dams on a second stream, Anderson Creek.

East of the mountains where surface sources were more scarce and water demands greater because of irrigation, wells became an important supplemental source of water. It seems that most would-be town founders dreamt of finding an artesian well, but few succeeded. In the late 1890s, when a well was being dug on Main Street for the Palouse Hotel in Pullman, water jetted twenty feet out of the ground. After drilling and finding several more wells that discharged an average of 100 gallons per minute, Pullman residents capitalized on their lucky find, promoting the town as

CITY
WATER-WORKS

"Artesian City." One Pullman entrepreneur, J.W. Thompson in 1891 took advantage of the city's artesian water, touted to be beneficial to the health as well as abundant, and built a public swimming pool, heated by the city water works station alongside it. The charge was high — twenty-five cents with season tickets available — but 200 people plunged into the 24 x 35-foot tank the first day, some coming from as far as Moscow, Idaho. The Chalybeate Swimming Baths didn't last, however, for the city council the next year decided it needed the space the pool occupied.

Of course, most early Washington towns enjoyed neither swimming pools nor artesian wells and only developed minimal water systems in a rudimentary and piecemeal manner. The City of Toppenish in Yakima County provides a good example of the way some of Washington's early municipal systems were built. During the first stage of settlement, the town pump and water trough outside the trading post were all that was needed. When the population rose, the town council voted to build a water system financed by a bond issue that required about all the citizens could afford. To save money the system was designed without the aid of a professional engineer, and a shallow well, a pump, and a tank were installed without standard specifications. After several heated council meetings about the need for expanding the system, an 8-inch wooden stave pipe was laid from the well up Main Street for five or six blocks. It was followed later by a few laterals of 4-inch pipe into the residential district.

Next, the old well was enlarged and deepened. A 10-inch cast iron main was installed to replace the wood pipe that was leaking badly. More laterals were added to serve additional customers. However, because of the serious strain on the town's budget, the city fathers planned the system only to meet the current needs of a population of 846. What they bequeathed to the future water superintendent and 4,000 residents of Toppenish in 1940 was a literal bottleneck — an incorrectly mapped system of leaky pipes and services laid even to vacant properties. Gate valves were haphazardly installed and some had never been opened and poor mapping made repairs difficult.

A more common pattern of municipal water development was for communities to buy existing private systems and improve them. In the early 1890s the town of Aberdeen purchased the pumping plant, water mains, and other facilities of the Aberdeen Water Company, which had been unable to keep pace with demand. After the town built another pumping station and intake dam on Stewart Creek, the water department proudly reported to the city council at the end of 1894 that they had pumped 106 million gallons of water during the year and chopped and burned 527 cords of wood for the steam-powered pump. In 1899 the city of Walla Walla took over a local enterprise, the Walla Walla Water Company, and continued to divert flow from Mill Creek, which has been the city's principal supply ever since. Not until 1917, when the town and Navy shipyards were burgeoning with war workers, did Bremerton voters approve a $225,000 bond issue to purchase the city's privately owned water system. The largest of the municipally owned waterworks were built by the cities of Tacoma, Seattle, Spokane, and Everett.

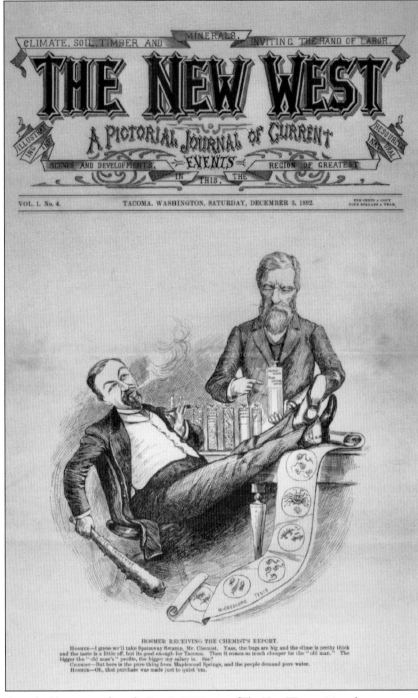

A muckraking cartoon from the Dec. 3, 1892 cover of The New West *satirizes the customers of the Tacoma Light and Water Company and its president, Theodore Hosmer. Courtesy, University of Washington Libraries, Special Collections.*

TACOMA

In 1925 Tacoma's Superintendent of Water works, W. A. Kunigk, found it hard to imagine that only fifty years earlier Tacomans who wanted to cook, bathe, or get a drink of fresh water usually had to haul it themselves. At least, there had been no shortage. The hillside of the future Tacoma business district teemed with springs. One of the most popular was the "Presbyterian Font" at South Eleventh Street and Broadway, whose waters were considered not only thirst-quenching but therapeutic.

In 1873 New Tacoma was a town of tents pitched on newly burned slash. It had been created by the Northern Pacific Railroad about three miles south of the original Tacoma settlement as the western terminus of its transcontinental line. Despite its highly sought-after status, the town did not get off to a very good start. An

A sample of Tacoma's many reservoirs. Above: Hood Street Reservoir. Top right: An early view of McMillin Reservoir. Right: The Alaska Street Reservoir in 1964, before it was covered. Courtesy, Tacoma Utilities.

informal census that year counted 375 residents, two-thirds of whom were laid-off Chinese railroad workers. Before the line that was to connect Tacoma to Kalama on the Columbia was finished, the Northern Pacific went bankrupt and was unable to pay the men putting in the tracks. Then, when the first construction train rolled into Tacoma in November, it also rolled over as the tracks gave way at the foot of the bluff below Eleventh Street. Soon after the line was finished in December most of the construction workers left, and New Tacoma's population shrunk to approximately 220.

One of those who stayed, Chinese immigrant Tom Quan, found new employment as the town's only public utility. To the relief of many housewives and children, Quan began carting water in barrels from house to house on a mule cart. W. J. (Billy) Fife, store operator and town postmaster, was able to improve on Quan's system when he completed the town's first piped supply in 1878. Fife dug a couple of small earthen reservoirs on the west side of Ninth Street at Broadway and channeled water into them from a nearby stream. From these holding ponds, he piped water down to Pacific Avenue and A Street through bored logs that he brought from Olympia.

In 1883, with the completion of the transcontinental line, Tacoma's long-expected boom finally got underway. Billy Fife's little system could not keep up with the thousands of newcomers. Many Tacoma residents had to continue to service themselves even after John E. Burns and Philip Metzler formed the town's first water company. They bored a tunnel into the hill on South D Street to tap a number of springs behind Burns's house. The tunnel, driven through hardpan, connected to a 350-foot-long flume that ran to a small reservoir on the same street between South Ninth and South Eleventh. The combined storage capacity of the flume and reservoir, Superintendent Kunigk noted in 1925, was 100,000 gallons, "not quite enough to supply one of our present day fire service pumps for a period of two hours." From the reservoir the water was piped downhill through a 4-inch main, supplying a Chinese laundry on Broadway along the way, to Pacific Avenue near Eleventh Street. There it branched into smaller pipes running south to the main business district and north to "Whiskey Row," as Pacific Avenue between Ninth and Seventh was called.

Although Burns and Metzler's system was a big improvement over Fife's, it was still not enough. Water pressure was low, the incidence of contamination high, and the need for more flow for fire protection immediate. Skeptical that the company would ever be able to provide an adequate and safe supply for the booming town, the city council refused to grant the partners a franchise. The council had more faith in a company founded by Charles B. Wright, Philadelphia financier, Northern Pacific official, and

president of the Tacoma Land Company. In June 1884 Wright was granted a franchise and incorporated the Tacoma Light and Water Company. The company first tapped Tule Lake, a small body near Spanaway Lake. But the supply soon proved to be inadequate, so the canal was extended to Clover Creek and Spanaway Lake. The water glided into town through a broad 50,000-foot-long wooden flume that emptied into a 2.5-million-gallon reservoir at Hood Street. (This reservoir, built in 1885 and enlarged in 1909, served the city until it was replaced by a new one on the site in 1987.) In 1891 the system was drawing 2 million gallons a day from Galliher Gulch and 2.5 million gallons from Clover Creek and Spanaway Lake.

Since the Clover Creek flume was mostly uncovered, cows found it a convenient water trough; children, a stream for wading; and housewives, a self-replenishing washtub. Several Tacomans, including two Chamber of Commerce members, soon died of typhoid and customers became suspicious of their water supply. When complaints about the company's rate increases and poor service also multiplied, the city council studied possible new sources. However, all of them cost more than the city was willing to invest. The least expensive alternative was to buy out the Tacoma Light and Water Company. In 1893 Tacoma voters, some seriously doubtful about the ability of city bureaucrats to manage the system, approved a bond issue by a slim margin. After negotiating with the private utility's president, Theodore Hosmer, a price of $1.75 million for Wright's light and waterworks was agreed upon, and the City of Destiny prepared to test its municipal mettle.

Tacoma officials shortly discovered that some of the facilities had been grossly overvalued and that the company had been dipping into Clover Creek illegally. Tacoma firemen had to be called out to pump emergency supplies from nearby streams until a deal could be struck with the Clover Creek area farmers who had legitimate water claims. Worse yet, there was no money left over from the bond issue to make improvements to the system. The city sued the company for misrepresentation, asking for $1 million in damages. Five months after C. B. Wright died in Philadelphia in March 1898, the city agreed to a compromise settlement of approximately $375,000. It was not enough, especially for a city hit hard by the Panic of 1893, and the system continued to deteriorate faster than it could be repaired.

By the first years of the new century, however, Tacoma had

recovered and like other Washington cities underwent its greatest growth since the 1880s. Fueled by an expanding lumber and wood products market, the city's population more than doubled from 37,714 in 1900 to 83,743 in 1910. Tacoma boosters were bullish, if unoriginal, when they awarded the prize in a city slogan contest to "Watch Tacoma Grow."

This time Tacoma's boom was accompanied by a lucky "strike." It appeared that the city would not have to build an expensive new gravity system to tap the glaciers of Mount Tacoma (Mount Rainier) after all. In 1903 the water department drove three 12-inch diameter wells into the gravel deposits left behind by the Vashon Glacier in the South Tacoma area along the right-of-way of the Clover Creek Flume between South Sixty-second and South Seventy-sixth streets. Air compressors powered pumps to lift water from the massive aquifer 150 feet to the surface into the flume and to the Hood Street Reservoir, the city's low service supply.

Above: Pierce County Bridge No. 7195-A over the Puyallup River at McMillin. The City of Tacoma pipeline is to the left. Courtesy, Pierce County Public Works. Below: Tacoma's Palmer intake on the Green River. Courtesy, Tacoma Public Library.

The wells were so successful that during the next four years eleven more were drilled and tapped. Some of the pumps forced water into a high service distribution system where it was stored in the Alaskan Street Reservoir, completed in 1889, and the J Street standpipe, built in 1891. Because of the ample supply found in the Vashon Glacier deposits, the Galliher Gulch source was abandoned. From that time on, the new wells and Clover Creek were the city's sole source of water until the Green River gravity system was installed in 1913.

Green River Gravity System

Tacoma's well water was pure and plentiful, but it was not enough for a city whose leadership aimed to make Tacoma the premier city on the Sound. By 1903 Tacoma was developing into an important industrial and international trading center. That year the Chamber of Commerce counted at least 300 mills and factories — mostly lumber-related — employing nearly 8,000 workers; six healthy home-grown banks; the largest flour mills on the coast; and "the only large starch factory in the West." Such potential, city leaders reasoned, could not risk being frustrated by an unsafe or unreliable water supply. The solution for pulp, pastry, and people was the Green River gravity system.

Investigations into using the Green River for a municipal water source had begun as early as 1889. F. L. Davis, Tacoma's city engineer, worked out a general plan in 1907 and Tacoma voters passed a $2 million bond issue in 1910 and 1911. By May 1913 city engineers and crews had completed a 17-foot-high concrete diversion dam and intake works in the Cascade foothills near Palmer and 42 miles of single conduit wood stave pipe to carry the water to town. The completed system was very close to Davis's plan. It supplied 42 million gallons a day, enough water for a city twice the size of Tacoma. Of course, more storage reservoirs and distribution lines also had to be built to handle all that water.

Today, as then, at the intake gates at the north end of the diversion dam, the water is screened and sent through a short tunnel to a small settling basin. From there the water passes to a treatment plant where it is chlorinated. Moving out of the chlorination plant, the water flows through a concrete and steel pipeline for twenty-six miles until it reaches the McMillin Reservoir. Enroute, the pipeline crosses under the White River stream bed and then over the Puyallup River on a three-span steel bridge. Because the original untreated wood staves had deteriorated in a number of places by 1923, the line was gradually replaced between 1926 and 1952 with permanent steel and concrete pipe.

McMillin Reservoir, the main storage on the Green River system, consists of three concrete-lined reservoirs — two of 55 million gallon capacity built in 1913, and a third of 100 million gallon capacity which was completed in 1957. A second treatment plant was added at the reservoir in 1941 so that the water could be rechlorinated before passing into the two large supply lines feeding the distribution system in town.

Following World War II and throughout the 1950s, the greatest challenge to the Tacoma water division was keeping up with the many extensions that had to be made to the distribution system. Postwar

Above: An amazed Tacoma Utilities employee, Peggy Ervin, poses in front of "the amount of water used daily by an average Tacoma household in 1959." Bill Dugovich, Tacoma Public Utilities public relations legend, used considerable artistic restraint in limiting his display to roughly 600 milk bottles. By recent statistics, Dugovich's collection would represent about half of a single day's portion of the 112,000 gallons of water that an average Tacoma home used in 1997. On a hot August day in Tacoma, Ms. Ervin's bottles might have irrigated her lawn. Below: The J Street Standpipe across 19th Street from Tacoma's St. Joseph Hospital is not currently used except as tower for a department antenna. Courtesy, Tacoma Public Library.

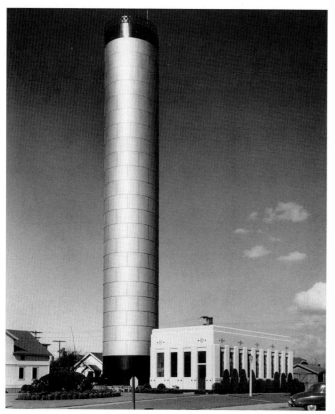

housing developments cropped up like the early settlement's abundant springs. But since most of the new extensions were developed through local improvement districts, the utility did not have to overextend its finances to make them. In fact, the Tacoma water division did not have to raise its rates between 1919 and 1954.

To protect the purity of the Green River supply, the water division tries to keep the watershed above the city's intake closed to all but authorized personnel. But because the city owns only a small percentage of the watershed acreage, its success in keeping people and contamination out comes from its control of key bits of land like the riverbanks and roads into the property. (See Watersheds below.) No matter how well it controls access, the city can't control the weather. During the fall and spring, heavy rains and melting snows wash excess soil into the river causing it to cloud. Since the Tacoma system is a run-of-the-river supply and has no lake to settle out suspended particles that cause this seasonal turbidity, the community must sometimes turn off its river supply. In those instances, lasting at times for weeks, Tacoma's wells serve as a supplementary source.

In 1930 the demand for a larger industrial and domestic supply prompted the city to drive five more wells into the aquifer. Equipped with multistage, turbine-type deep well pumps, the large-diameter wells supplied about twice the water produced by the original well system. In 1940 three more wells were dug and put into service. Cold War anxiety about more emergency and peaking capacity spurred another expansion of the well supply in the late 1940s. Some of the wells were even housed in heavy reinforced concrete designed to withstand bombing. Today, about twenty-two wells in and around the city operate to meet peak demand and supplement the gravity supply during times of high turbidity.

Eventually, the wells developed their own problems. They tapped an aquifer that extends into Lakewood and Parkland, and is largely supplied by surface water recharge. Overuse between 1970 and 1980 caused a drop in the water level and made it necessary to closely control withdrawals. Effluent from septic tanks and pollutants from industrial activities also caused contamination in some wells. Septic tank restrictions and sanitary sewers helped alleviate the problem. In 1988, after a well in the South Tacoma area was found to be contaminated by industrial solvents, the city adopted an aquifer protection district. The district serves as an administrative mechanism for regulating underground storage tanks and the handling of hazardous chemicals above the aquifer.

Demands on the aquifer are increasing. In 1990 Tacoma's average per day use was around 79 million gallons. Its peak loads, however, could reach as high as 130 million gallons. In winter when water needs drop, Tacoma's requirements almost matched what it could draw from the Green River. In summer the utility relied also on its wells. The water department began looking for ways to augment its supply and reduce demand. One proposal, which was approved for a pilot project in 1991, was to recharge the aquifer by pumping in water from the Green River during the winter. However, this solution was complicated by the contamination already present. Adding too much water to the aquifer might spread the underground pollution to more wells. Another plan involved the reuse of waste water. Since 40 percent of Tacoma's water supply was going to one customer, the Simpson Tacoma Craft Co., a major conservation program at the paper mill would improve the standing of the whole system. In 1990 the utility proposed that Simpson send its effluent to the city's new treatment plant on Portland Avenue for "polishing" and then pipe it back to reuse instead of using the city's drinking-quality water.

By 1990 the Tacoma Water Division had begun to think regionally as utility planners considered the needs of fast-growing communities in south King County, such as Kent, Lake Meridian,

Covington, and Federal Way. In 1988 the U.S. Geological Survey found that there was very little additional ground water available in the area. A potential solution nearby was Tacoma's long-proposed second pipeline from the Green River, which was designed to pass through south King County. Projected to draw another 65 million gallons a day (added to the 72 million that the utility was then taking into its first Green River pipeline) the estimated $60 million, 33-mile pipeline could be paid for in large part by the King County communities that would use most of its supply. The construction of this regional solution, however, was restrained by the Muckleshoot Indian tribe, which depends on fish from the Duwamish River and its tributary, the Green. The tribe holds considerable power in the matter, backed up not only by the decision of the Ninth Circuit Court of Appeals protecting tribal fish habitat, but by Section 404 of the Federal Clean Water Act, which insures that tribes participate in decisions regarding pipeline construction over or under streams used by them.

SPOKANE

In 1881 with a population of about 900, Spokane Falls was one-fourth the size of Walla Walla, the dominant eastern Washington city. However, that ratio would soon change and dramatically so. That year in late June, the first railroad line in the area reached Spokane Falls and the town's hegemony in the Inland Empire began. When Northern Pacific president Henry Villard and a "coterie of capitalists" arrived on the freshly laid tracks, the citizens of Spokane Falls gave them a rousing reception and filled their ears with stories about the young city's promising future. A visiting newspaperman, Will B. Turner, was as impressed with the town's water drawn from the town well as with its commercial and social potential. On the front page of the four-page weekly *Spokane Falls Chronicle*, he gushed that the water "absolutely discounts anything in the line of aqueous fluid that the writer hereof has ever absorbed."

But the wheel and bucket well in front of the hotel at Howard and Main, despite the pure and restorative water it brought up, clearly was not a system designed to impress eastern investors.

Top and above: Lithograph renderings of Spokane Falls and the Echo Mill, where a waterwheel and pumps were installed to lift and move the river water through the city's main service mains. Below: View of the original, left, and the later rebuilt, right, Upriver Dam and pumping station. Courtesy, Spokane Water and Hydraulic Services.

Neither were the two Spokane Indians who outfitted themselves with wooden shoulder yokes and a couple of five-gallon oil cans and delivered water from the pump to hotels, restaurants, and a few private residences. The town had neither fire department nor distribution system and had already suffered major fire losses.

In early 1884 Frank R. Moore, a prominent Spokane Falls businessman, devised a plan for building a municipal waterworks. After Moore was granted a franchise by the town council, he signed a contract with a San Francisco manufacturing company for a $30,500 pumping and distribution system. Unfortunately, Moore had more enterprise than cash. When he couldn't make the payments, the California manufacturer prepared to ship the equipment back to the factory. But a local hardware store proprietor, Louis Ziegler, was not about to see the plan die. Ziegler had come to Spokane because he believed the Spokane River's "cataracts would in time attract capital and industries and compel

Above: An early pump used in Spokane's water works. Courtesy, Eastern Washington University Archives. Below: Ninth Avenue and Pine Street Reservoir, Spokane. Courtesy, Spokane Water and Hydraulic Services.

the rise of an important commercial center." And if the falls wouldn't, Ziegler would. On September 3, 1884, he called an emergency meeting at Joy's Opera House, at the corner of Wall and Riverside. There he convinced thirty of the town's leading citizens to sign an agreement whereby each pledged $200 to bail out Moore's system. In another emergency meeting the following week, the group formed the Spokane Falls Waterworks Association and agreed to pay the California contractor an initial $6,000 to install the system. The balance would be secured by a mortgage until the next year when, they hoped, the town would vote to take over the system.

The municipal takeover soon became part of a spirited — and closely supervised — mayoral race. The town's civic leaders allegedly intervened to make sure that J. N. Glover, who represented the partners in the water association, won and that the water proposal and bond issue carried. With the legalities taken care of, $50,000 in bonds were issued, and the town took over the water system which included a waterwheel and two pumps installed in the Echo flour mill on Havermale Island. The pumps pushed the river water through a few hundred feet of 12-inch service mains up Howard Street to Main. One of the city's first improvements was to extend the lines south on Howard Street to First Avenue, west of First Avenue to Chestnut Street, and on Main Avenue east to Washington Street.

By 1888 railroads ran to and from Spokane Falls in all directions, soon making the city the marketing center for the Inland Empire. Responding to the Northern Pacific's worldwide advertising, or just the urge to move to the wide-open West, hundreds of people arrived every month. The city banks bulged with deposits, many of them flowing from the Coeur d'Alene mines whose owners preferred to live in style in Spokane. Carpen-

ters worked furiously to keep up with the real estate boom and a population that within two years would balloon to nearly 20,000. The city water department also scrambled to keep up. That year, with the help of a $75,000 bond issue, they built an enlarged pumping plant on Middle Island.

However, even this improvement could not save the city from its worst fire yet. On August 4, 1889, when flames swept over the business area, the firefighters' hoses went limp. The only man who knew how to turn up the pressure, the water superintendent, was away on a fishing trip in Idaho. Nearly all the clapboard business buildings burned down. But the fire did not destroy the mettle of their owners who went heavily into debt to replace the ashes with ornate brick and granite. Four years later the building owners were ruined by the Panic of 1893, while the imposing six- and seven-story structures survived. Along with the rebuilders, seven out of ten banks in Spokane went under as wheat prices crashed and the money supply dried up during the mid-90s depression.

Despite the slump, the city again outgrew its waterworks. However, the funds needed for building a new pumping station were lacking. At the suggestion of an eastern lender, the city issued what are believed to have been the country's first municipal revenue bonds, warrants payable from future utility revenues, to finance the necessary improvements. While Spokane weathered the economic downturn, the city built the Upriver pumping station in 1894. Located five miles upriver from the city center near Minnehaha Park, the project included a dam with a timber spillway, a canal, and hydraulic turbines to drive the pumps. The Upriver plant was capable of delivering up to 10 million gallons per day of river water through a 24-inch-diameter riveted steel pipeline that extended along Sprague Avenue and connected with existing service mains.

By late 1897 most of the region and the country had pulled out of the economic doldrums. Emigrants from the East and Midwest, responding to the glittering advertisements about Washington in pamphlets and newspapers, again flocked westward. By 1898 Spokane's population had grown to 42,000 and the number of retail and wholesale businesses had more than doubled. That year alone an estimated 450 new residences and 50 new commercial buildings went up. The number of mining companies based in Spokane rose from three in 1889 to 239 ten years later.

However, population and business booms brought problems along with prosperity — like the dumping of more sewage into the Spokane River. Just as the river water was becoming dangerous to drink, Spokane officials stumbled onto an underground "gold mine." While work was being done on the Upriver plant in 1907, water was discovered seeping into the excavation at a level well above the surface of the river. Further investigation revealed a vast underground "river" underlying 350 square miles and ranging in depth from 50 to 200 feet. The water in the Spokane-Rathdrum aquifer was harder than Spokane River water, but it was pure and stayed at a temperature of 48 degrees F. year round. The supply appeared to be inexhaustible, and it solved the problem — at least for awhile — of what to do about the pollution of the river. When the city sunk the first well, 28 feet in diameter and 40 feet deep, engineers found they could pump at the rate of 28 million gallons a day and still draw down the aquifer only 24 inches. Between 1910 and 1912 two more open wells, each with a capacity of 12 million gallons a day, were dug and put into operation at the Upriver plant. In 1925 the city topped that with the Well Electric

Top: Spokane's Shadle Reservoir. Above: Spokane's 33rd Street and Lamont Avenue Reservoir. Courtesy, Spokane Water and Hydraulic Services.

wartime labor and material shortages, the Parkwater plant was claimed to be the largest well pumping station in the world. Two deep-well turbine pumps of 600 to 900 horsepower lifted water from each of four wells 140 feet to the surface. Designed to pour 63,000 gallons of water a minute into the city's mains, the pumps had a capacity of 92 million gallons per day. The new plant was completed just in time to catch up with the postwar housing developments that had been taxing the Upriver system.

For more than forty years, the city had merely to chlorinate the water drawn from the plentiful Spokane-Rathdrum aquifer. But by the mid-1970s the slow-moving underground river, which had become the sole source of drinking water for more than 350,000 people in the areas of Spokane and Coeur d'Alene, Idaho, was showing signs of the area's development. Tests performed by the U.S. Army Corps of Engineers and the U.S. Geological Survey found high levels of nitrates, phosphates, and chlorides — all components of septic tank effluent — in the wells. Over 30,000 homes and businesses and several major industries in the valley had been discharging waste water directly into the soil above the aquifer. In 1977 Spokane County imposed a brief moratorium on federally funded housing projects using septic tanks with drainfield disposal and began formulating a coordinated comprehensive land use plan and a wastewater management program in order to develop a general sewer plan for the greater Spokane area.

The following year the Spokane-Rathdrum Aquifer became one of seventeen aquifers in the nation to be designated as the only source of potable water for the community it serves. Under the Sole Source Aquifer Protection Act, whose passage and amendments were fostered by Congressman Tom Foley of Spokane, federal matching grants became available for projects to protect the aquifer. In 1985 Spokane area voters overwhelmingly voted to tack an additional fee to their utility bills and raise the county sales tax. The revenues fund new sewerage facilities and the management of an aquifer protection area. Spokane County also created an Aquifer Sensitive Zone, which established requirements for commercial and industrial businesses using critical or hazardous chemicals, to prevent possible leakage seeping into the ground.

SEATTLE

Seattle's first Euro-American settlers picked Alki Point for its proximity to salt water, not fresh. From the Point they could see in all directions and there was also a security in being easily seen — especially by other Midwesterners searching for homesteads. But the spit was dry. Within a half year, most of Seattle's original pioneers fled across Elliott Bay to a hill sprouting with springs. The generous hydraulics of their second choice came from the aquifer that flowed below glacial hills and was replenished by the region's reliable rain. This easy water helped convince Henry Yesler to set up Puget Sound's first steam sawmill on Elliott Bay in 1853. (See Waterways Chapter.)

John Leary, a sometime partner of Yesler, was one of a group of local movers who first attempted in 1881 to build and organize an integrated distribution system. The Spring Hill Water Company diverted spring water into a dozen or so wooden tanks along the ridge between First and Beacon hills and laid some sizable water mains beneath the business district's principle streets. However, the most auspicious moment for the future of community water in 1881 was the September 25 arrival of Reginald H. Thomson. At daybreak the young teacher stepped from the steamer *Dakota* onto Yesler's Wharf and was greeted by Yesler himself. Besides his baggage, Thomson carried ashore a predisposition to public service and a fervent belief in the importance of fresh water. "Clean water and sufficient water is the life blood of a city," he liked to say. "My father drilled that into me."

In the year Thomson came to Seattle his cousin and host, city engineer F. H. Whitworth, advised the city council that the Cedar

Station, a pumping plant with a capacity of 80 million gallons a day. Part of the Upriver group, the station was built over two 49-foot-diameter closed wells.

In 1933 a record-breaking flood on the Spokane River forced the city to modify its well-water system and pumping plant. As water from the river seeped into the wells, the city was compelled to put its eight-year-old chlorination system into operation for the first time. Although the Upriver plant escaped damage, officials realized that the Well Electric Station was potentially vulnerable to flooding. This and the need for a greater supply resulted in the eventual construction of the Parkwater station on higher ground nearby at the southwest corner of Felts airfield.

When it was completed in 1950, after being held up by

River was the best potential source for an abundant supply of pure community water. However, in 1881 the council's interest in building a water utility was as remote as the recommended river which flowed from Cedar Lake some thirty-five miles southeast of the city. The council chose to rely on Spring Hill instead. But the company's Lake Washington plant (now the site of Colman Park), which began pumping lake water to its new Beacon Hill reservoirs in 1886, could not keep up with the city's requirements. Its delivery was also less than heroic on June 6, 1889, the day thirty blocks of the business district burned to the ground.

For the price of $352,265.67 the city purchased Spring Hill's system and the responsibility of supplying its 12,000 customers. The remainder of Seattle's 42,000 citizens were serviced either from their own wells or by smaller water companies which the city utility eventually subsumed. Shortly after the fire destroyed most of downtown in 1889, Seattle Mayor Robert Moran hired Chicago waterworks engineer Benezette Williams to devise a plan for increasing the city's water supply. Williams warned against relying on the pumps at Lake Washington. Not only was the supply inadequate but the lake was already showing signs of pollution. The new municipal utility installed another pump at Lake Washington anyway, but as soon as R. H. Thomson became city engineer, on June 1, 1892, he forbade expansion of the Lake Washington plant and put his formidable will to the task of bringing Cedar River water to the city.

Cedar River System

During the summers of 1893 and 1894 Thomson and an assistant made several trips on the night train to Maple Valley. There they unrolled their beds in the woods and rose with the light to tramp along the line of Benezette Williams's proposed gravity line. Persuaded that Williams's plan for an open V-shaped flume was "very bad engineering" as well as unsafe and unsanitary, they rough-sketched a route for a buried pipeline. However, Thomson's plans were soon buried by the hard times of the Panic of 1893. Two years later, funding problems were resolved after the state Supreme Court approved the city of Spokane's proposal to rebuild its water system with revenue bonds redeemed solely through water utility receipts and not from the city general fund. Using the Spokane model, Thomson and his assistant, George Cotterill, wrote an ordinance for a Cedar River system to be paid for by revenue bonds. The new bonds, however, required voter approval. A contemporary characterized the election that followed as "waged with a fury scarcely equaled in any other campaign that the city has experienced."

Above: The oldest surviving photograph of Seattle is of the Yesler home, and includes a portion of the town's first water system. Yesler's pile-supported flume descended James Street, turned in front of his home on Front Street (First Avenue), center, and continued on to his mill. The flume was supplied by a tank set close to where the cleared townsite bordered the forest, near the present line of Fifth Avenue. The view is commonly dated 1859.

Above: In a second view, photographed about one year later, the flume is gone; and the Yeslers have buried their waterworks. The new system was constructed of hand-bored fir logs. The roughly six-foot sections were joined by wooden spigots and driven together with a wooden mall. Log pipelines became quite commonplace in the small water systems that individually serviced a few pioneer businesses and households. Although they leaked, some lasted a long time. In 1926 workmen uncovered a log pipe still in use below the intersection of First Avenue and Pike Street, at the entrance to Seattle's Public Market.

Seattle City Council members sample Cedar River water and joyfully approve, ca. 1899. Photo by A. Wilse. Courtesy, Seattle Municipal Archives.

Support for Thomson's plan came from an combination of Progressives and Populists. The opposition was led by eastern capitalist Edward Ammidown, who allied with some prominent Seattle businessmen to incorporate the Seattle Power Company and build a Cedar River system that would sell its water to the city. The well-funded privatizing forces hired bands and speakers and hurled accusations of socialism at the public utility advocates. Federal judge J. J. McGilvra, a Lincoln appointee and respected Seattle civic leader, published a letter in the *Post-Intelligencer* supporting Ammidon's plan and urging a nay vote on city ownership. This apparent setback set the stage for Thomson's strategy. Pioneer Seattle historian Clarence Bagley noted Thomson's "masterful fighting" qualities, and the engineer's assistants said he hunted "with a rifle, not a shotgun."

Thomson set his sights on McGilvra. After several meetings with the city engineer, the judge ten days before the election wrote a second letter to the *P-I,* calling for approval of the bond issue. McGilvra then paid for the bands and speakers supporting public water. The combination of populism and respectability won the day with 2,656 votes for the measure to 1,665 against. As Thomson's assistant George Cotterill later noted, "What we accomplished here in 1895 . . . within a few years every state did the same. Hundreds of millions of utility bonds were issued,

Above: Concrete pier construction for the dam at the Landsburg intake on the Cedar River, ca. 1898. Photo by A. Wilse. Insert: City Engineer R.H. Thomson. Bottom left: Laying the Cedar River Pipeline through its lowest elevation near the Black River in Renton. Bottom right: The original 1900 ornamental standpipe on Queen Anne Hill and, on the left, its later unadored second. A portion of Fire Station No. 8 and its drying tower appear at far right. Courtesy Seattle Municipal Archives.

interest rates were lowered, and utility bond investment was among the safest and most desirable."

When Thomson and Cotterill emerged from the Cedar River watershed with their completed surveys in 1897, the city was alive with the stimulating effects of the Klondike Gold Rush. The following year the city acquired Landsburg for the site of its supply intake. The timber-crib dam there was constructed on concrete piers set at an elevation of 536.4 feet, a head high enough to carry water by gravity twenty-eight miles to the city reservoirs at Volunteer and Lincoln parks on Capitol Hill. From the headworks

the water was delivered a few hundred feet downstream through a 54-inch pipe to a settling basin where the flow passed through screens, initially operated manually, to remove coarser materials like sticks and leaves. Over twenty-two miles of the pipeline were constructed of wood staves bound with threaded steel bands of the latest design.

On Christmas Eve, 1900, the system tested so satisfactorily that on January 10, 1901, the waters of the Cedar River were let loose into the Volunteer Park reservoir. After a decade of riotous development, during which Seattle's population grew from 80,000

Above left: Before the third Cedar Pipeline reached West Seattle through a tunnel beneath the Duwamish River, water was piped there across the Spokane Street swing bridge over the East Waterway, an arrangement that stopped service whenever the bridge swung open for ships. This 1918 view looks west toward the Riverview business district and shows the pipeline (far right). Courtesy Seattle Municipal Archives. Above right: Aerial over Seattle's Maple Leaf Reservoir and I-5 to Green Lake Park. Roosevelt High School is at bottom-left. Courtesy Seattle Municipal Archives.

in 1900 to nearly 240,000 in 1910, a second pipeline, which paralleled the first, was added in 1909. With the two mains the Cedar system capacity increased to 67,269,000 gallons a day. Two additional city reservoirs with a 110 million-gallon combined capacity were also built atop Beacon Hill.

In 1928 the Seattle utility began diverting Cedar River water to the 500-acre Lake Youngs (formerly called Swan Lake and named for Water Superintendent L. B. Youngs), seven miles west of Landsburg, for settling and storage. The following July Seattleites complained about the taste when the heavy summer draw lowered the lake level and raised its temperature. Eventually, a pipeline was added, which allowed the utility to bypass the lake when the river waters were cool and clear and did not need settling. From Lake Youngs, water was sent through the system control works where it was screened and chlorinated before being delivered to its users.

In 1923 the city completed a third Cedar River pipeline that ran parallel to the first two. A fourth line was dedicated in 1954. Its path was entirely separated from the first three lines, in part as a precaution against any disasters that might sever the triad of pipes that ran through Renton and up and along the ridge of Beacon Hill

to the city reservoirs. The fourth Cedar River line, or the Bow Lake Pipeline as it was originally called, entered the city from the southwest after running west from the control works to near Bow Lake in the neighborhood of Sea-Tac Airport.

Water for the Suburbs

Getting water to Alki Point and the rest of West Seattle was still a problem sixty years after most of the first settlers left. West Seattle was annexed in 1907, following proclamations that the two communities were "plainly designated by nature to form one community." However, the Duwamish River, which at the time was being developed into the Duwamish Waterway, inhibited the transport of Cedar River water to the annexed neighborhoods. The swing bridge over the Duwamish, built for wagons and trolleys in 1910, also carried the city's main water lines to West Seattle. The effects on West Seattle plumbing were easily calculated. Whenever the bridge swung open for a boat or barge, the taps of West Seattle went dry. This intermittent service continued until the bridge was scrapped in 1918 and the mains submerged beneath the river's traffic. The underwater solution was improved in 1924 when an 8-foot, concrete-lined tunnel was dug beneath the river and a steel main with walls three inches thick was laid within it. The desire for Cedar River water also figured prominently in Ballard's annexation in 1907. In the "Shingle Capital of the World," the campaign for "pure and sufficient water" was helped considerably when a dead horse was found floating in the Ballard reservoir on the eve of the election.

More water had to be crossed in the city's extension of service to neighborhoods on the north shore of Lake Union. A pipeline from the Volunteer Park reservoir was run across the old Latona Bridge, which spanned the lake's narrow neck to Portage Bay in line with the future I-5 Ship Canal

Left: Early view of the Tolt River pipeline near its source below the reservoir's earthen dam. Courtesy Seattle Municipal Archives.

Bridge. Beginning in 1911 an extension of Cedar River Pipeline #2 was carried parallel to the Latona bridge on its own timber-pile span until 1916, when nearly 2,000 feet of 42-inch steel pipe were laid through a concrete tunnel built beneath the lake at the same passage.

Flood and Famine

In 1906 the City of Seattle made a widely unpopular decision to allow the Milwaukee Railroad to run its electric line to Snoqualmie Pass twelve miles through the lower Cedar River watershed. Five years later on the Sunday morning of November 19, 1911, the church bells of Renton called not for worship but for flood, sending its citizens scurrying for the hills. A warm Chinook wind released a downpour which swelled the river and undermined the bridge that carried the two Cedar River pipelines just downstream from the Landsburg intake. The railroad construction along the river was determined partly responsible for making the pipeline's own supports vulnerable. The collapsing bridge broke open both pipes, adding their volume to the already overflowing river and flooding the valley.

Soon after the streets of Renton flooded, bottom, on the morning of Sunday, Nov. 19, 1911, the streets of Seattle and much else went dry. Residents of Seattle's Capitol Hill, above, bring buckets and bottles to fill from the city water truck during the nearly week-long Seattle water famine. The cause — a break, below, in the Cedar River pipeline downstream from its Landsburg outfall.

A water famine in Seattle followed. Citizens were encouraged to fill their bathtubs with lake and rain water and the health commissioner's precaution "BOIL YOUR WATER" blazoned across the front pages of the dailies. Since the limited supply in the city reservoirs was released only to the business district, entire families from more affluent neighborhoods fled their homes for downtown hotels. Schools closed for want of steam heat, and on Wednesday 2,000 bundles of Seattle's dirty laundry were shipped to Tacoma. By week's end water department crews had restored the pipelines.

Tolt River Development

In 1936 city officials applied for the water rights to build two reservoirs on the Tolt River. But it was not until almost twenty years later that the utility actually prepared to tap the river. In 1955, 650,000 people were being served by the Seattle Water Department. Water Superintendent Roy Morse calculated that the Cedar River would be pushed to its capacity by 1970, and by 1980 about 900,000 people would be using the system. A second major source besides the Cedar would have to be used. Once the city council was convinced of this, it went ahead with development of the Tolt. In 1963 the river's waters began flowing through the 25-mile Tolt River pipeline. As it turned out, Morse's predictions were about right. In 1989 the Tolt and Cedar rivers together served over one million residents in an area whose size had grown to nearly 450 square miles. As parts of an integrated system, the two sources, plus a small amount pumped from the Highline Well Fields, could deliver up to 350 million gallons a day in 1990.

East end of Break in Pipe Line at Bridge #1 as it appeared Monday, Nov 20 1911, one day after Break which occured Sunday at 11 A.M.

Seattle's water system includes Bellevue, Kirkland, and Redmond, together with a number of other cities and water districts. Each community acts as a separate purveyor purchasing water from Seattle, the wholesaler, and reselling it within its service area. Although Seattle aggressively pursued water customers to the north, the city had to be wooed for nearly thirty years to supply the Eastside. In 1937 Eastside residents petitioned the city council to allow them to connect into either the Tolt River or Cedar River lines. The construction of a pipeline from the Cedar would have involved no insurmountable engineering obstacles. (The Tolt waters were still a quarter century from being tapped.)

But the Seattle City Council didn't think there was enough population to support the service, and not even the prospect of $900,000 in federal employment grants persuaded them to build the connection.

Eastside residents themselves were ambivalent about requesting the gravity system to supplant their wells. In a 1939 election a new water district, which included Bellevue, voted 891 in favor and 899 against requesting Cedar River water. Seattle's relaxed water department superintendent, W. Chester Morse, remarked, "Take as much time as you want. Every month's delay saves this department over $15,000 dollars. We certainly are in no hurry." Ultimately, the utility would change its mind as postwar growth brought increased water needs to the Eastside. Three years after he succeeded his father as superintendent in 1949, Roy Morse advised the city to speed its development of the Tolt River, in part to supply the Bellevue area. In 1963 that community came on line with the Seattle system's new Tolt pipeline. Eventually, the Tolt Eastside supply line was connected with a new Eastside line laid from the Cedar River at the pump station in Bellevue's Lake Hills district. In 1998 construction began at a 25-acre site overlooking the South Fork of the Tolt River on a filtration plant capable of filtering 120 million gallons of water a day when it opens in late 2000.

Tolt River Reservoir. Courtesy Seattle Municipal Archives.

Conservation

With the considerable population growth that occurred in King County by the 1980s, Seattle water department officials quickened their search for new sources of supply and their investigations into conservation methods. In 1985-86 the water department tapped its Highline Well Fields for a ready daily supply of 10 million gallons. Typically this new source was used only during the dry summer season when the average daily demand of 170 million gallons could rapidly inflate up to 300 million gallons. Restraining the public's wasteful over-watering of residential lawns became the key to the utility's development of a conservation program.

During the drought of 1987, the utility was forced to innovate when the level of Chester Morse Lake (Cedar Lake) dropped below the elevation of 1,532 feet — the minimum level for moving lake water by gravity. Department officials outfitted a barge with a pumping plant capable of moving nearly 120 million gallons a day from the lake into the lower-elevation pool behind City Light's masonry dam from which it flowed into the system. The experience resulted in plans for installing a permanent on-shore version of the barge-mounted pumps. The Cedar Watershed is capable of supplying a volume considerably greater than that which it now delivers through the four Cedar pipelines. However, fish using the stream to spawn could be adversely affected, and new transmission lines would be needed if a permanent deep-water pump at Chester Morse Lake were to be useful year round. Two other possibilities for increasing supply are to add a filtration plant to the Tolt River system, making it usable during periods when heavy runoff makes the water turbid, and building a second intake on the river's north fork.

However, even during the more severe drought of 1992, department spokesmen admitted that any such expansions were at least ten years away. In the meantime, Seattle and other Puget Sound area water departments and districts hurried work on their conservation plans as they implemented drastic conservation measures, such as a total ban on lawn watering. The reuse of treated waste water and the distribution of low flow shower heads were just two of the measures Seattle officials promoted as a way to save the 47 million gallons a day the department needed to conserve through the end of the decade.

Above: Depression-time WPA work on 28-foot wood stave pipeline in South Everett. Courtesy, WA State Historical Society, Tacoma. Right: Everett tank wagon #1 filling up at a city hydrant. Courtesy, Snohomish County Historical Society.

EVERETT

The city of Everett did not get into the water utility business as early as Spokane, Tacoma, or Seattle but it eventually built a system in the same class as these larger cities. Everett's first domestic water supply was installed by the Everett Railway, Light and Power Company. In 1915, when Everett residents voted to purchase the company's system, they also approved the construction of a timber diversion dam and pipeline to bring water by gravity from the Sultan River twenty-five miles away. Construction of the latter began in April 1916 but was slowed by the wartime manpower shortage and two floods which damaged the partly completed work. When the first water through the system reached a reservoir in town at 7 p.m. on July 17, 1919, Everett citizens proudly celebrated the culmination of four years of planning and two years of pipeline construction. The twenty-five miles of pipeline and three tunnels, totaling 1,355 feet, had a capacity of 11 million gallons a day.

Most of the pipe was 28-inch-diameter wood stave. In three places where the pipeline crossed stream beds, 30-inch cast-iron "subaqueous" pipe was installed — but not without difficulties. At the Snohomish River crossing, the contractor failed to properly align the underwater pipe. When the city demanded that it be removed and relaid, the contractor refused. With the help of lumber-industry technology, city engineers removed the pipe themselves. Using a donkey engine securely anchored 400 feet back from the river bank, steel cables, and a double system of pulley blocks, as well as a government snag boat to separate the line in the middle of the stream, they pulled out the pipe without damaging it. Then the 360-foot, 90-ton pipe was reassembled along a greased skidway on the bank, caulked, and dragged into place by the cables and pulley blocks operating from the donkey engine. The entire launching operation took only fifteen minutes.

In 1930 the city built a new diversion dam and tunnel to send the Sultan River flow into Lake Chaplain. The diverted river waters and a 22-foot-high earthfill dam raised the level of the natural lake, creating a storage capacity of 1.4 billion gallons — enough to supply the city with 50 million gallons a day. From the lake, which doubled as a settling basin, a second tunnel sent the flow to the screening and chlorination plant from which it exited into the town's distribution system. In 1941 the original earth

Old Sultan River Dam at Everett Headworks after the 1931 flood. Courtesy, Snohomish County Historical Society. Bottom left: Sultan River Conversion Dam, May 5, 1931. Courtesy, Everett Public Library. Right: Construction at intake to Culmback Dam, 1965. Courtesy City of Everett.

dam was raised and a second dam installed to the north, increasing the lake's capacity to approximately 4.4 billion gallons and doubling the daily flow to the city.

Since 1957, when the Snohomish County Public Utility District was given federal approval to use part of the Sultan River flow for power generation, Everett's water supply and the PUD's hydroelectric projects have been intertwined. In 1965 the city and the PUD built Culmback Dam, twelve miles upstream from Lake Chaplain. The 200-foot-high earth and rockfill structure created the three-and-a-half-mile long Spada Lake reservoir, which has a surface area of 770 acres. In 1966 the Everett water system provided an average daily flow of 120 million gallons of water to its customers. Approximately 100 million gallons of this amount was used by the three major pulp and paper plants in the area — the Scott, Weyerhaeuser, and Simpson Lee companies.

By 1982 Spada Lake had become the main supply for 250,000 people in Everett and south Snohomish County. That year the PUD began work on the second phase of the cooperative Culmback project — the construction of the power generating facilities. To achieve optimum hydroelectric capability, the dam had to be raised sixty-two feet, creating a larger reservoir. Because

clear-cutting in the basin would release higher levels of naturally-occurring asbestos, plus soil and other residue from the shoreline into the reservoir, the PUD agreed to finance a portion of the filtration plant. The controversial plant was completed in 1983.

Watersheds

Despite the increasing importance of groundwater, most Washington residents, particularly those west of the mountains, get their water from lakes and streams. The urge to protect these natural waterworks from contamination often involves precautions that seem excessive to fishermen, hikers, hunters, loggers and others who want to enter the land. Typically, state and county health officials have sided with city water departments who argued that if people were allowed into the area surrounding the water supply, they would cause contamination, and the utilities would have to build expensive purification plants.

Above: Spada Lake Reservoir, 1965. Courtesy, City of Everett. Below: Chester Morse Lake and the line of logged-off land. Courtesy Seattle Municipal Archives.

Cedar River

The Cedar River provides about 70 percent of the water supplied by the Seattle Water Department to more than 1 million people in the Seattle-King County metropolitan area. The river produces power at City Light's masonry dam, and the dam also helps control one of the river's few disservices to developed areas — floods. The Cedar hosts the largest sockeye salmon run in the continental U.S., an achievement which requires care on the part of both City Light and the water department. The Cedar's waters are so low in mineral content that they require artificial hardening with lime and soda ash to prevent corrosion of home plumbing. The river waters also have low levels of bacteria and bacilli, a purity which is maintained by the utility's long struggle to acquire and protect the river watershed.

The Cedar River watershed is about the size of the City of Seattle. The watershed's 91,400 acres — or about 143 square miles — are conventionally divided into upper and lower parts. The upper part contains everything above Cedar Falls and includes Chester Morse Lake, formerly called Cedar Lake and renamed for the Seattle Water Department superintendent from 1938 to 1949. Morse's links to his namesake lake went beyond his administration of it. He homesteaded on the eastern shore of the lake in 1896. Except for less than 100 acres cleared by homesteaders like Morse,

in 1900 the upper watershed was an untouched stand of old-growth fir, hemlock, and some cedar. Logging began on the lower watershed below Cedar Falls in the 1890s, and the water department's first purchases and condemnations there introduced it to the difficulties of managing and acquiring a watershed which is also of intense interest to loggers, railroads, and sportsmen.

By 1912 the city owned nearly 38,000 acres in the watershed. Since logging rights were usually retained by the former owner, logging activity was heavy even on lands purchased by the city. In 1924 the water department became responsible for management of the watershed, which included plans for reforestation, fire protection, the development of a tree nursery, and the hiring of the department's first forester. That year also the city acquired 11,997 additional acres in the watershed from the Northern Pacific Railroad, with the company retaining rights for a time to remove timber in ways not injurious to the water supply.

Water department officials were generally sanguine about the logging. Chester Morse noted in 1943 that even without reforestation practices the resilient logged-off lands were almost all covered by second growth timber. The city determined that the Cedar River water was excellent and that the typical hazards attending it were present with or without logging. In 1945 Morse concluded a historic arrangement that established strong sanitation requirements and eventually put most of the private land within the watershed into the water department's hands. He also agreed to extend the logging rights of the Weyerhauser Company and the Northern Pacific Railroad on watershed land in exchange for logged-off lands the companies owned outside the watershed. The U.S. Forest Service agreed to exchange its forested lands within the watershed for those logged-off properties. The first acreage was traded between the city and the forest service in 1953 and under a later agreement in 1962, the city continued gradual acquisition of watershed lands. By 1992 the city owned about 80 percent of the watershed, with the forest service the only other landowner.

In 1989 the utility began implementing a new watershed management plan, which, in addition to its primary mandate of producing pure water, shifted emphasis from timber harvesting to preservation of wildlife and old-growth forest. The importance of remaining old-growth forests was underscored in the controversy surrounding the protection of the spotted owl and its habitat, which came to a head in 1990 when the species was officially declared endangered. For those wishing to preserve the old forests, the owl was another reason for protecting the complex ecology there. The panel of federal wildlife biologists, headed by spotted owl specialist Jack Ward Thomas, recommended a 100-year plan for preserving a well-distributed spotted owl population from San Francisco Bay to the Canadian border. The Thomas plan described the Cedar River Watershed's remaining old growth as an important link in the owl's West Coast habitat, recommending that some of it be preserved. Although the Seattle City Council favored the proposal, the decision would finally rest with the U.S. Forest Service, which still managed about 80 percent of the 15,000 acres of old growth in the watershed. In 1992 Congress passed the Cedar River Watershed Land Exchange Act directing the forest service to complete its exchange of federal lands with city-owned lands. With this final transfer, the City of Seattle will have achieved its goal of sole ownership of all land in the Cedar River watershed.

Green River

The Green River watershed is large — 231 square-miles — but the City of Tacoma owns little of it. Extending to the summit of the Cascade Mountains, two-thirds of it lies in the Snoqualmie National Forest. When the gravity system was first completed, a number of logging camps and sawmills were still operating in the area. Since then the city, with the help of the U.S. Forest Service, has been able to control the timber operations and reduce their number to a fraction of the original total. But despite an agreement with the Forest Service in 1914 to keep the area restricted, Tacoma utility officials have not been successful keeping trespassers out. In the early 1960s, while watershed patrolmen skirmished with interlopers, the city fought in the courts for the right to condemn a half mile of land on both sides of the stream. The city eventually won and bought the land enabling them to legally enforce trespass laws, at least along the river. But Tacoma officials wanted to keep people out altogether, so they tried to control the access roads as well.

In 1962 the Tacoma utility erected a gate at Palmer Junction, the western entrance to the watershed. The citizens of Lester, a railroad town more than twenty miles into the watershed near its eastern border at Stampede Pass, were informed that they and their registered guests would be allowed through the gate but only at posted hours. During any other times they wished to visit the Puget Sound basin, they would have to go east over Stampede Pass and join Interstate 90 before turning west for a second climb over Snoqualmie Pass. The seething Lesterites revolted. Appealing to

Citizens of Lester mobilize to keep their road through the Green River Watershed open to Puget Sound. Above: Lester citizens post a cartoon lampoon of a napping King "County Commissioner" with legs on his desk while "Letters from Lester" collect in his wire wastebasket. The commissioner's snoring sends a line of Zs out the office window that frames Seattle's Smith Tower. Photo dated Aug. 7, 1947. Courtesy, Museum of History and Industry, Seattle P-I Collection.

the right of public access, they found allies in the King County engineer who, accompanied by a chief deputy prosecutor and workmen, took an acetylene torch to the gate and hauled it away. Two hours later a Tacoma water department sanitarian directed another crew to weld a chain and hasp to the gate posts that had survived the work of the King County demolition crew. That night some Lesterites blew off the locks. The utility promptly replaced them.

The citizens of Lester were not only angered by the gate, but also anxious for their ultimate fate. The Lester schoolhouse was filled with virtually every able-bodied resident on March 20, 1963, when they voted to form a "Save Lester" committee. Rumors that Tacoma was planning to condemn and buy the land out from under the community and evict all its residents were only partly true. Ultimately, the city did purchase Lester from the railroad, but rather than kick its citizens out the utility gave them lifetime leases to the lots they lived on. Tensions over access lingered, until by the late 1980s the remaining Lesterites had removed themselves, leaving the abandoned town to rot and rust. In 1990 the utility, however, was still guarding its gate at Palmer Junction.

The Tacoma Water Division has been more liberal with hunters. Every year Tacoma cooperates with the state Department of Wildlife in managing a controlled hunt in which hunters compete for elk tags in a lottery draw. For the winners the week-long sortie into a watershed, which for fifty-one weeks of the year is practically a wildlife preserve, is a thrilling experience.

In 1962, King County officials join the fight when they order the Tacoma Utility's locked gate at Palmer opened and dismantled by acetylene torch. Courtesy, MOHAI, P-I Collection.

Above: Posting for Roslyn City Ordinance 560, at the community's intake pond, requiring permits for entry into its Domerie Creek watershed. Photo by Jerry Gay. Courtesy, City of Roslyn. Bottom:: Tacoma billboard. Courtesy, Tacoma Public Utilities.

Domerie Creek, Roslyn

For both Seattle and Tacoma the successful restriction of public access to their watersheds meant that they did not have to install expensive filtration systems to maintain water purity. The relationship between filtration and watershed access was also a concern of the old mining community of Roslyn in Kittitas County, about thirty miles east of Snoqualmie Pass. Roslyn's watershed was owned partly by the Forest Service and partly by the Northern Pacific Railroad. It was the railroad that first opened a coal mine on the Roslyn site in 1886 and it was the railroad that years later abruptly quieted the community by shutting down the operation.

In 1910 the railroad built the town's present gravity system from Domerie Creek. The town had only to add chlorine to the water to safeguard against giardia and other mountain-area microbes. However, when the Plum Creek Timber Company, a child of the Northern Pacific, announced its intentions in the 1970s to improve an old logging road through the Roslyn watershed, Roslyn citizens spoke up. Recalling the railroad's abandonment of the community, Mayor Dave Divelbiss noted that the company now wanted to "ruin our watershed" as well. Another Roslyn resident told a Seattle *Post Intelligencer* reporter, "If our watershed is damaged, the whole damn town will just dry up and die. The water here is just about all we've got left."

The tiny Roslyn watershed of only 2,200 acres had never been logged, and the citizens prudently calculated that an improved road would open its old growth of scattered Douglas fir to a flood of "wetsiders" in their "four-wheelers and their campers and their motorbikes." The town first attempted to stop the road work with an appeal to the state Department of Resources, only to discover that the logging company was not required to make an environmental impact statement. Feeling abandoned, the community took its watershed into its own hands. They annexed the land and passed environmental legislation that required a permit for any activity — including those of the forest service and the timber company — that could affect the public interest. Although the logging company refused to recognize the town's action, it retreated.

As long as surface water systems remain unfiltered, their purity depends on the safeguarding of their watersheds. This linkage makes political allies out of municipalities and environmentalists who might otherwise part company. But federal legislation threatens this alliance. The Environmental Protection Agency was instructed in 1986 to develop guidelines requiring filtration of all surface water systems to protect against the spread of the giardia microbe and other contaminants. Once the water is filtered, an important rationale for restricting access to watersheds is removed. Although Seattle and Tacoma are sure to claim exemptions from the expensive requirements, there is a growing likelihood that filtration will eventually be required for even the most protected and purest of surface water systems in the state.

WATER TREATMENT

Filtration

When Americans first began purifying water, they aimed to improve its taste, color, and odor. If these qualities were amended, it was believed the water would be safe to drink. As it turned out, the filtration process they used to make these aesthetic adjustments did remove most bacterial contamination.

Experiments with water filtration began in the United States in the 1830s. The early systems, later called slow sand filters, consisted of beds graded from top to bottom from fine sand to pea-sized gravel. As the water flowed through the beds, solids and organic material containing bacteria stuck to the sand particles in the upper layers. Despite their effectiveness, these trial systems were not adopted by the nation's larger cities for another forty years. Part of the initial reluctance of the municipalities was due to the great cost of installing and maintaining the systems. The slow sand filters quickly clogged and had to be cleaned frequently. Not until the 1870s, when the germ theory had gained wider acceptance and it was established that impure water was often the cause of the spread of typhoid and cholera, did scientists and city engineers begin to investigate the effectiveness of sand filters for removing the organic matter that carried micro-organisms.

The slow sand filter became an effective system for water drawn from relatively clear streams, although it remained too costly for smaller cities. By the early twentieth century the rapid sand or mechanical filter, which forced water through the filter under pressure, came into general use, largely replacing the earlier installations. The rapid filters could be operated at a high flow rate and were more easily cleaned by using a reverse flow. They could also clarify turbid waters without presedimentation when coagulants added to the water caused suspended matter to bunch together and thus be trapped in the filter media. In 1935 there were at least eleven water systems in the state using rapid sand filtration: Ferndale, Lynden, Burlington, La Conner, Mount Vernon, Kelso, Wenatchee, Dayton, Bucoda, Arlington, and Anacortes.

In the early 1940s, motivated by the critical wartime need to produce much lower turbidity water for processing radioactive materials, engineers working at Hanford began experimenting

with high rate, dual media filtration. The dual media filter developed by Hanford engineers Raymond Pitman and Walter Conley was perfected as a mixed media filter by the early 1960s. Composed of coal, sand, and garnet, the mixed media filter could produce a better water faster and more reliably than the sand filter. By the beginning of the 1970s mixed media filtration was rapidly becoming the industry standard.

Chlorination

At the beginning of the twentieth century, waterborne disease was common in the United States. Typhoid fever alone took a toll of 36 out of 100,000 Americans in 1900. By the end of the 1930s the number of deaths reported from typhoid had fallen to 3 per 100,000. In Washington state the decline was even more dramatic. Deaths from typhoid dropped from 44 per 100,000 in 1908 to 1 per 100,000 in 1937. State health officials attributed the decline primarily to the increase in chlorination of municipal and domestic water supplies.

As early as the 1830s efforts were made to improve the odor of water supplies with chlorine. Foul-smelling water was believed to be responsible for the epidemics of typhoid and cholera that nineteenth-century Americans so frequently suffered. But a misunderstood theory of disease transmission retarded the widespread adoption of chlorination until decades later. Not until after 1908, when a New Jersey water company convinced the courts that chlorine gas and bleaching powder were effective disinfectants, did chlorine became available for municipal water treatment. It took another dozen years and more, after improvements were made in chlorine compounds and disinfection techniques, before chlorination of water supplies became common. In the mid-1920s Washington State Board of Health regulations required virtually all water supply systems to chlorinate, even those drawing water from lakes and rivers at high elevations and from protected watersheds. In 1931, when ninety-two cities and towns sterilized their water by chlorination, 62 percent of the state population was receiving chlorinated water. In 1935 the percentage rose to 85.

Top: Tacoma Public Utilities billboard promoting the dependence of community growth on access to its water. Below: Water system intake for Leavenworth on the Wenatchee River. Photo by Simmer.

Controlling Contamination

It took a long time for the State Board of Health to achieve these results, however. Matters had not looked so promising in 1908, when deaths from typhoid stood at 82 per 100,000 in Chelan and Yakima counties. Most of the victims were male, between twenty and thirty years old, and their deaths could be traced primarily to contaminated irrigation ditch water used for drinking and washing milk containers.

West of the Cascades, young men often fell victim to typhoid in the filthy conditions of the forest industry camps. In one case, public health inspectors reported that a sawmill employing a few hundred men had installed outhouses emptying into the river only a short distance above the intake of one city's water supply. After inspecting railroad construction camps on the Wenatchee River upstream from the town of Leavenworth, the health board concluded "that danger to Leavenworth had only been averted by an act of Providence."

The board had been given the authority to enforce state health regulations when local health officials failed to do so. This gave them much to do. In the first two decades of the century a large number of Washington lakes, rivers, and streams used for water supply by small communities were being contaminated by sewage. Local officials did not understand the dangers of the pollution. Even the state legislature failed to enact laws recommended by the health board for controlling the fouling of state waters. So, in 1908 the board itself adopted a regulation forbidding municipalities from discharging untreated sewage into any body of water used for drinking purposes.

Compliance was slow. In 1910, Cle Elum, Ellensburg, and North Yakima all dumped their waste directly into the Yakima River, used downstream for drinking water by the people of Union Gap. Waitsburg, on the Touchet River, was another recipient of an upriver city's leavings. To illustrate that there was at least some public awareness of these "intolerable" conditions, the health board's 1910 biennial report quoted graffiti in a Dayton public toilet: "Urinate here. Waitsburg needs the water."

Residents of small towns were not the only people who had to cross their fingers, if they were not already holding their noses, before taking a drink of water. In 1907 Seattle experienced its largest typhoid epidemic after the Cedar River pipeline was shut down for repairs and water was temporarily drawn from Lake Washington. As a result, 238 Seattleites died. Two years later the director general of the Alaska Yukon Pacific Exposition in Seattle was advised by the state health commissioner shortly before the opening of the fair that plans to service fairground restaurants with water from Lake Washington were illegal. Although the AYP director general insisted there was no such intention, city health inspectors shortly discovered that most of the fairground buildings were connected to mains taking water from the lake. Worse yet, the intake of the mains had been installed only 300 feet from the outlet of one of the exposition's main sewers. The state commissioner ordered the Lake Washington pumps to close down immediately. But the damage had been done. The result of using polluted lake waters during the first ten days of the fair was a substantial increase in the number

of typhoid cases which reverberated for months in numerous minor epidemics throughout the western part of the state.

After Washington's experience with the 1919 worldwide epidemic of Spanish influenza, the legislature dismantled the health board and created a state health department. Among its other duties, the department was instructed to examine all public water supply systems and issue orders necessary to prevent contamination and secure purification. After a survey of state streams found 485 contaminated by sewage, the department required all public water systems to submit regular samples to the department's laboratory. Generally, contaminated water supplies were not dangerous enough to prohibit domestic use, and the need for state supervision of public water supplies in the larger cities was slight. It was in the towns of 10,000 or less population, where water facilities were supervised by officials subject to frequent political turnover and where treatment plants were often staffed by inexperienced operators, that state supervision was most needed.

In the upper Columbia Basin during the 1930s, the most serious stream pollution was found along the Yakima and Spokane rivers. Here sewage from towns along the river was being distributed over irrigated lands, endangering farm water supplies that came from shallow wells or from irrigation water stored in cisterns over the winter. Consequently, Yakima County had the highest typhoid rate in the state, and the health department ordered the

Cartoon panels shown on this page are selected from the State Health Department's 1939 Annual Report. Courtesy UW Libraries, Special Collections. Panels 1 and 2: The old way where, after county public assistance programs had been funded, there was typically little money left for public health work. AND SO…

Panels 3, 4, and 5: The "new way" began in 1940 when monies proposed under Senate Bill 438 sent funds directly to the State Department of Health. Combined with county funds… AND SO…

valley communities to build sewage treatment plants. In 1934, after conducting an inspection survey of tourist camps around the state, the department found that 279 of them, or 54 percent, had "unacceptable" water. During President Franklin D. Roosevelt's visit to the site of Grand Coulee Dam that year, three water supplies were studied before one was selected for his use. Special service lines were also installed and carefully sterilized before the water was delivered to the "President's Special" train.

DRINKING WATER STANDARDS

After sand filtration and chlorine disinfection were adopted, the incidence of serious disease spread through drinking water dropped to low levels. But the potential for contamination still remained. As new evidence of potentially health-threatening contaminants was discovered, state and federal lawmakers enacted increasingly stringent water quality standards.

The federal government took its first action in 1912 when it prohibited the use of the common drinking cup on all interstate railroad trips. Not everyone approved. Some people argued that if clean cups became unavailable, those deprived of water could have their health seriously threatened. Prohibitionists warned that the cupless might even be forced to succumb to the temptation of alcohol.

The first federal standards specifying maximum bacteriological counts were adopted in 1914 by the U.S. Public Health Service. Although these standards were legally binding only on water supplies used by interstate carriers, they were widely used as guidelines by state and local governments. The federal government updated the 1914 standards in 1925, 1942, 1946, and 1962. In 1925 chemical standards were included, and in 1942 the number of required bacteriological samples from distribution

systems was increased. When the latter regulation was instituted, Seattle Water Department Superintendent W. Chester Morse complained that the health service had far exceeded its authority. The department was already suffering a wartime shortage of manpower and yet was required to increase its number of samples from fifty to 250 a month.

The 1962 standards were the most comprehensive yet, setting mandatory limits for health-related chemical and biological impurities, and recommending limits for impurities affecting appearance, taste, and odor. An additional requirement specified that water supply systems be operated by qualified personnel. Still, in 1970, when the Nixon administration established the Environmental Protection Agency (EPA) and transferred to the new agency the responsibility for reviewing drinking water standards, a state survey revealed that only half of Washington's water systems serving 500 people or fewer met the 1962 norms.

The statistic was not surprising. According to state regulations, any water system serving two or more families was a public system subject to state and federal water quality standards. For years the high cost of extending water lines to outlying areas had made it cheaper for small groups to create their own independent water system than to hook up to larger existing ones. Usually built early in the century, these rural waterworks have typically been underfunded, simple systems, sometimes no more sophisticated than a pipe stuck in a stream. Some have had no formal operator or company organization that can be held accountable. Their rates have been too low to pay for system improvements and sometimes too minimal even to sustain basic operations. The cost of installing expensive purification systems and testing devices for measuring contaminants would have to have been borne by only a few customers.

In some areas such as near Ocean Shores and in Island

County, water systems were originally built to service summer homes. Now subdivisions in those areas have year-round residents. Volunteer water system managers, who have limited time and knowledge about operations and regulations, also have trouble convincing residents to fund improvements before problems become severe. In 1980 residents in the Grays Harbor County Water District No. 6 voted to dissolve the district after its commissioners passed a resolution to finance improvements with a $3 million revenue bond. The residents figured that it would have cost each of them $3,947.

As long as the water looked, smelled, and tasted pure and it came out of the faucet when they wanted it, many small systems were not troubled about possible contaminants or health department regulations. In the mid-1970s local residents and a water supplier in Selleck, in the foothills of southeastern King County, rejected the warnings of state and county health officials that their water posed a health risk. After all, they reasoned, they had been drinking it all their lives. About the same time, in the little community of Baring, near Skykomish, runoff from the road went directly into the town's drinking water. It took King County health officers two years to get some Vashon Island residents to keep their cattle from cooling themselves in springs used for drinking water.

But even the larger systems were found to be deficient. In 1967 the state health board reported that of the eighty-one Class I utilities (of 100 service connections or more) in King County, only two met bacteriological standards. Because of these kinds of statistics, in 1971 the health board adopted new regulations for public water supplies. For the largest systems of 1,000 connections or more, comprehensive planning, filtration of all water drawn from lakes and rivers outside of unprotected watersheds, and covered reservoirs were prescribed. The state ordered the smaller class II systems (under 100 services) to meet 1962 federal standards and make more frequent chemical and bacteriological tests. The small water purveyors also were directed to control cross connections to eliminate the illegal pipe arrangements that had drawn dirty water, sewage, and even gasoline into public water supplies.

In 1974, Congress enacted the Safe Drinking Water Act. The legislation for the first time gave the federal government the authority to regulate drinking water contaminants in the nation's largest 50,000 public systems. The EPA was authorized to set national comprehensive standards for turbidity, bacteria, and chemical compounds and to oversee state enforcement of these standards. The standards were to be phased in over a period of several years, and federal grants were made to help the states, particularly their smaller systems, meet them.

Enforcement in Washington has been slow and difficult. Seattleites raised such a ruckus over the required lidding of the Volunteer Park reservoir that alternate protective measures had to be taken. In 1976 the City of Port Angeles, which for some time had been resisting the state's mandate to filter its water supply drawn from Morse Creek, found itself up against the combined forces of state and federal agencies. The state Department of Social and Health Services (DSHS), to whom the regulation of water quality enforcement had been transferred, filed a suit against the city claiming that the water supply failed to meet bacteriological and turbidity limits. The EPA, at the state's request, forbade ships, ferries, and buses engaged in interstate commerce from supplying themselves with the city's drinking water. Then the Seattle office of the federal Department of Housing and Urban Development determined that it would no longer insure home mortgages in Port Angeles because of the substandard water quality. In July 1977 the city capitulated and, with state and federal financial assistance, began construction of a Ranney radial well to tap the sand and gravel aquifer below the lower Elwha River. (A radial well uses a system of laterals projecting out like spokes of a wheel from the

Above: Port Angeles pumping station with a schematic drawing of its Ranney radial well. Courtesy, Port Angeles Deptartment of Public Works. Bottom: Everett filtration plant, 1983. Courtesy, City of Everett.

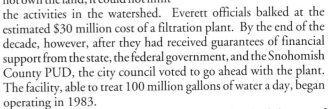

base of the caisson.)

Everett also attempted to put off the day of reckoning. In the early 1970s DSHS directed the city to filter its water because it was being contaminated by disease organisms and naturally occurring asbestos dislodged by logging operations in the watershed surrounding Spada Lake. Since the city did not own the land, it could not limit the activities in the watershed. Everett officials balked at the estimated $30 million cost of a filtration plant. By the end of the decade, however, after they had received guarantees of financial support from the state, the federal government, and the Snohomish County PUD, the city council voted to go ahead with the plant. The facility, able to treat 100 million gallons of water a day, began operating in 1983.

In June 1986 after legislation was passed in both houses of Congress by overwhelming majorities, President Reagan signed into law the 1986 amendments to the Safe Drinking Water Act. The amendments established new requirements for public water systems, including stricter measures for monitoring, filtration, and chlorination. The EPA was directed to work with the states in order to regulate more than eighty contaminants and authorized to distribute federal grants to help the states upgrade their public systems. County and state health officials continue to see that the state's ever-growing number of public water systems comply with the new standards.

Above: Aberdeen's depleted reservoir during the February 1950 water famine. Courtesy, MOHAI, Seattle P-I Collection. Right: Wynoochee Dam. Courtesy, Army Corps of Engineers.

WYNOOCHE DAM

"Our woodbox is full but our water bucket is empty" a citizen of Aberdeen reflected on the eve of construction for the Wynoochee Dam. Sponsored by most of Grays Harbor's big players, including the cities of Aberdeen, Cosmopolis, and Montesano, Grays Harbor County, the Port of Grays Harbor and the county P.U.D., the Army Corps built the 175-foot-high dam in the summer of 1969 in a narrow canyon about forty miles north Montesano. These usually sodden and often flooded coast communities needed even more water, not particularly for themselves, but for the impressive collection of thirsty lumber and pulp mills that then crowded the region. Aberdeen's first serious look at the Wynoochee as a source for its industrial demand ended in 1928 with the "Aberdeen Folly" when the two mills which lobbied for the service could not as promised help pay for the Wynoochee outfall. Gradually, however, the investment paid off as new mill after mill came on line. The grander dream of a high dam originated with Aberdeen's longtime city employee and master mechanic Joe Malinowski who filed a water rights claim on the Wynoochee in 1921 and later sold it to his hometown for one dollar. After working for forty-five years as its promoter, the retired Malinowski was on hand for the Wynoochee Dam's August 26, 1973 dedication following the filling of its five-mile-long reservoir with 70,000 acre-feet of water.

On one occasion, the mills of Aberdeen gave back water to its citizens. On the night of February 1, 1950, when the thermometer dipped to fourteen degrees, city reservoirs quickly went dry, depleted in part by the common precaution of keeping faucets dripping to prevent freezing. However, the principle cause of this widely reported Aberdeen water famine was the 3,000-foot section of antiquated wood stave pipes below the system's Wishkah River outfall. The frozen pipes soon burst and the town quickly went dry. Aberdeen Mayor Ed Lundgren noted that it was the first time he had had to wash his hands and face in the snow since he left Sweden. The mayor also closed Aberdeen theaters, public meetings, dance halls, and — perhaps the greatest hardship — its taverns; he shut down the town's nine mills and borrowed water from their reserves, sent the police to patrol for running faucets with the recommendation to make arrests in the event of drips. In five days, the inevitable thaw began, repairs were made, and the reservoirs filled. Four days later the Aberdeen City Council raised the monthly water rates from $1.50 to $2. It was the first increase in thirty-three years.

WATER UTILITY COORDINATION

More stringent standards for improving water quality meant little if utilities were incapable of putting them into effect. In 1968 state officials estimated that it would take over $220 million to bring all state waterworks facilities up to the 1962 standards. Most of the improvements were needed by the smaller utilities who could least afford them and who often could not get a bank loan. Recognizing these limitations, in 1972 the legislature and governor's office agreed to allocate $50 million of bond proceeds approved by the voters in Referendum 27 for municipal and industrial water supply development. Distributed in the form of grants and loans, the state funding was meant to help public systems plan for their own needs and coordinate with neighboring systems. In 1974, state statistics showed that Washington residents used an average of 75 gallons of water per person every day. When industrial demands were added, per capita use totaled 160 gallons a day, or 58,400 gallons a year, enough to fill a small lake.

In the general election of 1980 Washington's voters ratified a continuation of Referendum 27 when they passed Referendum 38. Seventy-five million dollars of the bond issue were dedicated to helping public utilities correct their deficiencies and upgrade their systems. Between 1973 — when the municipal water supply funding began — and 1985, 718 grants totaling over $95 million and 144 loans totaling over $5 million were made to 470 water utilities. The grants ranged from $129 to the town of Rockford to purchase a chlorinator to $7.5 million toward the construction of Everett's new filtration plant.

However much the capital was needed, it alone could not overcome a major failure of the water supply industry since its beginnings — the decentralized and uncoordinated manner in which it operates. In the tradition of American political institutions, public water utilities have functioned as small governmental units, each with considerable autonomy and planning powers. Consequently, there has been a natural distrust of regionwide planning and coordination. As one industry official wrote recently, an interconnection between water systems is about as simple as spanning the Grand Canyon with a pipeline. Such fragmentation of the industry has prohibited sound and economical management nationwide for tens of thousands of small public systems.

Washington's utilities have followed this pattern. Small systems have proliferated in the state, from 559 in 1960 to 2,500 in 1971, and to 12,245 in 1989. In Snohomish County alone there were more than 850 in 1989. Some public systems have overlapping service areas or are totally within a service area of another system, causing competition for customers. Other utilities have duplicated supplies or storage reservoirs that could have been more economically operated by sharing facilities and operation costs.

Boundaries have tended to follow political lines, often making little economic sense. In 1981, when a private elementary school attempted to build within the City of Kent water district, it was informed that the city could not afford to extend its nearest water line to the school site. Water District 75, serving unincorporated King County, operated a line forty feet from the site, but because of jurisdictional boundaries the school could not tap into it either. Water districts also have failed to consult city and county planning departments about future land use plans. In some cases there have been no ordinances to consult, particularly in areas undergoing rapid transformation from rural to urban.

The state's Public Water System Coordination Act of 1978, which was promoted by the Washington chapter of the Waterworks Association and public health officials, attempted to remedy these kinds of problems. The two main objectives of the legislation were to achieve an organized development of water utilities within a given area and to integrate water system development with city and county land-use planning. In the spirit of the law, experts suggested more efficient alternatives for small systems, among them joint operation of treatment plants and reservoirs and even the sharing of a "circuit-riding" certified treatment plant operator to oversee several systems.

One of the first entities to initiate a coordinated water system plan according to the state guidelines was Spokane County. More than eighty utilities in the greater Spokane area in 1978 reached agreements establishing legally binding borders of their service areas. Minimum design standards that promoted consistency between adjacent utilities and ensured the potential of hydraulically compatible interconnections were also adopted. Some of the utilities even began plans for sharing facilities. One of the program's more recent success stories was an intertie project undertaken in the Walla Walla-College Place area in 1985. Rather than building several separate storage tanks and additional wells, five water utilities completed interties between their systems in order to share their water supplies and expenses. They saved enough in power costs to pay for the construction of the intertie within four years. Additional benefits included an emergency source of water, increased fire-fighting flows, and reduced wear and tear on the consolidated district's pumping equipment.

GROUNDWATER SUPPLY

Until recently groundwater was not an important part of most of the state's domestic and irrigation water supply. Surface water was much easier to find and, compared to the costs of well-drilling and the electricity needed for pumping, considerably less expensive to develop. Also, little was or is yet known of the exact location, extent, and geologic conditions in which underground water can be found. Today we do know that the subterranean supply is by far the largest part of the state's freshwater resource, and that it can be obtained nearly everywhere in Washington, although supplies in some places are small. In 1986 over 40 percent of the state's population was drinking groundwater,

Spokane pump. Courtesy, Water and Hydraulic Services, City of Spokane.

compared to 20 percent fifty years earlier. By 1997, that had risen to over 60 percent. As many of the state's rivers and streams have become fully appropriated and cost-effective surface water reservoir sites have been claimed, groundwater, particularly in the eastern part of the state, has become increasingly important.

Although it is less subject to evaporation, pollution, and temperature changes than surface flows, groundwater is not limitless. During the past three decades the basalt aquifers below Walla Walla, Odessa-Lind, and Pullman have declined markedly. In the early 1960s several dryland wheat farmers around Odessa in Adams County, where rainfall averages nine to thirteen inches a year, dug deep wells and began experimenting with large irrigation sprinkler systems. The wells were expensive but the economic returns were high. Their normal yields of twenty to thirty bushels per acre nearly tripled when they added less than one foot of water to the soil. The water also allowed them to abandon the summer fallowing method and to grow a crop every year. When word about the bonanza yields spread, farmers stood in line to buy deep well pumps and circular sprinkler equipment.

It took only a few years of this enthusiastic pumping to reveal that there were limits to the underground "mother lode." In some places the water table was receding as much as twelve feet a year by 1965. In 1968 Governor Dan Evans imposed a moratorium on new well drilling around Lind and Odessa. Shortly afterwards, the Water Research Center, a joint agency of Washington State University and the University of Washington, began studies. The researchers found that the Odessa-Lind aquifer was extensive, underlying most of an 1,800-square-mile area. It reached down through several water bearing zones to at least 2,000 feet below the surface, where the water was found to be from 2,000 to 7,000 years old. Since there was practically no recharge from precipitation, pumping had depleted the stored water and required well operators to keep drilling deeper as the water level declined. In 1974 the state Department of Ecology adopted regulations that established a maximum of thirty feet of drawdown over a three-year period.

A similar problem was found in the Moscow-Pullman basin where the water in the underground aquifer had been age-dated at between 10,000 and 20,000 years old, indicating that it had been deposited as ice sheets at the end of the last Ice Age. The dense well spacing, high pumping rates, and low precipitation threatened to drain a source that could take decades, if not centuries, to refill. Heavy reliance on wells in the Toppenish Creek basin since the mid-1950s has also caused significant declines in water levels. Today the situation is critical in much of east-central Washington. A network of observation wells installed over the past forty years has helped state officials monitor changes in groundwater levels in many of the principal aquifers. In 1985 the legislature tightened the regulations in the state's original groundwater code of 1945 to protect the rights of prior appropriators, prevent overdrafts, and ensure safe, sustaining yields.

Not all groundwater sources in eastern Washington are in danger of being depleted. In the Spokane Valley the coarse sand and gravel laid down by Ice Age glaciers and floods holds extensive amounts of underground water even after seventy years of municipal use. In the western part of the state, there also are some highly productive aquifers located in the Puget Sound lowlands and near Vancouver.

Coastal aquifers present a problem of another kind. Large withdrawals have resulted in salt water being drawn into the freshwater aquifers. Between 1940 and 1979 the population of Island County — which consists of two major islands, Whidbey and Camano, and several smaller islands in Puget Sound — rose from 6,700 to 40,200. By the late 1960s county planners had become concerned about the extent of the groundwater and the potential for seawater intrusion. In 1971 the Coupeville City Council considered (and later abandoned) the idea of installing the Northwest's only desalinization plant to convert sea water into fresh. During the drought of 1977 some Whidbey residents thought their water tasted salty. Others had their wells go dry. Island County health department officials, acting on the advice of state health inspectors, temporarily blocked further housing development in 1979 when the water quality in some areas became substandard. In 1985 a survey of the county's public water systems showed a number of incidences of seawater intrusion and supplies inadequate to meet the existing demand, but residents have been reluctant to fund improvements. Because water districts in the area are small with few financial reserves, residents in both Island and Kitsap counties have asked state and federal agencies to help them determine the extent and condition of their underground resource.

Water Rights

Washington's territorial legislature and courts seldom had reason to concern themselves with water use issues. There was usually more than enough water to go around during the first forty years of settlement. However, by 1889 when the state constitution was adopted, farmers and irrigation companies in fertile eastern Washington valleys had begun squaring off over their rights to water.

During the territorial period and later, Washingtonians claimed a right to use water according to two different legal traditions. According to riparian law, an inheritance from British common law followed in the eastern part of the United States, landowners were entitled to a share of the water passing through or alongside their property as long as they did not unreasonably affect the ability of downstream landowners to use the water. According to appropriation doctrine, a western legal tradition initiated by California miners during the Gold Rush, those who first claimed the right to take water from a particular source for their "reasonable" needs, irrespective of any property rights, had first priority to it. In other words, the "first in time is first in right."

Water rights became complicated when territorial and later state courts upheld both types of doctrine. In 1891 the state legislature passed an act declaring that all state waters used for

Built in 1889 to service Calkins Resort, East Seattle's first public destination, this ornate Victorian water tower included living quarters. It served as the spring-fed reservoir for Mercer Island's first water system. The tower was torn down after a 1974 fire ruined plans to restore it. Photo by Hugh Paradise.

irrigation, mining, manufacturing, municipal, and domestic use were to be considered a public use acquired by appropriation. The lawmakers reasoned that appropriation was better suited to the agricultural conditions of the eastern part of the state. Riparian law might be more practical west of the mountains where water was plentiful, but no one was likely to invest in or attempt to farm land east of the Cascades without a sure supply of water.

In 1917 when legislators adopted the first state water code, they declared the appropriation doctrine to be the law of the land for allocating public water supplies. Just as the first miner to stake a claim was considered to have the sole right to work it, so the first water user to claim a portion of streamflow established first priority to divert whatever he felt he needed. Once the state granted the claimant a permit, he was assured of a legal property right to the water in perpetuity. Of course, claiming by appropriation meant that the stream was not shared equally, and that users with less seniority could be left high and dry when stream or lake levels sunk.

To be granted a state permit, a water user was supposed to demonstrate that the water was actually being diverted out of the stream for a "beneficial" purpose — for irrigation, manufacturing, or domestic or municipal supply. The concept of beneficial use was intended to prevent water users from diverting more water than they could actually use. However, administration of the code fell short of its intent. For instance, the law required adequate diversion works and measuring devices essential for the proper distribution and regulation of a stream. Yet, watermasters and

Below: "A cast-iron horse trough, a relic of the 1894 boom, in ghosty, reminiscing Northport." Caption taken from Sunset magazine. Photo by Hugh Paradise.

stream patrolmen complained in the 1920s that they had no means of enforcement. Even today state administrators have difficulty enforcing the code because they lack accurate data about the amount of water available in streams and how much is actually being used and for what purposes.

Throughout the nineteenth and most of the twentieth century, few people in Washington or the West questioned the belief that intensive development of water resources was essential to economic growth. Generally, it was assumed that the larger public interest was served with every private withdrawal of state waters because the public benefited, at least indirectly, as a result of the development. However, by the late 1960s and early 1970s, many began to challenge this assumption. Environmentalists, fishermen and others argued that the traditional test of beneficial use was no longer adequate and that water must be regulated as a limited and essential resource. The concern for future municipal supply, recreational water uses, and the protection of wildlife and the environment, along with court decisions protecting the treaty rights of Native Americans, is beginning to wrench Washington's water allocation policies away from their nineteenth century origins.

To be acceptable to a new environmentally conscious and more politically active society, state water law had to broaden the meaning of beneficial use beyond the traditional extractive uses. With the passage of the Water Resources Act in 1971, Washington lawmakers acknowledged the public's demand for reasonable limits on private uses and their concern about aesthetic, recreational, habitat, and other environmental values. The new law outlined revised fundamentals of water resource policy in order that the "allocation of waters among potential uses and users shall be based generally on the securing of the maximum net benefits for the people of the state." Unfortunately, the statute failed to define the scope or extent of the public interest or how benefits deriving from diverse economic, social, and environmental uses should be weighted and compared in order to determine maximum net benefits. This left state Ecology Department administrators to set policies that attempted to accommodate a number of competing water users.

Following the directives of the act, the department implemented a comprehensive state water resources program. The goal was to determine how much water was available in the state, how much was currently being claimed and used, and how much would be needed in the future, allowing for population growth and minimum flows essential to maintain fish and wildlife. Researchers verified what state officials had suspected — the permit system was not managing state waters efficiently. In some places permit holders were using as little as 30 percent of their water allowance, denying junior appropriators access to the difference. However, inventorying all the streams and lakes in the state so that they could be managed more effectively was an enormous task. The work was only a few years underway when the droughts of the late 1970s caused lawmakers and administrators to shift priorities.

Instream Water Uses

The dwindled flows and dried-up stream beds of 1977 and 1979 reawakened state policy makers to the condition of over-appropriated bodies of water and their impact on the survival of fish and wildlife. They put aside their basin inventories in order to determine and prescribe minimum water levels necessary for the preservation of fish and animal populations and their habitats.

The Ecology Department's policies setting minimum or base flows were controversial but were not without precedent. As early as the 1930s, the state Division of Hydraulics and Water Resources began cooperating with the Departments of Game and Fisheries

Early-century headwaters on McAllister Creek. Sign reads, "Olympia Waterworks, No Trespassing."

to maintain enough streamflow for migrating fish, even though there were no statutes specifically requiring it. In 1949 state lawmakers approved legislation that put the necessary teeth into the agreements being reached among these departments. Consequently, approximately 250 small streams were closed to new water withdrawal claims.

In 1967 this legislation was bolstered by the Minimum Water Flows and Levels Act that gave the state the authority to establish minimum stream flows and lake levels to protect recreational and aesthetic values, and fish, game, and other wildlife resources. However, due to a lack of basic data and a definitive methodology, only one minimum flow regulation, for the Cedar River, was established under this law by 1977. And this river was particularly problematical. Because the City of Seattle had managed the Cedar River for so many years, water experts had no clear idea of the size of the natural flow. To resolve these kinds of problems, the Water Resources Act of 1971 directed state administrators to adopt whatever requirements they found necessary to set and retain base flows. Like the earlier legislation, the instream flow protection program was opposed by out-of-stream and hydroelectric water users.

In the 1980s the state, along with the federal government, continued the emphasis upon instream water uses and the maintenance of levels essential for fish passage and production. The Regional Power Act, passed by Congress in 1980, although primarily concerned with regional planning for the conservation and production of electric power, made fisheries protection a major provision. (See Power Chapter). Officially recognizing the appalling decline of salmon runs on the Columbia and other Northwest rivers, the legislation required hydropower developers to repair damaged fish habitat and to help salmon and steelhead run the gauntlet of dams. During 1981-82 the Ecology Department imposed minimum flow standards on the main stem of the Nisqually River, which was heavily utilized for power production by the cities of Tacoma and Centralia. McAllister Creek, the major source of municipal water supply for Olympia, was closed to further appropriation to protect existing water rights, fish runs, and a new hatchery. The 1985 Pacific Salmon Interception Treaty between the U.S. and Canada committed both countries to the conservation and long-term management of salmon. By 1987 the state had adopted minimum flow standards for 172 major streams.

Although stream closures were generally necessary only during the low flow periods of late summer and early fall, utility officials and eastern Washington irrigators complained that the state's emphasis on instream flows was too narrow. The priority being given to fish did not take into account the needs and priorities of agriculture, power, and municipal and domestic water use. In order to take action quickly, state administrators had set minimum flow standards without a clear idea of how much water was actually being withdrawn. A provision of the 1971 water resources law that allowed waters to be reserved for future beneficial use, even though it might constrain present beneficial use, also seemed to eastern Washington farmers and ranchers to

Pathe News Photographer Will Hudson's portrait of a fish counter at Bonneville Dam soon after its construction. Courtesy, Jean Hudson Lunzer.

enough for all users at the same time. Hydropower remains the region's only source of electrical peaking capacity and that means that when all the Columbia and Snake River dams are operating together at maximum capacity, other uses of the river are jeopardized.

The first to suffer from an overcommitted river were the salmon, some species of which have been driven nearly to extinction (See Power Chapter.) About thirty years ago another water user began to feel the Columbia River water squeeze. But irrigators, unlike fish, had enjoyed a long tradition of legal protection and could lobby on their own behalf. In the mid-1960s the state issued a large number of permits to ex-

discriminate against their traditional water rights. These agricultural permit holders wanted to maintain the certainty that the original 1917 water code guaranteed by appropriation — a vested right to use the water forever. Proponents of instream or optimum flow levels, on the other hand, argued that the state should not issue any water permits on streams where instream flows had not yet been set. As far as they were concerned, fish, wildlife, and recreational water users had as much right to establish valid claims to state waters as diverters had.

Needless to say, the calculation and comparison of the present and future public benefits of various water uses, some of which cannot be assigned a dollar value, has been a difficult and controversial task. By the late 1980s state water allocation policies had become complicated even more by international salmon agreements, the courts' recognition of Native American treaty rights, federal and state environmental programs, and the resource demands of a growing economy and population. Current laws and policies, which in some cases conflict or are ill-defined and unintegrated with federal laws, have created much confusion and uncertainty. In 1988 an independent fact finder, after interviewing water purveyors, irrigators, hydropower operators, fisheries and recreational-use spokesmen, and Washington tribes, reported his findings to a legislative committee. Although there were many clashing opinions and priorities, the water users agreed that the legislature needed to provide more guidance in balancing competing interests.

This consensus was reinforced by a state Supreme Court decision in September 1993 that could have broad implications for the future of water rights, if the legislature does not draft new legislation for a comprehensive water policy. The court ruled that the Ecology Department had exceeded its authority in taking sides in a controversy between ranchers and irrigators over dwindling groundwater reserves in the Sinking Creek area south of Wilbur in Lincoln County. Only the courts, they said, could adjudicate water-rights disputes. Justice Richard Guy, who did not agree with the majority opinion, claimed that the legislature must now consider "whether Western water law meets today's societal needs, given the understanding that water is not an infinite resource."

Hydropower vs. Irrigation

All the water that Northwest farmers, industries, and communities extract from the Columbia River and its tributaries amounts to only a fraction of its total annual volume. Nevertheless, although there is enough water for all users, there is not always

tract groundwater in the Columbia Basin, pending completion of the second half of the Columbia Basin Project. (See Irrigation Chapter). Then when the Odessa-Lind aquifer showed alarming drawdowns, the state placed a moratorium on further withdrawals. Now the Columbia Basin Project is on hold, and Basin farmers wonder how long they can afford to pump from such deep levels and how long their underground supply will last.

The uncompleted second phase of the Columbia Basin Project provides a good example of the competition that exists between irrigation and hydropower users of Columbia River waters. Irrigation is by far the largest consumer of water in the state and it is also a major consumer of electric power. It competes with the water used for hydroelectric generation in two ways. First, there is the electric energy needed to divert, lift, and deliver the water and pressurize the large circular sprinkler irrigation systems. Second, water that goes onto fields is not available to flow through the turbines of dams downstream. The link between irrigation and hydroelectric generation is further complicated by the state's heavy dependence on hydropower and the predominant importance of agriculture to the state's economy. Although environmentalists and fish and wildlife advocates have cited irrigation's effects on stream flows and water quality, state officials have weighed development primarily in terms of its costs and benefits to the agricultural sector. Will the value of crop production and jobs created in the agriculture-related industries ultimately exceed the cost of finishing the Columbia Basin project?

Because of the long time, roughly fifty years, it would take to complete and pay for the project, researchers attempting to calculate a comparison of benefits and costs have played an educated guessing game at best. Their findings vary according to their basic assumptions about future agricultural productivity, markets, and prices. However, they do agree that the cost of the project must take into account not only the usual expenses for building and financing the system, but also the cost of the hydroelectric power that would be lost by diversion above the dams.

Since water that is withdrawn from the river does not go through the turbines of the hydroelectric plant, the further upstream it is diverted the more dams and turbines it bypasses and thus the greater the loss in hydroelectric generation. Each acre-foot of water taken above Grand Coulee, researchers calculate, has the potential of producing 1,025 kwh if left to go through the turbines of the eleven downstream dams. If the additional acreage in the Columbia Basin that is now under dryland farming were to be irrigated, it would reduce hydropower output by 1,811 billion kwh per year. And since the river's hydroelectric potential is already fully utilized, the energy lost would probably have to be replaced by more expensive thermal generation. According to one 1984 estimate, this would cost the region's ratepayers an additional $63 million per year. Following Bureau of Reclamation policies, most of the cost of power for pumping water to the project would also have to be borne by all of the Bonneville Power Administration's customers through higher utility rates.

Naturally, the electric utilities do not want withdrawals that would force them to incur high thermal replacement costs. Since practically all streams in central and eastern Washington are tributary to the state's "powerhouses," the Columbia and Snake rivers, any irrigation diversion east of the Cascades has the potential of affecting electrical energy production. On the other hand, if irrigation developers were forced to reimburse hydropower producers for their losses at thermal replacement costs, they would not be able to afford new irrigation projects.

Legally, the irrigators have the upper hand. Current water rights laws and policies in the Northwest continue to favor irrigation development over hydropower generation. The customary lack of protection from irrigation withdrawals and of guarantees for optimal flow levels for instream uses such as hydropower, has made a transfer of water use from hydropower to irrigation legally possible without regard to the economic effects of the transfer. Water rights of 11,500 cubic feet per second with a priority date of 1938 have been reserved by the state for the remaining half-million acres of the Columbia Basin project. Legally, the second part of the basin program has priority for the water over the federal and non-federal hydropower dams downstream.

Whether the irrigation project is politically and financially feasible is quite another matter, however. The cost of enlarging eighty miles of existing major canals, building seventy-two miles of new primary canals and associated secondary delivery and drainage systems, and pump lifts would be approximately $2 billion. On the plus side, the Ecology Department has estimated that the additional irrigated acreage could increase annual state agricultural production by over $300 million. (A 1976 WSU College of Agriculture study argued, however, that this increase could depress crop prices and that the market for most products grown under irrigation in Washington showed little prospect of becoming stronger for a long time.) The program has had the active support of the late Senators Magnuson and Jackson, former Senator Dan Evans and Senator Slade Gorton.

However, the only way the state and the Reclamation Bureau can complete this massive project is by persuading Congress to appropriate the funds. And the attitude of the government toward vast federal water resources development has changed considerably since the first half of the project was built in the 1950s and 1960s. The go-ahead also requires a commitment from the state to pay up front from 10 to 30 percent of construction expenses, an acceptable environmental impact statement, and an agreement with project farmers on repayment. The government now requires a much higher percentage of construction costs from project beneficiaries than in the past. Although the farmers' share, according to one estimate, would amount to only 22 percent while the nation's taxpayers would eventually shoulder 78 per-

cent of project costs, their annual per acre payments would be several times what farmers in the first half of the project pay. Consequently, they have mixed views about the desirability of the project, especially when they consider the current surpluses in some commodities and the difficulty they have recently experienced competing in a world market.

INDIAN WATER RIGHTS

In the early 1960s a fish of another kind began swimming upstream against the current of traditional western water law. In 1963 the U.S. Supreme Court dispelled any lingering doubts that the reservations of Indian lands also included rights to water. For over fifty years the United States government, in encouraging the settlement of the West, had disregarded the 1908 Supreme Court decision of *Winters* v. *United States*. The "Winters doctrine" awarded reservation Indians the right to use as much of the waters located on and adjacent to the reservation as they needed to continue their traditional ways of livelihood or to develop new ones. It has since become a kind of Magna Carta for Native Americans seeking to reclaim reserved treaty rights.

Following the 1963 Supreme Court ruling and other state Supreme and lower court decisions, Washington has recognized the Indians' rights to waters within and bordering their reservations. But the state did not agree that all available reservation waters were necessary to satisfy tribal claims. In 1980 the Ninth Circuit Court of Appeals ruled that the state had the authority to issue water permits for reservation water that was surplus to that used by the tribe. The Department of Ecology has been committed to following this policy. Of course, in order to enforce such a ruling the department first had to determine the total amount of reservation water available and how much was needed by the tribe. That has been a formidable undertaking, one that will probably take many more years to complete.

Low water at Bumping Lake. Photo by Hugh Paradise.

Washington tribes, particularly the Yakamas, have long been leaders in the national Native American water rights movement. In 1905 the U.S. Supreme Court ruled in the *Winans* case that the Yakamas' treaty, negotiated by Territorial Governor Isaac Stevens in 1855, was intended to preserve their traditional supply of fish and the use of their accustomed fishing areas, even if these sites were not on reservation lands. In 1960, after nearly fifteen years in the courts and two appeals, celebrated Indian rights lawyer William Veeder won back the Yakamas' irrigation rights on Ahtanum Creek, which forms the northern border of the reservation. As a result, the non-Indian farmers in the area who had long been withdrawing water from the creek hurriedly began investigating groundwater sources.

In the drought year of 1977 the Yakama Nation filed suit under the Winters doctrine, claiming that 95 percent of the water in the Yakima Valley had been illegally diverted from them. The tribe maintains that their treaty reserved to them 2.25 million acre-feet of water annually, which is about as much as non-Indian irrigators diverted in 1988. The suit forced several thousand Yakima Valley farmers to defend their state water permits. The case was still going through the courts in 1994. It also led irrigators to seek the expansion of the Bumping Lake Reservoir.

The Yakama and other Washington tribes also have attempted to maintain stream flows for the benefit of anadromous fish. In 1980 the Yakamas again invoked their treaty right to the once abundant fisheries resource of the Yakima River, claiming that the state and federal governments were responsible for maintaining the habitat of fish passing through or destined for traditional tribal fishing grounds. At a time when the Yakima Irrigation Project reservoirs were low, the tribe requested water to protect the spring Chinook spawning beds in the river near Cle Elum. Their claim is involved in the second part of the controversial tribal fishing rights litigation, the first part of which was resolved in 1974 by George H. Boldt, senior judge of the Federal District Court in Tacoma. Phase two of *U.S.* v. *Washington*, the so-called Boldt decision, has yet to be settled.

The outcome of the Yakamas' water rights case will likely have wide ramifications for all state streams where there is a tribal fishery, and that is most of them. If the trend in recent court decisions continues, treaty rights will be found to supersede state laws and non-Indian water claims. (Water implicitly reserved to guarantee a stream level needed to protect aboriginal fishing rights has been given a priority date of "time immemorial.") Valid state water permits could be subject to prior Indian rights. Operators of irrigation and hydroelectric projects have already felt the effects of these legal precedents. In the early 1980s the City of Seattle gave up its preliminary permit to build the Copper Creek hydroelectric project partly because of treaty rights claims. The Snohomish County PUD settled tribal claims by agreeing to pay $1 million for mitigation and fish enhancement. If reserved tribal rights were to be fully honored, it could prevent additional withdrawals for municipal water, even from rivers such as the Cedar and Green used for large metropolitan systems. At least, it is likely that Washington's indigenous people will become ever more significant participants in the management of the state's increasingly precious resource.

COMPETITION FOR THE COLUMBIA

Water for the Southwest

In 1964 California officials began reviving plans, derived in part from Bureau of Reclamation studies conducted two decades earlier, for the diversion of Columbia River waters to the arid Southwest. The thirsty looks that Californians and Arizonans cast northward were part of a nationwide concern over dwindling water resources. In 1960 the United States was using over 60

percent of its water resources for domestic, industrial, and agricultural purposes, up from 8 percent in 1900. With this rise and the increased number of water resources that had become unusable because of pollution, public water supplies in a number of areas began coming up short. If the trend continued, newspapers and magazine articles warned, within a few decades large areas of the country would experience a serious water famine.

Although some experts objected that water was not scarce on a national level, but only in certain limited areas because of pollution and wasteful overuse, Congress voted funds for research on ways of increasing local supplies. To obtain more irrigation water in eastern Washington during the summer, the state and federal government cooperated in the mid-1960s in an experimental cloud-seeding program intended to induce more precipitation in the Cascades, and build up the snowpack. In 1969 a U.S. Geological Survey research glaciologist, Dr. Mark F. Meier of Tacoma, suggested tapping the huge reserves of fresh water locked in glacial ice. Meier claimed that Washington state had more than 70 percent of all glaciers in the lower forty-eight states. He calculated that each summer they released as much water as was pumped out of state groundwater reserves all year.

Most proposals of this kind produced more headlines than water, but in the midst of the perceived national water crisis they were taken very seriously. The plan to deflect Columbia River waters into the Colorado River to be delivered to the fields and bathtubs of the Southwest was for Northwesterners a grave and threatening proposal. Not only skeptical of the feasibility of diverting water such a long distance, they were above all suspicious of the actual needs of their expanding southern neighbor. "California is experienced and ruthless and fights with vast money resources to strip all she can from her neighbors before she turns to her own watershed," a Seattle *Times* reader wrote to the editor. Gov. Dan Evans along with Senators Henry Jackson and Warren Magnuson argued that conservation or desalinization would make a "water raid" unnecessary. Before billions were foolishly spent to divert Columbia River waters, the Southwest should prove that it was making proper use of the water it had, Magnuson insisted in April 1966.

Evans, Governors Mark Hatfield of Oregon and Robert Smylie of Idaho, and the congressional delegations from the three states all opposed the plan, citing the adverse effects it would have on Northwest fisheries, power producers, industry, and recreation. But in Congress, which had the power to authorize such a project, Northwest representatives were outnumbered by their more influential Southwestern counterparts. And Washington had no firm data on how much water its own residents were withdrawing from Columbia Basin streams. This kind of information was needed to make a strong case for present and projected needs.

Fortunately for those rooting to keep the Columbia's waters at home, Senator Jackson held the powerful position of chairman of the Senate Interior Committee. Jackson and University of Washington law professor Ralph W. Johnson, chief consultant on water resources to Jackson's committee, believed that what Southwest irrigators really lacked was not the water itself but a cheap source of supply. In July 1965 Jackson attached an amendment to the 1902 Reclamation Act requiring the Bureau of Reclamation to come to Congress for authorization to conduct interbasin diversion studies. A request for a Columbia River study that could potentially provide ammunition to diversion advocates would be unlikely to get through the Interior Committee with Jackson in charge.

That fall, however, state officials placed an advertisement in the *Wall Street Journal* that played into the opposition's hands. Signed by Governor Evans, it was headlined, "If Water were Gold, Washington State Would Be Fort Knox." The ad told industrial investors that the Columbia "pours 6.8 billion gallons of water an hour into the Pacific — enough to provide twice the present industrial requirement of the entire nation." An anonymous Northwest legislator told the press he could easily imagine a congressman from California or Arizona reading the ad into the record at the next hearing on water resources.

A more serious threat was the House Irrigation and Reclamation Subcommittee, dominated by Southwestern representatives. Here in June 1966, freshman Congressman Thomas S. Foley of Spokane in vain opposed committee members who voted in favor of a Columbia River diversion study. On the other side of the hill, however, the Senate Interior Committee held hearings on Senator Jackson's alternative bill, designed to deflect attention from the Northwest by calling for a commission to study the water problem on a nationwide basis. Interior Secretary Stewart Udall voiced the Johnson administration's support for the Jackson bill, and Jackson became fond of quoting the late President Kennedy, who once said that "anyone who can solve the problem of water will be worthy of two Nobel prizes — one for science and one for peace."

By September 1968 the powerful alliance of Arizona and California delegates had come apart, and Senate and House conferees agreed to a ten-year moratorium on Columbia River diversion studies. Jackson, the architect of the compromise, called it the greatest victory for the Northwest in the past decade. Ten years later, a drowsy Congress passed a new ten-year moratorium on Columbia River water diversion. During a marathon session just before adjournment, Jackson tacked a little amendment on to some dam safety legislation Sunday at 3:51 a.m. The chairman of the Senate Energy and Natural Resources Committee had no apologies for his eleventh-hour tactics. "You have to move when they're not looking," Jackson told a Vancouver gathering in October 1978. "A lot of them [senators] go to sleep."

Since that time state officials, relying on estimates of present and projected use, have continued to insist that Washington has no water to export. Federal policy makers have also become more realistic about the costs of large-scale, publicly financed interbasin transfers. Any future diversion proposal will have to be cost-effective as well as politically and environmentally acceptable, a difficult combination to achieve.

SHARING A LIMITED RESOURCE

By the mid-1990s unchecked population growth, with its accompanying demands for water, tested the state's ability to sustain high quality supplies. Moratoriums on building and new water service hookups were not uncommon, especially in the Puget Sound region where water districts reached the limits of their system capacity. By 1994, confronted with a backlog of nearly 5,000 water rights applications, the Ecology Department's Division of Water Resources strained to keep up with its watershed surveys. In 1995 the division published sixteen basin assessments

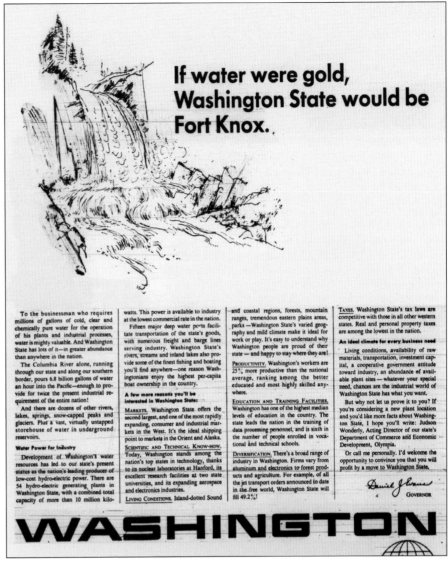

Washington State's troublesome "If Water Were Gold..." advertisement in the Sept. 28, 1965 issue of the Wall Street Journal begins "To the businessman who requires millions of gallons of cold, clear and chemically pure water for the operation of his plants and industrial processes, water is mighty valuable. And Washintgon State has lots of it — in greater abundance than anywhere in the nation. The Columbia River alone... pours 6.8 billion gallons of water an hour into the Pacific — enough to provide for twice the present industrial requirement of the nation!" Signed by Governor Dan Evans, the ad copy concludes "Or call me personally. I'd welcome the opportunity to convince you that you will profit by a move to Washington State." Courtesy, UW Libraries, Newspapers and Periodicals Division.

that calculated and compared the amount of water available in each basin with the registered water rights and other use claims made on it. In most cases, the results showed that stream levels had declined partly due to less than average precipitation, more ground water pumping, and more paving over natural areas, reducing water recharge to aquifers. Consequently, the division denied about as many permits as it approved, even turning down some large municipal requests.

Almost all the denials were based on what the state insisted was a "hydraulic continuity" between virtually all surface and ground water sources. That is, a decision whether to allow a well to be drilled had to consider not only water table levels but also assess the impacts to surface water flows. Before making new water rights decisions, department officials welcomed input from the local community so that all possible alternatives for sharing and conserving water could be considered. The department was also willing to allow the issuance of "interruptible" permits, rights that would be in effect except during periods of low flow. Whether an underfunded Ecology Department would be able to enforce such partial rights, however, seemed doubtful.

PULLMAN: THE ARTESIAN CITY

In 1988, the one hundredth year of its incorporation, Pullman's powers that be, including many of the Chamber of Commerce's honorable Artesians, gathered on an April afternoon to dedicate the town's new Centennial Fountain. The speakers included Mayor Carole Helm, who also cared for the time capsules; Judge Wallis Friel, who recalled Pullman's history; and W.S.U. President Samuel Smith, who retold the story — a local favorite — of how his school wound up in Pullman and not Colfax, Ritzville, Walla Walla or any other of the state's dry side communities. They gathered with the Pullman Community Band on three sides of the new fountain's octagonal base, their circle completed by a marble plaque explaining it was "a replica of artesian well Number Seven."

Number Seven was first framed in 1891 with a concrete base ten feet in diameter, one foot less than the vertical reach of the fountain itself. The proposal to "beautify the 'Artesian City' with a proper fountain" was made by the local newspaper, the *Herald*. As the name suggests, Number Seven was not the first of Pullman's

Mark C. True, the hotel keeper who discovered Pullman's first artesian well in 1889, managed the Artesian Hotel after his own Palace Hotel burned in 1894. Courtesy, Dan Kerlee.

spouters. That discovery belonged to Palouse Hotel proprietor Mark C. True, or more precisely to J.J. Shupe who for two weeks drilled for True sixty-some feet through the rich soil, called loess, that made the Palouse famous for its wheat. This fertile soil forms the ordinarily treeless rolling hills on all sides of Pullman from less than one foot to several hundred feet deep. The speculation is that in a Pleistocene dust storm it was piled over the normally flat formation of Columbia River basalt that is itself thought to be more than 1,000 feet thick. Pullman's great reservoir of groundwater lies within this basalt, and in downtown Pullman the water under pressure is close to the surface.

When J.J. Shupe had dug nearly 65 feet on May 24, 1889, he punctured the first impervious layer below the loess, releasing the trapped water with an eruption onto a lot beside Pullman's Main Street. Five more artesian wells quickly followed. None of them, however, saved Main Street from the ruin of Pullman's great fire of 1890.

Spurred by the fire, the city ceased trying to persuade True to share his wells and instead drilled its own on the Olsen Street side of Block 36 from the 1883 pioneer plat. This "City Artesian" was the "lucky number seven" which enabled Pullman to quickly build that year its first water works. The artesian pressure carried the water to a city reservoir built on Pioneer Hill at Alder Street. Late in 1890 the city's 150,000 gallon tank was filled and seven hydrants were installed on downtown streets. For a community that was dipping for its water in a few shallow wells of low yield only a year earlier, the sudden overflowing of the artesian wells was like discovering oil. For Mark C. True it was the iron. True moved his Palouse Hotel to the site of Shupe's dis-

The Artopho studio's early-century postcard reads 'Pullman's Great Artesian Well' — but it was not the first one. Courtesy, Pullman Public Library.

covery, promoting the water's relatively high ferrous content as medicinal for dyspepsia and rheumatism.

With their discovery Pullman's artesian wells were soon used as props on the stage of the city's promotion. In 1890 when state commissioners visited Pullman in search of a college site, True's wells were an asset. They were, however, not as great an asset — to repeat again the old story told by President Smith at the 1988 centennial dedication — as the performance put on for the commission. Every available citizen and farmer turned out for a kind of street theater with but one stage direction, "keep moving around." To the visiting inspectors Pullman appeared to be very much a boom town. In 1892 Washington State College opened on College hill. (See Public Buildings Chapter.)

Also in 1892 Pullman was ready to advertise itself as "The City of Flowing Wells" in the October issue of *Northwest Magazine*. The copy extols the community for "having nine artesian wells throwing their cold, clear streams of sparkling

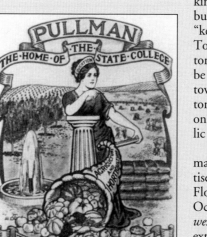

Courtesy, Washington State University Library.

"Souvenir" postcard showing artesian well in setting of Main Street. Courtesy, Barbara J. Collins.

waters high into the air, forming fountains that for beauty rival the famed founts of Cashmere." A souvenir postcard produced in the 1890s shows Number Seven framed by an elegant Pullman street scene. In fact, however, the fountain was well off the street. In the 1911 publication *Pullman Washington, The Commercial and Educational Center of the Palouse Country*, the number of wells had grown to eighteen. The illustrated handbook claims that the "excellent water supply must be numbered first among the many natural advantages of Pullman."

Only a year earlier, Pullman's "water supply" from another source had disastrous effects. As a wet Chinook wind hit the snow pack on the Moscow Mountains to the east, the South Fork of the Palouse River soon swelled its banks and flood waters raced through the business districts of both Pullman and the Whitman County seat of Colfax. (See Flood Control Chapter.) Many buildings were swept away including Pullman's first city hall, a modest false-front clapboard which started as a bank on Main Street which the city purchased in 1890 and moved to Block 36 just in time for it to escape the 1890 fire on Main Street. Returned later to Main as a barber shop it did not escape the 1910 flood.

Pullman's greatest loss from the 1910 flood was the undermining of every bridge including that on Kamiaken Street at the northeast corner of Block 36. The bridge was one block from the site of the first city artesian (number seven) and even closer to the second City Hall which, although flooded, stood firm at the northwest corner of Kamiaken and Olsen. In its considerable life — 1893 to 1986 — this modestly ornate municipal building with a Romanesque belfry, also had stints of service, long and short, as fire station, police department, jail, library, school, Methodist church (when their sanctuary's furnace cracked), city council assembly room with kitchen (for the weekly Chamber of Commerce luncheon), and pump room. During its first remodel in

1915, the city water works' old pump was moved out and replaced, in part, by a dog pound. During its second remodel in 1934 the structure was stripped of its corner tower, arched windows and accenting masonry. This depression-time disfigurement made it easier, perhaps, to abide the 1986 loss of what was by then merely a box of a building.

Pullman's 1988 dedication of its fountain was the first of the community's three centennial celebrations. It was followed by

Members of the Pullman Chamber of Commerce's Artesian Ambassadors pose beside the community's commemorative fountain. Courtesy, Pullman Chamber of Commerce.

Pullman's part in the Washington State Centennial of '89 which was followed by the 1990 commemoration of Washington State University's first one hundred years on the hill east of downtown. Actually, the "Artesian City" might have began its centennials in the mid-1970s. The first claim was taken at the future Pullman site around 1875 by the farmer Bolin Farr and his family. Their home from the early 1880s survives at 320 Park Street. And there might have been other centennials: in 1983 for the town's platting, in 1985 for the arrival of the railroad and an 1989 centennial for the first grading of Pullman's streets. Besides the balloon ascension, ribbon cutting, and the lighting of the Kamiaken Street bridge, the 1988 festivities were fulfilled, of course, by turning on the fountain.

Although the aquifer's elevation has been declining since measurements were begun in the late nineteenth century, Pullman's domestic water supply is still drawn from the groundwater reservoir. No longer bubbling to the surface, the city's four production wells in 1998 pumped its community water from deeper sources. Little of the total withdrawal is used for crop irrigation — most is for domestic purposes — and W.S.U. maintains a separate water system within the city of Pullman, although the two systems are connected for emergency situations. Of course, the size of the University is a matter of considerable local concern when the community's future water needs and their effects on their ancient supply in the Pullman-Moscow Groundwater Basin are considered.

1910 flood — view north on Alder (Kamiaken) Street looks across the intersection with Main Street. City Hall is in the center and the South Fork of the Palouse River just beyond it.

223

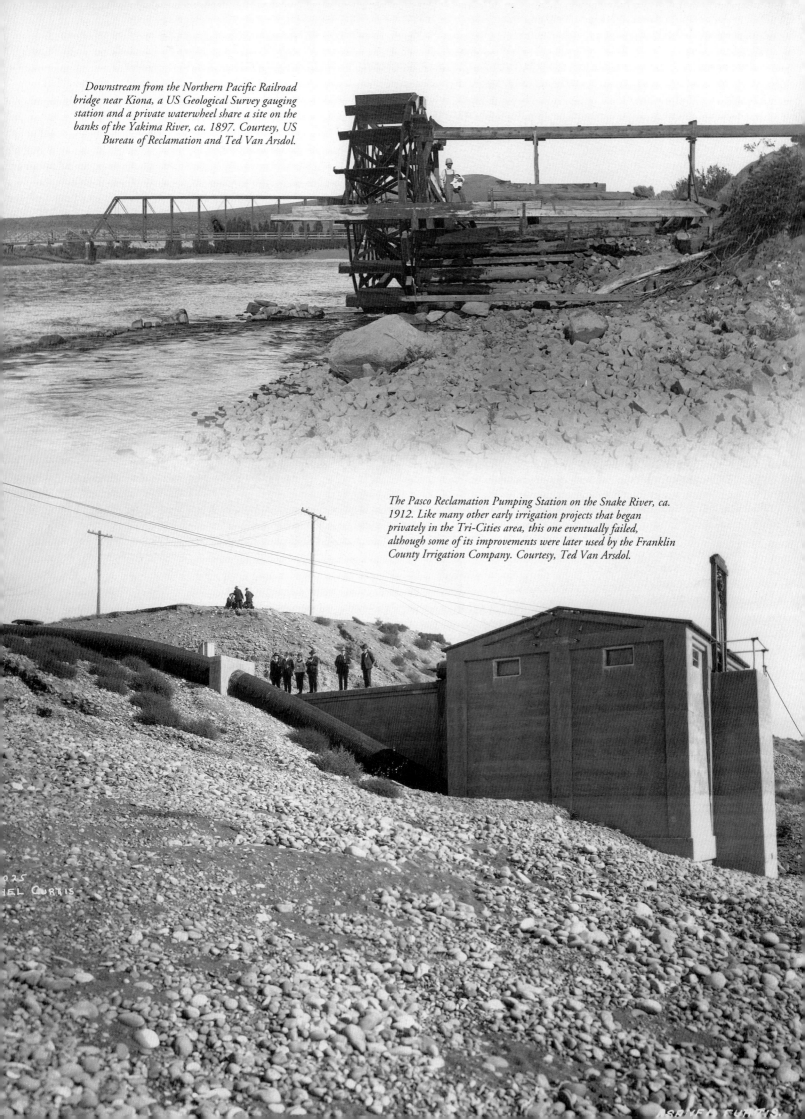

Downstream from the Northern Pacific Railroad bridge near Kiona, a US Geological Survey gauging station and a private waterwheel share a site on the banks of the Yakima River, ca. 1897. Courtesy, US Bureau of Reclamation and Ted Van Arsdol.

The Pasco Reclamation Pumping Station on the Snake River, ca. 1912. Like many other early irrigation projects that began privately in the Tri-Cities area, this one eventually failed, although some of its improvements were later used by the Franklin County Irrigation Company. Courtesy, Ted Van Arsdol.

IRRIGATION

DRYLAND FARMING

When the Oregon Trail overlanders of the mid-nineteenth century reached the last leg of their journey, between Walla Walla and the Dalles rapids on the Columbia River, they cast a weary eye on the desiccated, barren hills and eagerly hurried on. Most were farmers from the humid Mississippi Valley, and they had made the long cross-country trek expecting to find similar conditions in the rich, evergreen valleys near the coast. Some among the enterprising — or the aimless — found their way to the mines and dusty grazing lands of the future Inland Empire. Gold strikes sent miners by the thousands stumbling over trails in the northeastern part of Washington Territory, where they mercilessly panned the streams of the Pend Oreille, Kootenai, and Nez Perce countries. Many fewer cattlemen stayed to mine the rich Okanogan, Big Bend, and Palouse grasslands and a booming market in the gold rush "towns."

Unfortunately, for most of the ranchers and miners, the adventure of coming out west had to be its own reward. Although the ranchers outlasted the placer miners, poor markets, overgrazing, and some uncommonly cold winters in the 1880s put some of even the biggest stockmen out of business. Nor could the open-range cattlemen any longer stem the tide of settlers arriving from California and the Great Plains in ever greater numbers to homestead upon the choicest grasslands. The population east of the Cascades rose nearly six fold between 1870 and 1880, yet it still totaled only 36,902 in an area of approximately 40,000 square miles. By the 1880s the demographic movement to the west side of the mountains, which would forever leave the eastern region on the high end of the population see-saw, was well underway.

This left the pioneer agriculturists. But to extract their share of profits from the eastern drylands, they had to find ways to water

Above: Before irrigation was introduced to the Big Bend, the hopes of its farmers were often abandoned to sagebrush and winds. Courtesy, WA State Historical Society, Tacoma. Below: East of the Big Bend the Palouse country was covered with loess, a deep fertile soil able to hold water and grow wheat, thousands of acres of it. In the Palouse there was little need for windmills. Courtesy, Ethel M. Hagen.

them. At first, the most obvious solution was to settle alongside creeks and rivers. Often the first farmers laid out their homesteads to control both sides of a stream to make sure they could draw out enough water for themselves, their stock, and their gardens. In the northern Columbia Basin the early settlers tried farming the lowlands first, but they soon discovered that the soil of the higher ground was less alkaline and held more moisture, retained from spring snowmelt. So they learned to grow wheat, rye, and barley on the high plateaus and rolling prairies without irrigation. This usually involved alternate-year planting in which a farmer allowed half of his land to lay fallow each year in order to gather moisture from the limited rainfall.

East of the basin, in what would become Stevens, Spokane, and parts of Walla Walla and Whitman counties, rainfall and spring freshets generally supplied enough water to make irrigation unnecessary. As the miners poured into the territory, a few pioneer farmers discovered that the hills of the Walla Walla country, bounded by the loop of the Snake and Columbia rivers, were valuable for something besides grazing. During the short-lived placer mining boom, a harvest of wheat was as good as gold. By the 1860s the Walla Walla region produced the future state's first

Evolution of Sickle and Flail—33 Horse Team Combined Harvester—Walla Walla Washington   Copyright 1902 by Underwood & Underwood

commercial crop to feed the hungry miners. By 1885, when the railroad brought another boom and new markets, the Walla Walla and Palouse country yielded over seven million bushels of grain. In 1909 Whitman County was a major grain producing area and claimed to be the richest county per capita in the country.

Walla Walla and Palouse area farmers proved that dryland wheat farming could be profitable, but it required a lot of land since per-acre yields were low in comparison to irrigated fields. When the public lands in these areas were taken up, home seekers moved further west along the Columbia Basin to the territory between Pasco and Ephrata. Finding there the same good quality soil, they cleared and fenced the land, and built homes, churches, schools, and roads. But within a few years the plowed soil was dryer than the hot wind that lifted it through the cracks of their wood frame cabins. They had not counted on the difference in rainfall between the two areas, which amounted to the difference between success and failure. Most gave up and headed for wetter regions. Behind them the plowed fields, marked here and there by their graying abandoned homes, reverted into a vast desert of stunted sagebrush.

This 32-foot high irrigation wheel was constructed near the mouth of the Yakima River in the mid-1890s by Richland pioneer farmers Mary and Benjamin Rosencrance. Courtesy, Franklin County Historical Society.

EARLY PIONEER AND COMPANY SYSTEMS

In the Yakima and Kittitas valleys, weather conditions were ideal for agriculture except for the lack of summer rainfall. The soil was exceptionally rich, porous, and easily worked; so it was here that farmers built most of Washington's first small irrigation systems. For when they were not dried up, the streams flowed rapidly over land that lay with a grade nearly perfect for irrigation. Large areas could be watered with short canals.

However, it was to the northeast, in the Okanogan Highlands, that Hiram "Okanogan" Smith established what was probably the first large irrigated orchard in Washington. A former printer for Horace Greeley's *New York Tribune* turned Fraser River miner, Smith became an Okanogan Highlands farmer about 1860. On the east shore of Lake Osoyoos close to the Canadian border, he built a log cabin and trading post and set out 1,200 apple trees, which he watered by a ditch tapping Ninemile Creek. One after another, Smith's few Okanogan neighbors stopped by to visit and find out how he lured the water to his thirsty land. His ingenuity earned him legendary status — at least for reminiscing Okanogan pioneers who liked to call him Washington's "father of

irrigation." Smith was hardly the first irrigator in the region, however. Fur trader Donald McKenzie of the North West Company had established irrigated gardens around Fort Walla Walla in 1818.

Like the ranchers and wheat growers before them, some ambitious central and eastern Washington fruit and vegetable farmers of the 1870s recognized in the miners a potential market. In this first stage of the future state's agricultural development, they began experimenting with familiar techniques for watering crops and orchards. Some, like the Yakima Land Company in the Moxee Valley of the Yakima Basin, "struck gold" when they hit an artesian vein of water which bubbled to the surface without pumping. But that was rare. For most the water, like the gold before it, had to be pulled from the streams.

Since that was a job few people could take on single-handedly, irrigation in Washington, like elsewhere in the West, was initially a neighborhood effort. In the Kittitas Valley farmers toiled with shovels and horse teams to build canals that were usually six to eight miles long, five to seven feet wide, and watered 400 to 500 acres. Because they had little money and only their backs to invest in the projects, neighbors sometimes labored into the night by lantern light. When they finished, they divided the ditch water equally. A group of families living along the Wenatchee River worked together for over a year digging a seven-mile-long ditch to their apple orchards.

With water from these small, experimental ditches, Yakima and Wenatchee valley farms in the 1880s produced vegetables and fruits never before seen in the area. Land values rose and drew the attention and dollars of Tacoma, Seattle, and Spokane investors, soon to be followed by the bankrolls of eastern capitalists. Not long after the twenty-two-mile-long Selah Valley Canal, financed in part by two Tacomans, began delivering water to 5,500 acres in the Naches and Selah valleys near the end of the decade, Chester A. Congdon, a Chicago-Duluth copper magnate, financed and built the Yakima Valley Canal.

The flip side of this early-century postcard of Kennewick Canal is posted to Serene Grambo of Prosser from Mabel of Kennewick and reads, in part, "We have been very busy this week with peaches... Have shipped about 1600 boxes so far. Was it hot up there last week?" Courtesy, Ted Van Arsdol.

In 1893 the Yakima Irrigating and Improvement Company, headed by Frank A. Dudley, a New York railroad builder who purchased 23,000 acres from the Northern Pacific Railroad, platted the town of Kennewick.

Valley farmers were willing to temporarily set aside their distrust of big businessmen and distant corporations, for they knew that the capitalists alone had the money to pay for the more extensive systems. Until the 1890s neither the federal nor state government was willing to offer much help with irrigation development. At most, the state encouraged efforts to find the elusive artesian bonanza. During the administrations of territorial governors Watson Squire and Eugene Semple in the second half of the 1880s, the legislature appropriated small grants to Yakima, Franklin, and Adams counties to help them locate artesian wells, but Congress turned down the territory's request for financial assistance in this effort.

So private enterprise led the way. But it took more than the success of a few irrigation projects to convince savvy financiers to gamble their dollars on the remote and meagerly settled Washington Territory. The railroad, so often resented for the high rates it charged, was the primary engine driving the area's development. The Northern Pacific created new markets, otherwise inaccessible to most farmers. It also opened up new land. As a result of the federal government's exceptionally generous land grant, the railroad owned huge tracts that it wanted to sell. First, however, it had to make the land more desirable. To spur the development that would yield freight and passengers, the railroad sold acreage at low prices as an incentive to land companies to build irrigation works. In 1890 the state legislature pitched in and granted railroads the authority to organize and operate reclamation companies of their own.

Private water companies that took advantage of the railroad's land and financing offers built the first large-scale irrigation systems. The Ellensburg Water Company tapped the Yakima River for its twenty-mile-long, twelve-foot-wide ditch, the first big canal in the Kittitas area. The "town ditch" not only irrigated about 10,000 acres but doubled as Ellensburg" water supply. Spokane financier of railways and mines, D.C. Corbin, headed the construction of a $200,000 system of canals delivering water to 15,000 acres between Spokane and the Washington-Idaho border. However, most of these firms were more interested in making big profits on land sales than in supplying efficient water delivery. The results of these exploitive, get-rich-quick schemes were usually poorly planned and hastily built canal systems that quickly deteriorated and hindered more efficient water delivery. Sometimes the companies, through incompetence or dishonesty, ruined farmers' hopes and cost them their investments even before they built the projects. A. B. Frame of Portland was summoned before Superior Court in Walla Walla County in 1906 by some angry land purchasers who alleged that none of the lands his company had sold belonged to him. And after he had collected over $63,000 in land payments, he still failed to deliver any water. In Wahluke, in Benton County, land buyers in 1910 leapt at the sale of 800 acres to be developed by the DeLarm and Biehl Company. The company had ambitious plans to deliver water from the Columbia with the help of a big steam-driven pumping plant. Within two years the company was bankrupt. When federal authorities began investigating their activities, the company managers disappeared.

Wenatchee Valley Irrigation

The Great Northern Railroad built Wenatchee. When the company finally announced the route it would take through the valley, the town got up and moved itself a mile to meet it. The railroad managed the new town, and railroad money made it possible for local men to enlarge the pioneer irrigation ditches and produce the particularly successful Gunn-Shotwell and Jones-Shotwell canals. By 1902 these ditches tapping the Wenatchee

Located about 16 miles west of Wenatchee, the Dryden waterslide releases excess irrigation flow from a flume above the Wenatchee River. Photo by Hugh Paradise, ca. 1970.

River watered about 2,500 acres lying north and south of Wenatchee and between Cashmere and Monitor. The resulting rise in land values prompted the building of the Highline Canal along the north side of the valley over difficult terrain. In 1903, when the forty-mile-long canal was finished to water 7,000 acres, a bumper crop of newcomers had descended on the town bloating its population and its land prices, which went from $25 an acre or less to $400 or more.

Within a few years the Wenatchee Canal Company, the builders of the Highline Canal, came up with a bold scheme for extending it over the Columbia River to the present site of East Wenatchee. They enlisted Great Northern president James J. Hill and Thomas Burke, a Seattle business leader who laid out the Wenatchee townsite, to help raise money for a bridge that would carry a pipeline along each side. Completed in 1908, the span became the first highway bridge to cross the Columbia River. (See Bridges Chapter.) The water it carried, along with the horses and buggies, reclaimed an additional 4,000 acres and set off a new land rush that brought 6,000 more settlers into Douglas County within months. Yet, for all its ingenuity, the company went broke for the same reason so many cash-short water companies did — for spending too much on land and failing to charge enough for system maintenance. Area water users, however, formed a reclamation district in 1914 and saved the Highline Canal by purchasing it.

Walter Granger and the Sunnyside Canal

The largest irrigation system in the Northwest in the 1890s was also built as a prerequisite to the sale of land. But the Sunnyside Canal endured and transformed the Yakima Valley into one of the country's greatest fruit baskets. When a champagne bottle smashed against the headgates of the diversion outlet on March 26, 1892, to celebrate the official opening of the first twenty-five-mile section of the canal, the *Yakima Herald* crowed that it marked the "beginning of the most important system of canals in America."

Only three years earlier Walter N. Granger had stood atop Snipes Mountain, gazing down into the fertile but brown-dry valley and envisioning a vast canal over 100 miles long. Then the experienced irrigation engineer from Montana awoke from his

Left: Early-century Sunnyside.
Above: The Yakima River Canyon between Ellensburg and Yakima. Photo by Hugh Paradise.

reverie, came down to earth, and turned his musings into matter. Granger surveyed the lower Yakima Valley, organized the Yakima Canal and Land Company, and accepted Northern Pacific president Thomas F. Oakes's offer of 90,000 acres of valley railroad land at $1.25 an acre. Granger's plan to sell the land with a perpetual water right at a substantial profit looked so promising that the railroad bought half the company's stock and furnished construction funds while Granger built the canal.

Work on the Sunnyside Canal began in late 1890 after the company took over the three-mile-long Kennewick ditch, dug a few years earlier by stockmen in Parker Bottom. The ditch became the initial unit of the new canal. At the intake, just below Union Gap, Granger and his engineers built a new head gate and a new movable diversion dam that backed up water during low flow periods and thus maintained a constant flow into the canal. The crew enlarged the Konnewock ditch until it was enormous. At eight feet deep, thirty feet wide at the bottom, and sixty-two feet wide at the top, the Sunnyside Canal surpassed all others in the Northwest.

By the time the canal reached Zillah in 1892, the area was beginning to fill up with farmers, but company funds were beginning to dry up. The national financial panic hit the next year and sent the Northern Pacific reeling. When the railroad withdrew from the company, Granger had to come up with a plan for operating and enlarging the system without money. For eighteen months he issued his workers time checks, redeemable only for the yet undeveloped land, and convinced town merchants to accept them. Finally, when local banks were choking with them and merchants would no longer take them, an irate crowd armed with

guns and clubs descended on Granger's office. Somehow Granger managed to pacify them. Later, after their land was irrigated and soared in value, some of the involuntary landowners profited many times over.

The Sunnyside manager could not, however, turn away the national financial collapse that first swept the Northern Pacific, and then his company into receivership in 1895. But Granger still refused to quit. Throughout the receivership proceedings he continued to operate the system and even built twelve additional miles. In 1900 the project was purchased by the Washington Irrigation Company, a syndicate of Portland and Seattle entrepreneurs including Roland Denny, son of one of Seattle's founders. To no one's surprise, they invited Granger to be project manager, and under his direction the company extended the ditch from its halting place near Sunnyside to near Prosser.

By 1905 the company had spent over $1.5 million and had expanded the system to more than 700 miles of canals and laterals which irrigated almost 44,000 acres. The main canal had a carrying capacity of 800 cubic feet of water per second (c.f.s.). It seemed that Granger's vision of a canal watering the entire valley would come true after all. The Washington Irrigation Company had conducted an aggressive settlement campaign aimed at the midwestern and eastern states. They lowered land prices and shamelessly extolled the Sunnyside project in extravagant pamphlets, picturing farmworkers harvesting fruit from heavily laden branches. The several thousand mostly inexperienced farmers who responded and bought land and water rights from the company were usually satisfied with their rates and service — that is, if they were among those who lasted through the first few years. For it

Main Street, Granger. Courtesy, Michael Maslan Historic Photographs, Postcards, and Ephemera, Seattle.

usually took them six to eight years to learn how to correctly prepare their land for irrigated agriculture. In the meantime, although the company attempted to instruct them in rudimentary land preparation and irrigation techniques, those who failed to prosper often blamed their poor results on Granger's management. Competition for canal waters also became keen. Many of the original land purchasers, tired of battling for water and trying to meet land payments, sold their tracts and left within three years.

In the first four years of the new century, each new influx of settlers to Sunnyside country brought on a water shortage. The threat of these shortfalls made farmers in the valley even more fearful of monopoly. Irrigation "battles" between companies began after the Washington Irrigation Company, the state's largest irrigation corporation, attempted to get control of the lakes that fed the valley streams. Well aware that Yakima River water had been over-appropriated, the company was anxious to build storage facilities and guarantee itself a reliable flow. In August 1905 there were fifty-five canal systems taking water from the Yakima and Naches rivers between Cle Elum and the mouth of the Yakima, and their canals diverted 1,995 c.f.s. — practically all the water in the rivers. That month the Yakima reached its lowest recorded level and Granger prepared to build a wooden crib dam at the outlet of Lake Cle Elum. But the state legislature, pressured by other irrigation companies, stepped in and refused him or anyone else the right to obstruct the stream flow. Unimpressed with state regulations, another company began building a temporary dam at the lake's outlet on Washington Irrigation Company land, using Granger's timber. Granger sent in a dynamite crew, and the Sunnyside irrigators got their water — at least as much as the undammed and multi-diverted river could give.

These kinds of incidents required the U.S. Reclamation Service to play the role of peacemaker before it took over the canal. (For the federal Sunnyside project, see below.) But once the Yakima Valley warriors were quieted and the Washington Irrigation Company agreed to the sale, there was no conflict among federal officials over whom to put in charge. By the time Walter Granger retired from the Service in 1910, he had spent over twenty years on the Sunnyside project. He had built, sustained, and guided it through two eras of state irrigation development. Today portions of the canal built by Granger and his crews are over 100 years old — and still delivering water.

IRRIGATION DISTRICTS AND LAND SETTLEMENT EXPERIMENTS

In 1890 and 1895 the legislature followed California's example and authorized Washington landowners to form irrigation districts. The districts were intended to help farmers raise money to build and improve irrigation works. Under the law these organizations became municipal corporations with the power to issue bonds (using property and water rights as security), condemn right-of-way, and levy assessments. Only seven districts were formed during the decade, however, due to the poor reputation irrigation bonds had at the time and the depression that began in 1893. Not until after the federal reclamation projects superseded the land promotion companies and more effective organizational legislation was passed about twenty years later did districts multiply.

At the urging of Gov. Ernest Lister, the legislature voted in 1919 to approve the state reclamation revolving fund. By this time the number of Washington farms using irrigation had increased from 1,046 in 1889 to 13,271. A one-half mill tax was levied on all taxable property to create a fund from which loans could be made to irrigation, drainage, and diking districts for improving and expanding their systems. Within two years the program proved to be a miserable failure. Acting more out of sympathy for

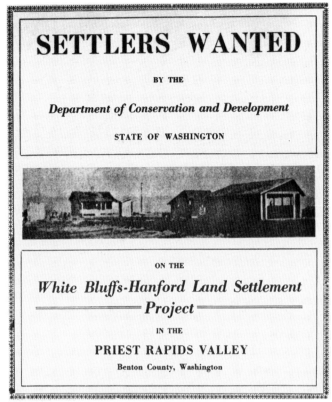

SETTLERS WANTED

BY THE

Department of Conservation and Development

STATE OF WASHINGTON

ON THE

White Bluffs-Hanford Land Settlement Project

IN THE

PRIEST RAPIDS VALLEY

Benton County, Washington

Courtesy Washington State Archives, Olympia.

the homesteaders than on an objective assessment of their proposed projects, state officials spent about half a million dollars on ill-planned district systems that could not work. The legislature discontinued the tax for 1926 and afterwards but continued to help existing systems with financing through low-interest loans secured by bonds. In 1948 the state Department of Conservation and Development reported that the program over the years had furnished funds for repairs and improvements in "urgent emergencies" and saved "deserving districts from failure in bad times."

When the United States declared war on Germany in the spring of 1917, most Washingtonians, like most Americans, supported the war effort. Their patriotism was still strong after the war ended, and in 1919 state irrigationists and a newly formed land settlement association convinced the legislature to fund a settlement program for the returning veterans. They had been inspired by a nationwide response to a well-publicized letter from Interior Secretary Franklin K. Lane to President Woodrow Wilson about the doughboys' employment needs. The former Tacoma newspaperman and others were concerned that the veterans, after all the sacrifices they had made, would return home to find only unemployment and financial distress. The state's land settlement, approved at the same time as the revolving fund, passed easily. The legislators, in fact, were uncommonly generous and invested a half million dollars in the program so that the settlers would prosper. They selected White Bluffs and Hanford as the sites for the initial experiment. Each of the project homesteaders received twenty acres of land, a three-room house, a well, pumping plant, barn, chicken house, and financial aid to help with clearing, leveling, and seeding — all for a 10 percent, $600 down payment. The state even purchased sixty-three cows for the first sixty-nine homesteaders, all but six of whom were veterans.

For all their good intentions, the settlement planners had not reckoned on the shrunken markets, deflated agricultural prices, and drought conditions that followed the war. Four years after the project began, over a third of the tracts remained unsold, and settlers complained of misrepresentation and demanded adjustments on their contracts. Criticism came from all sides — especially from farmers and others who complained that the state should not be encouraging agricultural development when even established farmers could not make a living. By 1925 the legislature's postwar patriotism wore thin. Hoping that their first state-sponsored irrigation project would also be their last, the legislators threw in the towel and deeded the tracts to the settlers for $1 each.

In 1926 Earle Barnes, director of the Conservation and Development Department, which administered the state reclamation act, described "the whole land settlement scheme" as "uneconomic, un-American, socialistic, paternalistic, . . . unwarranted and harmful." Like his employer, Gov. Roland H. Hartley, Barnes was a staunch believer in individual initiative, public frugality, and "the natural law of supply and demand." Barnes refused to make any more state reclamation funds available to new district projects.

Times had changed. National supporters of the program, like Secretary Lane, had envisioned the soldier-settlement program as a way to return

Bureau of Reclamation employee and farmer pose to either side of the early fruits of federal irrigation in the Yakima River Valley. Courtesy, UW Libraries, Special Collections.

young veterans to the farms, away from the disturbing conditions and tendencies in the cities. (A local advocate, Seattle Mayor Ole Hanson, backed the program but for opposite reasons. Fearing radical action if the veterans returned to the cities, he favored keeping them happy and peaceful down on the farm.) The settlement concept was also based on the Progressives' belief that organized communities participating in cooperative marketing and scientific production could effect a revolution in American farming. But this idealism was not shared by the Congress and many farmers and local politicians in the more conservative times and depressed agricultural conditions of the 1920s. The determined opposition of commercial farmers and the agricultural recession undermined similar experiments in five other states as well.

The 1930s depression gave Washington's irrigation farmers even more cause to worry. Still heavily in debt for equipment and other purchases made during the wartime agricultural boom, many came close to abandoning their homes. Irrigation districts could no longer meet their loan payments nor collect assessments for maintaining their systems. But this time the government was more responsive. The Reconstruction Finance Corporation (RFC) approved a $50 million appropriation to help refinance the nation's drainage, diking, and irrigation districts. With these loans and some state-approved funds, approximately thirty state irrigation districts survived until World War II brought higher agricultural prices and more prosperous times.

FEDERAL RECLAMATION

Before the twentieth century the federal government had resisted any direct involvement in irrigation development. In the 1877 Desert Land Act, Congress amended the 1862 Homestead Act with some slight recognition of the problems of farming land in the arid West. The new law enlarged the amount of public land a homesteader could buy to 640 acres, but it required that he irrigate a portion of it within three years, which most settlers were not able to do. The Carey Act of 1894 was essentially an extension of the earlier policy, except that it made the states rather than

individuals the custodians of the arable public lands. But because of the limited financial resources of the western states, as well as a number of technical and administrative problems, the act — like its predecessor — largely failed to achieve its objectives. Mostly, it resulted in an excessive number of land frauds. In Washington, no projects were approved under the Carey Act. When President Theodore Roosevelt signed the Newlands Act in June 1902, he effectively inaugurated the commercial agricultural development of eastern Washington.

In the first years of the century, national irrigation leaders, aided by the vigorous support of President Roosevelt, aroused a new public awareness of western irrigation. In the spirit of the Progressives, they promoted the prospect of turning millions of acres of desert land into productive farms — not so much for its economic value as for its ability to effect social reform. Fear of domestic turmoil still lingered from the depression days of the "terrible 90s." The idea of the West as a safety valve for redistributing potentially dangerous surplus workers from the East was the most common theme in congressional speeches favoring the Newlands Act. Washington's Rep. Wesley L. Jones was one of those who believed that if the government gave the unemployed easterner a desert home, "the seed of anarchy and lawlessness will shrink and die, while love for family and country will well up in the heart and grow stronger and stronger." Irrigated farming could also reverse the ominous flow of rural residents to the cities through the intensive cultivation of small tracts that would allow families to be in almost urban contact with each other. The national reclamation proposal, sponsored by Nevada Congressman Francis G. Newlands, won widespread support throughout the country and sailed effortlessly through Congress.

Like the Carey Act before it, the Newlands legislation required the western states to ultimately pay for their own irrigation projects. In this case, the proceeds from the sale of public lands within their borders were to be placed in a revolving fund to finance the irrigation works. The settlers were to repay the government within ten years for the major portion of land irrigated under a federal project, and then management and operation of the system would pass from the government to the landowners. In

theory, it sounded good. But it became clear almost from the start that receipts from public land sales and settlers' construction repayments would not keep the fund in the black. By 1922 only 10 percent of the $135 million the government had invested in reclamation had been repaid. Until the late 1930s the reclamation fund tottered on the edge of bankruptcy most of the time and had to be supplemented with funds from the general treasury. Not until then did revenues from the sale of hydropower generated by government dams rehabilitate and, in fact, revolutionize reclamation financing. From then on water power became the cornerstone of federal reclamation.

In limiting the number of acres a settler could irrigate from a federal project, the Newlands Act preserved the tradition of earlier reclamation legislation, which was dedicated to the homestead ideal of an agrarian society. Since the time of Thomas Jefferson, many Americans and their political leaders believed that the happiest people and the soundest political conditions existed where farmers owned their own land and formed a large segment of the population. According to Frederick H. Newell, first chief of the Reclamation Service, the promotion of "home-making" by "the most desirable class of citizens" was the law's objective. Like Rep. Jones, Newell believed that once a man owned and cultivated his own land he would be "transformed politically and socially from a man, almost a danger to the community, to a citizen of the type that forms the foundations of strong, intelligent democracy." Yakima Valley residents, however, who had no desire to promote their region as a haven for the urban poor, did not share Newell's and Jones' idealism.

Yet the Newlands legislation went much further than the attempt to revive traditional institutions and reclaim wasted lives along with wasted lands. The federal reclamation program was infused by new intellectual currents and ideals which were part of the Progressives' "gospel of efficiency." The direct participation of the government in financing, building, and operating irrigation works was intended to inaugurate a scientific and more orderly approach to reclamation and reduce the widespread land speculation that dominated the disposition of public lands. Engineers were "logical thinkers," men of vision, and eminently suited,

Newell believed, to become the agents of twentieth-century technological change and material and social progress. Other proponents argued that the government's role in developing the arid West would bring prosperity to the whole country because settlement of the area would create a new source of agricultural products and a new market for manufactured goods from the East.

Okanogan Project

In 1903 local settlers, eager to participate in the new form of government largess, petitioned the Reclamation Service to survey for a canal project on the west side of the Okanogan River. The results of the report by Theron A. Noble, a Seattle civil engineer

Above: Mt. Adams rises above the edenic floor of the Yakima Valley. Courtesy, WA State Historical Society. Photo by Asahel Curtis. Below: Irrigation flume above the Similkameen River in Okanogan County. Photo by Hugh Paradise.

A promotion for the fruits of Okanogan irrigation. Courtesy, Dan Kerlee.

hired by the Service, convinced the government engineers to drop the project, but political pressure from Washington's congressional delegation caused them to reconsider. The initial reluctance of the Reclamation Service turned out to be well-founded. The agency had problems with the project from the start. The most serious was its underestimation of the amount of water needed. Even after steps were taken to expand the completed project, the water supply kept coming up short. Expenses mounted beyond all estimates, fueled in part by labor and material shortages resulting from the boom in railroad building and the reconstruction of San Francisco after the 1906 earthquake. The Service soon found itself in the red and unable to recoup construction costs.

When their land assessments nearly doubled, orchard owners in the project, few of whom were experienced in irrigation methods, sank deeper into debt. The project caused two private contractors to go bankrupt, and seepage water damaged so many basements in Conconully that the government was forced to buy the town. When they could find buyers, the original settlers fled. One disgruntled settler wrote now-Senator Wesley Jones in 1918 that if the Okanogan system "had been privately owned the promoters of such a wildcat would be put in the penitentiary." That year the Service relieved itself of its millstone when it sold the project to the Okanogan Irrigation District. But for the Okanogan farmers, who put great hope in the federal system, the period from 1910 to 1930 was a time of hardship and disappointment.

Like the failure of many of the Service's first projects, the shortcomings of the Okanogan District stemmed in part from the government's misconceived notion of reclamation as social reform. Homes for the homeless, jobs for the jobless, and food for the hungry were worthy goals, but were not the ingredients for a successful irrigation project. Until 1924 the government did not require settlers to have any farming or irrigation experience or sufficient capital to establish their farms. Nor did the Reclamation Service offer instruction or aid in clearing and leveling the land, digging ditches, and building houses and roads.

Perhaps because of its dedication to high standards of scientific efficiency, the Service devoted its attention to the engineering side of the program and rushed the construction of its first projects without sufficiently examining a number of variables that effected the productivity of project tracts. Soil conditions, the amount of available water, the need for fertilizer and drainage, and potential markets for crops had not been adequately studied and incorporated into the program. The Reclamation Service also miscalculated costs and completion schedules so that some settlers were left high and dry waiting on land that would not receive water for years. Some of the homesteaders simply could not adapt to pioneer conditions. Others filed on more land than they could reclaim and cultivate and had to pay taxes and construction repayments for barren ground. Most found that they were not able to make the large capital outlays needed for land preparation, farm buildings, and machinery. The Okanogan, Yakima, and other federal projects eventually increased the value of the land several times over, but farmers had to be able to stick it out for a number of hard years before they enjoyed the reward of good crop yields.

Neither was the Service able to eliminate the land speculation that plagued and nearly destroyed its first projects. Gambling on the prospect that land would be included in a federal project, speculators bought acreage and then sold it to project settlers at vastly inflated prices. The government had no

Top: Similkameen River Siphon Irrigation Ditch. Courtesy Dan Kerlee. Above: Lengthy portions of the main federal canal for the Okanogan were cut through rock. Courtesy, UW Libraries, Special Collections.

232

way of controlling the resale of public lands or the sale of private lands watered by the federal works. Often the first homeowners on project lands were speculators themselves and bought the land with no intention of developing it or staying longer than a few years. By the time a tract changed hands a few times, the last buyer was so saddled with financial obligations that he put off and usually defaulted on his payments to the government. Between 1902 and 1913 when the price of farmland in the West rose an average of 110 percent, land within the Yakima project, although still unwatered, increased by 5,400 percent — more than any other Service project in the country.

Because problems like these existed on all the government irrigation projects, Congress passed bills in the mid-twenties to reform the original reclamation act and reorganize the Service as the Bureau of Reclamation. No new projects were to be approved until accurate information was available concerning the cost of construction and land, the availability of water, the fertility of the soil, and the likelihood of a project returning its cost. Applicants for project lands were to be screened for their experience, capital, *and* character. The period of repayment to the government for construction costs was doubled and then doubled again — from twenty to forty years. The Kittitas division of the Yakima project became the first Bureau project to test new antispeculation legislation passed in 1926. Here, apparently, the new regulations were successful. Of the total 70,000 irrigable acres in the division, 60,000 acres were privately owned, yet there were no speculation scandals connected with them.

Yakima Valley

Although the Yakima Valley was one of the nation's most promising agricultural areas, the U.S. Reclamation Service was at first reluctant to enter it. The policy of the Service was to give priority to undeveloped lands, and the valley, it reported, was already "well covered with irrigation systems" and most of the land was in private hands. The agency also had little desire to participate in the irrigation wars caused by squatter's rights water claims that appropriated more than twice the low flow of the Yakima River. But Yakima farmers, eager for a government benefactor, petitioned their representative, U.S. Congressman Wesley L. Jones, a member of the committee on irrigation and reclamation of arid lands, to appeal to the Service for reconsideration.

Jones, who had witnessed the manipulation of reclamation funding but loved the sound of "farms for the homeless, [and] homes for the farmless," was equally eager to advance his political career. He persuaded the Service to reconsider a Yakima project, if the state passed enabling legislation and resolved the water rights conflicts. Returning to the state with that assurance, the plain and platitudinous Jones convinced Yakima businessmen that the ball was now in their hands. Sporting the campaign slogan, "It's up to the people," they took up the challenge and successfully canvassed farmers up and down the valley to reduce their water claims by more than half. In December 1905 the Reclamation Service officially approved the first federal irrigation project in the valley, the Yakima and Tieton systems.

Tieton Canal

The canal built along the sides of the steep Tieton River canyon was the first monumental work the Reclamation Service had yet built and one of the first really difficult jobs

Above: A leak in at the Tieton Dam. Below: Looking downstream across the spillway of Tieton Dam. Photos courtesy, National Archives, Alaska-Pacific NW Region.

executed in modern American irrigation technology. The gravity canal had to rest securely on a 60 percent slope and convey water across an unstable, porous soil, inclined to slide at any provocation. To overcome the inhospitable terrain, the engineers adopted unprecedented large-scale sectional methods that expanded the limits of reinforced concrete in irrigation canal construction. They cast the canal sections in molds at camps on the canyon floor and conveyed them on a tramway, which resembled a carnival roller coaster, up the canyon wall to the canal bed where they were joined. Rather than build flumes around the cliffs, the Service drove five sets of tunnels through them. Because of the extreme difficulty of the project, only one contractor responded to the government's call for bids. So the Service did most of the work itself.

Materials and labor were also scarce. Even though the government raised laborers' wages from the usual $1.50 to $3.00 per ten-hour day, they still had to recruit and transport men to the job site. Many of them were drifters rounded up in Portland saloons. Some took advantage of a free ride and hopped off the train before it got to the construction camps. Others made it to the job but didn't stay long. Those who had too good a time in the high spots of North Yakima sometimes found themselves the next day working with the chain gang on the city's streets. (In 1910 when the

Wobblies agitated for shorter work days, the North Yakima chain gang struck against the city, refusing to work more than eight hours a day.) The Service tried to get more reliable workers by hiring foreigners, but the European immigrants tended to storm out of camp en masse when they found camp conditions below their standards. A group of Greeks and Bulgarians quit when forbidden to prepare their own meals.

Problems like these, according to the engineers in charge of the project, were responsible for extending the construction period on the twelve-mile canal from the anticipated two years to five. Once the system was completed, in late 1911, Tieton project lands became the most expensive on any of the Service's projects. But they also eventually became the most profitable. They were so highly productive that in 1947 the Tieton owners were the first on any federal reclamation project in the country to repay the government all of its construction debt. On Valentine's Day that year, the Tieton division sent President Truman and each member of Congress a large red apple grown on the reclaimed desert land.

Sunnyside Division

At the same time that Congressman Jones pushed the campaign to limit Yakima River water claims to the much smaller amount of water that irrigators actually used, the government negotiated with the Washington Irrigation Company for the sale of its Sunnyside Canal. The canal and its system of laterals lay in the very heart of the valley. The Reclamation Service figured that it would be more efficient to absorb it into a larger project than to duplicate another system alongside it. Initially, the company had opposed the Service coming into the valley. The firm had pressed the legislature to pass a bill that would have given them control of the basin's irrigation through the right to develop the upstream lakes into storage reservoirs. However, the legislature, after two years deliberation, instead granted the U.S. government the right to acquire by eminent domain sites for storage reservoirs and canals in the valley.

This left the company with no option but to sell the canal, since without more water it was unable to enlarge the system or sell more land. After the firm signed a sales contract on very favorable terms, the government acquired reservoir sites from the Northern Pacific Railroad at Lakes Kachees, Keechelus, and Cle Elum.

In October 1906 the Service began working on its plan to upgrade and expand the Sunnyside Canal into an integrated system from the Cascade lakes to Kennewick. They started construction at the diversion dam and headworks, just below the

location of the original intake built by Walter Granger's company in 1892. The movable crest dam constructed six years earlier was replaced with a fixed-crest, concrete weir-type dam, and a mile-long dike above the dam to prevent flooding during high water. The new headgate structure, which increased the flow by about 65 percent, was made of concrete and retained the original hand-operated, six-foot-square cast iron gates. (In 1962 a radial sluice gate was added.) The main canal was enlarged to eight feet deep and was typically forty feet wide at the bottom. With the exception of a 600-foot-long flume, originally, no part of the main canal was lined. When it was finished, the new canal had a carrying capacity almost double that of the initial system.

The fifty-six-mile-long canal purchased by the government was solely a gravity system and watered only the land on the north side of the river. To supply water to land across the river, the Service built pressure pipelines, composed of wood staves and concrete, from the main canal. The nearly three-mile-long Mabton pipeline carried water under the river bed, while the Prosser pipeline transported water across the river on a steel truss bridge which still stands. Today pressure pipelines dominate irrigation construction, but they were not widely used at the beginning of the century. The government also enlarged the main lateral of the Snipes Mountain Canal, built by the Washington Irrigation Company to divert water on the south side of the main canal. After installing Cippoletti weirs and other devices for measuring and regulating the amount of water going to farmers' ditches, Service employees completed the gravity system part of the project in April 1912. The first flows watered 62,800 acres.

To irrigate the higher lands, government crews in 1915 began work on pumping plants at six locations along the canal. Although pumping operations formed part of the earliest irrigation projects in the state, they were rarely used because of their high operating cost. The Sunnyside system became the first large-scale effort in the state to pump water for irrigation. Except in one case, the Sunnyside plants were built along drops in the canal, and they slowed the increased water velocity caused by the slope of the enlarged canal. The head of water at the drop turned the turbines that operated the pumps to lift water to the benchland. The construction of the pumping plants and subsequent development of lands adjacent to the government canal was directly related to the formation in the mid-1910s of irrigation districts that financed and operated the plants. Like the canal itself, many of the original pumps were still in use three-quarters of a century after installation.

Above: Trimming the flume, Kittitas Irrigation Canal, Aug. 8, 1928. Right: Sunnyside Canal outfall on the Yakima River. Photos by Asahel Curtis. Courtesy, WA State Historical Society.

Above: Lining a portion of the Kittitas Canal, Aug. 8, 1928. Photo by Asahel Curtis. Courtesy, WA State Historical Society, Tacoma. Right: Broadside evidence of the federal Indian Service's fight against sabotage and water theft on the Yakima Reservation canal. Bottom: Horse teams drag-cleaning the main canal on the Yakima Indian Reservation, November 1910. Courtesy, National Archives, Seattle.

Wapato Division

The third federal system built in the valley was on the Yakama Indian Reservation, bordered on the east by the Yakima River and on the north by Ahtanum Creek. Technically, the Wapato project was not part of the Service's Yakima system because it was built by the Bureau of Indian Affairs. However, it had a history of government involvement in irrigation construction that predated the federal Sunnyside system, and its feasibility was dependent upon the use of the Yakima project's vast storage facilities. Unlike the first two Yakima River projects, the Wapato system was relatively easy to build. The accessible and gently sloping terrain provided ideal conditions, making it possible to construct a low-cost canal. Here the challenges were not so much of an engineering nature, but rather political and legal.

Irrigation began on the reservation sometime before the Yakama tribe signed its treaty with Gov. Isaac I. Stevens in 1855. The authors of the treaty, in which the Yakamas ceded a large area of land to the United States and reserved for themselves over a million acres, intended the Yakamas to become an agricultural people for which they would need the use of reservation waters. Catholic missionaries on the reservation first helped the tribe dig ditches from Ahtanum Creek. Later, government Indian agents helped the tribal farmers take water from the Yakima River to water their stock and gardens. In 1897 the Office of Indian Affairs built the first large-scale system on the reservation, the Erwin Ditch, later called the Old Reservation Canal — a twelve-mile-long ditch tapping the river just south of Union Gap. A few years after that Congressman Jones urged the Indian Bureau to construct a second irrigation canal through the reservation. The Indian Service built the New Reservation Canal in 1903.

Jones's objective for a larger reservation system, however, was not to foster a class of Indian agriculturists so much as to open the reservation to white settlers who would lease irrigated lands from tribal members. He was acting in harmony with the provisions of the Dawes Act of 1887, which called for the opening of a portion of reservation lands to white settlement. His views also conformed with the

common attitudes of valley settlers and reclamation officials, who considered the reservation a waste of good land that might otherwise be put to profitable use. In its 1905 water-limiting agreements on the Yakima River, the Reclamation Service registered the reservation for only a fraction of what its system was designed to use. According to Lucullus V. McWhorter, the tribe's great advocate and spokesman, this heavy cut in water rights was due to unjust encroachment by ambitious non-Indian irrigators. However, because the tribe under the Dawes Act sold and leased much of their allotted land, most of the reservation's prime irrigated land came into the hands of white, and later Asian, farmers. (In 1911, in the future Wapato project area, tribal members farmed approximately 5,000 acres while white farmers leased and owned 54,000 acres. In 1927, after the government's gravity system was in operation, there were five non-Indians for every Indian farmer.) The Washington Irrigation Company, which had opposed the second reservation canal from the beginning, sued the tribe and then destroyed the diversion dam of the

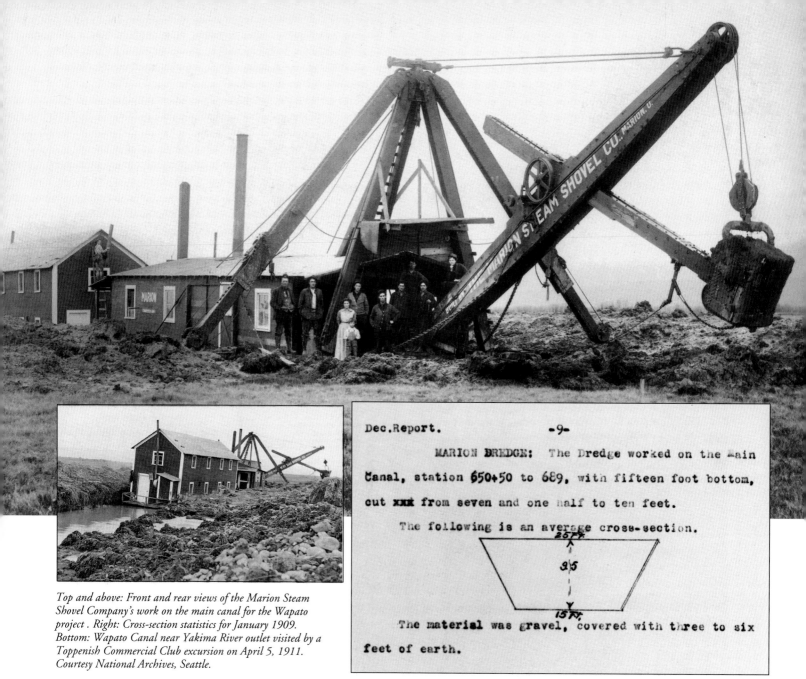

Dec.Report.   -9-

        MARION DREDGE: The Dredge worked on the main

Canal, station 650+50 to 689, with fifteen foot bottom,

cut xxx from seven and one half to ten feet.

        The following is an average cross-section.

                                25 FT.

                              9.5

                          15 FT.

        The material was gravel, covered with three to six

feet of earth.

Top and above: Front and rear views of the Marion Steam Shovel Company's work on the main canal for the Wapato project . Right: Cross-section statistics for January 1909. Bottom: Wapato Canal near Yakima River outlet visited by a Toppenish Commercial Club excursion on April 5, 1911. Courtesy National Archives, Seattle.

new canal, which was a little upstream from the head gate of the Sunnyside ditch. Meanwhile, on the other side of the reservation, whites and Indians fought over water rights on Ahtanum Creek. (See Indian water rights in Public Water Chapter.)

Before government engineers could begin work on a new large-scale system for the reservation, the water rights disputes between white settlers and the tribe had to be resolved. In 1914 after a congressionally appointed committee had investigated conditions on the reservation, Congress directed the Secretary of the Interior to see that the Indians received enough water to irrigate at least half of the eighty-acre allotment of each tribal member in the Wapato unit — almost five times what the Service had originally allocated.

Work finally began on the Wapato division in 1916. The gravity system came first between 1917 and 1923. The main canal and laterals followed the contours of the land to minimize construction costs. Pumping plants and hydroelectric facilities followed between 1928 and the early 1960s. Excess grade was concentrated in a few places so that power could be developed for pumping water to the elevated land. The Wapato system increased irrigated acreage on the reservation from 35,000 in 1909 to 118,637 in 1939. By 1977, 150,000 acres of the total 160,000 in the project received water.

Kittitas, Roza, and Kennewick Divisions

As early as 1892 settlers in the Kittitas Valley, the bottomlands surrounding Ellensburg, began investigating the possibility of building a large irrigation works. In 1905 the Reclamation Service made some preliminary surveys in the area and determined that the uneven topography and the great distance of the land to be irrigated from headworks on the Yakima River would make it too expensive. They decided to build the less costly projects in the lower Yakima Valley first. Twenty years later the government finally entered the valley when the Bureau of Reclamation formed the Kittitas division of the Yakima project.

Unlike the earlier Service projects, the Kittitas

system was built by private contractors, among whom were three companies that later worked on Hoover Dam. The twenty-six-mile-long main highline canal, built parallel to the Yakima River, conveyed water to approximately 72,000 acres. The uneven terrain made heavy side hill excavation necessary. In one place a bench flume and combination spans were built in a vertical wall on the south side of the Yakima canyon. The most formidable feature of the job was the construction of a 3,600-foot-long pressure tunnel which operated under hydrostatic pressure to carry water under the Yakima River and up a hill on the opposite bank. In 1929 a diversion dam, unique for its time, stretched across the river at Easton, about sixteen miles east of the Snoqualmie summit. A series of gates in the concrete gravity-type structure were designed to maintain a constant water level in the reservoir, making it possible to regulate diversion into the intake. When the High Line canal and laterals were completed in 1932, the system delivered water to approximately 45,000 acres.

The Roza division, completed by the Bureau in 1946, was designed to irrigate a strip of high land adjacent to the Sunnyside tract. The intake was situated between Yakima and Ellensburg on the Yakima River's west bank, but a large inverted siphon sent the water under the river to the Yakima ridge. A generating unit, operated by a penstuck at mile 12 of the main canal, transmitted power to eighteen pumping stations along the lower canal to lift water as much as 200 feet to the higher benchlands. Competition for project lands was keen. In 1947, the names of over 1,200 veterans and others who met government qualifications were mixed in a goldfish bowl in a drawing for twenty-eight project parcels.

Located furthest downstream in the Yakima Valley, the Kennewick division occupies a narrow strip of land thirty-two miles long and from one-quarter to four miles wide on the south side of the river between Chandler and Hover in Benton County. Completed in 1957, it receives its water supply almost entirely from upstream spills or return flows from the Yakima River. The Chandler pumping and power plant delivers the flow to over 19,000 acres.

Storage Reservoirs

The Service's reclamation projects would not have been of much help if the water the canals and laterals were designed to carry had not been available when it was needed. The capture and storage of flood waters for later release during the irrigation season was an essential part of the system. As quickly as federal funds were appropriated, the Service built permanent dams that enlarged existing mountain lakes or created reservoirs that fed the tributaries of the Yakima. The Clear Creek (1918) and Tieton (1925) reservoirs on the Tieton River were crucial to the success of the Tieton division; while the Kachess (1912), Keechelus (1917), and Cle Elum (1933) reservoirs supplied water primarily to the Wapato and Kittitas divisions. Because the Tieton unit would divert part of the Tieton River, which flowed into the Naches River, the Service gave priority to replacing the low flow of the Naches for the Sunnyside division with its first permanent storage project in the Yakima Basin, the Bumping Lake Dam.

Like the other early projects, Bumping Lake allowed the Service to improvise solutions to unanticipated problems and test experimental construction techniques. The first problem was finding a contractor. After twice advertising, the Service did not get a single bid, forcing it to hire laborers and do the work itself. First a wagon road had to be built from the nearest railway station at Naches City through forty-seven miles of rugged country. Once the road was in, horse teams pulled wagons of equipment and materials from the train station until they reached snow and the freight was transferred to sleds.

Construction began on the earthfill dam in May 1909. Quarries were located, a canal and flume built to carry water to the dam for sluicing, and a 45-ton Bucyrus steam shovel and a 1-cubic

Roza Dam on the Yakima River canyon between Ellensburg and Yakima. Photo by Asahel Curtis. Courtesy, WA State Historical Society, Tacoma.

yard Hayward "orange peel" skid excavator were assembled. The steam shovel worked in the borrow pit at the south end of the dam, excavating earth and loading cars pulled by horses on railroad tracks. As many as ten trains of five to six cars operated at one time, dumping the material at the top of the embankment where it was sluiced down the sides with the water piped to the site. The engineers' experiment with sluicing was supposed to retain the finer material with as much silt as possible on the upstream side of the dam, while the downstream side was thoroughly sluiced to remove the finer particles and make it hard. Although the Service once again had a hard time finding and keeping workers, as many as 506 men and 160 horses worked at one time. When the dam was finished on November 26, 1910, it was 3,500 feet long, twenty feet wide and stood a maximum fifty feet high. It raised the lake level approximately thirty-three feet and created a storage capacity of 34,000 acre-feet.

YAKIMA VALLEY BOOMING

Despite their problems, the Reclamation Service's projects had ended shotgun rule at the headgates and brought to the valley a vastly improved storage and distribution system. But everyone knew that it was going to take more than advanced, even largely government-subsidized, irrigation systems to turn the rattlesnake-ridden desert into productive farmland. The Yakima Valley cried out for more settlers. Between 1905 and 1912 boostering became serious business for local civic leaders, individual speculators, the railroad, and the federal government.

Competing against their counterparts in Oregon and California, eastern Washington promoters sent eastward thousands of brochures lavishly illustrating the miracle of irrigation farming. The Midwestern farmers they targeted were unfamiliar with the practice. They had to be persuaded that they could be more successful growing fruit and alfalfa on small irrigated farms, than they had been doing on large corn and hog farms, in a region that received one-fourth as much rainfall. One Richland enthusiast claimed that a well-managed ten-acre farm would bring its owner a bank president's salary. A Zillah booster touted the area as "a port of call on the sea of prosperity." The Yakima Valley, writers sang, enjoyed 300 days of sunshine annually, a rich volcanic soil, reliable and expanding markets, ex-

Above: Cle Elum Lake and Cle Elum Dam near Ronald and Roslyn, Washington. Below: Early-19th century retouched postcard view of Lake Keechelus. Courtesy, UW Libraries, Special Collections.

tensive irrigation projects, stable and industrious inhabitants ("far above the average in intelligence"), fine churches and schools, and "no saloons, no gambling resorts," nor other "ruinous conditions." Promoters even sold tracts by mail order, sight unseen. Sometimes unsuspecting buyers arrived (years too soon for some speculators) expecting to find orchards well on the way to providing an easy-street income. Instead, they found only barren slopes and dry ditches.

While publicists extolled orcharding as a "delightful" and "fascinating occupation" and lauded the healthiness of a life out-of-doors, they often failed to mention the arduous work needed to prepare land for irrigated orchards. Those who did acknowledge the grubbing, plowing, grading, and ditching sometimes described it as so easy that even children could do it. The actual work was another story, but the advertising was effective. Between 1900 and 1910 the population, if not yet the apple trees, blossomed in North Yakima from 3,200 to 14,000, and in Prosser from 200 to 1,300. New towns along the Sunnyside Canal, like Kennewick, Sunnyside, and Granger, sprang up from the "wind and sand swept desert." The number of irrigated acres leapt from 135,500 to 334,400, a 146 percent increase. Not all who came and purchased a ten-acre tract were successful, of course. As a more restrained valley resident admitted, "Gold grows on trees here, but there must be the right kind of a man behind the trees." The most successful orchardists were usually those who already had some irrigation experience. Even more important, irrigation was not a poor man's game. It took a fair amount of capital to get started and to live on while the fruit trees matured.

Above: A visionary scene set up by the Bureau of Reclamation to suggest the promise of their big project. Rattlesnake Mountain in Benton County appears on the horizon in both views (see below). Courtesy, U.S. Bureau of Reclamation.

Below: Workers placing "Gunite" (also known as "Shotcrete") lining on a lateral canal on Block One in Pasco Heights before it went into service in 1948. This was a typical scene throughout the Columbia Basin Project construction.

COLUMBIA BASIN PROJECT

Prospective farmers lured by the Northern Pacific Railroad to the western side of the Columbia Plateau in the late 1880s found themselves in a perplexing situation. There they were surrounded by hundreds of thousands of fertile acres lying agriculturally useless for lack of rainfall, while one of the mightiest rivers in the country rolled around them on three sides in a canyon a thousand feet below. They called the high plateau, belted by the great loop of the river, the Big Bend. It was barren, parched, and starkly cut by stream-sculptured patterns left behind by the meltwaters of ancient glaciers. From Grand Coulee on the north to Pasco on the south, it encompassed the present Douglas, Grant, Lincoln, Adams, and Franklin counties.

The first farmers to settle there followed the example of those who had earlier homesteaded the rolling hills of the Walla Walla and Palouse country and taken up dryland wheat farming. But with the exception of the eastern end, rainfall was not nearly as abundant in the Big Bend. Prospects were worst in Franklin County, where around 1900 immigrants from the north central states came in large numbers to buy railroad lands at rock-bottom prices. Although they banded together and worked cooperatively, water was always a problem. By 1914 only a small percentage of the original settlers remained.

Initial efforts to irrigate sections of the area began in the 1890s and continued into the first decade of the next century. Some were joint ventures formed with the railroad. All were small projects undertaken by irrigation companies or groups of landowners hoping to cultivate vineyards and orchards. One group of North Dakota immigrants in the Winchester area of Grant County planted an orchard and tried to lift water from deep wells by gasoline-powered pumps. Some Moses Lake homesteaders built small steamplants, fired by coal hauled from Ephrata, to pump water from the lake onto their tracts. Willard H. Babcock attempted a novel but frustrating experiment when he tried to lift Columbia River water up the cliffs, now known as Babcock Ridge, using pumps powered by windmills. From 1902 to 1906 the Reclamation Service and the state mulled over plans for irrigating the Big Bend desert by gravity canal with water from the Pend Oreille or Coeur d'Alene and Spokane valleys. But when Seattle engineer Theron Noble estimated the cost at $26 million — $1,625 an acre — the Service's chief engineer, Frederick H.

Spokane printer Shaw and Borden's souvenir booklet was published in 1939, the year of Washington State's fiftieth anniversary—its "Golden Jubilee"—and two years before Grand Coulee Dam was completed. It is a photo essay of its early construction as well as a recitation of the dam's record-breaking statistics. Comparisons with another depression-era colossus, Boulder Dam on the Colorado River, were especially popular to state partisans. For instance, the caption accompanying a photograph of the completed foundations explains, "At this stage the Grand Coulee Dam, about one-third complete, contains several times the volume of concrete in Boulder Dam. In May of 1939 there was more concrete under water in the Grand Coulee Dam than was used in the complete Boulder Dam." However, apropos irrigation, the writers were cautious, noting that the "Columbia Basin Project cannot compete in the present agricultural market because it will require from five to six years to irrigate any of the Columbia Basin lands, and from thirty to forty years to complete the reclamation project." Actually, the first waters were released onto Block One in Pasco Heights in May 1948, and the grand project envisioned in 1939 had not yet been completed.

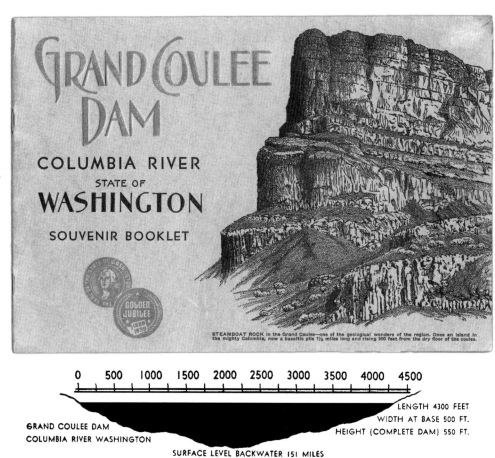

GRAND COULEE DAM

COLUMBIA RIVER
STATE OF
WASHINGTON

SOUVENIR BOOKLET

GOLDEN JUBILEE 1889 1939

STEAMBOAT ROCK in the Grand Coulee—one of the geological wonders of the region. Once an island in the mighty Columbia, now a basaltic pile 1½ miles long and rising 900 feet from the dry floor of the coulee.

0   500   1000   1500   2000   2500   3000   3500   4000   4500

GRAND COULEE DAM
COLUMBIA RIVER WASHINGTON

LENGTH 4300 FEET
WIDTH AT BASE 500 FT.
HEIGHT (COMPLETE DAM) 550 FT.

SURFACE LEVEL BACKWATER 151 MILES

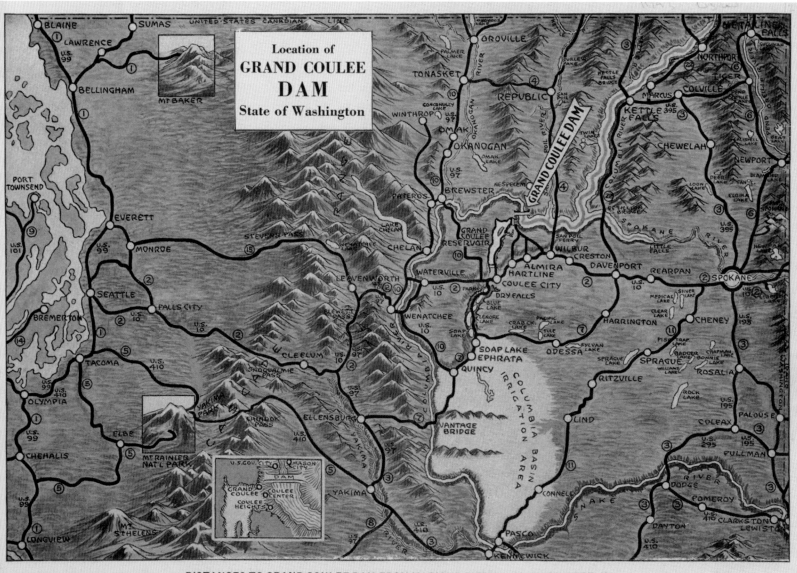

Location of
GRAND COULEE
DAM
State of Washington

DISTANCES TO GRAND COULEE DAM FROM VARIOUS CITIES SHOWN ON PAGE 10

Newell, decided the Big Bend should be left to a future generation.

Inevitably, all the private ventures failed within a few years. Crop returns were too low to sustain the high pumping costs. The Quincy Valley Irrigation District, attempting to overcome its financial disabilities, backed a proposal for a $40 million state bond issue to irrigate approximately 500,000 acres in the Quincy Valley with water from Lake Wenatchee. But state voters were not as enthusiastic about the idea and rejected the plan in the general election of 1914. The publicity for the referendum did, however, help awaken state leaders and residents to the call for reclamation in the Columbia Basin.

After thirty years of vacillation on irrigation issues on the part of Washington's governors, Governor Ernest Lister energetically backed the development of the Big Bend. In 1913 he approved a $10,000 state appropriation for a survey to be jointly conducted by the state and the Reclamation Service. Survey engineers identified four possible reservoir sites. But the high cost of the proposed project and World War I quieted the agitation for large projects in the Pasco basin. And there things stood. Until the close of the war, no development of any importance had been attempted, and the dry years caused more Big Bend farmers to flee their desert homes.

The Gravity Plan vs. the Dam

The same postwar patriotic spirit that had inspired the state's ill-fated soldier settlement prompted Elbert F. Blaine to go to Governor Ernest Lister with a plan in 1918. The Yakima orchardist and attorney, who became a forceful spokesmen for private irrigation in the state, wanted to turn the Big Bend into a huge breadbasket by reviving the idea of irrigating the area by gravity canal from the Pend Oreille River at Albeni Falls. The governor became so enthusiastic about the idea that he even took a train to the nation's capital to press the matter personally (and unsuccessfully) at the Interior Department.

Blaine also aroused the interest of the Spokane business community — so much so that the Spokane Chamber of Commerce eagerly adopted the plan and soon began considering the Big Bend its private commercial bonanza. They also liked the part of the plan that called for dumping water from the canal into the Spokane River during the non-irrigation season. The extra water, coming during the river's low flow period, would be sent through the turbines of the Spokane-based Washington Water Power Company dams and considerably boost their firm power output. Some historians suspect that the power company may have put the idea in Blaine's head to begin with. At any rate, the chamber formed a committee to promote the project to state and national lawmakers and even renamed the area the Columbia Basin so that it would be more recognizable in Washington D.C.

In 1919 the committee convinced the state legislature to form the Columbia Basin Survey Commission. The commission, charged with producing a survey and a report for the Reclamation Service, predicted that 1,753,000 acres could be irrigated by a gravity canal originating at Albeni Falls for an estimated $300 million. Such an expensive project necessarily relied on the generosity of Uncle Sam. But the Reclamation Service officials who reviewed the report had their doubts about the economic soundness of the plan. They asked the state to submit another study, including a closer look at the dam which the first study had quickly dismissed.

Rufus Woods and William "Billy" Clapp. Courtesy, Wenatchee World.

Meanwhile, on the opposite side of the basin, a group of men in Ephrata and Quincy were growing excited about a different Big Bend irrigation plan. The idea of building a dam on the Columbia River at Grand Coulee, where canyon walls reached over 800 feet above the mile-wide river, had been discussed for years. But no one had ever taken such a grandiose scheme seriously. Then in the summer of 1917, over a plate of ham and eggs in an Ephrata cafe, William (Billy) Clapp and a group of local men started talking about the war effort and the food that could be produced if the basin were irrigated. Clapp, an amiable Ephrata attorney, described his vision of a huge dam that would span the Columbia River at the head of the Grand Coulee. If glacial ice could block the Columbia and fill the coulee with water, Clapp mused, why couldn't a dam do the same and irrigate the entire Big Bend?

A year later, Rufus Woods, a boomer's boomer and editor and publisher of the *Wenatchee Daily World*, was looking for a story. In 1916, Woods had forced the opening of half a million acres on the Colville Indian Reservation to white settlers. After the Great Northern Railroad built a branch line north from Wenatchee to Oroville, Woods placed ads in about 400 newspapers and magazines west of Chicago promoting the reservation land which was legally open to settlement. Over 90,000 people showed up in the area for drawings for 5,500 homesteads. "It gave me some idea of the tremendous reservoir that could be tapped by advertising," Woods recalled. The publicist, who was probably more widely known than any other person in central Washington, was delighted that his efforts more than doubled the population of the Wenatchee area. When one of the men who had talked to Clapp told Woods to go see Billy because he had "a real big idea," Woods jumped at the lead and to the throttle of his Model T Ford, which

The pre-dam site where the Columbia River turns north below Grand Coulee. Photo by Asahel Curtis. Courtesy, WA State Historical Society, Tacoma.

he had customized with a built-in typewriter (see p. 292). Apparently, Woods found the plan newsworthy, but not anymore than other irrigation schemes he had pushed, for the story appeared as a relatively small piece on page seven of the July 18, 1918 *World*.

Nevertheless, neither the pumping plan nor the gravity plan disappeared. Sagebrushers living on the proposed project lands, who came to be suspicious of Washington Water Power Co. and the "power trust," favored the dam or pumping scheme. (See Power Chapter.) In fact, some Ephrata residents worked so hard and became so knowledgeable about aspects of the project, through their study of California dams, that the whole community was labeled the "Dam University." James O'Sullivan, the lanky head professor of this "college," had lived and worked in Ephrata as an attorney from 1910 to 1914. When he returned to Ephrata from his Michigan home in 1919, the pumpers persuaded him to work as chief publicist for the Dam at Grand Coulee. At Woods's request O'Sullivan, who was something of a self-taught engineer, surveyed the proposed site and determined that the dam was feasible — although the eager editor did not wait for his report before printing the positive results. In doing his research for the 1919 *World* articles, O'Sullivan hit on the idea that would make the pumping plan possible. He concluded that the huge dam would generate excess power which, when sold, would underwrite the irrigation component of the project. For a lump sum of $500, O'Sullivan crisscrossed the state over dirt roads in an open car, talking up the advantages of the dam.

In the early twenties backers of the two schemes faced off, matching report for report and expert for expert. Hugh L. Cooper, a well-respected engineer who later worked on the Muscle Shoals Dam, endorsed the dam. No doubt he gave an engineer's opinion, but he may have been influenced by hard feelings toward some Spokane residents who refused to return the family silver service he had earlier sold to pay bills. Spokane interests and the state Columbia Basin Commission, attempting to sidetrack the dam and improve their standing with the Reclamation Service, hired

Seattle engineer Willis T. Batcheller, who had worked on Seattle City Light's Skagit River project, for Gravity Dam. Although he had been privately instructed to turn in an unfavorable report about the pumping project, Batcheller instead reported that the dam would be less expensive and easier to build than the Spokane proposal adopted by the state. For his candor, the commission suppressed Batcheller's draft report and refused to pay his expense voucher. When word got back to the Reclamation Service, it became even more skeptical about the gravity proposal. The state's report, Service officials determined, deliberately underestimated the cost and difficulty of building the system, while grossly exaggerating the cost and engineering hurdles involved with the Columbia dam.

Resorting to new tactics, the state and Spokane Chamber of Commerce turned to public relations and hired a big gun — no less than General George A. Goethals, the builder of the Panama Canal and still a national hero. Many questioned the sixty-four-year-old general's qualifications for the job, but Goethals' six-day inspection of the canal route and dam site turned out to be a triumphal tour. Everywhere along his route, he was wined, dined, and celebrated, and farm people interrupted their chores to catch sight of him. At some point during his circuit, the general was reported to have said that if he were twenty years younger, he would love to tackle the dam. But to no one's surprise his report afterwards supported the gravity method.

For his two weeks of work, Goethals was paid $20,000, most of which was state money. (Goethals did hundreds of such consulting jobs in his later years. His biographer does not even mention the Columbia project.) Goethal's son remained behind and "finished" the report which was taken largely from the work of state engineer Ivan Goodner. At any rate, Goethals's findings were not the result of new surveys but a reassessment of earlier studies. He endorsed the gravity plan as less costly, simpler, and

Continued page 244

This map detail, which emphasizes the Washington State part of the Columbia River Basin, was taken from Plate One of the watershed "308" Report, published in 1931 by the North Pacific Division of the Army Corps of Engineers for the Sixty-ninth U.S. Congress.

PLATE I

COLUMBIA RIVER
BASIN

Accompanying Part One of Report on Columbia
River prepared pursuant to House
Document 308, 69th Congress, 1st Session.
Dated at Office of the Division Engineer,
North Pacific Division,
Portland, Oregon, July 31, 1931.

Above and top: Lodgings for project workers were provided in campgrounds and on barges, which were moved along the river to new work sites.

Top right: FDR's monument beside the lake which, after his death, was named for him by Secretary of the Interior Harold Ickes. Photo by Hugh Paradise. Below: The years of work were concluded on July 19, 1941 with the ceremonial felling of the last remaining pine tree in the reservoir. Inset: Frank A. Banks, Bureau of Reclamation, was at one end of the two-man saw that cut down the last pine. Years later the project's second lake, that above the dam in the Grand Coulee, would be named after Banks.

The work of clearing 52,000 acres for Roosevelt Lake, a 151-mile long reservoir, from Grand Coulee Dam to the Canadian border began in 1938. Some three thousand men from ten counties were employed in the W.P.A. program to clear 600 miles of shoreline. Entire communities like Kettle Falls and Marcus were moved to new townsites above the reservoir's high water line. Marcus (top right column) was one of the last towns to dismantle its depot (above), deliberately gut permanent structures like the brick school-house (below) using fire, and move its business district beyond the flood tide.

more comprehensive, and rejected the dam on the grounds that there was no market for surplus power. That same objection had often been made by the Washington Water Power Company, which did not welcome competition. The effect of the general's pronouncements was to jettison the dam proposal. For the next ten years the state officially accepted the gravity project as the only feasible method of irrigating the basin.

It seemed that the pumpers had lost hope. O'Sullivan went back to Michigan. From 1922 to 1929 the dam was not even mentioned in the *Wenatchee World*. The dam proponents' discouragement was understandable. For not only did they have the "Spokane gang" to compete with, but they would have had to overcome a great deal of skepticism about the need for any new large-scale, government-subsidized project. During the agricultural downturn of the 1920s, when prices slid and crops went unsold, many contended that it made no sense to bring new lands into production. Sunnyside project irrigators reminded now-U.S. Senator Wesley Jones that most of the state's irrigation districts were insolvent, their members unable to make water payments. Both the state Grange master Albert Goss and Earle J. Barnes, the state director of conservation and development, agreed that a new irrigation project would be "badly timed." Their feelings were shared by a majority of congressmen from the eastern and midwestern states who opposed any western irrigation project.

However, neither the pumpers nor the canal boosters gave up their vision of a Big Bend, lushly green and teeming with farms, towns, and industries. The Columbia Basin Irrigation League, a group formed by 500 friends of the gravity plan, lured members of Congress and the Coolidge administration out west so that they could view first-hand the region's possibilities. In 1926 Secretary of Commerce Herbert Hoover was a featured speaker at the league's annual convention in Seattle. While he vigorously urged that the Columbia Basin irrigation project begin as soon as possible, the future president got a bit confused about the methods. To a room full of gravity backers gaping in silent surprise, Hoover called the project "Grand Coulee" while he described the

Above: James O'Sullivan, key figure of the Columbia Basin Project, at his desk. Below: Construction work on the massive "flip-bucket" for the Grand Coulee Dam spillway. Photos courtesy, Bureau of Reclamation.

gravity plan. After that kind of endorsement league officials figured they had better see the president himself. At his vacation spot in Rapid City, South Dakota, President Calvin Coolidge graciously granted them a forty-five-minute interview so that they could display copies of their reports and the endorsements of prominent people.

"Cal" was characteristically cool but polite. Congress, however, was merely cool about such a huge public project. Even Senator Jones, who sat on influential committees, could not get his colleagues to approve a study of the Columbia Basin as a preliminary to construction. Finally, in 1927 Jones thought of the Army Corps of Engineers as a possible way to sidestep the political blockades in Congress. He threw a rider into an appropriations bill and had the Columbia included among the rivers the Corps was to survey for dam sites.

The Triumph of Grand Coulee

In 1932 when the army engineers submitted its plan for the river's development to Congress, the gravity scheme was finally put to rest. In considering all the potential uses of the Columbia, the Corps recommended several dams and among them a high dam at Grand Coulee to provide the major storage, reclamation, and power work on the river. By then it was clear that large expensive projects designed for a single purpose could not win congressional approval. The army's so-called "308 Report" was a comprehensive river plan that called for ten multipurpose dams to be used for navigation, power, reclamation, and flood storage. Tragically, the Corps engineers did not give much consideration to the millions of salmon that each year made the long swim upriver to their spawning grounds. This oversight would have a devastating effect on their numbers, even with the later provision of fish ladders at all the dams below Chief Joseph.

Even apart from their comprehensive river plan, the Army Engineers had favored Grand Coulee Dam over the gravity method because of its lower cost. The gravity canal, they figured, would cost twice the state's estimate — at least $750 million, while the dam would cost about $341 million and a large part of that could be recouped through power sales. The pumpers were ecstatic, especially Jim O'Sullivan who, although in poor health, had returned to Washington in 1929 to work full time searching for and promoting markets for the dam's power. At first Spokane men sulked but rather than lose out on a federal project altogether, they swallowed their pride and fell reluctantly in line.

In 1933 Gov. Clarence Martin, a strong supporter of the project, and a largely Democratic state legislature reestablished the Columbia Basin Commission to lobby for immediate construction. The commission immediately sent state Grange master Albert Goss, Rep. Sam Hill, and Sen. Clarence C. Dill to Washington to convince newly elected President Franklin Roosevelt to grant the state federal money for the project. Roosevelt reluctantly approved $63 million of Public Works Administration emergency funds to begin work on a low dam. It was a foot in the door for the controversial power part of the project, since under the provisions of the PWA, congressional approval, at least initially, was not required. After work had begun on the low dam, Grand Coulee's supporters figured, Congress might be more inclined to approve funds to raise it and thus make irrigation pumping economically feasible. (See Power Chapter.)

Colossal and magnificent, America's depression-era dams functioned as a purgative of national despair. More important, they employed tens of thousands of men, giving them a prominent role in the New Deal's program of relief and recovery. Reclamation works, on the other hand, did not fit easily into the scheme of employment and federal assistance. Bringing new farmlands into production would conflict with the administration's farm policy, which intended to raise farm commodity prices by reducing crop surpluses. It was the hydroelectric power to support new industry, jobs, and people in the region that Roosevelt wanted from Grand Coulee. And even with that he wanted to go slowly. Like so many others he was not convinced that a market would soon exist for the output of such a gigantic power plant.

However, just as the project's advocates had hoped, Reclamation Bureau Director Elwood Mead persuaded the administration in 1934 that a high dam would produce greater revenues and expedite the repayment of construction costs. President Roosevelt approved the high dam with an executive order in June 1935, and in August Congress passed a Rivers and Harbors Act that called for raising Grand Coulee Dam. The proposed 550-foot dam would decrease the difference in elevation between the reservoir level and the main canal, 280 feet above, and make reclamation of basin lands economically possible. The plan to turn the river back into the Grand Coulee and create a second reservoir (Banks Lake) to

Although remote, Grand Coulee Dam quickly became a destination for tours and field trips. Courtesy, National Archives, Alaska-Pacific NW Region, Seattle.

exclusively feed the irrigation canals was exactly what Jim O'Sullivan and the Ephrata pumpers had hoped for.

The Bureau's contractors and their crews worked around the clock. Mudslides and the cold winters of 1936 and 1937, when freezing conditions caused construction to shut down temporarily, were especially difficult. Yet, even with the delays, Grand Coulee was finished ahead of schedule in the spring of 1941 — just in time to supply the energy needed to power the region's wartime industries. The irrigation features of the project, however, did not have the same priority to a nation focused on winning the war. Consequently, irrigation survey work and planning slowed until after the conflict. At that time Congress, planning on the returning veterans' desire for farms, authorized large-scale construction.

In 1947 the Columbia Basin Commission resumed its activities with a stepped-up campaign of lobbying Congress for the necessary yearly appropriations. They kept a permanent lobbyist at the capital to make sure the commission was represented at all congressional committees considering reclamation legislation. Commission members and employees such as Woods, O'Sullivan, C. C. Dill, and Kirby Billingsley made long train trips across the country to put more logs on the congressional fires.

Together with the efforts of the state's congressional delegation, the commission over the years was remarkably effective. They convinced government officials to raise the maximum number of acres allowed for individual farm units on project lands. They helped talk government leaders into approving liberalized FHA mortgage terms for project settlers and pushed a revised sugar act that allowed basin acreage to be put into sugar beet production. For the first time ever, the group managed to get irrigation features authorized in a Corps of Engineers' project — the Chief Joseph Dam. Between 1933 and 1959 the commission and Washington's representatives secured federal appropriations for the Columbia Basin project of over $500 million.

COLUMBIA BASIN IRRIGATION SYSTEM

When it first began operating in 1952, the pumping plant at Grand Coulee Dam was the largest in the world. Its capacity was so great that initially only two of the planned twelve pumps were needed. Each pump could lift one billion gallons of water daily — enough to irrigate 100,000 acres or supply the water needs of New York City. At that time the twelve centrifugal-type pumps, officials claimed, could have supplied nearly all the people in the country with domestic water. But, of course, nothing so auspicious was required. All that was expected of them then was to lift water 280 feet from Lake Roosevelt behind the dam to Banks Lake in the coulee. Because a dam high enough to divert water directly from the river to the canals would have inundated parts of Canada, the dam and pumping project was designed to lift water from a lower to a higher reservoir.

Above: Nearing completion on the concrete lining for the project's main canal. Courtesy, Michael Fairley. Below: Summer Falls at Billy Clapp Lake. Photo by Hugh Paradise.

Banks lake was inspired by nature's own ice-age dam. During the Pleistocene period, the thick ice sheets that covered much of the area blocked the river's natural course and forced its glacial flood waters to carve spectacular canyons in the basalt plateau. The most impressive of the bigger canyons, called coulees, was the Grand Coulee up to 400 feet deep and from one to two miles wide. At the south end of Grand Coulee the Pleistocene Columbia dropped 400 feet over a sheer cliff that was once one of the mightiest waterfalls of all time. (When Harry Truman visited Dry Falls in May 1950, he suggested putting Republicans at the base of the cataract and turning the water back on.)

Many millennia later, after Ephrata area residents and the state's congressional delegation were able to convince the Roosevelt administration of the worthiness of the Grand Coulee project, work began on the dam on July 16, 1933. The dam was started partly because the government wanted to put thousands of unemployed men to work during the depression. Later it was rushed to completion in 1941 because of the country's need for power during the war. But the original inspiration for the project came from local residents who, during World War I, wanted to turn central Washington into a great breadbasket that could potentially help feed the nation. Their plan called for turning part of the river's flow back into the Grand Coulee, which would become a reservoir from which the water would flow out in huge canals to basin lands. The Banks Lake reservoir was constructed by building an earth-and-rock-fill dam across each end of the coulee. The lake fulfilled two functions — it replaced twenty-seven miles of very expensive canal and allowed a program of equalized storage, so that it was not necessary to pump a steady quantity from Lake Roosevelt to replace water being diverted into the canal. The pumps required a lot of electricity, but with the storage reservoir they could be shut down when power demands on the dam were high.

The water today moves south out of Banks Lake through the outlet gates in Dry Falls Dam near Coulee City. It then passes through two miles of concrete-lined main canal. The river-size main canal is fifty feet wide at the bottom and 120 feet wide at the top. From the main canal the water crosses John Paul Draw in the 1,038-foot-long Bacon Siphon and enters the two-mile-long Bacon Tunnel, which was laboriously bored through a hard basalt formation. Five miles below Bacon Tunnel the water plunges over a basalt cliff 165 feet into the upper end of the artificially-created Billy Clapp Lake. The appropriately named Summer Falls spills over the cliff only during the

Above: Excavating the prism of Eltopia Branch Canal, Feb. 27, 1963. Bureau of Reclamtion photo by Hertzog. Courtesy, Ted Van Arsdol. Below: Planning a home site within the Columbia Basin Project. Courtesy, Bureau of Reclamation.

irrigation season. Slightly south of the lake (about seven miles east of Soap Lake), the main canal divides into two branches. The East Low Canal flows eighty-seven miles down the eastern edge of the project and empties into the Scooteney Wasteway, which flows into the reservoir of the same name. The West Canal travels southwest to Soap Lake where it jogs around the lake and crosses the lower Grand Coulee via the Soap Lake Siphon, which at the time of its construction was the largest in the world. It ends near Lower Goose Lake, eighty-eight miles below the bifurcation.

In the center of the basin project, directly south of Moses Lake, is Potholes Reservoir. The reservoir, held back by the earth-fill O'Sullivan Dam, was designed to hold return flows coming from farms and system operations through drains, wasteways, and natural channels. So many seep lakes and marshes developed in the area, attracting many species of migratory water fowl and shore birds, that the government created the Columbia National Wildlife Refuge. From the reservoir the Potholes Canal flows southeast, paralleling the East Low Canal for about fifteen miles to the Scooteney Reservoir, from which it flows southwest before emptying into the Columbia River six miles upstream from Pasco. By 1978 in the Columbia Basin Project, there were 543,000 developed acres served by 333 miles of main canals, 1,959 miles of laterals and 2,761 miles of drains and wasteways.

Pumping Begins

The long-awaited Columbia Basin project formally opened in 1952, nearly twenty years after work had begun on the dam. Hoping to raise the basin's 35,000 population, the Columbia Basin Commission spearheaded a publicity campaign for the opening "that brought [the] attention of all parts of the nation and many parts of the world." That year they reported to the governor: "Coast-to-coast radio programs, a constant flow of news to the press of the nation, scores of national magazine stories and even television programs made this publicity campaign one of the greatest, if not the greatest, ever conducted in the history of the state. . . . Truly the eyes of the nation are on the Columbia Basin." Their advertising must have been effective, for 6,000 veterans put their names in the goldfish bowl for the first sale of 127 tracts of project land.

Before the first cubic yard of earth was excavated to start work on the canals, fifty-four agencies representing all levels of government as well as universities, trade associations, irrigation districts, and chambers of commerce spent three years planning for the project. Hoping to avoid the tragic difficulties that settlers on the early federal projects had experienced, the Reclamation Bureau sponsored the joint studies. The Columbia Basin Project became the largest and most carefully planned agricultural settlement in the Bureau's history. (In fact, the project is the largest single reclamation project ever undertaken in the United States.) The several committees studied and made recommendations for types of farm sizes, crops, irrigation techniques, crop processing industries, town layouts, transportation facilities, recreation, education, house construction, and even home furnishings. Their proposal that the size of farm units should be based on soil and topographic conditions and shaped to comply with the topography and the irrigation system inaugurated an entirely new policy for the Bureau.

One of the trickier problems for the sociologists was determining the acceptable "standard of living" for project families, which they admitted was "a psychological phenomenon [that] is difficult to measure." To find out the types of goods and services settlers might want, they conducted surveys of the spending habits

Grand Coulee's original six pumps were capable of lifting 4.3 million gallons of water per minute to the main canal. Photo by Hugh Paradise.

of farm families in the Columbia Basin and in the midwestern plains from which they expected to get many immigrants. They discovered that high- and low-income families in both areas considered food canning, washing machines, beauty parlor, barbershop, and physician services, automobiles, radios, reading material, motion pictures, and tobacco to be "necessities." Running water, dental services, and telephones were regarded as luxuries by low-income families; and central heating, electric sewing machines, and ironing machines were rarities in both areas and income groups. In the Northwest, kitchen sinks with drains, flush toilets, and electricity were considered necessities, while for the Great Plains people they were rarities or luxuries.

Project Acreage Limitations

Many of the investigators' recommendations were incorporated into the Columbia Basin Project Act of 1943, where the homestead ideal of earlier federal reclamation legislation once again appeared. According to the act, the project was supposed to "create opportunities for establishing homes and satisfactory livelihoods for the maximum practicable number of families, . . . not to create opportunities for a few families to obtain the largest possible income from farming." To carry out this purpose the planners had recommended that even with the poorest class of land, the maximum of 160-acre units should be maintained. Using their estimates, which became law when incorporated into the act, project officials restricted settlers to forty- and eighty-acre tracts if they found that soil and other conditions could support a family at a "suitable level."

Defining that "suitable" or "desirable" economic level proved to be an elusive goal. The project planners began their studies in 1938 before the war in Europe had begun. Basing their findings on the experiences of farm families during the later years of the depression, they had not considered the potential social and economic impact of war. Their prewar conception of the ideal farm was one just large enough to provide a family of four enough to live comfortably and to send their children to college — a

maximum of eighty acres of the best land and 160 of the poorest. By the time construction began in 1947 conditions had changed. Large-scale farm equipment and mechanization made it possible for farmers to cultivate extensive acreage. Expectations of a higher standard of living than project planners had anticipated, and the mobility offered the multicar family after the war, which made it possible for farm operators to live in town and commute to work, also created pressures for larger farm units.

Soon after the canals began delivering water to the basin in the early 1950s, project farmers started agitating for enlargement of their units. The planners' figures were outdated by the new postwar conditions, they argued. One of the original settlers complained in 1953 that the government was "living in the dark ages. You can only make a decent profit if you farm on a large scale." Encouraged by higher wartime agricultural prices and better yields obtained during a wet cycle that began in 1940, the dryland wheat farmers on the east side of the basin became even less enthusiastic about joining a project with acreage restrictions. Most already owned more than 160 acres of land and were not inclined to give them up. In 1947 the owners of three-quarters of the wheatlands in the East Irrigation District withdrew their land from the project. The removal of about a quarter of the project's more than one million acres made the proposed East High Main Canal impractical even before it was designed. In 1962, after the Columbia Basin Commission lobbied key lawmakers, Congress modified the 1943 law to allow for larger farms and put the project under the standards of the Reclamation Act's 160-acre limit for an individual and 320 acres for a man and his wife.

But many basin farmers continued to insist that even 320 acres was not enough. From the time the first federal systems began operating, commercial farmers throughout the West complained that the acreage limitation restricted their rights to acquire property and to be successful. According to the original 1902 and the 1912 reclamation laws, owners of land exceeding 160 acres could receive federal project water only if they sold their surplus property. However, Service and later Bureau administrators, except

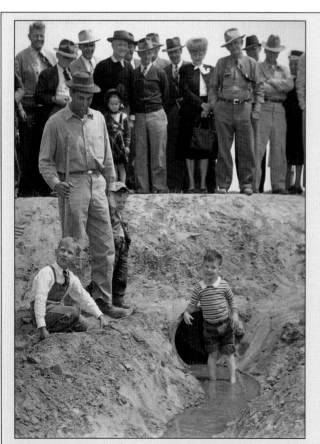

COLUMBIA IRRIGATION PROJECT

On May 5, 1948, the Columbia Irrigation Project commenced its services when Columbia River waters were pumped onto Pasco Heights' Block One, a section of the project's million acres, as a demonstration to publicize its progress. The project formally opened four years later in 1952, twenty years after work had first begun on the Grand Coulee Dam. O.C. Gillian, owner of the farm on Block One, and his two sons stood in the lateral canal at the moment the irrigated waters arrived. B.B. Horrigan, Franklin County Superior Court judge, gave the official signal for the pumping plant to start the pumps.

Block One was chosen as the demonstration site because the main canals leading up to Franklin County, which were being built southward from Lake Roosevelt behind Grand Coulee Dam, had not arrived in Franklin County yet. So the Bureau of Reclamation pumped water into Block One to show what the land could do once it was irrigated with an adequate supply of water. Since then, what was once desert is now the state's "breadbasket."

Left: O.C. Gillian, farm owner on Block One, and his sons stand in the lateral canal as the first waters of the Columbia Basin Irrigation Project are released. Onlookers include, from left: B.B. Horrigan, Franklin County judge; Loen Bailie, Columbia Basin Commission member; Mel Swanson, Pasco Chamber of Commerce chairman; Frank Lowden, Walla Walla resident; Art Garton, Columbia Basin Commission member; D.C. W. Neff, South Columbia Basin District Board member; and area residents A.H. Jaynes, Andy Job, and Fred Scott, Sr. Courtesy, Franklin County Historical Society.

Above left: Water from the Grand Coulee pumps unites first in this 25-foot-high siphon before reaching daylight and the main canal. Courtesy, UW Libraries, Special Collections. Right: The main canal and both Bacon Siphons, numbers one and two. The aerial was photographed in 1980, after the second siphon's first irrigation season. Courtesy, Bureau of Reclamation.

during the Roosevelt administration when the principle was resurrected, found the excess land provisions impractical or impossible to enforce.

So they modified them. Sometimes Bureau officials extended the 160-acre limit to every adult member in the farm family and permitted owners to deed lands exceeding the limit to their relatives and friends or anyone who would let them go on using it. Unlimited leasing of land was allowed, and residency requirements were loosened. By 1916 corporations were permitted to own federal project farms, which opened the door to large "absentee" corporations. During the Truman administration, when government and industry worked together to spur national production, ensuring a wide distribution of public subsidies became less important than promoting commercial agriculture and economic growth. Partly because the lengthy postwar recession did not occur and made veterans' settlement projects unnecessary, the Bureau overlooked the original intent of the federally funded projects that subsidized project farmers' water up to 75% of the cost in order to redistribute wealth and build agricultural communities that would not have been viable otherwise. In 1979 farmers and corporations in eastern Washington owned 24,180 acres of federally irrigated land in excess of the 160-acre limit. Smaller and resident farmers were not unaware of this situation. In November 1978 Washington voters approved Initiative 59, the Grange-sponsored plan to put restrictions on water permits to irrigators of over 2,000 acres.

Congress also watered down the law by creating a few significant exemptions. Yet, even into the 1980s some federal and state policymakers continued to portray and defend the projects as havens for "little farmers" who wanted to make a new life. President Franklin Roosevelt had consistently maintained that the Columbia Basin should be developed to aid the resettlement of the "Grapes of Wrath" farmers driven from their Dust Bowl homes. He hoped that the Columbia project would eventually support 80,000 new farm families and another 20,000 engaged in agriculture-related businesses. However, the Bureau at that time required that project settlers have at least $2,000 in capital. This would have excluded most of those fleeing the Midwest.

Despite the Bureau's liberal interpretation of it, the 160-acre provision continued to be upheld by Congress and the Supreme

Court until 1982, when it was finally changed. Then most members of Congress apparently were unconvinced by studies such as that performed by two agricultural economists at Washington State University in the mid-1970s that demonstrated that a 160-acre farm in the Columbia Basin could earn a family over $15,000 a year in after tax-income, compared to a national average of $10,037. Congress instead responded to the lobbying of the larger commercial farmers and their representatives. It finally gave up the long-standing agrarian tradition, which was portrayed as a sentimental and outmoded social ideal, and reformed the act to allow project families to own up to a maximum of 960 acres.

Columbia Basin, Second Phase

The construction of the irrigation works in the western, central, and southern parts of the basin began in 1946 and continued over the next twenty-five years until half a million acres were receiving water. By 1957 the first phase was 70 percent complete and had produced over more than $48 million worth of crops. Because of the withdrawal from the project of most of the wheatland on the eastern side of the basin, no work was attempted there. These higher lands were set aside as the second half of the project to be completed at some later date. The postponement, however, has continued much longer than anyone anticipated. Presently, there are serious doubts about whether the remaining half million acres will ever be developed by the government.

In 1967 Sen. Warren Magnuson, after a number of unsuccessful attempts, was able to convince his congressional colleagues to appropriate planning money for the second half of the project. From that time until 1975, in his powerful position on the Senate appropriations committee, "Maggie" managed to procure funds for the project, but officials in President Richard Nixon's administration refused to spend it. The administrative logjam was finally broken up in December 1975, when the Senate approved the use of impounded funds so that work could begin on the Second

Bacon Siphon and Tunnel project, the key component in the expansion of the system. The huge 1,150-foot-long siphon, like its antecedent of the same name, was designed to tap enough water from Banks Lake, the equalizing reservoir in the coulee, to irrigate the remaining project acreage.

By 1965 the Bureau of Reclamation had developed 80 percent of the irrigated land in Washington. By the early 1970s, however, Congress and the administration were not as willing as their predecessors to commit the nation's taxpayers and the region's electricity ratepayers to pay for large-scale reclamation that primarily benefited the local economy. In 1972 the National Water Commission, organized during the Johnson administration to reassess the nation's water management policies, reported that no new irrigation projects were necessary in the country for the next thirty years. The highly controversial report recommended that the government no longer assist irrigation systems through reduced interest rates, subsidies from hydroelectric projects, and other general support.

Columbia Basin farmers were appalled by the commission's findings. Russell Smith of Pasco, chairman of the Columbia Basin Development League and a former Reclamation Bureau employee, called the report "phony," "cockeyed," and based on "kiddy-car economics." At a commission hearing in Spokane in January 1973 local farmers, state officials, and businessmen complained that the government intended to halt all new water projects. Referring to the basin's large irrigated feed crops, they claimed that such a policy would force Americans to eat soybeans for protein instead of meat. Commission member Charles Luce, chairman and president of Consolidated Edison of New York and a former Bonneville Power administrator, explained that their proposal for ending federal water subsidies was based partly on the fact that crops grown on federally watered land were also subsidized by federal price supports. Due to crop surpluses, the government was currently paying American farmers large amounts to keep more than 50 million acres of land out of production. Four years later, while engineers were boring through a basalt mountain as they began work on the siphon and tunnel project, prices were down on three of the basin's four major crops. The market was

Five years work—1952 to 1957—of the Columbia Basin Project in the Quincy Valley. Both aerials look west towards Quincy, from above Naylor, and in line with the West Canal, Burlington Northern tracks and State Highway 28. Courtesy, Bureau of Reclamation.

Evergreen Ridge surge towers, between George and the Columbia River, are used for moving irrigation water uphill. Photo by Hugh Paradise.

glutted with potatoes, wheat, and sugar beets. Prices remained good only for alfalfa.

The basin farmers attending the meeting may not have been convinced by Luce's argument, but they did understand that the second half of the project was going to be more expensive than the first — and that they were going to have to pay a greater percentage of the costs. However, they balked at the amount the government had proposed. In 1964 when basin farmers voted to raise their government payment from the original $85 an acre to $132, their reimbursement covered about 11 percent of the capital cost of building the system. In 1976 the Reclamation Bureau proposed for the farmers' share of the estimated $2 billion second phase, a contribution of $1,600 an acre. According to reclamation law their payments would not begin until ten years after project construction began and would then be spread out over a fifty-year, interest-free period. Even though their suggested payment amounted to more than eighteen times the costs assessed the original tracts, they would still not be the main subsidizers of the irrigation works. Because most of the costs would be incurred during the first fifteen years of the project and the farmer's repayment period would extend over sixty years, an estimated 78 percent of the total construction costs, including financing, would be paid for by the region's electric ratepayers and the nation's taxpayers. (See Public Water Chapter.)

This kind of federal subsidy gave Gov. Dan Evans, the state's

congressional delegation, and the legislature even more reason to support the project. After the legislature and basin irrigation districts pledged a significant amount toward the Second Bacon Siphon and Tunnel, federal funds were finally released and the second phase of the Columbia Basin project got underway. On October 9, 1976, Interior Secretary Thomas Kleppe, Reclamation Commissioner Gilbert Stamm, Senators Warren Magnuson and Henry Jackson, Congressmen Mike McCormack and Thomas Foley, and Gov. Evans and local dignitaries gathered to celebrate the groundbreaking ceremony at Coulee City. The reclamation commissioner congratulated the state for pledging $15 million toward construction costs, the largest local share for a federal irrigation project ever made. Sen. Magnuson, praised by the other speakers for his efforts to win appropriations, said it was a great day for him and admitted that he had almost given up in the fight to obtain funds.

Top to bottom: Washington State College display at an unidentified fair. Courtesy, Dan Kerlee. Abandoned canal in Pend Oreille County. Courtesy, National Archives, Seattle. Early promotion for George, WA. Photo by Werner Lenggenhager, Sept. 1, 1957. Courtesy, WSU, Historical Photography Collections. Canal near Sequim. Courtesy, Harriett Fish.

Yet the battle was far from over. President Jimmy Carter had even less enthusiasm for massive government water resource development than President Nixon had. In October 1978 Carter vetoed a $10.2 billion public works bill that included $31 million for Columbia Basin irrigation development, calling it inflationary and a classic case of pork barrel legislation. When the Second Bacon Siphon and Tunnel was completed in March 1980, it was the only part of the expanded project under construction or even firmly planned. The first flows through the new structure had nowhere to go but to farmers on the original project tracts. Critics inside and outside the government continued to raise serious questions about the need for developing another half million acres in the Columbia Basin. Dryland farmers in the area of the proposed extension had mixed views about the desirability of the project, not only because of the high government repayments for system construction, but also because of the large capital expenditures they would have to make for equipment and chemical fertilizers to convert to irrigated farming.

Because of the nearly even split within its membership, the Washington State Farm Bureau, which represented 95 percent of the state's farm industry, in the mid-1980s chose not to take a position on the project's completion. Although Governors Dan Evans, Dixy Lee Ray, and John Spellman were each strong proponents of the second phase, Gov. Booth Gardner declined to recommend further development until the Bureau completed an environmental impact statement. When the draft EIS came out in September 1989, it estimated the cost of completion at around $2.5 billion and gave the project a cost-benefit ratio well below acceptable levels. Even if the state approves the completion of the project, eastern and midwestern congressmen are not likely to grant more federal aid for another western water project that provides their constituents no clear benefits. When Sen. Daniel Moynihan of New York announced in 1982, during congressional debates over the reformation of the reclamation act, that "the great barbecue is over," he pointed out that no major water resources authorization bill had been passed by Congress since 1972. At least for the foreseeable future, supporters of the Columbia Basin project's second phase will need to find many more logs than western congressman can roll.

READ A ROMANCE OF ANTIQUITY!!
THE GREAT MYSTERY FALLS OF WASHINGTON
3½ MILES FROM BANK TO BANK

A Mile and a Half of a Four Hundred Foot Drop for the Cataract of Waters that Beat Niagara's Volume as **40 to 1**
The Story of a Continent — Written as it was made — is in this Great Gorge.
Fifty Miles of Awe Inspiring Grandeur.
A Stupendous Mystery of One Hundred Thousand Years ago. ~~~~~~~~~~~~~~~~

G eologists Themselves can only Conjecture what Turned the Mighty Glacial Floods of the Upper Half of North America East and West from this Prehistoric Channel.
The Mighty Mississippi — The Columbia — The Fraser — The Yukon — even the Romantic M^{ac}kenzie — HERE LIES THE SKELETON OF THE FATHER OF THEM ALL

52 PARKS MAINTAINED FOR YOUR PLEASURE

STATE PARK COMMITTEE

-16430-

DRY FALLS STATE PARK

Above: The State Park's sensational "Mystery Falls" billboard at Dry Falls, ca. 1955. Courtesy, Dan Kerlee. Below: Part of the Dry Falls 3.5-mile-wide, 400-foot-high skeleton seen through a window of the state park's vista point, March 9, 1977. Photo by Glade Walker for the Bureau of Reclamation.

FLOOD CONTROL

COLUMBIA RIVER

Toward the end of the last glacial advance about 17,000 years ago, the Columbia Basin was violently reshaped by a giant flood. The torrent — as much as ten times the combined flow of all the rivers in the world today — was set in motion when a huge lobe of ice suddenly let go, releasing the waters of glacial Lake Missoula. The accumulated melt of mile-high glaciers moved west and south from a site near the present northern border between Idaho and Montana. The water pooled temporarily behind a ridge near Spokane, and then spilled onto the old lava plains of the basin. As it sped south, searching for the main stem of the Columbia River, the deluge broadened from about twenty miles to the width of Indiana. Pushing boulders the size of automobiles, it stripped away the top soil, ripped up bedrock, and carved deep canyons in the basalt plateaus. Within two to three weeks it was over. Left behind on the flat tablelands and between the rolling hills were solitary giant boulders, extensive gravel bars, and a scabland of canyons or coulees that would later perplex settlers and scientists alike.

Since the glaciers last receded from the northern tier of the future state of Washington, the mightiest river in western North America, the Columbia, has seldom escaped its banks — except at its mouth. According to evidence found below Grand Coulee near Nespelem, the river has overflowed only fifteen times in the past 1,900 years. However, when the Columbia slipped from its bed, it made up in volume for what it lacked in frequency. The first well-documented, massive flood released from the Columbia and its tributaries was the flood of 1894.

Flood of 1894

"Not only have thousands of dollars worth of property been destroyed and many lives lost, but business is practically at a standstill, owing to the communication with the east being shut off." Harry Chadwick, publisher of the weekly magazine *Argus* and spokesman for Seattle's business community, was incredulous that at this late date, the booming metropolis on Puget Sound could be cut from the rest of the world. "One of the most serious inconveniences," he fumed, that "might almost be called a disaster, is the non-arrival of the United States mails." While Chadwick and Seattle businessmen twiddled their thumbs during their unexpected vacation, others in the state also played a waiting game — but in much less comfortable circumstances.

The June flood of 1894 was the largest flood on the Columbia River since records were first kept in 1858. Fueled by snowmelt from a prolonged stretch of warm weather, it overwhelmed bottom lands along the river including the towns of Kelso, Kalama, Monticello (present-day Longview), and Vancouver, where it reached a maximum gage height of thirty-four feet, eighteen feet above the banks. A good portion of the railroad track along the lower Columbia also disappeared under the water. A correspondent for the Olympia *Washington Standard* described the owners of the flooded homes and farmlands as "quietly and patiently waiting for the waters to recede." There was little else they could do.

Above: Dry Falls Lookout. Photo by Hugh Paradise. Below: Scene from 1894 flood on the Columbia River near Vancouver. Courtesy, Ted Van Arsdol.

Years later during the depression of the 1930s, Mrs. Clara Davolt recalled how her father, having experienced the flood that swept away Monticello in 1867, built his house four feet above the high water mark of that year. But in 1894 the water "ran in through the windows." Luckily, the water rose slowly enough that most of the Cowlitz farmers could save their livestock and move their belongings upstairs in time. Another pioneer remembered the water was so deep in Kalama that the ferry sailed right up Main Street. In Kelso, where water was fifteen feet deep on Cedar Street, "people lived in their upstairs rooms and went back and forth by boat." The deluge that swept away crops, topsoil, trees, and buildings finally receded after five weeks.

Pioneer Flood Control

Far less spectacular than the Columbia's flooding but much more common were the seasonal overflows of other Washington streams. Before Euro-American settlers rolled into western Washington in the mid-nineteenth century, the lowland reaches of the larger rivers were an army engineer's nightmare — a bewildering maze of sloughs and multiple channels that were usually choked with snags or wholly blocked by log jams. When winter rainstorms or sudden spring snowmelt descended, the rivers swelled as they had for eons, escaping their beds and streaming across their

Above: Dike on the Cowlitz River at the Toutle River Bar, Aug. 20, 1892. Courtesy, National Archives, Alaska-Pacific NW Region, Seattle. Below: Early work on dikes (below) and drains (bottom) on the Skagit River flood plain. Courtesy, Skagit County Historical Museum.

floodplains for weeks, sometimes months, at a time. First order of business for newly arrived homesteaders was to take up their axes and saws and break up the jams to clear the main channels. Since the only practical means of getting crops to market was by boat, a clear waterway was as important for transportation as for curbing the destructive overflows.

SKAGIT SCOURGE

The Skagit is among the largest rivers on the Pacific slope and the second largest in Washington. Today its broad fertile delta, continually replenished by the river, comfortably spreads out more than twenty miles inland from Puget Sound. Beyond the delta narrow strips of arable bottom land flank the river along most of its winding fifty-mile course from Sedro Woolley to Marblemount. Holland-like with its low, flat profile, and fields of spring tulips, the delta has a long history of frequent and sometimes catastrophic flooding.

A tangle of trees, either undermined by the river or cut down by loggers and settlers, blocked the Skagit River in the late nineteenth century. Some of the jams were so old that full-sized trees grew on top of them. One of the largest, at Mt. Vernon, was three miles long and up to thirty feet high. Whether natural and or manmade, the debris dams gave the already flood-prone river even more opportunity to gambol unimpeded across the land during the annual spring and winter freshets. In the late 1860s pioneer valley farmers began building their first line of defense — earth dikes designed to restrain the waters both of the river and Skagit Bay. By the mid-1870s some areas, such as the Swinomish tidelands, were already producing sizable crop yields. But reclaiming the rich delta soils of the tideflats was a high-risk game. Farms on the delta and natural overflow plains remained at the mercy of the next unusually high tide, heavy downpour, and rapid mountain snowmelt. When they could not be restrained, the floodwaters sent lowland farmers fleeing for high ground with their livestock in tow. Residents of communities like Conway, who had witnessed one deluge too many, built the first floor of their homes high above the ground and stayed to ride it out.

Skagit settlers appealed repeatedly to the federal government for help. In the early 1880s, the U.S. Army Corps of Engineers was authorized to build one "snag-boat, well equipped" to clean out all the rivers flowing into Puget Sound. Congress finally appropriated $20,000, enough to build the sternwheeler Skagit but not enough to operate it regularly. (See Waterways Chapter.) At any rate, the Skagit's master was concerned primarily with clearing passage for

steamers in the boat's namesake river. Farmers were still left with the responsibility of holding back tidal and fresh waters alike.

Dikes and ditches were the obvious solution. Saltwater dikes were sheer drudgery to build. Because the tidelands were too soggy to use horses, farmers pushed wheelbarrows filled with mud, balanced on narrow planks across the tideland ponds. Along the river banks they used two-horse teams pulling scrapers, making the work easier and much faster. Drainage ditches were dug the old-fashioned way with shovels, strong backs, and help from the neighbors. In the Olympia Marsh Drainage District, farmers built submerged drainage ditches which they edged with cedar timbers well below the surface and then covered with cedar puncheons. The soil was then graded and planted over the top of the cedar planks. (In 1977 Skagit farmers began installing plastic tile and polyester tubing to drain their flat fields. The expense was great but the process was mostly automatic. Tile machines, manned by professional operators and sometimes guided by laser beams, installed up to 3,500 feet of drain in a day. The machines dug the ditches and laid the plastic tubing all in one operation.)

Valley farmers downstream experienced the greatest danger when high spring tides backed up flood water at the river's mouth. Even if the tides were successfully diked out, the land behind the dikes still had to be drained. Working cooperatively, neighboring farmers turned the river's smaller sloughs into drainage ditches which they dammed at the dike line to keep out the saltwater. The ditches were equipped with sluice boxes for letting the water drain

out when the tide was low. The system worked well under normal precipitation and runoff conditions, but it was useless when the water rose rapidly behind the dikes, as it did during a number of freshets in the early 1890s. The only alternative then was to break the dike and allow a large area to be flooded with saltwater.

Flood damage is calculated only for its effect on developed land, and it was not until a flood in 1880 that farmland along the Skagit had been developed enough to make flood losses significant. Cultivated land lay underwater for over a month or longer. Two years later the hapless dairy and crop farmers were hit again in a great summer flood that broke through dikes, damaged and destroyed homes, barns, and businesses, and submerged 2,500 planted acres. It was more than pioneer resignation could take. Attempting to find a permanent solution, local leaders organized public meetings and formed a committee, which determined that about $10,000 was needed to repair the dikes. A public subscription drive managed to raise about a quarter of that amount, but when the committee members could not agree about how and in what order the dikes should be rebuilt, the effort was abandoned. Some of the damage from these two floods was still evident twenty years later.

Despite the frequent inundations, the rich Skagit bottom lands continued to lure new homesteaders. In 1884 the federal Department of Agriculture calculated that in the Skagit River Valley 32,000 acres had been cultivated and were protected by about 150 miles of dike built by local residents. To help the farmers' drainage and diking efforts, the Skagit County Commissioners in 1888 voted to sponsor diking districts under the law passed by the territorial legislature that year. Several diking districts, formed voluntarily by groups of farmers from Sedro Woolley to the river's mouth, were approved by the county in the 1890s. The county raised and administered tax money to fund the dikes and ditches while farmers performed much of the work. By the turn of the century, the county was maintaining about 75 percent of the valley's small dikes and drainage ditches.

Above: Snohomish River flooding in 1909 at Snohomish. Courtesy Snohomish County Historical Society.
Below: Flood of 1909 at Edison on the Skagit River flood plain.

The county could help diking and drainage districts raise money, but it did not exercise regulatory controls or establish an overall development plan for the valley. County commissioners had enough trouble just getting district boundaries straight. Each district located its dikes as it saw fit and built them at whatever slope and height seemed right. Often the levees were built too close to the river, the sides were too steep, and the cross section too narrow to restrain the bigger floods.

Dikes also failed because of boils — channels that formed underneath them, often caused by muskrat burrows or by porous gravel and rotting logs buried below the surface. Even the more stable levees created hazards. Each levee that prevented the river from flowing onto its natural floodplains caused it to rise and put even more pressure on banks and dikes downstream. A habit of competitive diking ensued, in which farmers tried to build as strong a dike as possible so that the river would break through on someone else's land. By 1894 the river was substantially diked, in fact, over-diked from its mouth to points beyond Sedro Woolley. Yet when the big floods came, like the one that June, frustrated farmers sent enraged letters to the army engineers, blaming the logging boom companies whose stockpiles blocked the river.

When heavy rains brought expectations of a river overflow,

Above: WPA work on Drainage District #8, looking south from the north end of the dike, near Bayview, March 25, 1936. Right: WPA Drainage District #14, looking west along north spur of the Olympic Marsh ditch from the Pacific Highway crossing, March 26, 1936. Courtesy, National Archives, Alaska-Pacific NW Region.

farmers armed with shovels and old oat sacks filled with earth took turns patrolling the dikes twenty-four hours a day. Wives and children also helped, carrying messages and watching for weak spots in the levees. As long as the water in the river remained high but below the top of the dike, the dike watchers knew they were safe. A sudden drop in the water level meant that somewhere above them a dike had been breached, and that meant a quick retreat back home to see if the water was coming their way. Buildings caught in the direct path of the torrent could be swept off their foundations, or could fall into a hole dug by the current eddying around them. Such was the fate of the Nat Moore family home when the dike between Mount Vernon and Avon broke during the flood of 1909. In the middle of the night Moore and his four children barely escaped in a rowboat that was swept along in the raging current. The Moores were not the only family set adrift. After dikes broke in several places, the 1909 flood put most of the Skagit delta underwater all the way to La Conner.

Miraculously, no lives were lost in the Skagit Valley floods of the late nineteenth and early twentieth centuries. But the loss of stock and topsoil and the clean-up necessary to remove sediment and debris were disastrous for individual farmers.

UNCLE SAM'S RELUCTANT ROLE

It was not so much the spirit of pioneer independence that left flood victims to their own devices as it was the government's unwillingness to assume responsibility for flood control. In 1824 the Supreme Court ruled that the Constitution allowed the federal government to make river improvements for navigation purposes. But for many years Congress resisted the notion of implied powers that could have permitted federal assistance to states and afflicted localities for repair and reduction of flood damage. Not until 1917 did Congress pass the first federal flood control act in which the government accepted some responsibility for reducing damage in the lower Mississippi and the Sacramento river basins. And not until 1927 was the Army Corps of Engineers directed to make comprehensive surveys of the nation's principal streams where multipurpose projects providing navigation, power production, irrigation, and flood control might be feasible. Their first report, produced in 1931, recommended ten multipurpose dams on the main stem of the Columbia River. Despite the government's multipurpose commitment, flood control was not a primary consideration in the anticipated design and operation of these

dams. For, unlike power production and irrigation, flood control would not produce revenues for Uncle Sam. Also lacking was the backing of a powerful government agency. At any rate, dams on the Columbia offered no solution to the chronic overflows occurring on the streams in western Washington.

In fact, about 100 years elapsed from the time Henry Clay and John C. Calhoun made the first appeals for federally assisted flood protection until Congress passed the first comprehensive nationwide flood control legislation. A series of devastating floods in the 1930s and the New Deal work relief programs helped to change congressional and public attitudes about the government's role in flood protection. In the 1936 Flood Control Act, Congress for the first time asserted that flood control on all navigable streams and their tributaries was a federal responsibility in the interest of the general welfare. Constitutional questions were put aside by linking flood damage to the commerce clause — floods impaired navigable rivers, highways, and railroads, the channels of commerce between the states.

The government pledged to pay most of the costs and to work cooperatively with states and local governments in a two-pronged attack on flood problems. The Army Corps of Engineers was charged with designing and building structures downstream such as reservoirs, levees, and channel improvements. The Department of Agriculture was directed to develop land treatment programs that would reduce erosion and runoff originating in upstream watersheds. Participating local governments were required to provide land, easements, and rights-of-way, and maintain the works furnished by the government. The government's terms were generous, particularly after the Flood Control Act of 1938 reduced cost-sharing for local sponsors of channel improvements and reservoirs to nothing.

STATE DIKING AND DRAINAGE DISTRICTS

At the same time that they passed legislation supporting irrigation districts, state lawmakers in 1895 established diking and drainage districts. Like the irrigation districts, these organizations could be formed when a majority of local inhabitants petitioned for one. If approved, they became public institutions that could sell bonds and levy assessments to raise funds for construction and maintenance. Modifications in establishment procedures brought about diking and drainage improvement districts in 1913 and 1917. Along with the state's flood control districts, established later, the drainage and diking districts encompassed both private and public property and became the most important institutions in the state for dealing with local flooding. Most of the original districts were established west of the Cascades, along Puget Sound and the Columbia River in southwestern Washington. East of the mountains, they were formed mostly along the Colville and Pend Oreille rivers.

The decade of agricultural depression that followed World War I was not the best time to prove the potential of the new institutions. In the 1920s the state's reclamation division worked with county commissioners and engineers to help drainage and diking districts get organized, prepare plans, and build their projects. In Cowlitz County a diking improvement district received state planning and financial assistance to build a dike and pumping plant. The project was designed to protect 850 acres several miles west of Kelso against all except the most extraordinary Columbia River floods. The state helped a Grays Harbor district drain and dike 730 acres, the first large-scale attempt to drain the marshlands of Washington's southwest coast. By the middle of the decade, most drainage and diking districts were struggling to keep their heads above a rising tide of debt. Some had to be granted extensions on their state bond payments in order to avoid foreclosure after landowners failed to pay their assessments. Other districts, considered poor risks, were refused state reclamation funds altogether. It was a time of retrenchment when state reclamation funds were meted out sparingly to rehabilitate only those projects most likely to reach the high ground of financial solvency.

During the Great Depression, the diking and drainage districts were again preoccupied with staying fiscally afloat as they tried to pay loans for improvements built during more prosperous times. Landowners faced with assessment foreclosures barely avoided eviction when the districts were rescued by state emergency relief grants and refinancing loans from the federal Reconstruction Finance Corporation. Before the federal government began sponsoring the public works relief programs, the counties had had little to do with flood damage control and rural drainage. In the late territorial period, a few, like Skagit County, had begun to assume varying degrees of responsibility to open up and safeguard agricultural land. But nearly half a century later, in the late 1930s, state officials were still complaining that too few counties had a permanent program or a fund specifically dedicated to flood control.

Right: Collapse of the trestle on the electric "third rail" Seattle-Tacoma Interurban Railway by the 1906 Green River Flood. Courtesy, Lawton Gowey.

STUCK WITH THE WHITE

Farmers who settled along the White River in the late 1800s had little love for the river named for the glacial "flour" that gave it a milky color. Between the annual periods of heavy winter rain and springtime snowmelt, it could be counted on for at least two peak flows. Worse yet, the force of its current moving through a deep mountain canyon swept up tons of driftwood, gravel, and boulders that eventually jammed and blocked the channel, forcing the river to excavate new channels and making levees and other protective works practically useless.

During most of the nineteenth century and earlier, the main stem of the White River flowed northward to Elliott Bay in the channel of what is today called the Green River, which becomes the Duwamish River about twelve miles short of the bay. After each of the White's escapades, King County paid dearly for flood damage repairs to roads and bridges, only to have them once again destroyed or damaged. Lowland farmers and ranchers in the vicinity of Auburn, Kent, and Renton could do little but sullenly stand by and watch the floodwaters ruin their crops and drown their livestock.

For most of its course to Elliott Bay, the historical White River flowed to the north, except where it briefly looped to the south around the north end of Lake Tapps. Along this southerly meander the White River was paralleled by the Stuck River, a nine-mile-long tributary of the Puyallup River. For two miles the Stuck and the White ran within a quarter mile of one another, and at one point were separated by only a strip of earth about 200 feet wide. Beginning in the late 1870s the flood-fearing farmers of King County's White River Valley contrived an expedient solution to their overflow problems. Piling rocks, logs, and earth across the White River, they redirected flood waters down the Stuck River into the Puyallup Valley.

Enraged Pierce County residents who suffered the effects of these manmade diversions retaliated in kind, and throughout the 1880s and 1890s the White River channel was shifted back and forth. In one instance, Pierce County farmers dynamited a huge cliff above the rivers, hoping to force the waters of the Stuck into the White. But when the hillside came down, it partially blocked the White and thereby doubled the size of the Stuck. In 1899 when

Early 1915 scenes showing work on the county line cut-off of the Stuck-White River system. Courtesy National Archives, Alaska-Pacific NW Region.

the Stuck, without any human assistance, threatened to break through the slim earth barrier to the White, Pierce County farmers were jubilant. However, their King County counterparts, assisted by county commissioners, promptly set about building an embankment to stop it. Still smarting from the bluff-blasting fiasco, Pierce County then took King County to court, where King County officials claimed that they were only trying to prevent the Stuck from cutting across into the White. But "Pierce County placed a different interpretation on the proceeding," according to a government report, for the King County engineers, to obtain material for the dike, had dug a trench across the narrow strip.

Each county then produced a formidable array of evidence from engineers and old settlers to prove that the natural route of the White River to Puget Sound had always been through the territory of the other county. Any work that was done near the point of separation, they testified, had been only for the purpose of preventing the other county from interfering with natural conditions. The King County witnesses were apparently more convincing for the court ruled that King County was rightfully protecting property within its borders.

Court decisions could do nothing to restrain the whims of nature, however. In mid-November 1906, a combination of warm Chinook winds and heavy rain sent the snow-fed streams on both

Early flood control mattress at the Stuck-White River juncture. Courtesy, Tacoma Public Library.

sides of the Cascades surging in one of the most devastating floods the state had yet experienced. At peak stage the waters stood eight to twenty feet deep in the towns of the Green, White, Duwamish, and Puyallup river valleys. Lake Washington rose five inches in sixteen hours. Part of the flume that supplied water to the dynamos of the Seattle Electric Company's plant at Electron was knocked out, cutting out a crucial source of power to Seattle and Tacoma. Both cities, according to newspaper headlines, were "cut off from the world" as power, telephone, and telegraph lines were downed and roads, railroad tracks, and bridges were torn apart by the torrent. Several people clinging to logs and remnants of buildings were swept away to their deaths. At least fifty square miles, or 32,000 acres, were affected by the floodwaters in the area between Seattle and Tacoma.

Then, more suddenly than they rose, the Green, White and Duwamish rivers receded — in some places at the rate of four feet in an hour. It was several days before valley residents learned what had happened. The flood had torn through the Puyallup Valley, taking with it a shingle mill, a new steel railroad bridge, homes, barns, and a number of wooden bridges. When King County Sheriff Lou Smith went to investigate, he found that an accumu-

lation of trees, gravel, and other debris had blocked the White River and forced it to cut across the isthmus separating it from the Stuck River. The White had almost run dry while the Stuck, carrying nearly the entire volume of the White, had increased to five times its normal size, spreading out nearly 600 feet wide across the valley farms. The sheriff, a former King County commissioner, happily announced to a *Seattle Times* reporter that "today, King County is assured that practically the last dollar has been spent on rebuilding operations growing out of floods in the Duwamish, the Green and the White River Valleys.... The Lake Washington Canal, new county bridges, improved roads for miles and miles of territory in King County are problems that have been answered in a day by the conversion of the White River into the Stuck River."

The *Times* was not so sanguine the next day when it warned in a four-inch headline of possible "BLOODSHED!" if the "stern-faced, determined ranchers" from the Puyallup Valley carried out their plans to dynamite the mile-long jam. Convinced that if they got the flood-stage river back it would wipe out at least five county bridges, King County officials posted guards in the area and rushed to get a Superior Court injunction to stop the stockmen. Pierce County immediately began litigation to restore the rivers to their former channels. But Seattle and Tacoma civic leaders and county officials as well as representatives of several hundred property owners met together to find a better solution. After they appealed to the Seattle District Corps of Engineers for help, District Chief Engineer Major Hiram M. Chittenden agreed to head a group of engineers and surveyors to investigate the problem.

In 1907 Chittenden and the consultants concluded that "nature has transferred the course [of the White River] and it will be simpler to perpetuate it than to change it again." Nature's action had conveniently conformed with the engineers' penchant for efficiency, for the White River's new route to the Sound was now half as long as the old one through the Duwamish Valley. However, Pierce County had to be compensated for the greater expense and risk it now had to bear. The commission proposed that King County pay at least half of the costs of flood relief in the Stuck and Puyallup valleys.

Acting on these recommendations, the two counties overcame old animosities and by 1913 developed an intercounty agreement for a cooperative ninety-nine-year program of flood control. Pierce County would keep the troublesome White River if King County paid 60 percent of the total cost of improvements and maintenance on the former Stuck River and on a portion of

the Puyallup. In the first two years following their agreement, the two counties, with state financial help, together erected a 1,600-foot-long diversion dam, called the Auburn Wall, at the point where the White River used to flow north to join and continue with the Green to their Duwamish outlet. (The dam still functions and appears to be in good condition.) They also built a 2,000-foot drift barrier, bank revetments, and dikes, and dredged, straightened, and cleared the Stuck's channel of 35,000 cords of wood. Since that time the surface water agencies of the two counties have continued to operate and update their unusual intercounty agreement.

After floods in 1917 and 1933 destroyed most of these improvements, the counties persuaded the Army Corps of Engineers to build a flood retention dam upstream, hoping it would finally solve their problems. However, in order to win government approval, the Mud Mountain Dam (see below) had to be designed and operated primarily for the protection of the more heavily populated area of Tacoma and for navigation improvement on the lower Puyallup River. Consequently, parts of the White and old Stuck river valleys downstream from the dam were not protected against flooding in 1955, 1964, 1975, 1977, 1990, and 1995 when water in the Mud Mountain reservoir became dangerously high. In order to protect the Puyallup Valley, the dam operators released large flows, inundating parts of the White River Valley upstream.

THE WPA AND THE FLOOD OF 1933

The heavy rains and accelerated snowmelt that sent rivers roiling in the winter of 1933 caught Washington residents, local governments, and the state unprepared for the kind of damage that could occur when greater numbers of people lived and worked on river floodplains. In western Washington floodwaters inundated whole towns and marooned others as roads, highways, bridges, and railroad tracks were washed away. Thousands of livestock drowned, hundreds of people were left temporarily homeless, and many thousands of acres disappeared underwater. Several people drowned or were crushed by heavy slides. A United Airlines transport pilot, flying north from Portland on December 23, 1933, described western Washington as "almost one inland sea from Portland to Seattle." At least half of the estimated $7 million in losses were sustained in Cowlitz County and the other eight southwest counties.

The December flood also caused major damage in eastern Washington. Except for the flood of 1906, it was the largest on record in the Yakima River basin. About 700 acres were submerged in the Mud Lake area on the Yakima Indian Reservation, and over 400 feet of both the Sunset Highway and the Northern Pacific tracks were washed out when the Teanaway River, which joins the Yakima five miles east of Cle Elum, overflowed. Basements and first floors in Ellensburg, Yakima, Wapato, Toppenish, and Thorp were flooded after levees failed. All told, about 45,000 acres of developed and undeveloped land, more than half in the Wapato-Toppenish area, were inundated in the basin, and two lives were lost.

The 1933 flood was something of an antidote to the old condition of everyone wanting flood protection but nobody willing to pay for it. It caused Washingtonians, more than ever before, to look to the government for a permanent solution. Up and down the coast, flood victims spent the Christmas holidays consulting with engineers, attending meetings, adopting resolutions, and sending telegrams to President Franklin D. Roosevelt. In some cases, these newly galvanized public works activists invoked an old American tradition of protest, calling their gatherings "indignation meetings" because of the army engineers' rejection of projects they had requested just a year or two earlier. The Corps, insisting that they had stuck to regulations, replied that the landowners' applications had been turned down because the state had not yet completed the necessary stream surveys and flood damage reports. In eastern Washington representatives from Benton, Yakima, Walla Walla, and Kittitas counties requested the

Top: Flood of 1933 at Kelso on the Cowlitz River. Courtesy National Archives, Alaska-Pacific NW Region. Below left: Effects of the 1933 flood on the Yakima River. Right: WPA rock mattresse on the Yakima River. Courtesy, National Archive Alaska-Pacific NW Region.

All photos are examples of Depression-time flood control on Washington rivers. *Left:* Wheelbarrow line on the Cowlitz River.

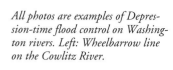

NN 293 to NN 340 W.P.A. and flood control
work on Cowlitz Lewis & Coweeman Rivers
Cowlitz County Wash.

NN 316	Hauling rock	4-24-36
NN 317	Loading barge	3-10-36
NN 318	Steam shovel at quary loading trucks with rocks for dikes.	
NN 319	Bank Protection.	1-17-36
NN-320	Unloading barge	1-13-36
NN 321	Rock after being unloaded	1-13-36
NN 322	Digging out stumps & removing logs	12-26-35
NN 323	Cutting brush before grading	12-26-35
NN 324	Removing old machinery from pump house for new	8-13-36
NN 325	Finishing dike along Col. River	6-30-36
NN 326	Driving Piling	6-7-36
NN 327	Dredge	6-30-36
NN 328	Finished dike looking up Lewis River	

Left: Cowlitz River rock barge. *Above:* Work list for WPA projects on the Cowlitz River. Courtesy, National Archives, Alaska-Pacific NW Region, Seattle.

Right: Concrete matress on the Stillaquamish River.
Far right: Protection mat on an unidentified state river. *Below:* Erosion protection mat on the Nooksack River.

Left: Part of 3,600-foot drift cable on the Puyallup River 1.5 miles south of Orting. Courtesy, National Archives, Alaska-Pacific NW Region, Seattle.

Top: Brush reventmment on the Skagit River at Lyman. Above: Folcrum device for tightening mat and wires, Skagit River. Courtesy, National Archives, Alaska-Pacific NW Region, Seattle.

Above: W.E.R.A. project on Inglewood Hill; work on overflow ditches and laterals at Holstein's Ranch. Courtesy, WA State Archives. Right: A partial listing of WPA flood relief projects for which photographic records were made. Courtesy, National Archives, Alaska-Pacific NW Region, Seattle.

W.P.A. FLOOD RELIEF PROJECTS NEGATIVE INDEX

O.P.No.	S.D.No.	STREAM
65-93-893	45	Nooksack.
894	81	Samish.
895	46	Skagit. - Burlington to Hamilton.
896	80	Skagit. - Hamilton to Marblemount & Delta.
897	57	Stillaguamish. - Stanwood to Arlington.
898	55	Stillaguamish. - North and South Forks.
899	59	Pilchuck.
900	58	Snohomish - Snoqualmie. Snohomish Co.
901	61	Skykomish. - Snohomish Co.
902	60	Sauk. - Snohomish Co.
903	82	Quinault, Humptulips Wynoochee, Satsop, Cloquallum & Ocosta.
905	99	Chehalis. Grays Harbor Co.
906	8	Bowley, Morse, Lees, Ennis Whites, Little, Valley & Peabody.
907	27	Quillayute, Dickey, Sol Duc, Bogachiel & Lake.
908	5	Jimmy-Come-Lately, Dungeness, Siebert & McDonald.
909	68	Hoh - Clearwater - Queets.
910	47	Docewallips, Big & Little Quilcene, Chimacum, Duckabush & Snow.
911	62	Snoqualmie - King Co.
912	66	Skykomish - King Co.
913	64	Cedar.
914	63	Green.
915	44	Skokomish.
916	101	Goldsborough - Coffee.
917	73	Puyallup - Carbon.
918	1	White, Stuck - Puyallup.
919	76	Des Chutes.
920	74	Yelm.
922	102	Chehalis. - Thurston Co.
923	75	Skookumchuck.
1949		South Aberdeen.
2100		Hott Slough.
	126	Nooksack
	128	Stillaguamish
	129	Skykomish
	138	Yakima

8 M for Miscell.

Corps do a survey of flood damage along the Yakima and Walla Walla rivers.

State and county administrators did all they could to help, even though the flood had struck a state drained of even the most basic operating funds. Although flood relief and control was beyond its ordinary scope, the Washington Emergency Relief Administration (WERA) distributed almost $1.5 million to the affected western Washington counties to help them rebuild dikes, revetments, and other damaged protective works. By this time the state's revolving reclamation fund was nearly broke. Finally, it was the Roosevelt administration's work relief programs, the Civil Works Administration (CWA), and the Works Progress Administration (WPA) that most helped communities like Castle Rock, Kelso, and Woodland with funds and labor to rehabilitate damaged parks, roads, and homes.

Municipalities and diking and drainage districts who needed emergency repairs applied for help to the state's WPA administrator, Don G. Abel. Those that Abel, and ultimately the president, approved were fully funded by the federal government. Since the primary purpose of the program was to give work to men on the relief rolls, WPA flood control projects required neither congressional approval nor did they have to meet the strict economic justification standard (benefit-cost ratio) normally prescribed for Army Corps work. The Corps, however, was put in charge of the projects which, according to a Seattle district chief engineer, were "not of such magnitude or nature as to have adverse effects on life or property in case of failure."

The army engineers requisitioned materials and supervised the workers who labored on the river channels performing snagging operations, building bank revetments and drift barriers, and rebuilding earth dikes. WPA workers, housed in camps at Longview and Woodland, substantially raised and reinforced dikes along the Lewis and Cowlitz rivers, including the destroyed low-level dike surrounding the town of Castle Rock. The latter had been built after the 1906 flood. They also dredged the channels and installed new pumping plants.

Uncle Sam's largess was a boon to the fledgling flood control programs of Washington counties. By 1938 the cost of WPA projects in twenty-one counties on rivers such as the Cowlitz, Chehalis, Puyallup, Snohomish, Stillaguamish, Skagit, and Nooksack, as well as several smaller streams, totaled over $5 million, of which local governments contributed $700,000. It was the most money ever spent on flood damage and protective works in the state's history — as much as the state reclamation fund had loaned to all the state's irrigation, diking, and drainage districts since its inception in 1919.

STATE FLOOD CONTROL LEGISLATION

The federal government's depression-era response was impressive, especially for a public work that it had until then largely avoided. But, as local officials ruefully realized, the money had been spent on flood "relief," not flood "control." There was no permanent nor comprehensive state program to help vulnerable localities protect themselves against these intermittent but inevitable catastrophes. A year and a half after Washington experienced its most costly flood ever, the legislature formally recognized the inadequacy of the state's piecemeal flood control programs. In 1935, to encourage more communities to build flood control works, the lawmakers passed the Flood Control District Act which allowed citizens to form districts having the same kinds of powers as drainage and diking districts. That way the flood-affected could vote to form districts with the power to build permanent flood control works paid for by their assessments and by federal and state aid. By 1936 four flood control districts had been established in the state, just in time to take advantage of WPA funds.

A second part of the 1935 legislation obligated the state to alleviate recurring flood damage caused by structures encroaching on the river channel. The Flood Control Zone Act authorized the state flood control supervisor to designate zones along the state's rivers in which all construction would be regulated. No flood control improvements or any other structures — whether bridges, culverts, channel alterations, bank protection, or dams — were to be built in these designated areas without state approval. The goal of the zone act was to keep channel constrictions, caused by construction adjacent to the river channel that raised the upstream water level, to a minimum. It also provided a way to oversee design and construction standards and coordinate local measures so that works built to protect one area would not increase the likelihood of flooding in another.

The first flood control zones were established on the rivers hardest hit by the 1933 flood. All but two of the sixteen zones were located on the west side of the Cascades. Most

A bank of the Snohomish River before and after its strengthening with a WPA improvement. Courtesy, National Archives, Alaska-Pacific NW Region.

of the permits issued for work in these zones between 1935 and 1966 went to the counties or state highway department for bridges, dikes, and bank reinforcement. In 1958 Washington was one of only seven states in the country that enforced this kind of regulation. However progressive for its time, the flood control

zone law had significant limitations. To avoid costly basin surveys, the zone boundaries followed government section and subdivision lines and, consequently, included land that might never be subject to flooding. The law, as administered, was concerned only with structures that might impede the passage of floodwaters in the main channel. Development in the floodplains was not at issue. Regulations were weakly enforced, and many unauthorized works were built by people who were unaware of or ignored the law. For thirty years no more zones were added, even though additional river basins experienced major floods.

In 1970 when the Department of Ecology was established, the state began to enforce the law more aggressively. Subsequently, a zone proposed for Asotin Creek drew stiff opposition. Five years before, floodwaters had washed out Asotin's water system and roads, requiring a quarter million dollars of federal emergency disaster funds for rehabilitation. Despite their recent experience, Asotin property owners protested that the flood zone law infringed on their private property rights. Like many others before and since, Asotins were willing to accept government responsibility and assistance for repairing flood damage but not governmental management of floodways and shorelines that might affect their property and buildings.

While the understaffed state flood control division had a hard time enforcing regulations, it had an equally difficult task convincing local governments to take responsibility for maintaining their government-subsidized protective works. In 1938 Lars Langloe, state flood control supervisor, was pleased with the work performed under the WPA program and with the federal government's generous cost-sharing terms. However, he was not happy with the ability and willingness of local interests to bear their share of federal project costs. Most counties claimed that they did not have the tax revenue to raise even the small percentage required from local sponsors. Only a few groups had yet organized the flood control districts that made them eligible to participate in the federal programs. Langloe complained that property owners seemed to believe it was the state's responsibility to pay all or most of the local sponsor's share. At least, he scolded, county commissioners should try to maintain their protective structures such as the many bank revetments built by the WPA, especially since bank erosion was the major cause of flood damage in rural areas.

However, no amount of pressure from state or federal officials could shake the lingering depression, and as the national economy went into a second slump at the end of the decade, counties and flood-prone residents could find few reserves in their squeezed accounts. In 1939 the Puget Sound Flood Control Council, a group repre-

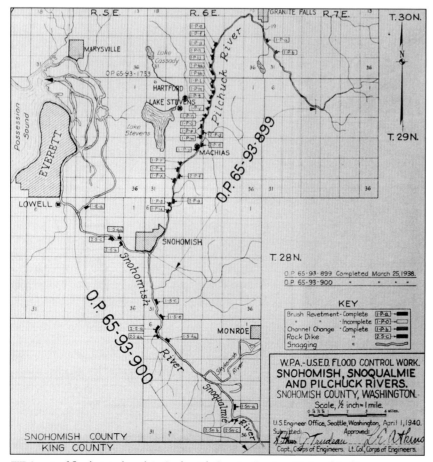

WPA map of flood control work in Snohomish County. Courtesy, National Archives.

senting Puget Sound counties, the University of Washington, and the state, recommended to the legislature that the state take even more of a lead by allocating funds and formulating a policy for maintaining local flood control works. In 1941 legislators followed the council's advice and approved a state flood control maintenance program intended to encourage localities to practice self-help. Under the law counties, municipalities, and soil conservation, diking, drainage, and flood control districts could receive from the state up to 50 percent of the cost of local maintenance and improvement projects. Although slow to get started, it eventually became a popular program. By 1960 the legislature's regular appropriations had assisted over 1,300 mostly county projects.

STRUCTURAL SOLUTIONS AND THE ARMY CORPS

Whether good engineering or good political largesse, Congress originally determined that structural flood control works were the best way to prevent flood damage. Dredging harbors, channeling rivers, building dams and creating reservoirs were the methods it explicitly directed the Army Corps of Engineers to use under the first national flood control acts. The 1938 Flood Control Act even relieved local beneficiaries of reservoir projects of any cost-sharing responsibility, thus largely explaining why dams became a common and popular solution in the Corps' early flood control program.

Mud Mountain Dam and the Puyallup River Channel

Although Pierce and King counties had had difficulty agreeing on joint management of the White River (see above), they could agree that an upstream retention dam — especially one paid for by federal tax dollars — would solve most of their problems. After the winter flood of 1933 wiped out much of their flood control works on the White River and inundated industrial sites in Tacoma where the lower Puyallup River ran unhindered, the counties joined with the City of Tacoma in appealing to the Seattle District of the Army Engineers. Their plea was answered when the Mud Mountain Dam was approved by Congress in the 1936 flood control act. It became the state's first large project scheduled to be built specifically for flood control. The Army's plan called for a retention dam and reservoir twenty-eight miles above the Puyallup River mouth, and a flood channel on the lower river where it passes through Tacoma.

Work began on the dam, named after the prominent hill nearby, in 1940. During the erection of what turned out to be one of the world's highest earth and rockfill dams (425 feet above bedrock), the engineers overcame an unusual problem. Normally in earthfill dams, water must be added in precise amounts to obtain an optimum compaction of the clay core material. At the Mud Mountain site, because of an extremely wet season, the earth was already too wet. The contractor, the Guy F. Atkinson Company, solved the problem by drying the clay in a rotary kiln, then remoistening it to the desired consistency before placing it in the core. To prevent the core from becoming oversaturated by rain, the contractor erected an enormous canvas cover over it. Held in place by an intricate maze of cables, it resembled a huge circus tent.

This technical novelty, however, turned out to be one of the few coups for the Corps on the project. Two major design changes and the cutoff of funding during World War II put construction several years behind schedule and increased costs by four times, causing even the army engineers to question the project's economic viability. Originally claimed to be an oversight and then acknowledged as a deliberate omission to save money, the dam was constructed without fish passage facilities. The dam was not completed until 1948, but to the relief of White and Puyallup valley residents, the partially completed structure began holding back floodwaters during a particularly damaging storm in December 1946.

Right: The Puyallup River's 1933 flooding throughout the reclaimed Tacoma tidelands was one of the principle stimulants for the eventual regulating of the river's winding channel (middle) with fewer curves, relocated bridges and higher banks (bottom). The work on the 2.2 miles of lower Puyallup Channel was completed in 1950. Courtesy National Archives, Alaska-Pacific NW Region, Seattle.

Usually the Mud Mountain reservoir, which stores approximately 106,000 acre-feet under normal weather conditions, is kept empty, and the river flows in a manmade tunnel around the former river bottom. During flood stage the water is stored and then released through two concrete-lined tunnels, permitting a controlled discharge of 17,700 cubic feet per second. During the December 1959 flood, the area's worst since 1933, dam operators regulated the outflow at 13,000 feet per second. This held the river at the city of Puyallup at a maximum height of twenty-five feet, six feet below the 1933 record.

The second portion of the project, the lower Puyallup River Channel, took longer to get started because of the need to condemn right-of-way and move bridges and utilities in Tacoma. Snagging and bank protection on the upper Puyallup outside the city was completed much sooner with workers and funds supplied by the WPA. Tacomans made no financial contribution to the $4 million channel, which was 2.2 miles long when completed. It extended from the Eleventh Street Bridge, located about three-quarters of a mile above the river mouth, nearly to the city's eastern limits. To give the channel a capacity of 50,000 second-feet (in order to protect against floods about 50 percent greater than the maximum recorded river discharge), the Corps had to remove and reconstruct six bridges, straighten and revet the channel, and build new levees. After three years of work, the Puyallup Channel was completed in 1950.

Top: Before its channel was improved, the mouth of the Puyallup River was an industrial mess. Above and below: Two views of flood control improvements on the lower river. Courtesy National Archives, Seattle.

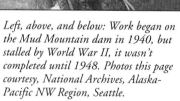

Left, above, and below: Work began on the Mud Mountain dam in 1940, but stalled by World War II, it wasn't completed until 1948. Photos this page courtesy, National Archives, Alaska-Pacific NW Region, Seattle.

Howard A. Hanson Dam

The next flood-prone stream in western Washington to be restrained by a Corps retention dam was the Green River in southern King County. From its source in the Cascade glaciers, the Green River flows west in a narrow canyon for forty miles to Auburn where the valley widens. Here the river turns north to eventually join the Duwamish River before emptying into Elliott Bay. The rich alluvial soil had made the Green River Valley by the 1870s the principal commercial farming area in King County. However, the river was a mixed blessing for the communities of Kent and Auburn and the surrounding vegetable, berry, and dairy farms. Between 1917 and 1933 sixteen floods were recorded, an average of one every year. Recurring floods also plagued the farming communities in the Duwamish River Valley. At the present site of the King County International Airport at Boeing Field, the water could reach seven feet deep.

Attempts to find a permanent solution to the flooding problem began around the turn of the century when valley settlers asked the army engineers to survey the Duwamish and Green River flood conditions. But the Corps had not yet been authorized to do work that provided only flood control, and Captain Harry Taylor of the Seattle District decided that any improvements to benefit navigation, other than occasional snag removal, would not be economically justifiable. Few boats were using the rivers of the Duwamish system when Taylor made his report to the chief of engineers in 1898, since cheaper transportation between Seattle, Puyallup, and Tacoma was supplied by the Northern Pacific Railroad. The captain disagreed with the "general impression" that dredging at the mouth of the Duwamish would allow a freer outlet for floodwaters and thus protect the rich bottom lands from overflows. Noting the settlers' uncoordinated arrangement of dikes built too low and too near the river, Taylor believed that the valley would not have adequate protection until a "complete and thorough system of dikes" was built. But that was not a "proper undertaking for the General Government."

In 1897, the year before Captain Taylor made these observations, there were about 65,000 residents in Seattle, as many as 15,000 living downtown. By 1905 when the Corps again reported on conditions along the Duwamish River, the city had soared to an estimated 150,000 residents, a population explosion that reached 237,000 five years later. As the city grew, it spread south. Businesses and manufacturers seeking more space and lower taxes moved onto the Elliott Bay tideflats as quickly as they were filled in. Farmland along the Duwamish was steadily subdivided into smaller farms and sites for warehouses, food processing factories, and iron, steel, and brick plants. Its brief slumber over, the Duwamish was once again a commercial highway.

By the late 1920s, the Green River Valley was covered with farms and food processing plants. The dredging of the river's mouth to permit deep water navigation had transformed the lower Duwamish Valley into one of the city's major industrial districts. But still the flooding continued. Finally, several Green River Valley commercial and improvement clubs resolved to do something about the problem that seemed like an ever-present rain cloud, ready to wash away their prosperity. Led by Howard A. Hanson, Seattle attorney and chairman of the rivers and harbors subcommittee of the Seattle Chamber of Commerce, the Seattle, Renton, Auburn, and Kent chambers of commerce in 1928 appealed to Congress for a flood control survey.

Howard Hanson Dam on the Green River, King County. Courtesy, Army Corps of Engineers.

This time the government agreed. The resulting reports completed by the Corps in 1933 and 1935 recognized the need for flood control in the valley, but the federal government still lacked the authority to do anything about it. They didn't have to wait long, however. In 1936 Congress passed the first flood control act and authorized the Corps to conduct a survey and prepare plans for rescuing the valley from its floods. The solution favored by local residents — the diversion of the Green River into Lake Washington or Puget Sound — was ruled out by the Corps as too expensive. Instead, the engineers proposed a dam and reservoir at Eagle Gorge, six miles above Kanasket and three miles above the city of Tacoma's water supply intake.

To help the Corps determine that the benefits from such an expensive project would equal or outweigh its costs (the favorable benefit-cost ratio required by Congress), Hanson and other project supporters went to work preparing studies focusing on the need for Seattle's industrial expansion into the upper Duwamish (Green River) Valley. But while the army engineers were making their own calculations of the dollars that would be saved by shielding valuable industrial, commercial, and agricultural property under the dam's umbrella, World War II intervened and postponed their work. Then, just as the Corps resumed its studies in 1946, a devastating flood hit the valley, causing more than $2 million in damage.

As it turned out, the timing of the deluge was fortuitous. It spurred local interests to push even harder for the dam and it supplied the Corps with up-to-date evidence of the cost of the kind of damage that would be prevented by the facilities — showing, in other words, that the dam's benefits would exceed its costs. After the state and King County pledged to contribute a total of $2 million, the proposal was approved by the Army Board of Engineers, and Congress authorized construction in May 1950. Still further delays, in part caused by the Korean conflict, deferred the start of construction until 1956. In 1958 the Eagle Gorge Dam was renamed for Hanson, who for over thirty years had led local government and civic groups in the drive to build it.

Before beginning work on the 235-foot-high, rockfill dam and the 106,000-acre-foot-capacity reservoir, the engineers had to relocate a mainline railroad and take steps to protect the Tacoma municipal water supply intake downstream. By the time the project was finished in April 1962, businesses and industries had already begun moving onto the flat farmlands of the Green River Valley. King County planners had been reluctant to rezone the farmland, coveted by developers and corporations, to commercial and industrial use because of the difficulty they anticipated providing urban services. But the valley cities, lured by the prospect of property tax revenue, were happy to oblige. Kent, Tukwila, Auburn, and Renton together annexed 14,438 acres of King County land, the majority of which was on the rich alluvial valley floor. With land prices and taxes soaring, many farmers sold out. By 1975 over 9,500 acres of prime farmland had disappeared — not under water but under a thick layer of gravel, trucked in from the surrounding hills, and sealed by a crust of asphalt and concrete. Homes and barns had been replaced by warehouses and industrial parks.

Although the Howard Hanson Dam has prevented the more disastrous floods in the valley, it has not been able to remedy the runoff and periodic ponding of water that has resulted partly from the impermeability of hard surfaces covering the soil. Water that once settled comfortably into vegetable fields has risen knee-deep and higher in poorly drained vacant lots, roadways, and parking lots. Consequently, the enlarged valley cities and King County, with the help of the U.S. Soil Conservation Service, have had to construct a network of channels to drain and pumps to lift the water over the dikes and back into the river.

Colfax Channels

While western Washington lowlanders braced themselves for floods caused by winter downpours, residents in the eastern part of the state kept an open ear for news about the spring snowmelt that could swell streams dramatically in a few hours. One of the areas hit hard by these flash floods, as well as by winter rainstorms, was the city of Colfax at the confluence of two branches of the Palouse River. On Sunday night, February 28, 1878, a sudden thaw sent ice crashing against the swollen banks and water sweeping away footbridges, a house, and a Prussian immigrant who had unwisely tried to cross the maelstrom clutching a rope. Seventy years later, again in late February, heavy rains pushed the river over and through its banks to cover downtown streets up to four-and-a-half feet deep.

The 1948 flood was the disaster that at last turned the townsfolk into flood control activists. A decade earlier, Colfax residents had persuaded the Corps to make surveys of the river as a preliminary step to a permanent solution. But by the time the project went through the usual government studies, negotiations, and reviews, the 1940s had nearly passed. The Corps ruled out a flood control or multipurpose dam as too expensive. Meanwhile, continued development on the floodplains made restudies essential and project costs multiplied. Then came the flood of 1948, and extensive modifications had to be made to augment the original plans.

The result in 1951 was a Corps proposal to build two concrete-lined, high velocity channels running through the heart of town. While the city and Whitman County agreed to jointly sponsor the project, it took until the end of the decade before Colfax residents gave up the required right-of-way and voted to raise their share of the project costs, and all the problems of putting two eighty-foot-wide channels through, around, and under existing buildings, bridges, and highways could be worked out. Construction on the main stem channel began in 1962. It was completed the next year, just in time to test its capacity in another February flood. After two years of work, the second unit along the South Fork, which passes through the business district, was finished in December 1965. By then the Colfax project had cost the federal government $5.5 million, twenty times the original estimate authorized by Congress twenty years earlier.

March 1, 1910 flood on the Palouse River running through Colfax, top, and destroying the Alder Street Bridge in Pullman and flooding the first floor of City Hall (above left).

Above: Palouse River flood waters of Feb. 3, 1963 enter the front door of the Whitman County Courthouse in Colfax. Courtesy, Colfax Gazette. *Below: Begun in 1962, the Army Corps' work on the Colfax Channels was completed in 1965. Courtesy, Army Corps of Engineers, Walla Walla District.*

Mill Creek Project

A smaller project in eastern Washington, which made it through government authorization channels with the comparative speed of a flash flood, was prompted by terrible flooding in 1931. On March 31 of that year, a sudden cloudburst over the Blue Mountains combined with melting snow runoff sent torrents of water rushing down the Walla Walla River and its tributaries. One of these, Mill Creek, flowed in a meandering channel through Walla Walla's business and residential districts. Rolling boulders, rocks, and other debris along with it, the water gnawed through the stream banks, undermining bridge approaches and building foundations. It raced down several principal business streets, scouring the roadways down to the buried water pipes and transforming them into rock-strewn creek beds. Even with the help of many trucks brought in from other towns to help haul away the tons of silt and debris, it took the city six months to clean up and make street repairs. WPA workers helped repair and improve the channel and concrete re-

Bridges throughout the state were tested by the 1933 floods. Above: In Spokane, the concrete Washington Street Bridge was inundated. Left: The reinforced banks of the Spokane River where it runs through the central business district. Courtesy, National Archives, Alaska-Pacific NW Region.

taining walls in town later in the decade, but the taming of Mill Creek would have to wait until after Congress approved a Corps project in 1938.

To deflect and hold floodwaters away from the city, the engineers in the early 1940s built a diversion structure from Mill Creek to send flows into an off-stream reservoir, Mill Creek Lake. The lake was formed by erecting a 3,200-foot-long earthfill dam across a valley. A division works, a half mile downstream, was also constructed to bypass flood flows and irrigation waters from Mill Creek into Yellowhawk and Garrison creeks. Toward the end of the decade the channel running through Walla Walla was lined, so that together the reservoir and channel could protect the city against floods equal to that of 1931, the greatest recorded on Mill Creek.

Government Channels

The benefits of these federally subsidized Corps projects to the cities of Kent, Auburn, Seattle, Tacoma, Bellingham, Colfax, and Walla Walla and their respective counties have been so considerable that one might wonder why more Washington localities did not participate in the federal flood control program.

Mill Creek also broke its banks in 1933 and ran through Walla Walla. Courtesy Walla Walla District, Army Corps of Engineers.

At least until recent years, it was not a lack of desire but rather the difficulty of getting approval from both the government and local citizens that stymied most large projects. All federally sponsored flood control projects had to pass through a series of stages, including initial authorization by Congress and the president and approval from several levels of the Corps. Each had to be "economically feasible," that is, its estimated damage reduction benefits, public and private, had to equal or exceed the estimated cost of building and maintaining it. The sponsoring locality had to meet certain conditions that involved financial contributions and/or right-of-way acquisition and other requirements within a specified time period. Clearance had to be given by a number of federal, state, and local agencies as well as by the governor. Finally Congress, concerned about a regional "sharing of the pork," had to give its approval for construction and make the necessary yearly appropriations.

According to an estimate of the Seattle District Corps in 1969, fewer than 30 percent of the navigation and flood control projects proposed to them by local interests since 1880 ever made it all the way through the political and bureaucratic obstacle course. Those that did often took not only years but decades from the time they were first proposed until they were completed. Smaller-scale projects, such as diking and revetment works, did not require so many authorizations and consequently took much less time. They were often completed within a few years.

One of the first Washington state projects to receive congressional approval, the Avon By-pass, initially proposed in 1921, never made it over the official hurdles. Intended to relieve Skagit Valley farmers of their perennial problem, the project, approved in the Flood Control Act of 1936, called for an eight-mile-long diversion channel off the Skagit River at Avon to carry floodwaters into Padilla Bay, five miles north of the river's natural outlet. Forty years later, the on-again off-again project was still making its way through institutional channels. By the late 1970s, the bypass no longer seemed to be the best solution. The Corps then proposed another plan that called for raising and strengthening existing levees and making minor river channel improvements. Yet even the vastly downgraded scheme, priced at an estimated $55 million,

Whatcom Creek channel looking upstream from the Dupont Street Bridge, Jan. 16, 1940. Courtesy National Archives, Seattle.

would have cost Skagit County residents $14 million. By a 72 percent majority in 1979, they voted down a proposition to fund the flood control facilities. The Corps then put this Skagit River improvement program, fifty years in the planning, into its inactive file. Since then, those most likely to be affected, the diking districts in the area, have had to shoulder the burden of flood prevention by upgrading their dikes. Existing reservoirs in the basin, owned and operated by Puget Sound Power and Light and Seattle City Light, have also been required to store storm waters, as much as is compatible with their power operations, to help reduce flood dangers.

WATERSHED TREATMENT

Along with the downstream structural flood control work assigned to the Corps, the 1936 flood control law directed the Department of Agriculture to develop a program for erosion and flood control in upstream watersheds, where a good proportion of damage was occurring. Even before the law was passed, the department had established erosion control demonstration projects in Pullman, Dayton, and Ellensburg. Civilian Conservation Corps (CCC) camps of 200 men worked on the projects built on farmland at nine locations so that farmers could see and study methods of protecting their land from soil erosion and also help decrease runoff, sedimentation, and downstream flooding. Edward Johnson, dean of the College of Agriculture at Washington Agricultural College (later Washington State University), became the director of the state's original experiment station at Pullman and worked aggressively to get research on soil erosion started in Washington.

In 1939 the legislature passed the Soil and Water Conservation District Law, which permitted Washingtonians to form soil and water conservation districts. Unlike irrigation, drainage, and diking districts, the soil conservation districts did not have the power to levy taxes, condemn property, or impose compulsory land-use regulations. However, working in cooperation with the federal Soil Conservation Service and the state/federal Cooperative Extension Service, they could make agreements with landowners or tenants to help them improve their land by assisting with technical advice, equipment, labor, and materials. In 1959 the state's Soil Conservation Committee proudly reported that the districts had reduced much of the former wasteful land management practices, erosion, and local flooding through such measures as strip cropping, stock ponds, terracing, grassed waterways, and drainage systems. (Although these kinds of methods could reduce runoff occurring during the average rainstorm, they lost their effectiveness after unusually heavy rainfall saturated the soil.)

By 1971 nearly the entire land area of the state, outside of incorporated municipalities, was within the boundaries of a soil and water conservation district. Originally directed toward individual land users, the districts by then were also giving assistance to local government units trying to deal with drainage and the problems associated with the transition from rural to urban land use. The Eastside Drainage Project in the Green River Valley, a system of drainage channels, pump stations, and wetland areas for which planning began in the early 1960s, was one of these directed by the federal Soil Conservation Service. Progress on both the Eastside and on the Westside project, which was started later, has since been slowed by environmental impact legislation and the reluctance of local interests to provide funding.

The scope of the watershed treatment program was greatly enlarged with the passage of the federal Watershed Protection and Flood Prevention Act of 1954. This law authorized the Agriculture Department, in cooperation with federal, state, and local agencies, to investigate, survey, and plan the coordinated development of watersheds of not over 250,000 acres. The act was intended to help local organizations plan and carry out works for flood prevention, drainage, water conservation, and fish and wildlife enhancement. In 1957 groups of farmers along Chimacum Creek near Port Townsend, along Saar Creek near Sumas, and along French and Marshland creeks near Snohomish seized on the cost-sharing opportunities offered under the federal watershed program.

MARSHLAND AND FRENCH CREEK PROJECTS

Lying on opposite sides of the Snohomish River, the Marshland and French Creek watersheds encompassed a total of 34,420 acres of floodplain on which over 9,000 people lived in 1957. Because of the frequency of floods in the area, an average of one every fourteen months between 1942 and 1955, drainage districts over the years had installed thirty-one miles of drainage ditch and five pumping plants. In the early 1950s the Marshland and French Creek Flood Control Districts were organized to build and rebuild dikes, with Snohomish County and the state's Department of Conservation and Development pitching in emergency funds for repairs. While these measures were effective in reducing and repairing damage, the lack of a comprehensive plan prevented any effective long-term improvements. Under the small watershed program, the county, state, and diking and flood control districts

Above and bottom, opposite page: Dedication of the Marshland Flood Control Dam, May 2, 1964. Courtesy, MOHAI, Seattle P-I Collection.

in the Marshland and French Creek watersheds were able to undertake a coordinated attack on the flood hazard.

The U.S. Soil Conservation Service designed and built the Marshland and French Creek systems that were intended to protect against major spring floods and minor winter storms with several miles of new and enlarged dikes and an extensive floodway. If the dikes were topped, the floodways, which terminated in massive, technologically advanced discharge structures, sent ponded floodwaters from the lowest part of the valley back to the river. The drainage system also reclaimed many acres of water-logged land, permitting a longer growing season for the valley's cash crops of peas, corn, and broccoli. However, despite the happy predictions that the projects would forever "take the meanness out of the Snohomish River," the dikes of both projects and the French Creek pumping plant were substantially damaged during a bad storm in December 1975. The plant alone required over $2 million of federal disaster relief funds to restore. The Marshland dike system broke again in two areas below the town of Snohomish when record rainfall and snowmelt engorged the river in November 1990.

EARLY FLOODPLAIN REGULATION

By the 1950s federal, state, county, and municipal governments and their subdivisions were spending more money on more flood control projects than ever before. Yet, while expenditures for flood protection grew, so did flood damages. During a twenty-three-day period in November and December of 1959, a major flood inflicted nearly as much in damage repairs in just two river basins — the Green and the Snohomish — as state and local authorities had spent on flood control maintenance statewide in the previous seventeen years. Under its 1941 maintenance law, the state could only reinforce or restore the original level of flood protection; it could not build new or improved structures. "In a manner of speaking," Greg Hastings, state flood control supervisor concluded in 1960, "our past seventeen-year maintenance program in cooperation with local authorities has netted us almost nothing." Even the $1.5 million spent on emergency repairs, mostly by the Corps but also by the counties and the state, "did not buy one dollar's worth of [added] flood protection." At that time the Corps estimated the state was suffering average annual flood damages of over $4 million. With the exception of the benefits derived from the few large Corps projects, Hastings seriously questioned the wisdom of the "maintain and hold" program that would inevitably result in increasing flood loss as the population and the value of property rose.

In order to shift from a limited skirmish to total warfare against flood damages, Hastings called for a comprehensive program in which the state would develop long-range plans for each river basin and enforce a reasonable but aggressive floodplain zoning law. In the absence of upstream storage, floodplain regulation and floodproofing were the only practical ways to reduce future damage on floodplains experiencing urban development. In response to similar concerns expressed by flood control specialists around the country, Congress enacted the Flood Control Act of 1960. The legislation authorized the Corps of Engineers to compile and disseminate information to states and localities that would help them identify flood-prone areas and guide their use of the floodplains. Gov. Albert D. Rosellini immediately applied to the Corps for floodplain studies on the state's most flood-prone streams — the Skagit, Snohomish, Stillaguamish, Nooksack, and Yakima rivers. U.S. Sen. Warren E. Magnuson was instrumental in getting congressional appropriations so they could be speedily carried out. The governor also pledged that the state would assume full leadership in developing a long-range, comprehensive plan for flood control and coordinated state water resources development.

But while the state had the police power to regulate activities on the floodplain, it did not have the funds nor manpower for enforcement. Regulation, at any rate, was more appropriately carried out at the county and municipal level where planning and zoning laws already controlled industrial and residential expansion. During the 1960s, local governments such as Skagit, Lewis, Cowlitz, King, and Snohomish counties and the city of Richland adopted comprehensive land-use plans and floodplain zoning ordinances under the state's supervision. However, they were the exception. In the state as in the nation, most counties and cities only slowly adopted floodplain ordinances. This was partly because they were unsure about their legality and partly because they lacked information about the frequency and extent of past flooding on which to base sound estimates for future flood risks. In the meantime, development on the rivers' natural overflow lands intensified.

The belief that structural works like levees and reservoirs would continue to be built and that they guaranteed a safe level of protection also kept many localities from acting. Also, the fact that the major flood control works until the late 1970s were largely paid for by the federal government made them the more desirable alternative to zoning restrictions. However, in many cases, structural solutions were impractical because acquiring adequate rights-of-way for dams, dikes, or channel alterations would have caused unacceptable destruction or modification of local properties. Moreover, the degree of damage control the engineering works were designed to provide had always been limited, based as it was on estimates about the size and frequency of future floods and the value of the property to be protected.

In the case of the Howard Hanson Dam, the reservoir's maximum available storage was limited not only by cost considerations, but also by the need to avoid damaging Tacoma's municipal water works. As a result, the Hanson structure, like the Mud Mountain Dam, cannot store all the water of the greater floods, even though it has been able to hold back lesser floods and limit damage to once in every ten or fifteen years. Neither has the dam nor the dikes along the Green River been able to relieve a serious drainage problem downstream. In December 1967 about 25,000 acres of pasture and farmland in the North Road District of the Green River Valley were flooded, causing about $500,000 damage. The constriction of the river behind dikes forces it to drop its silt inside the channel. Consequently, the river is now higher than its tributaries, causing the feeder streams to back up and flood and making it necessary to pump water over the dikes into the river.

The Corps of Engineers has an axiom that however great a flood on any stream may have been, time will bring a greater one. This means that structural flood control projects are always vulnerable. In Washington as elsewhere, they have had a long history of failures. Levees have been topped and breached, and bank revetments repeatedly washed away. When structural projects did protect against floodwaters, they too frequently encouraged a false sense of security among those who wanted to further develop the river's natural overflow plains. For before the government

On the delta's North Fork, about a mile-and-a-half below where the Skagit River divides at Skagit City, the river broke the dike on Nov. 11, 1990, flooding Fir Island. The Army Corps directed repairs, above, which began November 21 and were soon completed by private contractors. The work involved hauling 20,000 cubic yards of rock. On December 9, this dam also failed, washing away in about fifteen minutes. Work on the second dam was completed in April the following year. Total cost for the two efforts was about $1.3 million. Scene, upper right, shows the gap being closed during the second effort, and scene, right, records the application of clay to prevent seepage. During construction of the two dams, rock-laden trucks ran around the clock and virtually destroyed the Skagit City Road between the break and the South Fork Bridge at Conway. Photos by and courtesy of Arnie Garborg.

began subsidizing them, most people steered clear of these hazardous areas. The combination of new building on the floodplains and the occasional flood which exceeded the design level of the flood control structures has brought damage greater than would have occurred without them.

In the mid-1950s national flood-control research specialists began warning that with the explosive urban growth into high flood hazard areas, protective works would have to be supplemented by floodplain land-use regulations. Instead of trying to keep floodwaters away from people and buildings, public officials would have to reorient their thinking and keep people and buildings out of the way of floodwaters. In 1957 a housing development on the outskirts of Wenatchee sustained considerable damage from Canyon Number Two Creek partly because the houses were built with basements or on concrete slabs level with the ground. Had regulations prohibited basements and required the first floor to be two feet above ground level in this area, the damage would have been insignificant.

Researchers who advised local governments knew that floodplain zoning and regulation would have to be "reasonable" in order to be acceptable. For few localities were willing to give up the tax revenue and other income that residential and commercial development brought, just as individuals were unwilling to have state and local governments restrict their use of their property. The regulations, in other words, should allow land use whose economic benefits exceeded, or at least equaled, the potential flood damage. But calculations of this sort, which depended on a number of highly arguable assumptions, were easily influenced by the priorities of local government.

FEDERAL FLOOD INSURANCE

By the 1960s it was clear to federal lawmakers and flood control agencies that they were losing in their battle against the nation's floods. Since 1936, $11 billion had been spent in the country for dams, levees, and other protective works. Yet annual flood losses had continued to mount as urban communities spread into unprotected floodplains. Attempting to restrain the monetary outflows, Congress in 1968 adopted the National Flood Insurance Program which was intended to shift more of the responsibility for flood damage control to the local level by requiring localities to

adopt and enforce measures that would control future land use and thus limit losses in flood-prone areas. Under the program, once a locality's land-use plan was approved, existing structures in the area became eligible for the federal insurance. However, new structures, which were not to be encouraged to locate in the floodplains, were not.

Because so many communities lacked the necessary floodplain data on which to base regulations, few responded to the government's initial overture. So over the next five years Congress passed amendments that both sweetened and toughened the insurance program. Under an "emergency" phase, owners of both existing and new structures were allowed to purchase some insurance at subsidized rates before their community had yet drawn up floodplain regulations. Congress also made the federal flood insurance in areas identified as vulnerable to flooding a prerequisite for federal disaster assistance and for mortgages regulated or insured by federal agencies. These amendments resulted in a large increase nationally and locally in the number of communities enrolled in the program.

In fact, the government's insurance program has supplied the major incentive for local governments to adopt and coordinate regulatory actions. It has allowed them to use land considered essential to the community's economic health but subject to occasional flooding and protect their investment with affordable insurance. Washington cities and counties operating according to the federal standards required developers and builders to take floodproofing measures such as raising lower stories above flood levels or making them resistant to water entry and damage. Snohomish County residents living in high risk areas along the lower Snohomish and Stillaguamish rivers were among the first in the state to take advantage of the federal insurance.

However, the program, administered by the Federal Emergency Management Agency (FEMA), has far from accomplished its original objectives. Some critics believe that by allowing communities to participate before local regulations were completed and by providing subsidized rates, it has simply transferred federal subsidies from disaster relief to insurance. Others argue that because it reduced the economic risk, the insurance program actually reinforced floodplain development. Moreover, since the denial of relief funds has not usually been carried out, many in high flood hazard areas have not purchased the policies. At the end of 1991 only about 15 percent of state residents living in flood-prone areas were policy holders. After the flood of 1995, that percentage rose to twenty in Skagit County, where flooding occurs almost annually. The Thanksgiving Flood of 1990 damaged seventy of Skagit's town of Hamilton's ninety-three homes, only twenty-five of which were insured through the national flood insurance program. That year FEMA spent about 40 percent of its annual $5 million budget for property buy-outs in nine Washington communities. Federal taxpayers still reimburse most flood victims for their damage.

Implementation of the floodplain zoning ordinances has also brought objections. Property owners protested that land-use restrictions amounted to an unlawful appropriation of private property by the government. State and local administrators, in some cases, were forced to become legal experts on the issue to prove the constitutionality of the ordinances. However, as society became more aware that natural resources could be abused with long-term negative effects, courts began to uphold regulations that would have earlier been struck down. Neither was the idea of public responsibility for losses resulting from the private use of flood hazard areas as acceptable in the 1970s and 1980s as in the earlier growth-minded postwar period. Specialists at the Washington Water Research Center in Pullman reported in 1970 that public expenditures on flood control structures were actually "a financial contribution to the owners of floodplain properties." Building on the floodplain not only resulted in rehabilitation costs for occupants, but it could also raise the depth of floodwaters and affect residents who otherwise would not be flooded. Many discovered after the November 1990 flood, which caused approximately $170 million damage in nineteen Washington counties, that recent development in the floodplains had not only worsened chronic flooding but made floodplain maps obsolete, further hindering effective planning. Floodplain occupants also shifted costs to the community for those services — streets and utilities — that had to be repaired or made less vulnerable to damage. In addition to the fiscal costs, commercial and residential encroachment on the river's overflow plains drew environmental costs, adversely affecting fish and game habitat, creating more runoff and new drainage problems, and eliminating greenbelts and possible recreational uses.

ENVIRONMENTAL MEDIATION AND THE SNOQUALMIE MIDDLE FORK DAM

The view that large protective works produced environmental damage that outweighed their potential benefits was raised against a proposed retention dam on the middle fork of the Snoqualmie River. By the late 1960s the Snoqualmie-North Bend area, built largely on floodplains, had one of the highest flood damage potentials in the state. In March 1969 King County planners backed down from their proposed floodplain zoning ordinance for the Snoqualmie Valley after Snoqualmie and North Bend citizens protested that it would strangle the growth of their communities. Townspeople and farmers hoped instead that the Corps of Engineers' plans for retention dams on the Snoqualmie River would make zoning measures unnecessary. However the Corps' proposal for a multipurpose, earthfill dam on the Snoqualmie's middle fork drew loud and sustained opposition from those concerned about the loss of fish and wildlife habitat, white water recreation, and agricultural greenbelts.

Led by the Washington Environmental Council, the opponents protested that such a project would inevitably lead to the kind of rapid urban and industrial development that had occurred in the Green River Valley after the Howard Hanson Dam was erected and in the Sammamish River basin after even a modest

Examples of gauging stations on Washington State rivers. Courtesy National Archives, Alaska-Pacific NW Region.

Corps channelization and levee works was built to drain and protect farmland. They argued that a middle fork dam would result in the flooding of 950 acres of deer range and the loss of nine miles of white water. Local reservoir proponents called the environmental experts and recreational spokespersons "bird-watchers" and "kayakers," viewing them as outsiders who had no vested interest in the valley and who did not have to live with the regular and agonizing floods.

Gov. Dan Evans took a keen interest in the project and sided with the environmentalists, twice vetoing the Corps' plans. The second veto was delivered even after the army engineers had cooperated in a joint planning procedure — unprecedented for the Corps — with the state Department of Ecology, which also offered exceptional opportunities for citizen input. The King County Council, in the meantime, voted continued support for the middle fork dam, convinced that it could only help the Snoqualmie valley farmers, not force them from their land.

After Evans' second veto in 1973, a team from the Community Crisis Intervention Center of St. Louis offered to mediate between the two sides who, it seemed, could find no common ground. The late-1974 agreement the mediators secured was a genuine compromise. It called for a multipurpose dam on the north fork of the river, setback levees in the North Bend and Snoqualmie area, public acquisition of land or development rights on the floodplain for overflow and recreational purposes, and strict land-use management to preserve open space and forest and farm lands. It may have been the first time in the country that formal mediation, rather than litigation, had been used to resolve an environmental issue.

But for all its innovation in bringing the two sides together, the Snohomish Basin Mediated Agreement could not overcome the classic failure of local interests to fund a share of project costs. The economic feasibility of the dam and reservoir depended on a portion of the stored water being used for domestic supply. This would have cost local sponsors about half the cost of the facility, more than $80 million. Although City of Bellevue officials had considered using the north fork as a municipal water source, they didn't think that the city could afford the price tag. Without a local sponsor for the water supply, the Corps scrapped the project. In 1982 the Snohomish Basin Coordinating Council, a group representing basin municipalities and counties and the Tulalip Tribes, urged the Corps to reexamine the possibility of the dam in light of a new and less expensive dam construction technology. But the Corps once again ruled that a north fork dam, at least as a flood control project, was economically infeasible.

The Snohomish Basin compromise demonstrated that it was possible for advocates and opponents of large engineering structures to work together and develop an appreciation of each other's point of view. Through its rejection of the middle fork dam, it prevented the kind of industrial and residential development that followed on the heels, or, in reality, was led by the "toes" of projects such as the Mud Mountain and Howard Hanson dams. But it also finally resulted in the loss of the level of flood relief that Snoqualmie and Snohomish River valley residents had for so long lobbied. Since that time environmental mediation attempts to resolve disputes outside of the courtroom have had similar results in other parts of the country.

FUTURE FLOOD CONTROL — A CHALLENGE FOR LOCAL AUTHORITIES

By 1974 approximately $194 million had been invested in flood control measures in Washington by public agencies, about 75 percent of it by the federal government. Counties had spent about $34 million, cities less than $1 million, state agencies $14 million, and federal agencies, primarily the Corps of Engineers, $145 million. However, over the past three decades the responsibility for controlling flood damage has been moving steadily away from the federal and state level to that of the counties and municipalities. Following state legislation that encouraged this trend in 1961 and 1973, the legislature made substantial changes to the flood control zone law in 1987. They eliminated the eighteen flood control zones that had included only about one-third of the state's flood hazard areas. Instead, they authorized local governments to develop and enforce controls over flood hazard areas through floodplain management programs.

Presently, many questions remain for city and county officials trying to determine the best or "highest use" of the floodplains. The traditional higher use concept that weighed economic benefits only will have to give way to more recent public values that stress the quality of life. Today, environmental values and laws concerning fish and wildlife, recreation, and open space, not to mention the larger share of project costs that is now required of local beneficiaries, have made large-scale federal flood control works nearly impossible to build. And, since the best sites for major reservoirs already have been developed in many cases, the most

promising opportunities for reducing future losses will probably come in the form of smaller protective structures, rehabilitation and maintenance of existing flood control works, elevation and relocation of existing buildings, and nonstructural measures. Such measures could include the public acquisition of floodplains and the protection of wetlands so that these lands can perform their natural hydrologic function of detaining floodwaters and reducing downstream flows.

However, anticipated population growth in Washington, particularly in the Puget Sound counties, will continue to put great pressure on local officials to permit the development of these lands. Ways to raise money for new flood-control measures must also be found. Whether city and county officials will be able to control future development in flood-prone areas will depend largely on their adoption and enforcement of effective floodplain zoning and building code regulations and local taxpayers' willingness and ability to share the costs. Whatever the outcome, flood control measures will be back in local hands — hands resting comfortably on desks and computer keyboards as well as gripped coldly around shovels and sandbags.

MOUNT ST. HELENS — FLOODING AND SILT CONTROL

No one knows more about this mountain than Harry, and it don't dare blow up on him," Harry Truman told a *Seattle Times* reporter in the spring of 1980. In the few weeks before the eruption of Mount St. Helens on May 18 of that year, Harry Truman received a lot of media attention. So did the "harmonic tremors," those seismographic recordings indicating subsurface movement of magma. The tremors, earthquakes, and ash and steam eruptions that began in March had caused scientists to alert

After 123 years of quiescence Mount St. Helens rumbled again on March 20, 1980. Subsequent earthquakes within the mountain formed a 320-foot swelling on its north side which at 8:32 A.M. on May 18, 1980 exploded. Shaken by a magnitude 5.0 quake, the multifractured mountain gave way in an avalanche of historic size, repeated pyroclastic flows, ashfall and mudflows. More than 150 square miles of the Gifford Pinchot National Forest were leveled. A good part of the mountain slumped into the picturesque Spirit Lake basin, filling the lake with 150 feet of debris. In this view looking south-southwest from 7,000 feet ten days after the eruption, logs still cover 85 percent of the lake surface. The ragged-edged caldera left in place of the mountain's symmetrical crown continues to manufacture steam from the sporadically growing cone it nearly encircles. Photo by and courtesy of Elizabeth Pincha.

local agencies to prepare for a possible major eruption. On April 4 Washington Gov. Dixy Lee Ray declared a state of emergency and ordered roadblocks to keep people out of the most dangerous areas. But eighty-four-year-old Harry refused to leave his sixteen cats and longtime home on the shores of Spirit Lake.

Few of the 1,500 residents of Toutle, twenty-five miles northwest of the mountain, reported hearing any noise from the initial eruption at 8:32 in the morning on May 18. However, its effects soon reached them with a different sound, that of cracking windshields and trees, twisted by a sudden and uncanny increase in temperature. The hot lateral blast that exploded out of the side of the mountain with more than hurricane-force winds — up to 200 miles an hour — followed seconds after a massive landslide had carried the mountain's summit down its north flank. Almost every living thing within an area up to sixteen miles from the mountain was killed — including at least fifty-seven people, 2,300 big game animals, millions of juvenile salmon and steelhead, and trees comprising two billion board feet of timber. Harry Truman's lodge disappeared under a deep, steaming mass of hot mud and broken trees. One branch of the debris avalanche entered Spirit Lake, causing it to rise about 120 feet. The larger branch traveled down the north fork of the Toutle River.

By afternoon melted snow and water displaced from lakes and rivers had mixed with avalanche and volcanic debris to form huge mudflows, in places up to thirty feet deep. Sweeping through the Cowlitz and Toutle valleys, they destroyed or damaged over 200 homes, twelve bridges, log handling facilities, municipal water systems, and a fish hatchery. The lower Cowlitz River channel was filled with up to eighteen feet of mud, and the depth of the Columbia River channel was reduced from forty to fifteen feet, trapping thirty-one deep-draft ships upstream. Logs from the Weyerhaeuser Company's Camp Baker, along with other trees cut down by the blast, created a twenty-mile-long jam along the Columbia. A 200-foot-high wall of mud and ash, sixteen miles long, was deposited at the outlet of Spirit Lake, causing fears that if it should break the enlarged lake would cause massive flooding.

Once the immediate danger was over and emergency floodfighting concluded, the Corps began a crash program of dredging the Cowlitz channel and building levees at Castle Rock and Lexington. Three weeks after the disaster, the Corps and its sixteen contractors, with enough equipment to build a major dam, raced to dig out miles of the mud-choked Cowlitz and Toutle rivers before the autumn rains began. By February 1984 the Corps had removed enough volcanic debris to cover a football field more than a mile deep. However, the sediment was still being deposited. About 43,000 tons were eroding annually from each square kilometer of the Toutle River basin, making the stream one of the largest sediment carriers in the world. To slow the river flow and collect the silt as it came down from the mountain, the Corps built two debris-retaining reservoirs, which filled within two years, and eight sediment stabilization basins.

Meanwhile, as the water rose higher and higher behind the natural debris dam that blocked the outlet of Spirit Lake, residents of Longview, Kelso, and Castle Rock downstream became increasingly nervous. If the dam should give way, specialists warned, 100,000 acre feet of water would pour into the Toutle's north fork — more than twice the volume of mud and water that had rushed down the river after the May 18 eruption. At up to ten times the river's capacity, such a deluge would totally destroy the Cowlitz Valley. Because of this ominous prospect, Gov. John Spellman in the summer of 1982 declared a state of emergency and asked President Ronald Reagan to do the same so that federal emergency funds could be released.

After the president agreed and $7 million was authorized, the Corps began another rush rescue effort. In just forty-five days the engineers designed and built a pumping barge on Spirit Lake to send 5,400 gallons of water a second out of the lake and downstream into the Toutle.

Twenty pumps operated around the clock, consuming nearly 3,000 gallons of diesel fuel a day. The pumps ran until May 1985, when the Corps formally opened a $13.5 million tunnel from the lake, bored through 8,500 feet of solid rock. The eleven-foot-diameter tunnel could send 90,000 gallons of water a minute into the Toutle's north fork.

The tunnel relieved downstream residents of the threat of another catastrophic mudflow. But it could not hold back the heavy accumulations of silt and sand that continued to move down the mountain into the Cowlitz and Columbia rivers, posing risks to upstream fisheries and causing flood and navigation problems in delta areas. Suitable disposal sites were dwindling and dredging was expensive and inefficient.

In December 1986 the Corps began work on a $60 million silt-retention dam on the Toutle's north fork, about twenty-six miles upstream from Castle Rock. The state, Cowlitz County, and members of Washington's congressional delegation, including Rep. Don Bonker of Vancouver, had lobbied hard for the structure. The earthen dam, 1,800 feet long, 184 feet high, and capable of holding 250 million cubic yards of debris, was finished in December 1989 and dedicated on April 19, 1990, on the ten-year anniversary of the volcano's eruption. The structure was designed to trap sediment until the area behind the dam filled in about fifty years, at which time it was projected it could safely pour over the spillway.

Above: An old postcard scene of Mount St. Helens reflected in Spirit Lake. Courtesy, Fairlook Antiques, Seattle. Below: Aerial of the Army Corps-built Spirit Lake Silt Retention Dam.

A-116)(4-15-39-11A)(12-3000) COULEE DAM, WASH.

The early 1930s Bureau of Reclamation aerial of the Grand Coulee Dam site before construction (above left) can be compared to another Bureau aerial (above right) of early work on the dam and the communities beside it, and the Bureau's 1979 aerial (below) looking south over the new power house and dam to Banks Lake and Steamboat Rock.

Seattle City Light promotes municipal power with a light show from its Lake Union plant, ca. 1920. Courtesy Seattle Municipal Archives.

POWER

Shortly after noon on a 90-degree day in late September 1963, a ten-mile-long procession of cars slinked toward a dusty, desolate site in eastern Washington. A crowd of 40,000 people had come from all directions to witness the groundbreaking ceremony for the Hanford Nuclear Reservation's first electrical generating facility. The flat, featureless landscape in a strongly Republican area of the state was a strange backdrop for a platform of influential and urbane Democratic politicians. But local affiliations mattered little when the president was in the party. Behind the podium President John F. Kennedy charmed the crowd as he poked the air with an uranium-tipped wand and praised the peaceful and productive role the latest Hanford reactor would soon play. Alongside him stood Senators Warren G. Magnuson and Henry M. Jackson, proudly sharing the moment and the recognition that they had brought the state another federal public works project.

Two and a half years later the government's first dual purpose nuclear facility was in operation, generating electricity from the waste heat of Hanford's ninth plutonium reactor. The facility was also the second successful project to be sponsored by the Washington Public Power Supply System (WPPSS). Senator Jackson, a member of the powerful Joint Committee on Atomic Energy, had first proposed the project in 1956, but enabling legislation had not been able to break through congressional impasses until the summer of 1962. When it finally did, many in the private sector of the utility industry were outraged. Fearing that it would become the first link in a coast-to-coast, federally owned power grid, they called it contrary to American principles and the "first step to socialism."

The development of electric power in Washington has retold a familiar national tale of conflict between free enterprise and government control. By the time the technology reached its maturity in the politically somnolent 1920s, private industry had become the central character in the saga of American power. Most municipally owned and would-be public systems had been relegated to minor roles. Yet, Washington state introduced an unusual twist to the conventional power plots, for here the protagonist early on became embodied in the public power movement. This story line can be traced to a number of circumstances including the preeminent hydroelectric potential of the state's streams and the federal government's development of the Columbia River. But it is, perhaps, above all a chronicle of the unusual dedication of Washington citizens and lawmakers during the first half of the twentieth century to the principles of public ownership and control. The most recent chapters, covering the past two decades, tell a story of a state and a region coming to terms with new actors and unfamiliar conditions — conditions that have stubbornly defied the old subplots of historical precedent.

President John Kennedy at the 1963 groundbreaking ceremony for Hanford's first electrical generating facility. Courtesy, WWPPS.

PIONEER POWER

In 1845 Michael T. Simmons and a small party of emigrants, weary from the long Oregon Trail trek, established the first permanent settlement of Americans north of the Columbia River at New Market (later renamed Tumwater). The next fall they felled a giant tree across a stream, hollowed out a cedar log to make a flume, and built a water wheel of wooden buckets and gears to grind their wheat into flour. With the abundance of streams in western Washington, the early territorial settlers built a number of these primitive waterpower installations to perform routine labor. The mechanical hydraulics were first electrified when the Tacoma Mill Company built a small plant on Galliher's Gulch in 1882. (It was the same year that Thomas Edison put the world's first central steam electric station into service at New York City's Pearl Street Station.) So that the mill workers could put in longer hours, the com-

Above: Unidentified Tacoma Utility workers look over a model of the "First Tacoma Power Plant" (as the banner reads above the roof line); the original was built by the Tacoma Light and Water Company on Galliher's Gulch in 1886. Below: In 1893 the city took monopoly control of its electrical service and began the perennial search for more power. Courtesy Tacoma Public Utilities.

had a contract with one of the rare industrial users, few plants provided power during the daylight hours and they would usually shut off again at midnight. When patrons of the Saturday night dance in Quincy wanted to continue shuffling past midnight, they chipped in and paid the plant operator, C. R. Greenlee, to keep the current flowing. Sometimes when the moon was full on a cloudless night, Tacoma's early utilities would not come on at all. As late as the early 1920s the Oak Harbor area was served by a plant powered by a steam tractor. No kitchen appliances could be used, and only on Mondays was afternoon service offered for customers to do their electric washing and ironing.

Cautious and cost-conscious customers at first purchased only the lighting service, supplied by a single drop cord hanging from the center of the ceiling. The knob-and-spool type wiring was crude and service outlets in the walls were practically unknown.

pany installed a Brush arc generator to energize a string of arc lamps. The lights were powered by the same steam engine used to drive the mill.

Washington's original small light companies supplied small users. Generating a low-voltage direct current (DC) which petered out only a mile or two from the source, they carried virtually no industrial load. Until alternating current (AC), the transformer, and large steam turbines were perfected and service areas could be expanded, the larger the town, the greater the number of companies were needed to service its neighborhoods. Competition was intense, but the rates were still high — as much as $.25 a kilowatt hour — because of the great capital outlays that had to be made for generating equipment and transmission systems before any revenue could be collected. In the larger cities the first major producers of electricity were usually the traction companies whose franchised priorities were to keep the trolleys running. In the state's smaller towns electric power did not arrive until the first decade of the twentieth century and usually depended on the initiative and ingenuity of local entrepreneurs.

The one certainty with these early electric enterprises was the uncertainty of their service. Problems continually plagued the inefficient, jerryrigged plants and distribution systems, causing shutdowns that could last a week or longer. The town of Quincy's first generator was run by a single-cylinder Foos engine burning kerosene or distillate. Later, an old Model T engine was installed as a standby. Because the automobile engine tended to heat up, water from the radiator was piped up on the roof for cooling before it was recirculated through the radiator. The current produced was so weak that it took only a few light bulbs to cut down the voltage. Unless they

Light bulbs, usually about 25-candlepower, were shielded by a heavy frosted glass shade to minimize the "glare." After the lights, the electric iron was usually the first appliance customers wanted. It was easy to sell the relief an electric iron provided from the sweltering summertime routine of firing a coal stove to heat the flat iron. And once the electric companies ironed out their own systems, they were eager to persuade and sometimes push homeowners into the wonderful world of appliances.

The second but dearer purchase, and probably the most appreciated appliance, was the electric washing machine which replaced the old washboard and tub and the hand-cranked washer, so often powered and detested by the children. However, until twenty-four-hour service became available, not many households were willing to buy more than an iron, though they might occasionally rent the company's vacuum for twenty-five cents a night. Even with round-the-clock service, some of the larger companies had to aggressively push the sale of their appliances. Washington Water Power Company mounted a model electric kitchen display on the back of a flatbed motor truck that drove from town to town. One young promotional genius even hired camels from a traveling circus and strapped electric ranges on their backs.

In spite of all their inadequacies, the first electric systems continued to be a source of awe, especially for those who didn't yet have the service. One former Grant County resident recalls vivid memories of the summer of 1914 when "linemen replaced railroad engineers and cowboys as heroes among the youth" of Hartline. "All over town small boys were fastening a long belt around their waists, climbing clothesline poles and fence posts and leaning back in their 'safety belts' in imitation of the linemen." Sewing machine drawers were raided for empty spools to make the insulators on top of "power poles" which were strung with kite-string lines. The boys were stricken in admiration for one lineman who used to sing as he stretched out full length on his back on a cross arm above the schoolyard.

PRIVATE POWER

Born of a marriage between science and industry, electric power in the United States initially was the child of big business. Thomas Edison, J. P. Morgan, and George Westinghouse were among the first to realize the financial potential of turning darkness into daylight. In 1885 Henry Villard of Northern Pacific fame declined an offer by his friend Thomas Edison to represent Edison's Electric Light Company in the

Sidney Z. Mitchell

Northwest. Instead, twenty-three-year-old Sidney Z. Mitchell was sent west as the company's exclusive agent. By the following year the former naval cadet had sold the rapidly growing city of Seattle her first electric incandescent lights. With contracts signed for 250 bulbs on a flat monthly basis, Mitchell and his partner, F. H. Sparling, financed Seattle's first electric company, the Seattle Electric Lighting Co., and built a small steam generating station on Jackson Street. It was the first central station system for incandescent electric lighting west of the Rocky Mountains.

Unlike the small, isolated systems like that of the Tacoma Mill Company, central systems used one or more large dynamos and produced power for hundreds rather than a dozen bulbs. The Jackson Street station had two steam dynamos and a capacity of 600 lamps. On March 22, 1886, before a delighted group of dignitaries including Mayor Henry Yesler and the city council, the company switched on an exhibition of eleven 16-candlepower lights in their spartan Seattle headquarters. When the dynamo was started, the *Seattle P.I.* reported, "instantly the room was made brilliant with a clear white light." A month later another crowd packed into Toklas and Singerman's San Francisco Store, the company's first customer. Years later a spectator reminisced about how those who witnessed the flood of light from five 2,000-candlepower lamps that night "could barely believe their eyes."

Not to be outdone by their northern rivals, Tacomans

ordered 600 bulbs from Mitchell and Sparling. Mitchell successfully merged four Tacoma electric railway companies into the Tacoma Railway & Power Company. However, by this time the electric lighting industry in Tacoma was dominated by the Tacoma Light and Water Company, incorporated by Northern Pacific officials Charles Wright and General John W. Sprague. In Spokane Falls, Mitchell convinced local businessmen to invest in 1,200 bulbs and form the Spokane Falls Water Power Company. The Spokane investors agreed to use only Edison-patented equipment and to pay the Edison Company 30 percent of revenues as royalties. A generator, installed in a plant at the falls in a bay near the end of the Post Street bridge, supplied enough power to extend arc lighting across the bridge up to Main Avenue and east to Howard Street. It even lit Spokane's first opera performance.

Washington Water Power Company

Within a year the output of the little Spokane Falls plant was insufficient. In 1888 Mitchell supervised the installation of a new plant that had four times the capacity of the old one. The boost in power enabled the company to offer twenty-four-hour service, extend lines to residences for the first time, and to power the first electric motors, including some for the presses of the *Spokane Chronicle*. But when the company failed to secure the eastern capital needed to expand its facilities, the Edison-affiliate succumbed to the Washington Water Power Company, organized by local businessmen in 1889. Edison and his investors were convinced that water power had no future, but the Spokane entrepreneurs gazed knowingly at the spray of the lower falls and dared the opposite. The eastern steam technology and Edison-patented equipment were not indispensable, they believed, in a town built around and named after a powerful river falls. An article in *Electrical World* the next year revealed the debt Spokane Falls owed to the development of its hydroelectric power: "The remarkable electrical developments in the far west are nowhere more strikingly exhibited than at Spokane Falls. The rapid and phenomenal growth of this city finds its parallel in the growth of its electrical industries, and this is undoubtedly due in a great measure to the magnificent water power that the city possesses."

Washington Water Power president Rockwood Moore was a Spokane boomer—president of the First National Bank and

Two views of Washington Power's powerhouse at the base of Spokane Falls. The larger photo looks north, in line with the Monroe Street Bridge and across the river from the Spokesman Review Building, home of the city's daily morning newspaper. Courtesy, Michael Maslan.

When Washington Water Power's Long Lake Dam was completed in 1915, it was the highest spillway dam yet built. Courtesy, Michael Fairley.

of the lucky Last Chance Mine, organizer of two electric street railways, and one of the most extensive property owners in town. Moore and the company's other Spokane investors had good reason to be optimistic about their venture. Even after a fire wiped out the thirty-two-block business district in August 1889, the city of nearly 20,000 began rebuilding immediately and kept on growing. The demand for power increased so quickly that the company could not install new dynamos fast enough. By the early 1890s a half-dozen railroads and several electric streetcar systems ran their tracks through Spokane. The biggest of the railroads, the Northern Pacific, ran an aggressive Midwestern campaign touting the great agricultural potential of its land-grant tracts in eastern Washington. When nature cooperated in this promotion with above average rainfall from 1893-97, the railroad was rewarded with trainloads of immigrating families. That Spokane had developed into the "Heart of the Inland Empire" was precipitated by its railroads, but predisposed by its falls.

The electric company's decision to situate a large central station at the lowest falls on the south side of the river, "where the stations could be enlarged to meet the demands of a city of 100,000 people," was propitious. The original Monroe Street dam and power project began operation in November 1890. Its six Edison generators produced DC current with a capacity of 890 kw, of which a little over one-third was used to operate the streetcar system. In 1892 the station was expanded to 1,439 kw, which included a 60-kw AC generator. Eleven years later the facility was rebuilt and some of the DC works were replaced with AC equipment. Two of the 1903 generators, which are still in use, are believed to be the oldest operating electrical equipment in the state.

Washington Water Power grew slowly in its first four years and then nearly went under when the financial panic of 1893 swept the nation. But by the turn of the century the company had recovered and during the next thirty years it bought out approximately eighty-five existing small-town systems and brought first-time service to twenty-eight communities. A second and third hydroelectric project, Post Falls and Little Falls both on the Spokane River, were completed by 1910, by which time Spokane numbered 104,400 residents. The Long Lake plant and dam, which went into operation in 1915, was the company's largest and most difficult undertaking to date. At the time it was completed, the project boasted the world's largest turbines and the highest spillway at 170 feet. In 1962, after the completion of several more hydroelectric projects on rivers in Washington, Idaho, and Montana, Washington Water Power was one of the few investor-owned utilities in the nation that generated all of its electrical power through the use of falling water.

Puget Sound Power and Light Company

By 1890 Sidney Mitchell had organized incandescent lighting companies in Seattle, Tacoma, Spokane, Ellensburg, Bellingham, Colfax, and other towns and cities throughout the region. When the Panic of 1893 short-circuited Mitchell's plans

for a Northwest electric empire, he resorted to the advice and aid of Stone and Webster of Boston, M.I.T. whizkids and the country's most prominent electric power consulting firm. Following their directions Mitchell and his partners managed to consolidate practically all of the power, light, and railway companies operating in Seattle in the late 1890s into the Seattle Electric Company. In 1912 Stone and Webster combined the Seattle company with four other Washington traction and power companies and incorporated under Massachusetts law as the Puget Sound Traction, Light and Power Company.

As part of the merger the company acquired three major hydroelectric plants: Snoqualmie Falls, completed in 1898; White River, harnessed in 1911 to meet the demands of electric transportation companies linking Tacoma, Seattle, Everett, Bellingham, and Mount Vernon; and the 20,000-kw Electron plant on the Puyallup River in the foothills of Mount Rainier. The company also obtained the 15,000-kw steam plant built by Stone and Webster in Georgetown in 1906, the Nooksack Falls plant on the river of the same name, the York Street steam plant in Bellingham, the Seattle power distribution system, and gas properties in Bellingham and coal mines in Renton. At the Georgetown plant two 35-foot-high steam turbines, powered by coal and supplying a total of 11,000 kw, reduced operating costs and increased transmission distance to make power available to Georgetown and south Seattle homes. The company's interconnection of its power facilities with a 55,000-volt, 300-mile-long transmission line was an important step in the evolution of commercial power generation in the state. It was the first time an attempt had been made to link and unify the many individual systems, and it introduced electric service on a territorial basis in the Puget Sound region.

Snoqualmie Falls Project

Patterned after Niagara Falls and housed in a great cavern hollowed out of rock nearly 300 feet underground, the Snoqualmie Falls power project was the state's first large hydroelectric plant. The Snoqualmie Falls Project was certainly the most visually spectacular of the Stone and Webster acquisitions. One hundred feet higher than Niagara, the falls had for years inspired the reverence of the Indians and the awe of the first settlers and eventually the first tourists. When it was completed in 1898, the plant contained the works to generate 6,000 kw, 200 times the maximum output of the original Spokane Falls plant.

Five hundred feet back from the crest of the falls, a low dam diverts water into a vertical shaft excavated out of solid rock. Here the water drops 270 feet before the shaft turns an abrupt 90 degree angle and expands into a larger chamber at the level of the river below the falls. In the horizontal chamber penstocks discharge water through four water wheels before it escapes through a 400-foot-long tunnel to the foot of the falls. The Snoqualmie Falls plant was an engineering wonder, and even more remarkable, was completed in less than a year's time. Almost one hundred years

Puget Sound Power and Light Company's Georgetown steam plant.

after start-up, the original generators are still producing.

Electron

When it was completed in 1904, the 20,000-horsepower system at Electron on the Puyallup River generated more power than any other facility in the state. This distinction did not last long, but the Electron project remained significant as an example of the state-of-the-art of high-head power development and of the changes that occurred in hydroelectric technology as it moved west across the country.

Most of pioneering hydroelectric experimentation and development was based on the natural conditions that prevailed in the East. The typical eastern plant operated under a high volume and low head, or short fall, of water. The type of generating equipment used for low-head installations could not be adapted for high-head or long fall conditions. Consequently, a new design technology emerged for the vast high-head water resources of the West Coast.

An important innovation appeared in the 1880s, derived from the timber hurdy-gurdy wheel developed by California gold miners two decades earlier. It was the tangential impulse or Pelton wheel. In contrast to the old-style undershot and overshot water wheels, and the reaction or mixed-flow Francis turbines used in the East, the Pelton wheel used twin buckets with curved bottoms, inclined sides, and a raised center ridge which divided the incoming jet of water. This design permitted minimal interference between incoming and outgoing water and doubled the efficiency of the wheel. By 1900 the tangential impulse wheel had become the characteristic water turbine in high-head hydroelectric projects. The Electron water wheels at the time of their installation were claimed to be the largest impulse units in the world.

Another characteristic and indispensable feature in the evolution of high-head water power was the extensive water network that conveyed water to the turbines. The ten-mile-long timber flume at Electron is still the longest flume used for power production in the state. The technology for building concrete flumes existed when the project was under construction, but because of the high costs involved, especially for transportation in the mountainous region, the Stone and Webster engineers decided to use the abundant timber available nearby. However, the untreated timber had a life span of only twelve to fifteen years and required frequent and costly maintenance. To facilitate inspection and upkeep, a standard-gauge train track was laid on top of the structure. The rail line, which could not be run alongside the flume because of the steep terrain, became known

Snoqualmie Falls power postcard. Courtesy Old Seattle Paperworks. Bottom: Electron power house on the Puyallup River. Courtesy, UW Libraries, Special Collections.

to locals as "the world's crookedest railroad."

Approximately ten miles from the Mount Rainier glaciers which feed the river, a low timber crib dam across the Puyallup River diverts water into the flume. Built with pick and shovel on a uniform grade of 7.5 feet per mile, the flume carries the water across the rugged terrain into the reservoir on a plateau, 900 feet above the powerhouse. Penstocks, tubes through which the falling water is funneled toward the turbine blades, then carry the water down a 30 degree incline to the powerhouse. Here the water operates four twin Pelton Impulse turbines under a head of 872 feet.

The Electron project was built by the Columbia Improvement Company, formed by Stone and Webster and managed by none other than Sidney Mitchell. Samuel L. Shuffleton, a renowned construction engineer who managed all of Stone and Webster's operations west of the Mississippi, made the initial surveys and design studies. After it came on line, Electron supplied most of the power for Seattle's commercial, residential, and street lighting until Seattle City Light increasingly took over these services. It also boosted the power load of the expanding interurban electric railway system in Tacoma and Seattle and furnished power to a number of industries and small communities between the two cities.

White River Project

By 1910 the plants at Snoqualmie Falls and Electron could not keep up with the ever-increasing load demands of the Puget Sound population. Fluctuations in river flow were greater than had been anticipated, and neither installation had adequate storage facilities to provide reliable uninterrupted current. Dependable service was restored in 1911 with the coming on line of the White River installation at Dieringer, between Auburn and Sumner. Water was diverted from the White River near Buckley and flowed through a series of flumes and canals to an immense storage reservoir at Lake Tapps. Enough water was impounded there to operate the plant at full load, 20,000 kw, for an entire month.

By 1930 Puget Sound Power and Light, which had dropped the word "Traction" ten years earlier, was operating in nineteen counties of western and central Washington and supplying power to about half of the farms in its service area. That same year Puget Power began building the first dam to span the Columbia River. The Rock Island Dam near Wenatchee, completed in 1933, provided work for thousands during the early depression years. In 1938 Puget Power was furnishing electricity to approximately 450 communities in western and central Washington. By 1955 the company had absorbed nearly 150 smaller companies. Today Puget Power, despite losing the greater part of its 1940 service area to public utilities over the years, remains the state's largest electric utility company.

Progressive Reform and Utility Regulation

Mitchell's electrifying circuit around the region was an entrepreneurial model for other men lured by the promise of big profits. However, most of the smaller companies they founded were undercapitalized and too poorly managed to survive the Panic of 1893. The crash was a hard-times test in communities where competing companies ran redundant transmission lines at great cost to themselves and their customers. The conclusion that electric utilities had to be treated as natural monopolies came quickly. Agreement on who should control them did not.

The first rehearsals for the drama of public and private power in Washington got started in 1892. At their annual convention in Ellensburg the Peoples Party of Washington endorsed the national platform calling for government ownership of railroads and telegraph and telephone companies. Four years later the Populists added demands for municipal ownership of all street railways, and gas and electric lighting plants to supply customers at cost. In 1896 the party won the governorship and enough seats in the state legislature to control both houses. Yet, with the exception of Governor John R. Rogers, the Washington Populists proved to be inexperienced lawmakers, unable to agree upon and carry out their programs. When prosperity returned in the late 1890s, most of the Populists disappeared like vaudevillians yanked from the stage.

But the issues generated by rapid industrialization remained. Before 1910 another more successful reform movement was born uniting labor, militant farmers, and the burgeoning urban middle class. An effective lobby for reform, the Progressives in Washington changed public attitudes and introduced legislation that gave voters more control of the political process, forcing the state's largely Republican legislature to follow and eventually to lead. The initiative and referendum amendments, passed in 1912, later became important instruments in the grassroots battle for the creation of public utility districts.

In June 1911 one of the most reform-minded legislatures in the state's history established the Public Service Commission to regulate utility companies. The commission's primary function was to ensure that company rates represented no more than a "fair" return on their investments. They were also directed to make certain that firms met power load demands in their service areas. In 1919 the commission ordered the Wenatchee Valley Gas and Electric Company to boost its horsepower capacity in order to save the fruit crops that depended upon pump irrigation. When the company failed to meet the commission's order to secure additional power, a receiver was appointed and authorized to begin building an emergency steam plant.

Throughout its early history the utility commission had a difficult time keeping up with an overwhelming number of mostly minor complaints about utility companies. Although it was a phenomenon experienced nationwide, Washington's utility commission was unusually ineffective. In 1915 the city of Yakima obtained a rate reduction order from the commission to the Pacific Power and Light Company which operated in the south central and southeastern part of the state. Although the order still left rates nearly double those in Seattle, the company took the matter to court and the reduction was suspended. Commission members also lacked the staff and budget to perform the valuation of companies that was necessary for rate-making purposes. Moreover, the larger companies were part of an interstate utility empire that confounded the machinery of state regulation. However, while state regulatory controls were generally ineffectual, the growing competition from municipally owned systems and later more numerous public utility districts was not.

Formal opening, May 24, 1926, of Tacoma City Light's transmission line across the Tacoma Narrows from the Lake Cushman powerhouse. Courtesy, Tacoma City Light.

MUNICIPAL POWER

Unlike most other industrialized countries, the United States has left electric power primarily in the hands of private enterprise. Approximately three-fourths of the nation's consumers, including those in Oregon, Idaho, and Montana, pay privately owned utility companies for their kilowatts. In Washington the percentages are reversed. Sustained political support for public power made Washington the exception and a leader in the country's public power movement. Here the campaign for publicly owned utilities began with the cities. The largest municipal electric utilities in Seattle and Tacoma progressed at a pace matching the growth of the industry itself. Soon after their establishment the Seattle and Tacoma light divisions won national reputations as exemplary municipal systems.

Tacoma City Light

In 1884, two years after the Tacoma Mill workers began their evening shifts under electric lights, John W. Sprague and Charles Wright, the powerful capitalist, railroad president, and major stockholder of the Tacoma Land Company, incorporated the Tacoma Light and Water Company. In December 1886, after they had installed a small arc dynamo run by the waters flowing from Galliher's Gulch and strung up transmission lines, electric service became available to anyone in Tacoma brave enough to use it. On the day after Christmas 1886, the city became the company's main customer when the first electric incandescent street lights were switched on. By 1887 the firm could offer connections for inside and outside service for three-quarters of a mile along Pacific Avenue. Commercial rates were exorbitant — $10 a month per light if the light burned until midnight and $14 a month if it burned all night. That was equivalent to $20.53 per kwh in 1985 dollars.

Above: Construction work on Cushman Dam No. 1 on the Skokomish River, Sept. 19, 1925. Courtesy, Tacoma Public Library. Below: The completed Cushman Dam No. 2, a little less than two miles downstream from the first. Courtesy, Tacoma Public Utilities.

municipalities to exploit the hydroelectric potential of distant mountain-fed streams. In January 1909 Tacoma citizens approved a $2 million bond issue for a dam and powerhouse on the Nisqually River at La Grande.

Like the vote on the municipal takeover, the bond issue did not pass without controversy. Many Tacomans doubted that their city could ever use all the power generated by Nisqually's four 8,000-kw units. Some charged that the city was trying to supply power for the whole state. Two of Tacoma's three papers were owned by one man, and he bitterly opposed the idea, running editorials pilloring the proponents of the Nisqually plant as "enemies of a sound social order." But when the city reduced electric rates after the powerhouse came on line in August of 1912, most forgot their objections. By 1914 the rates charged domestic users in Tacoma were as little as one-fifth the rates paid by Seattle City Light residential customers. The next year the city inaugurated penny power by adopting a combination cooking and lighting rate of one cent a kilowatt hour (kwh). The City of Tacoma had established the lowest residential power rates in the country, a distinction it would maintain for decades.

The more rates went down, the more demand went up. By 1917 Tacoma's single municipal generating plant on the Nisqually could not keep up. Tacoma city engineers planned another hydroelectric project on the north fork of the Skokomish River on the Olympic Peninsula near Hoodsport. The site was forty-four miles northwest of Tacoma in an area where rainfall averaged ninety-five inches a year. During the construction of the Cushman dam and powerhouse during the winter of 1924-25, work was continually hampered by floods and mudslides. When the work was completed, one of its distinctive features was the enormous 440,000-acre-foot storage facility which assured a more reliable source of power. Even though the Nisqually plant had a 32,000-horsepower potential, it was reduced during low river flows to 9,200 horsepower because of its limited reservoir space. The Cushman reservoir could store almost twice as much. In May 1926 the two Cushman generator units were carrying Tacoma's entire load of 32,000 kw.

The high rates, however, did not dampen demand. Although the company kept adding dynamos, including a state-of-the-art Westinghouse AC machine with a 1,500-light capacity, they could not keep up with requests from a population swelling to an undreamed-of 40,000. But almost as soon as they were hooked up, Tacoma power users were unhappy with their service. They said the arc lights were not bright enough and the company took too long to replace broken lamps. As their dissatisfaction grew, many Tacomans began to favor municipal control. In 1893 a specially appointed committee advised the mayor and city council to buy the Tacoma Light and Water Company. The proposal stirred up immediate opposition. Many were appalled by the $1.75 million cost, and others claimed that the city did not need a power plant at any price. Public power advocates responded that if the city owned its own facilities it could produce adequate light and water at reasonable rates, and this would attract more business to the city and raise property values. The Tacoma *Daily Ledger* on the eve of the city-wide vote editorialized that the ballot would "show whether Tacoma is to take a long step forward, or… wait idly for something or somebody to push it forward." The voters approved the purchase on April 12, 1893, by 100 votes over the required three-fifths majority. The measure gave the city a monopoly on electric power which it used to reduce rates by 50 percent over the next two years.

However, city officials soon discovered they hadn't gotten all they thought they had paid for (see Public Water Chapter), and in spite of their efforts to repair and upgrade the system, the generating facilities acquired from the company proved pathetically inadequate. The municipal utility was still forced to buy most of its power from private companies, including the Seattle-Tacoma Power Company, one of the affiliates of Stone and Webster. City officials looked for more ways of producing power themselves. After City Attorney Theodore L. Stiles assured the city council that the city could condemn land outside its limits for public use and his opinion was upheld by the state Supreme Court, the way was cleared for Tacoma and other

Above: The U.S.S. Lexington *supplying emergency power for Tacoma City Light, 1930. Below, in order: The Mayfield and Mossyrock Dams on Cowlitz River and City Light's steam plant on the tideflats. Courtesy Tacoma Public Utilities.*

The remote Cushman plant required long-distance transmission. Part of the 11,000-volt transmission line to Tacoma spanned the steep-bluffed Tacoma Narrows crossing. When it was completed, it was the longest aerial electrical span in the world. During the formal opening of the project on May 24, 1926, army airplanes gave an aerial salute to "christen" the towers carrying the lines across the 6,245-foot-long gap over Puget Sound, while President Coolidge pressed a key in the White House that started the turbines humming. In 1930 a second dam was built two miles downstream from the first Cushman facility. Here water backed behind the 240-foot-high arch dam was sent through a 2.5-mile-long, concrete-lined tunnel to the powerhouse on the Olympic Highway, a half-mile south of Potlatch. The dam diverted most of the flow of the Skokomish's North Fork into the canal, resulting in the eventual destruction of the stream's salmon runs.

Since hydropower is dependent on streamflow, droughts caused power shortages. The dry year of 1922 pushed the Tacoma light division to complete its first steam generation plant in just three months. The drought of 1929-1930 caused such a critical power shortage that the steam plant could not meet demand, and Tacoma officials leased the turbogenerator aboard the U.S.S. *Lexington* docked in Commencement Bay. According to Ira S. Davisson, Tacoma public utility commissioner from 1918 to 1938, the private power companies seized upon these emergency measures "in an effort to discredit the municipal ownership and operation of utilities." The City of Destiny, they scoffed, had become the City of Darkness. Soon after the ship was tied into the city's distribution system, it began raining and the reservoirs filled to capacity. But the drought had brought home to utility officials the municipality's vulnerability to the whims of nature. Work began immediately on a second steam plant, located on the tideflats adjacent to the industrial district, that would supply an additional 25,000 kw of current.

From 1945 to 1947 the light division rushed the completion of two additional Nisqually River dams at Alder and LaGrande, thereby nearly doubling Tacoma's generating capacity. Both projects had been met with the traditional skepticism and court battles contesting the need for additional power. Yet by the time the last generating unit was installed in May 1947, Tacoma was utilizing the full capacity of each powerhouse and still had to buy additional outside power. Tacoma City Light spent the 1950s upgrading the capacity of its generating facilities, and in the 1960s it built the Mayfield and Mossyrock projects on the Cowlitz River to meet a load growth that had been doubling every seven or eight years.

Tacoma's residential rates, the first in the country to drop below one cent a kilowatt-hour, stayed at less than a penny from 1947 to 1971. The light division also claims the distinction of pioneering the use of underground lines. In the mid-1930s, underground installation in the business district was performed partly as a relief measure. Laborers on the project were selected from among those unemployed who were "unable to pay their light and water bills in cash" and allowed to work them off instead.

Seattle City Light

The early history of Seattle City Light is wound about a generator named James Delmage Ross. "Jay-Dee" was hired in 1902 to wire the public utility's first installation, the hydroelectric plant on the Cedar River, and he was with the utility for the next thirty-seven years. Ross grew up with electricity, and his engineering was largely self-taught. When the Seattle Electric Lighting Company first brightened Seattle streets in 1886, Ross was still in his early teens and living with his parents in Chatham, Ontario where he conducted electrical experiments powered by self-made batteries.

J.D. Ross

In Seattle, as elsewhere, the first electric service was balkanized, a patchwork of small steam generators feeding expensive and unreliable power to small territories. In its 1893 report to the city council, the Seattle Board of Public Works complained that "the difficulty of keeping an accurate check on which street lights are burning . . . and the impossibility of the city knowing whether the full candlepower of a light is being furnished or not . . . lead the board to believe that sound business judgment demands that the city own its own electric light plant." When the city composed its new charter in 1896, it explicitly empowered itself to provide for the lighting of streets, public buildings and residences and own whatever power facilities might be required.

Seattle's physical opportunity for public power came along with its new waterworks on the Cedar River. One year after the river's waters were first released into city reservoirs, city engineer R. H. Thomson recommended a dam site on the Cedar about a half-mile below Cedar (Chester Morse) Lake. When Seattle voters agreed in 1902 to support Thomson's proposal to exploit the Cedar River for municipal power as well as water, they were partly demonstrating their distrust of the Seattle Electric Co. (the future Puget Sound Power and Light), which was owned by eastern capitalists and had established a near monopoly on electric power and the streetcar service. During that and the

Seattle City Light generators (below left) and powerhouse (below right) below the Cedar (Chester Morse) Lake Reservoir. Center page: Seattle City Light's first timber crib dam on the Cedar River. Dec. 8, 1912. Courtesy, Seattle City Light.

following year, middle-and working-class Populists and Democrats managed to convince a majority of Seattle citizens that their best interests would be served by municipal control of "natural" monopolies. In the 1902 and 1903 elections voters approved the creation and financing of Seattle City Light.

What distinguished the city's plant at Cedar Falls was not its technology, but rather its status as the first publicly built hydroelectric installation in the country. The dam was of a timber-crib,

rock-filled design, and constructed entirely of lumber logged and milled at the site. About three miles below the dam, the powerhouse was connected to it by a four-foot wood stave pipeline. The current traveled forty miles to the utility's first distribution station at Seventh Avenue and Yesler Way. It was transmitted at 45,000 volts, which was a record level at the time.

Even so, the plant capacity was made rapidly inadequate by Seattle's alarming growth. In 1909 two additional generators raised it from 2,400 kilowatts to its limit:10,400 kw. In the following year the candlepower of the city street lights rose 600 percent, making it necessary to build a second generating plant that was also hydroelectric, although an oddity. The 1,500-kw auxiliary hydro unit used the overflow from the water department's Volunteer Park Reservoir. Installed in 1911 at an elevation about 300 feet below the reservoir, it was built at a site that was developed into the department's Lake Union steam plant. Steam units were added there in 1914, 1918, and 1921. The city's burgeoning appetite for electricity was due in part to the department's campaign, begun in 1912, to sell electric appliances, free wiring included.

The new department also worked to improve its stock at Cedar River. In 1914 a new 215-foot-high masonry dam was completed about midway between the original timber dam and its powerhouse. From the beginning the reservoir behind the new dam was plagued with seepage, making it practically useless as a reservoir for generating power. Observers feared that the bank might slip away, releasing a flood that could suddenly engulf not only the generating plant at Cedar Falls but also the water department's headworks further downstream at Landsburg. The steam generators at Lake Union made up the shortfalls in kilowatts until City Light could stop these leaks and develop an new site on the Skagit River.

The canyon on the Skagit was made of stiffer stuff than the percolating glacial till beside the Cedar River. Superintendent Ross was fond of reciting the "glories of the Skagit . . . lying entirely in hard granite." The Skagit site was not, however, his first pick. Ross first cast his eyes towards Lake Cushman on the Olympic

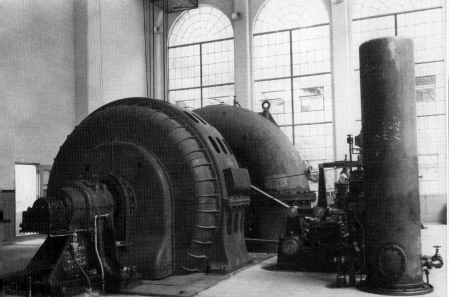

Peninsula. While Seattle voters approved condemnation and purchase of the Lake Cushman site in 1914 vote, they did not tally the required 60 percent majority to bond the actual construction of the facility. Later it was lost to Tacoma. When the department went searching elsewhere, on the Skykomish and White rivers, they were foiled by Puget Sound Power and Light, which quickly bought the sites before the city could act. The private company's mole-like talent for uncovering what Ross was up to may have even reached into his bedroom where his wife, Alice, dislodged a microphone from the chimney while burning trash in the fireplace. Ross returned the stealth in 1917.

Puget Power had the first rights to develop the Skagit River for power, but as Ross discovered, they had lapsed temporarily. Using his own and borrowed cash, Ross rushed his own application — in his name — to Washington, D.C., where the Department of Agriculture held authority over power sites on federal land. Ross told the federal officials that Puget Power grabbed the White and Skykomish river sites while still holding but not developing the Skagit. He characterized the company's greed as an instance "of the boy in Aesop's fable who put his hand in the jar of nuts and grabbed them all but could not get his hand out without dropping everything."

Ultimately, it was David Houston, the Secretary of Agriculture, who had to choose between the city and the company. His decision in Ross's favor arrived on December 25, 1918, just hours after Ross learned of the "Boxley Blowout." A large portion of the leaking reservoir on the Cedar River had suddenly washed away, destroying sawmills, railroad tracks, and the entire town of Edgewick to the north. Fortunately for Seattle's light and water plants on the Cedar, the flood ultimately drained into the Snoqualmie River basin. By the time the reservoir was at last made relatively safe and impervious, the Skagit's first two dams, Gorge and Diablo, were completed.

Linemen and lines behind Seattle City Light's first substation on Yesler Way near the site of the present Interstate 5 overpass. Courtesy, Seattle City Light

Skagit Project

The Skagit project was developed within the fifteen-mile stretch where the largest tributary to Puget Sound drops 700 feet through a gorge of solid granite. It sends the water through a succession of three plants, consisting each of a reservoir, a dam, two tunnels, and a powerhouse. In 1919 the city council allocated $432,900 for construction of a work town at Newhalem and a wagon road linking it and the first dam site at Gorge Creek with the head of the Great Northern Railway's tracks twenty-three miles downstream at Rockport. Ross substituted a railroad for the open road to more readily control access to the site — he feared saboteurs. When gold was discovered in the river during construction of the Gorge, workers temporarily abandoned their dam work for panning. Work on the dam was further complicated by forest fires, railroad wash-outs, and striking tunnelers. At last, in September 1924, President Calvin Coolidge switched on the first generator at Gorge Dam, and the current was carried to the new North Substation above Green Lake on East Seventy-fifth Street. With this fresh glut of power, rates fell to 3.41 cents per kilowatt-hour in 1925. Work began on Diablo Dam — the second of the three in the Skagit Project — in 1927, and it was completed nine years later.

During this time J. D. Ross's work with City Light got Franklin D. Roosevelt's attention. In 1931 Ross visited FDR, who was still governor of New York, to advise him on plans for power generation on the St. Lawrence Seaway. They became friends. Later as president, Roosevelt gave Ross three assignments: first in 1935 as chief engineer of the Federal Power Board organized to expedite Public Works Administration projects; soon after as a member of the Securities and Exchange Commission; and, finally, in 1937 as the first administrator of the Bonneville Power Administration (BPA). According to Jim Ross, a nephew whom Ross and his wife helped raise, the last assignment was accompanied by an instance of his uncle's obsession with electricity and the president's charm. Ross had given Roosevelt a copy of his book *New Views of Space, Matter and Time,* which was filled with his reflections on subjects more productively studied by Maxwell and Einstein. Roosevelt confessed to Ross that he was not able to make it through the first page, but added that "If I have any problems with the fourth dimension, I'll call you!" Later Ross heard from FDR, "Well, I've got the fourth dimension problem now. I want you to be the administrator of BPA."

By 1939, the year Ross died while recuperating from surgery at the Mayo Clinic, City Light had increased its generation by 1,200 percent since Ross engineered the first plant at Cedar River Falls. With few hitches, Ross had steadily increased power supply while lowering

Seattle City Light auxiliary hydroelectric unit (left) and the city's first steam unit (center) on Lake Union; April 5, 1919. Courtesy, Seattle Municipal Archives.

rates. And when the city utility initiated rate reductions, Puget Power, which still controlled a quarter of Seattle's electrical accounts, followed. Ross also covered the city with wires — except those the utility buried in the central business district during the late 1920s — including parallel distribution in the neighborhoods already serviced by Puget Power.

After Ross's successor, Eugene R. Hoffman, initiated a reduced "All-Electric Rate" for homes powered exclusively by electricity in 1940, Seattle-ites' consumption of power during the war averaged 3,246 kilowatt-hours a year, more than double the national average of 1,151. Residential power consumption continued to climb as veterans and their families settled down in new homes following the conflict. In 1949 Ross Dam was topped off at 540 feet, although it was designed to go higher. Three years later the first 90,000-kilowatt generator was installed in the Ross powerhouse. In 1954 the Skagit Railroad was dismantled — although the popular Skagit Tours continued — and the following year work began on replacing the original low Gorge timber dam with a new 285-foot masonry structure which, when it was completed in 1960, increased capacity at the Gorge powerhouse to 175,000 kilowatts. It was none too soon for by 1958 Seattle residents were using an average of 8,063 kilowatts a year, still more than twice the national average.

With the Skagit project nearing capacity, City Light began its search for other hydroelectric sources. In 1961 the utility was licensed to build at a dam on the Pend Oreille River in the northeast corner of the state just below the Canadian border. Construction on Boundary Dam began in 1963 and by 1967 the first of its four units was producing. After the installation of two huge Toshiba generators in 1986, the Boundary plant accounted for more than a third of Seattle's city-owned hydroelectric power supply. The utility has other interests on the Pend Oreille River as well, holding a contract for part of the output from the Pend Oreille County PUD dams at Box Canyon and Priest Rapids.

Two additions to the Skagit Project were given protracted study throughout the 1970s. In 1970 the city applied for a permit to raise Ross Dam to the full height envisioned in the 1930s, and in 1972 a fourth Skagit installation below the Gorge plant at Copper Creek was seriously considered. Neither project was built. The raising of Ross Dam, which would have extended Ross Lake further into British Columbia, was rejected by the Canadians. In 1984 Canada agreed instead to supply power equal in amount and cost to that which would have been generated by a heightened dam. In January 1980 Seattle Mayor Charles Royer and entourage took to rubber rafts for a float through the Copper Creek site. Their chilly experience confirmed his cool disposition to the dam proposal. The combination of uncertainties over Native American rights on the river, damage to the bald eagle's riverside habitat that would accompany the flooding of the valley, and the relatively minimal power promised — an estimated 3.5 percent of the utility's hydroelectric generating

Above: Steel plate Y for the Diablo plant. R.H. Thomson stands third from right, and J.D. Ross stands fourth from left. Courtesy, Seattle City Light. Clockwise from below left: 1. Inside Gorge powerhouse. 2. Ladder up the face of Gorge Dam, 1995. Photo by Nancy Ishii. 3. The two-mile-long Gorge tunnel measures 20.5 feet in diameter and supplies three 10-foot diameter penstocks. 4. Diablo Dam, 1995. Photo by Nancy Ishii.

capacity — scuttled the Copper Creek proposal.

By the mid-1970s, City Light officials had become worried about the economics of additional energy production. As an alternative to more hydroelectric generation, they considered nuclear power as a way to meet rising demand for energy. In 1975 City Light's administrator, Gordon Vickery, recommended the agency purchase a ten percent share in the WPPSS plants 4 and 5. (In 1971 the city had agreed to an 8 percent share in WPPSS plants 1, 2, and 3.) Reaction to Vickery's request was swift and sour. The Washington Environmental Council, an umbrella group of environmental organizations, filed suit to halt the purchase. When the Seattle City Council agreed to hire independent consultants to study both the problems and alternative solutions, the environmentalists dropped the suit but not their guard — a Citizens Overview Committee closely monitored the consultants' work.

The 1976 study, Energy 1990, was the result of this prudent politicking. As the title indicates, the consultants were hired to project Seattle's energy needs over fifteen years and recommend the best sources to meet those needs. In the mid-1970s the city's electric consumption was growing at a yearly rate of about 3.5 percent. The Energy 1990 report projected that Seattle consumers would use less electricity as prices rose, making additional nuclear investments unnecessary. It proposed a community-wide commitment to conservation, with a resulting annual growth rate of only 2.7 percent in the year 1990. Mayor Wes Uhlman split the difference between Vickery's proposal and the consultants' and recommended that the city commit to five percent of WPPSS plants 4 and 5. By the surprisingly wide margin of 6 to 3, the council rejected Uhlman's compromise and adopted the Energy 1990 report.

What actually transpired by 1990 is a happy advertisement

Diablo dam and Ruby Mountain. Courtesy, Seattle City Light.

for the consultants' and the council's wisdom in 1976. The utility had projected a growth in demand of 3.24 percent a year and estimated that the city would require 1,379 average megawatts. The actual average load in 1989 was 1,059 megawatts and growth in 1990 was projected at 1.1 percent per year. Periodic rate increases had encouraged consumers to take Energy 1990's prescriptions for conservation seriously.

In 1977, the year City Light opened its conservation office, the worst regional drought in a century required the utility to purchase power from other sources. In addition to a rate increase, the out-of-area purchases were subsidized by drought surcharges. With conservation the first priority, City Light began experiments with residential solar energy and offered free home energy checks, with free home insulation for elderly and low-income home owners. Fifteen years later during the severe drought of 1992, expanded numbers of City Light customers were becoming accustomed to the idea of water shortages and the consequent rise in water and power rates. Snow packs were so low that year that the Ross Lake reservoir could not meet both local power needs and the $25 million in outside power sales on which the utility usually counted. Consequently, for the first time in its history, the utility faced a deficit.

J. D. Ross's vision of more and cheaper power produced by a natural — and public — monopoly in a natural wonderland was bound to eventually reach its limits. Still, the relatively low cost of Ross's "municipal miracle" on the Skagit continued to partly subsidize the rates of City Light customers who through the 1990s became increasingly aware of the conservable side of this precious resource.

PUBLIC UTILITY DISTRICTS

In 1920 while Seattle and Tacoma residents were enjoying the low rates charged by their municipal light departments, King and Pierce county residents living outside city limits had to pay several times as much for private power. Washington law forbade municipal utilities to sell power outside their city limits. Inspired by the big cities' low rates and encouraged by public power advocates such as J. D. Ross and Homer T. Bone, the Washington State Grange in the early 1920s began a movement to bring low-cost power to rural people. In a decade known for its political complacency, Washington farmers worked doggedly for the passage of a law that would authorize publicly owned systems of basic utilities to operate in agricultural areas.

First organized in Washington in the early 1870s, the Grange

Ross Dam under construction (below) and as photgraphed by Nancy Ishii in 1995 (above). Courtesy, Seattle City Light.

became the mouthpiece of Populist agrarian protest and anti-monopoly sentiment during the depressed days of the mid-1890s. The Populist Party collapsed when prosperity returned, partly in the form of Klondike gold, but Washington Grange leaders did not abandon their drive for political reform. During the period of Progressive reform preceding World War I, the Grange discovered allies in organized labor and its greatest political weapon in nonpartisan appeals to the electorate. The initiative and referendum measures for which they had campaigned became the means by which the Patrons of Husbandry were able to circumvent an unsympathetic legislature and submit their proposals for economic and political reform directly to the people. Twice, in 1915 and in 1921-22, the legislature passed bills that would have made it virtually impossible for municipal systems to condemn the property of private utilities. In each case the Grange and the State Federation of Labor led successful campaigns to put the issue before the voters in the form of a referendum. And each time the legislature's action was decisively rejected. The Grange first went on record in favor of rural public utilities in 1916.

It was not ideological conviction that motivated the farmers' drive for public ownership as much as practical economics and daily frustration. By 1920 most of cities and towns in Washington had been enjoying the electric age for at least a decade or two; yet many in the state's large rural minority — 45 percent according to

Above: Skamania County PUD activists (from left), Chauncey Price, PUD commissioner; Clyde Linville, PUD attorney and county prosecutor; and Harry Card, PUD commissioner, pose at the front steps to the county courthouse in Stevenson, 1940.

the 1920 U.S. census — remained in the dark. Companies such as Puget Sound Power and Light devised rate schedules according to population density, distance from generating facilities, and the amount of competition. In 1925 Puget Power rates per kilowatt hour varied from 5.5 cents for the first block of power in Seattle, where the company had public competition, to 12 cents in the vicinity of Chehalis.

Conditions for getting rural service could be as irritating as the rates charged. Often, farmers had to supply the poles, lines, and equipment necessary to tie in with the power company's system and deed these improvements over to the company. And then their rates were based on the value of the company's property, including the farmers' lines. Indeed, they paid several times over for the extension lines, according to the *Washington Grange News*.

Yet the costs of bringing power to isolated regions were real. The larger companies, such as Puget Power and Washington Water Power, were proud of the extent of their rural electrification programs. A fact that public power advocates often overlooked was the high rate of electrification in rural Washington compared to agricultural areas in other states of the region. In 1935 — before the activation of the state's public utility districts — 48 percent of Washington's 40,000 farms were receiving central station electric service, compared to 30 percent in Oregon and in Idaho, and six percent in Montana. But such statistics did little to quiet those who still were without power.

Fred J. Chamberlain, a Puyallup berry grower who was nicknamed the "old Grange warhorse" for his longtime crusade for the public power cause, became the chief spokesman for the aggrieved farmers. Chamberlain attributed the farmers' activism to "the arbitrary control of the Legislature, the dominating tactics of the Power Trust, and their reckless use of propaganda, and the success of the Ontario system [state ownership] in Canada

Above: Energized on Jan. 1 1940, the Skamania County Public Utilities District was the first of the regional full-county PUDs. Lineman Sparky Meyers is at the front door. Below: Citizens meeting in the formative years of the Skamania County PUD. Photos this page courtesy, Skamania County PUD.

[which] created a spirit over the State for public ownership." In 1921 Chamberlain was elected president of the "Super Power League of Washington" formed by farm and labor groups and liberals of both major parties to consider a number of public power proposals. In mid-December 1923 the Seattle Municipal League sponsored a statewide hydroelectric conference that was attended by mayors, city officials, and Grange and labor union members. The committee they elected, which included Chamberlain and state Grange Master Albert Goss, decided to back the Bone Bill.

The bill, written by Tacoma city attorney and state legislator Homer Bone, would have permitted cities owning their own power systems to sell surplus power outside their corporate limits. A Farmer-Labor Progressive, Bone had just begun his political career, having been elected to the state House of Representatives in 1922. Bone's bill, he recalled in 1948, "precipitated what was then declared to be the bitterest fight the Legislature had ever witnessed. The power companies got busy and really went to town on that fight. The Legislature was deluged with printed propaganda and the power lobbyists were as thick as bees around a hive."

After the bill went down to defeat in the legislature, Bone was determined to put the issue before the people using the initiative law which he had helped write. Campaigning in "hundreds of places around the State" before the fall election of 1924, Bone charged that the power companies had spent a million dollars to defeat the bill. "Hundreds of thousands of pieces of literature were put out by the private companies and were distributed by hand, by mail and in public meetings." They disseminated their point of view even in the schools and set up committees around the state. J. D. Ross, who was also an effective platform speaker, toured the state with Bone, campaigning for the measure. But the public power proponents, split by factions representing the more conservative and rural eastern side of the mountains and the more liberal and urban western side, could not match the industry's recently invented "public relations" assault. Initiative No. 52 was voted down by nearly 2 to 1.

During the rest of the decade while the issue languished in the public's eye, membership in the Grange soared. The *Grange News* began publishing legislators' voting records, and farmers were encouraged to run for positions in the state house. Goss and Chamberlain led the Grange's power development committee, and they refused to give up the idea of public utility districts. In 1926 at their annual convention the Grange endorsed Goss's speech, one that echoed Bone's argument that "to permit Stone

Vote Him a Change of Diet

The Grange News was one of the prominent voices urging passage of Initiative No. 1 in 1930. This cartoon appeared on the eve of the election.

The Grange, an early advocate of public power, used its organ to attack the private companies' monopolist iniquities as the Grange saw them. Courtesy Washington State Grange. Below: Later Puget Power Co. responded with its own cartoon campaign against PUD condemnation of private power facilities. Courtesy Puget Sound Power and Light Co.

and Webster to take the power from our hills which is the heritage of our children is a crime against the coming generations." Stressing the failure of regulation by the public service commission, the group passed a strong resolution calling for public ownership of hydroelectric facilities. The Grange leaders argued that low-cost public power would stimulate urban industrial activity and in turn create a market for farm products. The public power projects could also serve as an important relief measure for those put out of work by the postwar slump in the agriculture and lumber industry.

All fired-up, Chamberlain once again called on Homer Bone who had considerable experience with utility law and continued his passionate quest for public power. (Bone, in fact, molded his party affiliation around the power issue, running sequentially for local, state and national offices as a Socialist, Farmer-Laborite, Progressive, and Republican. In 1932 he would be elected to the U.S. Senate as a Democrat.) After many meetings and months of study, Chamberlain's committee drew up a bill that would give rural citizens the same right to form public electric systems as that city residents enjoyed. The measure would authorize the formation of public utility districts as municipal corporations, consisting of one or more counties, with powers to issue revenue bonds and levy property taxes, and buy, construct, or condemn privately-owned power facilities. The districts were to be formed by means of a petition and majority vote of the electorate. According to Bone they had written into the bill "every conceivable power which then appeared possible of realization." In 1929 the District Power Bill was presented to the legislature and became Initiative No. 1. When the lawmakers, "still dominated by the power trust" according to Bone, refused to pass the bill, it went on the ballot for the general election in November 1930.

In the late 1920s muckraking revelations made it obvious to anyone with a habit for the daily newspaper that the "power trust" was more than a local slur. By 1925 the rapid expansion of the electrical industry had created an ideal arena for the operation of shady business practices. Sixteen holding companies controlled 85 percent of the nation's electricity production, and most of Washington's private utilities were controlled by six of them.

Public power advocates found it easy to tap the western farmer's and working man's traditional animosity toward eastern capitalists, who were portrayed as in control of both the state legislature and the national Congress. The depressed condition of agriculture in the 1920s also contributed to the common practice of skapegoating big business.

In 1934 Chamberlain, who had learned to match the best of the industry's public relations rhetoric, recalled what the public power advocates had been up against in the twenties:

"Our nation was parceled out to various interlocking corporations over which princes and czars held sway. . . . Here in the State of Washington the Washington Water Power Company was supreme on the East side. The Puget Sound Power and Light Company held dictatorial sway on the West side and the Pacific Power and Light Company captured the southern central section. They usurped the political reins, they captured the legislature, they dominated the government, they invaded the schools and polluted the pulpits."

Above: This scene, taken July 30, 1930, shows the Grays Harbor Railway and Light Company's powerhouse and public swimming pond, which were part of the facilities taken over ten years later by the Public Utilities District No. 1 of Grays Harbor County.

The image of a thoroughly corrupt industry was reinforced when the Federal Trade Commission completed two lengthy investigations of the power industry at the end of the 1920s. The commission reported to Congress a number of fantastic stock manipulations, pyramiding of holding companies, and evidence of stock watering and high profit margins — which involved a number of companies operating in the Northwest. Company efforts to control public opinion and to influence local, state, and national governmental regulations inspired several books about the "machinations of the power trust." Public confidence in the companies was undermined further by the collapse of the stock market in November 1929.

Wiser for the mistakes they had made six years earlier, the Grange was prepared to do in 1930 what it had failed to accomplish in 1924. Public power advocates had little money to spend, but they responded to the companies' newspaper ads and "canned" editorials with a well-organized campaign conducted by hundreds of volunteers — and by C.C. Dill. Washington's U.S. senator from Spokane, who had helped initiate the Senate probe of the power industry, campaigned for the power bill around the state, releasing strategic revelations from the FTC investigation.

The vote was close and early returns were not encouraging for public power. But after the rural ballots came in late, the day after the election, the Grange was rewarded for its perseverance. After ten years of losing battles, Homer Bone, Fred Chamberlain and the public ownership forces were finally victorious with a 22,000 vote majority. The Public Utility District Law, which adopted the provisions of Bone's bill, authorized Washington residents to establish public utility districts (PUDs) as municipal corporations, coextensive with existing county lines. The PUD could acquire private utility property by condemnation; it could tax, issue revenue bonds and a limited amount of general obligation bonds on its own motion without going to the people. These awesome powers enabled Washingtonians to make by far the most extensive efforts to establish PUDs in the region and elevated Washington into the top three PUD states in the country. Along with the districts in Nebraska, an all-public power state, the Washington districts were cited by the editors of the Yale law journal in 1951 as "the most effective non-federal public power device yet developed." The District Power Act was followed in 1933 by state legislation, gladly resurrected by now-U.S. Senator Bone, which permitted cities to sell their power outside corporate limits.

Enabling legislation alone was not sufficient to spur state residents to immediately start up their own utility districts. Political observers at the time claimed that the vote legalizing the establishment of PUDs was more a protest against the private utility industry than an affirmative vote for public power. By 1935 only Mason County had created a district that actually provided service, and it was a small one, serving only a corner of the county. In 1936, Washington voters helped President Franklin Roosevelt win a landslide victory and also approved fifteen new PUDs. But by 1939 only four districts had solved all the problems involved in supplying power sources and building transmission systems. The technical difficulties were formidable. Private industry also helped to delay the formation and operation of the districts by filing a number of initiatives and legal challenges that tested the constitutionality of the PUD law. And the hard times of the Great Depression caused farmers to think twice about attempting to finance costly new power systems.

But the economic collapse actually aided rural electrification when it brought to the presidency Franklin D. Roosevelt who, as

Far left: Heye Meyer, Clark County PUD commissioner, activates service for that PUD in 1942. Courtesy Clark County PUD. Left: The 1940 transfer of Grays Harbor Railway and Light Company's properties to Grays Harbor County Public Utilities District No. 1. The meeting concluded with the passing of a $2.842 million check from county to company. Courtesy, Jones Photo Company, Aberdeen.

Above: Transmission line construction. Courtesy, Chelan County PUD.

governor of New York, had undertaken an ambitious state power program. In a campaign speech delivered in Portland in September 1932, Roosevelt called the distribution of electricity "a national problem." State regulation had failed to prevent unreasonable profits, and public power, he believed, could be used as a "yardstick" against which the rates of private companies might be measured and held in line. New Deal legislation supplied a further thrust for public power. The 1935 Holding Company Act facilitated the transfer of electric company properties to public ownership. The Rural Electrification Administration (REA), also passed in 1935, offered low-interest government loans to non-profit cooperatives for the construction of power lines in areas currently unserved by any electric utility. The state's congressional delegation between 1932 and 1942, all Democrats including some of the most liberal in the state's history, prodded the government toward a more aggressive power program in the Northwest. But the greatest impetus to the PUD movement was the construction of Bonneville and Grand Coulee dams.

Not until cheap federal power became available through the Bonneville Power Administration (BPA) did more public utility districts come on line in the 1940s. At the time of the drafting of the PUD bill, Homer Bone claimed, "no one envisioned such later developments as Grand Coulee and the Bonneville Power Administration." The BPA not only built transmission facilities from the federal dams to the major load centers, but it also provided legal and technical assistance to those PUDs attempting to purchase or condemn private distribution systems in order to tie in with the Bonneville system. The appointment of public power enthusiasts J. D. Ross and his successor, Dr. Paul Raver, as the first Bonneville administrators resulted in a BPA policy of active support for PUDs in the region. Faced with competition, private utility rates fell. Between 1935 and 1940 their cumulative reductions in the region equaled about $13 million annually.

In 1940 when it became the first Washington PUD to receive the federal Columbia River power, Skamania County PUD also began operating as the first full-county district, having acquired by condemnation the properties of the West Coast Power Company. Kittitas, Cowlitz, Clark, and Grant counties followed in the next two years. As BPA expanded its interconnections, other districts including Wahkiakum, Pacific, Klickitat, Lewis, Chelan, Snohomish, and Grays Harbor came on line in the late 1940s. By 1949 twenty public electric utility districts were operating in the state's thirty-nine counties. In 1954 only nine counties had not established a PUD. Most of the operating districts were located in the western and central part of the state. Other than the rural cooperatives, the eastern third of Washington remained largely in the private industry camp. The good service and customer relations established by Washington Water Power over the years quieted the few voices calling for utility districts in their service area.

RURAL ELECTRIFICATION AND REA COOPERATIVES

Electric power came last to those areas of rural eastern Washington that private utilities had found unprofitable to serve. Soon after the Rural Electrification Administration was established in 1935, groups of farmers in eastern Washington counties began organizing electric cooperatives. An electric cooperative, according to state law, was a group of customers who controlled the agency by electing its trustees and shared equally in its gains or losses. Unlike the public utility districts, they were not given the power of eminent domain. The REA operated as combination banker and consulting engineer and offered 100 percent loan financing. Farm families found time after a full day of chores to attend community meetings and help sign up members. It was not uncommon to hear the local preacher include a request for electric service in the Sunday morning service. Between 1937 and 1941 seven rural electric coops were energized in Washington.

In March 1937, Whitman and Spokane County farmers formed Inland Empire Rural Electrification Inc. to hook up farmers living within the service area of Washington Water Power Company. Using its REA loan, Inland, which was supplied by Washington Water Power for a few years before tying into the BPA

Above: Five years after the Public Power Act won its statewide referendum in 1930, the State Supreme Court validated it. In 1935, Mason County No. 1 became the first PUD to begin operation in the state. The following year, Lewis County's was one of fifteen new PUDs approved by voters. Courtesy Lewis County Public Utilities District.

HYDRO BUILDS THREE SHIPS WHERE ONE WAS BUILT BEFORE

THROUGH THE MAGIC OF ELECTRIC WELDING

BONNEVILLE FIGHTS TIME

Above: Chelan County PUD's Lake Chelan Dam where the lake outlet passes through the town of Chelan. Courtesy, Chelan County PUD.
Left and right: Examples of Bonneville Power's World War II posters promoting public power as a hardworking weapon.
Below: The electrifying acts of nature and man along a Bonneville Power transmission line.

Let 'em have it with hydro

YOUR JOB IS A WAR JOB!

BONNEVILLE IS ON THE WAR FRONT

YOUR JOB IS WAR

THE ENTIRE NATION IS LOOKING TOWARD THE PACIFIC NORTHWEST FOR POWER · · POWER TO FORGE THE WEAPONS WE NEED FOR VICTORY!

TURN YOUR TIME INTO POWER

Above: Early view of the completed Grand Coullee Dam. Bottom left: Back of Grand Coulee from the east side of the dam. Photos courtesy U.S. Bureau of Reclamation. Bottom right: Grand Coulee Dam promoter and The Wenatchee World *editor Rufus Woods. Courtesy,* Wenatchee World.

grid, was able to build nearly 500 miles of line to bring power to its first 1,530 members. The cooperative completed the backbone of its system of 1,500 miles by the end of 1941, but electrifying new and old farms continued into the late 1940s. Washington Water Power Company at times accelerated its line construction to compete with the growing coop and attempted to buy it out in 1940. But Inland was determined to stay in business and continue to bring service to "ALL rural people." In 1976 with over 12,000 members mostly in Spokane, Whitman, Pend Oreille, Stevens, and Garfield counties and 5,000 miles of line in low-density regions, Inland was the largest electric cooperative in the state and one of the largest in the nation.

Few farmers had to be persuaded of the advantages that electric power could bring them. During the mid-1930s most eastern Washington farms of 1,500 to 2,000 acres barely grossed $2,000 a year. Yet many of their owners were willing to make financial sacrifices in order to build lines and tie in with the closest system. Power meant a release from the drudgery of a wood stove that burned as hot during the summer as the winter and whose wood box always seemed to be empty. It brought an end to the tedious hauling of water from the hand-cranked pump and heating it on the stove. And the electric stove allowed the farmwife the marvelous and unprecedented freedom of being able to leave the kitchen, and even the house, while the stew simmered and the pies baked.

In the mid-1920s Washington State Agricultural College (later Washington State University) conducted research, sponsored by the state's three largest private utilities, into a number of

other ways that electricity could save farmers time, work, and money. Some of their projects included electric oat-sprouters, water trough warmers, milking machines, irrigation sprinklers, hay dryers, potato and apple washers, fans as orchard frost expellers, and lamps for pig brooders and hen houses. These experiments would eventually profit the utilities as well as the farmers since their adoption resulted in a vastly heightened use of power and made the building of new transmission lines worth the investment.

FEDERAL HYDROPOWER

The Columbia River is the nation's greatest hydroelectric power resource. Since the federal government began to harness it, the Columbia has produced the major portion of the state's, the region's, and the nation's inexpensive electricity. Its development was a catalyst to mid-twentieth-century Northwest economic growth and revolutionized the state's industrial base.

In 1881 Lieutenant Thomas W. Symons of the Army Corps of Engineers in a thirty-foot wooden boat, manned by four native oarsmen shouting in "wild savage glee," took an adrenaline-raising trip down a 360-mile stretch of the Columbia River. His assignment was to examine and report on the river between Colville and the mouth of the Snake River noting developments that could open the river to navigation and commerce (see Waterways Chapter). Along with the copious professional notes he made about river conditions, Symons interjected personal observations about "the complete silence and lifelessness" which made the scene "exceedingly wild, almost unearthly." Fifty years later little had changed in the scenery of looming basalt cliffs and empty coulee-scarred tablelands. But by then the Army Corps had made plans that would forever alter the wild unearthliness of Symon's vision. Between 1923 and 1928 army engineers conducted surveys for a river development plan that called for multipurpose projects for navigation, flood control, irrigation, and hydroelectric power. The Corps' 1,850-page "308" report of 1931 recommended for the Columbia ten multipurpose dams between the Canadian border and tidewater to be erected at Grand Coulee, Foster Creek, Chelan, Rocky Reach, Rock Island, Priest Rapids, Umatilla Rapids, John Day Rapids, The Dalles, and Bonneville at the Cascades. In 1932 the availability of the army's recommendations and the lobbying efforts of the state before Congress and the administration combined to get the development of the Columbia River underway.

Grand Coulee Dam

The greatest of the Columbia River projects was proposed years before the corps' first 308 report. Grand Coulee Dam was originally the brainchild of central Washington boomers. Rufus Woods, editor of the *Wenatchee Daily World*, and

Above: FDR at the Grand Coulee Dam construction site, August 1934. Courtesy, WA State Historical Society, Tacoma. Below: A young Grand Coulee Dam beyond Mason City. Here the irrigation component (top center) is still under construction. (Compare to photos at beginning of chapter.) Courtesy, U.S. Bureau of Reclamation.

Billy Clapp, an Ephrata attorney, began promoting their schemes for a huge dam spanning the river at Grand Coulee in 1917. Woods was a born enthusiast for anything in which he believed, and above all he believed in the development of the latent resources of north central Washington. Throughout the twenties, Woods advocated a high dam to be used primarily for irrigating the Columbia Basin drylands. According to Kirby Billingsley, longtime manager of the Chelan County PUD who previously worked under Woods for thirty-five years, "You couldn't work for the *Wenatchee World* and Rufus Woods without being in the 'dam' business." Woods won the support of the state Grange which had initially opposed the plan to bring more land under irrigation, believing that increased production would prolong the agricultural depression. By 1930, however, it had become clear that there would be a great block of cheap power for sale above the power needed for irrigation pumping — power the farmers could use. Holding strong convictions about private ownership and free enterprise, however, Woods would not swap with the Grange his support for their 1929 District Power Bill.

James O'Sullivan was another indefatigable champion of Grand Coulee Dam. The former Ephrata attorney returned from the Midwest to carry the banner for the project around the state and back to the nation's capital. The drought conditions between 1917 and 1929, that cut wheat production in Douglas County in 1929 to one-tenth of what it had been in 1917, bolstered O'Sullivan's conviction that irrigation was the only salvation for the Columbia Basin.

Grand Coulee Dam was a controversial project from its inception throughout its construction. When Wood's radical proposal for a huge dam at Grand Coulee was finally taken seriously, aroused power companies, particularly Washington Water Power, began organized attempts to block any government

project. To derail the dam, which would create a vast and competing source of power, the company and other Spokane interests in the 1920s backed a plan for a gravity-flow system of irrigation that would divert water from Lake Pend Oreille in Idaho. (See Irrigation Chapter.) In 1933 Washington Water Power protested the Federal Power Commission's grant of a preliminary permit for a high dam at Grand Coulee on the grounds that it would interfere with the Kettle Falls site for which the company already held a preliminary dam permit. They also argued that a surplus of generating capacity existed in the Northwest and that it would continue for a long time.

The colossal size and cost of the proposed dam and its location in such a thinly populated area of the country put local supporters and government planners on the defensive. In the 1930s before the widespread use of pump irrigation in the Northwest, there was no industry that consumed large amounts of electricity, except for the paper and pulp industry which had traditionally generated its own. The regional economy was dependent on the extraction and processing of raw materials in agriculture, forestry, fishing, and mining. In comparison to other parts of the country, there was very little manufacturing. During a time when corporate profits had all but disappeared, state and federal authorities could not be certain that a large market for the amount of power a dam the size of Grand Coulee would produce would ever exist. Still, they tried to disarm objections about an overabundance of power by devising plans for attracting power-consuming industry to the area. Studies by the State College of Washington at Pullman were commissioned on the use of electricity in aluminum production and on the possibility of developing a phosphate fertilizer industry using the electro-thermal process. Another engineering experiment was conducted by the future Washington State University at Mason City, the contractor's camp at the dam site. Built by the contractor, Mason-Walsh-Atkinson-Kier Company, the town had 340 residences, twenty bunkhouses, a hotel, recreation hall, general store, bank, post-office, theater, firehouse, baseball park, tennis courts, two churches, and a general hospital staffed by four doctors and twelve nurses. The entire complex was built in ninety days. First of its kind in the country, the revolutionary all-electric town had no chimneys so that researchers could determine the feasibility of heating houses with electric heat so that the dam might generate another source of revenue.

Between 1935 and 1937 national magazine articles scoffed at the dam, calling it a useless monument and a huge white elephant. A *Collier's* writer contended that the "dead land, bitter with alkali" around the project was so poor that even when irrigated it would never produce crops. And as for who would use the power, some joked, if there wasn't an electric light bulb in every gopher hole in the Northwest, American taxpayers would get stuck paying the tab. Congressmen from eastern states asked why their constituents should be taxed to pay the enormous cost of federal dams in a region that had less than 3 percent of the country's population, especially when they created power no one needed and reclaimed land no one wanted improved. The electrical industry also complained about unfair competition and priority being granted to a "socialistic" program. Even the president of the American Society of Civil Engineers declared that the dam would be no more useful than the pyramids of Egypt.

But there were powerful exceptions to this derisive chorus. Foremost among them was Rep. Sam Hill and state

Top: Governor Clarence Martin makes the first concrete pour at Grand Coulee, December, 1935. Above: Dam construction from the reservoir side. Photos courtesy, WA State Historical Society, Tacoma. Below left: The largest cement mixer in the world at the time, with a capacity of 16,000 yards in 21 hours. Below right: inspection tunnel. Courtesy, John Cooper.

QUEEN MARY · QUEEN MARY · QUEEN MARY · QUEEN MARY

Queen Mary
1018 Feet Long

L. C. Smith Bldg., Seattle
462 Feet High

Capitol, Washington, D. C.
288 Feet High

Statue of Liberty
305 Feet High

Niagara Falls
167 Feet High

World's Greatest Dam

THE Grand Coulee dam will be the largest dam in the world. Its striking features are tabulated below:

Length—4200 feet.
Height—550 feet.
Width at base—500 feet.
Width at crest—32 feet.
Spillway—1654 feet.
Handles 1,000,000 feet per second.
Concrete—11,250,000 cubic yards.
Weight 23,000,000 tons.
Capacity—2,640,000 horsepower.
Two power houses, each 765 feet long.
Each 292 feet high.
Creates lake 151 miles long.
Generators weigh 2,000,000 pounds.

GRAND COULEE DAM
550 FEET HIGH

NIAGARA FALLS
167 FEET HIGH

GRAND COULEE DAM
2,640,000 HORSEPOWER

BOULDER DAM
1,500,000 HORSE POWER

* COMPARATIVE POWER GENERATED AT GRAND COULEE AND OTHER LARGE DAMS

WILSON 610,000 H.P.

BONNEVILLE 360,000 H.P.

WHEELER 360,000 H.P.

NIAGARA (CANADA) 208,200

GRAND COULEE DAM 2,640,000 H.P.

WHEELER 360,000 H.P.

WILSON 610,000 H.P.

BONNEVILLE 360,000 H.P

NIAGARA (CANADA) 208,200

GRAND COULEE RUNOFF 81,000,000 ACRE FEET

BOULDER DAM RUNOFF 16,000,000 ACRE FEET

Under the caption "Facts—Not Fancies," Reclamation Era, *organ of the U.S. Bureau of Reclamation, presented the following Grand Coulee highlights:*

The ultimate Grand Coulee Dam will be as high as a 46-story building (500 feet) and as long as 14 ordinary city blocks (4,200 feet). It will contain 11.25 million cubic yards of concrete masonry, which is about four times the volume of the great pyramid, the pyramid of Cheops, and three and one-half times that of Boulder dam, largest concrete dam in the world.

The bulk of Grand Coulee exceeds the combined bulk of the 20 largest concrete dams in the country. This huge mass of concrete will weigh 23 million tons. It would build a monument 100 feet by 100 feet, 5.75 miles in height; or if placed on an ordinary city block would rise 2.7 times the height of the Empire State building in New York City (1,248 feet), or to a total height of 3,375 feet, more than three-fifths of a mile.

It would build a standard paved highway, 16 feet wide, from New York to Seattle and return by way of Los Angeles. The concrete will require 12.5 million barrels of cement, weighing 2.35 million tons. If this were all shipped in one freight train, it would be 500 miles long and contain 50,000 box cars.

The maximum daily requirement for cement will be 60 cars. With two mixing plants running at full capacity, it is estimated that a cubic yard of concrete will be placed in the dam every five and one-half seconds. The base of the dam covers 34 acres. The capacity of the power plant will be 2.7 million horse power, 50 percent larger than the Boulder plant (largest in the world) and equaling the combined installed capacity of the 12 largest plants (with the exception of Boulder) in this country.

Each of the generators will be 40 feet in diameter, 34 feet high, and will weigh more than two million pounds. The amount of electrical energy to be provided yearly would light four million homes. Each of the two powerhouses will be 765 feet long, 112 feet wide, and 292 feet high, or the height of a 24-story building. Power can be generated at a cost of 2.25 mills.

The average annual run-off of the Columbia river at Grand Coulee is 79 million acre feet, with a record maximum of 101 million acre feet, or enough water to cover the six New England states with two-and-one-half feet of water, or supply metropolitan New York city for nearly 100 years.

A spillway, 1,654 feet long, with a capacity of one million cubic feet per second will be provided. This spillway can discharge 450 million gallons a minute.

A pumping installation exceeding in magnitude any yet devised by pump manufacturers will include 12 pumps of 1600 cubic-feet-per-second capacity. There will be imbedded in the dam a system of pipes containing more than 2000 miles of one-inch steel tubing, through which cooling water will circulate to remove chemical heat due to setting of the cement in the mass concrete.

The original drawing of the dam, shown here with the capitol building superimposed, was made by George H. T. Brinkerhoff, Spokane artist. It hangs in the Civic Building in Spokane. The other drawings were inserted by the staff artist of *The Spokesman Review.*

Grange Master Albert Goss who convinced a reluctant Senator Dill of Spokane to make an appointment for them to meet with the president. During his presidential campaign in 1932 Franklin Roosevelt promised Dill and others that if he was elected he would "build that dam" at Grand Coulee on the Columbia. Soon after Roosevelt took office, Dill and Goss confidently strode into the Oval Office to remind the president of his promise. (Hill got stuck in traffic and missed the meeting.) However, Roosevelt had also become skeptical about the need for so much power in the skimpily settled Northwest. "It's too big," he kept repeating. Besides, he objected, it was going to cost more than the Panama Canal. But Goss successfully sold the president on the idea, while Dill made it sound like it was all his idea and that he alone got the president to approve the dam. As he reminisced:

"I was desperate. I didn't even hesitate. I knew he might order me out of the White House, but I saw my dam being thrown out the window.... He had tried to interrupt me, but I was talking too fast. I had him on the defensive. I was like Joe Louis raining punch after punch on his opponent with his left hand, after having hit him a stunning blow on the jaw with his right."

By the time FDR visited the dams under construction at Bonneville and Grand Coulee in August 1934, the president, as Dill would have it, had been brought entirely around by the senator's mean left jab. For he told the huge crowds assembled at each site to see him: "I don't believe that you can have enough power for a long time to come." Spokane residents were elated and planned a civic celebration, complete with brass band, to greet the returning senator at the train station. The community of Wenatchee also broke out the champagne and celebrated with a "Carnival of Joy." So many people began trooping off to the dam site, the *Spokane Chronicle* reported, that "the rattlesnakes have retreated from the area." The proprietor of a Spokane cafe honored the occasion with a new creation — a "Coulee Dam sandwich with Dill pickle." One half consisted of lettuce and tomato, representing the produce which the reclaimed land would raise, and the other half was spread with "current" jelly.

After President Roosevelt set aside $63 million in emergency funds mostly from the Public Works Administration, the Bureau of Reclamation on September 9, 1933 began construction on what would become the world's largest concrete structure. When Congress approved a high dam in 1935, funding estimates jumped to $181 million. First the builders bored 6 miles of holes in the granite bedrock to test its ability to support the weight of 11 million cubic yards of concrete. Then the engineers drilled grout holes into the granite and forced in concrete under pressures up to 600 pounds per square inch until the bedrock was ready to support the gigantic load. Coffer dams were built to divert the flow of the river. Although plagued by slides and exceptionally cold winters, construction crews excavated nearly 22 million cubic yards of dirt and surface rock. Then to prepare the riverbed to receive the concrete, all the available tombstone polishers in the area set to work scrubbing the granite with brushes and soap and water.

In December 1935 Governor Clarence Martin, clad in overalls and brakeman's cap, inaugurated the concrete pour when he officially dumped the first bucket of what would eventually amount to nearly 21 million tons of concrete — three times as much as in Boulder Dam. (For his labor he received from the contractor a check for $.75 for one hour's pay.) Concrete was poured a block at a time into wooden frames five feet high and from thirty to fifty feet square. In the summer of 1937 employment on the dam peaked at 7,798 men and the contractor, the Mason-Walsh-Atkinson-Kier Company, set a new world's record of 15,844 yards for daily concrete placement. The next year it was surpassed by the finishing contractor, Consolidated Builders, when they placed 20,685 cubic yards in one 24-hour period, a record that still stood in 1976. By the time it was finished, according to Northwest historian Murray Morgan, there was enough concrete in Grand Coulee "to build a six-lane highway around the United States, enough to bury the state of Montana three inches deep or — to some a better idea — Texas more than an inch deep."

The dam superlatives go on and on. At 4,173 feet or twelve city blocks long, "four battleships the size of the U.S.S. *Missouri* could be placed bow to stern and not reach across Grand Coulee's crest." At 530 feet high, the height of a 46-story building, water pouring over the 1,650-foot spillway drops three times as far as water going over Niagara Falls, and there can be eight times as much of it. The dam covers an area of twenty-six football fields or thirty-five acres. On either side of the spillway is a powerhouse more than two blocks long and 200 feet high; each holds nine 108,500-kilowatt generators. At the time it began operating in March 1941 Grand Coulee produced more power than the combined output of all seven Tennessee Valley Authority dams; it was the largest hydroelectric power plant in the world. Later, it was surpassed by two plants in the U.S.S.R., but with the completion of the third powerhouse in 1980, it again for a short time regained first place with a capacity of 6,500 megawatts (Mw). Today, it has bowed to the world's largest project, the Itaipu Dam on the Parana River between Paraguay and Brazil rated at 13,000 Mw.

Bonneville Power Administration

At least four years before Bonneville Dam's first generator began delivering power in July 1938, controversy developed over how and to whom the power from the two dams should be distributed. President Roosevelt and some of the state's public power supporters favored the creation of a Columbia Valley Authority (CVA) based on the precedent of the New Deal's recently-enacted Tennessee Valley Authority as the best type of agency to sell and deliver federal power. The reaction of most of the region to this proposal was overwhelmingly hostile. The opponents primarily in Oregon, Montana, and Idaho represented commercial interests who feared the concentration of power in a remote federal bureaucracy, and arid-region farmers who feared the proposal would rob irrigation of its power subsidy. For some just the word "authority" when used by a federal agency was enough to scare them off. Support for the valley-authority movement came chiefly from Washington and from organized labor, some farm groups, and the Washington State Planning Commission which, while not necessarily advocating a CVA, favored a single regional administrative agency. The issue split public power supporters among those who favored national, regional, and local control.

Another divisive issue was the question of who should be the main beneficiaries of the river's power development. The struggle which developed over rates was basically between industry and Oregon on one side and agriculture and Washington on the other. The Portland Chamber of Commerce and businesses in the vicinity of the dam, including Vancouver, favored "busbar" rates. According to this policy, rates would be higher the further the electricity had to be carried from the power plant. Users such as factories located "at the switchboard" near the dam would be able to get

Left: View of Bonneville Dam spillway photographed in the late 1930s by Pathe Newsreel photographer Lew Hudson.

large blocks of power at low cost. This would be a way of attracting manufacturing and industrial capital to the area, particularly to Portland. Industry congestion near the dam was precisely what President Roosevelt, J. D. Ross, Homer Bone, and other public power advocates opposed. Reasoning that the Bonneville dam belonged to all the public, they argued that its power should be available to all at the same cost. The blanket or "postage stamp" rate would average the cost of long distance transmission into everyone's rates. With postage stamp rates, the power would still be cheap and it would be available to far more customers in the region.

In 1937 Bonneville Dam was nearing completion and Northwest congressmen had not yet agreed upon a compromise bill. As an interim expedient President Roosevelt and Congress that year endorsed the Bonneville Project Act. Following most of the recommendations of the Pacific Northwest Regional Planning Commission, the act created the

Above and below: Scenes beside BPA transmission lines. Photos by Hugh Paradise.

Bonneville Power Administration (BPA) as a temporary administrative organization within the Interior Department. The wording of the act implied that the BPA would eventually become a permanent valley authority. But later, home rule advocates defeated several attempts in Congress during the 1940s and 1950s, including a compromise bill introduced by Senator Bone, to adopt a CVA-type administration. With the passage of time the BPA became permanent. BPA was authorized to market the power of the dams and instructed to encourage the widest possible use of electrical energy throughout the region in order to stimulate economic and social development. The agency was also instructed to operate primarily for the benefit of domestic and rural customers. Intending to provide a stimulus to PUD formation and following a precedent set by the 1902 Reclamation Act, Homer Bone wrote the clause in the Bonneville act that directed the agency to give preference in power allocation to public bodies. The social engineering incorporated into the act ensured future conflict between public and private utilities. Except in Washington, most domestic and rural customers were and are presently served by private companies. Of the four states in the Northwest region, only in Washington did state law effectively foster the creation of public utility districts that were then able to profit from this priority status.

The Bonneville Act in conjunction with the District Power Act of 1930 opened up new markets in Washington for the public power movement in the 1930s and 1940s. The preference policy guaranteed the publicly owned utilities enough hydroelectric power to meet their demands before any power was sold to BPA's other two types of customers: the privately owned companies, and the direct service industries, primarily aluminum companies. Until the 1970s the preference policy involved few hardships for the unpreferred. There was usually a surplus of hydroelectric power even after the public agencies had met their needs. There were exceptions, however. In the early 1950s when the region began experiencing serious short-term power shortages, the Public Service Commission restricted some of the private utilities from taking on new industrial loads because of their insufficient generating resources. Consequently, in 1951 the Scott Paper Company located its new plant in Everett rather than in Bellingham because the Snohomish County PUD could do what Puget Power could not — assure the company access to BPA's firm power resources.

On November 1, 1937, despite the opposition of the electric utility industry and conservative local politicians, J. D. Ross, the human dynamo behind the spectacular growth of Seattle City

Light, took on the BPA as its first administrator. While Governor Charles H. Martin of Oregon and many of his constituents believed that the Bonneville administrator should help the states utilize cheap power to attract industry and turn a profit for private enterprise, Ross felt the social factor should have priority. Bonneville, he admitted, was a financial institution. But "It is also humanitarian. I think the humanitarian use is by far the greater," he said. "It is not just what the electricity costs; it is what our people can do with it that constitutes the help to humanity and makes it a real success." Sharing with his personal friend, President Franklin Roosevelt, the public power credo that cheap electricity would bring everyone a higher standard of living, Ross immediately took charge of the Bonneville act. He interpreted that charge to include the establishment of uniform rates and the construction of a region-wide power grid that would make power available as widely as possible. Congress had made no provision for a transmission system in its initial appropriation for the agency. So Ross's first task was to persuade Congress that the government in building the system would not be pouring tax dollars into the Columbia River program like water spilling over the dam. An eastern engineer who visited the Northwest in 1936 had ironically remarked that: "The Columbia is certainly a wonderful river. It waters four states and drains forty-eight." All that Ross wanted was the wherewithal to get the power from the two dams to those preferred and distant rural users.

Within a year of his appointment, Ross had convinced the administration and Congress to appropriate $3.5 million of PWA funds to build a two-circuit, 220-kv transmission line from Bonneville Dam to Vancouver. Since the lines crossing the river would not be completed until the end of 1939, Ross, to prove that BPA could accomplish its mission, hastily built a 13.8-kv line to connect with its first customer, the city of Cascade Locks, Oregon. In August 1938 Ross won another allocation of $10.75 million in PWA funds for 550 miles of transmission lines, including a 235-mile intertie between Bonneville and Grand Coulee dams. Expediting the start of the project, several thousand Works Progress Administration (WPA) laborers were put to work surveying and clearing the rights-of-way of the lines and preparing substation sites. The BPA's survey techniques were primitive by today's standards. Even at the time some were characterized as being "unusual field operations" — such as the night surveys using automobile headlights and sky rockets.

Although Ross is sometimes credited with designing the specifics of the regional "Master Grid," its original configuration had been worked out some years earlier by Professor Charles McKinley of Reed College and Charles E. Carey, an electrical engineer with the Pacific Northwest Regional Planning Commission. McKinley had prescribed a triangular-shaped grid system with Puget Sound, Portland, and Spokane forming each apex. Carey, who became Ross's assistant at BPA, originated the idea that the grid, in addition to handling power generated by the federal dams, could "wheel" or carry the energy of other regional power systems as well. At the hub of the grid, the agency established its main distribution station on the north edge of the city of Vancouver. When completed, a skeletal network of 230,000-volt transmission lines linked the major population centers and generation plants in what was called "the loop." Distribution lines of lesser voltages radiating outward from the loop were then built to connect individual customers such as municipalities, industrial plants, and utility districts.

As long as the New Deal was in place, public power in the state thrived. Using their ability to acquire private utility properties by condemnation or negotiated purchases and backed by BPA, the PUDs accelerated their takeover of private utility properties in the 1940s. Federal courts upheld the constitutionality of the 1935 Holding Company Act, and the Securities and Exchange Commission ordered the holding companies controlling the state's three largest companies — Puget Power, Washington Water Power, and Pacific Power and Light — to divest holdings and reorganize. By the early 1940s Puget Power was the largest private utility in the state, serving nearly all of the western counties and several east of the mountains. BPA was eager to help the PUDs bring about a transfer of Puget Power facilities and territory to public ownership. In 1934 J.D. Ross had proposed that the City of Seattle buy the entire company and then divide and sell parts to other municipal systems and PUDs.

The plan was pursued by Ross's successor at BPA, Dr. Paul J. Raver, who interpreted the Bonneville act as a mandate to promote public distribution and consumption of Bonneville power. Raver, who had initially found that objec-

Aluminum Company of America plant at Vancouver WA., Sept. 9, 1940. Courtesy, MOHAI, Seattle P-I Collection.

tive thwarted by the Washington PUDs' inability to acquire distribution systems, was willing to personally help them negotiate acquisitions. He viewed the takeover of Puget Power as a way to create a large and steady market for BPA power and eliminate the need for parallel facilities. President Roosevelt personally backed the plan and even recommended a bill that would amend the Reconstruction Finance Act so that the public utilities could be permitted a loan to acquire private utility property. But after fifteen years of negotiations, legal and financial obstacles and the split within the public power forces over the CVA foiled the takeover. Even so, during the late 1940s Puget Power lost 60 percent of its territory in twelve of the twenty counties in which it was operating in 1940 as the PUDs individually acquired by sale or condemnation the company's distribution lines and facilities.

NORTHWEST POWER POOL AND WORLD WAR II

The coming of World War II interrupted the public power drive. In 1942 the private and public utilities were forced to cooperate when the newly organized federal War Production Board, faced with growing demands for war-related industrial output, directed the BPA to interconnect the federal system with all the major electric systems in the region. Prior to the linkage with the region's eight major private utilities, BPA was tied to only the Seattle and Tacoma municipal systems. The Northwest Power Pool which resulted linked together the region's utilities, public and private, from the Canadian border south to Salt Lake City and from Puget Sound east to Fort Peck, Montana and served about five million people. Built around the exchange and sale of bulk power transmitted over the federal grid, the pool allowed the region to use temporary surplus power and save thousands of barrels of oil and great quantities of coal. During the war the interconnection allowed about 20 percent of the federal hydropower to be sent to private utilities which otherwise could not have met the additional load from the war-time industries.

The power available through the pool became the most important factor in establishing defense production in the Northwest and helped put Washington among the top five states in the number of government contracts. The War Production Board assigned the Columbia River project priority status in the requisition of materials so that the power installations at the two dams and the grid could be completed ahead of schedule to meet the new loads. Bonneville and Grand Coulee dams were completed just in time to make a considerable contribution to the war effort in power supplied to Hanford, and to the aluminum, shipbuilding, aircraft, and other wartime industries. In fact, recognition of their importance led to the government's decision to begin building more dams that would exploit the Columbia's power, irrigation, and navigation possibilities to the fullest. During the war BPA delivered more electricity for war-related purposes than all the other power systems in the region had developed and marketed up to that time. By 1942 the agency had committed 92 percent of its load to industry. Its high voltage transmission grid grew from 37 miles in 1939 to 2,720 miles in 1945, making it the second largest power system in the nation.

ALUMINUM INDUSTRY

Within a few short years of the skeptics' harangue against Columbia River dams with "power to burn," the region had acquired a resident power hog that was gulping down kilowatts as fast as they could be generated. It was the aluminum industry. In an effort to step up production of the light metal, needed for the building of airplanes at the nearby Boeing Company plant, the government sponsored the construction of some of the wartime aluminum plants. The first and largest, built at Vancouver, was privately owned and operated by the Alcoa Company. The reduction plant began operating in the fall of 1940. In September of the following year the Reynolds Metals Company, with a BPA contract for 60,000 kw, fired up its three potlines at its new plant at Longview. The government's Defense Plant Corporation built and leased the next three plants in Tacoma, Mead (near Spokane), and Troutdale, Oregon. By the end of the war the region was producing over one-third of the nation's aluminum output, enough to build 10,000 B-29s or 150,000 fighter planes. It was a startling statistic considering the fact that before 1941 no aluminum at all was produced west of the Mississippi.

The region's cheap power, which made cheap aluminum possible, enabled the region to become the center of the aircraft industry. The effect on Seattle's economy was stunning. Before the war, in 1939, the total output of all the city's manufacturers was $70 million. In 1944 the Boeing Company alone produced $600 million worth of airplanes for the government. The production of aluminum, as one the first large-scale manufacturing processes to come to the state, helped rescue Washington from the boom-bust cycles of agriculture, lumbering, and fishing. Since the Alcoa Company became BPA's first direct service industrial customer in 1939, the industry has located over 35 percent of the nation's aluminum reduction capacity in the Pacific Northwest. The aluminum industry has remained BPA's largest industrial customer. However, later when energy shortages loomed, it became the target of much criticism precisely because of the huge amounts of power it consumes.

The "B" canyon building at Hanford at the time of its late-1950s reactivation from retirement to provide storage space for waste management. Courtesy, General Electric Company and Ted Van Arsdol.

HANFORD ATOMIC WORKS

In 1943 a "mystery load" came on line at the Bonneville Power Administration and soon became, after the aluminum industry, the second largest single user of power in the region. The army arrived in Hanford, population about 100, in February of that year to begin condemnation proceedings against the few townspeople and peppermint farmers in the area. Immediately rumors began circulating about what the government could be up to. One story told that the Corps of Engineers was fronting for the DuPont Company, the army's chief contractor, which had discovered that the sands around Hanford were rich in alumina. Others speculated that the project must have something to do with producing poison gas. A more pleasant fantasy had DuPont and the Corps making nylon using a new, top-secret process.

The project, which the government complimented the locals by naming after their town, the Hanford Engineering Works, was supposed to be secret — as secret as it could be when 60,000 workers from all around the country had to be recruited. Although

Below: The farming community of Hanford, ca. 1911. Courtesy, Michael Maslan. Right: The Tri-Cities' Monday surprise, as revealed on the front page of the Pasco Herald *Aug. 6, 1945 Extra edition, could not compare to the devastating surprise dropped on the city of Hiroshima, Japan, where 130,000 people were killed, injured, or missing, and 90 percent of the city was leveled as a result of the first atomic bomb ever dropped in a populated area.*

299

publishers of the local newspapers agreed to the Hanford commandant's request for voluntary censorship for the duration of the war, Columbia Basin residents could not ignore the transformation of their area. The huge building project required 8,000 pieces of construction equipment, 748,000 cubic yards of concrete, and 160 million feet of lumber. By the middle of 1944 Hanford with a population of 41,269 was the fifth largest city in the state.

From 473 kw of electricity in 1943, the mystery load grew to 55,000 kw in 1945. In that last year of the war, all the residential customers of the PUDs, municipals, and cooperatives in the state used 45,000 kw. Of the 137,000 people who worked on the Hanford project during the war, some with the highly technical procedures involved in separating plutonium from uranium, probably only a hundred or so knew what was going on. Some Hanford scientists believed they were working on experiments to help soldiers who contracted jungle diseases in the South Pacific. Even the War Manpower Commission, to whom the army applied for an expeditious assignment of workers, was kept in the dark. Resenting the army's refusal to provide details about the nature of the project, the commission took its time, and a near-emergency worker shortage threatened the continuance of the project in early 1944. Not until after the bombs exploded over Hiroshima and Nagasaki did the "engineering works" employees, Tri-Cities residents, and even the state's powerful representatives in Congress, Senator Warren G. Magnuson and Congressman Henry M. Jackson, discover that Hanford had been part of the government's Manhattan Project and producing plutonium for the world's first atomic bombs.

POST-WAR PARTNERSHIP

By the end of the war a new relationship had begun to develop between the region's private utilities and its public power establishment. The participation of the commercial utilities in the coordination of facilities and defense industry power planning had given them a social importance equal to that of the public's — even in the eyes of the Roosevelt administration. Also, their large wartime power purchases had made them major BPA customers. Most power planners had expected sharp cutbacks in energy usage with the shutdown of the wartime industries, and even the possible demise of Northwest aluminum production. Although BPA's load dropped by one-third immediately following the end of the war,

Above: Construction at Rocky Reach Dam seen from Highway 97, ca. 1959. Bottom: Chief Joseph Dam spillway. Photos by Hugh Paradise.

by 1946 the high price of steel and other building materials, including Pacific Northwest lumber, created a new interest in cheap aluminum. It began to replace steel in motor vehicles, wood in construction, and glass in bottles. Aluminum was given an additional boost by the mid-1948 rearmament program.

In short, the lengthy post-war power surplus never materialized. The substitution of electric power for fossil fuels in many small industrial establishments also helped replace the wartime power load sooner than anyone had expected. And a huge migration of people into the region between 1940 and 1949, which raised the population of Oregon and Washington by an average 46 percent, together with the electrical consumption stimulated by the low BPA rates increased power demands even more. By 1947 the region was experiencing an unprecedented power shortage more critical than at any time during the war. Federal appropriations for carrying on new Columbia River projects were slow and too little to keep up with the energy demands. This led the cities of Seattle and Tacoma to join with the major private utilities and appeal to the government for funds that would allow approved federal dam projects and extensions to the BPA transmission backbone to be completed as quickly as possible. Federal Power Commission data confirmed that the Northwest was experiencing uncommon load growth. Between 1940 and 1946 the peak load demands in the region increased by 102 percent compared with a national average of 58 percent.

When General Dwight D. Eisenhower returned the White House to the Republicans in 1953 after 20 years of exile, the national public power movement lost the administration's support. President Eisenhower, who "just [didn't] believe that the Federal Government should be in these things," instead elaborated a "partnership policy." This plan encouraged public utilities to cooperate with private companies in the joint construction and operation of power facilities. Aiming to stem what some viewed as a move toward a government monopoly of the power industry, the administration also wanted to eliminate disparities in retail rates charged by the public and commercial utilities. Eisenhower's attitude toward federal involvement was summed up in a "no-new-dams" policy, and during his two terms in office no new federal projects were authorized. However, he could not stop the projects already underway or previously authorized by Congress. Strong Democratic support in Congress supplied the appropriations needed to complete the commissioned dams and boost the Columbia River power system capacity from 2,462,400 kw in mid-1952 to 6,033,250 kw in mid-1960. In the same period, the number of miles of BPA transmission lines nearly doubled. Neither was the nation's favorite ex-general able to repeal the public preference clause which remained entrenched in the Bonneville Project Act, securely protected by congressional powers. Subsequent attempts to write public preference into post-New Deal federal power legislation were not successful either, however.

Eisenhower's power policy may have been circumscribed in Congress, but partnership had already become a social and economic reality in a region experiencing rapid industrial expansion and linked by a single high-voltage grid. Much of the old antagonism that existed between leaders of the two types of utilities dissipated as both, deprived of Uncle Sam's aid, looked for ways to fund new facilities. The public utility districts with their firm-power BPA contracts had sufficient power for their current loads, but without help they could not possibly finance the expensive new generating facilities needed to meet future demands. However, as public bodies they enjoyed access to cheap money — low-interest municipal revenue bonds. The private companies, already short on generating capacity, also could not afford to finance such costly projects on their own. But together, the public agency could sponsor the project and secure the favorable financing, and the private company could supply revenue in the form of additional customers to help repay the low-interest government bonds.

One of Washington's partnership projects actually predated the president's policy. The expansion of the Rock Island Dam, undertaken by the Chelan County PUD in 1951, used a novel financing agreement. Chelan leased the dam from Puget Sound Power and Light which had built the project in 1930 but could not afford to improve it. The PUD agreed to raise the height of the dam and install six additional generators, allowing them at the same time to sign a contract with the Alcoa Company for a four pot-line smelter south of Wenatchee. With the aluminum contract and Puget Power sales agreement in hand, the PUD was able to secure municipal revenue bonds for the upgrade. Five years later it purchased the dam from the company. The Chelan PUD-Puget Power combination became the prototype for the other mid-stem Columbia River projects which followed; and in fact, it became a national model for the industry.

Starting with the construction of Priest Rapids Dam in 1957, five new hydroelectric power projects were built as joint ventures in which the PUDs own and operate the dams, which are being paid for through long-term power contracts with private and other public utilities. The next four dams upstream are: the Wanapum Dam, which along with the Priest Rapids Dam, is owned by Grant County PUD; the Rocky Reach and Rock Island dams owned and operated by Chelan County PUD; and the Wells Dam, built by Douglas County PUD. The building and upgrade of these dams added substantially to the region's power supply.

The partnership policy fizzled on the lower Snake River after Franklin and Benton County PUDs were unsuccessful in their attempts to finance a power project at Ice Harbor in 1954. Senator Warren Magnuson, who had long battled for construction funds for the project, managed instead to push through the necessary appropriations legislation for another Army Corps assignment. Three additional Corps multipurpose projects, the Little Goose, Lower Monumental, and Lower Granite dams, followed. (See Waterways Chapter.)

CANADIAN STORAGE AND THE SOUTHWEST INTERTIE

Except for the reach of the river within the bounds of the Hanford Reservation, the remaining hydroelectric sites on the Columbia River within Washington were exhausted with the completion of the PUD middle-stem dams. Yet, there still remained a substantial power capacity that could be developed by storing water in the upper basin in Canada, where 30 percent of the river's streamflow originated. The reservoir capacity of the existing main stem projects was not great enough to regulate river flow over the whole year and allow for maximum efficiency in hydroelectric operations. During spring and early summer high volumes caused by melting snowpack had to be spilled over the dams, while during low flow season in winter, generation was limited by

In anticipation of the filling of the Lake Celilo reservoir behind The Dalles Dam (above left), Native American remains in the ancient burial grounds on Memaloose Island (above) were moved to Wish-Ham Cemetery, where new graves (far left) were marked with the names of those who were known. A memorial obelisk (left) was also erected for these and all the unidentified members of the "Yakima and confederated tribes" whose bones were reinterred.

Days before John F. Kennedy's January 1960 inauguration, President Dwight Eisenhower met with Canadian Prime Minister John Deifenbaker in Ottowa for the signing of the Columbia River Treaty. British Columbia's objections delayed Canadian ratification until 1964. That year, on Sept. 6, President Lyndon Johnson met Canadian Prime Minister Lester B. Pearson under the International Peace Arch at Blaine to exchange signed copies of the treaty. Courtesy, BPA.

the amount of water in the reservoirs. In 1964 the Canadian government, after a long period of negotiation between the two countries, ratified the Columbia River Treaty. The agreement called for the cooperative development of the upper Columbia through the construction of three Canadian storage dams — Arrow, Duncan, and Mica — and Libby Dam in northwestern Montana, which would flood lands 42 miles into Canadian territory. By retaining water during high flows and releasing it when natural flow was low, these upriver dams doubled the storage capacity of the Columbia system and allowed the downstream dams to produce nearly three million more kilowatts of firm power.

As part of the deal, half of the power benefits of the arrangement were assigned to Canada. But neither western Canada nor the Pacific Northwest yet had a need for the extra power. So plans were resurrected for a high voltage intertie to send the surplus current to the power-hungry southwest. As early as 1919 Professor C. Edward Magnusson of the University of Washington had suggested the idea of a west coast "inter-tie," extending from the Canadian border to Los Angeles to interconnect the systems of Washington and Oregon with California transmission lines. The plan received further support from J.D. Ross in his 1938 master plan for the BPA grid. During the 1940s and 1950s studies conducted by BPA and the Federal Power Commission reaffirmed the economic advantages of a Pacific Northwest-Pacific Southwest interconnection. Southwest power demands increase in the summer due to irrigation and air-conditioning, but streamflows do not reach their highest stage there until the fall and winter. In the Northwest power demand is highest during the winter when stream flows are low. High flows do not begin until the late spring and summer. The dissimilarity between peak supply and use created strong incentives for cooperation. But political opposition was not overcome until the late 1950s when BPA began experiencing annual deficits of nearly $50 million caused by poor sales due to a soft economy and the start-up of the non-federal mid-river dams. During the same period, from 1958 to 1962, BPA was compelled to spill water which if it had gone through turbines and had been sold would have generated $150 million. The surfeit of power produced by the Canadian Treaty and the ever-expanding loads in southern California made a good marriage which could be consummated only by the intertie.

At first, the idea was not warmly received by the Northwest power establishment which feared that such an arrangement

Top: John Day Dam. Courtesy, UW Libraries, Special collections. Above: McNary Dam spillway. Courtesy Corps of Engineers, Walla Walla District. Below: Wanapum Dam. Courtesy Grant County Public Utilities District. Bottom: Priest Rapids Dam with Native American wood gatherer in foreground. Photo by Hugh Paradise.

would give priority to the federal hydropower to public utilities in California before BPA's private utility and industrial customers could meet their loads. Washington senators Henry Jackson and Warren Magnuson made it clear, however, that they would oppose the intertie unless legislation gave preference to Northwest utilities. Their promise resulted in the 1964 Northwest Regional Preference Act which limited BPA exports to surplus power for which there was no demand in the Northwest. On September 16, 1964 President Lyndon Johnson and Canadian Prime Minister Lester Pearson signed the Columbia River Treaty at the Peace Arch at Blaine. This was followed the next morning by an intertie "victory" breakfast in Portland where Johnson described the intertie "as the most exciting transmission system in history," one that would "carry from the Peace River to the Mexican border enough power for five San Franciscos."

After four years of work from 1966 to 1970, the largest single transmission system in the country, which was jointly sponsored by BPA, five private utilities, and the City of Los Angeles, ran from northern British Columbia to the Mexican border. It served electric systems in eleven states. The extra high voltage connection of two 500-kv AC lines and one 1,000-kv DC line enabled BPA to sell its surplus power and use the revenues to help keep Northwest power rates low. It also provided a means of bringing power into the region when demand soared during unusual cold spells and regional water supplies dwindled, as they did during serious droughts in 1979, 1987, and 1992.

HYDRO-THERMAL POWER

By the late 1940s when the region began to experience its first serious power shortfalls, utility leaders began to realize that the Columbia was not, as J.D. Ross used to say, an oil well that would never run dry. It had its limits — as the once free-flowing river, transformed into a series of long lakes backed up to one other behind massive concrete dams, demonstrated. Soon the Eisenhower administration proved that the government also had limits — on subsidizing huge public works projects. But to utility planners in the late 1950s, after a decade of tremendous post-war economic growth, there seemed no clear limits to the demand for more electricity. If hydropower could not alone meet projected loads, then thermal plants would have to be built. In their "308" report of 1958, the Army Corps of Engineers recommended the introduction of thermal-generated electric energy to augment the Northwest's hydroelectric system. Eight years later BPA Administrator Charles Luce predicted that thermal plants would be carrying much of the region's baseload by 1982. The transition from predominately hydropower to hydro-thermal operations was being planned and made by large utilities across the country, including the Tennessee Valley Authority which started out to build seventeen nuclear plants. There seemed no doubt that nuclear power, which experts in the early 1960s predicted would eventually become "too cheap to meter," was the wave of the future.

In 1966 the Joint Power Planning Council led by BPA was formed by representatives from 180 utilities in the region. Two years later they had developed a plan which called for a gradual conversion from regional dependence on only hydroelectric power for baseload demand to a mixed base of hydroelectric and thermal sources. The plan proposed that the utilities, public and private, would build the large nuclear and coal-fired plants, while the Bonneville Power Administration would supply the transmission grid, the reserve power, and the hydroelectric peaking capacity. Initially, the group proposed an awesome 20-year, $15 billion program to meet projected regional demand through the installation of twenty nuclear and two coal-fired plants. These facilities would more than double the 10,600 megawatts of firm hydroelectric capability available in 1970. In 1969 the group scaled down its

The WPPSS (Washington Public Power Supply System) Hanford generating plant on the Hanford Reservation beside the Columbia River was a precedent for the Hydro-Thermal Power Program, but not part of it. The Hanford plant was put into service in 1966, three years after President John Kennedy participated in the groundbreaking ceremonies. Courtesy, WPPSS.

original projections into a 10-year, $7 billion program that entailed seven thermal plants, involving the participation of 109 utilities. The development of any new hydroelectric resources was relegated to increasing peaking capacity only.

Today such estimates of future power use seem astounding. But in the late 1960s the state had been experiencing at least two decades of what appeared to be unstoppable economic and population growth. Few utility operators, if any, questioned the load forecasts made by the council, BPA, and others which were extrapolated from the recent six and seven percent annual increase in electrical usage. The traditional association between power consumption and economic prosperity, accepted by the utilities and the business community, left little reason to expect anything less. The public power community relied implicitly on the indefinite availability of ever greater quantities of power which BPA had continued to deliver over the years through its policy of encouraging increased sales and supply. Besides, hydropower was cheap and there was little penalty for overestimating usage since at least some of the extra power could be sold to California or possibly lure another aluminum plant to the area. Until it made a small increase in 1965, BPA had never raised its rates since it began sending current to its first customers in 1938. Likewise, some of the PUDs had not raised their rates in over a quarter century.

The Northwest region's hydro-thermal concept promised to break new ground in utility economics. Since electricity cannot be stored, it must be generated as it is needed, and the need can vary substantially with the seasons and time of day. Generally, in electrical utility operations the cheapest generating system is used for the base load: that constant around-the-clock supply of power necessary to meet the lowest period of demand during the day. As demand rises above the baseload, more expensive generating methods are used until the peak load is met with the costliest source of power. Because of the inherently flexible nature of hydroelectric generation, the hydro-thermal system projected for the region operated the other way around. Here thermal energy, although costlier than hydroelectric power, would provide the baseload supply of power because thermal plants are most economical when operated at constant output. Hydroelectric systems would primarily supply the peaking capacity to meet the high periods of demand by releasing more water behind the dam to the turbines. The BPA's policy of "wheeling," or carrying over the grid electricity produced by non-federal generating facilities, sends surplus power wherever it is needed and thus also enhances the flexibility of the region's hydropower system.

POWER PEAKING AND FISHERIES

Yet for what seemed to be an efficient combination, the intended hydro-thermal program would have extracted significant environmental costs. The current operation of dams to meet peak or daily high periods of demand has already adversely affected river habitats. By blocking upstream migration and altering river flow, the approximately 130 Columbia Basin dams have destroyed one-third of 12,000 miles of salmon and steelhead habitat. Before 1850 an estimated 10 to 15 million salmon fought their way through the rapids of the lower river; in 1984, 2.5 million made the same trip. When dams are used primarily for peaking power, there is little water going over the spillways. Slowing the flow of the water slows the downstream migration of young salmon. Although the larger fish somehow survive a trip through the turbines, the fry suffer an estimated five to thirty percent mortality rate at each dam. Even when salmon are washed over the spillway they can suffer the fish equivalent of the bends in the nitrogen-saturated water. They can also become stunned and easy prey to predators in the stilling ponds below the dams. Fluctuations in flow also erode river banks, destroying shallow water habitats necessary for the hatching of eggs and nurturing of the young fish.

Testifying to the low priority anadromous fish had in the government's early river development plans, the original design of Bonneville Dam did not make any provision for the passage of salmon. In 1935 New York Congressman Francis D. Culkin became enraged over a $3 million allocation for a fish ladder at one of the reclamation bureau dams, calling it simply "an aid to the salmon . . . when they feel the urge to go to the upper stretches of the river on their honeymoons." Puget Power's Rock Island Dam was exceptional. It featured not one but three fish ladders, including one placed innovatively at the center of the spillway.

Efforts to mitigate the effects of the dams on fisheries began with the control of the fishermen. However, regulations shifting catches from in-river to ocean harvest did less to replenish the salmon run on the Columbia than their artificial production in large-scale hatcheries. By the late 1960s hatchery output of steelhead, chinook and coho salmon had far surpassed natural yields. Extensive scientific study of the "fish problem" did not become commonplace until the early 1970s. Besides catch restrictions, and fish farming and ladders, other solutions have included the removal of natural and manmade barriers (other than dams) affecting migration, and the installation of screens on irrigation diversions. Since 1981 the Army Corps of Engineers has directed "Operation Fish Run" in which as many as 15 million fry a year are taken around the dams to the sea by truck or barge, with mixed results. The fisheries issue has endured as such a serious concern that fisheries protection became a major sticking point in the three-year Congressional deliberations over the Regional Power Bill passed in 1980. (See below)

Below: Portion of the Bonneville Dam fish ladder under construction. Courtesy, BPA.

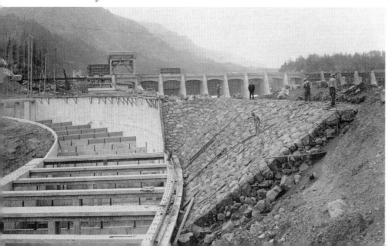

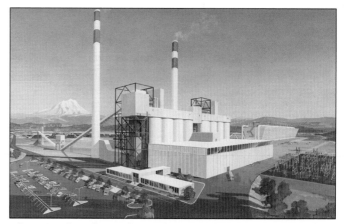

Above: Artist's rendering of Centralia Steam Plant. Courtesy, NWPP.

Centralia Steam Plant

The first large-scale thermal electric plant in the state was built by several private utilities whose access to federal hydroelectric power was curtailed under BPA's policy giving priority to public bodies. In 1968 Pacific Power and Light and Washington Water Power companies led a consortium to build the two-unit, coal-fired plant at Centralia. The plant was completed in 1972 just under the wire of a new awareness about the environmental dangers accompanying the combustion of coal. Since they began operation, the Centralia facilities have emitted sulfur oxides and other air pollutants which produce acid rain in the Puget Sound region. Despite significant advances in air pollution control technology, experts in 1980 expected acid rain to continue to be a problem whenever electricity was derived from burning coal. Partly for this reason, the construction of a third unit at Centralia was indefinitely deferred.

When the Joint Power Planning Council first made its recommendations for future thermal facilities in 1968, the federal and state environmental protection laws requiring environmental impact statements had not yet been passed. Even without the costs associated with these regulations that would later add significantly to the expense of building coal-fired and nuclear generating plants, the region's private utilities recognized that building nuclear reactors was beyond their combined financial capability. Nor could the public systems, who typically had little capital or no collateral, obtain financing on the scale that was needed to pay for the thermal plants. And BPA, the leading actor in the Northwest power trinity, was not authorized to build and operate power plants without congressional approval.

WASHINGTON PUBLIC POWER SUPPLY SYSTEM

When Senator Henry Jackson was finally able to convince Congress in the late summer of 1962 that the production of electricity from the Hanford dual purpose reactor would not result in "energy socialism" or a government monopoly in the production of nuclear-generated power, it was because he had conceded to the private utilities an equal share of the reactor's electrical output. Jackson's compromise brought a new collaboration between the utilities and the federal government in the financing of major thermal power projects. No private utility in the country could by itself finance a nuclear plant. But the private utilities had lobbied against any plan that might give public agencies or the federal government control of the technology and, in this case, the output of the Hanford plant and make it the government's first venture into commercial nuclear generation. But with Senator Jackson's concession a tripartite — government-public-and-private-utilities — method of financing and sharing in the output of such projects was established. The arrangement that BPA and the utilities worked out was made with the Washington

Public Power Supply System (WPPSS).

The supply system was born in 1957 partly as a result of the concerns of the public power establishment that the

WASHINGTON PUBLIC POWER
SUPPLY SYSTEM

Eisenhower administration wanted to remove the federal government and public preference from the power industry. Fearing that the private utilities might monopolize construction of new power facilities and the Eisenhower administration would try to sell the Columbia River system, in 1955 representatives from Washington public utilities successfully lobbied Governor Albert Rosellini and the legislature for a revised joint operating agency law. As a result, the WPPSS emerged, effectively freed from prior political and legal control governing joint operating agencies. Originally composed of seventeen public utilities, WPPSS was intended to serve as a construction and finance vehicle for projects beyond the capability of a single public utility. But for the first few years of its life, it had little to do. By 1961 it had built only one small hydro project at Packwood Lake and legislators talked of decommissioning it. So, when the prospect of sponsoring the Hanford project came up, the supply system leapt at it.

To help WPPSS secure financing for the dual purpose-reactor, BPA agreed to exchange power from its hydro system for Hanford energy. The public and private utilities that subscribed to portions of the Hanford plant output received credit from BPA for the cost of the thermally-generated power which they paid to WPPSS and these credits were then deducted from their BPA hydropower bill. It was a way of melding the much greater cost of the thermal power with the low-cost federal hydropower, and it became the prototype for the net billing system that would later finance WPPSS plants 1, 2 and 3. (Later it was found that it masked the true cost of the thermal plants.) According to the arrangement, any losses that BPA incurred because of the net-billing trade-off would "be borne by [all] its system customers through rate adjustments." Terms such as these were hard to turn down, and 71 utilities over-subscribed the plant's output by January 1963. After a $122 million bond issue was sold in May, President Kennedy broke ground in September. Three years later in April 1966 the steam plant was finished under budget, and for the first time nuclear-generated power began flowing into the Northwest power grid.

Two year later WPPSS officials proudly reported on the status of the Hanford project. It produced more than three times the output of any other nuclear power plant in the country, and the next year it was expected to generate more than 4 billion kilowatt hours and set another record for itself and the nation. Never mind that WPPSS actually had no experience building or operating nuclear plants — it had not built nor operated the reactor, only the generating portion that turned the steam from the reactor into electricity. With that kind of results and with the example of utilities around the nation committing themselves to a nuclear future, WPPSS became the agency the region's utilities naturally turned to.

Like the enormous load projections made by the power plan-

Washington Public Power Supply System Nuclear Project No. 2. Courtesy, WPPSS.

ning council, the decision of WPPSS and BPA officials to go ahead with the building of five large nuclear plants, the largest nuclear plant construction project of all time, today makes us wonder about their professional competency. However, in the late 1960s Northwest power planners were confident that their growing power needs were immediate and that the nation's reactor vendors and the Atomic Energy Commission (AEC) were sufficiently experienced in the construction and economic operation of the plants. Yet in the mid-1960s the power industry had built and operated nuclear plants of no more than 200 megawatts. Prompted by the AEC, which tried to minimize regulation to promote the new technology, soon utilities were ordering reactors of 400-500 Mw and then over 1,000-Mw plants even before the middle-range plants were up and running. Throughout the country utilities embarked on major projects, assured by reactor manufacturers that nuclear fission was just another way of boiling water to run a turbine. By the end of the decade the AEC and the power industry were discovering that they had sorely misjudged the complexity of the technology.

In 1971 when ninety-four Northwest utilities signed contracts with WPPSS for the first plant, designated WNP 2, the voices they heard were not words of caution about nuclear technology, but rather warnings that if they did not build and do it now, the consequences could be catastrophic for the region. To BPA the need for new non-hydroelectric power sources was unquestionable. The danger signs power planners posted were so clear that they brought the public and private utilities together in a new type of partnership policy. The Public Power Council and WPPSS's twenty-three public utility members agreed to allow private utilities to participate in some of the WPPSS projects since their involvement would facilitate financing and the output of the plants would exceed the normal needs of WPPSS' public members. A drought in the winter of 1972-73, which resulted in the shutdown of aluminum potlines, a number of conservation measures, and a greater consciousness of the power industry's dependence on regular precipitation helped to spur the utilities to sign contracts with WPPSS for plants 1 and 3. Then in 1973-74 after the OPEC nations slowed the flow of Middle-Eastern oil to the United States, the nation's obsession with the "energy crisis" reinforced the appeal of non-fossil fuels. After BPA began predicting that the region would experience serious power shortages by the middle of the 1980s, even with the completion of five nuclear plants, even the Seattle and Tacoma light divisions, which had historically avoided dependence on BPA and other agencies, joined WPPSS.

And if all that wasn't enough to convince Northwest power producers and consumers about their need for another source of power, there was BPA's net-billing arrangement which was once again able to sweeten the deal utilities made in their agreements with WPPSS. The financing plan, encouraged by the Nixon administration and approved by Congress, not only watered down the effect of the thermal

The 212-foot-high concrete containment silos of WPPSS plants WNP-3, on the right, and WNP-5 at Satsop, Aug. 22, 1983. Courtesy, WPPSS.

power costs, but guaranteed participating public agencies sufficient power to meet their total loads even if the nuclear plants never went on line. In this way the public utilities participating in the projects could be assured that if a plant turned out to be a "dry hole," its costs would be shared among all of BPA's customers, not just the participating utilities, in higher wholesale rates. According to two experts on the subject, Kai Lee and Donna Lee Klemka, "Net billing was an offer too good to refuse."

But it was not enough. By the time plant construction began in the fall of 1972, the cost in constant dollars of building a nuclear plant had more than doubled since 1967. Orders for plants had dropped off drastically around the country. Then the financing plan came under scrutiny. A 1972 IRS tax ruling that limited the financial advantage for private utilities participating in joint public-private ventures, effectively destroyed the net billing arrangement on which the financial feasibility of the projects largely depended. Net-billing, at any rate, was limited to a percentage of BPA's preference customer billings, and it had not been able to keep up with the skyrocketing costs of the thermal plants. Eventually, the financing system was dropped for projects after 1973. The Northwest's hydro-thermal program also ran afoul of unanticipated environmental opposition. Environmental groups that had once favored nuclear power over building more hydroelectric dams, began to fear its potential safety hazards and circulated antinuclear petitions in Washington and several other states. BPA Administrator Don Hodel in July 1975 before the Portland City Club alienated the environmentalists even more with his famous "Prophets of Shortage" speech in which he called them "a small, arrogant faction which has dedicated itself to bringing our society to a halt."

The loss of net-billing for plants 4 and 5 meant that WPPSS and the utilities participating in these projects ould have to directly fund them. Without the financial backing of BPA, they alone would have to bear the risk of potential unsatisfactory performance. Consenting to "take or pay" contracts, which were common in the industry and had been upheld by the courts, the utilities obligated themselves to pay for the plants whether or not they ever produced any power. They were willing to take such a risk partly because BPA warned on several occasions between 1972 and 1975 that it could not guarantee it could meet the firm load demands of even its preference customers after 1982 unless more thermal plants were built. At meetings they conducted around the Northwest, BPA officials encouraged their public utility customers to sponsor WPPSS plants 4 and 5, warning them that if there was a power shortage the preference clause might not mean very much. Most of those who signed agreements with WPPSS for shares of the generating capacity of plants 4 and 5 were already participants in the first three projects. Many of them expected that eventually BPA would be allowed to purchase the power output of the facilities and spread their costs to all BPA customers as the agency had done with the original three facilities through net billing.

Shortly after eighty-eight utilities signed agreements to go ahead with projects 4 and 5, a number of regional forecasts questioned the need for their power. The Environmental Research Center at the University of Washington became one of the first of a number of critics to challenge the high load projections sponsored by BPA and the region's utilities and adopted by WPPSS. But the WPPSS board of directors, composed of representatives from each of WPPSS' twenty-three member utilities, was determined to proceed with the plants based upon their original 6 to 7 percent annual load growth forecasts. Most of the WPPSS board were small-town businessmen, and local PUD commissioners whose experience consisted of approving budgets for small utilities and promoting local power use. None of them had backgrounds in heavy industry, nuclear engineering, investment banking or corporate management. At various times wheat ranchers, apple orchardists, a muffler shop owner, and veterinarian sat on the board. They implicitly trusted the judgment and expertise of their architect-engineering firms, who were experienced in building reactors, to manage and oversee construction.

WPPSS's directors were strong supporters of public power, committed to continuing the BPA and PUD tradition of keeping power rates as low as possible. In order to avoid asking the utilities sponsoring plants 4 and 5 to make payments for the projects before they began producing power, WPPSS management had to set aside enough money from every bond issue in order to pay the interest on the bonds for two years. This "build now, pay later" financing could only work if the plants remained on schedule and within budget. For example, interest payments on bonds for plant 2 came due in 1979, two years after the facility had been optimistically scheduled for completion. At that time BPA had to begin paying $6 million per month in interest on the still unfinished plant at Hanford, forcing BPA to announce a nearly 90 percent rate increase.

By 1982 delays caused by work stoppages, late equipment arrivals, design changes, and safety modifications required by the Nuclear Regulatory Commission (the former AEC) caused WPPSS to fall far behind construction schedules. When word of the construction problems and delays reached the New York bond brokers in mid-1981, WPPSS' bond ratings fell and the system's interest rates rose. (Altogether the agency issued more than $8 billion in tax-exempt bonds, more than any public agency or private company in American history.) By 1982 the New York financial market was saturated with WPPSS bonds, again putting the supply system at the mercy of the bond raters. Some estimates attribute about half of the amount of cost overruns on the five plants, originally priced at $4.1 billion and escalated to nearly $24 billion by 1983, to the cost of the bond financing. In 1980 when the five unfinished plants were priced at $11 billion, their cost exceeded all the capital currently invested in the federal Columbia River dams and the 12,500 miles of line in the BPA transmission grid.

Meanwhile, amidst all the construction problems and delays, contractors attempted to speed up construction by taking advantage of new building techniques. At the Satsop units, plants 3 and 5, in Grays Harbor County, two contractors, the Boecon Corp. of Seattle and the Fegles Power Service Corp. of Minneapolis, jointly installed what were believed to be the largest and perhaps most complicated slipform structures ever built at an American nuclear project. With the help of two 25-ton-capacity jacks, used for the first time at Satsop, the two 212-foot-high concrete containment silos were molded in record time. Fegles' project manager credited the vastly improved slipforming methods, which placed the three-foot-thick concrete walls using fewer and larger jacks than before, with a $1 million savings. At plant 3 engineers and contractors broke another construction record when they lifted a self-supporting reactor dome to top off the reactor containment. The steel forms allowed the dome to be lifted in one piece and left in place which eliminated stripping wooden forms after the concrete was poured. On the Hanford Reservation at plant 2, a specially fabricated derrick permitted installation of a 966-ton reactor pressure vessel. Because work on the reactor building was behind schedule, R. C. Root, resident construction chief for Burns & Roe, the architect-engineering firm on the plant, proposed lowering the completed reactor vessel into its containment shell before the building was finished. The lift made by a $2.5 million twin-boom derrick, called the Hanford Giant, was said to be the largest of its type ever made. Root figured the six-hour operation cut six months of construction time off the project.

Reports on construction feats such as these, however, were not the type of stories that Northwest ratepayers were reading and retelling as the nuclear plant "fiasco" unfolded in 1981 and 1982. Most common were reports that told of the most expensive atomic powerhouses ever built, construction several years behind schedule, faulty designs that had to be redesigned and rebuilt several times, and whole construction crews lying around on the job on full pay while they waited days, even weeks, for custom-designed parts to arrive. But the most remarkable tale of all had to be how WPPSS, with its insatiable financial appetite, from 1973 until 1978 managed to add billions of dollars in additional costs and get years behind schedule without serious investigations being made by BPA, the state legislature, bond raters, or the press. It was not until 1979 when the first large BPA rate increase, which included the impact of the soaring plant costs, took effect, and a report by a consulting firm about WPPSS' management problems was released, that BPA, the legislature, and the press finally noticed.

Following the appointment of Sterling Munro as BPA administrator in 1978, the agency attempted to distance itself from WPPSS by launching a highly visible and aggressive campaign of criticism. When the legislature's senate energy committee held hearings in 1980, letting witness after witness testify about WPPSS' problems, the effect was to dramatize further the rate increases beginning to affect household bills. The senate committee concluded that mismanagement was the major cause of WPPSS' cost overruns. WPPSS officials countered that costs had escalated because of regulatory requirements, inflation, labor strikes, schedule extensions, and "other authorized costs." Consultants hired by WPPSS and BPA had earlier reported that the supply system was still being managed as it had been when it began the projects as a small group of 81 employees in 1971. In 1981 WPPSS had over 2,000 employees, not counting the 14,000 construction personnel working on the projects. (On the national level a Department of

When it began operating in 1984, seven years behind schedule, Plant 2 at Hanford was the only completed WPPSS project. Top: Number 2 under construction in 1974. Above: Same perspective of Number 2 in 1984. Courtesy, WPPSS.

Energy study concluded in 1984 that most of the worst problems the nuclear power industry had incurred were a "result of its own management failures.") With these kinds of revelations, WPPSS became such a political hot potato that no elected legislator or administrative official could afford to be seen as having anything to do with it, especially at a time of worsening recession.

1980 Northwest Regional Power Act

By the late 1970s construction delays on the WPPSS plants, dwindling federal hydropower, and a growing rate disparity between the public electric agencies in Washington and the private utilities in Oregon had outstripped BPA's ability to formulate the political compromises necessary for cooperative regional power planning. The PUDs, municipals, private utilities and aluminum companies all wanted to know how much new power the region was going to generate, how it was to be priced, and who would have access to it. Since its creation in 1937 BPA had functioned as the regional planning authority by default — primarily because it operated the grid and, due to the defeat of the CVA proposals, no other federal agency had been commissioned to do so. The region had reached a planning deadlock that could only be remedied by federal legislation.

In late 1980 the Pacific Northwest Electric Power Planning and Conservation Act, also known as the Regional Power Act, broke the impasse. The legislation, which took three years to formulate and win congressional approval, established a regional energy council. The council was a response to demands for more public involvement in major regional energy issues and recognition of the fact that most of the region's electric power issues were less technical than political. It was composed of two representatives from each of the region's four states who were directed to draw up a regional energy plan. Responding to conservation and environmental interests, the act required that in acquiring new regional power sources the council must first consider conservation and renewable energy resources before any thermal generating stations were brought into the federal system.

One of the most crucial aspects of the act was the equalization of power rates for BPA's preference and non-preference customers. In 1976, when BPA supplied fifteen times as much power to the publics as to the privates, the latter paid almost twice the wholesale firm power rate that was charged the public utilities. The rate differential between residential and farm customers of the public and private utilities was reduced by raising the rates of BPA's direct service industrial customers, mostly aluminum companies, which would, in effect, partially subsidize the residential and farm customers of the private utilities. The regional power act left the Bonneville Project Act's preference clause intact, and BPA's public customers were offered new twenty-year firm power contracts to meet their projected loads. So, while the public utilities were still guaranteed priority to BPA-marketed power, their economic advantage would not be as great as in the past.

The top priority given to fisheries and wildlife protection and conservation in the Regional Power Act clearly represented the beginning of a new era in Northwest power planning and development. Over the years the price of the region's hydroelectric power had been kept low partly because the cost of the impact on fish and wildlife resulting from system operations had not been incorporated into the rates. Such losses were no longer acceptable. In the future, fish and wildlife in the Columbia Basin were to be given "equitable treatment," even if it caused significant constraints on power system operations and expansion. In 1982 the regional council promulgated a remedial program which was designed to increase spring flows, on which downstream migrating fish depended, boost protective fish by-pass facilities, and take other fish and wildlife enhancement measures. During the 1980s BPA spent over $100 million on more than 250 fish and wildlife projects. It cost them another $45 million in 1987 alone to release sufficient water for fish at critical migration periods.

Until 1980 conservation attempts in Washington to slow the rate of power use and facility expansion had been weak and few. After environmentalists challenged Seattle City Light's proposed participation in WPPSS plants 4 and 5, the city council in 1975 voted not to take part and instituted a conservation program instead (see above). This decision, a result of the Energy 1990 study, which uncharacteristically brought citizens into the energy planning process, was reached more for its economic than environmental benefits, however. Before the region's electric ratepayers began to experience large rate hikes, the anti-nuclear drives of the mid-1970s failed to arouse much public interest. It was not until the November 1981 general election that Initiative 394 became the first of the anti-nuclear campaigns initiated by environmental groups, to achieve wide support. Although concern about the safety of the environment in the vicinity of nuclear plants had risen sharply after the accident at the Three Mile Island plant near Harrisburg, Pennsylvania in March 1979, safety was not the main reason for the initiative's broad appeal. Rather, it was the issue of fiscal responsibility and the enormous sums that had been spent by WPPSS without ratepayers' consent that converted the measure into a vehicle of popular protest against the perceived incompetence of government bureaucracy. The initiative passed by a large majority but was later found to violate the federal constitution's contract clause. It would have required a vote of the people in effected service areas before bonds could be sold for any new power project of more than 250 megawatts or for any project under construction whose costs had doubled.

The Great Default

The overwhelming approval of Initiative 394, together with the considerably lower electric load projections made by a new group of Northwest power planners in the early 1980s, and the provisions of the Regional Power Act made support of plants 4 and 5 untenable. After the bond market suspended the ratings on these plants in the summer of 1981, WPPSS management had no alternative but to mothball the projects. Initiative 394 had put the plants in a fiscal and political limbo and the utilities participating in the projects were in purgatory, hounded by their angry customers. Led by Clark County PUD and Tacoma City Light, the utilities began to pull out of their mothballing agreements. The I-394 campaign had helped shape the popular perception of WPPSS' role as a major factor in the state's economic downturn. It had also fostered hopes of economic relief which were soon dashed by BPA rate hikes and the expectation of further increases to cover the costs of mothballing. Particularly in counties suffering record unemployment due to the worst recession in the state's wood products

Above: Seattle Sun *photographer John Stamets' record of the unfinished cooling tower of the Satsop's WNP-5 on June 18, 1981, the day the Supply System Board of Directors voted unanimously, bottom, to slow down construction on WNP-4 at Hanford and WNP-5 Satsop. Courtesy, WPPSS.*

and other major industries since the Great Depression, angry ratepayers turned out in unprecedented numbers to protest the actions of their utility commissioners. In hard-hit Grays Harbor County, PUD commissioners and local and state officials faced an angry group of approximately 3,200 people who jammed into a high school gym to demand an explanation for the recent doubling of their electric rates. With this kind of pressure and demands for the recall of PUD commissioners and WPPSS directors coming from dozens of activist ratepayer organizations and the press, the majority of the 88 utilities participating in projects 4 and 5 flatly refused to go along with the mothballing plan. Then termination of the facilities became almost certain. By this time ratepayers were suing their cities, their PUDs and WPPSS. Cities and PUDs were suing WPPSS and BPA. And WPPSS was suing BPA and the PUDs.

Probably no one worked harder to put together alternative plans to rescue the two plants and save the credit ratings of WPPSS and state agencies from the anticipated financial fallout of an uncontrolled termination than Governor John Spellman and BPA administrator Peter Johnson. Yet, the real power behind the "Don't Bankrupt Washington" slogan lay with the supporters of the anti-nuclear, anti-WPPSS initiative. Finally, all the governor's alternative termination plans were rendered moot by a decision of the Washington Supreme Court on June 15, 1983. In the Chemical Bank vs. WPPSS case, the high court held that the 29 Washington PUDs participating in plants 4 and 5 were relieved of their debt because they did not have the legal authority to enter into take-or-pay agreements. With those contracts voided, WPPSS could not pay back the $2.25 billion ($7.5 billion with interest) it owned the 78,000 bondholders for the projects.

Since that time, Chemical Bank, trustee for the WPPSS 4 and 5 bondholders, pursued a suit against the supply system on behalf

of some 24,000 bondholders. Most of the bonds on these projects were sold when bond ratings were still high — Moody's A-1 and Standard and Poor, A-plus. And most of those who purchased the $5,000-denomination bonds were over 60 years old, retired, and expecting to use the income from the bonds to supplement their social security. Among other charges, the bondholders have contended that WPPSS and the securities dealers fraudulently misled investors about its ability to pay back the bonds. Fearing that if they allowed the case to go to the trial scheduled in September 1988 the jury would likely render verdicts settlements in favor of the bondholders, most of the utilities involved agreed to settlements out of court. The bonds on the first three plants, two of which were uncompleted and mothballed, are currently being paid off by all of BPA's customers according to the original net-billing agreement.

In 1984 the only completed WPPSS project, plant 2 at Hanford, which ended up costing $3.2 billion, began operating, seven years behind schedule. By 1992 it had cost the agency about $220 million a year to operate at 50 percent of capacity, which was in the bottom 25 percent in the nation in efficiency. However, between 1994 and 1997, the WPPSS raised that rate to 70 percent of capacity and reduced the plant's cost of power by 30 percent to 2.6 cents per kilowatt-hour. Plant 2 was, by then, the country's only commercial plant that ran on a twelve-month operating cycle, in order to meet the fluctuating load demand of BPA, its sole customer.

Because of the high cost of mothballing plants 1 and 3, $11.5 million a year, the unlikelihood that they would be needed for future demand, and no prospective buyers, WPPSS's board of directors resolved in 1994 to terminate the unfinished projects, WNP 1, 3, 4, and 5. They are currently examining another unprecedented American project — the first demolition of full-sized nuclear plants. At an estimated cost of $200 million, directors pondered over ways to destroy the plants with their concrete cooling towers as high as 500 feet, floors as thick as 20 feet, and reinforcing bar in the 5-foot-thick containment building walls more than two inches in diameter.

WPPSS AND THE LEGACY OF PUBLIC POWER

Agrarian populism and the PUD movement bolstered by the New Deal's Columbia River system and BPA's public preference policy created the conditions in which an institution like WPPSS could flourish. As a result of the state's long commitment to public power ideals and the extraordinary success of BPA, the PUDs, and the municipals in the development and delivery of electric power, state lawmakers granted WPPSS a degree of legal, financial, and political freedom that they would not have entrusted to private power. In an ironic reversal of history, the public power institution embodied in WPPSS found itself in the early 1980s in a position resembling that of the state's private utilities fifty years earlier. In the late twenties and early thirties the investigative probes of the press and lawmakers and the progressive thrust of the people's initiative had been directed against private industry and the holding companies. Half a century later the charges of extortionate rates and abuse of the public trust were hurled by the legislature, the media, and the people at the public power establishment.

The public power movement in Washington succeeded in its original mission of bringing low cost hydropower to the majority of the state's consumers. But enduring public support depended upon the continuation of low and stable power rates. The Washington Public Power Supply System brought on the greatest municipal bond default in history because it tried to maintain its heritage of producing the country's most abundant per capita supply of electric energy at the lowest possible cost. It was a tradition that was not compatible with nuclear power generation, at least not as the industry had developed in the United States, and certainly not on the scale that was attempted. By 1984 every reactor in the country ordered since 1974 had been canceled at some stage of construction, and stockholders and ratepayers were expected to have to pay off $11 billion spent on 100 canceled plants. Of the reactors that were operating or near completion at that time, all had increased in cost several times over their original estimates. No new nuclear power plant has been ordered in the country since 1978.

In January 1983 the four-state council created by the Regional Power Act issued its first twenty-year plan. Forecasting that power demand would grow at an annual rate of between 0.8 percent and 2.8 percent per year, they concluded that no additional thermal plants, beyond the three remaining WPPSS plants technically under construction, would be needed through the end of the century. In fact, until 1992, when the Northwest suffered a power deficit primarily because of a prolonged drought, the state and the region enjoyed a surplus of electric power. Four aging and abandoned but expensively-guarded WPPSS plants, in various stages of completion, stand in silent testimony to the failure of power forecasters in the 1960s and 1970s to anticipate a number of hard-to-imagine factors. In the 1980s a recession, the drop in oil prices, tax incentives that encouraged private utilities to build additional generating facilities, the greater use of energy-efficient machines and appliances, and especially the "rate-shock" induced by the sharp increases in power rates all coalesced by the middle of the decade to produce an energy surplus in the Northwest. Yet by the beginning of the 1990s BPA and other regional power planners had begun to warn in familiar tones that that surplus was fast dwindling.

The April 1982 demonstration at WPPSS Corporate Headquarters in Richland to continue construction of WNP-1 was to no avail when the Supply System Board of Directors voted in May 1982 to delay construction on that project as it had done several months earlier on WNP-4 and WNP-5. Courtesy, WPPSS.

The Vancouver sewage treatment plant serves the community as a waste treatment facility and as a wetlands protection area. The plant was built over the demolished site of the previous facilities, but had left bordering trees to buffer the wetland —one of the last urban wetlands on the Columbia River Basin — from the treatment facilities. When the old treatment facilities couldn't adequately service the growing city population, planners had wanted to add onto the existing grounds by expanding into the adjoining land, part of which was a park "loaned" to the community. By then community objections forced planners to think more progressively. That is why the American Public Works Association recognized the City of Vancouver sewage treatment plant-marine park natural resources area as a 1997 Public Works Project of the Year. The $35 million Marine Park Water Reclamation Facility established a model for treatment facilities that integrated aesthetics, environmental responsibility, cost-effectiveness, and state-of-the-art waste treatment technology. Photos courtesy, City of Vancouver.

WASTE MANAGEMENT

When Washington became a state in 1889, its waste stream consisted of mostly organic material. Now it includes as well an abundance of synthetic and some toxic materials that will lie buried in state landfills well into the next millennium. The management of our waste is an issue of ever-increasing complexity. Recent municipal and county programs encouraging householders to recycle materials from their garbage is just one example of the demands that will continue to be made on waste makers and waste managers in the future. The most complicated attempts to control solid and water wastes have been those that try to correct the hazardous mistakes of previous work. Consequently, while responding to the public's desire for a non-polluted future, today's waste managers must often research the dumping habits and sites of the past.

"OUT OF SIGHT, OUT OF MIND" — THE EARLY WASTE MANAGEMENT ETHIC

Waste disposal practices in Washington during the nineteenth and early twentieth centuries are best characterized as a form of "in situ placement." The scant population allowed almost any convenient location to become a waste receptacle. Although homeowners used backyard tin dumps for cans and bailing wire, pigs for kitchen scraps, and burn barrels for small combustibles, larger items were thrown haphazardly in dumps in vacant lots or just beyond the border of town, homestead, or work camp. Where available, streams, lakes, and bays received gifts of noncombustibles, oversized discards, and a range of putrescible material. In fact, the largest solid waste contribution pioneer citizens made to their communities usually followed the death of their horses. Since the removal of dead animals from the public streets was the responsibility of the city Board of Public Works, a Seattle citizen might have felt relieved if the family steed dropped dead on the streets and not in the yard. In 1894 Seattle Health Department inspectors recorded complaints about thirty-nine abandoned dead animals, 102 filthy privies, and eighty-nine garbage-strewn alleys. In 1901 an unfortunate public health officer in Everett fell from his bicycle into the bay beside the rotting carcasses of two horses. "I am saved," he gasped to an *Everett Herald* reporter, "I didn't swallow any of it!" Obviously, the natural flushing qualities of Washington's rivers and tidal basins did not always provide the desired result.

Besides public health officers, newspaper editors were the most likely to publicly express concern about the sanitation problem. In 1889 the editor of the *Snohomish Weekly Sun* complained that "a great many people are dumping all their swill and

Above: An early lesson from the state Board of Health on separating outhouses from wells. Courtesy, Washington State Archive, Olympia. Below: Everett dump. Courtesy, Everett Public Library.

garbage into the river at the west end of town and greatly inconveniencing the residents of that section." In 1915 across the mountains in Okanogan County, the editor of the *Oroville Weekly* criticized those Orovillians who unloaded their garbage "any place on the outskirts of town that seemed the most convenient," leaving the town fringed with "humps of refuse." No one seems to have objected when the Seattle Engineering Department happily concluded in 1892 that garbage from the business district was easily dumped from a scow into the deeper reaches of Elliott Bay. (However, the department sternly restricted the collection of garbage, swill, and "night soil," which was transported in tight-bodied wagon boxes to between the hours of midnight and 5 a.m.)

Health officials were initially the only public authorities responsible for overseeing the disposal of domestic and commercial wastes. In 1910 state Health Commissioner Dr. Elmer E. Heg blamed the contamination of state water supplies on local officials and waterworks operators who failed to understand the conditions causing pollution. He also found that "a false idea of economy" caused "many cities to take a chance on pollution" rather than spend money to prevent it. Not until 1924 was the commissioner able to report to the legislature that communities were finally becoming aware of the dangers of contaminated drinking water. Yet the statistics he had

compiled for cases of typhoid and cholera-related ailments in Washington during the previous year, including 548 deaths, were alarming. Two cases of typhoid in Snohomish County were traced to Marysville's municipal water system. Spokane County's Clear Lake, which supplied water to the Medical Lake custodial school, was polluted, resulting in twenty-five cases of typhoid and three deaths. Lake Keechelus was being fouled by vacationing autocampers and residents relaxing at their mountain retreats. Ferndale, a small community in Whatcom County, drew its water untreated from the "grossly polluted" Nooksack River. While some of the enteric diseases could be attributed to other sources such as contaminated milk, state health officials had established a clear relationship between sewage pollution and waterborne disease.

In the 1930s with the help of the federal government, Washington municipalities made their first large-scale efforts toward cleaning up their water supplies. But the "out of sight, out of mind" ethic continued to shape much of waste disposal thinking throughout the first half of the twentieth century.

EARLY WASTEWATER SYSTEMS AND SEWAGE TREATMENT TECHNOLOGY

By the 1880s flush toilets were fairly common in the more developed areas of the country, encouraging the speedy development of subsurface sewage systems to collect and dispose of the increasing volumes of wastewater. After statehood was achieved, municipal sewer construction programs were among Washington's largest public works projects. Like other burgeoning municipalities, Seattle, Spokane, and Ellensburg (each a victim of downtown fires in 1889) had to rethink the state of their public utilities. In Ellensburg a contract was let to J. J. Stroud to build a city sewer system projected to cost about $15,000 and designed to serve about 1,000 people. Spokane began to systematically divert its sewage into the Spokane River in 1889. Except for one separated storm and sanitary system built in Browne's Addition west of downtown, Spokane's sewers were combined.

Shortly after the Civil War ended, Seattle citizens, numbering about 700, installed a crude system of open wooden troughs that individually conveyed the untreated sewage to the closest shore of Elliott Bay or Lake Union. By 1875 the town's population had doubled and a more organized approach to sewer planning and construction was required. After Seattle voters passed a sewer construction bond levy, the city in 1883 installed its first permanent sewer line, made of "iron stone," a mixture of clay and iron slag, along Madison Street from Fifth Avenue to Elliott Bay. In 1900 Seattle had more than 80,000 residents who were using sixty miles of city sewer line. By 1924 population growth had slowed,

but the city's lines had swelled to over 625 miles to provide what the engineering department called a "moderately adequate network of sewers."

During the first quarter of the twentieth century, other Washington communities, such as Tacoma, Walla Walla, Chehalis, Hoquiam, Centralia, Renton, Auburn, and Aberdeen took their first steps toward the management of their wastewater. The fundamentals of sewage technology, which involved primary and secondary treatment, were fairly well established by then. Primary treatment removed 50 to 60 percent of the floating and suspended solid matter in raw sewage by filtering, screening, or by gravity through storage in holding tanks. Secondary treatment enabled plant operators to remove up to 95 percent of suspended solids. At the second level, primary-treated sewage was sent to another tank or set of tanks where the natural process of organic decomposition was hastened by the introduction of bacteria to feed on and decompose the remaining suspended organic matter. When bacteria fed on the particles in the water, they fattened and settled to the bottom as part of the sludge.

One of the first treatment methods, which came into use in the United States in 1899, was the contact bed. These "beds" were actually tanks filled with broken stones or other coarse material that provided a relatively large area for the solids to settle and a place for microorganisms to grow. After the solids had settled and the bacteria had performed their service, the water could be withdrawn and sent into the river, lake, or bay. In another process called the "trickling filter," first used in the country in 1908, untreated effluent was sprayed over rock beds covered with colonies of microorganisms. The introduction of oxygen into the sewage by spraying it through the air sped the biological oxidation and mineralization of the organic matter.

The Imhoff tank, introduced around 1911, attempted to facilitate disposal of the sludge, the sewage solids left undigested by bacteria. Usually twenty-five feet deep, the tanks consisted of a sedimentation and a sludge chamber. Solids introduced into the sedimentation chamber fell through slots into the sludge chamber where they were allowed to digest. The remaining sludge that was not gasified or liquefied was then dried and dumped or used as fertilizer. Imhoff tanks were popular in Washington's small towns. Plagued by sandy soil, Elma residents in Grays Harbor County spread the sludge from the town tank on their lawns. Although these early treatment processes used both physical and biological methods, the percentage of organic solids that they removed was comparable to that of later primary treatment facilities.

The solids-removing potential of secondary treatment was significantly expanded with the introduction of oxidation ponds and activated sludge technology. The latter technique, introduced into the U.S. in 1916, put heavy concentrations of aerobic microorganisms into the raw sewage and also pumped air into the

Above and left: Put into operation in 1928 Walla Walla's trickling filter plant was an early state example of effective waste treatment. Courtesy, Walla Walla Department of Public Works.

mixture to stimulate bacterial decomposition. Some of the "activated" sludge left over from the process was then retrieved and put to work on a new stream of wastewater. The system was eventually widely adopted by larger municipalities in the state because it required a smaller area of land than systems like the trickling filter.

Oxidation ponds or lagoons, although first promoted in the 1920s, did not become common until after World War II. The lagoons were large, shallow ponds that allowed sunlight, oxygen, and algae to interact with the sewage. Depending on how long the water was allowed to "brew," it could be restored to a level of purity that equaled or exceeded that achieved by other types of secondary treatment. The ponds, which required a lot of land, were usually built by Washington's rural communities where the availability and cost of property were not a problem. Small municipalities also favored the lagoon treatment because the ponds were relatively inexpensive to build and could provide both primary and secondary treatment.

Primary Treatment in the 1920s

Aiming for the least expensive solution, most Washington cities and towns did not consider treatment facilities in their initial sewage projects. Instead, they concentrated on adequate transportation systems for carrying sewage from business and residential areas to the nearest large body of water. There, it was believed, nature would take care of the rest by diluting and dispersing any toxins. Their systems followed the standard pattern of a network of conduits called laterals that collected the discharge from homes and businesses and fed it into larger pipes called collectors. The collectors emptied into larger mains, also called trunk sewers, that terminated at an outfall into a body of fresh or saltwater.

By the 1920s, often because of an order by the state health department, a number of municipalities had built treatment facilities. In 1925 the department reported that ten Washington cities and towns were practicing primary treatment by a variety of means. Among them Ritzville, Grandview, Olympia, Enumclaw, Pacific Beach, and Puyallup had built municipal septic tanks. Wapato and Cashmere used both septic tanks and contact beds. Seattle and Cedar Falls treated their wastewater with modified Imhoff tanks, and Renton built two sedimentation tanks. Renton's twin rectangular tanks were designed by city engineer S. L. Hanley and built at a cost of $9,000 in 1922. The state sanitary engineer was impressed, noting that the Renton plant "creates no noticeable nuisance, and its cost of operation averages three dollars per day (including electric current and chlorine gas) for approximately 350,000 gallons of sewage daily." In 1925 the city of Pullman installed state-of-the-art Imhoff tanks, designed to serve 2,000 residents and 2,800 faculty, staff, and students at the Washington Agricultural College (later Washington State University). The system was used until the late 1940s when a new trickling filter treatment plant was built. Toward the end of the decade Chelan, Roslyn, and Sunnyside all installed hopper-bottom settling tanks with unheated sludge digesters.

R. H. THOMSON AND SEATTLE'S NORTH TRUNK TUNNEL

R. H. Thomson, Seattle's most famous city engineer, got hired in June 1892 because the North Trunk Sewer was full of water, that is, clean water. Also called the Lake Union Sewer Trunk, the tunnel was being dug from the intersection of Westlake Avenue and Republican Street to the foot of Depot Street (now Denny Way) to divert into Elliott Bay the sewage currently being sent into Lake Union. It was a massive project and it was in serious trouble.

The idea for the huge collector had originated with Col. George E. Waring, a nationally known sanitary engineer who built

Courtesy, WA State Archive, Olympia.

the country's first separated sewer system at Lenox, Massachusetts in 1875. The city hired Waring to design a comprehensive grid needed to accommodate Seattle's swelling population. True to his separate-system inclinations, Waring's 1889 plan for Seattle called for the collection of storm water by surface diversions and a separate underground system for sanitary flows. According to the colonel's design, the Lake Union Tunnel would divert the sewage from the district naturally draining into the lake into the Sound and thus remove the source of pollutants that had turned the lake into a virtual cesspool. Had it been adopted, Waring's plan would have been a farsighted milestone in the development of Seattle's wastewater system and, would, no doubt, have prevented the overflow and related problems of the city's present combined system. But at the time the design was considered, concerns about its carrying capacity and cost resulted in its rejection. Actually, the city council's thumbs-down decision was reasonable considering the current state of wastewater treatment, which was largely restricted to the removal of grit, trash, and other solids.

Instead council members authorized Benezette Williams, a Chicago engineer who had been commissioned by Seattle Mayor Robert Moran as consultant and chief engineer for the city's water system development, to suggest an alternative plan. Two years later Williams' proposals were adopted and began to set the pattern for Seattle's future sewer improvements. Williams had thrown out the separate system concept, arguing that a combined sewage and stormwater works would be adequate and could be built at an estimated cost of $600,000. Dividing the city into three districts, each with between fifty and sixty miles of mains, the plan called for tunnels and outlets to carry the normal-level flows to the Sound. High stormwater (and thus also sanitary) overflows would continue to drain into the lakes. However cost-effective Williams' plan may have been at the time, in later years combined sewer overflows (CSOs) would become the single greatest problem for Seattle's sewer system, requiring millions of dollars to correct. As early as 1914 trunk line overloading caused storm and sanitary wastes to be discharged into the city's three lakes, and in some cases, onto public streets through manholes.

While he rejected Waring's two-system design, Williams kept the colonel's plans for the Lake Union sewer tunnel. After Seattle voters authorized bonds for the North Trunk line, city workers in

~LAKE UNION SEWER TUNNEL~
~ Forcing steel roof ahead ~

~LAKE UNION SEWER TUNNEL~
~ Tunnel a subterranean reservoir ~

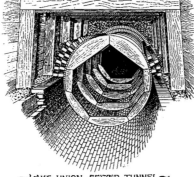

~LAKE UNION SEWER TUNNEL~
~ Masonry — Building the arch ~

~LAKE UNION SEWER TUNNEL~

The Board of Public Works report, included in Seattle's published Municipal Report for 1892, was stocked with detailed descriptions of projects as well as these illustrations for the often heroic construction of the Lake Union Sewer Tunnel, which was then still a work-in-progress.

~LAKE UNION SEWER TUNNEL~
~ Completed section ~
~ Centre not removed ~

March 1891 began excavation for the 72-inch-diameter tunnel, starting at both ends of the mile-long route. Initially, the digging of the tunnel through sand, gravel, and clay formations went along smoothly. Then the diggers hit a pot hole that turned out to be a small underground lake. A deluge poured in and collapsed the face of the tunnel. When the men tried to route the tunnel around the "bad ground," they still came up against a huge volume of sand and water and they even lost a man in the process. The council decided to abandon the project in the spring of 1892 until another plan could be conceived. By then all the money approved for the project had been spent, and the city engineer, Albro Gardner, resigned in frustration over the "impossible North Tunnel sewer."

When James T. Ronald took over the mayor's office, he found the city engineer's resignation on his desk and 25,000 north Seattle residents still sending their sewage into Lake Union. The new mayor quickly scheduled hearings and met with engineers to get opinions about what the city should do next. One of the experts he consulted was R. H. Thomson. With a background in mining engineering, Thomson was happy to oblige and gave the mayor and city council a quick lesson in Puget Sound geology and groundwater deposits. The mayor was impressed, and after the city engineer's position was turned down by an expert who had only to take one look at the project, he offered Thomson the job. And *That Man Thomson*, as he would later title his autobiography, took on the "impossible."

First Thomson hired Edward T. Morgan, "an able miner," who admitted he knew nothing about glacial sand but knew a lot about "working behind breast boards." Morgan was confident that they could finish the bore of the remaining 1,200 feet. After refilling the abandoned ends, Morgan's crew drove through new ground. In his 1894 annual report Engineer Thomson described their progress:

> *"In driving forward, heavy timbers set by hydraulic jacks were used to support the excavation. The flow of water was enormous, the work at times progressing under perfect torrents. For some weeks this flow averaged 437,554 gallons per day. At the point where the original face had been lost, wooden lagging was insufficient to sustain the pressure, and the driving for 20 feet was done under cover of a roof of steel rails advanced with the heading."*

After eleven months of "fighting our way through such ground… with water pouring in upon workmen constantly from sides, roof and face," the tunnel burrowers met about mid-point on May 1, 1893.

Once the difficult bore was completed, masons went to work lining the tunnel with vitrified brick produced to withstand a tensile strain of up to 400 pounds per square inch. By this time the 1893 national financial crash had made its way to Seattle, and Mayor Ronald, hoping to help some of the city's unemployed, directed Thomson to hire heads of families "regardless of whether they were Republicans or Democrats." The men were to be given two weeks of work and then replaced by another group so that the work relief could be spread around. The city Board of Public Works didn't like this arrangement, however, and particularly didn't like Thomson's refusal to negotiate with them about other terms. As a result, Thomson explains in his book, he was fired.

He was not long out of a job, however. In his one-month absence, at least as Thomson tells it, graft, political corruption, and "general confusion seemed to abound." When Mayor Ronald became suspicious that his two-week rotation rule was not being followed, he called in the bookkeeper and

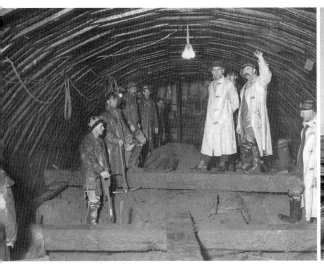

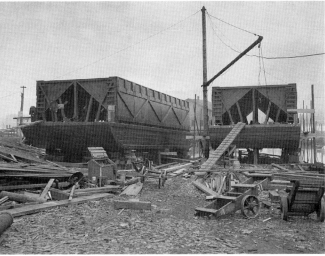

Far left: Work on Seattle's North Trunk Sewer, Siphon Tunnel, Jan. 27, 1913. Left: Seattle garbage scows, 1913. Courtesy Seattle City Archives. Bottom: An exposed section of the North Trunk Sewer as it appears in a postcard advertisement for Seattle Superior Portland Cement. Courtesy Old Seattle Paperworks.

found that some men were being paid too much — "one man having to his credit twenty-six hours for one day." Equally unaccountable, as the sewer line was built down First Avenue from Union to King streets, it had risen toward the level of the street. This time the mayor called in Thomson's replacement who reported that "someone had cut off part of the staff which was used in measuring the depth from the surface line to the top of the sewer."

For years later, Thomson recounts, sewer department employees greeted each other with the salutation, "Who cut the stick?" Mayor Ronald, however, wasn't amused. He fired the offending board members, apparently responsible for the misappropriated funds and botched work, and reappointed Thomson as city engineer. It was under Thomson then that the "impossible" Lake Union tunnel was finished in November 1894. Just one of his self-described "visions" for Seattle, the tunnel, he proudly concluded, would allow the North Seattle neighborhood to "advance along lines of permanent progress, having means at hand for perfect sanitary facilities." During Thomson's tenure the South Tunnel, also known as the South Bayview Street Tunnel, was also completed in 1894. It discharged wastewater collected from the south side of the city onto the Elliott Bay tideflats.

On the east side of the city, sewer mains continued to discharge their contents directly into Lake Washington. Williams had figured that because there was so little development on the east slope, or the west shore of Lake Washington, sewage could continue to be safely sent into the lake even though city health officials had warned that the lake water was unsafe to drink. In 1922, with thirty-three separate outfalls emptying into the lake,

the city proposed to correct the problem with a $2.5 million program that called for sixteen Imhoff-type plants along the lake shore. Three were built by 1924. But in the following year nearby residents complained about the tanks' operations, and state and county health boards passed resolutions requiring the effluent to meet Public Health Service drinking water standards. This the tanks could not do.

In a redesigned program the city built a primary treatment plant and overflow structures and interceptors to carry the combined flows from the eastern slope to the existing salt water diversion systems. That way only high water overflows would be released untreated into the lake. By 1936 the last of the raw sewage outfalls to Lake Washington had been intercepted, and three years later Seattle completed its first primary treatment plant. With a design of 32,000, or approximately ten percent of the city's population, the Oregon Street plant became one of about fifty treatment facilities operating in the state before World War II.

DEPRESSION AND WARTIME WASTEWATER PROJECTS

The money that became available through the New Deal work relief programs of the 1930s helped Washington municipalities fund facilities that otherwise would probably not have been built until many years later. The state's first secondary treatment system, however, was built before the federal government got involved in local public works projects. It was in Walla Walla and it was built only after the state health director issued a formal condemnation order against the town in April 1924. Three years earlier a state health officer had investigated the city's trash disposal system after "the man who had the contract for the removal of garbage in Walla Walla lost all of his [garbage-fed] hogs and threw up his contract." (Hogs would continue to provide rural communities a common disposal method until the 1950s when the spread of trichinae infection in humans was traced to these public service porkers.) The director had calculated that approximately 60 percent of the city's untreated sewage was being discharged into Mill Creek, which ran through the center of town, and the balance wound up in irrigation ditches on nearby land. The results were "obnoxious exhalations offensive to the public," the gross contamination of shal-

70,000 BARRELS OR 405 CAR LOADS OF SUPERIOR PORTLAND CEMENT USED IN NORTH TRUNK SEWER, SEATTLE. SUPERIOR PORTLAND CEMENT IS MADE AT CONCRETE, SKAGIT CO., WASH. YOUR HOME COMPANY

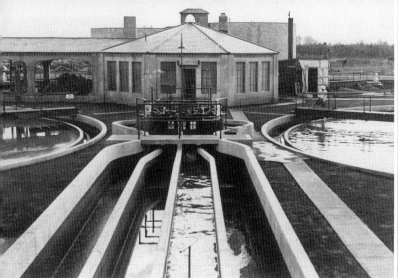 

Above left: Yakima's primary treatment plant as recorded for the WPA, the depression-time agency that helped build it. Courtesy, Franklin D. Roosevelt Library, WPA Collection. Above right: Aerial of Yakima's considerably enlarged treatment facilities, 1985. Courtesy, City of Yakima, Wastewater Division.

low wells, and a number of cases of typhoid and other intestinal diseases.

Five years after the condemnation order was issued, the Walla Walla treatment plant was completed. The facility included an impressive arsenal of sewage treaters including the first trickling filter unit in the state, as well as bar screens, grit chambers, mechanical settling tanks, chlorination, unheated sludge digesters, and open sludge beds. In 1937 the City of Colfax in Whitman County used federal assistance to become the second municipality in the state to use secondary treatment. The Colfax plant featured a mechanically equipped primary clarifier, a rotary-type trickling filter, a mechanically cleaned secondary clarifier, a heated digester with sludge stirring equipment, sludge drying beds, and chlorinators.

That same year in Yakima County the cities of Selah and Yakima put primary plants into operation to retard the growing degradation of the Yakima River and adjacent irrigated tracts subject to contaminated return flows. Yakima's works accommodated daily flows ranging from four to twenty million gallons, making it at the time the state's largest plant. Continued concern about the river's water quality led to the completion of primary treatment plants by the cities of Wapato and Ellensburg and a secondary plant by the City of Zillah. Designed by Yakima engineer G. D. Hall, the Zillah project was notable on several accounts. Besides being the first municipal plant in the state to use the activated sludge process, it was hailed by the state health department as "one of the most unique in the state for location, architectural treatment, and landscaping." Except for the sludge drying beds, it was entirely underground and located next to the city park and swimming pool.

The City of Lynden in Whatcom County also completed its WPA-sponsored treatment facilities in the late 1930s. Located on a landscaped site amidst a grove of trees, the plant was equipped with a circular trickling filter with a three-arm rotary distributor and a sludge digester with gas collector. It was the first secondary treatment plant west of the Cascades. In Grant County, the City of Ephrata inaugurated an activated sludge system which it promised would produce an effluent so "highly polished" that it could be used for irrigation. During the depression decade in rural areas throughout the state, the CWA and WPA employed men to build nearly 5,000 "sanitary privies" according to U.S. Public Health Service specifications with materials supplied by their mostly homeowner beneficiaries.

In another attempt to help localities improve sanitary conditions, state officials initiated a treatment plant operator training program. Realizing that plant efficiency largely depended upon the knowledge and abilities of their operators, the state health department, together with the University of Washington Engineering Department and the Pacific Northwest branch of the American Water Works Association, sponsored the first three-day

training course for waterworks and sewage plant treatment operators in November 1938.

Funding available through the New Deal and for defense-related projects during the war years caused the number of sewage treatment plants in the state to rise from thirty-six in 1934 to 120 in 1946. The postwar plants served 16 percent of the state's total population, 22 percent of those in densely settled areas. Secondary treatment was provided by the facilities in Walla Walla, Moses Lake, Colfax, Lynden, Dayton, Zillah, Ephrata, Issaquah, Leavenworth, Goldendale, the Renton Boeing plant and war housing project, Seattle's Sandpoint and Kirkland's war housing projects, and King County's Val Vue Sewer District. During the war the government funded much of the state's sewer line construction primarily to serve military bases, war-related industries, and housing projects for war-industry workers. As the state population grew by 15 percent from 1940 to 1945, the portion of the population served by sewers almost kept up, rising from 46 to 59 percent. The corresponding figure for metropolitan areas increased from 75 to 78 percent.

WASTEWATER MANAGEMENT IN SPOKANE

Although it took awhile to build, Spokane's postwar remake of its sewage collection and treatment system eventually culminated in some award-winning public works. It took thirty-one years, from 1946 when the Chamber of Commerce described the water in the Spokane River as becoming "more obnoxious every day," until 1977 when the National Society of Professional

Below: WPA project, Hoquiam storm sewer construction, April 2, 1937. Courtesy Washington State Historical Society, Tacoma.

Spokane treatment plant beside the Spokane River. Courtesy, City of Spokane Public Works.

Engineers named Spokane's new treatment plant one of the ten outstanding engineering achievements in the country for that year.

Spokane's habit of using its namesake river as a convenient dump for raw sewage was as old as the settlement. Years before the grand waterfall in the center of town began generating the state's first hydropower, it diluted the first settlers' sewage. For a long time the low population and plenteous supply of water in the river and the huge aquifer underlying the city (See Public Water Chapter) put off concerns about the disposal of wastewater. However, after the Grand Coulee and Bonneville dams went on line and the Kaiser Aluminum Company built the second largest aluminum reduction plant in the country in Spokane, the city's population began to climb. Uncle Sam also decided that the "Heart of the Inland Empire" would be an ideal site for military airbases. By 1942 war-industry workers were streaming into Spokane, contributing an additional 20,000 souls to the city's population. The housing that the newcomers needed could barely keep up with their numbers and the city utilities could not.

In 1946 the war was over but the aluminum industry did not peter out as expected, and many servicemen decided to make Spokane their permanent home. That year Spokane voters were asked to approve a $1.7 million bond issue to finance a system of intercepting and transmission lines that would carry the area's sewage to a treatment plant instead of the river. The urging of the Chamber of Commerce that "Spokane is 20 years behind now on its sewage disposal" probably influenced at least some Spokane residents to vote in favor of the controversial issue.

The bond issue passed but it took another twelve years before the city treatment plant was up and running. In the early 1960s the plant was expanded and pre-aeration, a primary clarifier, and increased chlorination and digester capacities were added. But even these enhanced functions could not bring the river up to state and federal water quality standards. In 1968 the state's Pollution Control Commission gave the city a 1972 deadline for meeting the standards. The result was the considerably updated, award-winning $55 million treatment plant that went on line in 1977. It was capable of treating 44 million gallons of sewage per day with an additional 77 million gallons of stormwater receiving primary treatment and chlorination.

The success of this advanced treatment facility shone brightly at Long Lake, located on the Spokane River about fifteen miles northwest of Spokane. Before the new plant began operating, nutrients expelled from the city's old sewage treatment plant clouded the lake with excessive algal growth. The new facility brought a steep dip in the lake's phosphorus levels and a big improvement in water clarity.

WASTEWATER MANAGEMENT AND WATER POLLUTION CONTROL, 1950-1990

Federal Water Quality Legislation

Prior to the June day that Harry Truman put his signature on the 1948 Water Pollution Control Act, the federal government had had little to do with monitoring the pollution of the nation's waters. The 1899 Rivers and Harbors Act had authorized the Army Corps of Engineers to control the dumping of refuse into navigable waterways, "other than that flowing from streets and sewers." State health departments had received some federal aid for studies involving waterborne disease during the 1910s and 1920s. But for the most part water pollution control and the overseeing of waste disposal was carried out by local and state health officials under the authority of state public health statutes with limited local and state funding. The New Deal public works programs of the 1930s brought a revolution in community sanitation when they funded and put men to work on water and sewer systems in 8,000 communities across the nation.

The New Deal activities also laid the groundwork for the 1948 Water Pollution Control Act that called for comprehensive planning and interstate cooperation to reduce pollution in interstate waters. The legislation provided the states technical services and financial assistance, although at the beginning there was not much of the latter. It gave Washington municipalities the incentive to plan their first long-range comprehensive waste management systems. In 1951 fourteen communities on the urban side of Puget Sound — Seattle, Tacoma, Puyallup, Bellevue, Snohomish, White Center, Richmond Beach, Edmonds, Bothell, Redmond, North Bend, Fall City, Duvall, Black Diamond, and Des Moines — lacked adequate sewage treatment plants. By 1954, of the above, Tacoma, Puyallup, Bellevue, Richmond Beach, and Edmonds, as well as Bremerton, Olympia, Shelton, Sumner, White Center, Buckley, and Tumwater had updated or built new treatment facilities with government aid.

In eastern Washington, Othello in Adams County put its federal grant to work in 1955 on its first and badly needed sewer system. Numbering only 526 residents in 1950, the town by 1960 had increased in population by five times after the Columbia Basin Project irrigation canals began delivering water to the area in 1953.

The irrigation project brought unprecedented prosperity along with new problems. More homes in close proximity with each other and each using septic tanks and drainfields resulted in greater potential for contaminating the town's well water supply. Poorly draining soil and a dramatic rise in the water table caused by the irrigation flows also created problems for the septic system. The completion of sewer lines and the primary treatment plant on Owl Creek came none too soon. In fact, by the early 1960s the plant was already seriously overloaded, and in 1963 the city was compelled to build a twenty-acre lagoon. The lagoon allowed both primary and secondary treatment for both the town's domestic and the local food processing plant's industrial waste.

It was President Eisenhower who put his signature on the 1956 Water Pollution Control Act, which made the 1948 law permanent and allocated more federal assistance for the states. Following the government's lead, the Washington Pollution Control Commission (PCC) put community sewerage at the top of its program priorities. In 1956 the commission counted 188 treatment plants of "various types and capacities" operating in the state, with 48 needing enlargement or improvement. There were 64 cities and sewer districts that had sewer systems but no treatment works. The commission directed all communities to give their liquid waste at least primary treatment, including any industrial waste that was connected to their works.

The PCC's attitude towards industrial waste, its second priority, was somewhat more relaxed. Their list of the approximately 1,500 Washington industries that produced liquid wastes reads like a Whitmanesque catalogue of industrial muscle — breweries, grain elevators,

Top: Edmonds waste treatment plant, ca. 1955. Courtesy, HDR Engineering.
Above: Work-in-progress, May 1990, on the contemporary Edmonds waste water treatment facility. Courtesy, Edmonds Public Works.

laundries, dairies, oil refineries, rubber and food processors, smelters, tanneries, woolen mills, chemical plants, plastic manufacturers, packing houses, and more. Years before toxic chemicals were discovered in industrial waste streams, commission members had no reason to suspect that public health could be threatened by the "by-products" of these industries since they did not ordinarily contain disease-producing organisms.

The concern about industrial wastewater was primarily for the effect it might have on other sectors of the economy, such as fisheries, recreation, and irrigated agriculture. During the 1950s industrial and sewage treatment plant discharges sometimes forced beaches and recreation areas to close. Obnoxious odors, pollution slicks, and fish kills began to draw more public attention. In 1955 the legislature passed a bill requiring commercial and industrial establishments to obtain permits prior to discharging waste into public waters. However, the PCC had not been given the wherewithal to enforce the new law, a situation that was typical across the country. Until the federal government stepped up its participation, enforcement depended largely upon the voluntary cooperation of local officials and industry representatives.

By the early 1960s ever greater numbers of people were going to state and national parks to hike, swim, and fish, and they began to realize that pollution could affect far more than their drinking water supplies at home. The toxic effects of water pollution on the health of both humans and the ecosystem became a subject of congressional investigation. The 1965 Water Quality Act, resulting from the congressional debates, won strong support from the Johnson administration. It set up the Water Pollution Control Administration, the first federal agency to be given specific charge of water pollution control. The law also required all states to establish minimum water quality standards subject to federal review and doubled the number of grants for municipal waste treatment plants.

In 1969 during President Richard Nixon's first term, Con-

gress adopted the National Environmental Policy Act (NEPA), making it the greatest year yet for environmental legislation. With the NEPA the government for the first time acknowledged its responsibility to act as a "trustee of the environment for succeeding generations." One of the goals of the act was to "attain the widest range of beneficial uses of the environment without degradation, risk to health or safety, or other undesirable and unintended consequences." The most important and enduring lever of the law was the mandate for environmental impact statements (EIS) for all federal projects. In 1970 Congress created the Environmental Protection Agency (EPA) which was given authority to establish and enforce uniform standards for water pollution control.

One of the biggest challenges for the EPA was establishing controls on industrial waste discharges. For several years in the 1960s, data on industrial discharges, which was needed for the drafting of legislation, was delayed because the federal budget bureau's industry-dominated committee on report forms objected to the proposed form for data collection. Not until Congress passed the 1972 Clean Water Act did the government have the authority to require industries to disclose such information. The act marked a turning point for the nation's public waters. No longer would it be legal to discharge contaminants into streams and lakes. Because conformance with the act meant substantial and costly technological adjustments, industry representatives resisted the EPA's policies, but ultimately the courts sided with the federal agency. Consequently, the act stimulated much innovation in industrial wastewater treatment, such as that adopted by the lower Columbia River pulp mills. (See below.)

The ambitious goal of the 1972 legislation to eliminate all pollutant discharges into American waters by 1983, except for "necessary and justifiable" economic and social development, also applied to municipalities. But communities were given even less time to comply than industry. Municipal sewer system operators were directed to install secondary treatment facilities by July 1,

Right: Moses Lake Sewage Treatment Plant in 1957, after its first upgrade. Photo by Duane Allen. Below: The same lakeside site reconstructed as the landscaped Central Operating Facility. All photos courtesy, City of Moses Lake.

MOSES LAKE WASTEWATER TREATMENT

The World War II development of Larson Air Force Base required Moses Lake to develop a wastewater system greater than the capacity of its citizens' septic tanks. And the Air Force helped, constructing the original sewer system in 1945. The primary treatment plant, built then a few blocks south of downtown on the west shore of the lake's Pelican Horn, treated the community sewage with a variety of clarifiers, trickling filters and digesters before releasing the treated effluent into Moses Lake. With periodic upgrades this system worked well enough until it was determined that the plant outflow was feeding the algae which was increasingly fouling the lake. Construction of an environmentally friendly system began in 1982. Forty-five percent of the $7 million-plus project was borne by the community — the rest came from the state Department of

Above: The system's new secondary treatment facility, the "Sand Dunes Plant," three miles south of the city, seen here at the top of the photo.

Ecology and the U.S. Environmental Protection Agency. For secondary treatment, a wastewater treatment plant — the "Sand Dunes Plant" — was built about three miles south of the city. It was connected to the central operating facility at the site of the old secondary treatment plant by a five-mile-long force main, the first 1,500 feet of which crosses the lake with 24-inch polyethylene pipe. For safety, a variety of pressure-sensing devices, mobile emergency units, alarms, and bypass devices were built into the system. In 1998, eighty-four miles of collection mains, twenty-eight lift stations, and two wastewater treatment facilities of the Moses Lake system were maintained by five city employees.

1977. It was an unrealistic deadline. Many Washington communities were still trying to comply with earlier state requirements. In 1967 the state Pollution Control Commission had adopted a program directing municipalities to have the "best practical treatment" system in operation within five years. Construction schedules, however, were often slowed due to the difficulty of obtaining funding. Many small towns could not even raise the amount required to match state and federal grants. As a result, in 1971 over a dozen communities missed the state's deadline for upgrading their sewer systems. In 1988, 54 percent of Washington's public plants failed to meet the deadline for installing secondary treatment which had been extended to July 1 of that year. After Hawaii, it was the worst compliance rate in the country.

Duvall's waste treatment plant with two 12-foot cage rotors and two 16-foot Spiraflo clarifiers. Courtesy, City of Duvall.

Washington voters had opted to help localities fund improvements in 1968 when they approved Referendum 17, a $25 million bond issue, some of which was distributed in 1973 to over forty sewage treatment construction projects. Money also became available after Referendum 26, a $225-million bond issue for waste treatment and water supply systems, was passed by the voters in 1972. Some of those who benefited were: Bellevue for an interceptor sewer; Duvall for secondary treatment facilities; Lynnwood for a force main; Marysville for chlorination equipment; Tacoma for a system treating Point Defiance Park; and Olympia for treatment plant improvements. That year Gig Harbor was also given funding for interceptor sewers, a treatment plant, and an outfall line.

HARBOR POLLUTION AND RESTORATION

Everett Harbor

By the mid-1930s the fouling of state waters by industry and municipalities had reached alarming levels. In 1937 the legislature created the Pollution Control Commission to investigate and protect the condition of Washington waters. That year the commission began studying Everett Harbor. Their research discovered extremely low dissolved oxygen levels in the water, resulting from the discharge of sulfite waste liquor by two local pulp mills. When measured in terms of oxygen demand alone, the effect of the mills' emissions was equivalent to that of sewage produced by four and a half million people. The commission as yet had no enforcement powers and the pollution was a problem that could not be easily corrected. So the commission recommended a stopgap solution, directing the mills to use better diffusion methods at their outfalls, which were then located at low tide elevation on the beach beneath the mill docks.

When commission researchers returned to Everett in the fall of 1949, they found that salmon and herring in the bay were still suffocating from the lack of oxygen caused by the mills' sulfite discharges. They also uncovered a deposit of decomposing organic matter covering a large portion of the harbor bottom. As it decayed, the mix of fish cannery waste, pulp mill emissions, and domestic sewage further robbed the water of its oxygen. At this time untreated sewage from Everett's 33,000 residents was being carried through combined sewers to eleven major outfalls along the Lower Snohomish River and Port Gardner Bay. Bacterial contamination levels were so high that the commission considered the lower river frontage and shores of the bay "undesirable for human habitation."

It took the City of Everett five years to gather the political will to begin correcting these conditions and another six to put the first public works on line. In July 1954 the city established a reserve account to fund system improvements by charging sewer utility customers an additional service fee. They also required all sewer line extensions to separate stormwater from sanitary flows. In 1960 Everett completed its sewage treatment facility, an oxidation lagoon providing secondary treatment and capable of removing an estimated 80 percent of the biochemical oxygen demand (BOD) carried in the waste flow of the community of 40,000. (High BOD

Above: At its southern Everett end, the old U.S. Highway 99 bridge over the Snohomish River runs between the riverside mills of Everett, ca. 1940. Courtesy National Archives, Seattle. Bottom: North of its bridge over the Snohomish River, Interstate 5 runs between the river and the Everett waste treatment lagoon, 1997. The Cascade Mountains are on the horizon. Photo by James Arrabito.

levels are caused by large quantities of oxygen-consuming organic material that reduce the amount of dissolved oxygen concentrations in the water, thus endangering aquatic life. The BOD has become a standard measure for determining water purity.)

Reducing the toxicity of industrial wastewater going into Everett harbor would be more difficult. In 1958, as was true twenty years earlier, the combined wastes of the Weyerhaeuser and Scott Paper mills accounted for 99 percent of the total BOD load in Port Gardner Bay. In 1967 a joint federal-state investigation was still listing the damage. The deepwater outfalls installed by the mills were an improvement, but discharges of sulfite waste liquor and occasional toxic chemicals were still injuring larval forms of indigenous fish, contributing to the harbor's toxic bottom sludge, and suppressing phytoplankton activity. In 1967 the Washington State Enforcement Project, conducted under the authority of the federal water pollution act, directed the mills to provide primary treatment of all solids-bearing wastes, reduce the quantity of solid waste liquor discharged into the harbor, construct a submarine outfall with an adequate diffuser to discharge residual wastes outside the harbor, and dredge and bury the existing sludge deposits.

This time industry went on parade in a steady march to dramatically reverse its past abuses. In 1970 the waste load discharged through the mills' deep water diffuser routinely exceeded 2.5 million pounds of total solids per day. After the Scott Paper Company completed installation of the first stage of its recovery furnace in March 1974, the waste load declined to less than two million pounds. In 1975, after the Weyerhaeuser mill converted from a sulfite pulping process to a thermal-mechanical operation, the waste load declined further to about half a million pounds per day. Following the installation of a secondary treatment facility at the Scott plant in 1979, the total solids discharged to Port Gardner Bay averaged 50,000 pounds per day, or about two percent of the pre-1970 solid waste level.

Grays Harbor and Chehalis River

The Pollution Control Commission's 1938 findings about Grays Harbor and the lower Chehalis River were as disconcerting as those at Everett. Hundreds of dead and near-dead silver salmon were discovered drifting helplessly in the current as large numbers

Above: Chehalis treatment plant, 1949. Courtesy Ravenna Rare Books, Seattle. Below: Hoquiam Lagoon, Oct. 1, 1958. Photo by Jones Photo Co.

of shrimp flipped spastically at the water's surface. Unnaturally low dissolved oxygen concentrations were found throughout a twenty-mile area extending from the Grays Harbor estuary up the Chehalis River and beyond Cosmopolis. Throughout the dry summer, the oxygen-depleted water shifted back and forth in the harbor along with the tide.

A second commission study in 1950 identified the principal sources of pollution as the solid waste liquor discharges from the ITT Rayonier pulp mill near the mouth of the Hoquiam River and the untreated domestic effluent of the several municipalities along the Chehalis River and the harbor. The mill's contribution to the harbor's BOD was 150 times that of the domestic sewage. Although Hoquiam and Aberdeen, which together accounted for nearly two-thirds of the sewage-contributing population, were both over 90 percent sewered, in 1950 neither municipality had yet constructed treatment facilities. Neither had the upstream communities of Centralia, Montesano, McCleary, and Cosmopolis.

At that time the only municipalities in the basin with treatment were Chehalis, Elma, and Pe Ell. The Chehalis facility, constructed in 1949, was the first to use secondary treatment. Providing comminution, primary and secondary sedimentation, filtration, solid digestion, and chlorination, the facility was reportedly capable of 75 percent BOD removal and approximately 90 percent removal of suspended matter. In 1951, following the PCC study, Centralia constructed a secondary treatment plant similar to the Chehalis facility. That year also Montesano initiated a storm water removal project, and in 1953 McCleary built a sewer system and secondary treatment plant that discharged chlorinated effluent. The last significant source of untreated domestic discharge on the upper Chehalis was eliminated in June 1957 when Montesano began operating a primary treatment plant.

Despite all these improvements in the upper Chehalis River, in 1956 commission investigators found that the contamination of Grays Harbor had increased in the Aberdeen-Hoquiam area. Pulp mill sulfite liquor was responsible for most of the estuary's pollution, but untreated domestic waste from Hoquiam and Aberdeen was also contributing to the water's high oxygen demand and bacterial contamination. The low-lying sister cities shared formidable sanitary engineering problems that stemmed mostly from the proximity of their sewer lines to bodies of salt- and groundwater. Yet both communities complied with the commission's recommendations and by the early 1960s were operating sewage treatment facilities. Aberdeen chose a primary plant consisting of settling tank, heated sludge digester, and chlorination units, while Hoquiam built a lagoon that provided secondary treatment.

It was not until the 1970s that Grays Harbor received considerable relief from the excretions of the pulp mills. In 1969 the ITT Rayonier mill installed a chemical recovery furnace to remove toxic pulping chemicals prior to discharge. Two years later a primary treatment system was added and, in 1977, a biological wastewater treatment system. Concurrent with these efforts, the Weyerhaeuser mill completed a biological treatment system and upgraded its river outfall. With the completion of these facilities, the combined daily BOD load produced by the two mills was drastically reduced to about 10,000 pounds, or about 3% of the mid-1960s level.

Lower Columbia River

Pollution from cities and pulp mills had become clearly evident in the lower reaches of the Columbia River by the late 1930s. The first sulfite pulp mill in Washington was constructed in 1893 at Camas, about ten miles east of Vancouver. In 1921 a second major sulfite pulp mill was built at Vancouver, and by the mid-1930s a third had begun operating downriver at Longview. The combined effects of these mills became painfully apparent in the summers of 1939 and 1940 when commercial fishermen cast a chorus of complaints over dead fish and a "slime" that was collecting on their nets. When the state fisheries department investigated in 1941-1942, they identified the slime as a strain of sphaerotilus, a filamentous, sheath-forming fungus that grew only where sulfite waste liquor concentrations exceeded 50 parts per million (p.p.m.).

As expected, water sampling revealed that the greatest slime concentrations occurred adjacent to the Camas, Vancouver, and Longview pulp mills. The plants were daily discharging several million gallons of sulfite waste liquor that produced concentrations of more than 100 p.p.m., a figure that the Pollution Control Commission ordered to be cut by half. The fisheries department also reported bacteriological problems in the lower Columbia, especially in the vicinity of Vancouver, Camas, Longview, and Kelso which together were discharging the untreated sewage of more than 50,000 persons directly into the river. The researchers concluded that although the Columbia was "not at the present time grossly polluted by sewage," swimming had to be considered dangerous, and nowhere should the water be used for drinking unless adequately treated by filtration and chlorination.

The first big break for restoring and preserving clean water in this part of the Columbia came in the early 1950s when nearly all the communities discharging raw sewage into the river, including Camas, Vancouver, Longview, and Kelso, built primary treatment

plants. During the same period, the principal sulfite pulp mills installed waste recovery and diffusion equipment. Yet, even with these efforts, by the early 1960s the slime was back, to the consternation of both commercial and sports fishermen. This time the federal government stepped in. The Lower Columbia River Enforcement Conference in 1965 directed all pulp and paper mills to install within the next two years treatment facilities for removing settleable solids and at least 70 percent of volatile suspended matter in their effluents. The conference also ordered the Crown Zellerbach mill at Camas and the Boise-Cascade mill at Vancouver to reduce their sulfite waste liquor-related BOD loadings by at least 70 percent by the end of 1969. The industries complied and when the 1972 fishing season began there were no reports from gillnetters of slime in their gear.

The river's fresh water revival received another boost as the cities of Camas, Vancouver, Longview, and Kelso upgraded their treatment facilities from primary to secondary. In addition, by 1986 all of these cities except Vancouver were collecting their wastewater through separate sewerage systems, thereby minimizing the periodic fouling caused by raw sewage overflows and treatment plant overloading occurring during storms. However, the cleanup of the lower Columbia was not over. In 1990 the EPA announced that it had found dangerously high dioxin levels in bottom fish in the waters where the mills released their wastewater. A result of the use of chlorine bleaches, the cancer-causing dioxin contamination was found to be serious enough to impose stringent new controls.

Commencement Bay

In 1981 the Environmental Protection Agency awarded Tacoma's Commencement Bay the distinction of being one of the ten most dangerously polluted sites in the nation. Agency researchers estimated that up to 200 sources of chemical pollutants were contributing to the bay's mix of poisonous metal compounds and organic toxicants. Some of the waste leaching from pre-World War II chemical dumps was found hidden under 500 feet of water. In 1984 state Ecology Department investigators confirmed the presence of toxic metals in the water and toxic compounds in the sediments of the inner bay along the industry-lined Tacoma waterfront. A significant part of the pollution was coming from the City of Tacoma's storm sewer system that swept in high levels of fecal coliform, metals, and hydrocarbons.

After studying Commencement Bay for six years, EPA and DOE were finally ready in 1989 to begin implementing a cleanup plan that was expected to take from ten to twenty years to complete. Nine areas were identified for the removal of 1.6 million cubic yards of mud loaded with arsenic, lead, zinc, mercury, PCBs, and other toxic substances. Through the Superfund Program approved in 1980, the federal government agreed to contribute $300,000 per year to increase the number of DOE enforcement personnel. But with cost estimates for dredging the contaminated sediments alone ranging up to $100 million, the cleanup promised to be an expensive project for state and local agencies, Tacoma's industries and utility customers, as well as for federal taxpayers.

And the vexing problems didn't end with the price tag. Difficulties in tracking the sources responsible for the pollution have been matched by uncertainties about where to direct the final disposal of the contaminated sediments. The cleanup has also been slowed by the chronic contest of wills between government and industry, the latter which, according to the Superfund act, is liable for the cost of removing the pollution it has caused. A Kaiser

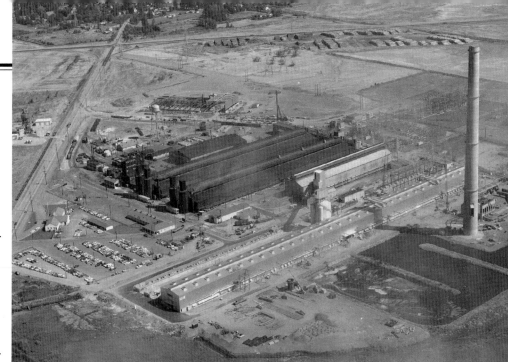

Kaiser Aluminum on Tacoma's reclaimed tidelands, ca. 1969. Photo by Bud Kimball. Courtesy, Tacoma Public Works.

Aluminum Company spokesman may have expressed the skepticism of many of Tacoma's processing and manufacturing firms when he told a reporter in July 1989 that "This place has been used for industry for a hundred years. To try to turn it into a pristine bay now is sort of like suggesting downtown Tacoma be returned to virgin forest." However, in June 1991 the EPA announced that the St. Paul Waterway, which was probably the most contaminated part of the bay, had become the first Superfund marine site in the nation to be cleansed of pollution.

GREATER SEATTLE WATER POLLUTION CONTROL AND THE GROWTH OF METRO

By 1945 evidence of the residence of one-third million waste producers in the Northwest's largest metropolis was showing in the waters of Puget Sound. According to the state health department, the coliform count, used as an indicator of fecal contamination, in the water off Seattle's public saltwater bathing beaches was so high that it was unsafe for swimming. Health inspectors noted complaints about "floating solids, scum, and slicks throughout all of Elliott Bay and extensive stretches of the Sound," and found levels of dissolved oxygen so low in the Duwamish Waterway "that fish cannot exist." The Seattle City Council hired Dr. Abel Wolman, a nationally recognized authority on wastewater management, to propose a solution.

In 1948 Dr. Wolman announced his findings, claiming that because Puget Sound was so deep and cold and had such swift tidal currents, it could be used safely and indefinitely for the disposal of Seattle's raw sewage. City officials were pleased. Wolman's recommendations seemed to confirm the soundness of their current disposal method, making a costly treatment plant unnecessary. The state Pollution Control Commission reacted less positively. Citing the high coliform counts recorded at Seattle's Alki and Golden Gardens beaches and warning of a possible epidemic, PCC biologist Dr. Nathan Fasten confessed to being "horror-struck" that a sanitary expert could recommend that any large city discharge untreated sewage.

In fact, Wolman's conclusions and recommendations were much more than a vindication of the city's current sewage practices. He also advised that the city extend marine outfalls to greater depths and expand trunkline capacities to minimize overflows. Further construction of combined sewers should be prohibited and a master plan ought to be developed for additions to the system. The city adopted Wolman's plans and by the summer of

1949 began extending the city's southern outfalls while working on plans to divert the northern outfalls at Salmon Bay and Golden Gardens into a single discharge point at West Point. But the PCC wanted the city to do more and quickly. In a notice to Seattle Mayor William F. Devin, the commission urged the city to take immediate steps to initiate a sewer separation program, reminding him that separation was one of Dr. Wolman's proposals.

A jurisdictional contest between the city and the commission continued into the spring of 1950. Seattle City Engineer R.W. Finke reported to the city council that the PCC would not approve its plans for an outfall off Alki Point until the city committed itself to a permanent sewage disposal solution for "the entire West Seattle area." Vocal Alki Point residents, who preferred the commission's solutions, demanded the construction of a sewage treatment facility that would clear up the problem rather than merely divert it to beaches further south. Subsequent negotiations between the commission and the city opened the door for a Seattle waste management system committed to treatment. In March 1951, a half-year short of the centennial marking the arrival of Seattle's first settlers at Alki Point, the Seattle City Council voted to authorize the construction of a sewage treatment plant to serve the West Seattle area. After a variety of delays arising from neighborhood protests, financing problems, and disputes over the plant design, the West Seattle interceptor system and the Alki Point primary treatment plant were completed in early 1959.

The West Seattle program set important precedents, and it marked the recognition that Puget Sound could not indefinitely be used as a dump for untreated sanitary wastes. By placing a substantial portion of the storm and sanitary waste stream entering the Sound under the control of a rudimentary management plan, the experience helped predispose Seattle and surrounding communities for the coming of the Municipality of Metropolitan Seattle, or Metro.

A Regional Solution

Even early in the 1950s the desirability of long-range planning and the concept of a regional waste management system ought to have been evident to city planners familiar with the impact of another type of public work — the Lake Washington Floating Bridge. While West Seattle residents were pressing the city to rethink its position on waste treatment, the berry farms of

Above: The reach of Metro's hopes for cleaning King County waterways in 1963, the license date on the Chevrolet. Courtesy, Metro and Washington State Archives, Bellevue.

what was once called East Seattle were rapidly being developed into the bedroom communities of Bellevue, Kirkland, Redmond, and their unincorporated satellites. Easy access across the lake brought more subdivisions, more septic tanks, more uncoordinated small sewer districts, and more runoff from streets and highways. This added up to more raw and inadequately treated sewage flowing into what was considered the most stunning jewel in the Queen City's crown.

When Kirkland became a boomtown, with the mobilization of the Lake Washington shipyards for war production during World War II, the water off the city's shores became heavily polluted by sewage. Before the conflict, the shipyard rest room consisted of a sixteen-hole outhouse on the dock emptying directly into the lake. Soon after the war began, a chemist analyzing the water in Yarrow Bay off the shipyards exclaimed, "My God, this is almost pure urine!" Fortunately, grants from the Public Works Administration (PWA) were still available and in 1942 the town began work on a municipal sewage system and primary treatment plant financed by the federal program. However, the lake continued to be used as a convenient receptacle for the treated and

Bottom left: In the famous pose, photographed siblings Susanna, Jonathan, Kenan, Daniel, and Adam Block make real the message for Metro's campaign to clean up Lake Washington. Right: In 1988, the Block children returned to the same lake shore with thumbs up for Metro victories on the occasion of the thirtieth anniversary of its founding. Courtesy, King County Transportation and Natural Resources Library.

untreated sewage of small communities like Kirkland along its eastern shore throughout the decade.

With more and more people opting for the Eastside's affordable ramblers and large backyards, the practice of lake and other indiscriminate dumping soon reached critical levels. In July 1948 the Seattle Municipal League, an influential group of citizen activists, cited sewage disposal in rural King County as the most critical health and sanitation problem facing suburban residents. Two years later James A. Gibbs, chairman of the Board of King County Commissioners, helped organize preliminary discussions about a metropolitan sewage system encompassing Seattle and the communities bordering the lake. A major objective of these talks was to establish uniform specifications that would guide all future sewage and drainage development and ultimately make it easier to convert to a regional scheme. Following these initial organizational efforts, the Seattle Municipal League and King County called for the hiring of a nationally recognized consulting firm to prepare a plan for the formation of a metropolitan sanitation district. In 1952 the Seattle City Council and the Board of King County Commissioners met in an unprecedented series of monthly gatherings, about which City Council President David Levine noted, "For the first time in history, the city and county are getting together to iron out problems for the community benefit."

Getting local taxpayers to fund such an extensive and unusual plan was not as easy as luring young families to GI bill-financed homes in the suburbs. In 1954 Seattle voters defeated a $5 million bond levy to fund additions and improvements to their own wastewater disposal system. The prospect of coordinating a plethora of independent small sewer districts that had haphazardly cropped up with the sprawling subdivisions was a utility official's waking nightmare. But happily the region was not lacking managerial talent. In the early 1950s James R. Ellis, who was barely out of law school, took a leave of absence from his law firm to help draft a new King County charter that would try to control the unregulated suburban sprawl. King County administrators were convinced that it was a good idea but county voters were not and turned down the charter in 1952.

Four years later Ellis, assisted by his wife, Mary Lou, led a group of longtime Seattle-area residents, all concerned about the dramatic effects caused by only a few years of postwar boom. As chairman of a citizen's advisory committee, Ellis and the volunteer members drafted and lobbied for legislation that would allow for the formation of a metropolitan corporation empowered to deal with such matters as public transportation, sewage disposal, and regional planning. This time Ellis was successful, although just barely, when the proposal was approved by the state legislature by one vote on the last day of the 1957 session.

The following year the plan to form a metropolitan council of fifteen members, including eight representatives from Seattle and seven from the suburbs, was placed on the general ballot. The ambitious plan to set up an agency that would supervise the construction of a greater-Seattle area sewer system *and* engage in comprehensive growth planning *and* develop a mass transit program apparently asked for more authority and more money than county voters were willing to grant. The proposition passed within the city but failed without. The following September a well-pruned proposal limiting the agency's authority to sewage disposal development only was returned by the voters. The $125 million sewage system to serve 231 square miles was the largest and most expensive sewer construction program of any metropolitan area of comparable size in the country.

The official ground breaker for Metro's $12-million West Point Treatment Plant came with his shovel, pail, and mother. Alexander Brenner Hepler II had other qualifications. He was the great-grandson of R.H. Thomson, Seattle City Engineer who more than sixty years earlier selected West Point for the city's major sewer outfall. Besides his mother, others witnessing "Aleko's" shovel work that Sep. 19, 1963 were (left to right) Seattle Councilman M.B. Mitchell, County Commissioner Scott Wallace, Seattle Mayor Gordon Clinton, County Commissioner Ed Munro, and Metro Council Chairman C. Carey Donworth. All, except the Heplers, were members of the Metro council.

First-Stage Construction

Metro moved rapidly. Less than two years after its creation in 1959, the Metro council adopted its first ten-year sewage system plan. The $125 million in construction costs were to be financed by revenue bonds to be repaid by a $2 per household monthly sewage charge. Metro entered into 50-year contracts with member cities and neighboring sewer agencies, guaranteeing connection to its interceptors that would direct waste flows to Metro treatment plants before discharge into Puget Sound.

By 1962 Metro had signed contracts with fifteen municipal sewage agencies and districts representing one-third of a million customers. That year the agency assumed operation of all sewage treatment plants, major trunk sewers, and pumping stations within its boundaries and completed the Carkeek Park primary treatment plant. The following spring the new Richmond Beach primary treatment plant went on line, just two years before the Renton secondary plant was completed. In July 1966 the agency dedicated its West Point plant. At that time it was the largest treatment works in the Northwest and the last of the four treatment facilities to be built under the agency's initial ten-year plan. Reaching 3,600 feet offshore, the West Point outfall was 240 feet deep, reportedly the deepest of its type in the nation. In 1971 Metro completed its first-stage construction program, which also included more than 100 miles of large trunklines and sewers, on schedule and at a cost that was only two percent over the original 1961 estimate.

Lake Washington and Duwamish Waterway Cleanup

Before Metro began intercepting the sewage of the many small treatment plants discharging effluent into Lake Washington, the lake was receiving up to twenty million gallons per day. In February 1968 the last of these pollution sources was eliminated and the lake's cleanup campaign received national attention. According to the *Municipal News*, "Thanks to Metro, citizens of Seattle and King County will now have . . . a water recreation area unparalleled by any comparable metropolitan area of its size in the country." The visual effect was dramatic. In 1950 a white eight-inch disk could be seen to a depth of twelve feet in the lake. By the summer of 1967, the disk could be seen only to a depth of 2.5 feet. In the summer following the last of the effluent diversions, sightings as deep as nine feet were recorded, and since June 1977 Lake Washington's standard disk visibility has remained in the twenty-foot range.

Metro's first-stage work produced a similar reduction of bacterial contamination and biochemical oxygen demand in Elliott Bay. The health of the industry-lined Duwamish River was much harder to restore. In 1955 the Duwamish, the only river flowing into Elliott Bay, was a foul waterway with high levels of bacterial contamination, low levels of oxygen, and all levels of toxic compounds. In its worst spots, the river was a lethal cocktail mixed from the discharge of raw and insufficiently treated waste from the cities of Seattle, Kent, and Auburn, and several suburban sewer districts, and the promiscuously dumped waste of a panoply of manufacturing industries in the valley. Originally a pristine stream meandering through rich agricultural land, the Duwamish River over the past century, according to one Metro expert, had experienced "just about every possible pollution problem."

The river began to experience some relief between 1964 and 1967 when treatment facilities were built by some of the bordering communities, including Kent and Auburn. New interceptors and the opening of the Renton treatment plant also helped to boost the river's dissolved oxygen levels, which by the late 1970s consistently met state and federal standards. This was a happy consequence for both the salmon and steelhead that used the river to spawn and those who harvested them.

However, the steady improvement in the river's coliform bacterial levels was not accompanied by a decline in other sources of pollution — including surface water runoff, contaminated dust and groundwater, accidental chemical spills, and continued illegal dumping into storm drains and the waterway. Their combined effects created several highly contaminated "hot spots." In June 1983 the Metro Council responded with an eleven-point plan that was able to bring about a variety of controls to prevent further contamination. For instance, some industries built berms and similar devices to contain spills, while others installed pretreatment equipment or oil and water separation systems to facilitate the safe disposal of petroleum products. Large quantities of contaminated sediment were removed from storm drains near the river — in one operation over 100,000 pounds of PCB-tainted sediment. In another, the sediment removed was so contaminated with lead, up to 31 percent, that it was sold to a smelter in Oregon.

Looking south over Metro's Renton treatment plant to a slightly flooded Longacres Race Track and a still agrarian Green River Valley, ca. 1968. Inset: Details of the Renton plant and Governor Dan Evans (lower left) being interviewed at its 1965 dedication. Courtesy, Washington State Archives, Metro Collection, Burien.

The agency also stepped up enforcement against illegal dumping, in one case resulting in a $1 million fine and sixty-day jail sentence for the president of a wood treatment company. Although the cleanup of the Duwamish River has come a long way, it will require continued monitoring, tough enforcement action, and cooperation from valley industries before it can be fully restored for the public's safe use and enjoyment.

Metro and the Secondary Treatment Debate

In September 1970, when the Metro Council authorized its second-stage construction program for 1971 to 1985, probably none of them imagined the problems they would encounter. The trigger for the turmoil was built into the 1972 Clean Water Act which directed all publicly owned sewage works to provide secondary treatment by July 1977. Although the prescription was sweetened by the offer of federal grants covering up to 75 percent of construction costs, it was not well received at Metro headquarters. In fact, the council directed its staff "to do whatever is necessary," including court action, to resist what it considered a wasteful and unnecessary requirement. Secondary treatment, they believed, would produce little or no water quality improvement in the Sound since sewer overflows and stormwater runoff accounted for a major source of water quality degradation and these flows could not be treated with the present combined system. Like Dr. Wolman, twenty-five years earlier, the officials reasoned that Puget Sound was a well-flushed body with a large capacity to dilute and disperse pollutants.

As it turned out, the 1972 act had a loophole that directed agencies to provide the "best practicable treatment" methods by July 1983. Determining that the latter could be met by continuing their research into the effects of Metro discharges on Puget Sound, Metro officials opted to "leapfrog" over the 1977 deadline and concentrate on the less stringent and far less costly "best practicable treatment" requirement. Metro's leapfrog strategy was, in effect, supported by Congress in a 1977 amendment to the Clean Water Act that waived secondary treatment for some marine dischargers. In 1981 the agency won even more time when the Reagan administration's EPA waived secondary treatment for Metro's West Point plant, along with several other facilities in Alaska, California, and Hawaii. Dispensations soon followed for Metro's other plants. However, all the waivers depended upon the agency's compliance with federal EPA monitoring and discharge requirements and the concurrence of the state Department of Ecology. After overcoming his initial reservations, DOE Director Don Moos agreed to the waivers on condition that Metro take steps to prepare for secondary treatment at the West Point plant if water monitoring showed the need for it.

West Point. Top to Bottom: 1) The West Point Lighthouse with a portion of the U.S. Navy's Great White Fleet during its 1908 visit to Puget Sound. Courtesy, National Archives, Seattle. 2) Early-century map including platted streets for the proposed reclamation of the tidelands south of West Point. 3) Construction scene. 4) Dedication in 1966. 5) Construction scene looking east towards Fort Lawton. Courtesy Washington State Archives, Bellevue.

Moos's decision immediately elicited a suit against the department and Metro by a coalition of environmental groups. The protesters were armed with new scientific evidence that challenged the old orthodoxy of a self-cleaning Sound. National Oceanic and Atmospheric Administration (NOAA) scientists reported in 1982 that because of its shape, tidal actions tended to keep pollutants in Puget Sound rather than flushing them out to sea. University of Washington

Metro control central. Courtesy, Washington State Archive, Bellevue.

runoff overflowed into Lakes Union and Washington, instead of being sent to the Elliot Bay outfalls. The problem did not go away after treatment plants were built, for the surge of water that overwhelmed the capacity of the sewer mains also exceeded that of the treatment plants, and consequently, had to be redirected into nearby water bodies. Otherwise, the sewage would have backed up into homes, businesses, and streets.

oceanographers confirmed the NOAA findings. The central Puget Sound basin is shaped like a bathtub with abruptly sloping sides and a broad, flat bottom and is bounded on the north and south by shallower sill-like areas. Because of these physical features and the intermixing of incoming ocean water with less saline outflowing water, about one-half to two-thirds of the Sound's seaward flowing water, the scientists estimated, was carried back into the central basin. There much of the solid material it carried, including that suspended in treatment plant effluent, was deposited in bottom sediments.

In May 1984 these grim findings appeared even grimmer. At that time Metro released a study indicating that the West Point plant was releasing effluent that about five percent of the time exceeded either existing water quality or toxicant discharge standards for cyanides, PCBs, and a few heavy metals. It also acknowledged that secondary treatment was at least fifty percent more effective in removing heavy metals than primary treatment and about seven times better at removing toxic organics such as PCBs and pesticides. In the nation's capital, meanwhile, the tide was turning against secondary treatment waivers. In its 1984 review of the Clean Water Act Congress dropped them. But to soften the blow, special appropriations, including $250 million for Metro, were promised to localities to help defray the cost of the upgrade. Almost immediately the Metro Council agreed to discontinue its decade-long opposition to secondary treatment, citing a better understanding of the Sound's limited flushing capacity and the toxicant loadings coming from Metro plants. Under court order from the EPA to complete the work by late 1995, the agency began a tight work schedule on the $600 million West Point expansion, for which Metro customers will pick up most of the tab.

Sewer System Overflows and Nonpoint Pollution

When combined sewers were built in the nineteenth and early twentieth centuries, horse manure was a regular part of the street debris. Partly because of this and because most municipalities did not then envision treating their sanitary wastes, it made good sense to combine sanitary and stormwater flows into one sewer line. It was certainly much cheaper and had only one drawback. Overflows would occur from time to time during heavy downpours because pipes large enough to carry or store all the rainwater were too expensive to install. However, the limitations of the single design turned out to be much greater than expected. For instance, during rainstorms in Seattle large volumes of raw sewage and

In Seattle, Metro officials began to build separate lines for sanitary waste and stormwater in the 1950s. But by then most of Seattle was already using over 1,000 miles of combined sewers that periodically overflowed at points along Lakes Washington and Union, the Lake Washington Ship Canal, the lower Duwamish River, and Elliott Bay. New interceptors and separated sewers, the West Point Treatment plant, and a computer monitoring system that enhanced use of available storage capacity helped to reduce the overflows. However, in the late 1970s ten to twenty billion gallons of raw sewage and stormwater still entered Seattle area waters every year. In conjunction with a 1985 state law directing municipalities to reduce combined sewer overflows (CSOs), the Metro Council adopted a CSO control plan in 1986. They aimed to reduce the volume by 61 percent by the year 2005, but the state Ecology Department raised the figure to 75 percent. If the program, a mixture of tunnel enlargements, better storage controls, and separation projects, achieves the higher goal, annual overflows will be reduced to about one-half billion gallons by the year 2005, about two percent of what they were in 1960.

Agencies working to restore and preserve water quality have also recently begun to develop programs for controlling the "nonpoint" pollution that is carried in stormwater runoff. Separate systems for the most part eliminated the overflows typical of combined works, but the storm drain system that efficiently collected runoff and routed it to the nearest water body contributed to another type of pollution problem. Rain draining from neighborhoods can carry waste oil, pesticides, pet manure, household chemicals, and residue from failing septic tanks. Water flushing from streets and highways bears auto exhaust particles, oil, gasoline, and metals. Storm sewers that quickly flushed water from streets and driveways did not allow the natural cleansing process to take place when rainwater flowed through grasses and other vegetation on its way to the stream. Heavy metals such as lead and zinc, oil hydrocarbons, and high coliform counts mostly from pet feces have consistently been found in Washington's suburban streams. In both rural and urban areas, stormwater has been found to contain nutrients such as nitrogen and phosphorus that are picked up from fertilized fields and lawns. Phosphorus, in particular, stimulates the algae growth that has so often been found on lakes ringed by homes. Streams receiving stormwater flows have also been subject to greater flooding levels, stream bank erosion, bed scouring, and sedimentation, all of which impair fish habitat and, consequently, have dramatically reduced the survival rate of anadromous fish that use the streams to spawn.

Bellevue's Surface Water Management. Salmon returning from the Pacific Ocean use the Mercer Slough, above, as a passageway from Lake Washington to their spawning grounds on Kelsey Creek. This open creek and others, along with underground pipes, 11 regional stormwater storage facilities, over 200 neighborhood stormwater storage sites — and Mercer Slough — make up Bellevue's drainage system. Photo by Peter C. Fisher. Courtesy, City of Bellevue.

BELLEVUE'S STORM DRAINAGE

The City of Bellevue became a national leader in stormwater control with its development of a revolutionary storm drainage utility intended to preserve and restore natural streams and wetlands as much as possible rather than encasing runoff in the usual concrete culverts. In 1972 the city passed ordinances to control clearing and grading adjacent to drainage areas and water bodies and began planning a comprehensive approach to storm drainage. After considering a range of alternatives the city decided to use both conventional storm pipes and open streams to convey stormwater to lakes and wetlands, which would slow erosion and flooding, retain flood waters, and filter out pollutants. Their creation of a separate storm drainage utility in 1974 was initially challenged by utility customers unhappy about additional charges. However, two years later, when alternative means of funding were proposed, Bellevue citizens, in an advisory vote, approved the initial plan that based rates on the amount of impervious surface on a property. Because these charges were also levied on the city and state transportation department for roads and highways, they helped overcome opposition to the so-called "rain tax." By 1997 the drainage utility tax cost the average Bellevue homeowner over $100 a year, but it had allowed the utility to purchase and protect 250 acres of stream corridor and wetlands.

In addition to constructing storm sewers, the Bellevue Storm and Surface Water Utility has improved stream channels for carrying capacity, wildlife habitat, and fish passage and built on the stream system eleven small flood control dams designed to withstand the one-hundred-year-storm. Because buildings and street surfaces alone did not account for all the contaminants in stormwater runoff, the Bellevue Storm and Surface Water Utility incorporated a variety of related programs. Among them were an annual household hazardous waste pickup day, an oil recycling program through local gas stations, and a round-the-clock chemical spill response hotline.

SOLID WASTE MANAGEMENT

Aside from state and county health officers and the occasional outraged newspaper editor, most Washingtonians prior to World War II, especially in rural communities, did not concern themselves much about where or how they dumped their garbage. Only after the war when they found their garbage cans, dumps, and incinerators swollen by a greatly enlarged stream of paper, packaging, and plastics did they begin to become aware of the inadequacy of their collection and disposal systems.

Before 1945 Wenatchee's garbage collection system was a business operation franchised by the city. Although a 1935 city ordinance required universal collection, it was not enforced and only about 40 percent of town residents received service. The refuse was burned in an incinerator, but it was not broken down entirely and neighbors complained about the smell. In 1944-45 the Chelan County Health Department examined the city's waste practices and advised it to go into the garbage business. The mayor agreed and the city bought a twenty-acre tract at the corner of Crawford and S. Mission streets, about a mile from the center of town. The site was a deep gorge, called Dry Gulch, that had been used unofficially as a dump for years. There were the usual protests about the taxes and fees that were expected to accompany the municipal takeover. However, when the person who started the petition to halt the new landfill was photographed dumping garbage into the gulch illegally, the city went ahead with its plans in the early 1950s. Wenatchee officials followed the state's recently developed guidelines for sanitary landfills and included a drainage system, maximum depth, and daily covering with a layer of earth.

In the early 1950s the city of Anacortes in Skagit County and the town of Wilbur in Lincoln County requested help from the state health department when they found themselves feeding a sizable rat population. In both municipalities garbage collection was optional and cans were typically left uncovered. Following the department's advice, Anacortes officials moved the dump outside town where it was operated as a sanitary landfill, and both town councils made garbage collection mandatory. Unfortunately, for the health department there were few other successes it could describe in its 1955 literature promoting sanitary landfills. Too many communities continued to put off the day of reckoning.

Left: Seattle's Montlake Dump, 1959. Courtesy Seattle Municipal Archives.

Seattle's Early Solid Waste Disposal

Engineer R.H. Thomson was as eager to solve the city's garbage as its wastewater problems. In 1905 he traveled to England to study British systems of sewage and solid waste disposal. There he was particularly impressed by London's Shoreditch incineration plant that not only burned the neighborhood trash but produced steam to heat water and buildings. Similarly, Seattle's first refuse-burning plant at the south end of Lake Union was designed to steam heat a neighboring lumber kiln and laundry. However, Thomson's system of four energy-producing incinerators did not work as well as planned. By 1913 only three of the plants were still operating and only part-time. Although the strategically located plants did not require long hauls for trash collectors, it was still cheaper to carry the city's refuse to landfills than operate the plants. Most of the city dumps were established at wetlands and ravines, considered to be useless mosquito-breeding swamps and holes in the ground. In 1911 there were nine dumps within the Seattle city limits, including those at Interbay, Washington Park, Salmon Bay, and at the foot of Wallingford Avenue at the north end of Lake Union. The first of these was on Queen Anne Hill on Crockett Street between Nob Hill and Third Avenue North.

As long as dumps were located downwind and at least partially concealed from view, their users would usually tolerate their presence for the convenience of the short haul. A central location was desirable even in the larger cities for once they were filled the city could build parks, playgrounds, and even streets on top of them. In 1926 the City of Seattle began dumping rubbish in what is now the Montlake area between the east border of the University of Washington campus and the shore of Lake Washington's Union Bay. The area was a wetlands that had been created by the lowering of the lake that resulted from the building of the Lake Washington Ship Canal. Two goals were achieved by the Montlake dump. The University campus was expanded at low cost, since the filling and grading were paid for by the city refuse disposal operations, and the city got a centrally located dump site.

However, by 1954 neighbors' complaints put an end to open burning and after the legislature passed new sanitary landfill requirements, the city was obliged to cover each day's deliveries with a layer of earth. This caused the rate of fill to increase, ensuring it would soon reach capacity. From the mid-1950s until 1965 when it was closed, the site handled about 110 truckloads of domestic garbage daily. When maximum levels were reached, the university built parking lots, playing fields, and a golf driving range over the fill.

By the early 1960s Seattle had closed most of its in-city landfills, the last choked with construction debris from freeway projects. This forced city planners to come up with alternatives and to levy a charge on customers to pay for it. Until the fall of 1961 garbage collection was paid for by the city's general fund. But the hauling of domestic garbage to landfills outside the city would cost households $1.25 a month. After an incineration plan was turned down, a specially constituted citizens' panel recommended that transfer stations and long-haul trailers be incorporated into a regional land disposal plan that included King County. In 1965 the city leased sites for three landfills at Midway and Kent Highlands in the Kent area, and at Cedar Hills southeast of Issaquah, which was to be shared with the county as its principal landfill. Midway, which opened in 1966, was originally designed to handle commercial or nonputrescible wastes, while Kent Highlands, which opened in 1968, was to take Seattle's residential waste.

Although the Kent Highlands and Midway landfills would eventually develop serious problems requiring expensive cleanup operations, in 1965 Seattle's waste disposal program was one of the more farsighted in the state. Most smaller Washington communi-

The Joy Parlor's portrait set, top, parodies both the city's early-century "Seeing Seattle" open-air tour buses and especially its garbage wagons, above. Both were often stuffed to the limit. Courtesy, Old Seattle Paperworks.

ties continued to follow turn-of-the century waste practices — dumping their refuse at unsupervised sites, feeding it to the hogs, or burning it. In 1966 and 1967 the state health department and federal health service conducted a survey of the state's municipal solid waste facilities. About 40 percent of the communities surveyed had no regulations governing the storage of either domestic, industrial, or commercial wastes and of those that did, more than forty percent failed to enforce them. Of the 339 official disposal sites inspected, only fourteen met sanitary landfill standards. The majority were open dumps that practiced burning and were infested with rats and breeding flies. (Sanitary landfill standards had recommended over the years such things as the layering of organic garbage with rubbish or cinders to retard putrefaction, the addition of poisons and other chemicals to kill flies and rats, a daily covering of earth, and fencing, regular hours, and an attendant to control the materials dumped.)

Solid Waste Legislation— From Dumps to Sanitary Landfills

Similar findings across the country prompted Congress in 1965 to pass the Solid Waste Disposal Act. The law was a recognition that while waste collection and disposal were properly a state and local function, localities needed technical and financial assistance. In 1969 state solons passed their own watershed legislation with the Solid Waste Management Act. It required cities and counties to prepare plans for adequate solid waste programs and for vigorous regulatory enforcement. In 1972 the legislature passed the state's first solid waste management plan that stressed

Above left: Early Bow Lake transfer station. Right: King County transfer truck. Courtesy, King County.

the importance of developing regionwide disposal solutions and of upgrading dumps to sanitary landfills. By this time the central Puget Sound area had experienced such growth that sites originally expected to last from forty to fifty years were filling two to three times as fast as had been anticipated. And land that might formerly have been used for new landfills was quickly being developed for suburban homes and shopping malls. However, the legislators' studies revealed that, due to the high cost of incineration and for lack of a better technology, sanitary fills were still the preferred method of disposal.

The 1972 legislation seemed to propose the most practical and forward-looking solutions to the safe disposal of rapidly growing mounds of garbage. But administrators at the Department of Ecology (DOE), to whom authority for solid waste planning had been transferred from the health department in 1970, were not prepared for the bold and innovative solution proposed by the state's chief engineer, Gov. Dan Evans. According to Evans's plan, a strip coal mine near Centralia would be converted into a solid waste disposal and recycling center serving western Washington and Oregon. There, refuse shipped from cities and counties in covered railroad cars would be picked for recyclables before being sanitarily buried. The DOE could not couple with the governor's rail-hauling vision because their studies showed that the regional center could not compete with the convenience and cost of local landfills. They also determined that the recycling proposal was premature. In 1972 it was still "more economical to produce commodities from abundantly available virgin materials."

Solid waste management planning fared better under the 1969 law. By 1975 the DOE was able to report that thirty-seven of the thirty-nine counties had submitted solid waste management plans for state approval. Eighty-four percent of the dumps found substandard in 1966 were on compliance schedules to be eliminated by the end of 1975, and the number of sanitary landfills had increased. Yet even with these improvements, at the end of 1975 two-thirds of the state's solid waste disposal facilities were either open dumps or non-sanitary landfills where burning was commonplace and no precautions were taken to block or treat toxins and leachate that could percolate into groundwater. For instance, in 1972 more than half of the residents of unincorporated Pierce County had no municipal or company collection and disposal service. Dumps at Carbonado and Buckley were polluting nearby rivers and those at Eatonville and Roy were cited by air pollution authorities. Pierce County's 1973 management plan called for the closing of these as well as a number of other rural dumps, some of which were to be replaced with drop boxes (small transfer stations). Rural collection systems were also to be added and leachate drainage ditches installed for fills polluting the ground water.

Through sanitary landfill practices communities learned how to reduce the health risks associated with promiscuous dumping. They also learned how to increase the efficiency of landfill sites by reducing volumes through the separation of materials, compaction, and controlled incineration. But finding new disposal sites acceptable to both the community and increasingly stringent pollution laws was not as simple. Large landfills presented other problems that had not been fully anticipated. Seattle garbage utility officials had known at least since the 1950s that landfills could emit methane gas produced by the breakdown of organic materials. In 1956 the University of Washington drove pipes into the refuse piles at the Montlake landfill and experimented with controlled burning of the gas. Their objective then was to reduce the odor that neighbors frequently complained about.

In 1983, when Seattle's Midway landfill was closed, it was more than just the odor that had driven protesting neighbors into city hall and the courts. Methane concentrations had become so great that they could not all be burned off. The city was forced to purchase the homes of Midway-area residents, who could not sell them at market price, when explosive levels of methane gas were found to have migrated outside the area of the landfill. Although the city originally planned to bury only construction waste at Midway, little control was exercised over the type of garbage dumped and industrial waste was also taken to the landfill. Because of the contamination of the leased site, its owners went to court and forced the city to purchase it for approximately $1 million in 1986. Midway was placed on the Environmental Protection Agency's Superfund cleanup list.

The highly contaminated Kent Highlands landfill, which also took industrial waste in addition to residential, was closed in 1986 after leachate was found to be entering the Green River and zinc, copper, and other metals were found in site wells. In 1988 the cleanup of the two landfills was expected to cost about $100 million, costs that largely accounted for the steep increase in garbage collection fees. With the closure of the two landfills, the county agreed to allow the city to temporarily send its trash to Cedar Hills, which was the only major landfill still operating in King County. In 1992 the county council considered proposals from a number of firms interested in buying the methane produced at Cedar Hills and using it to generate electricity or as a substitute for natural gas. At this time Metro was daily selling 500,000 cubic feet of methane gas from its Renton treatment plant to the Washington Natural Gas Co. — enough to heat 5,000 homes.

Disposal problems in Snohomish County were primarily caused by growth. In 1967 the City of Everett agreed to allow the county to send 80 percent of its solid waste to the city's landfill after the county's principal disposal site was filled to capacity. Before the county could implement plans for a new sanitary landfill, both the county and city were forced to temporarily use the county's few remaining small dumps after the city landfill closed in 1975. When the county's new 55-acre Cathcart landfill, east of Mill Creek and south of Snohomish, opened in 1980, growth in the county had already cut its expected lifetime to ten years. Snohomish County officials immediately began making plans for a new site. By the end of the decade, preparations quickened for building a 125-acre landfill on a site contiguous to the Cathcart installation. The county also promoted recycling and waste reduction to extend the lifetime of its landfill.

By the 1980s the era of close-in dumping sites in metropolitan areas of the state had clearly come to an end. Site degradation caused by unanticipated factors, the escalating cost of urban land, and costly legal challenges made the hauling of refuse to remote sites the most acceptable solution for large solid waste producers. In 1991 the Chicago-based Waste Management Co. began transporting Seattle's refuse to a site near Arlington in eastern Oregon. In order to extend by a few years the lifetime of its new Cathcart space, Snohomish County agreed to send part of its solid waste to the Rabanco Company's private landfill in Klickitat County.

Incineration or Waste-to-Energy

While some cities and counties decided to stick with landfills that were built or upgraded to limit contamination of the surrounding area, others experimented with ways to recycle or recover refuse in energy through incineration. In 1973 the City of Tacoma's landfill was the only disposal site in Pierce County that met state standards. As a way to extend the life span of its site, the city agreed to purchase a refuse shredder in 1972. The facility was originally designed to shred paper, plastic, and other combustible material in order to produce "refuse-derived fuel" (RDF) that could be sold to local industries. But by the time the shredder was ready in 1979, oil prices had dropped and the anticipated market for alternative fuels had evaporated. Instead the city used the shredder to reduce the bulk of its waste.

When an Idaho firm in 1984 suggested how the city might be able to use some of its RDF, officials were interested. The company proposed that it renovate the old Steam Plant No. 2 in the Tideflats district (see Power Chapter) and fire it up again with RDF and coal and wood waste from local mills. After the firm's financing fell through, the utility took over the project and reconfigured the old plant to burn up to 300 tons per day of filtered garbage, wood waste, and coal and produce steam to generate power for about

Top: Pierce County's Hidden Valley Landfill. Courtesy, Land Recovery, Inc. Above: Cedar Hills Landfill. Courtesy, King County.

21,000 homes.

However, in 1989 the nearly completed incinerator was waylaid by the objections of area residents and by Gov. Booth Gardner, who in May of that year signed a bill requiring environmental impact statements on all such projects. Opponents were concerned about air pollution, the effects of toxic-ash disposal, and the destruction of otherwise recoverable materials. Critics objected that Tacoma's garbage utility had not made adequate efforts to reduce the waste load by methods such as recycling. Proponents answered that modern "waste-to-energy" incineration technology produced dioxin emissions well below state and federal thresholds and that ash could be safely buried at specially equipped landfills. The burning of organics would, moreover, eliminate the source of toxic gases and leachate found at landfills.

After a Pierce County Superior Court judge struck down the controversial amendment in January 1990, the city was able to go ahead with its tests. For several months operational problems with the plant kept consultants, working on an environmental study for the state Department of Ecology (DOE),

Bottom: Snohomish County, Tulalip barge landfill. March 11, 1969. Between 1964 and 1979 an estimated four million tons of commercial, medical, and industrial waste were barged to an island in the mouth of the Snohomish River. In 1997 the work of containing and managing the resulting pollution was negotiated by the Environmental Protection Agency under the federal Superfund law. The work of covering the closed 147-acre Tulalip dump with a layering of sand, plastic liner, topsoil, and grass was scheduled for completion by the fall of 1999. Courtesy, Seattle Municipal Archives.

Left: Spokane incinerator. Courtesy, Spokane Regional Solid Waste System. Right: Tacoma's RDF facility. Courtesy, Tacoma Refuse Utility Division.

from collecting reliable data. The city had bowed to the pressure from the DOE, Tacoma-Pierce County Health Department, and Tacoma citizens to do an environmental impact statement (EIS). But since it was not legally necessary they were able to proceed with testing and even begin commercial operation, using performance data for their draft EIS. Several months before it began full-time operation in August 1991, the utility's draft EIS estimated that the project could cause twenty cancer cases for every one million people exposed — a level twenty times what the Puget Sound Air Pollution Agency considered acceptable. However, in 1993 Tacoma utility officials reported that the plant was producing less than 1 percent of carbon monoxide and 23 percent of sulfur dioxide emissions allowed by EPA safety standards. That year Tacoma's revamped steam plant generated enough power to service approximately 10,800 homes.

In 1987 the county and the city of Spokane in a cooperative regional plan adopted an incinerator or "waste-to-energy" system as part of a program for waste reduction and recycling. Spokane's solution to disposing of an enlarged and more complex waste stream seemed to hearken back to its original disposal method. Spokane County had relied on burning dumps and the city on incinerators. Ash from the municipal incinerators was hauled to an open dump on a large tract west of the city. However, even by the late 1950s, the incinerators could not keep up with the growing pile of trash, resulting in the opening of two sanitary landfills.

When air pollution control laws in 1969 made outdoor burning illegal, the county was forced to make greater use of landfills. This caused the cost of their disposal program to almost double between 1968 and 1970. Through the 1970s the city sent most of its solid waste to the sanitary landfills at Indian Trail and Moran Prairie, which both lacked leachate and runoff collection and treatment. The county's 1986 solid waste proposals approved by the state DOE focused on the incinerator program as the chief way to overcome the landfill problems. But fear about possible air pollution, and perhaps the memory of burning dumps, prompted citizen objections to the modern incineration plan. By this time incineration had acquired a reputation for being costly and polluting the air with heavy metals and the gases responsible for global warming and acid rain. But in 1987 a Spokane Superior Court judge overruled a challenge to the project's EIS findings and the city was able to secure an air quality permit from the EPA to begin operation. Wheelabrator Spokane, Inc., builder of the $106 million plant which is capable of burning 800 tons of garbage daily, began test operations in September 1991. When the power plant came on line at that time, it began selling power mostly to western Washington customers, primarily Puget Power and Light

Company, earning the city $1.4 million by June 1, 1992.

Recycling

During both world wars recycling was used around the country as a way to overcome wartime shortages of materials such as rubber, metal, and glass. However, after the conflicts were over and the government lifted its restrictions on materials deemed necessary to the war effort, interest in recycling rapidly declined. In 1920 a Seattle health commissioner noted that contractors no longer sought salvaged paper and the "fancy prices that war activities gave these by-products have disappeared." It wasn't until after the prosperity of the post-World War II period began to falter in the late 1960s that the recycling of materials again became attractive. And by then more than economic considerations were involved. Experts and the public had begun to realize how much the success of the country's manufacturing and extractive industries had cost the purity of their water, soil, and air.

In 1970 the federal government passed the Resource Recovery Act that authorized the EPA to study and encourage methods for recovering materials and energy from solid waste. During the 1970s the recycling of materials such as scrap iron and steel, aluminum, newspapers, and cardboard was conducted primarily by private firms who found it profitable to sell the salvaged material to foreign markets. However, some public agencies began studying and experimenting with recycling projects at this time. The City of Seattle tried out a six-month program in 1971 that was almost able to pay for itself. In 1975 the Department of Ecology established a toll-free hotline that gave state residents information about collection sites for paper, glass, and metals.

By 1980 myriad problems associated with solid waste disposal and the concern about dwindling natural resources spurred by the energy crisis convinced DOE that it had to persuade manufacturing, governmental, and commercial establishments, as well as consumers, of the importance of reducing their amount of waste. Included in DOE's 1980 solid waste management plan were recycling and possible waste-to-energy goals, a significant shift in emphasis from the 1972 plan that focused on proper handling and disposal methods

When Seattle began implementing its recycling program, there were good markets for the materials and high citizen and commercial interest. In 1978 the city was recycling about 14 percent of its residential and commercial waste. City administrators aimed to increase that percentage to 22 percent by 1985, a goal missed by only one year. A year after the city began its curbside recycling program in February 1988, an astonishing 60 percent of eligible households in Seattle were using the program, raising the

Above left: Spokane's joy of recycling. Photo by J. Craig Sweat for Spokane Solid Waste. Above right: Opening day of curbside recycling in Seattle. Courtesy, Seattle Municipal Archives.

city's percentage of recycled solid waste to 28 percent. Mayor Charles Royer and city officials had earlier decided to put off their prior endorsement of incineration partly because of the opposition by environmental and neighborhood activists and partly because it would compete with a recycling program that promised to be cheaper. After only one year of curbside recycling, the Seattle Solid Waste Utility was able to sign new contracts with garbage collectors that cut annual pickup costs by over one-quarter, and the city had received two national awards from national recycling institutes for operating the best urban program in the country. The steeply increased and variable can rates helped convince garbage utility customers that recycling was worth the effort. King County and a number of cities in the county shortly followed Seattle's example with programs that were equally popular.

However, before solid waste officials in Seattle, Olympia, Spokane, and other Washington municipalities and counties had time to bask in the success of their recycling programs, they were facing problems largely created by that success. Companies, contracted to separate, store, and prepare the materials for shipment to Asian markets, had trouble keeping up with the mountains of paper, glass, metal, and plastics. The market responded to the surpluses and prices plunged. The economic downturn that began in 1990 also made shippers reluctant to transport material that took up so much space and was worth so little. The year before the legislature had passed the Waste Not Washington Law which required every municipality to cut its residential garbage in half by 1995. However, the lawmakers had not anticipated the missing markets for millions of tons of recyclables. Neither had they foreseen that the two huge landfills recently built in Klickitat County and Arlington, Oregon, with a third planned for Adams County, would moderate landfill costs. By 1994 Eastside Disposal, which served customers in Seattle's Shoreline and the Eastside's Northshore and Juanita districts, paid as much to unload recyclables at a reprocessing facility as it did to dump a load of garbage into the King County system— $66 per ton.

Lately, solid waste utility officials have been working with local businesses and business organizations to encourage industries and commercial establishments to use or make products from recycled materials. With paper there has been an additional incentive. As Washington sawmills shut down in the early 1990s, the paper and pulp industry became more interested in recycled

newspaper, cardboard, and high grade paper as a fiber source than the now scarcer and more expensive wood chips. Experts estimated that between 1989 and 1995 paper mills in Washington and Oregon would nearly triple their ability to use recycled paper. Mixed-waste paper has remained a high-volume, low-value problem, but aluminum has enjoyed a consistently strong market since bauxite, the raw material for aluminum, has to be imported. It also takes 90 percent less energy to produce cans from recycled aluminum than from raw bauxite. While savings from recycling will continue to depend on the unpredictability of the market, the DOE reported that in 1995, of the 6.5 pounds of waste generated daily by a person, 2.5 pounds were recycled. It appeared Washingtonians had largely accepted the environmental ethic of reuse — even if it sometimes cost them more than throwing things away.

Hanford and Hazardous Waste

In December 1942 Col. Franklin T. Matthias of the Army Corps of Engineers, under orders from the top-secret Manhattan Project, conducted a whirlwind tour of the West to find the best site for a plutonium production complex. Within two weeks he had found that site with all the necessary conditions — isolated, large and open, and accessible to great amounts of water and power. With only the few hundred townspeople, orchardists, and peppermint farmers in and around Hanford, Richland, and White Bluffs, made the area was mostly uninhabited. After a quick lookover, the colonel scribbled some notes and sketched a diagram the size of a matchbook cover. It was the closet thing to an environmental impact statement the future Hanford Nuclear Reservation would have.

The following month the government hurriedly bought out the small population, acquiring a 570-square mile tract west of the Columbia River and north of the mouth of the Yakima in Benton County. Thousands of men were recruited and quickly transported to the site to begin building the six major plutonium production facilities. There were three water-cooled graphite reactors, which made the plutonium from uranium and loaded it into aluminum tubes, and miles away, three chemical separation plants, known as "Queen Marys" because of their size, that handled the final processing. Of course, most of the tens of thousands of workers at the "Hanford Engineering Works" had no idea about the true purpose of the complex. It was not until several days after the world's second atomic bomb was dropped on Nagasaki that the *Seattle P.I.* wrote of the "gay mood" of Mrs. Matthias, the "first lady of Hanford," as she "described the unveiling of the atomic bomb mystery."

Hanford's accomplishment, whether considered horrible or benign, had to be the most significant undertaking ever to occur in Washington, according to one historian. But its mission did not end with the Japanese surrender as anticipated. Less than a year later, in June 1946, the War Department hired the General Electric Company to replace DuPont as contractor at the site, and the production of plutonium resumed in August. In 1950 the government began work on five additional plutonium reactors and three more chemical processing plants in the largest peacetime construction job in the nation's history.

The Cold War tensions with the U.S.S.R. kept the Hanford reactors busy producing plutonium for the nation's nuclear weapons through the 1980s. From the 1950s until 1987 when Hanford discontinued all plutonium production, it manufactured from one-third to one-half of the nation's weapons-grade plutonium. However, between 1964 and 1971 all of the reactors, except the recently completed ninth, dual-purpose N-Reactor, (see Power Chapter) were shut down due to a decreased need for plutonium and pollution problems in the Columbia River. In these "single-pass" reactors, river water used to cool the reactor core came into contact with the irradiated uranium fuel rods. It was held for only one-half to six hours before being pumped back into the river, at a thermally and radioactively hotter temperature than when it went in.

General Electric photographers prepare to record activity within a Hanford waste storage tank, ca. 1960. Courtesy, Ted Van Arsdol.

The Atomic Energy Commission (AEC), the first federal agency in charge of operations at the reservation, had used two types of waste disposal. The high level radioactive waste was routed to single-wall steel storage tanks underground, with the understanding that the storage would be temporary until a permanent solution was found. Material considered to be less dangerous was injected directly into the ground. Hanford geologists and chemists believed that it was safe to dump the highly acidic, low-to-intermediate level radioactive waste from the chemical separation process into trenches or holes called "cribs." They figured that a process of "absorption" or ion exchange with the soil would occur and reduce the radioactivity to safe levels. The engineers did not realize that some of the liquid they dumped into the ground contained two long-lived radioactive materials, technetium 99 and iodine 129, with half-lives of 212,000 years and 16 million years respectively, and that soil could become saturated with fission by-products and lose its ability to hold them back. From 1951 to 1957 an estimated 26.7 million gallons of high level waste was poured directly into the ground.

Production took precedence over all other considerations at Hanford. The AEC, which was created by Congress in 1946 to regulate and promote nuclear operations, was more concerned about efficient production than reactor safety and waste disposal. When accidental or intentional releases of radioactive materials occurred in the ground, water, or air, the public was usually not informed. For instance, in 1949, shortly after the Soviet Union conducted its first atomic weapons test, Hanford conducted its infamous "Green Run" experiment. In order to discover how far airborne fission products could be detected so that they could monitor future Soviet tests, the government directed Hanford scientists to release high levels of radioactive Iodine-131 into the atmosphere above the Columbia Basin. The early December release caused vegetation contamination readings throughout eastern Washington to climb to several hundred times the prescribed "tolerable limit." Yet, no milk supplies from local dairies were withheld from the market and the public did not learn of the experiment until almost 37 years later.

By the 1950s the groundwater underneath and

The Hanford 300 area sits on the Columbia River, across from the outfall for the Columbia Basin Irrigation Project's Esquatzel Diversion Channel, seen here in the foreground. After it opened in 1960, the Hanford 308 Fuels Development Laboratory (FDL) pioneered a variety of innovative fuels technology and fabrication, largely for the Atomic Energy Commission's non-defense "Atoms for Peace" program. Because of its proximity to Richland — about three miles north of the city's northern limits — deactivation of the 94,000-square-foot structure began in 1991 with the removal of the building's working inventory of plutonium. At its peak, the 308 Building held as much as three metric tons of encapsulated plutonium. The deactivation was completed on March 31, 1994. Photo by Hugh Paradise, ca. 1970.

The 100-C site was home of the B-Reactor, the first of three reactors constructed on the Hanford Reservation during the World War II. (Reactor A did not proceed beyond the design phase.) This aerial looks toward the installation over its outfall and jetty on the Columbia River. B-Reactor began operation September 27, 1944, only thirteen months after construction had begun. The plutonium from B-Reactor was used in the Trinity test bomb in New Mexico and also in the "Fat Man" bomb that was dropped on Nagasaki, Japan. Eventually six Cold War reactors were built at Hanford. B-Reactor continued to operate through February 1968. Courtesy, Flour Daniel Hanford Company.

near Hanford was becoming contaminated. In 1956 Hanford scientists discovered large bulges in the water table on the west and east sides of the reservation. After drilling wells, they discovered that some of the wastewater, instead of percolating downwards through soil, had contacted a permeable substrata of gravel that transmitted it laterally down the hydraulic gradient to the water table from which it exited into the Columbia River. There was no time for radioactive decay and insufficient soil for ion exchange to take place. The results of these well tests, conducted in the 1950s and later, were kept secret in most cases until 1986 and 1987.

The culture of secrecy in which the Hanford project had been born was maintained nearly throughout the duration of the Cold War. When accidents occurred or safety problems arose, the contractors who ran the operations often did not report them to the AEC, later the Nuclear Regulatory Commission (NRC), for fear they might stop work. The contractors were given bonuses for meeting production goals, not for making safety or environmental improvements. According to a former AEC general manager, chemical engineers in the 1950s and 1960s "were not interested in dealing with waste. It was not glamorous, there were no careers, it was messy. . . . The AEC neglected the problem." The U.S. Department of Energy (DOE), which later became responsible for the Hanford site, continued to argue that national security superseded all other concerns. Using this argument, they were allowed by Congress and the administration to escape state and national hazardous waste laws until the extent of the pollution became known in the late 1980s. A 1985 federal court ruling that federal facilities like Hanford had to comply with state and federal environmental laws also helped break down the legal barricade.

When two public watchdog groups filed a request under the Freedom of Information Act in 1986, the DOE was obliged to release about 39,000 pages of documents, many of which had been classified, that concerned Hanford's operations since 1944. The records revealed the extent of contamination and safety problems that Hanford, AEC, NRC, and DOE officials had so long concealed. According to investigators in 1991, at least 66 of the 149 single-wall and 28 double-wall tanks holding millions of gallons of liquid containing plutonium, other radioactive elements, toxic solvents, and unidentified chemicals were leaking into the ground. An estimated one million gallons of what one analyst called a "terrible cocktail" had been absorbed by the Hanford soil from the tanks alone. And some of the tanks that didn't leak had other problems. The haphazard combination of chemicals caused one tank to actually boil and another to "burp" when it formed a build-up of hydrogen that could potentially explode and send highly radioactive material into the air. The failure of the ground to act as a sponge and retain the dangerous liquid has meant that at least 230 square miles of groundwater, underneath and near the reservation are contaminated with long-lived radionuclides that cannot be prevented from traveling in underground springs to the river. Hanford had become the most polluted and dangerous compound in the country.

After the extent of the contamination became public, in 1989 Secretary of Energy James D. Watkins announced a plan to improve operations at the nation's nuclear production facilities and promised to make the cleanup of Hanford a first priority. In May of that year state Ecology Department Director Christine Gregoire signed an agreement with the DOE that committed the government to a 30-year restoration program, which could cost taxpayers at least $30 billion. By July 1990, 1,200 sites on the reservation were identified as containing radioactive or hazardous chemical contaminants requiring some kind of treatment. Congress followed up with large appropriations. In 1992 President George Bush recommended a 1993 cleanup budget of $1.38 billion, a 30 percent increase over the previous year. Although the annual funding was not enough for some critics of the Hanford site, the federal dollars created a boom town environment for environmental and engineering consultants, Hanford public relations firms, and building contractors in Richland. In 1995 a congressional oversight committee found there was little actual cleanup work performed to account for the $7.5 billion that had already been spent. The ranking members of the Senate Energy and Natural Resources Committees attributed these results to "grotesquely inflated overhead costs, murky and contradictory regulations, and cleanup goals that are so vague it is impossible to know if anything is being accomplished." However, employment at the reservation stood at an all-time high — 20 percent higher than during the Cold War period of plutonium production. The local Tri-Cities economy had discovered that there was gold along with toxins in those leaky tanks and radioactive soils.

PUBLIC BUILDINGS AND PUBLIC ART

EARLY NORTHWEST BUILDINGS

Native American quarters varied considerably in the degree to which they were communally constructed and used. A longhouse, or winter residence, was often owned in parts which were marked with headposts depicting the guardian spirit of those who built and lived within the section. The potlatch house used for initiations and intercommunity rituals was ordinarily more of a public work, for it was usually constructed by an entire community. Of all native structures — sweat lodge, latrine, smokehouse, longhouse, stockade, menstrual lodge, potlatch house — the type most like a public work was the salmon weir. The effort both of constructing and repairing these fish traps usually required the entire able-bodied community. Although platform sections attached to the weir and the dip nets used to fetch the salmon were owned individually, and often passed down through families, permission for others to use these without rent was expected and commonplace.

The first public buildings on the European model constructed in the future state of Washington, or for that matter west of the Rockies and north of San Francisco Bay, were the barracks, palisades, storehouses, bakery and other modest structures of the Spanish settlement at Bahia de Nunez Gaona (Neah Bay) on the Strait of Juan de Fuca. The American fur trader James Boit aboard Capt. Robert Gray's *Columbia* described it in the summer of 1792, the season of its construction, as "a few huts and tolerable good garden." The fort was large enough to accommodate seventy seamen, thirteen soldiers, four officers, and a chaplain. However, six months after the Spanish began building their camp they abandoned it and returned to Nootka Sound on Vancouver Island. Yet they did leave their mark. Bricks from the oven were uncovered at the site in 1917.

In the half century that followed the Spaniards' short stay at Neah Bay, non-native construction in the future state was the work of trappers and traders, a caste eventually dominated by the Hudson's Bay Company. Soon after the U.S. Naval Expedition led by Lt. Charles Wilkes arrived at the HBO's Fort Nisqually on May 11, 1841, they raised a sixty-foot flagpole. The standard flown was not the Union Jack. But the English company was hospitable and loaned Wilkes oxen to drag logs for building cabins for an observatory and chart room where pendulum and astronomical observations were completed on Independence Day. At the next day's boisterous patriotic party — endured by the British and their French Canadian employees — Wilkes hosted a dinner for the officers of his ships and the company. The observatory, nicknamed the "Hall of Science," was converted into a flag-draped banquet hall with the large drafting board covered by a Hawaiian mat serving as a table. The site for these celebrations was appropriately named American Lake.

An accurate listing of either the total number of public buildings ever built in Washington or of those which survive would both show that the largest collection of them are at or near American Lake in Pierce County. Strung out from where Wilkes's men built their observatory are the 4,600 buildings of Fort Lewis. (See below.) Add the federal government's other seven bases and the number of military structures in Washington exceeds 10,000. The remaining statewide tally for post offices (about 515), federal office buildings (15), court houses (3), warehouses (11), and special buildings like laboratories and border patrol buildings (36) is dwarfed beside that of the military, a significant presence in Washington's history.

According to the 1996 inventory of the state Office of Financial Management, Washington has an estimated 6,500 public buildings. However, this figure is low because it counts, for instance, the Department of Corrections' 25 sites, rather than its buildings which number more than 300. State institutions of higher learning — universities, colleges, and technical schools — have at least 1,940 buildings, about the same number as state parks. A quick accounting of buildings used by other state agencies reveals that the Department of Transportation uses 833 buildings; the Department of Social and Health Services, 412 buildings; the Department of Natural Resources, 346 buildings; the Department of Wildlife, 304; buildings and the Liquor Control Board, one building — its liquor stores are leased.

Counties and communities, of course, vary widely in the number of structures they own. The least populated county, Pend

Above: Portrait of an "Indian family near Chimacum Creek." Signed by Port Townsend pioneer photographer Torkas. Below: Fort Lewis barracks by Tacoma photographer Boland. Opposite top: Painter Jacob Lawrence with his mural inside Seattle's Kingdome. Opposite bottom: Old Whatcom City Hall, now Whatcom County Museum with "Heron" sculpture by Phillip McCracken. Both photos by Mary Randlett.

Above: Statehood celebration, Nov. 18, 1889. The old territorial capitol building continued to serve until 1903 when government moved into the Thurston County Courthouse, below, which the state had previously purchased. Courtesy, Washington State Capitol Museum.

Oreille, counts 11 buildings; and King County, the state's densest, claims an inventory of 257 buildings. Seattle hedges its collection at about 250; Poulsbo's 11 include four park restrooms. Bellevue's 14 buildings include nine fire stations, but this figure does not include its park structures, nor does Tacoma's count of 71 municipally owned buildings. Obviously, the buildings treated below, historical and contemporary, are a minority. They have been chosen either for their excellence or for their exemplariness.

STATE CAPITOL

In the nineteenth century, towns in developing frontier areas vigorously vied for institutions such as capitols, courthouses, universities, and even penitentiaries as indications of their future prosperity and stability. When Washington Territory's first governor, Isaac I. Stevens, arrived at his welcoming banquet on November 25, 1853, trail-scruffy and hungry after an arduous cross-country trek, he went unrecognized and was directed to the kitchen for scraps. Even so, two days later Stevens made his capital choice official. Olympia's status seemed assured after town founder, Edmund Sylvester, offered twelve acres for a capitol site. Olympia, also the seat of Thurston County which still included Mason and Chehalis (Grays Harbor)

THURSTON COUNTY COURT HOUSE

counties, had 996 residents, or about one-fourth of the entire territorial population. Washington Territory was also much larger then, including all of Idaho and much of western Montana.

While contention over the capital's location continued to surface over the years, even after statehood, the legislature continued to meet in Olympia. From the downtown rented quarters it first used, the legislature moved in 1856 to its own building on Sylvester's donated land, beside the site of the present Legislative Building. Intended to be temporary, the two-story, wood-frame building served the territory and then the state until 1903. On November 18, 1889, one week after the official declaration of statehood, celebrants erected a bunting-wrapped stage in front of the old capitol building.

Along with his approval of the state's new constitution, President Benjamin Harrison helped fund its permanent legislative quarters with the donation of 132,000 acres of land. The state was free to choose the acres from among any unappropriated federal lands within its borders and use the income from the timber sales to fund construction of the capitol buildings. In his excellent account, *Washington's Audacious State Capitol and Its Builders*, Norman J. Johnston quotes a state official's assertion that the capitol structures "will not cost the taxpayers one cent" — a promise that would later fizzle.

Ernest Flagg, a rising young New York architect, submitted the winning plans for the **Capitol Building** in an 1893 nationwide competition. Although Flagg's Neo-Classical monumental design had a definite "Gilded Age" ornateness, particularly in the dome, the state capitol commission was satisfied with the cost estimates, and the hopeful 1895 legislature authorized the necessary funds. However, the effects of the Panic of 1893 and the 1896 election of the cost-conscious Populist governor, John R. Rogers, terminated construction of the building at the basement level. As an economical alternative, Governor Rogers proposed and the legislature approved in 1901 the purchase of the Thurston County Courthouse in downtown Olympia. From 1905 until 1927 the legislature crowded into the multi-turreted, castle-like courthouse, while the brick and stone foundation of the Flagg building patiently awaited construction of the present Legislative Building.

By the time the legislature decided to hold another national competition for a capitol design in 1911, American architectural styles had been influenced by the imperial "Great White City" style of the buildings at the 1893 Columbia World's Fair Exposition and the Beaux Arts school of design. It was a propitious time to solicit designs for a group of capitol buildings. Two young New York architects, Walter Wilder and Harry White, submitted the winning plans for the site, the Legislative Building, and the **Temple of Justice**. The Olmsted Brothers were hired to do the landscape planning, part of which, two monumental stairways and a grand esplanade, was later abandoned. Capitol Lake, although it was not completed until 1949 with the damming of the Deschutes River, was retained.

After delays caused by World War I and insufficient legislative appropriations, the Wilkeson sandstone-sheathed Temple of Justice, with Doric columns supporting its portico, was ready for occupancy in 1920. The **Legislative Building**, the centerpiece of the capitol campus, was constructed on top of the existing Flagg

foundations. It was designed with a rectangular shape, Doric-colonnaded wings to the north and south, and central colonnaded and pedimented entrance porticoes between. From this base rises the dome, one of the highest in the world, weighing 15,400 tons and encircled by a Corinthian colonnade. The Tokeen and Gravina marble from southeast Alaska used in the north main entrance, vestibule, rotunda, and public corridors creates a majestic impression. More than 500 workers, including marble setters and stone carvers using hand tools, worked for five years on the building.

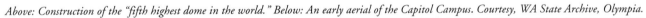

Above: Construction of the "fifth highest dome in the world." Below: An early aerial of the Capitol Campus. Courtesy, WA State Archive, Olympia.

Above: Fort Vancouver officers quarters. Courtesy, U.W. Libraries, Special Collections. Right: Fort Nisqually remnant removed to Point Defiance Park, Tacoma. Photo by Hugh Paradise. Right below: Fort Steilacoom officers quarters at the turn of the century.

FORTS

All of Washington's first public buildings were forts, built either as posts for trading furs with the Indians or as block-houses to protect settlers against them. British and French Canadian employees of the mighty Hudson's Bay Company finished building the first **Fort Vancouver** upriver from the mouth of the Columbia in 1825 at what is now the site of the Deaf School. Soon, however, the company moved a short ways west to build another larger fort. Surrounded by a stockade 600 by 525 feet, with 12-foot bastions at two corners, the fort protected houses, storehouses for furs and trading goods, and workshops for carpentry, blacksmithing, and barrel making. After Britain gave up its claim to the territory south of the Forty-ninth Parallel in 1846, the Hudson's Bay Company began sharing the fort with U.S. Army troops in 1849. The Army built on a rise above the company trading post with buildings on a line 2,000 yards from the river bank. The commanding officer's house, built in 1849-50 when Ulysses S. Grant was quartermaster at the fort, is now a museum. By 1875 the military had built two double-story barracks, and seven log and four frame buildings that served as officers quarters. Because the latter were designed with two rooms on either side of a corridor, they were known as "four pens and a passage."

To supply Russian fur traders in Alaska, the HBC in the 1830s formed the Puget Sound Agricultural Company and conducted commercial farming and ranching at Cowlitz Farm and **Fort Nisqually**. Naturalist George Gibbs in 1854 described Fort Nisqually as "a cluster of small buildings, of no great value, within a stockade." However, at its conception twenty years earlier, Fort

Nisqually was a crucial part of the British effort to bolster territorial claims to the Northwest region. Located seventeen miles south of present-day Tacoma on a bluff overlooking the Sound, the stock-aded fort with blockhouses at each corner surrounded a store, granary, blacksmith shop, and chief factor's and employees' houses. The original granary and factor's house, enclosed by a log stockade, were reconstructed at **Point Defiance Park** in 1934 in the post-and-sill construction favored by the company with uprights, planks, hand-split shakes, hand-forged hardware, and oak pegs salvaged from the site. The reconstructed log granary is probably the oldest surviving building in Washington.

Left: Fort Simcoe Commandant's dining room. Brick fireplaces built in every room by five-dollar-a-day masons were criticized by military superiors in Washington D.C. The major who ordered them considered his parsimonious critics unreasonable and, fortunately, remote. Photo by Hugh Paradise. Above: Fort Simcoe exterior. Courtesy, Washington State University Historical Photography Collection.

In 1849, two years after the Whitman mission massacre, the government replied to settlers' pleas for protection from the local tribes with **Fort Steilacoom.** Strategically located at the western end of a military road built in 1853 over the mountains from Fort Walla Walla (see Highways Chapter), the fort served as Army headquarters in western Washington until it was abandoned in 1868. Of the original fifteen buildings within the post, only four officers' homes, which have been painstakingly reconstructed, remain. While **Fort Simcoe** was also built to protect local settlers, it did not, however, sacrifice style for defense. Army architect Louis Scholl (who also designed **Fort Dalles**, sixty-five miles to the southwest) employed the picturesque Gothic Revival style in Fort Simcoe's officers' quarters from a plan straight out of the design bible of the time, A. J. Downing's *Architecture of Country Houses.* Feeling confident that the Indians were nearly vanquished, Scholl even gave the four post blockhouses large windows and doors that could easily be converted to peacetime use.

Beginning in the winter of 1854, eastern and western Washington Indian tribes banded together to drive out the white settlers. Finding that the few Army troops in the region could not give them the protection they wanted, frightened settlers, urged by Governor Stevens, constructed local blockhouses to which they could flee in case of attack. During the 1850s settlers built twenty-three neighborhood forts, while the militia built another thirty-five. Oregon volunteer militiamen built **Fort Borst** to protect the nearby Chehalis River crossing on the military road between Fort Vancouver and Fort Steilacoom. Its construction was typically strong and utilitarian with thick log walls, shake roof, and dirt floor. Rifle slits in the second-story walls and overhung floor allowed for firing down at those below. Almost as soon as it was finished, Fort Borst became a supply depot for protecting grain instead of people. During the remainder of the war with the Yakama Indians, the fort functioned as a forwarding point and storage house for supplies unloaded from large canoes for overland shipment. Meanwhile, settlers who needed safety rushed to **Fort Henness**, ten miles to the northwest.

In January 1917, 86 percent of Pierce County's patriotic and economically hopeful residents voted to bond themselves for $2 million for the purchase of 70,000 acres to be donated to the federal government for use as a military base. The future **Camp Lewis,** (named for Capt. Meriwether Lewis, commander of the Lewis and Clark Expedition) offered a perfect terrain for military training, part of the American Lake-Nisqually plain having long been used for militia and National Guard encampments. Over that summer nearly 10,000 men built 1,757 buildings and 422 other structures to accommodate the anticipated 50,000 troops. The workers even subscribed $4,000 of their own money to build the main gate. Constructed of field stone and squared logs and resembling the old blockhouses, the gate has been moved but is still standing.

After the war most of the troops were removed from Camp Lewis, and the post's quickly built wooden structures almost as quickly declined; many were torn down. Reflecting the public mood, the *Tacoma News Tribune* demanded that the Army "Give us a payroll or give the land back to the county." And the camp nearly reverted to county ownership until Congress and the War Department decided in 1926 to raise the camp to the status of fort. The ten-year building program that followed saw the raising of the first permanent brick barracks. **Fort Lewis** was an important participant in mobilization for both World War II and the Korean War, when additional permanent buildings and facilities were built, including the **Madigan General Hospital** in 1945. In 1972 Fort Lewis became headquarters for the Ninth Infantry Division, the first "all volunteer" division in the U.S. Army, which it remains today.

A number of federal forts were built in Washington at the turn of the century. Like the coast defenses at the entrance to Puget

Top: Gate to Camp Lewis. Above: Fort Borst on the Chehalis River. Bottom: Engineer Ambrose Kiehl, who supervised the clearing and early construction at Fort Lawton, with his family beside their temporary lodgings in one of the officers quarters. Courtesy, Frederick Mann.

Sound, most were constructed during the mobilization attending the Spanish American War. However, the opening of Spokane's **Fort George Wright** in 1897 preceded that excitement. Like Seattle's Fort Lawton, the 1,500-acre Spokane fort included some military use well into the twentieth century, and both forts were subsequently developed for park and heritage purposes. After its closure in 1958 the preservation of the stately brick buildings arranged along tree-lined boulevards was ensured in the formation of the Fort George Wright Historic District. Many of **Fort Lawton**'s frame quarters were razed after its demobilization in 1970. The fate of those preserved remained a point of contention between those who wanted to turn the old fort's 640 acres on Magnolia Bluff overlooking Puget Sound into a park and those

Right: Olympia Armory. Photo by Clark Gilman. Bottom (clockwise from upper left): 1) Seattle Armory on Western Avenue. Courtesy, John Cooper. 2) Tacoma Armory with Pierce County Courthouse behind. 3) Fort George Wright, Spokane. Photo by Jack Arkills. 4) Bellingham Armory.

who preferred a mixed use including preservation. The latter prevailed — Discovery Park includes as one of its attractions the twelve restored Georgian Revival homes along Officer Row.

The military institution that melded most with the community was the armory. In 1897 Walla Walla staged its first Fruit Fair in the local armory. The first **Seattle Armory** on Union Street between Third and Fourth avenues was constructed ostensibly for the drill practices of its several home guards and rifle units, but was more often used for a variety of other meetings and entertainments. After the fire of 1889 it served as a temporary city hall. Seattle's second armory, which opened at Western Avenue and Virginia Street in 1909, quickly became the center for local auto shows. A third Seattle Armory built in 1938 at the Civic Center was later converted to the Food Circus for the World's Fair in 1962 and has since been remodeled a few times as the Center House. Tacomans donated their armory site at Eleventh Street and South Yakima on the condition that the building also be used as a community center. Appropriately, its dedication on January 1, 1909 featured a New Year's Ball. Thereafter, the Tacoma Armory was used for auto, boat, and flower shows, as well as high school graduations. These playful uses were prohibited when armories nationwide temporarily closed to public use early in World War I. The Olympia Armory was built during the depression with PWA funds. With its smooth white surfaces, long recessed windows, and restrained Art Deco details, it is one of the state's better examples of the then popular Moderne Style.

COUNTY COURTHOUSES

The urge for home rule, which in 1853 "liberated" that part of Oregon Territory lying north of the Columbia River into Washington Territory, was repeated on a smaller scale with the division of Washington Territory into counties. This began in 1844 when the Oregon provisional government created the Vancouver district north of the Columbia River and the following year divided that immense territory along the line of the Cowlitz River. The lesser half to the west of the river was named Lewis County, and the much larger section to the east was first named Vancouver and later Clark County. Pacific County at the mouth of the Columbia was divided from Lewis County in 1851, and the next year Thurston County was created to include everything west of the Cascades and from its existing southern border as far north as the Forty-ninth Parallel. The first Washington legislature created several new counties in 1854, including Cowlitz, Clallam, and Whatcom. At the other corners of the state, Asotin County was carved from Garfield County in 1883, and Pend Oreille became the last of the state's thirty-nine counties, separated from Stevens County in 1911. This division followed the legislature's agreement that it was too much to expect residents of the Pend Oreille Valley to take a four-day round-trip train excursion through Spokane for business at the Stevens County seat in Colville. Then the routes between the valleys of the Pend Oreille and Colville rivers were little more than mountain trails.

When **Asotin County** was created, the towns of Asotin and Asotin City competed with each other for the county seat by extending the county free quarters. Choosing between the offers was difficult, but finally Asotin resident Theodore Schank's new home was accepted when he promised to also include free fuel, lights, tables, desks, and a safe for the commissioners. In other new counties the commissioners sometimes first met in the local general store for official versions of cracker barrel politics. Once the enticing period of free rent ran out, counties would either lease quarters for a recorder's office, sheriff's office, jail, and courtroom, or build one. **Whatcom County**'s early commissioners in the future Bellingham first met in 1854 at member R. V. Peabody's home. In 1858, the county was able to move into its own two-room wooden building which it occupied until it purchased Washington Territory's first brick structure, the five-year-old **Richards Building**, in 1863. The bricks had come around the Horn as ballast for a ship that also took on California goldseekers heading to Bellingham Bay enroute to the latest strike on the Fraser River.

The more common temporary and even flimsy nature of early county quarters often had as much to do with a town's tenuous claim to county seat status as it had to do with economy. In the days of early settlement and even later, struggles among rival communities competing to become the county center were more often the rule than the exception. As populations grew, speculators, town boomers, and newspaper editors led this civic fuss, combing the countryside for voters and peppering newspapers with their advocacy articles.

In Spokane County the seat switched back and forth between two communities. After a lively 1880 sparring contest between newspaper editors in the two towns, Cheney won the **Spokane County** seat away from Spokane Falls. Six years later another vote moved the county seat back to Spokane, where the commissioners quickly erected a temporary courthouse on donated land. **Cowlitz County's** seat of Kalama fought repeated attempts by Kelso and Castle Rock to steal its status. After seven Kalama victories, Kelso was finally able to muster enough votes for the transfer in 1922.

Snohomish County acquired its seat of the same name after an initial contest between Mukilteo and Snohomish in 1861. More than thirty years later the city of Everett developed a shrewd plan to win the county capital when it proposed a vote for a

Top: Built during the Gold Rush of 1858, the Richards Building, Washington Territory's first brick building, was purchased by Whatcom County in 1863 to use as its courthouse. Courtesy, Galen Biery. Above: Skamania County Courthouse in Stevenson. Below: Snohomish County Courthouse in Everett. Photo by Juleen. Courtesy, Everett Public Library.

$30,000 bond issue to fund "a public place or park." The bond issue for the new courthouse won overwhelmingly. The election, however, started one of the state's most spectacular legal battles over a county seat, requiring three separate state Supreme Court decisions before the question was finally settled in Everett's favor. One of the many architects imported by the railroad, A. F. Heide, stayed on to become Everett's first resident architect. Heide's Romanesque-Chateau-style **Snohomish County Courthouse** resembled the earlier heroic courthouse creations of Seattle Architect Willis A. Ritchie (see below). Completed in 1897, Heide's first creation burned in 1909 at a time when Mission Revival architecture was sweeping the country. So Heide laid the more au courant Mission exterior over the burnt core of the original building.

Sometimes county seat contests went beyond the war of words and influence peddling to fist fights and post-election abductions. In 1893 "a group of rowdies" raided the small county office in Cascades, **Skamania County's** seat, and carted the records to Stevenson. Cascades threatened to take the thieves to court, but

Above left: Postcard produced for Montesano's fight to keep the Chehalis County Courthouse. Right: The clapboard Chehalis Courthouse's Beaux Arts replacement in Montesano, for the seat of the since renamed Grays Harbor County. Courtesy, Jones Photo Company, Aberdeen.

the great Columbia River flood of 1894 did so much damage to the town that they conceded the records would be safer in Stevenson where they remain. In **Pacific County** a group of "volunteers" decided that the county commissioners were not moving quickly enough to South Bend, which voters had approved as the new county seat in 1892. So they broke into the courthouse at Oysterville and packed off the records themselves. Two decades later South Bend possessed a beautiful Classical Revival style courthouse with art glass dome over a rotunda, sitting on a landscaped park overlooking the city. In 1907 **Franklin County** built in Pasco another design of the same architect, C. Lewis Wilson — a Neo-Classical courthouse of buff brick and limestone, with Corinthian columns and a gilded dome visible for miles.

Chehalis County experienced its biggest political uproar and a near civil war in 1905 after the much larger lumber towns of Aberdeen and Hoquiam lost by a few votes in their electoral bid to wrest the county center from Montesano. But after winning the

vote Montesano, which had argued economy as a reason to reject its much larger neighbors' proposal to build a new courthouse beside the harbor, proposed the construction of its own lavish seat to replace the worn clapboard county courthouse built in 1890. Aberdeen and Hoquiam seized this opportunity to try again, and in 1907 the big harbor cities petitioned the state to create a new county with Hoquiam as its seat. Both state houses passed the bill and the governor signed it. The state Supreme Court, however, found the whole affair unconstitutional and ordered the seat kept in Montesano. Years later, in 1915, the county name was changed to the name proposed by the Aberdeen-Hoquiam advocates, but Montesano retained the courthouse for the new **Grays Harbor County**.

An 1884 election over the permanent location of the county seat in **Lincoln County** resulted in more votes than there were people. Charges of fraud flew between Davenport and Sprague, the main contenders. However, the commissioners ordered the

Clockwise from below left: 1) Franklin County Courthouse, Pasco. Signed by Bryan. 2) Pacific County Courthouse, South Bend. 3) Laying the cornerstone for the Chelan County Courthouse, Wenatchee, 1923. Signed by Simmer. 4) Completed Chelan County Courthouse. Courtesy, North Central Washington Museum, Wenatchee.

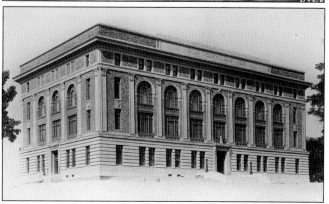

Above: Flipsides of a postcard published by the advocates of keeping the Douglas County Courthouse in Waterville. Courtesy, Dan Kerlee.

county office moved from Davenport, the temporary seat, to Sprague, which had received the most votes. Davenport residents, refusing to give up the county records, dug a trench, set up a breastwork, and posted armed guards inside and outside the town to prevent their removal. After three weeks of day-and-night guard duty, the men tired and went home. Sprague was ready and sent an armed force to Davenport, capturing the records before the farmers could regroup. The courthouse remained in Sprague until an 1895 fire nearly wiped out the town and county residents voted to move the county capital back to Davenport.

When **Douglas County** was created in November 1883 and Okanogan became its capital, the town's population consisted of one man living in a tent. Three years later Waterville challenged the "town" and won the seat. However, the county auditor at the Okanogan townsite refused to release the county records — until the sheriff delivered a court order. Eventually the town of Okanogan got its position back, although not for Douglas County. When **Okanogan County** was divided from Douglas County in 1888, the mining town of Ruby was chosen for its temporary county seat, until nearby Conconully took it in that year's November election. Soon, however, Conconully was visited by a sequence of disasters, beginning with the 1892 fire that consumed two business blocks, the Salmon River flood of 1894 that destroyed forty-two structures, and the deflation of silver. The county seat was subsequently moved about fifteen miles downstream to Okanogan, where the Salmon River enters the Okanogan River. The existing courthouse which is a fanciful rendering of the Spanish Mission style, opened in 1916. A year earlier, Okanogan's old rival Waterville opened its unique new courthouse, a Richardsonian Romanesque construction topped by a Queen Anne cupola.

More substantial courthouses, built of brick and stone, came to Washington with the settling of county seat disputes, a population boom, and statehood. The late 1880s and afterward was period of opportunity for ambitious young architects coming west. One of these, twenty-five-old Willis A. Ritchie, arrived in Seattle just two weeks after the Great Fire. With six years experience but no formal architectural training other than a correspondence course, Ritchie submitted the winning design for the **King County Courthouse** on Seattle's First Hill. This first success would be followed by several others until he had produced plans for courthouses in Thurston, Whatcom, Jefferson, Clark, and Spokane counties, as well as for several schools. With the exception of a Classical-style King County Courthouse, since replaced, most of Ritchie's large public projects used the Romanesque Revival style.

Ritchie's **Thurston County Courthouse**, finished in 1892, was constructed of Chuckanut sandstone from Whatcom County. Originally it was topped by a 150-foot octagonal tower with clocks on each of its eight sides. After the state purchased the building for its capitol in 1901, Ritchie designed a new wing so that the building then featured three twenty-foot-wide domed skylights

LINCOLN COUNTY COURT HOUSE.

Above: Lincoln County Courthouse, Davenport. Left: Okanogan County Courthouse, Okanogan. Courtesy, Dan Kerlee.

345

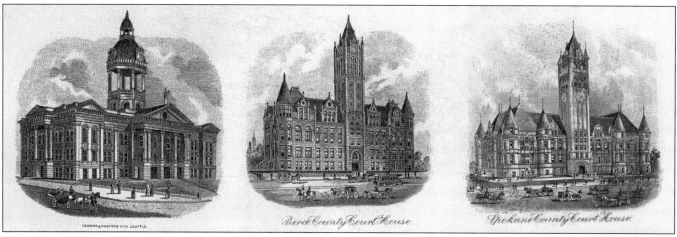

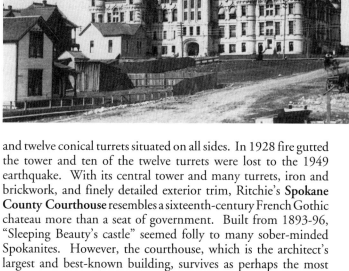

Above: King County Courthouse, ca. 1900. Right: Spokane County Courthouse, ca. 1895. Courtesy, Michael Maslan. Below: Jefferson County Courthouse, Port Townsend.

and twelve conical turrets situated on all sides. In 1928 fire gutted the tower and ten of the twelve turrets were lost to the 1949 earthquake. With its central tower and many turrets, iron and brickwork, and finely detailed exterior trim, Ritchie's **Spokane County Courthouse** resembles a sixteenth-century French Gothic chateau more than a seat of government. Built from 1893-96, "Sleeping Beauty's castle" seemed folly to many sober-minded Spokanites. However, the courthouse, which is the architect's largest and best-known building, survives as perhaps the most auspicious county landmark in the state. The brick and carved stone **Jefferson County Courthouse** (1890-92) in Port Townsend, with its off-center main tower, remains Ritchie's most inventive use of the Romanesque Revival style. It too survives. However, Ritchie's other county landmarks, the brick **Clark County Court-**

Right: Fire gutting the towers of the old Thurston County Courthouse, 1928. Far right: Thurston County Courthouse after its 1903 purchase by the state to use as the temporary capitol. Courtesy, Washington State Archives, Olympia.

*Above: Pierce County Courthouse.
Below: Whatcom County
Courthouse.*

*Top: Dedication of the new County-City Building on April 10, 1959; a
remnant of the abandoned Pierce County Courthouse peaks behind it.
Courtesy, MOHAI, Seattle P-I Collection. Above: Early photo of the
Columbia County Courthouse, Dayton (which is still used and recently
restored). Courtesy, Columbia County Historical Society.*

house (1891-92) and the stone **Whatcom County Courthouse** (1889-91) have both been razed.

The **Pierce County Courthouse** (1893), which looked like another Ritchie creation but wasn't, was modeled after H. H. Richardson's Pittsburgh courthouse and jail. Built of blue sandstone from Wilkeson, it was the first Tacoma landmark sighted by ships' pilots entering Commencement Bay. The *Tacoma Ledger* reported that "when the 999 electric lights outlining its tower were lighted at night, the building glowed like a dowager in a diamond necklace." Cracked by the 1949 earthquake, the courthouse eventually was torn down and replaced by a parking lot for the new County-City building.

The **Columbia County Courthouse** in Dayton (1886-87) is the oldest courthouse in the state still used for county government purposes. Designed by Dayton resident and architect William H. Burrows,

*Etching of the Walla Walla County Courthouse in Walla Walla from the 1890s.
Courtesy, Marsha Rosellini.*

the Italianate-style building has twenty-two-inch-thick brick walls that were originally finished in stucco with ornate trim features. At the center of the mansard roof Burrows set a twenty-four-foot-square platform supporting a twenty-two-foot cupola, topped by another iron-fenced platform. Much of this elegance was subsequently stripped away and Columbia County was left with a box for county offices after the building's cupola was removed in 1947. Recently, however, most of the courthouse's original features, cupola included, have been returned to it in one of the state's best examples of historic restoration.

The Columbia County Courthouse in Dayton resembled the slightly larger Italianate courthouse built for **Walla Walla County** in 1881. In 1916 this elegant box was replaced by a fine example of Ecole des Beaux Arts Classicism. The exuberantly detailed limestone exterior of the building complements its fine black-veined white marble interior. It is one of the prominent landmarks on Walla Walla's Main Street.

MOUNT ANGELES FROM PORT ANGELES, WASH.

Top left: Port Angeles Carnegie Library, high school (above it), and the Clallam County Courthouse. Courtesy, Clallam County Historical Society. Top right: Clallam County Courthouse, Jan. 4, 1962. Courtesy, MOHAI, Seattle P-I Collection. Left: Garfield County Courthouse, Pomeroy. Courtesy Garfield County historical Society. Above: Thurston County Courthouse, Olympia.

Built to survive the type of fire that destroyed its predecessor, the **Garfield County Courthouse** (1901) was made of stone and brick with stucco covering. The unique design, resembling part Queen Anne-style residence and part Romanesque-style public building, survives in Pomeroy.

The **King County Courthouse** (1912-16) illustrates the shift from a style in which the courthouse resembles a monumental temple of justice to the restrained aesthetic of an office building. It does, however, hold its own against the otherwise undistinguished four-block-square enclave of modern county and City of Seattle governmental quarters off of City Hall Park.

With its two-story brick exterior and nicely detailed bell-clock tower, **Clallam County's** Federal-style courthouse (1915) is considered by many the most distinctive building in Port Angeles. It is now the home of the Clallam County Historical Society and its museum, and a new courthouse has been built behind it.

The present **Thurston County Courthouse** (1930), designed by Joseph Wohleb, is described in Woodbridge and Montgomery's guide to state architecture as a "proto-Modern stripped Classic block with a Beaux Arts plan and massing and ornament from the Art Deco vocabulary." In its massing it shares the austere symmetry of the **Island County Courthouse** at Coupeville (1948).

PROPOSED ISLAND COUNTY COURT HOUSE

Above: King County Courthouse facing City Hall Park, Seattle, Oct. 17, 1932. Left: Plans for the Island County Courthouse at Coupeville and as built. Courtesy, Island County.

Clark County Courthouse. Courtesy, Ted Van Arsdol.

Clark County could not have been prepared for the local demands of the Second World War when it dedicated its new modern courthouse on Nov. 29, 1941 just days before the attack on Pearl Harbor. The extraordinary boom of Vancouver's wartime industry soon taxed the the capacities of the new courthouse. However, new county facilities were not added until after the war, and the courthouse continues to be a center of county affairs.

Olympia City Hall with fire department headquarters.

CITY HALLS

While towns were small and taxpayers few, cities typically housed all their services in one building. Often city halls were attached to fire stations. Smaller community examples of these "duplexes" include Marysville, Mabton, Elma, and many others, but this combination was commonplace even in towns as large as Olympia. Designed by George Gove of Tacoma, the Neo-Classical Revival **Olympia City Hall**, built in 1912, still functions as a city fire station. The **Montesano City Hall**, built in 1914, is another city headquarters that accommodated the fire department. Its Mission Revival design may seem an unusual style for the wet Pacific Northwest, but it was all the rage throughout the country during the early twentieth century. The building has since been altered to house larger fire engines and its original arched windows have been rudely squared off for aluminum frames.

A few of Washington's larger communities, especially those which had some hope of prospering from connection with a railroad, built lavish city halls in the late-Victorian era. The **Whatcom City Hall** (1893) was big enough for a community many times it size. The three-story, red brick superstructure trimmed with gray Chuckanut sandstone remains one of the region's finer examples of Victorian Second Empire architecture. The building, which rises from four corner cupolas to a high

central bell tower, was used as a city hall until 1939. Afterwards, it became the Whatcom Museum of History and Art and is still Bellingham's major landmark. After the mansard roof and central tower were destroyed in a fire in 1962, a group of local citizens organized as the Whatcom Museum Society to raise funds to restore it. Architect George Bartholic oversaw the restoration.

Another municipal headquarters that conveyed the city's sense of civic pride and promise was built in Tacoma. **Tacoma's "Old City Hall"** was designed by E.

Above and top: Early and later views, respectively, of Whatcom City Hall. Below: Montesano City Hall.

A. Hatherton of San Francisco and constructed in 1893, just before the nationwide economic crash. An outstanding example of the Italian Renaissance style, the building features light-colored pressed brickwork, terra cotta ornamentation, and a copper-tiled roof. The elaborate arched and bracketed tower still houses a clock and chimes that were donated in 1905 by Hugh C. Wallace, later United States ambassador to France, in memory of his daughter. After city offices moved to join Pierce County in a modern structure in 1959, Old City Hall stood vacant for more than ten years until it was transformed into an assembly of shops and restaurants — what Tacoma historian Murray Morgan described as a "vertical shopping mall." The renovation incorporated a

Above: The King County Courthouse, ca. 1885, was purchased in 1890 by Seattle for its City Hall when the county moved into its grand Willis Ritchie-designed courthouse on Seattle's First Hill, then known as "Profanity Hill" because of the expletives trumpeted by the courthouse litigants. Courtesy, Seattle Public Library.

structural system that closely followed the original engineering diagrams and included novel work such as mosaic tile floors. Unfortunately, Tacomans were not persuaded to patronize the landmark's new boutiques and restaurants in sufficient numbers, and Old City Hall was reworked again in the 1980s for professional offices.

Unlike its counterparts of the same period in Bellingham and Tacoma, **Seattle City Hall** was a dilapidated object of ridicule. After King County moved into its new courthouse atop Seattle's "Profanity Hill" (First Hill) in 1890, the city moved its offices into the county's old frame courthouse at Third Avenue and Jefferson Street. In the nineteen years that Seattle government resided there, it put the 1882 structure through changes so elaborate and irregular that it was popularly known as the "Katzenjammer Kastle" after a popular comic strip in which jumbled constructions were commonplace. The patch-ons were necessary, for between 1890 and 1909, the year the "Kastle" was abandoned for a proper municipal building, Seattle's population exploded from 40,000 to more than 200,000. A comparison of an 1880s view of the structure with one recorded in 1909, its last year, would reveal the additions that attempted to keep pace with a city that grew in the years of its use from 40,000 to more than 200,000 citizens.

The Everett City Hall, designed by architect A. H. Albertson and built in 1930, is one of the state's best examples of the architectural style that came to be called "PWA Moderne." The classical detailing of the Beaux Arts style has been replaced by

Above: Late 1890s etching for Tacoma City Hall. Below: The landmark Old City Hall in 1996.

Below: Everett City Hall. Courtesy, Everett Public Library.

Left: The unidentified board-and-batten post office may be a branch P.O. for the lumber town of Fremont at the outlet to Lake Union. The satchel, far right, is signed 'Buck Photographer, 3418 Fremont Avenue.'
Above: Turn-of-the-century Shelton Post Office shared a building with a newspaper and photographer. Courtesy, Mason County Historical Society.

popular geometric and foliate ornament. PWA Moderne was commonly used for government buildings throughout the country from the late 1920s to the early 1940s. Albertson also had a hand in designing the Moderne-style **Seattle Tower** (1928).

Built in 1891 the brick-and-stone facade of **Port Townsend's City Hall** originally had an "Old English Revival" look. The carved sandstone used for its foundation, window sills, lintels, and

Above and bottom: Old Port Townsend City Hall, ca. 1898 and 1996. Contemporary photo by Miguel Edwards.

capitals was a popular material of the time. Edward A. Batwell and Andrew G. Patrick, the building's local architects, also experimented with the application of decorative sunbursts made from sheet metal. The structure originally had a gable-roofed attic story and a square corner tower, both of which were removed in the early 1940s because of storm damage. Today the building houses the museum for the Jefferson County Historical Society.

FEDERAL BUILDINGS

Aside from the military additions to Fort Vancouver in the late 1840s, the first federal construction in the future Washington Territory was probably William Winlock Miller's improvisation on the beach at Nisqually. In April 1851 with two crates borrowed from the Hudson's Bay Company, Miller opened the federal customs office. The larger box he used for a desk and the smaller for a chair. Miller was assistant to Customs Collector Simpson P. Moses who arrived from the east later that year. Moses quickly moved his customs station into the upper floor of "Colonel" Michael Simmons's home, the largest in Olympia. After the schooner *Exact* from Portland let off one of Seattle's two founding parties at Alki Point on November 11, 1851, it proceeded south to the new federal customs, where it was cleared on November 19 to continue its journey to the gold diggings off the Queen Charlotte Islands.

Besides housing the U.S. customs officer and his family, Olympia patriarch Michael Simmons also ran a store and the post office in his big home. Simmons performed as postmaster with an impediment — he was not "book larnt." So his post office was run on the honor system where patrons helped themselves. Before statehood, especially in rural areas, the "mail service" often had to rely on volunteer letter carriers, and postmasters could seldom supply a dedicated building. But as populations grew, the one-room, wood-frame post office became the norm for small communities. When a town seemed to have real promise or ambition, as did Port Townsend in Jefferson County in the early 1890s, a more permanent brick or stone structure was constructed to house federal functions. The 1893 **Port Townsend Customs House**, now the post office, is as monumental as the rest of the edifices built in the city that had once seemed the most likely to succeed on Puget Sound. The Richardsonian-Romanesque building was originally planned with a six-story entrance tower, later truncated to three to save money.

Spokane's post office, made of Bedford limestone, was another government structure that clearly announced the civic pride of its citizens. When the Classical Revival landmark went up in 1909, it was widely considered the most beautiful structure in the city. Nearly sixty years later the new **Federal Building and U.S. Courthouse** made a poor comparison alongside it. According to Sally Woodbridge and Roger Montgomery, authors of *A Guide to Architecture in Washington State*, the latter is "a blockbuster that

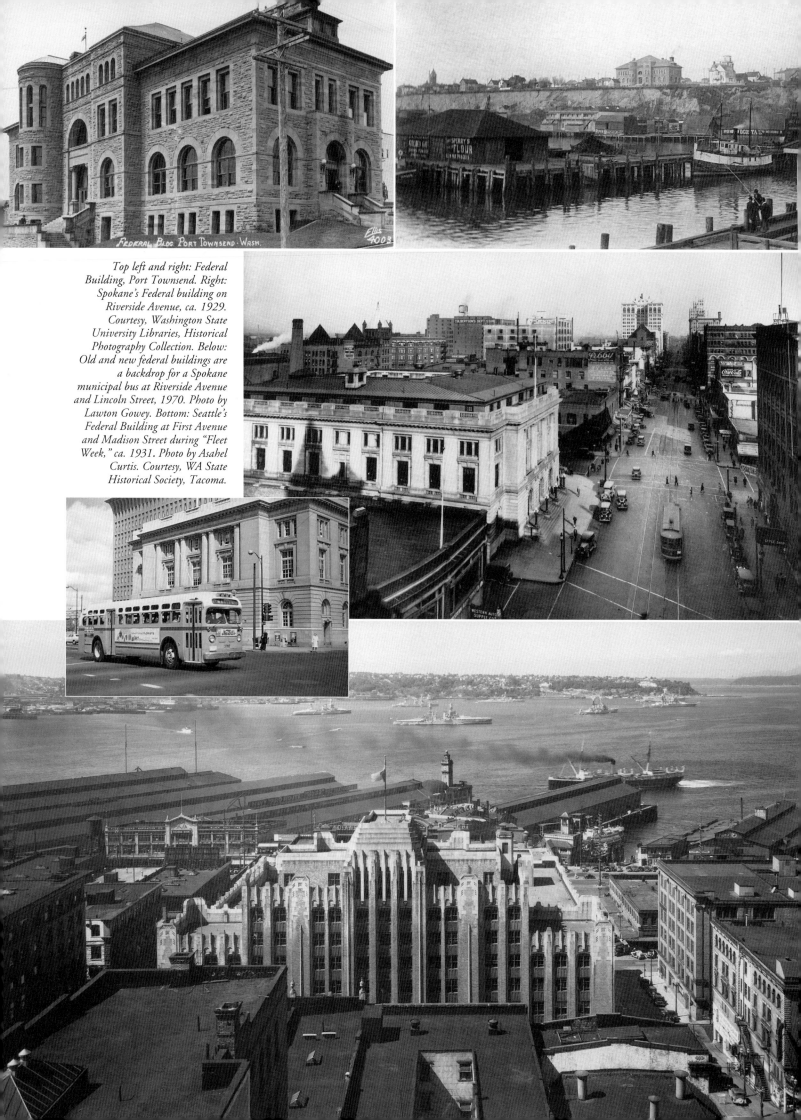

Top left and right: Federal Building, Port Townsend. Right: Spokane's Federal building on Riverside Avenue, ca. 1929. Courtesy, Washington State University Libraries, Historical Photography Collection. Below: Old and new federal buildings are a backdrop for a Spokane municipal bus at Riverside Avenue and Lincoln Street, 1970. Photo by Lawton Gowey. Bottom: Seattle's Federal Building at First Avenue and Madison Street during "Fleet Week," ca. 1931. Photo by Asahel Curtis. Courtesy, WA State Historical Society, Tacoma.

FEDERAL BLDG. PORT TOWNSEND. WASH.

Yakima Post Office. Courtesy, Michael Fairley.

mostly negates the urban design potential of its site in the Riverside historical district."

During the first half of this century it was common for the federal building and post office to be combined. The Classic Style of the Beaux Arts, which conveys massiveness and authority as well as beautiful detail, was generally chosen as the most appropriate architectural design for these structures. **Bellingham's Post Office** on West Magnolia Street is a good surviving example. The **Yakima Post Office** also employs a Beaux Arts facade in limestone, while **Tacoma's Federal Building and Post Office** (1908-10), still used for its original purposes, was built in another Neo-Classical variation, the Roman-Classical Revival style. The post offices at Omak, Shelton, and Auburn are examples of a later popular federal style, the Colonial.

LIBRARIES

In his first official message to Washington residents Gov. Isaac Stevens reported that with the congressional appropriation for Washington's territorial library he had purchased 2,000 books, most of which had already arrived from the east. Beyond this original federal allotment, no public funds were directed for the support of Washington libraries for years to come. Libraries were usually not of great importance to frontier towns and city boomers, so book lovers could usually not expect support from city coffers. Communities in the 1860s through 1880s acquired their first libraries ordinarily through the efforts of local women who formed library and literary clubs. These private and semiprivate "local improvement" associations donated their own books and reading rooms, usually in a member's home, and raised funds through subscriptions and charity balls.

The great unfolding for community libraries came with the 1901 retirement of United States Steel Company magnate An-

Above: Seattle's old, bottom, and new, above, federal buildings face each other across First Avenue between Marion and Madison Street. Architect James A. Wetmore's 1932 creation is notable for the light-colored terra cotta capping that defines the ascending steps of a structure faced with darker brick. (The stepping is best exhibited in the view printed at the bottom of the facing page.) Across First Avenue, Fred Bassetti's 1974 Federal Building resembles a highrise palazzo with its red tile roof and brilliant white exterior.

drew Carnegie into a life of philanthropy. In the years left to him Carnegie donated $56 million to help build over 2,500 public libraries, with few exceptions all in the United States, England, and Canada. The Carnegie Corporation required that land for a site be donated and that the community provide sufficient funds for

Left: Spokane's Carnegie Post Office restored as architect's office. Courtesy, Integrus Architects, Spokane. Above: Colonial-style Federal Building in Auburn recorded by ubiquitous Washington State postcard artist, J. Boyd Ellis. Courtesy, John Cooper.

Renton Carnegie Library. Courtesy, UW Library, Special Collections.

the library's support. Typically, it would then allocate the funds needed for the building — $10,000 was a common appropriation for smaller towns — and recommend a standard interior design. **Olympia's Carnegie library** (1914) at South Franklin and Seventh was built of Chehalis brick in the "public library" style with a columned main entrance and terra cotta detail. The **Walla Walla Public Library** moved into its Carnegie-financed building in 1905, the same year the first **Spokane Carnegie Library** was occupied. Spokane opened three more Carnegie branch libraries in 1914, when **Renton** also used its Carnegie grant, however, with no books in sight.

Ellensburg Carnegie Library. Courtesy, Michael Fairley.

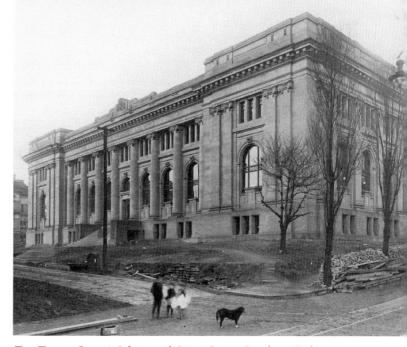

The Ladies' Municipal Improvement Society of **Ellensburg** won its Carnegie grant in 1908; however, over the next two decades an apathetic city council left it to the women to raise funds for both the librarian and books. Until it acquired a Carnegie library in 1911, Edmonds residents borrowed books from the state's traveling library, shipped to the waterfront town by steamboat. The **Edmonds Library** (1911), which also housed city offices on its lower floor, was one of only 271 Carnegie library buildings still intact in 1990. It is now home of the Edmonds South Snohomish County Museum. With the help of a $75,000 Carnegie grant, **Tacoma** in 1903 built a new public library in the French Renaissance style, where it maintained a large collection of books on forestry-related subjects. Its central dome was removed after it was damaged in the 1949 earthquake.

Less than two years after opening to the public on December 19, 1906, the front doors to the **Seattle Main Branch Public Library** (financed largely by a $220,000 Carnegie grant) were exposed ten feet above Fourth Avenue during the cutting stage of the Fourth Avenue Regrade. The staircase that greeted users until the library's destruction in 1957 added grandeur to the already monumental Beaux Arts landmark.

Originally sent to Seattle by a New York architectural firm to

Top: Tacoma Carnegie Library with Pierce County Courthouse (right-center) and Central school (far-left) behind. Courtesy, MOHAI. Above and below: Exterior and main lobby of Seattle's Carnegie Library, Central Branch. The street scene is an early view photographed before the 1908 regrade of Fourth Avenue. Courtesy, Seattle Public Library.

supervise the construction of St. James Cathedral, W. Marbury Somervell and Joseph S. Cote won commissions to design several of Seattle's Carnegie-financed branches between 1906 and 1910. The **Greenlake Branch** (1910) uses what the partners considered a "modern" French Renaissance style. To fit in with the neighborhood they chose a Tudor Revival style for the **Queen Anne Branch** (1913). The two architects also designed the **University and West Seattle branches** (1910), and the **Columbia and Douglass-Truth branches** (1914).

The last of Seattle's Carnegie libraries, the **Fremont Branch** (1921), was designed by Daniel R. Huntington and has little in common with the others. Eschewing the symmetrical Beaux Arts scheme, the Mission-style building was even outfitted with Stickley Arts-and-Crafts lounge chairs built by McNeil Island prisoners.

A. F. Heide, the designer of the Snohomish County Courthouse (see above), also drew the plans for **Everett's Carnegie**

Carnegie Libraries at: 1) Green Lake, circa 1910; Seattle. 2) Green Lake Library, 1996; Seattle. 3) Aberdeen. 4) Early-century municipal street crew pose in front of the Walla Walla Carnegie Library. Courtesy, Penrose Library, Whitman College. 5) Sedro Woolley. 6) Chehalis. 7) Snohomish. 8) Wenatchee. 9) Anacortes. 10) Vancouver.

library (1905) at Oakes and Wall. Heide took his inspiration from a Mediterranean-Renaissance style library in Pomona, California. **Everett's second library** (1934) was designed by Carl Gould in a streamlined Art Deco style, its red brick trimmed with terra cotta and its marquees faced with aluminum. When the Everett Library's main branch was remodeled with an addition in the 1960s, Gould's son, Carl Gould Jr. complained that much of the original structure's Art Deco ornamentation had been either

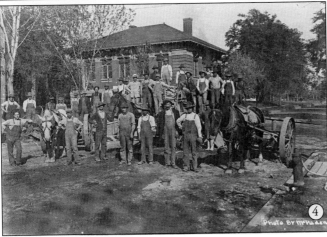

Proposed Library University of Washington

The variety of architect Carl F. Gould's designs is illustrated with the Art Deco-style Everett Public Library, right, and the Academic Gothic Suzzallo Library on the U.W. campus. Gould's architectural drawing of the Suzzallo, above, features a tower which was never built. Courtesy, U.W. Library, Special Collections.

removed or hidden. Almost thirty years later, during a time of greater appreciation for architectural continuity, his father's work was restored with another expansion in 1989-91. The new part of the library features a large reading room with a thirty-five-foot cathedral ceiling paneled in maple and topped by a copper roof.

The Everett library is an illustration of the eclectic interests of an architect who is most often associated with his work on the University of Washington campus. As founder of the university's School of Architecture, Carl F. Gould shared a vision with University President Henry Suzzallo that the library should dominate the university campus and express "our intellectual and spiritual ideals in education" through "appropriate architectural treatment." The central **University of Washington library** (1922-26), later named after President **Suzzallo**, was Gould's most impressive building on the campus. Its western facade is the grandest expression of the Academic Gothic style chosen for the campus buildings constructed in the years following the 1909 Alaska Yukon Pacific Exposition. Its English Gothic details incorporate inscriptions, university crests, and terra cotta statues in the buttresses.

Suzzallo and Gould were able to complete most of their vision for buildings on the campus, but not before losing their jobs. In

1925 soon after Roland Hartley took over the governor's mansion, the conservative chief executive focused his sights on the "tax spenders" at the University of Washington and its "extravagant library." When the new governor could not get his way with the University Board of Regents, he replaced its uncooperative members with cronies who fired President Suzzallo. Gould, who was also forced to resign, happily returned eight years later when the regents again appointed him and his partner, Charles H. Bebb, as the university supervisory architects. In 1934 Gould saw to completion a south addition to his beloved library project, although the central tower in its original design was never built. Later additions to the university's central library were generally

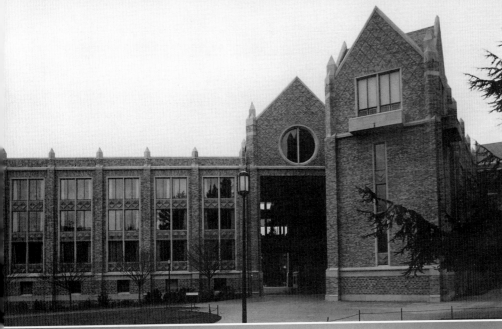

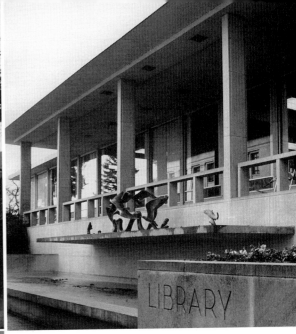

Above: Architect Paul Thiry's modern Washington State Library (1954-59), Olympia. Photo by Clark Gilman. Top left: **University of Washington Allen Library**. Left: The **Bellevue Regional Library**, designed by architect Zimmer Gunsul Frasca. This library, the largest of forty libraries in the King County Library System, was completed in June 1993. It was one of only thirteen winners nationwide of the American Institute of Architects (AIA) Honor Award for 1997. The new structure was earlier recognized by the American Library Association which, with the AIA, honored it with an Award of Excellence in 1995. Photo by Timothy Hursley. Courtesy, King County Library System.

undistinguished, until the 1990 addition of the five-story **Kenneth S. Allen Library**. Named for one of Suzzallo Library's longtime top librarians, it is connected to the Suzzallo's four-story south wing by an eighty-foot-high arcade that serves as both a bridge between the two buildings and as a gateway to the yard of the "HUB" student union building. Although clearly contemporary, the Allen Library is built of brick of several colors using five different patterns and blends well with the older campus buildings. It uses Indiana limestone at belt courses, window frames, and parapets, and sculpted terra cotta panels under the windows in geometric patterns and forms.

The contemporary colonnaded **State Library Building** (1959-61) in Olympia is probably more notable for its art and sculpture than for its architecture. Directly in front of the building stands a hand-hammered bas relief sun dial by John W. Eliot. It is six feet

across and divided into seven panels depicting early events, discoveries, and accomplishments in Washington history. Just inside the library's main entrance is a twenty-foot by sixteen-foot-high freestanding mosaic. James Fitzgerald used chipped marble to produce the abstract design which suggests a Northwest scene of forest, foliage, and water. In the Washington Room downstairs four panels painted by Kenneth Callahan create a panorama of state history from pre-European contact through the early twentieth century. Mark Tobey, probably the Northwest's most famous painter, also created an original work for the library.

The modern **Renton Library** (1966), designed by Renton architect Felix M. Campanella, has won national acclaim for its unique approach. The building has an exterior of aluminum, brick, sculptured concrete, and cement plaster with marblecrete finish — and it spans the Cedar River near Liberty Park.

Left: **Spokane's South Hill Branch Library**, winner of the American Institute of Architects, Spokane Chapter, 1996 Award of Merit. Courtesy, Integrus Architects, Spokane. Bottom left: **Shoreline Public Library** opened its new 20,000-square-foot space in 1993. Designed by the Portico Group in association with Johnston Architects, the library was constructed and furnished with funds from a 1988 King County Library District bond issue. Below: Renton Public Library spanning the Cedar River.

HOSPITALS

As one of its first acts, the territorial legislature of 1854 passed a poor law that made the counties responsible for the care of indigents who had no family support. However, this responsibility was soon returned to the legislature with the law's first test. When a pauper named Edward Moore was found crazed and frostbitten on a Seattle beach, King County officials asked the legislature to assume his care. Wanting to avoid a costly precedent, the legislature procrastinated before finally assigning the care of the insane to the governor and auditor of the territory. The Sisters of Charity at Vancouver were contracted to provide this care, but the policy of awarding the contract to the lowest bidder soon put the work into the hands of two Monticello men whose custody could be described charitably as minimal. Learning from this experience that the lowest bidder policy was not conducive to good health care, the solons decided to build a permanent territorial asylum. The two dozen military buildings at the abandoned Fort Steilacoom seemed ideal for these purposes.

Above: Harborview Hospital, Seattle. Bottom: Health Science and Medical Center, University of Washington.

Above: Western Washington State Hospital, Steilacoom. Courtesy, Tacoma Public Library.

In 1871 the Hospital for the Insane of Washington Territory, later **Western State Hospital,** opened its doors, soon adopting the "Kirkbride Plan" that separated patients into different wards and used new, more humane treatment. Permanent buildings for staff and patients, made of bricks from the clay of Steilacoom, were raised in the late 1880s. Over the years building programs attempted to keep up with the patient load, but overcrowding was a chronic problem until the introduction of drug therapy in the 1950s. In 1891 the state opened the **Medical Lake or Eastern State Hospital** near Spokane to care for patients east of the Cascades. When both institutions became overcrowded in 1909, the legislature purchased 1,100 acres of rolling pasture and crop-

land, just north of the Skagit River Valley. **Northern State Hospital** was dedicated by Gov. Marion E. Hay in May 1912 and opened the following year. Its attractive two- and three-story buildings use cream-colored stucco exteriors, bay gables, cupolas, and columned entranceways, topped with red-tiled roofs with broad overhangs. Surrounded by well-kept gardens and spacious lawns, some are connected with covered walkways. Unfortunately, additional structures dating from the mid-1960s reveal no continuity with the hospital's original architecture.

Despite its many mediocre additions, the Moderne exterior of **Harborview Hospital** (1931), formerly the King County Hospital, is still impressive with what Woodbridge and Montgomery call its "mountain-like mass" and "stylized craggy brick walls." Inside is the nation's premier burn treatment center and the region's foremost trauma unit. The former Marine Hospital (1932), now **Pacific Medical Center,** is another hilltop Seattle landmark. The complex of Zigzag Moderne buildings, employing a rich variety of patterns in brick and terra cotta, was designed by University of Washington architects Charles Bebb and Carl Gould. One of the first hospitals to use a high-rise form, the award-winning landmark commands a magnificent position within a campus-like setting atop Beacon Hill. The recent addition of a north wing was done in satisfying sympathy with the original style.

The University of Washington **Health Science and Medical Center,** designed by Naramore, Bain, Brady and Johanson, was

Above: Marine Hospital (now Pacific Medical Center), Seattle.

completed in stages between 1949 and 1972. The first stage of offices, classrooms, and laboratories included eight wings projecting from a center corridor, five stories high. This plan allowed maximum window space and the most direct lighting. Large vertical columns and the exterior walls bear all the building's weight, so that interior partitions may be easily shifted about. The second stage of the Modern-style complex was the 300-bed teaching and research hospital which received its first patient in May 1958. An eight-story addition to **University Hospital**, designed by the original architects, was finished in 1972.

JAILS AND PRISONS

The old blockhouse at Seatco in Thurston County that held the first territorial prisoners was so insecure that its inmates were chained night and day. The private contractors hired to supervise the felons were more concerned about the pay they also got for the inmates' labor than for their living conditions. These conditions helped convince the legislature to move the ninety-eight prisoners from Seatco to Walla Walla, which in 1886 had won the competition among Washington communities for the territorial-run prison. Most of the prisoners carted over the pass on May 1, 1887 had been convicted for rustling, robbery, arson, assault, second-degree murder, or like William Murphy, who wore convict number "1," manslaughter. The new prison walls were breached that summer when two inmates took advantage of Independence Day celebrations to escape. They were soon caught, however, and returned for an additional punishment of thirty days of bread and

Early-century views of prisons. Bottom left: Entrance to the Walla Walla State Penitentiary. Above and top: Views of McNeil Island Prison. Photos courtesy, U.W. Library, Special Collections.

water. Thereafter guards were stationed on top of the prison walls, and in 1888 the prison was outfitted with a jute mill plant for manufacturing grain sacks to keep the inmates working. After Washington became a state the following year, **Walla Walla State Penitentiary** became the state's maximum security institution. Its original brick administration building resembled a medieval fortress, a common style for late-Victorian prisons.

McNeil Island Prison opened as a U.S. Marshal's jail in 1875 on 27 acres of the island's 4,400 acres of forest. The original cell house, designed according to the then-favored Auburn Prison plan, had massive walls of brick and stone and 48 double cells. More cellhouses followed in 1911, 1921, and 1929. As the government gradually purchased the entire island, the prison became nearly self-sufficient with its own dairy, orchards, cannery, farm lands, and water system and resembled an industrial community more than a prison. During World War II some cells served as Navy barracks for newly trained sailors awaiting assignment.

With its campus of low-silhouette brick and concrete buildings surrounded by tall evergreens, the **Purdy Treatment Center**

Above left: Built by citizen subscription in 1898 as a strategy to beat back rivals hoping to replace Colville as the county seat, the Stevens County Court-house and Jail served side by side on Oak Street in Colville until both were razed and replaced in 1939 by a WPA-built courthouse, which is still being used today. Courtesy, Old Seattle Paperworks. Right: Martha Schwartz's Jail House Garden at the entrance to the otherwise undistinguished King County Correctional Facility in Seattle.

for Women (1971) resembles a community college. The structure of the buildings and their layout reflects the concept of "progressive freedom" implemented by the state's first correctional facility for women. One-story residential structures bordered by flowerbeds sit on a slope above the central complex. From the balconies of these apartments, the residents can look down on the intake unit, where they arrived, and up to the road along which they hope to someday, or year, depart.

Pioneer municipal jails were commonly reinforced shacks or log structures improvised with bars and locks. When communities reached a size requiring construction of a city hall, jail space would often be included in the back or the basement. The few dedicated jail houses were usually the least ornamented boxes that a community could tolerate. The original 6 x 12-foot **Colville Jail** was made

of handsawed timbers and stood across Main Street from the Stevens County Courthouse in the former Pinkney City, between the general store and the saloon. Colville's second jail, although larger, was only slightly more lavish. In 1888 a Whitman County judge declared the county's jail "unfit for any human being" and ordered the prisoners be transferred to nearby Walla Walla County. The modern **King County Correctional Facility** in downtown Seattle continues the austere tradition of jail architecture, except at its ground level plaza. There the county's "1% for Art" program has enlivened the jail's public entrance with Martha Schwartz's Jail House Garden. This gentle parody of a formal garden, where dark green ceramics substitute for shrubbery and dazzling tiled pathways lead to what seems, ironically, like an opening in the jail wall, is not open to inmates.

The main fire station in the Tacoma business district was a next door neighbor to the stately Tacoma Hotel (bottom right). Photo taken in 1894 by A.H. Waite from the tower of then new Tacoma City Hall. The Puyallup Indian School can be seen across the tideflats on the left, beside the Northern Pacific Railroad. Mount Tacoma (now known as Mount Rainier) surmounts the scene. Courtesy, U.W. Library, Special Collections.

Combined city halls and fire stations in 1. Lynden, 2. Dayton, 3. Marysville, 4. Elma, 5. Walla Walla Fire Station, ca. 1895. Courtesy, Penrose Library, Whitman College, Walla Walla.

Above: Spokane Station #3 photographed 1893. Courtesy, Thomas Heckler.
Below: Tacoma's Engine House #9. Courtesy, Tacoma Public Library.

FIRE STATIONS

Originally, fire fighting in America was a community obligation like jury duty or road work. But after the Civil War, when citizens grew dissatisfied with the volunteer system, city governments increasingly took control of the fire service and the fire station became a public building. As part of city government fire stations had to be functional and ceremonial, yet appear less important than a city hall or courthouse. (When attached to city hall their part was often subdued.) Because they served all sorts of districts and neighborhoods, fire stations required designs that fit in with the industrial, commercial, or residential character of the area surrounding them. Consequently, the diversity of community fire stations makes them one of the most inventive and often times even elegant of the public building genres.

Eighteen eighty-nine, the year for fires in a number of Washington communities — Spokane, Seattle, Ellensburg, Aberdeen, and Vancouver — revealed the woeful inadequacies of urban water systems and fire service. Following this destruction, cries for greater protection translated quickly into more stations and rigs. Seattle in its first year of reconstruction after the June 6 fire built four new stations. Except for **Firehouse No. 1**, a brick and stone edifice that doubled as department headquarters (razed for the I-5 freeway in 1963), all were fanciful clapboard and shingle structures with wooden detailing, distinctive towers, and second-floor balconies. Between 1890 and 1910 when the Seattle population rose from 43,000 to 237,000, the fire department kept apace with eighteen more stations.

More stations meant better response time and greater safety, but neighborhoods also had aesthetic concerns. In the teens and twenties "bungalow-type" fire stations, designed to look like houses, became popular because they helped appease disgruntled neighbors and needed only a single level to house both the engine room and the firemen's

living quarters. **Tacoma's Engine House No. 9** (ca. 1910) resembles a residence so closely that only its oversize doors and a small sign identify its function. A commercial style, generally used downtown, employed stone or brick fronts, heavy cornices, and round-arched windows and doors. Three extant examples of the many fire houses designed by Daniel. R. Huntington, architect for the City of Seattle from 1912 to 1921, are the large Bungalow-style **Wallingford Station No. 11** (1911-12) and the two commercial looking stations built in 1920 — **Station No. 2** at Fourth Avenue and Battery Street and **Station No. 7**. Designed exclusively for a motor apparatus, the latter facility was smaller than the horse-era station which preceded it at the Fifteenth Avenue E. and E. Harrison Street site. Station No. 7 and Wallingford Station No. 11 are good examples of how these comely and substantial landmarks have been preserved for conversion to other uses: shops, clinics, libraries, condominiums. With its stepped brick gables **Fire Station No. 18** in Ballard (1910-11), designed by Charles Bebb and Louis Mendel, suggests a German Rathaus. Until replaced by a modern structure nearby in 1975, Firehouse No. 18

Top: Seattle's old post-1889 "Great Fire" Fire Station #4 at the northeast corner of Fourth and Battery before the Denny Regrade razed it and lowered the intersection. Above: Fire Station #2 at the southeast corner of Fourth and Battery after the Denny Regrade.

was the oldest active station in Seattle.

Many firehouses built in the thirties and forties reflected the popular architectural styles of the time, yet with varying effect. **Fire Station No. 6** (1931) in Seattle's Central Area, with its zig-zag patterned transom, used variations of the ubiquitous Moderne or "streamlined" style that combined asymmetrical planes with horizontal lines and rounded corners, all meant to evoke images of mechanical power. **Renton's** WPA-funded Art Deco style **Station at Houser Way and Mill Avenue** (1940), now converted to a local museum, uses a simpler design emphasizing the utility of its solid construction. Since World War II the science and technology of fighting fires has considerably improved, while the civic status of most of the state's newer firehouses has not. They are generally among the least impressive public buildings in the community. Some notable exceptions are the Streamline Moderne Revival **firehouse on Bellevue Way S.E.** in Bellevue (1976) and the decorated concrete Brutalist-designed **Fire Station No. 1** (1970) in Yakima.

Top (this column): Yakima Fire Station #1. Courtesy, Yakima Fire Department. Above: Renton Historical Museum, formerly community fire station. Below left: Seattle's Fire Station #6. Below right: Bellevue Fire Station #1.

WORLD'S FAIRS

AYP, Century 21, and Expo '74.

Washington's first world's fair, the 1909 **Alaska Yukon Pacific Exposition** (AYP) on the University of Washington campus, repeated the basic design, themes, and architecture of its many predecessors including those at Portland (1905), St. Louis (1904), and most important, Chicago with the 1893 Columbia Exposition. Like the others, the AYP had its gleaming "white city" of grand but temporary structures built in the French Classical Renaissance style. In Seattle this imperial look celebrated the Klondike Gold Rush and Seattle's extensive influence in Alaskan affairs, and the city's anticipated development of trans-Pacific markets. The stately buildings and formal grounds were also intended to convince the rest of the country that Washington State was not part of the wild west and that Seattle, its principal city, was no longer a frontier town but a culturally sophisticated metropolis in which businessmen could confidently invest and new inhabitants could live safely and comfortably. The AYP's most important legacy for the university was not its grander buildings, of which only Architecture Hall (called the Fine Arts Building during the fair) survives, but a campus design based on that drawn for the fair by the Olmsted Brothers. The fair never attracted the new capital, residents, and trans-Pacific trade that promoters had hoped for, but it did strengthen Seattle's progressive urge to develop its parks and improve its streets, especially its boulevards. (See Streets Chapter.)

A half-century later the AYP served as the inspiration for another Seattle World's Fair — the 1962 **Century 21 Exposition**. Again the city was motivated to advertise itself and the region to bring in new business, and to demonstrate that Seattle was neither remote nor the "aesthetic dustbin" that English conductor Sir Thomas Beecham called it during his brief stint as conductor of the

Above: Balloon view of the Alaska Yukon Pacific Exposition's Artic Circle on the University of Washington campus, 1909. Left: Washington State Forestry Building at AYP. Photos courtesy, U.W. Library, Special Collections.

Seattle Symphony in 1941. Century 21 was also meant to boost the city's retail core to compete with the proliferating outlying shopping malls and subdivisions. Fair planners chose the somewhat dilapidated Civic Center neighborhood at the foot of Queen Anne Hill and just north of the Denny Regrade in part because a number of its buildings, including the Civic Auditorium and the Armory, could be remodeled for the exposition. They also hoped to draw the central business district northward into the Denny Regrade, a neighborhood that had resisted development ever since

Below: Senators Henry Jackson and Warren Magnuson (right) discuss Century 21 plans with the fair's early publicist James Faber (left). Left: Retouched aerial of 1962 Century 21 World's Fair, Seattle.

Left column: Pacific Science Center at Century 21 World's Fair. Photos by Ken Hodgeson. Courtesy, Seattle Center. Right column: Spokane's railroad center on Havermale Island and south bank of the Spokane River above the falls before and after its tranformation into Expo '74 site, bottom, the city's World's Fair. Courtesy, Spokane Public Library, Northwest Room.

Denny Hill had been leveled.

"America's Space Age World's Fair" attracted international attention and was one of the last world's fairs to be a financial success. However, planners did not achieve their downtown agenda. The development of the fairgrounds into a cultural center did not stimulate growth in the recalcitrant Denny Regrade. Nevertheless, the Seattle Center with the permanent buildings remaining after the fair — the Opera House, Exhibition Hall, Seattle Repertory Theater, Coliseum, and others — has become one of the Puget Sound region's most popular destinations and has substantially enriched Seattle cultural life with its spaces for the arts, recreation, and folk fairs.

Spokane was likewise forever changed with its sponsorship of **Expo '74.** The jumble of railroad tracks, deteriorating warehouses, taverns, and flophouses along the riverfront had long withstood redevelopment. When the City of Spokane acquired the land and demolished the railroad property to make way for the world's fair, it promised that once the six-month exposition was over, the 100-acre site would be transformed again into an urban park. Although the 1974 fair did not turn a profit, according to King F. Cole, Expo president, Spokane gained "about $500 million worth of improvements downtown at a cost to the city of not quite $6 million." Among them were the Spokane Opera House and Convention Center, built and operated by the state during the fair and turned over to the city in 1979. (See below.) The fair also bolstered the modernization of the downtown, boosted its retail trade, and greatly expanded the convention business.

Riverfront Park is, no doubt, the "environmental" fair's most popular legacy. Where once there were noisy trains and trucks, people now play and picnic on acres of gently sloping lawns, admiring the flowers, watching the river and one another. The former U.S. Pavilion, a huge modernistic structure, helps pay for the park's maintenance. In winter the pavilion houses an ice rink for pleasure skating, hockey and ice shows, and in summer it is converted into a children's zoo. Many Spokane residents believed that with Expo '74 the Lilac City took a vital turn toward the future.

Museums, Pavillions, Theaters, Stadiums

Seattle Art Museum (1932, 1991)

According to its designer, Pritzker-prize winning Robert Venturi, the **Seattle Art Museum** (SAM) is a simple angular building or "decorated shed" that saved most of its ornamentation for the interior. The postmodern character of the limestone museum (1991) which incorporates references to pre-Modern styles and popular cultural imagery, can be seen in the Art Deco-design strip of the facade. The monumental staircase that ascends along the windowed south wall echoes the University Street hillside. Outside the entrance, the forty-eight-foot high steel and aluminum, black slab sculpture "Hammering Man" silently moves his motorized arm up and down four times per minute. (Detractors

The Washington State Museum and beyond it the federal offices and courtrooms housed in the restored Northern Pacific Depot facing Tacoma's Pacific Avenue. Below right: Cheney Cowles Museum.

Below: The old Seattle Art Museum, now the Seattle Asian Art Museum, in Volunteer Park. Bottom left: The new Seattle Art Museum and the monumental "Hammering Man" sculpture towering above the main entrance to the museum are the centerpiece of a three-block-long hill climb along University Street that begins near the waterfront with Harbor Steps (bottom) and concludes with the Washington State Memorial Garden and the Seattle Symphony's Benaroya Hall (center-right) between Second and Third Avenue. First Avenue is in the foreground.

see the Hammering Man hitting his own hand.) SAM's original museum in Volunteer Park (1932) was also an Art Deco creation, designed by Carl F. Gould and paid for and donated to the city by Richard Fuller, president of the Art Institute of Seattle.

Washington State Museum (1995-96)

Architect Bruno B. Freschi, adviser to the Washington State Historical Society in their search for a design for their new museum in Tacoma, described the process of choosing the architect as "the most important architectural competition in the state since the 1911 competition for the capitol group in Olympia." The new museum's relationship to its next-door neighbor, the landmark Union Depot facing Pacific Street, was a major consideration. In the words of the jury, the museum designed by Charles W. Moore and Arthur W. Andersson, winners of the competition, "sensitively displays respect for Union Station through the strong rhythm of arches and vaults executed in substantial, complementary materials. The lofty vaulting, in the long tradition of railroad structures, creates an implied extension of the station without diminishing its presence."

Cheney Cowles Museum (1924, 1960)

Kirkland Kelsey Cutter was once the architect of choice for Spokane Brahmins in the early twentieth century. Among Cutter's big homes in the "Browne's Addition," the A. B. Campbell mansion stood out in its stucco and timber Elizabethan style. Bequeathed to the Eastern Washington Historical Society in 1924, the house was for years the home of the Cheney Cowles Museum. Now the Campbell home has been restored and is open to tours. Adjacent to the mansion the historical society operates a modern museum that holds many of the items once displayed in the mansion, as well as the society's library and extensive archives.

Above left: Washington State Convention and Trade Center in downtown Seattle. Above right: Spokane Opera House, Convention Center and Floating Stage beyond the Washington Street Bridge. Photo by Alan Bisson. Courtesy, Spokane Convention and Visitors Bureau.

Washington State Convention and Trade Center (1988)

The six-level, glass-and-concrete Washington State Convention and Trade Center, which encloses several columnless and football-field-sized meeting rooms, also performs functions other than those described in its name. Like Freeway Park to which it is connected, the center takes up the unused "air space" over nine lanes of I-5 freeway and two city streets. The Convention Center has also helped revitalize the area around it, although at this writing plans for its expansion include a grand new entrance with an arched covering of Pike Street and the destruction of the landmark Waldorf Tower Apartments.

Above: Seattle Repertory's new Leo Kreielsheimer Theatre. Photo by Patrick Benett. Courtesy, Seattle Repertory Theatre.

Bagley Wright Theater (1983)

Rather than a premier piece of architecture, the Bagley Wright Theater at the Seattle Center, initially became a premier piece of capital construction litigation. Soon after it opened the light steel-framed and stucco building, which had already risen in cost to several times the original estimate, developed cracked walls and a leaky roof that caused considerable interior damage. After repairs were made and the suits settled in 1988 and 1989, the Streamline Moderne-style building with its exaggerated horizontal painted joints was finally able to escape the controversies and become simply the outstanding home of the Seattle Repertory Theater. The Rep's new **Leo Kreielsheimer Theatre** was added in 1996 with a new south wing.

Spokane Riverpark Center Opera House (1974)

The principal architectural legacy of Expo '74, the former Washington State Pavilion, overlooking the Spokane River, was converted by the city into an exhibition hall and opera house theater, seating 2,700. Made of concrete and dark glass, the building's profile angles upward from the auditorium to the stagehouse on the west. Steps down to the river serve as seating for outdoor summer concerts.

Above: Makah Museum at Neah Bay. Photo by Arlene Wade. Below: View east across 15th Avenue NE to the Henry Art Gallery with recent Fay Allen addition (right foreground); remodeled Meany Theatre (center-right); Odegaard Undergraduate Library (center-left); and front of Suzzallo Library, in distance across Red Square.

Neah Bay Makah Museum

Situated at the eastern end of the Neah Bay community, the Makah museum is a functional fire-proof structure designed by

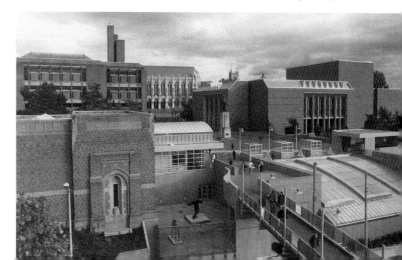

Spokane Veterans Memorial Arena. Photo by Thomas Heckler.

Fred Bassetti to display the mostly wooden artifacts of the Makah tribe. Inside visitors find a number of large scale dioramas with photomural backdrops, and part of a longhouse in which drying salmon releases an aromatic introduction to the exhibit. The museum houses an assortment of artifacts and implements, at least 500 hundred years old, discovered at the Ozette village on the Pacific Coast. The work of the Makah Cultural and Research Center is a continuing process of discovery, interpretation, and preservation of the region's ancient heritage.

U. W. Husky Stadium (1920, 1951, 1987)

The basic horseshoe bleachers of the University of Washington Stadium were completed in 1920 in time for the football game with Dartmouth College. The Huskies lost 28 to 7. The south side of the stadium was considerably enlarged in 1951 when a covered second deck, featuring a cantilevered roof with a 145-foot span, was constructed. The most striking design element of this addition was its pedestrian access up two monumental spiral ramps of reinforced concrete. In January 1987 new north stands with a similar cantilevered roof were built — twice. When the steel framework for three of the stand's nine sections was nearly complete, it fell into a twisted wreck. To the university's embar-

rassment, one of Seattle's more attentive architectural photographers, John Stamets, happened to be cycling on the Burke Gilman trail and recorded the collapse. The fall did not prevent—barely—the university from having its enlarged Husky Stadium ready for the September fifth game with Stanford University. The city permit to use the new stands was awarded at four o'clock in the afternoon of the day before the game which, this time, the Huskies won 31 to 21.

ACT–A Contemporary Theatre (1997)

The conversion of Seattle's Eagles Auditorium at Seventh Avenue and Union Street into the new home for A Contemporary Theatre not only saved a terra cotta landmark, but created one of the country's unique theater spaces.

ACT's new $30.4 million Allen Theater, 1997, formerly the Grand Ballroom for the Fraternal Order of Eagles, is one of the country's unique theater venues with three separate stages. Photo by Chris Benion.

Spokane Veterans Memorial Arena

The Spokane Arena was built in 1996 on the site of the city's old post–World War II coliseum just north of the central business district and the Spokane River.

Below: Husky Stadium on opening day, Nov. 27, 1920. Bottom: An embarrassment for its builder, the Feb. 25, 1987 collapse of the first sections of Husky Stadium's new north stands was a serendipitous opportunity for photographer John Stamets, who was happening by on the adjacent Burke Gilman Trail.

Seattle Center Key Arena

Seattle Center Key Arena— (1962, 1995)

City officials discovered that they could keep the Seattle Super Sonics at home and avoid the high cost of a new sports arena by recycling the 1962 Seattle Center Coliseum. By lowering the court's elevation, the new Coliseum, or "Key Arena," retains its original roof line and seats more than 17,000 in a high-tech pit. Although the old World's Fair structure did not require additional tax dollars for its revival, it did acquire a new name from the bank that directed the most cash towards its enlargement.

This artist's rendering of a new open-air Seattle Mariners stadium was drawn before the 1997 statewide vote directed the Kingdome's destruction for the construction of a new open-air Seahawks stadium on Seattle's reclaimed tideflats. The combined football/soccer/convention facilities are projected for completion in 2002. A portion of the fated Kingdome is included here upper-right. Bottom: Tacoma Dome, 1997.

Kingdome (1976)

Considering its size the Kingdome gets little attention, aside from reports of its foibles and travails. Designed by Naramore, Bain, Brady, and Johanson, this enormous concrete structure, which holds up to 72,000, has been called the "Orange Squeezer," "King-Dumb," and other names that convey its appearance as well as its unfortunate history of maintenance problems. Two public votes added to these travails. First in 1996 the region's baseball

Poster for a big show at the Tacoma Stadium, early July 1910. Courtesy, Tacoma Public Utilities.

team, the Mariners, won an election for the public construction of a new open-air baseball stadium to the south of the Kingdome. A year later, Seattle's "other billionaire" (other than Bill Gates) Paul Allen ran a statewide campaign and won a second stadium election against relatively impoverished Kingdome proponents. The "yes" vote also meant that Allen finalized his purchase of the region's National Football League team, the Seahawks. This second open-air stadium, which requires the demolition of the Kingdome, is scheduled to be completed in 2002.

Stadium at Stadium High, Tacoma (1909)

When the Stadium High School stadium, built on the site of an overgrown ravine descending to Commencement Bay, was dedicated on June 10, 1910, its concrete horseshoe of terraced seats surrounding the field was described as "a poem in masonry." The stadium, fronting the "Brown Castle" high school on the hill, became the city's entertainment center, featuring football, baseball, fireworks displays, balloon ascensions, Wild West shows, military demonstrations, even opera stars.

Tacoma Dome (1983)

Although considerably smaller than Seattle's domed stadium at 530 feet in diameter and 152 feet tall, the Tacoma Dome is widely considered a more satisfying structure. The 28,000-capacity auditorium was painted to blend harmoniously with the horizon, and, fittingly for Tacoma, uses wood frame construction. In fact, at the time of its completion it was the largest wooden dome structure in the world. Unlike the Queen City's, the roof of this dome has neither leaked nor have parts of it fallen down, although at one of its first concerts it was temporarily set afire by a rock n' roll fan with a flare gun.

Martin Stadium, Pullman (1936)

Cost-conscious Washington State College officials chose a site for their athletic stadium that would do part of the work for them. The seating was made to conform to the natural contours of the rolling Palouse which at the construction site sloped down toward the athletic field.

Bainbridge Island High School Stadium. Photo by Art Grice. Courtesy, Bainbridge Island Historical Society.

Bainbridge Island High School Stadium and Grandstand (1951)

The timber-and-corrugated aluminum grandstand, built by the students of Bainbridge High School under the direction of their manual arts instructor, David H. Morley, is believed to be the largest public school student-built project in the nation. Constructed with hand tools only, the project was completed between 1947 and 1951 and dedicated to the sixteen island men who died during World War II.

SCHOOLS: HIGHER EDUCATION

University of Washington

Built in 1861 at the edge of the woods on a donated knoll overlooking Seattle (population about 200) and Elliott Bay, the Territorial University in its main two-story hall with Classical Revival detail and bell tower marked the beginning of the future state's largest institution. The "new campus" north of Portage and Union bays to which the university moved in 1895 today possesses Washington's greatest store of architectural landmarks. The more than 200 permanent buildings include the 1895 **Denny Hall**, which as the first building on the new campus enclosed practically every school function: offices, classrooms, library, bookstore,

Top: Denny Hall, first structure on the "new campus" of the University of Washington north of Portage Bay, Lake Union. Courtesy, Old Seattle Paperworks. Above: The old territorial university bell in its second belfry, the Denny Hall cupola. Left: U.W. at its old campus in Seattle's central business district, ca. 1893.

Above: U.W. buildings in 1912, including many "temporary structures" surviving from the 1909 Alaska Yukon Pacific Exposition. Photo by L.G. Linkletter. Courtesy, U.W. Library, Special Collections. Below: Panorama of a portion of "Red Square" in 1997. Structures (left to right) Meany Auditorium, Odegaard Library, exhaust campanile towers (from underground parking), Kane Hall, and Suzzallo Library.

museum, laboratories, and an auditorium seating over 700. Happily, the three-story French Renaissance structure survived a 1950s effort by a minority of the Board of Regents to replace it with a modern hall. A recent cleaning of the exterior returned the reflective sparkle of the light-colored sandstone and pressed brick trimmed with terra cotta. The bell in its central cupola is the same 400-pound clapper which pealed from the bell tower at the old campus. It is still rung each homecoming day by Brewster Denny, a university emeritus professor and descendent of the building's namesake, Arthur Denny.

Denny Hall stands near the top and north end of the campus. The buildings constructed after it were sited according to several different campus plans. Most important of these was the Olmsted firm's intersecting axis designed for and refined after the 1909 Alaska Yukon and Pacific Exposition held on the campus (see above). The science quadrangle was constructed in line with the axis of the fair's Rainier Vista and the academic buildings were built along the other. The two axes meet and cross in the central plaza or "Red Square," where acres of brick are surrounded by the Suzzallo and Odegaard libraries, the Meany and Kane performance halls, and the Administration Building. The formalist austerity of **Kane Hall** and the campanile towers, which vent the garage built beneath the plaza, make the Gothic stone detailing of **Suzzallo Library** and

the Administration Building seem playful. Built in 1949, the **Administration Building**, recently renamed in honor of the university's longtime president William P. Gerberding, was the last of the campus' many Gothic structures.

The English collegiate Gothic style is especially coherent in the classroom buildings which surround the **Academic or Liberal arts Quadrangle**. Besides its obvious association with medieval university sources, university architects Bebb and Gould chose the style because of its adaptability to concrete and steel framing that allows high, wide windows. **Raitt Hall** (1916), the home economics building, was the first of the four liberal arts buildings to be completed. The terra cotta finishing around the cornice with figures of women performing domestic tasks illustrated the building's original use. **Savery Hall** (1920) was also trimmed in terra cotta figures, although not confined to the subject matter of the building, and its variously colored and patterned brick walls varied from Raitt Hall's. Across the broad brick walkway from Raitt Hall, **Miller Hall** was added in 1921; and across from Savery, **Smith Hall** was built in 1935. In 1950 the Gothic quad was completed by Spokane architect Harold Whitehouse's **Music and Art buildings**.

From its original configuration the university campus has developed a number of adjacent campuses including the medical science buildings of the South Campus and the athletic facilities of the East Campus. Most of the dormitories are set in the northeast corner of the original acres. But others are sited along Campus Parkway, west of Fifteenth Avenue NE, where the buildings are distinctly modern

University of Washington. Above (left to right): Condon Hall; Aerial of U.W. liberal arts quadrangle and a portion of "Red Square" below it. Courtesy, U.W. Public Relations; Physics-Astronomy Building.

and include the Law School's award-winning **Condon Hall** (1974). Its candid but inventive use of concrete as the principal building material is an unusually elegant example of Brutalist design.

Concrete is the exception on this campus, however. Since cleared and graded for the AYP, the campus grounds have been lavishly landscaped and provide a green backdrop for the warm colors of the campus "skin" — the brick which is the principal component of the built campus, whether Gothic, Romanesque, Neo-Classical, or Modern style. A recent addition to this brick élan is the **Physics/Astronomy Building** (1994), a six-story office and library tower with four-story wing for labs, auditoria, and offices, and a basement that comprises a third of the entire working space. Besides the architectural continuity of the brick, the structure's reflecting copper roof represents a victory of postmodern contextualism. Details on the exterior walls announce the building's functions. On the south wall facing Pacific Street, architects Cesar Pelli and Naramore, Bain, Brady, and Johanson installed a huge sundial of green tubing, designed by UW astronomy professor Woodruff Sullivan. Around the tower at eye level are thirty formulae and diagrams blasted into the cast stone. Inside the glass dome of the auditorium wing is a Foucault pendulum that demonstrates the earth's rotation.

Washington State University

Among the first issues for the new Washington state legislature to settle was the location of its agricultural college. The small town of Pullman, promoting its artesian waters and itself as "the center of the garden spot of the state," offered the state 160 acres. With a population of only 350, Pullman would have been an unlikely candidate were it not for its persistent lobbying and the fact that two of its principal competitors had previously received significant state patronage — the mental hospital for Spokane County at Medical Lake and the penitentiary for Walla Walla. Pullman residents also made the most of their numbers by crowding the town streets with every available citizen during the visit of the college siting commission. Soon after the Pullman choice was announced another competitor, the nearby Whitman County seat of Colfax, sent the county sheriff to Pullman with a restraining order. Alerted, the college's board of regents hastily approved a sketch of a building and arranged for a contractor to submit a bid. The fait accompli worked.

Washington State University. Above: Stevens Hall. Below: Adminstration Building (Thompson Hall). Courtesy, U.W. Library, Special Collections.

Later the board ambitiously adopted more formal plans for a huge castle-like structure, the estimated $300,000 price of which far surpassed the legislature's $60,000 biennial appropriation for all campus buildings and their maintenance.

The first students of the **Washington Agricultural College and School of Science** were greeted in January 1892 by a modest structure set on the treeless summit of the campus. The original class of sixteen called these less than grand quarters the "crib," for the building was regularly rocked by the sweeping Palouse winds. The winds also worried Enoch Bryan, college president, who

Washington State University. Above left: Bryan Hall. Above right: Fine Arts Building. Courtesy, W.S.U. News and Information Services, Pullman.

doubted the capacity of **Ferry Hall**, the campus' second structure completed that summer, to withstand the blasts that blew across the unprotected Palouse. As it turned out it was not wind but fire that in 1897 put an end to the five-story dormitory, described by Bryan as "ungainly." A year earlier there were, besides Ferry Hall, five major buildings on the campus, and two of these, the turreted brick and granite **Administration Building (now Thompson Hall)** and **Stevens Hall**, survive.

A sudden burst of campus construction occurred in 1908 when **Bryan Hall**, used for an assembly hall and library, **Van Doren Hall** for home economics, and **College Hall** for "recitation" classrooms were all built of brick. The school's original dedication to agricultural and science was ultimately rewarding and much of this support was federal. By the time the college became Washington State University in 1959, its campus had matured with scores of structures and a covering of trees and bushes that transformed its hill into a kind of Central Park for the Palouse. WSU's more notable modern campus landmarks include the Moderne-style **Regents Hill Dormitory** (1952) designed by Paul Thiry, who contributed regularly to the design of state college campuses in the postwar period; and the concrete **Physical Sciences Building** (1973) and the **Fine Arts Center**, both Brutalist-Formalist designs by Naramore, Bain, Brady, and Johanson. One of the largest projects of the state arts commission's Art in Public Places program involved the work of artists George Traka of New York and Catherine Howett of Georgia at the **Glenn Terrell Friendship Mall**. The work, which began in 1988 and was completed six years later, redesigned the campus core — its walkway, lighting, seating, terraces, and building facades.

As part of Washington State's Enabling Act of 1889, the

Above: Circa 1910 view of a young Washington State College campus topped by the brick tower of Bryan Hall and the smokestack for the school's heating plant. Courtesy Old Seattle Paperworks. Right: The campus in mid-1990s. Courtesy Pullman Chamber of Commerce.

372

federal government provided a land grant of 600,000 acres for the erection and maintenance of public schools of higher learning. The University of Washington received 200,000 acres. A one-sixth share of 100,000 acres was directed to the state agricultural college in Pullman and to each of the state's three normal schools or teachers' colleges. As with the siting of other state institutions, the normal schools became the object of competition among communities across the state, and Ellensburg, Cheney, and Bellingham were the eventual winners.

Old Main at Western Washington University in Bellingham. Courtesy, U.W. Library, Special Collections.

Central Washington University, Barge Hall. Courtesy, Michael Fairley.

Central Washington University

Enjoying a boom economy in the late 1880s, Ellensburg boosters were initially more interested in running for state capital or in becoming the "Pittsburgh of the West" than in acquiring a state normal school. Almost unnoticed, their state senator convinced the legislature to approve the Ellensburg Normal School, however, initially without funding. For its first three years the school occupied the second story of the new Ellensburg public school building. The hard times and unemployment that followed the 1893 market panic were intimated a year earlier in many rural communities, including Ellensburg. Then the advantages of possessing a normal school, especially the building funds that came with it, appeared more attractive. The Washington State Normal School, now **Barge Hall** (1894), was designed by a local architect in a high Victorian style with a basalt stone basement, brick walls with white sandstone trim, and an imposing stone tower. Over the winter of 1893-94 in snow and temperatures that hovered at zero, workmen labored on the 152 x 20-foot, three-story building, and completed it at just $3.31 under the $60,000 appropriated.

Western Washington University

Old Main (1896), the all-purpose administration building on the future Western Washington University campus, was designed by the prominent Seattle firm of Skillings and Corner and patterned after the Italian Palazzo-styled Boston Public Library. The board of trustee's architectural choice was a disappointment to many, for the elaborately florid and ornamental High Victorian style was more popular at the time. One disgruntled architect used the wall of the local post office to display his ornate design and captioned it, "This is what you might have had." Alongside he posted a newspaper clipping with the accepted plan and labeled it, "but this is what you get." The latter was a five-story building of pressed red brick with belt courses, buttress caps and trim of sandstone quarried from near the site, topped by a hipped roof.

Old Main survives but stands apart from the central campus quadrangle. "Red Square" is a mid-1960s creation of architect George Bartholick featuring a brick paved square surrounded by mostly contemporary brick structures and featuring a fountain and large sculpture, *Skyview*, by Isamu Noguchi. WWSU's **Ridgeway Dormitory** complex is an award-winning synthesis of landscape design by Richard Haag Associates that imaginatively exploits the often steep hillside site and tasteful architecture by Fred Bassetti and Company. Both Haag and Bassetti have many Northwest credits in school and school grounds design.

The liberal arts **Fairhaven College**, which opened in 1968 and features independent study and experimental teaching and curriculum, is a "cluster college" designed for future growth. It has a village style campus, and shares some services with its neighbor, Western Washington University.

Entrance to Eastern Washington University in Cheney. Courtesy, John Cooper.

Eastern Washington University

The town of Cheney lost in its race with Spokane to become the capital of the Inland Empire, but it won Eastern Washington's normal school. During the 1890s Cheney citizens donated both land and a building, and the faculty agreed to work without pay until the legislature made the necessary appropriations. **Showalter Hall** (1915), with its Classical styling in buff brick and ivory terra cotta trim, was Cheney Normal School's second administration building. (The first was destroyed by fire in 1912 nearly taking with it two faculty members asleep in the tower's music room — sixty feet up and too high for a ladder. Firemen confiscated a carpet from a house nearby and used it half effectively as a life net; both men were seriously injured.) Like Barge Hall, Showalter is a good example of the early college buildings which accommodated virtually all school functions. As in Bellingham such buildings were often named Old Main.

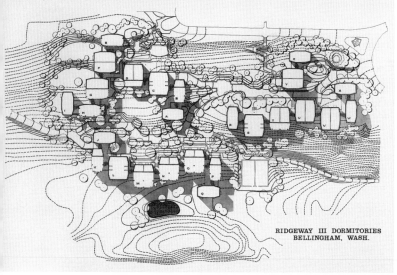

Top left: Detail of Fred Bassetti and Company plan and Richard Haag Associates' contoured plan for landscaping and structures at Western Washington University's Ridgeway III Dormitories. Courtesy, Richard Haag. Above left: Detail of Ridgeway Dormitories. Top right: View to the south over Western Washington University's Red Square towards Huxley College. Courtesy Western Washington University Public Information Office. Above right: Evergreen State College Laboratory Building. Courtesy, Evergreen College Campus Planning.

Evergreen State College

When it opened in 1971 **Evergreen State College** in Olympia was the first new four-year public school of higher education founded in Washington in the twentieth century, and, perhaps, the last. Incorporating a variety of innovative urban design and landscape ideas, the college is the work of a number of different architects and planners. To protect the natural flora and topography of the site, campus planners banned cars from the central core. Concrete-framed buildings grouped around a mall and adjacent landscaped areas are tied together by patterned brick pavements.

Reflecting the school's interdisciplinary curriculum, the modernistic **Laboratory Building** addition contains spaces ranging from greenhouses to ceramic studios, from self-paced learning centers to areas for nuclear magnetic resonance spectrophotometers, as well as batik and silk screen laboratories.

The **Arts, Music, and Drama Complex of Columbia Basin Community College** (1977) has been called one of the most imaginative buildings in the country. This Brutalist box is nearly as self-reflective as a piece of monumental minimalist sculpture. However, the austerity of these blocks of nearly windowless concrete is deceptive. As Woodbridge and Montgomery explain in *A Guide to Architecture*, the building has been "cut into and pulled apart to create a complex interior circulation pattern with small courts at the ground level and open bridges connecting upper floors." At night the exterior walls can come alive with images cast from projectors in turrets placed in the berms.

Above: Main building at Fairhaven College, Bellingham. Courtesy Western Washington University. Right: Details of the Arts, Music and Drama Complex at Columbia Basin College. Courtesy, Columbia Basin College.

374

Above: Flag drill at Novelty School in King County in 1909. Photo by Edwin Pierson. Courtesy, U.W. Library, Special Collections. Right: Board and batten pioneer school at Napavine. Bottom: Abandoned school in the Big Bend. Photo by Hugh Paradise.

PRIMARY AND SECONDARY SCHOOLS

In the nineteenth century and earlier, school was often held in homes, stores, saloons or tents. The teachers were ordinarily volunteer parents. Or if compensated, the generally female instructors lived and boarded with students' families as the greater part of their pay. The first departure from these informal arrangements in Washington came in 1850 when Lewis County collected $918.35 to help build at **Monticello** (Longview) the first public school north of the Columbia River. This was money assessed from property taxes authorized in a bill passed the previous year by the Oregon Territorial Legislature. The schoolhouse which the settlers built during the winter of 1850-51 is described by Angie Bowden in her *Early Schools of Washington Territory* as "constructed along the lines of architecture then in vogue — a square pen something like an Illinois corn crib of Pioneer days — log walls, roof of four-foot shakes, puncheon floors, mud and stick fire-place and chimney, and benches without backs made of split logs." That winter a schoolhouse built by Olympians the previous fall caved in under heavy snow. The Monticello school was sturdier but equally primitive, and the innovative schoolhouse that replaced it only a few years later featured a floor built on an incline so that the teacher could monitor students in the back seats. The board-and-batten **Napavine Primary** and **Hubbard School** near Colfax are two other examples of how austere these early structures could be. As a clear sign of its progress, the Lewis County lumber town of **Yacolt** made a point of comparing its primitive pioneer school with the towered frame box that replaced it in a postcard.

Above: The elementary school (inset) is the landmark featured in this late 1880s birdseye sketch of Pullman before it was chosen for the site of the state agricultural college in 1890. Pullman's primary school is repeated in the photo above right. Courtesy, U.W. Libraries, Special Collections.

This column. Top: Hubbard School north of Colfax. Courtesy, U.W. Library, Special Colllections. Middle: Primary school in Omak. Courtesy, Michael Maslan. Above: Central School in Port Angeles. Courtesy, Dan Kerlee.

For most Washington school districts the single-room school house was the norm well into the twentieth century. As late as 1947 Spokane County still had ten one-room schools within twenty minutes of the city center. In a situation where all classes were grouped together, students' ages might range from five to twenty-five, with the older students often of necessity used as teacher's aides. In the beginning, school terms rarely ran longer than three or four months in a year. Some teachers moved from district to district hoping to stay employed and also worked as janitors and domestic caretakers. In Douglas County, school teachers were prohibited from loitering in ice cream parlors, dressing in bright colors, staying out after 8:00 p.m., or having any contact whatsoever with men other than their fathers or brothers.

Especially for rural districts, the schoolhouse was easily the most important structure on the landscape. The school often doubled as a public building and community center. There one might attend political debates, socials, court, fraternal meetings, church, spelling bees, weddings, even funerals. And one would almost certainly vote there. As Washington grew, so did its schools and school districts. In the four years between 1872 and 1878, generally years of economic depression, the number of schools in Washington Territory more than doubled, from 144 to 326. When a district became too crowded it usually split and built a second school rather than add a second classroom to its first structure. Dividing districts allowed students to be instructed closer to home.

School overcrowding became commonplace in the larger communities as early as the 1870s. Within a few years after its construction in 1866 the two-room frame school built in Walla Walla for 100 children had to rotate groups of students between the classrooms and the playground. Seattle's first tax-supported public school, **Central School**, built at Madison Street and Third Avenue in 1870, originally had two large rooms in two stories. Later a third-story attic was built, requiring students sitting near

Below: New and old early-century schools at Yacolt. Courtesy, Dan Kerlee.

Top: Newport High School. Above: Cle Elum High School. Courtesy, Michael Maslan.

the rafters to stoop during their recitations. In 1881 the legislature stimulated the building of larger schoolhouses with a law that required the uniting of all school districts within incorporated towns of over 300 population. The law also established the primary system of eight grades. The state requirements meant local communities would have to plan and pay by levy for the professional construction of multi-room schools.

Both Walla Walla and Seattle opened grand schoolhouses in 1883. The Walla Walla **Baker School** was the first brick school in the territory, and Seattle's new Central School was the largest, dominating the city skyline until it was destroyed by fire in 1888.

Top: Seattle's Central School on the horizon and Providence Hospital at mid-ground. Photo taken by Charles Morford from the Territorial University, 1887. Courtesy, Kurt Jackson. Above: Baker School in Walla Walla. Courtesy, Dan Kerlee. Bottom left: Tacoma Central School. Courtesy, Tacoma Public Library.

Spokane and **Tacoma** also dedicated their first multiroom central schools in 1883. Tacoma's was much the larger and its twelve rooms were quickly filled to capacity with 425 scholars. Still, by 1889, the year of statehood, only 49 of the 1,044 schools in Washington were yet graded. The proliferation of rural schools where all levels were taught together was finally reversed only by twentieth-century forces — especially the school bus, which made it possible to transport students beyond the proverbial two- or five-mile walking distance.

What was probably Washington's first high school opened in **Dayton** in 1881, not in its own building but on the top floor of a grade school. Separate high schools did not become commonplace until the twentieth century. **Seattle High School** (Broadway High), Seattle's first dedicated secondary school, opened in 1902. The further division of grades into junior high schools did not begin until the 1920s.

Architecturally, the one- or two-room schoolhouse could become a thing of beauty in the hands of skilled carpenters working from pattern books or using the opportunities represented by a bell tower, a porch, or anteroom for improvising

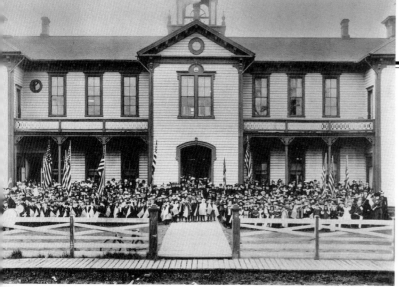

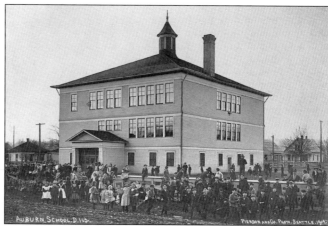

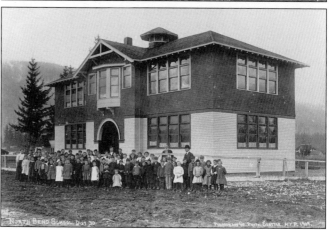

Above: Dayton School. Courtesy, Columbia County Historical Society. Below and bottom: Portraits by Edwin Pierson of King County school and scholars at Houghton (now Kirkland), and Vashon in 1909. Courtesy, U.W. Library, Special Collections.

variations in both mass and ornament. Photographer Edwin Pierson's 1909 record of all **King County schools** outside of Seattle is a luxuriant revelation of this creative carpentry. Especially with the increase in state settlement that followed the arrival of the railroads in the 1880s and 1890s, the sudden proliferation of school districts meant greater opportunities for school designs. As the frame structures grew, projecting pavilions, balconies, ornate fish scale shingles, multigabled roofs, and landmark bell towers became the woodworkers' last and best creations before the masons took over. **Winlock**, **Burlington**, **Tumwater**, **Centralia**, **Chehalis**, **Vancouver**, **Sumner**, and **Bellingham** all built traditional wood schoolhouses, many of them ornate, with impressive towers and asymmetrical massing. In Seattle, official school architect James Stephens created a simpler — but still huge — wooden schoolhouse in which a Colonial Revival model was used

King County Schools, 1909. Top to bottom: Auburn, North Bend, Veasie, and Juanita. Photos by Edwin Pierson. Courtesy, U.W. Library, Special Collections.

King County Schools, 1909. Top to bottom (this column): Tolt, Redmond, Skykomish, and Bellevue. Photos by Edwin Pierson. Courtesy, U.W. Libraries, Special Collections.

Above: Stanwood School. Courtesy Dan Kerlee. Below: Burlington School. Bottom: Maple School in Georgetown (now Seattle). Courtesy, Loomis Miller.

several times with variations in the first years of the twentieth century. Many of Stephens' schools survive — **Seward**, **Latona**, **Frantz Coe**, **John B. Allen** — and one, Interlake, was saved for conversion into the popular **Wallingford Center**: a combination of second-story, high-ceiling condominiums above main floor and basement retail shops.

Although the material of choice for school houses in the quarter century between statehood and World War I was generally wood, there were many exceptions of both material and style. A fair number of Victorian Gothic and Victorian Romanesque structures were raised. Like the Central School built in Seattle on

Above left: Lincoln School, Walla Walla. Above right: Aberdeen's Central School under construction, 1892. Courtesy, Jones Photo Company. Right: Seattle's Central School at Sixth and Madison, ca. 1900. Below right: Secondary School, Pullman.

the same site as its frame predecessor destroyed by fire in 1888, these vaguely medieval schoolhouses featured multicolored brick work and massive towers. **Spokane High School** was another of these scholastic monuments, and the central tower of **Walla Walla's Lincoln School** impressed more than one teenager of the inassailable virtues of a secondary education. **Tekoa**, **Centralia**, **Granger**, **Snoqualmie**, **Lynden**, **Sedro Woolley**, **Dayton**, **Anacortes**, **Pasco**, **Ellensburg**, **Garfield**, **Everett**; all built landmark brick schools often with impressive central towers.

James Stephens, Seattle's official school architect, had his hand in the design of over fifty schools during the city's great early-century population boom. Interlake School, above, was typical of his classic box model. Constructed in 1904, Interlake was adapted in 1982 for the mixed residential and retail use of Wallingford Center. Right: Ronald W. Petty's sculpture "Animal Storm" marks the corner of 45th Street and Wallingford Avenue North. Historical photo by Asahel Curtis.

Many public schools built in these years were fanciful, and one was also almost beyond dreams — **Stadium High School** in Tacoma. Begun as a hotel-castle by the Northern Pacific, construction was stopped by the market panic of 1893. After the structure later burned to its shell, the Tacoma School Board revived the ruins in 1903. With its steeply pitched roofs, towers, and tall chimneys, the Chateau-style Stadium High cuts a spectacular figure above its namesake hillside stadium. While Stadium High soared, Seattle's **Broadway High School** sat — a Richardsonian Romanesque mass of gray stone. Only the entrance

Spokane South Central High School. Destroyed by fire in 1910 and replaced by Lewis and Clark High School.

New $40,000 School Building Wilkeson, Wash.
Erected by Dolph Jones, Contractor & Builder. 1913

Top (from left): Brick schools in Ellensburg, Anacortes, and Dayton. Above: Wilkeson stone school. Below: Lynden High School, 1914.

Above: Pasco High School. Bottom (from left): Union High School in Burlington; Elma High School; Irene S. Reed High School in Shelton.

facade of Broadway High survives. When most of the school was razed in the early 1970s for the construction of the Seattle Central Community College campus, the stone arch was dismantled and used to frame the front entrance to the old high school's only surviving wing, its Renaissance Revival performance hall.

Lewis and Clark High School in Spokane was an early example of how great a high school might become. Plans for the new school were made while the ruins of its predecessor, South Central High, were still cooling after its 1910 fire. (See previous

page.) The formidable Tudor Gothic structure was built so rapidly that its cornerstone was laid in backwards, hiding the engraved quotation of Theodore Roosevelt. After sharing North Central since the beginning of the fall school term, the school's 2,300 students returned to the South Hill site at Fifth and Howard for the April 8, 1911 dedication. Following World War I, Eatonville, Enumclaw, Cheney, Colfax, Everett, Kirkland, Tonasket, Shelton, Port Angeles, Mount Vernon, Burlington, and Sunnyside were a few of the Washington communities that built brick high schools big enough to include large study halls and auditoriums capable of seating the entire student body. Many would also need parking lots for the school buses delivering students from distant communities.

After the war, busing rapidly consolidated school districts. The name of Mount Vernon's **Union High School** refers directly to this merger. For the 1921 opening the town shut down for a mass parade to the Union High front steps. Seventy years later when its time capsule was opened for the rededication of the modernized school, "Old Main," as it was called, was still intact. It was not, however, the largest structure on a campus which had swelled to nine buildings. By 1933, 67,500 students were being bused statewide, and by the end of World War II, most of the smaller schools were closed. A few rural institutions, like the **Dungeness School** which was converted into a community center, were saved for other uses. Adams County, which once had a hundred school districts, had five by 1971.

Depression-time relief assisted not only the unemployed but a number of Washington's worn schoolhouses, mostly in the form of maintenance and minor renovation of the primping sort—a coat of paint here and some landscaping there. Very few schools built during the depression or the war were distinctive. One exception is **Bellingham High School**, a modern design in poured concrete completed in 1937. In Seattle no new schools were built during the depression and school enrollment dropped by 3,000 students between 1930 and 1938. Later, the population which swelled suddenly in Seattle and Tacoma for wartime construction required the addition of portables on many school grounds.

In the half century since the end of World War II, school construction in Washington, as elsewhere, has featured a variety of formalist and other vaguely modern styles. Function — sometimes mere function — has more often than not replaced the ornamental and the monumental. When Spokane needed a second high school on South Hill, the school board chose a design that cost half the price a four-story modern version of Lewis and Clark High School would have required. Nevertheless, after **Ferris High School** opened in 1963, it was lauded as much for its innovative pedagogy — team teaching, a mix of small classes and large

SARTORI SCHOOL

Clockwise from top right: Bellingham High School. Photo by Mark Cutler; Roosevelt Elementary at Fourteenth Avenue and Bernard Street is one of thirteen original elementary schools erected in 1980 as part of a $32 million building bond approved by Spokane voters in March 1978. These new elementary schools (now eighteen in all) are variations on a prototype designed by The Northwest Architectural Company in Spokane. Photo by Jack Arkills; Detail of Spokane sculptor Harold Balazs' art at Ferris High School, Spokane; Named for a Californian doctor who donated part of the school site, Renton's two-story frame Sartori School was built in 1907 on Gardner Avenue North to serve the children of North Renton. The first brick addition, also shown in this 1934 photo, was constructed in 1929. Courtesy Washington State Archives, Olympia; Sedro Woolley's Union School was a state leader in drawing students from far beyond city limits. Improvement in buses and highways allowed scattered rural school districts to cooperate in union schools. This Mack bus was one of seven used by School District No. 4., and it covered a daily route of sixty miles from Lyman to Clear Lake. Photo by Wathey Studio, Sedro Woolley, ca. 1926. Courtesy U.W. Libraries, Special Collections.

group lectures, and individual laboratories — as for the "quiet and pleasant landscape" of its campus. The campus features nine buildings with large hallways and several entrances, connected by covered walkways, surrounding a center courtyard with landscaping donated by descendants of the school's namesake, banker and local historian Joel Ferris. The school and its courtyard are also enhanced by the sculpture of Spokane artist Harold Balazs, whose work was donated by the school architects, Royal A. McClure and Thomas Adkison. In 1982, Lewis and Clark alumnae succeeded in closing Howard Street between Fourth and Fifth Avenues, connecting the school with its recreational facilities and thereby creating for their alma mater its own campus. They were motivated, in part, by the Ferris example.

Campus plans of single-story modulars attached by covered walks are especially popular on the more temperate wet side of the Cascades. The roofline can add some character to these sprawls of undistinguished structures. An example is the sawtooth roof of **Mercer Island's Island Elementary** (1960). The precast insulated concrete panel

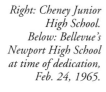

The old school in Dungeness, above (courtesy, Harriet Fish), has been preserved as a community center, top. Photo by Hugh Paradise.

walls used in the construction of **Cheney Junior High School** (1979) are effective energy savers, an important concern in eastern Washington. The otherwise austere uniformity of the walls are enlivened by artist Kay Slucarenko's sandblasted bas reliefs. Appearing from the outside like a monumental Egyptian mastaba, or burial chamber, the school interior is described by Woodbridge and Montgomery as like a "shopping mall with a variety of educational activities spaced along its length." Especially since the early 1970s movable interior partitions have become common in Washington public schools.

Right: Cheney Junior High School. Below: Bellevue's Newport High School at time of dedication, Feb. 24, 1965.

Above: Seattle Housing Authority's "poster children," ca. 1940. Bottom: Depression-time scenes from the decrepit housing on Seattle's "Profanity Hill," the site chosen for the Yesler Terrace housing project.

PUBLIC HOUSING

The National Housing Authority passed by New Deal social reformers in 1937 was designed to "remedy the acute shortage of decent, safe, and sanitary dwellings for families of low-income." The shack towns scattered about the tidelands and vacant lots of Seattle and other larger Washington communities were responses to this shortage — often ingenious ones. However, even the largest of these self-help communities — called Hoovervilles for the president under whose term the Great Depression began — were hardly "decent, safe (or) sanitary solutions" to this housing crisis. By June 30, 1940 the federal housing agency had opened 73,132 units in 230 developments, and more than 94 percent of them were occupied. The following year in Seattle, **Yesler Terrace**, a public housing paragon, opened on First Hill and was quickly filled. Beyond meeting the federal standards for open space, Yesler Terrace offered panoramic vistas, proximity to work, tasteful wood residences imaginatively arranged, and a bold novelty for the time, racial integration. Jesse Epstein, the housing project's creator and director of the Seattle Housing Authority, had insisted on the latter, thus predating President John Kennedy's executive order establishing the same policy in public housing by more than twenty years.

World War II soon transformed the federal low-income housing policy into a temporary war-time housing program for

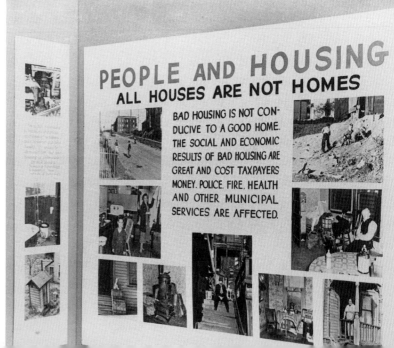

Above: *Typical units in Yesler Terrace, Seattle. Courtesy, Seattle Housing Authority.*
Below: *World War II housing and the Kaiser Shipyards at Vancouver. Courtesy, National Archives, Alaska-Pacific NW branch, Seattle.*

Top: Seattle's largest depression-time "Hooverville" filled the waterfront acres south of Pioneer Square that were previously crowded with the Skinner and Eddy Shipyards. The neighborhood of inventive squatters resisted efforts to destroy it in the early 1930s to become an established community of mostly out-of-work single men with its own post office, sheriff, and mayor. America's many Hoovervilles were strong evidence of the need for public housing. Courtesy, Seattle Municipal Archive.

defense workers. One of the Public Housing Authority's greatest efforts was in Vancouver, Washington, where Henry Kaiser established a shipyard in 1942. The government developed several housing sites to handle the Kaiser workers who numbered 38,000 late in the year; a fourth of these were women. More than 140 ships, including 50 carriers, were built at the Kaiser yards during the war.

The emergency housing dismantled at war's end was not regularly replaced with affordable units for the returning vets, and they joined in the chorus of complaints over the postwar housing shortage. The 1949 Housing Act projected the construction of more than 800,000 units within six years, but it took more than twenty years to reach the figure. In the interim anti-public housing forces, primarily realtors and developers, effectively slowed government participation in the construction of affordable housing. In Seattle a housing program referendum was successfully stopped with the slogan: "Can you afford to pay somebody else's rent?" It was a campaign strategy used throughout the nation. Its opponents also associated public housing with socialism and, pointing to Jesse Epstein's example, with racial integration. In 1958 Congress failed to enact any public housing legislation.

Public housing experienced a revival during the Kennedy-Johnson administrations and was extended to include innovative programs such as rehabilitation of existing housing, rent supplements, tax breaks for low income homeowners, and "turnkeys" in which private developers were allowed to build government housing. The Nixon Administration's 1974 Housing and Community Development Act put housing within the context of a variety of community concerns including jobs, health, and public safety. At that time a number of Washington communities instituted community development departments to select projects for the block grants awarded through the 1974 act.

Above: View from the Volunteer Park Observatory to the park's conservatory (upper right), High Reservoir (left), Lake Union, a portion of the Lake Washington Ship Canal, and Puget Sound (upper left). Courtesy, Seattle Municipal Archives. Right: Volunteer Park Conservatory, Seattle. Below left: Duncan Gardens, Manito Park, Spokane. Bottom right: Seymore Conservatory, Wright Park, Tacoma.

PARK STRUCTURES

Nearly one-third of the 6,151 buildings owned by the state (1995) are park structures. Add those included within Washington's ten federal parks, those in its 271 municipalities and 39 counties, and the number of all park structures in Washington State is second only to the more than 10,000 military buildings within its borders. Some are mere sheds, but others are distinguished landmarks like: the **Seymore Conservatory** in Tacoma's Wright Park and Seattle's **Volunteer Park Conservatory and Grounds**; the **Duncan Gardens and House** in Spokane's Manito Park; the fanciful stone creations in Anacortes's **Causland Park**; the **Point Defiance Park** boathouse and octagonal beach Pavilion

(since destroyed by fire) in Tacoma; the Peace Arch in **Peace Portal Park**, Blaine; **Paradise Inn** at Mount Rainier National Park; and one of the first bioclimatic zone exhibits in the world, the African Savanna in Seattle's **Woodland Park Zoo**. Some of the best-loved park structures were built during the depression by relief workers. The sandstone Observation Tower on top of 2,409-foot Mount Constitution in **Moran State Park** on Orcas Island was constructed in 1935 by members of the Civilian Conservation Corps (CCC), working from plans of architect Elsworth Storey.

Clockwise (from top left): **Blaine Peace Arch**, dedication ceremonies, 1921. The concrete monument to a peaceful border was another promotion of Sam Hill, the Northwest's good roads advocate and concrete crusader. Courtesy, Maryhill Museum. **Causeland Park**, Anacortes. Louis LePage's 1920 creation is one of the Northwest's most imaginative and charming community parks. Photo by Hugh Paradise. **The McKinley Stump**, Chehalis, Wash. The attached sign reads, in part, "Cut near Pe Ell May 1901 for President McKinley's reception. President Roosevelt spoke from this stump May 22, 1903. At base, 12 ft. 6 inches. Tree age, 360 years." When Mount Rainier's **Paradise Inn** opened in 1917 two-day visits were the norm for park visitors, and the new facilities allowed mile-high overnight comforts. Later, when day trips to the mountain were more common, the park service, as part of its Mission 66 (for 1966) plan to save the park's natural environment, proposed removing Paradise Inn and replacing it with night lodging outside park boundaries. Public outcry prevented the demolition. **Lookout Tower** on the summit of Mount Constitution, the San Juan Islands' highest point, was built in 1934-35 by the Civilian Conservation Corps of sandstone quarried on the northern end of Orcas Island. Although attributed to Seattle architect Ellsworth Storey, plans for the tower's final configurations are signed "Design by R. Koepf." The architect Rolan Koepf, who was attached to the CCC camp at Rosario State Park, no doubt worked with Storey, who supervised the 1935 construction of the fifty-three-foot sandstone observation tower. Photo by Art Lingenbrink, ca. 1930. Built in the 1890s by Tacoman George Austin for his hometown, the 250-foot-long rustic bridge spanning a ravine in Defiance Park was built with 3,500 logs. Courtesy, Rosa Morgan.

Above: New home at Gingko State Park near Vantage for a collection of Native American rock art salvaged from the rising waters of Lake Wanapum behind Wanapum Dam. Inset: Rock art on Harstene Island. Top right: Rustic gazebo at Chetzemoke Park, Port Townsend, ca. 1910. Courtesy, Dan Kerlee. Above right: Indian rock inscriptions near Victor on North Bay, Mason County.

PUBLIC ART

A melding of decoration and deeply human dreams, native art and craft long preceded the arrival here of Europeans. Curiously, the part of native culture that has become a widely popular type of public art, the totem pole, has more to do with the coast tribes north of Washington's border with Canada than those below it. Seattle's first Pioneer Square totem was stolen from Tongas Island on the Inside Passage by the city's Good Will Committee while returning from its tour to Alaska in 1899. The native art of Puget Sound and of the Yakamas, Spokanes and Nez Perce, from east of the mountains, is less monumental, but both spiritual and practical. A few of the first Euro-American settlers in Washington recognized its quality and collected it — baskets, masks, house posts, beadwork, canoes, and cedar boxes.

Preoccupied with subduing nature, most settlers showed little interest in the arts beyond the occasional book, that is when they could read. Art and ornament came slowly, for many first in church, and later for nearly everyone in the skilled handwork of frontier carpenters. Beginning in the 1880s the well-wrought ornamental cornices of fine homes, stained glass of large churches, and classical touches given public buildings were evidence that a community shared invigorating interests beyond those of mere survival or even growth. The preferred styles were generally Classical or Gothic. Triumphant arches built for visiting dignitaries or Independence Day visitors were popular as early as the 1860s. In nearly every town through which they passed, the inaugural entourage for the Northern Pacific Railroad's first transcontinental crossing in 1883 was greeted by an arch and expected to parade beneath it.

When the first wave of pioneer nostalgia swept the Northwest in the 1890s and joined with the rustic reaction to a flood of immigrant strangers, the twisting and piling of sticks and stones into park bridges, benches, and bandstands developed as a widely popular form of public art. Public sculpture, which became more commonplace on Washington streets and in its parks after the turn of the century, was ordinarily honorific, commemorating the heroic life of a public figure. The Spanish-American war spawned a pantheon of this sort, as did the 1909 Alaska Yukon and Pacific Exposition in Seattle. Subscriptions were the common source of funding, with the largest donations often coming either directly through the last will and testament of the honored or from his or her descendants.

Below left: Washington's oldest surviving depot in Dayton restored as a community and heritage center. Photo by Mary Randlett. Right: Arch erected at the intersection of First Avenue and Columbia Street in Seattle for the 1902 Elks Carnival, one of the state's finer examples of temporary public street art.

Above: "Chipping Rust" is one of eleven panels painted by Kenneth Callahan for the federal Treasury Art Project (TRAP) in 1936 and exhibited in the then new State Marine Hospital (now Pacific Medical Center) on Seattle's Beacon Hill. Callahan's murals were among the largest painted for TRAP, and "Chipping Rust" was first exhibited in a TRAP show in Washington D.C. in early 1937 before its installation in Washington State. Presently, eight of eleven panels are exhibited at the Museum of History and Industry in Seattle. Right: Display for Washington: A Guide to the Evergreen State. *The book by the Washington Writer's Project is considered one of the better state guides produced by the WPA American Guide program. Courtesy, National Archives, Seattle.*

The first significant public funding of art occurred during the New Deal era. At the state level, the Washington Emergency Relief Administration (WERA) sponsored some art projects such as a large oil painting for the Longview Public Library and orchestra performances in Seattle and Tacoma. Public art also issued from the National Youth Administration, notably a totem pole carved by Tulalip youths under the supervision of tribal elders. But most public art projects in the 1930s were the work of the WPA. The Works Progress Administration employed artists to sing, dance, act, design, sculpt, and especially paint. Many murals were completed in schools, post offices, and buildings on the Capitol Campus and other sites. Among the largest was the mural painted for the dining room of the Tacoma Indian Hospital. The dimensions of its main panel were 10 x 72 feet. A number of artists were simply paid to paint, and a few of them, like Mark Tobey and Morris Graves, later became internationally famous. Washington artists also participated in assembling the *Index of American Design*, the WPA's national project on the development of the decorative arts. And the still-read and enjoyed *Washington, A Guide to the Evergreen State*, is considered one of the best state

*Bottom left to right: Loredo Taft's monumental **George Washington** made for the 1909 Alaska Yukon Pacific Exposition on the U.W. campus; **Marcus Whitman** statue by Avard Fairbanks, Walla Walla. Photo by Mary Randlett; two Palouse monuments, the Colfax grain elevator and commemorative statue to the Grand Army of the Republic. Photo by Hugh Paradise.*

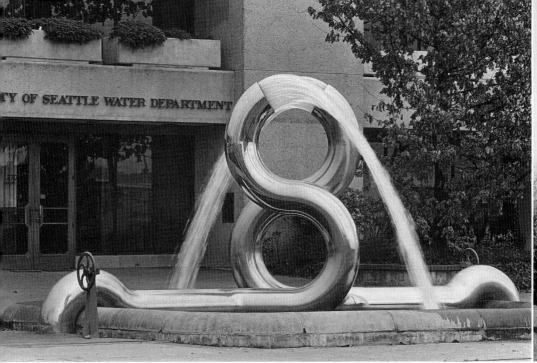

*Above: Ted Jonsson's untitled fountain at the Seattle Water Department Operations Control Center. Photo by Mary Randlett. Above right: **Dancer** by Phillip Levine on Capitol Campus in Olympia. Photo by Mary Randlett. Bottom left: Tim Sciliano's grand portal to Rainier View Elementary School in Federal Way. Bottom middle: Installing George Tsutakawa's silicon bronze **Naramore Fountain** at the downtown Seattle Public Library in 1966. Tsutakawa is at the far right. Photo by Frank Shaw. Bottom right: George Tsutakawa's fifteen-foot-high Naramore Fountain in flow.*

guides in the WPA Writers' Project.

The depression-time public support for the arts was, however, an anomaly. Following the war tax-supported art was a rare attachment to a few public buildings. A notable example is sculptor George Tsutakawa's *Fountain of Wisdom* at the Fifth Avenue entrance to the Seattle Public Library's main branch (1958). In Seattle the creation of the arts advocacy group Allied Arts in 1954 and of the volunteer Municipal Art Commission the following year primed the canvas for what became nationally recognized as a flourishing of public art in the "Northwest's premier city." Although it was rejected, the Municipal Art Commission originally proposed the dedication of a small percentage of the cost of major public buildings for their "beautification" with painting, sculpture, landscaping, and other arts. More than $750,000 was raised privately for public art associated with the World's Fair in Seattle. In 1962, the Kennedy Administration implemented through the General Services Administration a requirement that one-half of one percent of federal renovation and construction budgets be spent on art. The creation of the National

Endowment for the Arts followed in 1966.

Seattle Mayor Wes Uhlman's administration established and funded the Seattle Arts Commission in 1971. Soon after a statewide competition was held and selected sculptor Ted Jonsson's fountain for the entrance to the Water Department's operations control center on Airport Way South. The fountain was figured into the building cost. After Seattle's "1% for Art" ordinance was passed in the summer of 1973 such funding became commonplace, and the Arts Commission's Art in Public Places Committee has continued to guide the process. Seattle City Light's Viewland-Hoffman Electrical Substation (1979) is the city's first example of a commission in which the artists — Andrew Keating, Sherry Markovitz, Emile Gehrke, Veva Gehrke, and Lewis "Buster" Simpson — were involved in the total design of the electrical complex. The art of the Metro bus tunnel (see Streets Chapter) is another example of this cooperation. King County, Bellevue, and Everett also have 1% programs, as did Tacoma until it was rejected in 1985 by citizens unhappy with the Tacoma Dome neon work that used 1% funds.

*Left: Landscape architect Richard Haag and his "found art" at Gasworks Park. Photo by Mary Randlett. Above: Magdalena Abakanowicz's **Manus**, part of the W.W.U. Outdoor Sculpture Collection. Photo by Rod del Rozo.*

The Washington State Art Commission was formed early, in 1961. When its 1/2 of 1% for art program was established in 1974, Washington was only the second state, after Hawaii, to do so. Viewed collectively, the state art collection holds over 3,500 works of art in its Arts in Public Places Program. Notable examples include Magdalena Abakanowicz's Sculpture Garden at Western Washington University, Timothy Siciliano's **Balancing the Universe** sculpture at Rainier View Elementary in Federal Way, and Thompson Brennan's "River of Time" sculpture at Henkle Middle School in White Salmon.

*Right: Clair Colquitt's gate at Seattle City Light's Creston-Nelson Electrical Substation. Bottom left: **Seattle George Monument** by Lewis "Buster" Simpson at the WA State Convention and Trade Center. Middle: **High Tide** by Steven Jensen at Walla Walla College. Bottom right: Sculptor Lawrence Beck stands beside his **Inukshuk**, a two-ton stainless steel piece with an Eskimo name which translates as "floating shape." Boeing Field, 1980. Photos by Mary Randlett.*

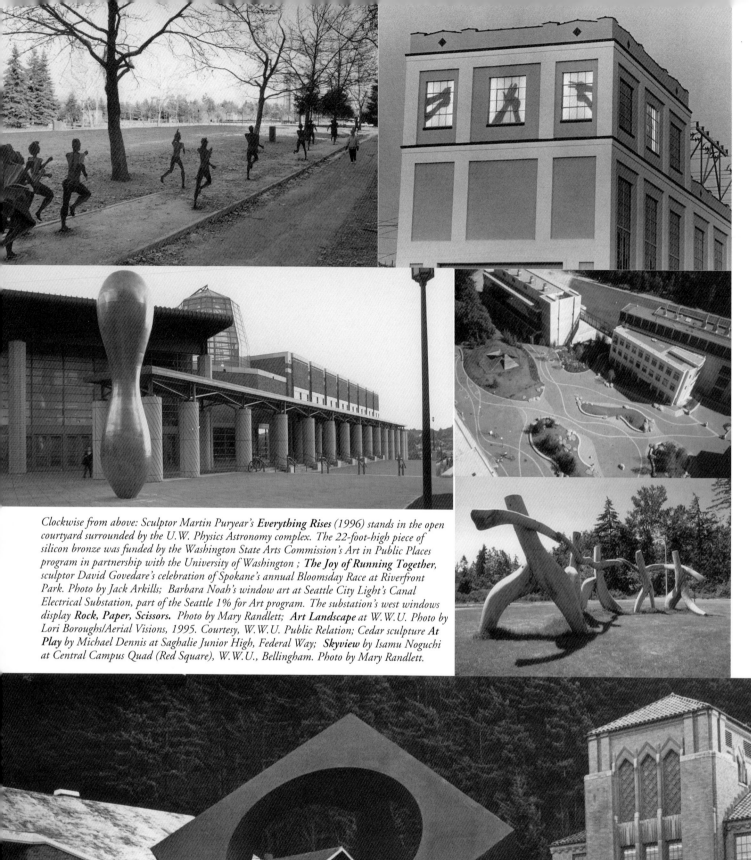

*Clockwise from above: Sculptor Martin Puryear's **Everything Rises** (1996) stands in the open courtyard surrounded by the U.W. Physics Astronomy complex. The 22-foot-high piece of silicon bronze was funded by the Washington State Arts Commission's Art in Public Places program in partnership with the University of Washington ; **The Joy of Running Together**, sculptor David Govedare's celebration of Spokane's annual Bloomsday Race at Riverfront Park. Photo by Jack Arkills; Barbara Noah's window art at Seattle City Light's Canal Electrical Substation, part of the Seattle 1% for Art program. The substation's west windows display **Rock, Paper, Scissors.** Photo by Mary Randlett; **Art Landscape** at W.W.U. Photo by Lori Boroughs/Aerial Visions, 1995. Courtesy, W.W.U. Public Relation; Cedar sculpture **At Play** by Michael Dennis at Saghalie Junior High, Federal Way; **Skyview** by Isamu Noguchi at Central Campus Quad (Red Square), W.W.U., Bellingham. Photo by Mary Randlett.*

Equality by Rolan Bart Garner, Don Scott, and Ken Leback (1997) includes the natural screen of incense cedars and the artifice of the city's skyline as aspects of an idea drawn from Alexis Tocqueville's Democracy in America. A plaque bearing the De Tocqueville passage interrupts the sculptures "residential rows." Photo by Arthur Aubry.

Sun and Raven (1973) and *Man riding on Tail of Whale (1971)*, Northwest Coast Indian carving by Duane Pasco at Occidental Park with the Smith Tower and Columbia Seafirst Tower in the background. Pasco's cedar carvings were given to the Pioneer Square Association by Richard White. Photo by Mary Randlett.

Left: One of several *Windmills* constructed by Emil and Veva Gehrke from discarded materials as part of 1% for Art Program installation at Seattle City Light's Viewland-Hoffman Electrical Substation. Photo by Mary Randlett.
Below: *Changing Form* by Dorris Totten Chase (1971) at Kerry Park on Queen Anne Hill in Seattle.

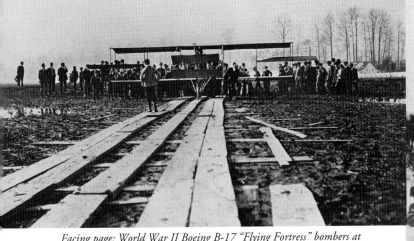

Facing page: World War II Boeing B-17 "Flying Fortress" bombers at Boeing Plant in Seattle. Courtesy, Boeing Archives. Above left: Charles Hamilton's rudimentary runway at the Meadows Race Track. Courtesy, Mary Randlett. Right: Hamilton in flight. Courtesy, Seattle Public Library. Below right: Flyer announcing Hamilton's flight.

AIRWAYS

And let your mind grasp this idea, that this thing was a man, and not a bird endowed by the Creator with the physical science of flying, and that this man rode a machine heavier than air...

—From a description of aviator C. J. Mars' October 5, 1910 flight over the Spokane fair grounds published at the time in the *Spokesman-Review*.

FIRST ADVENTURES

Using his mother's sewing machine, some basket wire, wood, fabric and a 40-horsepower engine, Herbert A. Munter bound together his home-made airplane to become the first Seattle citizen to fly solo. Munter throttled it aloft from the barren Harbor Island landscape in 1912. Eventually, Bill Boeing hired the young aviator, one of his first employees, and thereafter Boeing's company would proudly recall Munter's precocity. In 1937, in a variation on "look how far we have come!" Boeing celebrated the twenty-fifth anniversary of Munter's flight while promoting its new "flying boat," the Boeing Clipper. Herbert Munter's aeronautical contraption weighed less than a thousand pounds — the Clipper weighed 41 tons.

The first heavier-than-air itinerate adventurer to fly Washington airways was Charles K. Hamilton who pushed his leased G. Curtiss biplane airborne on March 11, 1910, two years before Munter's first flight. Hamilton took off from another clearing beside the Duwamish River at the Meadows — the area's race track. On the third day of his exhibition Hamilton crashed into a small lake beside the track thrilling the crowd including, perhaps, Bill Boeing. (Later that March, Boeing purchased a small shipyard — now the museum piece Red Barn — also on the Duwamish, where six years later he was building airplanes.) After the crash, the lucky Hamilton swam to a rescuer's rowboat and was taken to the hospital, where he soon recovered from his injuries. Less than a month later Hamilton continued his exhibition, without the swim, in the "blue empyrean" above Spokane's fair grounds.

William Boeing made his first flight on Independence Day, 1915, as a passenger aboard a Curtiss-type seaplane piloted by yet another thrill-giver, Terah Maroney. Boeing was so exhilarated by the airways above Lake Washington that he rushed off to Los Angeles to learn how to fly. Soon he returned to Washington with his own plane and, accompanied by a pilot friend, "bombed" downtown Seattle with red cardboard artillery shells printed with warnings of America's unpreparedness — a bold and prescient performance for someone who would become the builder of B-17s, B-29s, and B-52s. Less than two years after his first flight above Lake Washington, Boeing tested the "B & W," his company's first plane. When Herb Munter, who was to make its maiden flight from Boeing's hangar on Lake Union, was late for the event, Boeing took it up himself.

Will Fly Again Today

HAMILTON

The Crazy Man of the Air, Is Ready for More Sensational Flights and His Race With an Automobile

Notwithstanding injuries received in yesterday's closing dip to the ground, and the fact that he declares the course dangerous, the king of the bird men will attempt to achieve greater fame by making more dangerous plunges through the air.

Both Today and Tomorrow

General Admission $1; Children Under 12 Years 25 Cents

Northern Pacific Special Trains from the Union Depot every half hour, beginning at noon.

Interurban Trains from First Avenue and Main Street every ten minutes, beginning at noon.

Gates Open at Noon══First Flight at 2:15

EARLY PUBLIC FIELDS

The enthusiasm for flight, generated by daredevils before World War I, was well fed after the war, with the surplus sale of military aircraft. Of the estimated 1,200 civilian pilots operating nationwide in 1922 about half of them were unli-

Left: The Boeing Clipper's "roll out" onto the Duwamish River, Seattle. Courtesy, Teresa McCoy.

Above: An early aerial of Sand Point Field, Seattle. Courtesy, Museum of Flight. Inset: "Round-the-World Fliers" who began and concluded their record flight at Sand Point in 1924. Photo by Lew Hudson. Courtesy, Jean Hudson Lunzer.

censed and unregulated stunters flying itinerant "Gypsy Craft," many of them war surplus. With the Air Commerce Act of 1926 the federal government, at last, took responsibility for registering and licensing pilots and aircraft, designating civil airways, investigating accidents, and operating and maintaining air navigation aids — but not airports. Following maritime precedent, airports were treated like docks and left to either municipal or private developers.

A few Washington State municipalities had already acted, notably Spokane which opened its public landing field in 1920 in the valley just east of the city limits. Later named Felts Field, in 1926 it was one of the first landing strips officially designated an "air port" by the U.S. Department of Commerce. One year later the aviator who made every municipality, big or small, want its own airport, landed at Felts Field. Charles Lindbergh was on tour following his non-stop flight from New York to Paris.

King County also developed its first field in 1920. Under the urging of the Navy, the county cleared a strip at Sand Point. Used by Boeing early on as a test field, it was alternately dusty or muddy until the 2,000-foot runway was seeded with an all weather grass surface which required only an occasional cutting and a sentry to shoo away the ducks. In 1924 the Sand Point Field was both the starting and finishing field for the Army's first "Round-The-World Fliers." The *Seattle Times'* subsequent proud conclusion that "Sand Point will never fade from the air maps of the world; it is a historic spot forever!" was good promotion but not good prophesy. The Navy, after agreeing in 1926 to King County's urging that it develop the field, kept planes there until 1972. In the 1974 fall election local fliers lost their bid to convert the abandoned naval air station for civilian aviation. Instead, the Warren G. Magnuson Park and National Oceanic and Atmospheric Administration facilities were developed at the old field.

AIRWAYS SAFETY AND THE WASHINGTON STATE AERONATICS COMMISSION

Ten years after the first successful flight over the Cascades in 1919, the urge to cross the state along its airways was common enough that state aviators successfully lobbied the state legislature to fund construction of an emergency landing strip near the Snoqualmie summit. Gov. Roland H. Hartley, however, vetoed the bill. Although Washington pilots in distress could not count on their governor, they might have found some small consolation in the experience of one pilot who in the year of Hartley's veto landed his failing aircraft on the roof of the Seattle Bon Marche department store. A *Seattle Times* editorial concluded, "the time will come, of course, when every large city will have buildings designed to offer landing places for hard-pressed pilots."

Of course, it was the airways above mountain passes, not central business districts, that pilots hoped to make safer with the mountain airfields in case of emergencies. Help of this kind did not arrive until much later, in 1947,

New operations control tower at Ault Field, World War II. Courtesy, National Archives, Alaska-Pacific NW Region.

when the newly formed Washington State Aeronautics Commission chose as it first task the construction of emergency landing fields near the summits of both Snoqualmie and Stampede passes. The state split the costs with the CAA. The commission's first director, Joseph P. Adams, proposed to "make Washington the safest state in which to fly." The airways philosophy behind this goal was later explained by Robert Nuber, the commission's director in 1956. "Washington is interrelated not only by a network of concrete highways, but also sky routes laid out according to maps. Center markers of these air routes are not white-lines but radio beams. Along the sky highways... are landing points or airports." By then the state had completed eight emergency landing strips in the Cascades. Nuber proudly concluded, "we were the first state to launch an emergency-airport program to this extent."

Above: Snohomish County Airport (Paine Field) during its WPA supervision. Courtesy, WA State Historical Society, Tacoma. Left: WPA grading on Yakima Airport runway. Courtesy National Archives, Seattle. Below: Naval Air Station at Shelton in 1945 from 13,700 feet. Bottom: Checking bore-siting guns on a PV2 at Whidbey Island Naval Air Station. Courtesy, National Archives, Seattle.

GENERAL EFFECTS OF THE DEPRESSION AND WORLD WAR II

The risky eighteen years between Gov. Hartley's veto and the aeronautic commission's public works near the summit of the Cascades were shaped by more profound dangers and opportunities. First the Great Depression and then after World War II thoroughly accelerated the role of public works in the development of both airways and airports. Especially since World War I, the local opportunities attached to military funding were recurring preoccupations of municipal leaders. In 1929, on the eve of the stock market crash, Seattle Mayor Frank Edwards' public addresses over the military preparedness loudspeaker were typical.

> *Our coast defenses are out of date. The old guns at our fortifications are outranged two-to-one in shooting distance by the guns of the modern battleships. There seems to be no tendency on the part of the government to modernize these coast defenses... Without an ample force of war planes in the Western Washington district ready to go into action at a moment's notice, our Washington coast offers an open invitation at all times to attack.*

Although Edwards' attempts to land the proposed West Coast Army Air Base failed, federal assistance was soon being funneled from depression-era agencies. A good portion of Pres. Roosevelt's first relief work through the Civil Works Administration (CWA) was directed toward airports, although most of this was for "shovel work" to get the unemployed through the winter of 1933-34. The Work Progress Administration (WPA) which followed the Emergency Relief Appropriation Act of 1935 supervised airport projects from 1933 to 1939. In 1935 thirty-four airport projects in the state were approved for WPA funding by the Bureau of Air Commerce in Washington D.C. Included were construction of fields at Forks, Colville, and Clallam County and improvements to the municipal airport at Walla Walla. A request for $225,000 of WPA funds for work on the Snohomish County Airport (Paine Field) was approved by the War Department in 1937. The Snohomish County field was described at the time as but one post in an "imaginary fence" of airports then under construction between Bellingham and Vancouver. Included in this air guard were fields at Mount Vernon, Port Angeles, Sand Point, Boeing Field, Fort Lewis, Bremerton, and Grays Harbor, all of them approved by the military. Between 1933 and 1938 the federal government's share in the nationwide effort to build new airports and improve old ones was three quarters of the total dollars spent.

In 1938 the newly formed Civil Aeronautics Authority (CAA) directed the first federal funds to build airports that were not justified as CWA or WPA relief work. The CAA's success in overcoming the "except airports" clause, first introduced with the

original 1926 Air Commerce Act, was justified on the grounds of national defense. In 1940 the CAA announced plans to spend approximately $11.5 million on airport development in Washington State. Spokane was expected to receive the largest benefits, with Snohomish County airport next. Among the others were fields at Aberdeen, Anacortes, Arlington, Bremerton, Chehalis, Cle Elum, Clarkston, Colfax, Deer Park, Ellensburg, Ilwaco, Kelso, Monroe, Mount Vernon, North Bend, Olympia, Pomeroy, Port Townsend, Prosser, Pullman, Renton, Republic, Ritzville, Shelton, Tacoma, Toppenish, Twisp, Vancouver, Walla Walla, Wenatchee, Wilbur, and Yakima. Actually, the amount expended was considerably more.

In his postwar summary, Col. Conrad P. Hardy of the Seattle District Army Corps of Engineers calculated that more than $100 million had been spent in Washington State during the war developing thirty-five air bases, fields, and other airport projects. As predicted in 1940, the largest recipient was the Spokane Army Air Depot (Fairchild) in Spokane, which received $27 million. The colonel's short list included airports and/or additions to existing fields at Chehalis, $798,000; Ellensburg, $2.734 million; Ephrata, $9.211 million; Boeing Field, $4.849 million; Kitsap County, $1.551 million; Olympia, $934,000; Port Angeles, $1.19 million; South Bend, $392,000; Felts Field, $361,000; Pangborn Field (Wenatchee), $535,000. Other air base installations included McChord Field (Pierce County), $9.8 million; Paine Field (Snohomish County), $7.3 million; Arlington, $896,000; Bellingham, $1.049 million; Gray Field (Fort Lewis), $1.695 million; Mount Vernon, $1.579 million; Quillayute, $2.316 million; Shelton, $1.118 million; Yakima Air Base, $346,000, and $9 million for Spokane's second air base, Geiger Field.

The peaceful fruits of this wartime spending were the many new or improved air fields returned for community use after the war. In its efforts to provide a guard force for the Navy shipyard in Bremerton, the Navy expanded Shelton's Sandersen Field by overrunning a golf course bordering the field. Besides developing two runways, the military also constructed barracks, base operations buildings, officers housing, and even a tie-down pad for a blimp. Some of the housing was only recently completed when the naval air station was declared surplus soon after the war. Mason County took it over. Similarly, in Walla Walla the municipal airport, which the city had created by ballot in 1929 and improved with WPA funds in the mid-1930s, was commandeered for the war in 1942. Fire swept through the base while it was still under

Above and bottom: Inaugural 1926 air mail flight from Pasco to Elko, Nevada and connection with transcontinental postal service. Courtesy, United Airlines and Ted Van Arsdol.

construction damaging or destroying twenty-one buildings. Losses were three times higher than the reported $15,000, kept low for propaganda purposes. Between the time the first B-17s arrived in the summer of 1942 to the time the last B-24 liberator left the base three years later, a total of 594 bomber crews including 5,490 men and officers were trained at the base, which on August 31, 1947 was declared surplus and returned to the city and county as Walla Walla's municipal airport.

FELTS FIELD

The long and prosperous relationship between Spokane's airports and airways and the military was seeded in 1924 when the Spokane Chamber of Commerce quickly raised a $10,000 hangar at the city air field to house the 116th National Guard Observation Squadron — only the third such unit in the country. Spokane quickly became a Northwest center for aviation enthusiasm. When Rev. Margin, a local Methodist minister, persuaded Gov. Hartley to prohibit government airplanes from participating in an air circus scheduled there on a Sunday afternoon in September 1925, he soon learned the sacredness of Spokane's aeronautical interests. After two local pilots crashed and were killed while attempting to fill up the show for the missing military, they were described in the local press as "sacrificed on the altar of religious bigotry." Losing a good part of his congregation, Margin finally left town.

Members of the 116th Squadron and their craft were regu-

larly invited as guests to regional events like the dedication of Pearson Field in Vancouver in 1925. The 116th was also represented for the 1926 inaugural flight from Pasco to Elko, Nevada of the first Northwest air connection with the transcontinental airmail route. The troopers returned to Pasco three years later for the 1929 dedication of the new Franklin County Airport. In 1927, the squadron's leader, Major John Fancher, supported civic leaders in their bid to bring the National Air Races to the Spokane airport. Promotion for the six-day air derby was aided mightily by the visit of Charles Lindbergh and his *Spirit of St. Louis*, on the eve of the September event. During a pause in the races, the Spokane airport was dedicated and renamed Felts Field. Two years later Felts Field was home base for the *Spokane Sun-God* that set a record 7,220-mile, non-stop, five-day flight to New York and back again, refueling while in flight.

During the 1930s Felts Field, like so many other airfields in the state, benefited from depression-time relief funds. The 1934 construction of a new National Guard hangar was built with Civil Works Administration funds. A second hangar for Northwest Airlines was built, in part, with WPA labor. In 1937 the city offered Felts Field to the Army Air Corps in the Army's search for a maintenance and supply depot. The field, however, was soon rejected for its want of space and a paved runway. Two years later the Spokane County commissioners bought a 1,280-acre site west of town for development of a new "super airport" which was first called Sunset Airport. Early in 1940 WPA paid for the labor to clear and level the site for runways. Soon after, the entire site was transferred to the military. As part of the transfer the CAA promised to improve Felts Field for commercial use and the military soon paved the runway.

GEIGER FIELD/
SPOKANE INTERNATIONAL AIRPORT

The Army rented the Sunset site from the city for $1 a year. The new airport, named after a World War I veteran, was dedicated Geiger Field in 1941. The first B-17 of the 39th Bombard-

Spokane Municipal Airport Administration Building, Felts Field. Courtesy, WSU Library, Historical Photography Collection.

ment Group landed there in July, 1941. At the completion of field construction in December the Army Air Corps had two bombardment groups, five engineering units, and a variety of administration and supply personnel stationed at the base. In 1947 the original acreage at Geiger, including the runways and flight control building, were declared surplus and soon returned to the county for its originally intended use: the municipal airport. Some military presence at the field continued, however, until 1976 when the Air National Guard unit stationed at Geiger Field was relocated to the neighboring Fairchild Air Force Base.

The main transcontinental airlines returned to Geiger Field on July 22, 1946. The following year on October 27 it became the Spokane municipal airport. At first the airport operated out of a wood frame terminal built by the military in 1946. In 1965 these modest quarters were replaced by a domed structure with sweeping lines that was soon compared to the Indian Taj Mahal. Although predictable, the congratulations sent by Pres. Lyndon B. Johnson for the April 1 dedication were fitting. The aerodynamic architecture of the reinforced concrete terminal was described as "visible evidence

Right and bottom inset: Spokane Airport's new dome terminal, 1965. Courtesy, MOHAI, Seattle P-I Collection. Below: Aerial of Spokane International Airport runway with Spokane in the background. Courtesy, Spokane Airport.

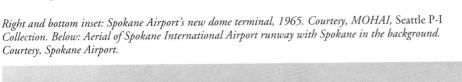

of forward-looking people keeping pace with the jet age." Spokane also kept up with the automobile, constructing a new freeway system which it promised could legally speed the motorist between the airport and the city center in seven minutes. Along with the terminal, field improvements included new taxiways, lighting, aprons, and landscaping. A number of additions were made in 1973-74 to both the terminal and field, including a runway widening to accommodate the increase in 747 service for visitors to Spokane's Expo '74 World's Fair. The 1976 exit of the military from Geiger Field and the release of fifty buildings to the city enhanced the community's strategy to develop a 300-acre commercial and industrial site at the airport. In 1997, the year the Spokane Airport Board began to serve as grantees of Foreign Trade Zone No. 224, Spokane International Airport processed 3.05 million passengers and 54,704 U.S. cargo-tons. These statistics more than doubled those of 1990. The board's responsibilities also included the general reliever airport Felts Field and the Spokane International Airport Business Park, a 600-acre industrial and office complex adjacent to the airport and Interstate 90. The park and two airports are owned jointly by Spokane County and the City of Spokane.

FAIRCHILD AIR FORCE BASE

Fairchild Air Force Base was still the largest military establishment in the inland Northwest in 1976, the year the Air National Guard moved over from Geiger Field. At the time it had a military population of over 4,000. Contiguous to Geiger, Fairchild was developed as the Army's maintenance and supply depot during World War II. It was the prize that most depression-burdened communities in the Northwest yearned for and many actively lobbied for in the late 1930s. Spokane's principal competitor was Everett, and its then still-young advocate, U.S. Rep. Henry M. Jackson. Jackson was so confident that the Snohomish County Airport (Paine Field) would be chosen as the site, that he advertised his intention to make an important announcement at the field on August 2, 1941. Jackson, however, missed the ceremony when his flight to Washington soon developed difficulties and he had to return to the Capitol. The representative's report to his Seattle office that he had been bruised in an aircraft accident was not, the *Spokane Daily Chronicle*

Below: Ault Field at Whidbey Island Naval Station, 1945. Courtesy, National Archives, Seattle.

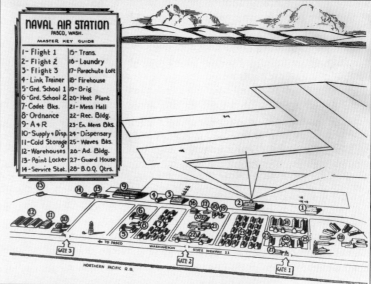

Top and above: The Naval Air Station at Pasco was one of many state airfields improved for WWII operations. Left: Navy blimp at Shelton Station. Courtesy, National Archives, Seattle.

pointed out, corroborated by Penn Central Airlines which reported no injuries on the interrupted flight which was quickly completed by a second aircraft. The *Chronicle* implied that Jackson was malingering because he had not yet won the battle for Paine Field. In any event, Jackson neither chose to board the second plane nor make an announcement. The Army, however, soon did, choosing Spokane's gift of 5,300 acres atop White Bluff Prairie west of town. More than $120,000 was raised after a one-week chamber of commerce campaign, an effort which so exhausted the city's charity that a month later the local community chest fell considerably short of its goal — $219,000, an ordinarily attainable sum. But Spokane had its Army air base.

The bombing of Pearl Harbor sped construction plans. More than 250 buildings were erected in thirteen months.

Included were a dozen warehouses each larger than a city block, and a repair hangar which covered twelve acres. More than $25 million was spent in building the installation, and when the base command headquarters were moved to the depot in the spring of 1943 more than 7,000 civilians were on its payroll, nearly twice the number employed by the city's private manufacturers in 1939. By the end of 1943 Spokane's three military installations, Geiger Field, Fort George Wright, and the Army Air Depot (it was renamed Fairchild in 1951) employed 15,000 civilians. By the end of November 1944, 1,250 B-17s had been repaired at Fairchild. Women comprised about 25 percent of the work force and in June 1945, three of them completed the base's 10,000th engine repair. Also in 1945 the depot retooled to repair B-29s.

At the conclusion of the war both the depot's maintenance and supply functions were drastically cut back. By the end of March 1947 the Spokane Headquarters of the Air Material Command was deactivated, and the Spokane Air Depot came to an end. Soon, however, the role of the base changed to one of active operations. First, two bombardment groups, the 92nd and the 98th, recently back from Europe with thirty B-29s and 3,000 men were located at the base in November 1947. The Air Force's post-war shift from Geiger to Fairchild added to this new role. In 1951 the base was renamed in memory of Air Force Vice Chief of Staff, General Muir S. Fairchild, a native of Bellingham. The July 20, 1951 dedication coincided with the arrival of the 92nd Bombardment Wing's first B-36. By 1957 the B-36s were being replaced by B-52s. This sequence of speedy Cold War conversions was made more complex in 1961 when the 567th missile squadron arrived with their Atlas ICBMs. However, within four years they too went the way of the B-36s. On May 25, 1994 the last B-52 left Fairchild in a transfer operation that began a little more than a year earlier. This ended the base's 52-year bomber mission. Soon after, Fairchild was made home for the largest air refueling wing in the Air Force and became known as the "tanker hub of the Northwest."

The airfields at Walla Walla, Whidbey Island, Pasco (see graphic previous page), Moses Lake (see below), and Wenatchee were beneficiaries of the federal government's WWII largesse. At Wenatchee's Pangborn Field, $50,000 was spent on three mile-long runways on the rationale that the bombers to be stationed at Moses Lake needed protection from the Pacific Theater. However, although improved, Pangborn Field was never used by Army Air Corps fighters and was returned to the community soon after the war.

Above: Tacoma Field prepared for the Army Air Corps by WPA laborers. Courtesy, National Archive, Alaska-Pacific NW Region, Saettle.

LARSON AIR FORCE BASE/ GRANT COUNTY AIRPORT

The air base built at Moses Lake was used for bomber training—its 3,502-foot runway is still one of the longest in the United States. After Larson AFB was closed in 1965, with a portion of it transferred to the Moses Lake Port District, the Grant County Airport was born, and it developed a unique niche. Because of the length of its runway, Japan Air Lines chose the airport for the center of its jet-crew training. Other more unconventional conversions included the use of one old B-52 hangar to grow mushrooms — about 400,000 pounds of them the first year. Another portion of the old base was taken over by Big Bend Community College whose flight training program kept the airport's air traffic controllers busy separating 747s from Piper Cubs. In 1975 the Grant County Airport tower was the fourth busiest — after Boeing, Boise, and Portland — in the Pacific Northwest. In 1982 it was still in fourth place, with Sea-Tac taking the third position from Boise. Periodically, the long runway at Moses Lake is mentioned as the likely choice for a regional airport connected to the Far East by supersonic jets and to Puget Sound by commuter flights or bullet trains. Partly with this in mind, the Grant County Airport hosted the supersonic Concorde for a series of icing tests in 1975. For a moment in 1984 the airport recalled its military past when the 62nd Military Airlift Wing returned to its former base while the runway at McChord Air Force Base was being resurfaced. In 1998, Grant County Airport expected to "follow" its 13,500-foot-long main runway into the third millen-

Two perspectives on the contemporary Grant County Airport. Courtesy, Port of Moses Lake.

Construction of the Boeing 747 plant in Everett during the late 1960s. Courtesy, Boeing Company Archives.

nium as a growing center for heavy-jet training and testing. Hopes for developing the airport as a hub for the handling of international cargo are encouraged by the size of the airport, with twice as much land as the cramped SeaTac International Airport near Seattle.

McChord Air Force Base

In the late 1950s Tacoma officials approached the Air Force about allowing joint military and municipal use of McChord AFB. They refused. Originally the site of the municipal Tacoma Field, the rough runway was improved by WPA labor in 1938 for use by the Army Air Corps. Renamed for William A. McChord, a colonel who died in a 1937 crash, the Air Corps opened its new base in 1940. McChord AFB first received the B-17 and B-24 bombers of the 17th Bombardment Group and soon thereafter received the B-25 medium bombers, some of whose aircrews participated in the first bombing of Tokyo — the Doolittle raid from the carrier *Hornet* in April, 1942. By 1943 Tacoma's ragged little field had grown into the largest bomber training base in America. Since the war McChord had gone through a variety of alterations to accommodate the "Jet Age," including an expansion in 1969-70 to accommodate jumbo jets like the C-5 Galaxy transport and the 747s contracted by the military for troop transport during the Vietnam War. Of all Air Force operations, McChord's were by far the most important in a 1981 inventory of the military's economic impact on the Puget Sound area. At the time it was the base for the 62nd Military Airlift Wing, the 38th Tactical Airlift Squadron, and the 318th Fighter Intercepter Squadron, with 5,300 military personnel and 1,300 civilian workers. Since then McChord has survived modern Air Force economics which has closed many bases. On January 1, 1995 McChord's territory of responsibility was doubled—as were the radar sites and aircraft under its control—when it assumed air defense responsibility for the entire western United States.

Paine Field

As at Pierce County's McChord base, Snohomish County's Paine Field was developed in part for its military potential during the depression with WPA funds. Unlike McChord, after the Army Air Corps took control of Paine Field, municipal use still figured in its postwar service. In 1937, the year $225,000 was designated for work on its north-south runway, the Snohomish County airport was also justified as an alternative to the growing congestion at Seattle's Boeing Field. Construction on the "new super airport north of the city limits" would give aircraft — especially commercial airliners — a second landing site when Boeing was fogged in. This civilian sanction was not needed with the beginning of World War II and the development of Sea-Tac.

During the war Paine Field boomed. However, unlike McChord at war's end, the Paine property commandeered from the county was returned to it. But the Air Force soon returned for the Korean conflict and stayed afterwards, buying a large section of the county property. The number of civilian landings first surpassed military touch downs: 37,000 versus 28,000 in 1965. Still, the Air Force retained its responsibility for operating the airport control tower, running the field fire department, and maintaining its runways, the longest of which has recently been lengthened from 7,300 to 9,000 feet.

Boeing's 1966 decision to build its 747s on a 700-acre site contiguous to Paine Field and the Air Force's exit in 1968 left the Snohomish County Planning Commission with a tangle of opportunities and problems. The flood of thousands of new Boeing workers and the opening of Paine Field for development generated a good deal of noise both political and auditory. In 1969 the commissioners described an airport that could develop into the air freight center of Puget Sound. When, within the year, the airport commission, planning to develop Paine Field into a regional airport, asked to extend its main runway to 12,000 feet, the proposal was crushed by the Snohomish County Commissioners who in 1971 informed the FAA of its "desire to withdraw" the airport's dreams of super-expansion.

Visions of a continuous merry-go-round of jets of all sizes was particularly noisome to the south county residents living beneath the airport flight paths. Of all the alternative roles described by the county planners, most of the residents polled — including Citizens for Responsible Development of Paine Field — favored the "do nothing" plan. The Snohomish County Commission's 1978 approval of their planning commission's recommendation of a general-aviation role for Paine Field was accepted by citizen activists as an acceptable compromise. The commission's assent, however, had a bizarre reversal when one of its three members claimed soon after the vote to have mistakenly chosen the planner's compromise proposal for more light planes when what he really wanted was the big ones. Ultimately, this political confusion brought all parties to the University of Washington's Office of Environmental Mediation where an agreement resembling the original compromise was worked out. Paine Field would continue to be oriented towards light aircraft while expanding its service to business and corporate aviation, public-service aviation, air-taxi, and commuter service.

In 1982 the FAA agreed with Paine Field manager, Don Bakken, that a second parallel runway 3,000 feet long and 3,000 feet east of the main runway would reduce noise by both shortening the time aircraft were kept waiting their turn to land and by moving general aviation landings and take-offs further east and away from the more developed area on the west side of Paine Field. The sensitivity to county-wide land-use goals included in the 1978-79 compromises was continued with the 1983 Paine Field comprehensive plan. This report predicted that the airport neighborhood, the area between Lynwood and Everett, Interstate-5 and Puget Sound, could eventually reach more than 200,000 residents. Also in 1983 the FAA designated Paine Field a "reliever" airport where jet airliners may land if Sea-Tac was fogged in — one of the original justifications for its construction in the late 1930s. In 1998 Paine was home for the production of the Boeing 747/ 767/ 777 models, and with the presence of B.F. Goodrich Aerospace's Tramco Division, it was also the site for the largest repair facility for commercial aircraft in the United States. The county's concern for the Paine Field environment is supported by its plans for a Wetland Education Park where an interpretive trail, greenhouse, and shelter will be featured with sixteen acres of enhanced and created wetlands. This "wetlands bank" is designed to mitigate the anticipated expansion of the airfield onto 5.5 acres of existing wetland.

AIRWAYS AND THE ENVIRONMENT

Environmental objections to airports and airways did not begin with the noise of the jet age. For instance, the long struggle to establish a seaplane site on Lake Washington during the 1930s was fought by the neighbors of Madison Park, who saw a site as more of a threat to the recreational values of the lake than to the peace and quiet of their homes. That the Seattle electorate agreed by rejecting the Madison Park site in a 1938 election was a convincing sign that it was not merely neighborhood activists who considered the lake shore part of their "back yard."

The variety of more recent environmental tests along Washington waterways includes the continuing contest between the birds of the Grays Harbor estuary and the aircraft using the Port of Grays Harbor's Bowerman Field. During spring migration more shore birds visit Grays Harbor than any other estuary on the Pacific Coast and Bowerman Basin, just north of the airport, supports nearly half of them. After nine years of studying the airport's impact on the special ecology of its immediate neighborhood, a sixteen-agency panel of experts in 1984 agreed in principle

Bill Broadhurst (left) and Leroy Gammon attend airworthiness test flights of the B-747 prototype, City of Everett. *Courtesy, Boeing Co. Archives.*

to move the airport to the south bay. However, "in practice" the airport has stayed at its Hoquiam site. At this writing (1998) the Port of Grays Harbor's 145-acre Bowerman Field is still coastal Washington's only jet-capable airport, with a 5,000-foot runway and parallel taxiway.

In Yakima it was not fowl but foliage that was threatened after the FAA in 1980 raised the airport's required visibility range from 2,400 to 4,000 feet. Fourteen trees were accused of forcing some commercial flights to land at Tri-Cities instead of Yakima. The city was not quick to act because the fourteen trees were well-loved in the arid valley where such foliage was a rarity.

In the same year that the trees beside the Yakima airport were besieged, the Port of Bremerton fought a television station's proposal to erect a 700-foot tower atop a 1,700-foot mountain only four miles from town on the grounds that it could dangerously interfere with the Kitsap County Airport's flight patterns. The FAA, however, demurred and allowed the tower construction on the condition that it be equipped with strobe lights. One year later, in 1981, Dean Willetts crashed his light plane into the tower and was killed.

Most often, of course, it is the noise that is found hazardous to the peace of citizens living nearby airports. In some situations, like that in Anacortes, airport officials can direct pilots on flight paths that take them far over water rather than above the homes of complaining neighbors. Occasionally, although rarely, a community like Moses Lake will develop an esprit de l'aeroport, and its citizens will hear music in the noise of even a Concorde. As noted above, Grant County's wide open and sparsely-settled spaces and the length of its airport runway support the recurring dream that someday Moses Lake will be the center for a regional airport receiving and sending with pride SSTs to and from the Far East. (Most recently this regional airport role has been linked with yet another great public works dream, that of a pneumatic tube delivering commuters between Puget Sound and Moses Lake via a high-speed surface transit.) But in the growing Pugetopolis it is principally the noise above and the vibrations below that stir the environmentalist urges, even within frequent fliers. And with the rapid escalation of passenger hours and the prospect of ever more noise, the conventional "not in my back yard" response expected of neighborhoods resisting the siting of prisons, landfills, freeways, and poorhouses is increasingly directed towards airports as well, though the development of fan jets and hi-bypass engines have significantly quieted aircraft since the 1980s.

In 1980 there were about 6,000 registered aircraft in the state and 23,400 licensed pilots. William H. Hamilton, then assistant

With Sand Point and Bellevue closed, Boeing Field saturated, and Paine Field too far from Seattle's business center, Bob Monroe, vice president of the Aircraft Owners and Pilots Association, warned that Seattle would lose business. In 1979 well over half of Boeing Field's airplane operations were for business-oriented visitors. The recent federal deregulation of airline operations permitted carriers to abandon flights to smaller communities, thereby increasing Boeing Field's service to corporate and charter flights. The current 55-mile-an-hour speed limit also encouraged flight and so increased airport congestion. In 1981 Boeing Field was the tenth busiest airport in the country in terms of take-offs and landings. The airport was also base for 645 aircraft, well above the 550 that the field's 1976 master plan said would mark the saturation point. The several small community fields at Auburn, Martha Lake, Kent, Snohomish, Sultan, and Pierce County's Thun Field near Puyallup — in 1979 the fourth busiest general aviation field in the state — offered some relief for light-aircraft pilots. For a few fortunates the Renton municipal airport provided an alternative closer to the Seattle core.

RENTON MUNICIPAL AIRPORT

In 1979 the U.S. Customs opened a port of entry at the Renton airport — on a call-ahead basis. At the time, most light aircraft coming from Canada were forced to clear customs at Sea-Tac. Renton Airport was first designated an entry port in 1928, when it was still called the Bryn Mawr Field. Its 2,300-foot sand runway, graded in 1922, lay between a lumber mill and the rechanneled Cedar River, which was a Black River tributary rechanneled into Lake Washington. The Black River dried up in 1916 with the nine-foot lowering of Lake Washington to the level of Lake Union for the opening of the Lake Washington Ship Canal. Renton's

Will Rogers steps ashore at Renton to meet the press. Courtesy, Harold "Jiggs" Hoyt.

secretary for the state Aeronautics Commission, predicated at the time that these numbers would double by the year 2000. Also in 1980 the state's Airport System Plan called for eight new general-aviation airports in the Puget Sound region by the turn of the century. The need for a new general aviation airport on the east side of Lake Washington was especially desired after the closing of the private Bellevue Airfield in 1980. Yet the prospects for such a development were not promising given citizen resistance. A series of eastside community forums in 1978 revealed that most residents of the area were unwilling to tolerate the added noise for the convenience of what they characterized as a few recreational fliers. An exasperated Gov. John Spellman concluded "there will be organized groups opposing any airport of any size anywhere."

AIRWAYS

airport began at the shoreline of the lake with a plank ramp for Eddie Hubbard's seaplane. The future Boeing vice president was awarded the right in 1920 to carry mail by air between Seattle and Victoria — the U.S.'s first international route. For about a year Hubbard operated this franchise with his Boeing B-I flying boat from Bryn Mawr, the community bordering Renton to the north on the west side of the lake. In 1929 Northwest Air Service built a hangar at the site and exploited its sea-land link by servicing Alaska bush pilots who ordered their floats changed to wheels or vice-versa. On August 5, 1935 Will Rogers and Wiley Post landed at Renton's "sand pile" to trade their wheels for pontoons. During their two-day wait Rogers fished in Elliott Bay and played some polo before resuming with Post their round-the-world flight from Lake Washington. Eight days later both men were killed in a crash on the tundra near Point Barrow, Alaska.

Boeing's part in the Renton story began early in World War II with a contract to build military flying boats for offshore patrol duty. With the company plant along the Duwamish dedicated to B-17s, Boeing purchased Bonnell's Nursery beside both the lake and the old Bryn Mawr runway as an ideal place to construct the Model XPBB-1 "Sea Ranger." However, by the time Boeing's Renton assembly line was ready, the order was changed to the land-based long-range B-29 bomber, for which the Bryn Mawr runway was considerably widened, lengthened, and paved in 1943. The Renton plant soon reached a production schedule of eighty-five planes a month and more than eleven hundred B-29s were delivered from the site. After the war, the vastly improved Renton field was returned to the city for a price of one dollar, and for a time the Boeing plant was used by the Navy to store surplus flying boats. Plane production resumed in 1948 with construction of military transport C-97s. In 1954 the Renton field first introduced the Boeing 707 prototype — the Dash-80 — to the skies, and in 1956 the Renton plant became the Boeing Transport Division. By 1962 the company had bought the land and facilities from the federal government, and soon occupied the majority of the airport's usable space.

Following 1973-74 improvements to Renton Airport, its traffic control tower was named "Tower of the Year" for the FAA's Northwest Region in 1975. Six years later the tower was temporarily shut down by its controllers who acted in solidarity with their union in a nationwide strike that was ultimately broken by the Reagan Administration in its first year. At the time Renton was handling an estimated 17,000 planes a month, most of them general aviation aircraft mixed with a few Boeing jets.

In 1997 the Renton airport had roughly 140,000 operations.

Because its mile-long runway is set in a narrow field— 800- to 1,900 feet-wide—the airport does not have the space required for the paraphernalia of an all-weather instrument landing system. Instead, Renton Airport expects that its number of operations will increase considerably as the all-weather accuracy of the Global Positioning System (GPS) for aviation improves. The airport also expects the increasing prosperity of business on both sides of Lake Washington to increase its service to corporate aircraft. And at its northwest corner, the airport continues its historic tie to seaplanes with the Will Rogers-Wiley Post Memorial Seaplane Base.

Top: Aerial of Boeing's 1928 dedication ceremonies. Courtesy, King County Public Works. Above: Cartoon from April 21, 1930 Post-Intelligencer *promoting Seattle Air Week activities at Boeing Field. Left: Aerial looking north over Boeing Field to Georgetown, 1949. Left of center is the Boeing plant between East Marginal Way and the Duwamish River. South Park is at far left. Courtesy, Boeing Company Archives.*

BOEING FIELD

O n Sept. 15, 1926 Grover Tyler landed an open-cockpit single-engine mail plane on a sandy field near Boeing's "Red Barn" plant on the west side of the Duwamish River. It was the beginning of coastwise mail service by Pacific Air Transport, a predecessor of United Air Lines. Ten months later this field and the one at Renton were two of the six sites investigated by the Seattle Chamber of Commerce's Aviation Committee for a large municipal airport. However, the acreage chosen was a seventh site set on county property across the river from the Boeing plant. Although this Georgetown location was neither on Elliott Bay nor featured a lake — a provision originally recommended by the chamber committee which desired an airport for both sea and land planes — the chosen site was large, located between two paved highways, beside four transcontinental railways, on two streetcar lines, and only ten minutes from downtown Seattle. The site's proximity to the Boeing company also figured in its selection. On dedication day, July 26, 1928, William Boeing told the 20,000 attending that "This day is just about the happiest one of my life." The new airport was named in his and his industry's honor. In touting the importance of the new facility before the crowd, state senator, W.W. Conner, culled a pioneer example. "Boeing Field today means more to Seattle and the Northwest than the building of the old Yesler Wharf meant to our pioneer citizens."

Runway construction at the county site had begun the preceding March. Among the crew were six prisoners, all serving on "lazy husband" charges. The field was graded, in part, by fill dredged from the Duwamish Waterway. It was a gift of the federal government which was pleased to find some useful place to dump it. Boeing Field quickly took shape. On May 14, 1929, the first large hangar was dedicated with what the *Seattle Times* described as "the greatest air circus Seattle ever witnessed." Among the speakers was Gov. Roland Hartley who declined the opportunity to a ride aloft but agreed to be photographed in the cockpit of an Arrow Sport biplane. (Having vetoed the legislature's bill for

Top: Boeing's original "Red Barn" plant at its original site beside the Duwamish River. Above: The restored barn at its new home next to the Museum of Flight at Boeing Field. Courtesy, Museum of Flight. (See p. 180 for record of the Red Barn's trip up the Duwamish to Boeing Field.) Bottom: Faye Dodd, Oscar Liebst, Nita Townsend, and Al Smith were among the hundreds of Boeing workers who painted their names on the 5,000th post-Pearl Harbor B-17 "Flying Fortress." Courtesy, Boeing Co. Archives.

Above left: The roof of the Boeing B-17 plant across the Duwamish from South Park as it was camouflaged during World War II. Above right: A Boeing employee stands above the Flying Fortress assembly lines at the intersection of Synthetic Street and Burlap Boulevard. Courtesy, Boeing Company Archives.

emergency airfields in the Cascades also in 1929, the governor might have had a fear of flying but not of photo opportunities.) Completed the following year were both the Boeing Company hangar and the airport administration building with its restaurant, ticket office, and quarters for the immigration department and the weather bureau. Also in 1930, Don Evans, a past county engineer who was then chairman of the King County Commissioners, advised that if an amphibian port was still desired at the Boeing site, then one of the drained sections of the old river, since abandoned with the construction of the Duwamish Waterway, could be dammed and refilled for seaplanes. It was an idea as ephemeral as the Port of Seattle's sproposal to build an airport at Fort Lawton that same year.

Most of the improvements made at Boeing Field during the depression — some of them with WPA funds — were illuminating and included a lighted wind indicator, fifteen floodlights, lights bordering the runway, and a light gun used to signal pilots landing or preparing to take off. On June 18, 1938 a radio landing-control system started beaming its signals to aircraft entering a fourteen-mile radius of the field. The new technology was a necessity, for Boeing Field was busy with three major airlines, hundreds of private planes and twenty-two transport operations. Already, in 1935 the Federal Bureau of Air Commerce was publicly contemplating the construction of a new "super-airport" near Seattle to handle the larger planes soon expected, aircraft for which the ridge bordering Boeing Field might present a hazard. In 1941 when a $223,000 defense appropriation was made for repaving the main runway and constructing a testing apron for Boeing's B-17 bombers, R.D. Bedinger, regional manager of the Civil Aeronautics Administration objected on the grounds that the federal funds should be used on a new airport. Boeing Field was then the busiest airport in the Northwest. In September of that year the field handled a record 16,079 takeoffs and landings. In October the new runway was opened and the numbers increased. Then suddenly in December Boeing Field was closed to everything except military aircraft. This extreme — although typical — reaction to Pearl Harbor was quickly rescinded. Soon United, Northwest and Trans-Canada Airlines, which had all been diverted to Paine Field, were invited back. In 1945 they moved again, this time voluntarily, to the new Seattle-Tacoma International Airport. Improvements, however, continued at Boeing Field.

In 1945 $2 million was spent in draining, paving, lighting, and strengthening the runway to counter the abuse from Boeing's new 120,000-pound B-29 bombers. Six years later it was extended to 10,000 feet to accommodate testing the then-new B-52s. The new runway was dedicated on December 7, 1951, the tenth anniversary of the bombing of Pearl Harbor. When the YB-52 was first tested no photographs were allowed, and guards surrounded

the airport to enforce the ban. More improvements were made for new generations of jets in 1958. Also that year the field's shorter light-plane runway was lengthened from 1,800 to 2,900 feet. By 1962, the year of Seattle's Century 21 Exposition, Boeing Field ranked second among Western airports in its peak-hour operations.

Boeing Field's 1965 national ranking of twenty-fifth in total aircraft operations was primarily the result of the volume of light planes using the field. In 1971, Hughes Airwest, the last major airline to regularly use the field, moved to Sea-Tac. According to field manager, Don Smith, the field which had once been crowded with DC3s and B-17s had developed into a general aviation facility — a base for commuter flying, charter airlines, and general and corporate flying. But by 1972 it was run down, although with income from its tenants and fuel sales it was also self-sustaining. Improvements costing $800,000 helped repair facilities, and the following year, 1973, the FAA built its new $2.5 million headquarters on the southwest side. Six years later King County purchased four acres nearby for the Pacific Museum of Flight, and soon Boeing moved its original "Red Barn" factory to the site.

In 1978 the federal government deregulated the airlines. The elimination of regular airline service to many smaller communities that followed increased the frequency of corporate and charter flights to Boeing Field and swelled the number of its operations to 419,484 in 1981. When these statistics propelled King County's airport to the status of the nation's tenth busiest airport in terms of takeoffs and landings, its assistant manager, Jack Frazelle, quipped, "We're now referring to Sea-Tac as 'the other airport.'" However, that year the field's air carrier operations, including cargo flights, scheduled flights, and the occasional diversion from Sea-Tac, numbered only just over 15,000. By 1997 Boeing Field's total operations had slipped some to 369,831, but the share of air carrier operations had increased to over 57,000. The airport master plan, to be published in the fall of 1998, is expected to emphasize service for mixed cargo and corporate users. Already in 1996 the latter role was advanced with the construction of Microsoft co-founder Paul Allen's hangar for his Boeing 757 at Boeing Field. That Bill Gates, the other of the area's two aging computer wunderkinds, was expected to purchase a jet of his own in 1998 was a matter of keen interest to both King County and Renton airports.

SEATTLE-TACOMA INTERNATIONAL AIRPORT

In 1994 the Seattle-Tacoma International Airport was a regional nexus for cosmopolitan culture regularly visited by sixteen international airlines and hosted by interpreters fluent in twenty languages. The notion of a super airport for Seattle became current in the mid 1930s because of the growing congestion at Boeing Field. Federal aviation experts were thinking big, contemplating the needs of planes too huge and too fast, they thought, for the hills beside Boeing Field. Perhaps even their most inflated dreams of speed and size could not have fabricated a Concorde or a 747 both of which managed well enough at the King County airport. But the super airport boomers did not need to deprecate Boeing Field to have their proposals ultimately realized in the concrete and steel of Sea-Tac's 11,900-foot runway and facilities. Pearl Harbor got them started.

With American entry into War II, the military immediately designated Boeing Field a reserve for testing Boeing's B-17 bombers, and bumped the airlines north to Paine Field. Although they were soon allowed to return, the search for an alternate Seattle runway became a priority. That the Bow Lake acreage was chosen over a site east of Lake Sammamish that was widely favored by both King County officials and the Army had, at least, something to do with the desire of United Airlines to keep control of their primary franchise to move passengers to and from Tacoma. The airline helped convince the trinity of Pierce County, the City of Tacoma, and the Port of Tacoma to put up $100,000 of the initial $1,660,000 required to build the new field. Five hundred and sixty thousand dollars was Seattle's share, but $1 million offered by the C.A.A. was initially described by the Port of Seattle as "hopelessly inadequate." Initially cool to the suggestion that it both manage the money and the airport, the Port of Seattle commissioners were warmed by the military's conviction that even without the war the new field was needed.

Warren Magnuson, the state's modern public works conjurer, was on hand at the 1942 ground breaking. On April 18th, the day Jimmie Doolittle's B-24s made the first raid on Tokyo, General Surveyor Ray Bishop's crew started work on the Highline site. Part of Bishop's survey took him over the short dirt runway of the private Bow Lake airport developed there in the late 1930s. Bishop's chainmen bumped into lovers, a gun-waving home owner, and an army machine gun nest hidden in the scotch broom covering the northwest corner of the field's original 906 acres. On October 31, 1944 a United Airlines mainliner DC3 carrying VIP officials from every relevant institution and agency — Port, CAA, UAL, Municipal League, Chamber of Commerce — hopped over from Boeing Field to Sea-Tac for the latter's first official landing. The airport, which officially

Jan. 31st/1947
First Temp. Term'l. Bldg.

No! This is not Sears Roebuck this is the Seattle Tacoma Airport

opened in 1947, wasn't fully appreciated until its full-service passenger terminal and administration building was dedicated on July 9, 1949 before 30,000 celebrants. The combined structure cost $3 million and brought total construction costs that time to $11 million.

The Alaska connection predicted for the airport when it was first proposed in the mid-1930's became a reality in 1951 as a key route flown by Alaska Airlines, in its operations out of Sea-Tac. (Twenty-five years later during the construction of the Northern Tier pipeline, freight bound for Alaska accounted for about 40 percent of the airport's total outbound cargo.) In 1953 the airport's Air Cargo Terminal was constructed and between 1956 and 1958 the main north-south runway was extended 1,900 feet to 10,400 feet to accommodate the new commercial jet aircraft. Japan Airlines, the first foreign overseas airline to operate in Seattle, arrived in 1959. That year, the North Concourse (D) was completed, and two years later the South Concourse (A) was added as well. By 1967, twenty years after the first temporary passenger terminal was constructed, the Port was preparing to make massive field and terminal improvements. Construction began in 1968 and continued through the 1973 dedication of Sea-Tac's new passenger terminal. Resembling a great boomerang, the new terminal was superimposed over the original administration building dedicated twenty-four years earlier. A new parking garage with dramatically corkscrewing ramps to its several levels was constructed in the arch of the terminal's swept-wing form. Two satellite terminals were linked to the main building by an underground subway negotiated by computer-controlled cars. The total cost of the five-year project was about $175 million financed by revenue bonds paid off principally by the airlines' landing fees.

By 1974, the year of the airport's silver anniversary, the 6,100-foot runway in use in 1949 had been extended to 11,900 feet and a second parallel strip 9,500-feet long was added. Work on the airport's north roadway access won the FAA's 1975 National Beautification Award for landscaping. Four years later Sea-Tac won an environmental award of a different sort when its anti-noise ST/Communities Plan, the first major off-airport land acquisition program in the U.S. designed to reduce the disturbing effects of aircraft noise on the community, won the American Institute of Planners Meritorious Program Award. By 1980 the FAA's part in this properties acquisition program at Sea-Tac amounted to $23 million for a process begun only five years ear-

Above: Snapshots by Ray O. Bishop, one of the original construction engineers at the airport, excerpted from his album "Sea-Tac from the Beginning." Scenes include the portrait, above, of the VIPs who completed the field's first official landing at the airport on Oct. 31, 1944, after a short flight from Boeing Field. Courtesy, WA State Archives, Bellevue, Sea-Tac Collection.

Left: Dedication ceremonies, July 9, 1949, for Sea-Tac's new passenger terminal gave celebrants access to the field and aircraft exhibited there. Courtesy, MOHAI, Seattle P-I Collection. Below: The new Sea-Tac Terminal and its surreal parking garage, 1973. Courtesy, Port of Seattle.

lier. Also in 1974, the airport won yet another FAA environment award, this time for its North Sea-Tac Park Plan that designated 420 acres of its newly acquired land as a park.

The Port of Seattle's sudden decision in 1983 to change the airport's name from Sea-Tac to the Henry M. Jackson International Airport was a quick lesson for its commissioners on the importance of names. On many previous occasions, the Seattle Port's candid desire to drop the 'Tacoma' from Sea-Tac was predictably met with such rebut from Pierce County that the proposal was withdrawn. But this time the criticisms arrived from all directions. Although the Washington State Board of Geographic Names does not name man-made structures like the airport, it did advise the Port commissioners to follow their policy of waiting for at least one year after a person's death before naming any natural feature for the deceased — to avoid hasty decisions based on sentiment. In 1984, before the scores of businesses surrounding the airport and often dependent on it had to order new stationery, the name was changed back to Sea-Tac. Clearly, the community identified with its airport and by its own investigations the Port might have known better than to suddenly switch the name. A 1984 Port study revealed that one in eight jobs in King County were Port-related. Included within this statistic were 25,580 jobs directly generated by Sea-Tac.

Nine years after first adopting its policy of abating noise by buying land, the Port committed to its 1985 Noise Remedy Program $140 million to buy more land, insulate homes, and offer home-selling assistance to its neighbors. Sea-Tac was, of course, busier than ever. Since the 1978 deregulation of airlines the number of its major carriers had more than doubled from a dozen to twenty-six. By 1989 more than half of Sea-Tac flights involved State III (the quietest) aircraft. That year its passenger total reached 15,241,072, a figure about thirty times greater than that enumerated when its first modern terminal was dedicated thirty years earlier in 1949. As constituted in 1990 the airport figured it could accommodate 25 million passengers a year.

Following the Noise Mediation Committee's 1990 agreement to reduce aircraft noise by at least 50 percent by the year 2001, Sea-Tac's noise control program became the most comprehensive in the nation, including nighttime restrictions on noisier aircraft. Rules required yearly noise reductions by the airlines, and it was expected that the ongoing Noise Remedy Program, begun in 1974, would ultimately involve the relocation of 3,000 residents and the insulation of 10,000 homes.

In 1991 the FAA upgraded Sea-Tac to a first class airport. Sea-Tac was first world-wide in one category, that of sea/air cargo. It also ranked number eight as an international gateway to Asia and Europe, number fourteen in the U.S. in total air cargo volume, and number twenty-two in total passenger volume.

In 1991, the year Sea-Tac was upgraded by the FAA to a First Class Airport, the Puget Sound Council of Governments' (PSCG) Air Transportation Committee concluded in its final report that "no configuration of Sea-Tac could, by itself, provide sufficient capacity to meet the region's commercial air transportation needs through the year 2020." Two years later PSCG's successor, the Puget Sound Regional Council, recommended both a second major airport for Puget Sound and a third runway for Sea-Tac.

In 1971, the first full year after the airport's second runway was opened 800 feet west of its first, Sea-Tac ran a total of 114,372 operations. Thirteen years later in 1984 the number of operations had nearly doubled to 223,828, accomodating 10,474,630 passengers. And in 1997, another thirteen years later, Sea-Tac handled a record 24.7 million passengers, a volume pressing its projected capacity of 25 million. In 1998, of the $1.7 billion projected for the Port of Seattle's capital improvement plan at Sea-Tac, $587 million was dedicated to building its controversial third runway. The runway's greatest objectors are its neighbors who are required to live with the growing noise and congestion that come with expansion of Sea-Tac's operations. A less noisy addition to the Sea-Tac skyline will be the new air traffic control tower, the plans for which the Federal Aviation Administration unveiled in December 1997. Considerably higher than the 100-foot tower it replaces, the new $20-million, 265-foot observatory will be paid for by passengers paying ticket tax into the FAA's Aviation Trust Fund.

Washington Territorial Council Bill No. 16 of 1854: 64

Washington territorial bill, 1853 (federal), 65

Washington territorial legislature 63-64

Washington Territory 338; bridge tolls 105; choice of capitol 338; county divisions 343; ferry regulation 36; separation from Oregon 65, 147; territorial proclamation 4; territorial roads 63-64; university 159, 169, 369

Washington (ferry) 36

Washington Toll Bridge Authority 36, 121-124

Washington Water Power Company 241, 244, 276, 277-278, 290, 294, 298, 304; Long Lake plant and dam 278; Monroe Street dam and power project 278

Washington Water Research Center 215, 271

Washington Writers Project, 1941: 166, 387

Washington's Audacious State Capitol and Its Builders 338

Washougal River bridge on "Evergreen Highway" 108

waste disposal: early practices 311-312

Waste Not Washington Law, 1989: 333

wastewater projects, 1930-45: 315

wastewater systems: combined sewer overflows 313-314, 327; contact beds 312; early systems 312-314; first secondary treatment system 315; nonpoint pollution 327-328; oxidation lagoons 320; plant operator training program 316; post-WWII plants 316; separated sewer system 313, 323, 327; sewer system overflows 327-328; trickling filter unit 316; West Seattle interceptor system 323

water conservation 198; irrigation sprinkler systems 215; minimum river and stream level requirements 217

water conservation districts 268

water pollution: aquifer protection area 201; aquifer protection district 198; bacterial contamination 320; controlling contamination 211-212; federal water quality legislation 317-319; fish kills 321; groundwater supply 215-216, 334; landfill contamination 332; public health 315; reuse of waste water 198; stormwater runoff 327

Water Pollution Control Act of 1948: 317

Water Pollution Control Act of 1956: 318

Water Pollution Control Commission 318, 320, 322

Water Quality Act of 1965: 318

Water Resources Act of 1971: 217

water rights 216-219; Ahtanum Creek 236; appropriation doctrine 216; competing uses 218; deficiencies of permit system 217; Department of Ecology 217; hydropower versus irrigation 218-219; Indian water rights 199,219-220; instream water uses 217-219; irrigation use 229; riparian law 216

water treatment 210-212; chlorination 211; drinking water standards 212, 315; filtration 210-211; municipal and industrial water supply development 214; slow sand filters 210

water utility coordination 214-215; Public Water System Coordination Act of 1978: 215

waterborne disease 211

Waterfront trolley (Seattle) 187

Waterhouse, Frank 112

Watershed Protection and Flood Prevention Act of 1954: 268

watersheds 206-210; Cedar River 208-209; flood control 268; Green River 198,209; Domerie Creek Roslyn 210

Waterville, WA 70, 80, 82, 345

Watkins, James D. 335

Wells Dam 28, 301

Wenatchee, WA 25, 91, 398; bridges 111; Carnegie library 355; Columbia River port 25-28; pioneer water service 194; population growth 241; solid waste management 328; Upper Columbia Navigational Conference 28; WPA funded school 14

Wenatchee Canal Company 227

Wenatchee River 211

Wenatchee Valley irrigation 226, 227

WERA, See Washington Emergency Relief Administration

West, A. J. 183

West Bridge (Aberdeen) 183

west coast intertie 302

west coast power grid 302

West Monitor Bridge 107

West Point (Seattle): lighthouse 56, 326; waste treatment facility 323-324, 326-327

West Seattle 35, 323, bridges 127, 179, 181-182; Carnegie library 357; WPA golf course 13

West Valley Highway (Green River) 83

West Wishkah River Bridge 107

Western Shore Magazine 137

Western Washington State Hospital (Steilacoom) 358

Western Washington University: campus structures 373; origin 222

Westinghouse, George 277

Westlake Mall (Seattle) 169

Weyerhaeuser Company 320, 321

Weyerhaeuser, Frederick 153

Whatcom 68, 149-151. *See also* Bellingham, WA.

Whatcom City Hall 349

Whatcom County 72, 77, 343

Whatcom County Courthouse 343, 346-347

Whatcom Creek 67, 149-151, 268

Whatcom Museum of History and Art 349

wheat growing 225

Wheelabrator Spokane, Inc. 332

Whidbey Island Naval Air Station 396, 397, 399

Whidbey Island: Possession Point 34

White, Aubrey Lee 178-179

White Bluffs, WA 229; White Bluffs to Othello Road depression-time funding 11

White, Harry 339

White Pass: CCC campgrounds 15

White River 32, 68. *See also* Green River; Auburn Wall diversion dam 259; flood control 257-259; flood of 1906 258; hydroelectric development 279-280

White River and Stuck Valley Road (1879 map) 68

Whitehouse, Harold 370

Whitman County 70; Courthouse 266

Whitman, Marcus 116

Whitman mission massacre 341

Wilbur, WA 82, 382, 398

Wilder, Walter 339

wildlife preservation 217

Wilkes, Lieutenant Charles (1841 Wilkes Expedition) 18-19, 29, 171, 337

Wilkeson, WA 347; school 381

Willapa Bay 19, 85, 143

Willapa Lighthouse 19

Willapa River 20

Willapa ("Mosquito Fleet" steamer) 35, 37

Williams, Benezette 202, 313

Williamson, Henry 139

Wilson, C. Lewis 344

Wilson, Major John 24

Wilson, Pres. Woodrow 229

Winlock, WA 378

Winsor, William W. 55

Winters v. United States 219

Wish-ham Cemetery 301

Wishkah River 182, 214; bridge 183

Wobblies 234. *See* International Workers of the World

Wohleb, Joseph 348

Wolman, Abel 322

wood block paving 139, 153, 172

Woodbridge, Sally 351

Wooden Boats Festival (Port Townsend) 51

Woods, Mrs. A. D. 182

Woods, Rufus 241, 292-293

workers' rights 233

Works Progress Administration (WPA) 10-16 87; airport projects 397-399, 401, 407; *American Imprints* 15; Bonneville Dam project 298; depression-era road building 86-87; Everett pipeline 206; flood control work 256, 259-261; Franklin Roosevelt Lake 243; 1941 statistics on work completed 14; public art projects 389-390; sewage treatment facilities 316; shovel work 11, 14; *Told by the Pioneers* 15; WA Writers Project 389

Works Projects Administration 10

World War I: postwar roads 81; postwar veterans' settlement program 229; Puget Sound industrialization 34; Puget Sound Naval Shipyard 53

World War II: coastal defenses 51; effect on airports 397-407; effect on Seattle waterfront 43; effects on public housing 384-385; exploitation of the Columbia 298; Histori-cal Records Survey 15; Puget Sound industrialization 34; Puget Sound Naval Shipyard 53; roads for defense 88; role of electric power in defense production 298

World's Fair, Seattle 96, 187-188, 342, 363, 390, 407

World's Fair, Spokane 175, 364, 400

World's Fairs 363-364

WPA. *See* Works Progress Administration, also Work Projects Administration.

Wright, Charles B. 196, 280

Wright, George 69

WWPSS. *See* Washington Water Power Supply System.

Wyckoff, Ambrose Barkley 52-53

Wynooche Dam 214

Y

Yacolt, WA 375-376; CCC clearing of Yacolt Burn 15

Yakama Indians and Reservation 220, 235-236, 259, 388.

Yakima, WA: 155-156; airport 397-398, 403; bicyclists 162; early streets 155; federal building 353; Fire station #1 362; trolleys 186; waste treatment 316

Yakima Canal and Land Co. 228

Yakima City. *See* Union Gap

Yakima County: typhoid rate 212

Yakima Indians. *See* Yakama Indians and Reservation

Yakima Land Company 226

YB-52 (Boeing bomber) 407

Yakima River 66; 1933 flood 259, 261; bridges 110; degradation of 316; diversion dam 237;over-appropriated use 229; pollution 211-212

Yakima (ferry) 26, 37

Yakima Valley: effects of irrigation 227, 238; population growth 240

Yakima Valley irrigation system 226, 233; diversion dam 237; Kennewick Division 237; Kittitas Division 233, 236; Roza Division 237; storage reservoirs 237-238; Sunnyside Division 234; Tieton Canal 233-234; Wapato Division 235

Yale Bridge 128

Yarrow Bay 323

Yellowstone Trail 83

Yelm Prairie 66

Yesler, Henry 40, 70-72, 171, 201, 277

Yesler Terrace (Seattle) 384

Young, Colonel Robert 21

Z

Ziegler, Louis 199

Zillah, WA 228; secondary sewage treatment plant 316

ABOUT THE AUTHORS

For years it was a popular curiosity at the State Museum on the University of Washington campus. This state map was painted on its raw indigenous "canvas" sometime between 1911, when Pend Oreille County was separated from Stevens County, and 1915, when Chehalis County was renamed Grays Harbor County. The line of Elliott Bay is defaced by the thousands of fingers that have pointed out where each finger's owner stood. The authors, who are also in Seattle (and near the U.W. campus) use this as a cautionary sign. In *Building Washington* they have tried to transcend any west or "wet side" bias. Paul Dorpat was raised and schooled in Spokane, and Genevieve McCoy also comes from the East Side — Kirkland, on the east side of Lake Washington. Dr. McCoy teaches history at the U.W. Bothell Campus, and the untitled Dorpat has several book titles on regional history.

Above: Harold Balazs stands next to his untitled stainless steel sculpture that was commissioned for the Spokane centennial. Photo by Mary Randlett.

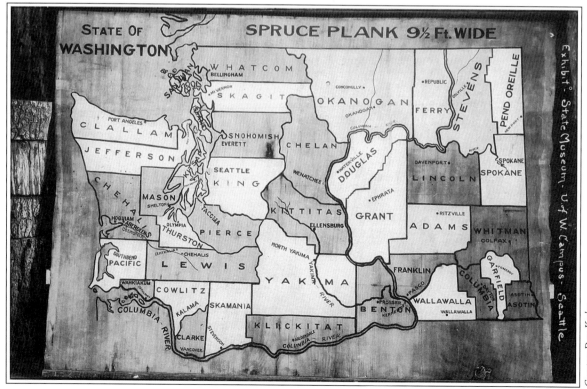

American Public Works Association Washington Chapter History

James Robertson

**ORIGINAL PETITIONERS —
WASHINGTON CHAPTER,
APWA 1955**

Chester L. Waggener, Pullman
Clyde Bergdahl, Richland
John R. Goggin, Richland
Harold N. Petty, Richland
Melvin Nilson, Richland
Rodney V. Colvin, Everett
Josehp F. Kulnush, Seattle
Walter Starkweather, Seattle
James Robertson, Seattle
William E. Parker, Seattle
E. H. Lindstrom, Seattle
J. Royal, Aberdeen
John J. Sleavin, Aberdeen
Alva Yeager, Centralia
Oscar E. Olson, Bellingham
F. L. Scholz, Bellingham
D. B. Wheaton, Bremerton
William A. Lyons, Spokane
Chester E. Murray, Wenatchee
G. M. Burns, Yakima
Grant E. Huey, Yakima
Stephen H. Suzer, Yakima
William A. Stancer, Tacoma

The American Public Works Association (APWA) was formed from the merger of two organizations. The oldest of these, the American Society of Municipal Engineers, originated in the midst of the economic depression that followed the financial panic of 1893. Twenty percent of the nation's labor force was then without work, and public works were looked upon by many communities as among the few opportunities available to alleviate the widespread distress. Jobs like park landscaping, sweeping alleys, and shoveling snow were examples of the largely unskilled day labor developed by municipalities to make jobs in a kind of rehearsal for a performance that would be commonplace during the Great Depression of the 1930s.

Like most other depressions, that of the mid-1890s encouraged an array of radical responses — socialist, populist, and utopian. Although not revolutionaries, the engineers who formed their society in 1894 were motivated by the progressive faith that relief would come more speedily to distressed communities by improving the quality of their public facilities and services as well as the public's understanding and support of them.

The APWA's second predecessor, the International Association of Public Works Officials, was formed in 1919, and 18 years later the two parents joined to form the American Public Works Association. Of course, this 1937 creation was also influenced by the profound role public works was playing in the national struggle to rise from the depression.

Another 19 years passed before the Washington Chapter of the APWA held its first annual meeting on May 9, 1956 in the Hotel Chinook in Yakima. Appropriately, the featured speaker during the noon luncheon was APWA Executive Director Donald F. Herrick who addressed the new chapter on the history, aims, and activities of the national association. Nearly a year earlier, on July 26, 1955, Herrick had notified J.R. Robertson, principal engineer with the Seattle Engineering Department, that the petition for chapter status by the Washington Chapter's temporary committee had been approved. The national APWA board of directors had given unanimous assent to the by-laws composed by the original 23 members of the temporary committee.

Most of the Washington Chapter's original petitioners, whose names are listed at left, were engineers working for municipalities. At their first annual meeting the charter membership discussed strategies for increasing chapter membership and including those in private industry whose activities related to the building and maintaining of public works. Another feature of the Yakima assembly which would become a regular part of the chapter's annual meetings were

panel discussions on a variety of public works related topics. In 1956 the meeting's organizers arranged panels on contract plans and specifications, storm drainage problems and financing, and sidewalk and street programs — all subjects of sustained interest to public works professionals.

The Washington Chapter developed a tradition of holding its yearly bi-annual conferences at different locations around the state. While each year members elect new officers and board of directors, there remains a significant continuity in the variety of professional and personal friendships which have developed in the chapter through its life. The meetings have also allowed hosting municipalities to exhibit not only their public works, but their cultural and recreational opportunities as well. Field trips have included visits to a new sewage treatment plant and a lake well-stocked with rainbow trout.

What follows is a year-by-year summary of events which highlighted the first 35 years of the Washington Chapter's history. Also included within this yearly catalogue are the names of the public works professionals who were elected by the membership to guide the association through the year. Many of these leaders will be familiar to persons connected in some way with public works in Washington. That only a few will be known by state citizens generally is evidence of the truism that the public is considerably more dependent on public works than conscious of them. Of course, *Building Washington* was written, in part, to expand citizen understanding of the helpful part public works and workers have played in their lives.

Seventy persons attended the first meeting of the APWA Washington Chapter. By 1966, ten years after it was formed, chapter membership had grown to more than 300, and by 1990 the rolls had swelled to more than 1,025 members.

Each year the APWA President's Plaque Award is directed to the one chapter of the 64 that make up the International APWA which has made the greatest advancement in growth and service during the preceeding year. Remarkably, in its first 35 years, the Washington Chapter has received this most distinguished award seven times. Included among the chapter's other historical honors are 11 APWA Membership Citation Awards, and three APWA Heritage Awards. Twice each year Washington Chapter members can review this meritorious history of their organization in the awards banner, reproduced on the previous page and above, which is displayed at the chapter's spring and fall meetings. ◆

1956 - 1957

William A. Stancer
Chapter President, 1956-1957

OFFICERS

President - William A. Stancer
Vice-President - C. E.Murray
Secretary-Treasurer - Chester L.
  Waggener

BOARD OF DIRECTORS

Robert Anderson
George S. McClean
P. N. Royal
L. P. Staman

The organizational meeting of the Washington Chapter APWA was held in the Chinook Hotel, Yakima, May 9, 1956. Conference topics included discussion of soils testing, construction standards and specifications, storm drainage, and a number of street maintenance topics. One year later, on June 5-6, 1957 the Washington Chapter held its first annual meeting, which was attended by 47 people, at the Hotel Leopold in Bellingham. The group continued its work of developing programs and policies for the fledgling organization. It was agreed that in addition to the spring meeting there should be a yearly fall meeting. Among the new activities adopted were the appointment of committees, one to study methods of financing storm sewers, and another to establish a recruitment and training program for attracting college graduates to the public works field. The latter committee was also asked to study salary schedules and job classifications. The need for an intensive membership drive was also discussed.

In addition to transacting chapter business, the conventioneers attended panel discussions on standardization, focusing on the report of the chapter's Committee on Standardization. Unquestionably, the most significant work undertaken in 1957, the committee's report set standards for curbs, gutters and sidewalks, driveway entrances, curb radii, and residential street widths. Chapter President Stancer sent a copy to the Association of Washington Cities, asking the organization to approve the standards and recommend them for adoption by its member cities. President Stancer pointed out that there was sufficient latitude in the standards to provide for individual or special cases, and that "Standardization of construction items in many public works projects would provide economic benefits of considerable magnitude. It would also expedite and simplify construction practices and planning of those projects and improvements." ◆

1957 - 1958

Chester E. Murray
Chapter President, 1957-1958

OFFICERS

President - Chester E. Murray
Vice-President - Roy W. Morse
Secretary-Treasurer - Chester L.
  Waggener

BOARD OF DIRECTORS

William A. Trezona
Oscar E. Olson
L. P. Staman
Phillip N. Royal

An air of urgency prevailed during the chapter's early years as population growth swelled Washington cities and unincorporated areas. There was a growing realization that there was little uniformity in construction or design standards and codes for municipal public works projects. Sidewalks, curbs, gutters, manhole covers and utility vaults were all individually designed. The need for greater efficiency and cost savings prompted the chapter to develop a closer working relationship with the Association of Washington Cities and the Associated General Contractors.

During 1957-1958 the chapter continued its efforts to create uniform construction standards for grates, meter chambers, catch basins, curbs, and sidewalks, which would economically benefit both state public works agencies and private contractors. Standardized designs, such as that for locking manhole covers, also provided tested safety features to avert potential accidents.

The first winter meeting of the chapter was held in Seattle with the AGC as the hosts. Significant discussion topics included "Proposed Metropolitan District for the King County Area," James R. Ellis, and "The Tacoma-Seattle-Everett Freeway." The spring conference was held May 20, 1958 in Spokane. Conference topics held attendees' interest and formed the lead in engineering sciences; "Electronic Computers in Municipal Engineering," and "Photogrammetic Engineering," and "Cooperation in Freeway Construction." ◆

1958-1959

Roy W. Morse
Chapter President, 1958-1959

OFFICERS

President - Roy W. Morse
Vice-President - Chester Waggener
Secretary-Treasurer - Earl W. Elton

BOARD OF DIRECTORS

William A. Trezona
Oscar E. Olson
L.R. White
Carl Arness

The chapter continued its work on construction standardization with Robert Anderson chairing this important committee whose work was gaining interest across the state, although not all positive. LID coordination was headed by Philip N. Royal.

On June 9-10, 1959 the Washington Chapter held its conference in Port Angeles. According to the secretary's report of the event, it was "considered highly satisfactory and an enjoyable one for several reasons. First there was a record number of members in attendance and this always starts the meeting off on the right level. Then, the day-and-a-half total meeting time had a balance that provided ample time yet did not tire those in attendance. The general theme was to have a full day of panels or speakers on well chosen subjects and a half a day for a business meeting. Since the full day's meeting started early in the morning, many of the delegates found it convenient and enjoyable to have a get together on the night before and renew acquaintances and relax with associates."

Those who attended the panels heard talks on: the "Impact of Annexation on Public Works," by Glen Sherwood, City Engineer of Kent; "Methods of Analyzing Water Systems," by Garth Anderson, Assistant City Engineer of Moses Lake; "Penalty Clause—When and How Much," by Earl Elton, City Engineer of Bremerton; "Recent Legislation Covering Public Works," by Phil Royal, Principal Engineer for Seattle; and "Progress Report on National Congress to be held in Seattle in September 1959," by Roy Morse, City Engineer, Seattle.

Chapter members distinguishing themselves at the national level were James Robertson who served on the National Organization Review Committee; Everett G. Henry who was on the AGC-APWA Coordinating Committee; and Roy W. Morse, among the top ten receiving the newly created "Public Works Man of the Year" award from the National Association. ◆

1959 - 1960

Chester L. Waggener
Chapter President, 1959-1960

OFFICERS

President - Chester L. Waggener
Vice-President - Myron Calkins
Secretary-Treasurer - E. J. "Bud" Dale

BOARD OF DIRECTORS

Glen Yake
L. R. White
Carl Arness
James Robertson

The chapter held its annual spring meeting at Wenatchee on May 11, 1960 when members voted to move the annual meeting to the autumn in the future. It was agreed that speakers at future conferences should provide copies of their papers, preferably in outline form, to the audience.

Interested in expanding the size and influence of the organization, members discussed ways to encourage city and county officials to urge their technical staff to join APWA. In addition, efforts were made to inform college and high school students of careers in the field of public works.

The Asphalt Paving Award was instituted. In establishing the Legislative Committee, the chapter moved toward taking an active role in shaping legislation affecting public works.

Chet Murray served as Region IX District Representative to APWA National Organization. ◆

1960 - 1961

Myron Calkins
Chapter President, 1960-1961

OFFICERS

President - Myron Calkins
Vice-President - Peder Hemstead
Secretary-Treasurer - Jean DeSpain

BOARD OF DIRECTORS

Ed Cameron
Glen Sherwood
James T. Robertson
Glen A. Yake

In 1961 the chapter met at the elegant Davenport Hotel in Spokane. The major push for the year was completion of the construction standardization handbook. Bob Anderson was remembered for his tireless work and great leadership in seeing that the book actually materialized. Chapter members were proud of this accomplishment because the standards of design and specifications were expected to be a great asset to public works planners and builders throughout the state. The chapter was also proud that Roy Morse served this year as APWA Region IX National Director, and Jim Robertson served as Region IX Washington District Representative. ◆

Conference center, Davenport Hotel, Spokane.

1961 - 1962

Peter Hemstead
Chapter President, 1961-1962

OFFICERS

President - Peder Hemstead
Vice-President - Jean De Spain
Secretary-Treasurer - Al Eschbach

BOARD OF DIRECTORS

Ed Cameron
Glen Sherwood
Hal Hagestad
Walt Winters

It was a productive year for the chapter. For its May meeting the chapter returned to Yakima, the site of its first annual May meeting in 1956. Louis Slyter, Jr. continued the membership drive and Ed Greathouse led the public relations efforts. The major accomplishment of the year, of which the young chapter was justifiably proud, was the completion of the *Standard Specifications for Municipal Public Works Construction*. While many contributed to work, Bob Anderson was the driving force bringing this project to completion. Roy Morse served as Region IX Director and James Robertson as Washington State District Representative.

This year the Washington Chapter created the James Robertson Award to recognize members who demonstrated leadership and made exceptional contributions to the chapter. It was named to honor the work and inspiration of James Robertson who was one of the chapter's founders. ◆

Peder Hemstead, Chapter President for the 1961-1962 term, is flanked by former presidents Myron Calkins on the left and Roy Morse on the right.

1962 - 1963

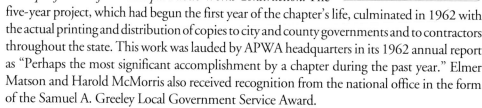

Jean L. DeSpain
Chapter President, 1962-1963

OFFICERS

President - Jean L. DeSpain
Vice-President - A. M. Eschbach
Secretary-Treasurer - Elmer J. Leland

BOARD OF DIRECTORS

Harold Hagestad
Walter Winters
George Fischer
John Warder

In 1962-1963 the chapter had 164 members, most of whom were active in the final stages of developing the *Standard Specifications for Municipal Public Works Construction.* The five-year project, which had begun the first year of the chapter's life, culminated in 1962 with the actual printing and distribution of copies to city and county governments and to contractors throughout the state. This work was lauded by APWA headquarters in its 1962 annual report as "Perhaps the most significant accomplishment by a chapter during the past year." Elmer Matson and Harold McMorris also received recognition from the national office in the form of the Samuel A. Greeley Local Government Service Award.

The 1962 fall conference was held in Olympia. It focused on the future of public works. It was clear to public officials that the Jet Age had begun, and growth and population increases affected all sectors of Washington State. Construction of the interstate highway system was well along. Conference topics included: "Transportation of the Future," "Highways of the Future," "Planning Utilities for the Future," "Preparing Ourselves, Materials and Specifications for Public Works Construction."

The 1963 spring conference was held in Yakima. Reflecting the expansion of chapter membership and a widening variety of public works topics, the fall meeting included three full days of papers and discussion sessions. Diversion was provided by a tour of a Hanford nuclear reactor plant and an afternoon of golf.

The Washington Chapter was well represented on the national level this year with Roy Morse continuing to function as Region IX Director, and James Robertson as District Represenative. Myron Calkins served on the Committee for International Relations; Bill Bugge and Roy Morse served on the Ethics Committee; Everett Henry served on the APWA-AGC Joint Cooperative Committee; D. A. Anderson on the Street Sanitation Committee; and E. E. Lewarch served on the Transportation Committee. ◆

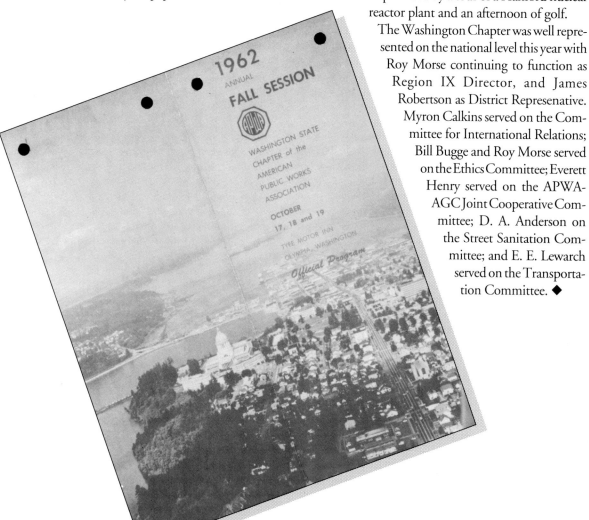

1963 - 1964

William E. Cameron
Chapter President, 1963-64

OFFICERS

President - William E. Cameron
Vice-President - H. C. Higgins
Secretary-Treasurer - Harold A.
    Hagestad

BOARD OF DIRECTORS

George Fisher
John B. Warder
J. Garth Anderson
Everett G. Henry

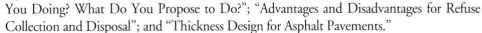

The fall 1963 meeting was held in Pasco, and for the spring 1964 meeting, chapter members visited Union on the Olympic Penninsula's Hood Canal. The conference featured a number of interesting sessions on topics such as: "Public Agency-Contractor Relationship. What have You Done? What Are You Doing? What Do You Propose to Do?"; "Advantages and Disadvantages for Refuse Collection and Disposal"; and "Thickness Design for Asphalt Pavements."

Field trips were an established tradition by now with attendees being offered the opportunity to enjoy a salmon and trout fishing excursion on Hood Canal, or take a field trip to the Tacoma City Light Cushman Power Project. Those attending the conferences agreed that the bi-annual meetings gave chapter members from all over Washington the opportunity to meet regularly and build strong professional and personal relationships by working together in the technical sessions and relaxing together in the evenings.

The Washington Chapter, which played an active role in assisting Oregonians organize and establish their own APWA chapter, gave the new Oregon group a vote of confidence by endorsing their bid to host the 1966 APWA Western Regional Conference in Portland.

In 1964 the Washington Chapter gained a prominent position on the national level when Roy W. Morse was elected APWA National President for the next year. Jean DeSpain succeeded Myron Calkins as Washington District Representative.

The major accomplishment of the year, which benefited the entire membership, was the establishment of a much-needed quarterly newsletter. National Public Works Week was observed by a chapter luncheon held in Seattle September 25th. William A. Bugge, former state highways director, was the speaker. Many local observances of Public Works Week were held around the state in conjunction with local Kiwanis clubs. ◆

Chapter President W.E. Cameron presents the James Robertson Award for 1964 to George Fisher as Director Everett Henry looks on.

William E. Cameron, Chapter President for 1963-1964, is flanked by his fellow officers and directors, left to right: John Warder, director; George Fisher, director; Herb Higgins, vice-president; (Cameron); Hal Hagestad, secretary-treasurer; J. Garth Anderson, director; and Everett G. Henry, director. The groups posed together at the 1964 May meeting at Union, Washington.

1964 - 1965

Herbert Higgins
Chapter President, 1964-1965

OFFICERS

President - Herbert Higgins
Vice-President - Robert Anderson
Secretary-Treasurer - Dominic Roletto

BOARD OF DIRECTORS

J. Garth Anderson
Everett G. Henry
Howard Godat
Louis R. Slyter, Jr.

The spring conference was held in Wenatchee, early in May, as had become the custom by this time. Conference attendees heard papers on such diverse topics as "Cooperative Planning of Urban Transportation in the Wenatchee Area," "Television Surveillance of Traffic," and "Results of 1965 Legislative Session as Pertains to Public Works."

The Washington Chapter was honored by the selection of member Robert G. "Bob" Anderson, Tacoma City Engineer, as the 1964 recipient of the Swearingen Award given for "outstanding service in the field of public works." Anderson received the national award primarily for his untiring efforts in spearheading the development of the Standard Specifications for Municipal Public Works Construction published in 1962.

As a part of the commitment to education and in-service training the chapter sponsored it first annual street maintenance school with a spring session in Pullman that was attended by 90 and an autumn session in Olympia that was attended by 125.

Roy Morse was elected APWA president and Jean De Spain was appointed Director for Region IX. Bill Bugge, former Director of Highways, was the speaker for the National Public Works Week luncheon in 1965. Bugge was Director of the BART (Bay Area Rapid Transit System).

◆

Chapter President Herb Higgins is greeted by Governor Dan Evans to recognize National Public Works Week, May 1965.

1965 - 1966

Robert Anderson
Chapter President, 1965-1966

OFFICERS

President - Robert Anderson
Vice-President - Dominic Roletto
Secretary-Treasurer - J. Garth
  Anderson

BOARD OF DIRECTORS

Howard Godat
Louis Slyter
George Oslund
Gilbert Schuster
Wayne Arrasmith

In 1965 the chapter passed its goal of 300 members. With twenty public agency members, the Washington Chapter had the largest number of such members of any APWA chapter in the country. President Anderson's words provide a sense of the organization's feelings about itself at this time:

> We have come a long way in a comparatively short period of time. To quote an old saying, "Success is a journey, not a destination," and we should be alert not only to bettering present procedures and methods of operation, but also we should be looking forward to new and revolutionary ideas whereby we will be better able to meet the needs of the State of Washington. We must enter into a program of training and recruitment of personnel for all levels of public works.
>
> The accelerated growth of our Northwest will make heavier demands for public works facilities as time progresses. We in APWA must play a greater part in the proper planning and development of these facilities.

Once again a Washingtonian made the national APWA's "Top Ten Public Works Men-of-the-Year" awards. Walt Winters, King County Engineer, was named as one of the ten national winners at the awards banquet in Chicago and thus joined Washington's Top Ten Award recipients, Roy Morse and Bill Bugge.

Public Works Week was observed in many places around the state this year, but the most ambitious program was held in Seattle. The entire week of September 26 through October 2 was observed as "Public Works Week in Seattle." The program, sponsored by the Uptown Kiwanis International Club and the Washington Chapter featured a number of engineering and equipment exhibits in the Westlake Mall downtown that changed daily.

Also in this the tenth year of the chapter's existence, one of its past presidents, Roy Morse, served as president of the national Public Works Association and presided over the National Congress and Equipment Show in Los Angeles. Gib Schuster was appointed Region IX Director, APWA. ◆

Past president Roy Morse, far right, stands beside Dominic Roletto, president for 1966-1967, and former director, E. G. Henry, center, while Seattle Mayor J.D. Braman signs the proclamation making the week of May 16, 1966 Public Works Week. Also witnessing are Dr. Peter Fisher of the Uptown Kiwanis, far left, and Lt. Col. Rupert Anderson.

1966 - 1967

Dominic Roletto
Chapter President, 1966-1967

OFFICERS

President- Dominic Roletto
Vice-President - J. Garth Anderson
Secretary-Treasurer - Chester J.
Woods

BOARD OF DIRECTORS

Paul A. Wiatrak
Joseph L. Thornton
Larry Larse
Wayne Arrasmith
John A. Bronow

The tenth annual fall meeting of the Washington State Chapter of APWA was held in Renton, October 1966, with a total of 150 attendees, 84 of whom were members. Hugo Erickson, national APWA president was on hand to address the group and present the chapter with the President's Plaque as the most outstanding chapter of the year in the United States and Canada. It was a proud moment for the Washington Chapter. The James Robertson Award for outstanding service to public works was given to Herbert C. Higgins, past chapter president.

The chapter's focus on productive activity was evident in its 16 committees, each of which was working on a specific concern such as construction standardization (the standards of the recently published handbook were being revised), APWA-AGC co-operation, honors and awards, research and storm drainage. The Education and In-service Training Committee again held spring and fall sessions of its street maintenance school. Another indicator of the growth of the chapter was the need to revise the bylaws which was accomplished in committee.

President Roletto observed that the Washington Chapter had received a great deal of national recognition lately, and it was a challenge to live up to that reputation. While President Roletto encouraged all committee areas of activity, he believed that the chapter's energies should be focused on standards specifications, public education, and recruitment of personnel. In the interest of advancing public education and interest in LIDs, the chapter completed a brochure, "The ABC's of LID's," in 1966. ◆

NEWS

PUBLIC WORKS---- Well Planned and Soundly Built
----THE FOUNDATIONS OF COMMUNITY PROGRESS

WASHINGTON CHAPTER
AMERICAN PUBLIC WORKS ASSOCIATION

June 1967

1967 SPRING CHAPTER MEETING

The Washington State Chapter of the APWA held its spring meeting in Bellingham this year. It was officially opened with a luncheon in the Ballroom of the Leopold Hotel. Jack Westford, Mayor of Bellingham welcome the members and President Dominic Roletto thanked him on behalf of the Chapter. Frank King, City Engineer of Ellensburg, acted as Master of Ceremonies. The keynote address, "Public Works in British Columbia," was presented by H.W. Buckley, President of the Public Works Association of British Columbia.

The Wednesday afternoon session began with a discussion on LID's, moderated by W.I. Friedline, Chief Engineering Division Public Works Department, Tacoma; followed by Frank Winslow, AGC, Spokane, with a talk on "L.I.D. Promotion". Ray Beauchamp, Office Engineer, King County, spoke on "C.R.I.D.'s" and James Gay, of Roberts, Shefelman, Lawrence, Gay & Moch, Seattle, spoke on "Legal Aspects of L.I.D.'s."

Garth Anderson, City Engineer, Olympia, started Thursday morning off by moderating a discussion on "Storm Drainage." Both Bob Sparling, Principal Civil Assistant City Attorney, Tacoma, followed with talks on "Comprehensive Planning and Legal Problems of Storm Drains." Engineer and Robert Hamilton, Chief Assistant City Attorney, Tacoma, followed "Design and Construction Problems of Sewer and Drainage Construction" was handled by Rogert F. Wilcox, Chief Engineer, Metro Engineering, Seattle, with Martin Dirks of Metro and Douglas R. Scheumann, Partner, Constructor Pamco, Seattle.

L to R: Gib Schuster, Tacoma; Dominic Roletto Seattle, Ed Henken, Bellingham

1967 - 1968

Garth Anderson
Chapter President, 1967-1968

OFFICERS

President - Garth Anderson
Vice-President - Chester J. Woods
Secretary-Treasurer - John B. Warder

BOARD OF DIRECTORS

John Bronow
Joseph Thornton
Paul Wiatrak
Larry Larse

By January 1968 Washington Chapter membership had climbed to 391. The most important on-going project was the Standardization Committee's work on a revised edition of the Standard Construction Specifications. A field engineers' manual was also suggested as a possible future publication. Roy Myklebust reported that his committee was attempting to prepare general information and standards for solid waste handling and disposal. The fall 1967 meeting was held in Walla Walla, and the spring 1968 meeting was held in Longview.

The long awaited loose-leaf style membership directory was completed. In the education and in-service training area, the chapter co-sponsored a sewer maintenance school in Seattle in May 1968. The Public Education Committee began a major new project with the creation of a film concerning street LID's. The plan was to make the completed film available to groups, organizations, and schools in order to inform the public on the benefits of and procedures for forming an LID.

Chet Woods was sent as a delegate to the APWA National House of Delegates. Glenn Yake, Director of Public Works and Utilities in Spokane, was honored as one of the "Top Ten" professionals in the field of public works by the National APWA. The spring meeting was held at Longview and the fall meeting in Yakima. As usual an excellent array of papers and panel discussions were presented to the attendees. The enjoyable field trips that characterized the annual meetings a few years earlier seem to have disappeared — at least for the time being. ◆

Local and state officials met with chapter officers to recognize the importance of public works to the community by proclaiming National Public Works Week in April of 1968. Top: Officers watch as County Commissioners John O'Brien and John Spellman sign the proclamation. Bottom: Chapter officers meet with Mayor J.D. Braman.

1968-1969

Chet J. Woods
Chapter President, 1968-1969

OFFICERS

President - Chet J. Woods
Vice-President - John B. Warder
Secretary-Treasurer - Edwin R. Henken

BOARD OF DIRECTORS

Joseph L. Thornton
Paul A. Wiatrak
Keith P. Nevins
Raymond C. Beauchamp

The Washington Chapter had a good year with many accomplishments. The engineer's field manual was completed. Two safety awards were initiated in each of three classes with the Chapter Safety Committee to determine appropriate eligibility and give the award.

The chapter put in its bid to host the 1976-77 National Equipment Show, an event typically attended by 6,000 people. The invitation was contingent on the construction of the Seattle domed stadium. The chapter established a committee to look into public works issues in disaster planning, particularly involving earthquakes, fires, floods, and for civil defense. The issue of hiring minorities in public works was discussed.

Among the major accomplishments of the year was the completion of the new LID film, "Action for Change." The film was very well received by APWA headquarters and it was anticipated that other areas in the United States would request the film. Twenty-five copies were made.

The fall 1968 conference was in Yakima, and the spring 1969 conference was in Port Angeles. Region IX National Director was Gilbert M. Schuster. Chapter delegate to the House of Delegates was John B. Warder.

The Executive Committee passed Resolution 68-1 revising the Chapter Bylaws to conform with National's organization of the House of Delegates. Newly elected officers would begin their terms on January 1. The change took effect in 1970. ◆

Washington public works officials, left to right, Brian Lewis, Kenneth G. Hoole, Everett Henry, and Dominic Roletto, join Governor Daniel Evans in recognizing Washington's participation in the 1969 National Public Works Week.

1970

John Warder
Chapter President, 1970

OFFICERS

President - John Warder
Vice-President - Edwin R. Henken
Secretary-Treasurer - Yoshio Kosai

BOARD OF DIRECTORS

John Berkowitz
Keith P. Nevins
Paul Sturmer
Raymond C. Beauchamp

The spring meeting, held in Portland, was a joint conference with the Oregon APWA Chapter on "Public Works and the Environment." Session topics were timely and well received. They included: "Regional Environmental Pollution Control Planning"; "Employing the Untrained and Underpriveleged"; and "Environmental Systems Planning—A Design Team Concept." The fall meeting was held in Pasco.

Activity during the year included a week-long public works improvement course that was held at the University of Washington and conducted by the university's School of Public Affairs. A sewage maintenance school was held in May in Olympia. The chapter also sponsored a management seminar.

The Region IX National Director was Gilbert M. Schuster. Also in 1970, Myron Calkins, who had been Washington Chapter president in 1960-1961, became National APWA president. ◆

Gilbert Schuster

1971

Edwin R. Henken,
Chapter President, 1971

OFFICERS

President - Edwin R. Henken
Vice-President - Yoshio Kosai
Secretary-Treasurer - Joe L. Thornton

BOARD OF DIRECTORS

John Lang
Dave Morris
John Berkowitz
Paul Strumer

City of
OLYMPIA

In 1971 the chapter reassessed its "state of organization" and developed new long-term plans The Past President's Advisory Committee concluded that the chapter should put primary emphasis on four broad areas including: chapter news and publicity, meetings, growth, and education programs. Supporting these objectives President Henken announced the goals of his presidency to be to continue the newsletter; send news of chapter activities to the *APWA Reporter*; survey other chapters to learn more of what they do at meetings; re-establish the Public Works Week Seattle Luncheon; increase membership; and continue progressive training and educational programs. In addition, he recommended that the chapter be divided into an east and west division that would conduct periodic area meetings in order that more members would be able to attend yearly conferences without extensive travel.

The chapter's 1971 fall meeting was held in Olympia in early November. The spring conference was held in Wenatchee. In the spring the Public Works Week Luncheon was held at the Seattle Center with speeches and awards highlighting the program. One of National's "Top Ten in Public Works Man-of-the-Year" awards went to Charles V. Gibbs, Executive Director of Seattle's METRO. The James Robertson Award went to Ed Kortnik. When Washington Chapter members received their May 1971 *Public Works* journal, they saw their own Jean DeSpain's genial face gracing the cover. One of the pioneers whose energy and vision was responsible for the founding of the Washington Chapter, Roy Morse, City Engineer of Seattle, was honored by a retirement dinner on April 23, 1971.

By this time the chapter had 24 committees to take care of organization activities. Public Works Education and In-Service Training committees had a productive year putting on a June workshop on "Public Works Planning and Engineering" in Vancouver, B. C.; a "Solid Waste Workshop" in November; and a December "Workshop on Sewage," in Portland, Oregon.

The chapter got involved supporting the state senate bill that would increase the gasoline tax by one-half cent per gallon and provide bonding capacity for the Urban Arterial Program. A resolution was sent to State Senator Nat Washington reaffirming APWA's support, and chapter members were urged to encourage their local elected officials to attend the hearing on the bill.

Recognizing the importance of political lobbying, the chapter established the Intergovernmental Relations Committee to participate in legislative activities pertaining to public works. The goal was to have each of the state's geographical areas represented on this committee.

Publications continued to be an area of chapter interest. The newsletter did not have a permanent editor, but somehow the *News* regularly appeared with various members seeing it through each time. In contrast, another writing project, the 1971 *Construction Manual for Municipal Public Works Construction* enjoyed the consistent attention of capable and dedicated members. The first chapter of the book was completed and sent out to the membership for review du ring the year. The State Highway Department had agreed to fund publication of the manual.

The Washington Chapter continued to expand and reach out to the public. The LID film was regularly being requested and the chapter succeeded in getting it shown at schools throughout the state. The Membership Committee launched a vigorous drive that included friendly competition for bringing in the greatest number of new members. Modest monetary prizes were given for those who recruited the most members.

The National Director of Region IX was Gib Schuster. ◆

1972

Yosh Kosai
Chapter President, 1972

OFFICERS

President - Yosh Kosai
Vice-President - Joe Thornton
Secretary-Treasurer - Edward Kortnik

BOARD OF DIRECTORS

Dave Morris
Al Coffelt
Gordon Fish
John Lang

The total chapter membership in late 1972 was 480, an increase of 29 members over 1971. The chapter sent word to the Oregon Chapter that they heartily supported Oregon's bid for the 1979 national APWA convention and would provide whatever help was necessary if Oregon was selected. The Asphalt Awards Committee reported that the number of agencies submitting projects for consideration had more than doubled in the past year.

The spring meeting was held in Port Angeles and the fall meeting in Walla Walla. The latter opened on the Tuesday before the formal sessions with a golf tournament that was enthusiastically supported by the chapter's golf buffs. Wednesday afternoon and all day Thursday papers were delivered and panel discussions in the sessions dealt with such topics as: "Results of the Environmental Impact Statement," "Uniform Traffic Control Manual," and "Public Employee Collective Bargaining Act and Rules."

By 1972, environmental legislation was making an impact on public works. Topics at the fall conference reflected the trend, for example, "Results of the Environmental Impact Statement." ◆

1973

Joe Thornton
Chapter President, 1973

OFFICERS

President - Joe Thornton
Vice-President - Ed Kortnik
Secretary-Treasurer - Dave Morris

BOARD OF DIRECTORS

Al Coffelt
Gordon Fish
Phil Buswell
Bill Howe

CITY OF YAKIMA

The 1973 spring conference of the Washington Chapter of APWA was held in Yakima. The board of directors convened at their traditional Tuesday evening dinner meeting. Sessions on Wednesday focused on a variety of timely topics including: "Occupational Health and Safety Act," "Urban Storm Drainage—Design and Finance," and "Computer Usage." On Thursday members attended panel discussions on "Planning and the Environment," "Washington State University Research," and "Landscaping for Highways."

The fall conference was in Bellingham the first week in October and started off with a good old golf session on Tuesday. Committees met on Wednesday morning. In the afternoon, after the conference's opening luncheon, attendees had two concurrent sessions to choose from — "Traffic Signals" and "1972 Amendments to the Federal Water Pollution Control Act." In their free time members could visit the display of traffic signals and associated equipment. Thursday morning sessions dealt with "Public Works Emergencies," and "State and Federal Revenue for Public Works Projects." The afternoon sessions offered the opportunity to learn more about "Law, Environment and the Public," and "Safety Legislation and Public Works— The Impact of OSHA—WISHA."

Ken Meng served as Region IX National Director. ◆

1974

Ed Kortnik
Chapter President, 1974

OFFICERS

President - Ed Kortnik
Vice-President - Dave Morris
Secretary-Treasurer - Pat Nevins

BOARD OF DIRECTORS

Phil Buswell
Bill Howe
Lee Spahr
LeRoy Bullard

Edward Kortnik's presidency began half way through Joe Thornton's term as the result of the untimely and shocking death of President Thornton. As vice-president, Mr. Kortnik immediately assumed full presidential responsibility. He was elected in his own right in the fall of 1973.

The chapter was honored when member Gilbert M. Schuster served as International APWA President. Schuster died unexpectedly on June 10, 1974, during his tenure as president. The City of Tacoma paid tribute to him on May 28, 1975 by naming their new parkway the "Schuster Parkway."

Dave Morris served as chapter representative to the APWA House of Delegates. The chapter achieved national level recognition when it received the President's Plaque award, Membership Drive Award, and the APWA Heritage Award — the Washington Chapter was the first recipient of this new award.

The chapter held its spring meeting as a joint conference with the Oregon Chapter in Vancouver, Washington. The fall meeting was held in Spokane. The Washington Chapter completed the revision of the *Standard Specifications for Municipal Public Works Construction* manual, originally printed in 1962. It also experienced vigorous growth in membership. A pin was designed for past presidents all of whom were honored at a presentation ceremony during the annual Public Works Week Luncheon in Seattle. ◆

Vintage cars provide the official escort following the dedication of Tacoma's scenic, two-mile Schuster Parkway, named for Gilbert Schuster, chapter member who died in 1974 during his tenure as international APWA president.

1975

David E. Morris
Chapter President, 1975

OFFICERS

President - David E. Morris
Vice President - Pat Nevins
Secretary - Phil Buswell
Treasurer - Frank Hansche

BOARD OF DIRECTORS

Allan Kimbel
Ken Fujuki
Dave Vargas
Jan Rosholt

The spring conference met at Ocean Shores with clam digging bringing members out to the ocean in the grey dawn. In the afternoon the traditional golf game was enjoyed by the golfers. The pipe equipment show was held concurrent with the conference, and conferees were able to learn of the latest developments in that industry.

Conference sessions focused on such topics as "Recent Development in Resource Recovery," and "Shoring and Cribbing." Proposed State Environmental Policy Act (SEPA) guidelines were evaluated in another. A popular bus tour took attendees to the Ocean City waste water treatment facilities, the ITT Rayonier Crane Creek site, a logging show, sorting yard, the Red Cedar Products shake mill, and the Hoquiam water treatment plant.

The fall conference was held in Richland. George Andrews, Director of Highways, gave the keynote address at the kickoff luncheon of this meeting which took on a number of controversial topics in the sessions. "Hazardous Waste Disposal—Passing the Buck" was the focus of the Wednesday panel. Another panel considered "Accommodating the Bicycle." Recognizing the challenges for public works administrators, one session dealt exclusively with management systems and problems. ◆

1976

Pat Nevins
Chapter President, 1976

OFFICERS

President - Pat Nevins
Vice-President - Phillip Buswell
Secretary - Leland Sphar
Treasurer - Jan Rosholt

BOARD OF DIRECTORS

Jack Locke
Ernie Geissler
Bill Butler
Kenneth Fukiji
Al Kimbel
David Vargas

The Washington Chapter was well represented on the regional and national levels with Jean DeSpain serving as Region IX Director and Roy W. Morse serving on the APWA Advisory Council. Nine additional national posts were held by Washington Chapter members.

The spring conference was held in Bellevue with 209 members and 37 guests attending. Wenatchee was the site of the fall conference which was attended by 167 members. National Public Works Week was celebrated at a luncheon at the SeaTac Holiday Inn on May 28. Jean DeSpain was honored as among the "Top Ten Public Works Leaders of the Year." Many members made the trip to Las Vegas, Nevada, to attend the APWA International Congress and Equipment Show.

The chapter had an exceptionally active year under President Nevins' leadership. High among its accomplishments was the production of a number of publications including "Public Agency Criteria for Engaging Consultants," developed by the APWA-Consulting Engineer Council Joint Cooperative Committee. Fifty copies of the National APWA's bicentennial history of public works were distributed free of charge to state colleges, and the Program Committee completed its manual, "Meeting Guidelines."

Education and in-service training activities were an important activity with two education foundation workshops being sponsored on "Sewage Collection and Treatment Systems," and "Motor Vehicle Equipment Mangement." In addition, the newly formed Public Relations Committee, headed by Robert G. Anderson, held a local workshop to educate and train public works members in public relations.

In keeping with the bicentennial mood, the chapter expressed its interest in the past through a special slide show on the building of the Lake Washington Ship Canal by Jan Klippert, and a special display for the fall conference on the chapter's history and its accomplishments. Interest in the future was demonstrated by the initiation of the first official APWA-sponsored golf tournament, the Thornton Tournament, named for past president Joseph L. Thornton, with proceeds to go to the student scholarship fund. The chapter received the National APWA Heritage Award in 1977 for its 1976 history activities.

In addition to the Heritage Award, the chapter was the recipient of the President's Plaque Award, and Robert G. Anderson won the Samuel A. Greeley Award. On the local level Venture Construction Company of Auburn won the Washington Chapter's Contractor of the Year Award. Robert Engle received the James Roberson Chapter Award, and two Gilbert Schuster Scholarships, of $500 each, were presented to promising students. ◆

Scenes from the fall meeting: Above left: Some of the participants in the Money for the Works workshop. Above right: President Pat Nevins presents History of Public Works *to Dr. William Steward, President, Wenatchee Valley College. Right: The head table at the conference banquet.*

1977

Philip M. Buswell
Chapter President, 1977

OFFICERS

President - Philip M. Buswell
Vice-President - Jan Rosholt
Secretary - Allan Kimble
Treasurer - Ken Fujiki

BOARD OF DIRECTORS

Jack Locke
Robert Engle
Ernie Geissler
June Rosentreter
Bill Butler
Monte Geiger

By 1977 the chapter committees numbered 34. According to the by-laws, the president was an ex-officio member of each committee. Realizing that he was getting "spread too thin," the president instituted the practice of assigning each board member responsibility for liaison with a group of committees. This system proved successful and was adopted by subsequent presidents.

Publications put out during the year were "Solid Waste Study," and the "Manual for Preparation of Chapter Programs."

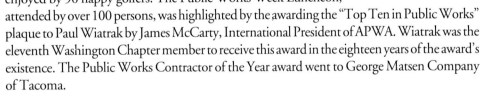

The spring conference was held in Renton in April with 245 members and guests attending. The fall meeting was held in Yakima with 221 attending. At the National Public Works Week Luncheon in Seattle, the Contractor of the Year Award was given to Tacoma general contractor Butler Jarvis for the Tacoma Spur project.

The new Public Relations Committee continued its commitment to developing awareness of public relations issues by holding a series of six public relations seminars throughout the state. The Gilbert M. Schuster Scholarship Fund was increased from two to three student scholarships with six annual scholarships the long-term goal. The chapter received the President's Plaque from National in 1978 for its 1977 accomplishments, and the 1977 Aedile award for its program to involve youth in government. ◆

1978

Jan E. Rosholt
Chapter President, 1978

OFFICERS

President - Jan E. Rosholt
Vice-President - Allan L. Kimbel
Secretary - Kenneth Fujiki
Treasurer - Leland Sphar

BOARD OF DIRECTORS

Jerry M. Fay
Robert R. Engle
June Rosentreter
R. Donald Horey
Keith Eggen
Warren Gonnason

In 1978 the chapter reported 684 members. The spring conference was held in Olympia and the fall conference in Walla Walla. The Joseph L. Thornton Golf Tournament, now a regular event, preceded the spring sessions and was enjoyed by 90 happy golfers. The Public Works Week Luncheon, attended by over 100 persons, was highlighted by the awarding the "Top Ten in Public Works" plaque to Paul Wiatrak by James McCarty, International President of APWA. Wiatrak was the eleventh Washington Chapter member to receive this award in the eighteen years of the award's existence. The Public Works Contractor of the Year award went to George Matsen Company of Tacoma.

Chapter members received a generous number of awards from national including the Honorary Membership Award, the highest award APWA bestows, which went to Roy W. Morse, and a Life APWA Membership award to Dominic Roletto. The Washington Chapter also won the President's Plaque for 1978, as well as the Heritage Award.

Don Horey and the Equipment Service Committee put on five workshops on equipment management throughout the state. The APWA specifications received approval from the Federal Highway Administration which resulted in a supplement to the APWA specs manual. Three thousand copies of the supplement were sent to cities across the state. The Intergovernmental Relations Committee, under John Ostrowski, put on two programs during the spring conference and worked on a guidelines brochure called "Working with State Agencies."

The chapter modified its old logo by placing it within the outline of the map of Washington. Reflecting the changing position of women within professional organizations, the chapter agreed from now on to use non-gendered words in the newsletter. ◆

1979

Allan L. Kimbel
Chapter President, 1979

OFFICERS

President - Allan L. Kimbel
Vice-President - Ken Fujiki
Secretary - Lee Sphar
Treasurer - June Rosentreter

BOARD OF DIRECTORS

Phil Butler
Robert Turner
Warren C. Gonnason
Jerry Fay
Donald Horey
Keith Eggen

Major activities of 1979 included the presentation of an APWA banner to the newly formed British Columbia Public Works Association Chapter. Through the effort of Don Horey and Phil Buswell, the banner was purchased by the Washington Chapter and APWA National Headquarters. It was presented to the B. C. Chapter by President Kimbel at a luncheon during the stormwater management workshop in Vancouver B. C. on March 2. Murray Brown, president of the B. C. Chapter, was the honored guest at the chapter's spring meeting in Bellingham. At this time William Korbitz, Director of Region IX, presented the Washington Chapter with the Membership Citation Award for 1978 — the fifth time the chapter had won this award.

On March 13 and 14 the chapter sponsored an employee relations workshop in Seattle with 45 attending. The annual Public Works Week Luncheon was held in Tacoma on May 23. John Warder was awarded an APWA Life Membership and Jan Rosholt, past president, received a Certificate of Appreciation for his valuable service in 1978. Several awards were presented to the chapter and its members at the APWA awards reception during the September International Congress and Equipment Show in Portland. Former President Rosholt accepted, on behalf of the chapter, the 1979 President's Plaque Award. Past President Dominic Roletto received the Harry S. Swearingen Award for outstanding service to the association. Kenneth M. Lowthian and Philip Buswell were recipients of the coveted Samuel A. Greeley Local Government Service Award.

At the late-October fall conference in Spokane, Don Horey received the James Robertson Award for outstanding service in the field of public works. The Asphalt Paving Association's and chapter's joint "Best Paving Award" went to the City of Tacoma. ◆

Lee Sphar, June Rosentreter, and Chapter President Allan Kimbel join Governor Dixie Lee Ray for her signing of the proclamation for 1979 Public Works Week.

1980

*Kenneth Fujiki
Chapter President, 1980*

OFFICERS

President - Kenneth Fujiki
Vice-President - Lee Spahr
Secretary - June Rosentreter
Treasurer - Jerry Fay

BOARD OF DIRECTORS

Phil Butler
Warren Gonnason
Jan Klippert
Jerry Newlin
Larry Southwick
Robert Turner

The spring conference was held in Seattle and hosted by the King County Department of Public Works. Its emphasis was on the developing use of computer technology in public agencies. Vendor exhibits included electronic telephone answering machines, word processing and data analysis systems, and potential computer applications for public works projects.

The fall meeting, held in Pasco, centered on "Disaster Action Planning." In the wake of the May 8, 1980 eruption of Mt. St. Helens, media representatives, APWA members, and other public works officials had held frequent meetings to coordinate assistance to stricken areas, and agencies around the state were still assessing the damage. Emergency preparedness, the effects of ashfall, and the dangers of flooding caused by volcanic eruptions were some of the topics discussed in sessions. The Research Committee held a competition for ideas on ways to use volcanic ash.

All of the Membership Committee's hard work during 1979 was rewarded when it received word in 1980 that Washington had received the President's Plaque, for the fourth consecutive year—an achievement unsurpassed by any other APWA chapter in the country.

◆

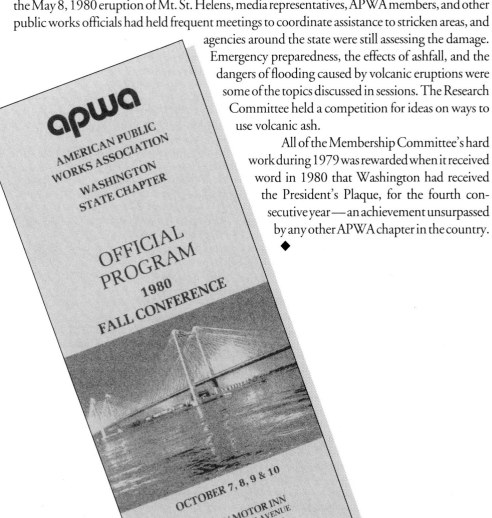

apwa

AMERICAN PUBLIC
WORKS ASSOCIATION

WASHINGTON
STATE CHAPTER

OFFICIAL
PROGRAM
1980
FALL CONFERENCE

OCTOBER 7, 8, 9 & 10

RED LION MOTOR INN
2525 NORTH 20TH AVENUE
PASCO, WASHINGTON

1981

Leland L. Sphar
Chapter President

OFFICERS

President - Leland L. Sphar
Vice-President - June Rosentreter
Secretary - Jerry Fay
Treasurer - Warren Gonnason

BOARD OF DIRECTORS

Jack Garner
Bill Howe
Jan P. Klippert
Jerry Newlin
Norman Skiles,
Larry Southwick

The year was one of steady non-spectacular accomplishment during a time of economic instability when many municipal programs had been put on indefinite hold. Membership grew, however, from 765 at the beginning of the year to 786 by September 30. This was a substantial increase in the rate of growth over the previous year. Constant, solid growth had been the norm for a number of years as a result of the chapter's efficient organizational structure capably managed by the committees, particularly the Program Committee.

The major accomplishment for the year was the compilation of the 1981 edition of the *Standard Specifications for Municipal Public Works Construction.* At the fall conference, the Samuel Greeley Service Award went to Ed Kortnik and the James Robertson Award to Pat Nevins. At the spring conference, held in Vancouver, Robert Flanagan, Chief of the Engineering Division of the Army Corps of Engineers, spoke about the Mount St. Helens clean-up effort. In a year of budget cuts and general "belt tightening," the meeting theme was "Doing More With Less." The fall conference was held at Moses Lake.

At the Public Works Week Luncheon in Seattle, Ron Dunlap, King County Executive, spoke on "Making Government Work Better." The Asphalt Committee, in cooperation with the Asphalt Paving Association of Washington, presented the year's Best Asphalt Paving awards to the City of Tacoma and to Woodworth and Company, contractor, for the paving of Portland Avenue between Fairbanks and East 44 Street. The Contractor of the Year award went to Bill Epping General Construction Company for the City of Port Angeles municipal pier project.

The chapter continued its energetic education program by sponsoring a series of workshops focusing on current needs and interests. A "Solid Waste Management Policy and Administration" workshop was held in Seattle in March and a two-day "Stormwater Detention" seminar, jointly sponsored by the chapter, the Seattle Section of ASCE, and the Pacific Northwest Concrete Pipe Association was held in Seattle in May. Stormwater Consultants of Chicago conducted the sessions. At the Association of Washington Cities Convention in Yakima in June, the chapter held a workshop on "Financing Streets and Roads," moderated by Dick Warren. ◆

AMERICAN PUBLIC WORKS ASSOCIATION
WASHINGTON STATE CHAPTER

OFFICIAL PROGRAM

1981 FALL CONFERENCE

HALLMARK INN
3000 Marina Drive Moses Lake, WA 98837
Phone 509/765-9211

1982

June Rosentreter
Chapter President, 1982

OFFICERS

President - June Rosentreter
Vice-President - Jerry Fay
Secretary - Warren Gonnason
Treasurer - Jan P. Klippert

BOARD OF DIRECTORS

Bill Howe
Norman Skiles
Jack Garner
John Ostrowski
Nelson Graham
Jack Pittis

W hen June Rosentreter was elected as chapter president, it was a history-making event for she was the first woman in the Washington Chapter's 27 years to hold the office. Rosentreter's presidency also highlighted the expanding role of women in engineering professions and management positions.

The spring conference was held at Ocean Shores and the fall meeting was in Wenatchee. National APWA President Robert Easterbrook was the fall meeting's honored guest. The chapter accomplished many things in 1982, and education/training and publications were among the most notable. In the wake of the emergency conditions created by the eruption of Mount St. Helens in May 1980 and the storms and flooding in October 1981, the focus was on emergency planning. The Chapter Emergency Management Committee, under Glenn Yake and Ken Nyberg, produced a report called, "Emergency Plan for Public Works Officials." Guidelines were published and both spring and fall meetings had educational sessions on emergency preparedness. The Safety Committee produced a publication, "Entry into Confined Spaces."

Education and training workshops were held on dealing with "On-the-Job-Safety," organized by Bill Strong, and "Urban Drainage," organized by Tom Huse. The Underground Location Coordinating Committee sponsored a symposium in Seattle conducted by Tom Odegaard.

Awards in 1983 went to Pat Nevins, 1976 chapter president, who was designated a Top Ten Public Works Official, and to Bill Bugge, who received the Honorary Member award in Boston at the national conference. ◆

1983

Jerry M. Fay
Chapter President, 1983

OFFICERS

President - Jerry M. Fay
Vice President - Warren Gonnason
Secretary - Jan Klippert
Treasurer - Jack Garner

BOARD OF DIRECTORS

John Ostrowski
Nelson Graham
Jack Pittis
William Gilbert
Rex Knight
Richard Warren

The spring conference in Bellevue was a joint meeting with the Institute of Traffic Engineers and the International Municipal Signal Association and was attended by over 400 members and guests. A major event of the year for chapter members was National Public Works Week when chapter officers met with Governor John Spellman. The luncheon was held at the Tacoma Dome, May 24, with Duane Berentson, Secretary of Transportation as speaker. A highlight of the day was a guided tour of the Tacoma Dome.

Sporting events enlivened the summer. The Thornton Golf Tournament held at Lake Wilderness in June raised $1,300 for the student scholarship fund. Chapter members enjoyed an APWA baseball challenge event at Port Angeles in August.

A variety of activities was accomplished including the recording of interviews with Bill Bugge as part of an oral history project. The *Standard Specifications for Road, Bridge and Municipal Construction* produced in conjunction with the Department of Transportation was completed. June Rosentreter served as Region IX Director and Roy Morse served on the National Advisory Council.

As usual a number of awards were given and won by the Washington Chapter and members. Awards received from National included: Honorary Membership to Bill Bugge; Top Ten Public Works Leader of the Year, Pat Nevins; and Life Membership, Phillip Buswell. The Public Works Leader of the Year Award went to Richard Warren. Jack Locke received the James Robertson Award. The Contractor of the Year Award went to J. A. Jones & Associates for the Hood Canal Bridge. Three Gilbert M. Schuster scholarships were given out.

Educational workshops included an urban drainage seminar in Bellevue in April and a sewer maintenance workshop in Seattle in December. A series of four one-day workshops on energy efficiency in water and wastewater facilities were held around the state. ◆

A work session during the spring meeting.

1984

Warren Gonnason
Chapter President, 1984

OFFICERS

President - Warren Gonnason
Vice-President - Jan Klippert
Secretary - Jack Garner
Treasurer - Larry Southwick

BOARD OF DIRECTORS

Hugh Warren
William Gilbert
Rex H. Knight
Richard Warren
Gwen L. Maxfield
Dave Rhodes

The Washington Chapter was well represented at APWA International with June Rosentreter continuing as Region IX Director; Kenneth D. Thomas as Executive Council member of the Institute for Transportation; Eugene Avery, member of the Membership Committee; Ron Button, member of the Program Committee for the Institute for Municipal Engineering; Don Broadsword, member of the Executive Council for the Institute for Equipment Services; Hector Cyre, member of the Executive Council of the Institute for Water Resources; and Eugene V. Avery, Chair of Committee on Intergovernmental Relations. June Rosentreter was also a member of the Executive Council of the Institute of Administrative Management and the APWA Insurance Committee.

The annual spring conference was held in Everett and the fall conference at Spokane. The Pacific Northwest Construction Exposition was held at the Seattle Center Coliseum jointly with the Associated General Contractors (AGC) and other interested groups. In June, the Ninth Annual Thornton Golf Tourney took place at Lake Wilderness and an area meeting was held in Kennewick.

The major accomplishment of the year was the chapter's and D.O.T.'s jointly published 1984 *Standard Specifications for Road, Bridge and Municipal Construction.* The culmination of years of effort, this publication brought the specifications of the two groups together in a single document for the first time.

Awards for the year included the following: Allen L. Kimbel selected as one of the Top Ten Public Works Leaders of the Year; Warren C. Gonnason was honored with an APWA Life Membership; the Merit Award went to Wayne Nelson; Chet Woods was designated Public Works Leader of the Year; Marve Seabrand received the James Robertson Award; and the Contractor of the Year Award went to Tacoma Dome Associates.

The award for the Best City Asphalt Paving Project in the state, a program which has been cooperatively sponsored since 1961 by the APWA and the Asphalt Paving Association of Washington, went to the City of Kelso for the Kelso-Longview Airport paving project paved by Lakeside Industries. ◆

AMERICAN PUBLIC WORKS ASSOCIATION

WASHINGTON CHAPTER

Official Program

1984 Fall Conference
October 2-5

Spokane, Washington

1985

Jan Klippert
Chapter President, 1985

OFFICERS

President - Jan Klippert
Vice-President - Jack Garner
Secretary - Larry Southwick
Treasurer - John Ostrowsk

BOARD OF DIRECTORS

Gwenn Maxfield
Dave Rhodes
Hugh Warren
Edwina Carlson
Angelo Bomben
Thomas Chini

The Washington Chapter in 1986 received the President's Plaque for the numerous accomplishments realized under President Klippert's able leadership. The spring conference was held in Olympia in April and the fall conference in Kennewick in October. The chapter was honored at the fall meeting by a public works delegation from Indonesia composed of Public Works Director General of Indonesia, Karman Somawidjaja and Planning Division Manager, Muhammad Muhtadi. Sponsored by Jess Abed and URS Company, Somawidjaja's presentation at the conference, "Balitbang," focused on the economic opportunities and changes occuring in Indonesia. The delegation visited several public works projects while in Washington including the I-90 Mount Baker Tunnel, the steel cable-stay bridge in Kennewick, and the Boeing Company ferries built for Indonesia. They also inspected irrigation and flood control systems.

The year was distinguished by a notable number of publications produced by chapter members such as the following technical reports: "Pavement Mangement System (PMS) Users Reference Manual"; "LID/RID Procedure Manual" by Celia Strong; and "Flashing Yellow Protected Permissive Signal Evaluation." Instructional brochures and guideline publications included: "Public Awareness is Everyone's Business," by Don Aicher and Dick Warren; "Guidelines for using APWA Display Materials," by Dick Warren; "Format and Guidelines for Preparing Committee Reports," by Al Kimbel; and "Risk Mangement, What is it?" How is it Done?" by Sonja Alexander. Two members, Edwin Von Borstel and Don Broadsword, published articles in national professional publications. At the end of 1985 the the Chapter Executive Committee decided to create this book, *Building Washington*.

Educational efforts were also prominent during the year. Equipment service workshops were held by Dave Ford and Win Mitchell. Faculty coordinators in six university engineering school programs were identified as liaison for expanding chapter scholarship opportunities. To help young people get into the public works field, Jack Pittis initiated a Computer Network Summer Jobs Program for engineering students. In order to make the chapter's collection of documents and information on public works more available for public use, the chapter library was transferred and integrated into the library of the Municipal Research Service Center in Seattle. ◆

Chapter President Jan Klippert joins Director Edwina Carlson and Vice-President Jack Garner to witness Governor Booth Gardner's signing of the Public Works Week Proclamation, May 19, 1985.

1986

Jack Garner
Chapter President, 1986

OFFICERS

President - Jack Garner
Vice-President - Larry Southwick
Secretary - John Ostrowski
Treasurer - Dick Warren

BOARD OF DIRECTORS

Gene Avery
Erv Bader
Angelo Bomben
Karen Brooks
Edwina Carlson
Tom Chini

One of the most significant activities for the chapter in 1986 occurred January 31 when the board voted to explore the feasibility of publishing a history of public works in Washington to coincide with the state's centennial in 1989.

The spring conference was held in Tacoma. This was the first Tacoma conference in the chapter's history, and it was well worth the wait. The Tacoma Sheraton Hotel proved to be an outstanding location and the local host committee did a tremendous job putting on a top conference. Keynote speaker for the Wednesday luncheon was Lenny Wilkens, NBA All-Star and coach of the Seattle Supersonics.

The fall conference was held as a joint meeting with the Rocky Mountain Chapter at the Coeur d'Alene Resort in northern Idaho. Aside from the usual excellent technical sessions, highlights included a visit by Region IX Director Deke Miller and a cruise around the lake sponsored by the vendors' group.

Other activities for the year included a May 20 luncheon at the Sea-Tac Marriott to celebrate National Public Works Week. Dick Sandaas was honored as a recipient of the Top Ten in Public Works Award for 1986. A joint board meeting with the British Columbia Chapter was held near Vancouver, B. C. in May. Two workshops were held during the year at the Doubletree Inn in Tukwila — "Vehicle Maintenance Facilities Management" in May and "Office Automation" in July.

Presentation of the President's Plaque to the Washington State Chapter APWA at the National Congress and Equipment Show, in September 1986 in New Orleans. From left: Carl Wills, national past president; Deke Miller, Region IX director; Jan Klippert, 1985 chapter president; June Rosentreter, 1986 national president; Jack Garner, 1986 chapter president.

Clearly, the high point of the year for the Washington Chapter in the area of national visibility was the National Congress and Equipment Show in New Orleans, Louisiana. At the congress, June Rosentreter was installed as APWA International President and the chapter received the President's Plaque for accomplishments realized in 1985. Another Washington Chapter member, Pam Bissonnette, was honored with the Charles Walter Nichols Award for achievement in the field of sanitation. ◆

1987

Larry Southwick
Chapter President, 1987

OFFICERS

President - Larry Southwick
Vice-President - John Ostrowski
Secretary - Richard Warren
Treasurer - Jack Pittis

BOARD OF DIRECTORS

Eugene Avery
Ervin Bader
Karen Brooks
Don Broadsword
David Ford
Celia Strong
Terry Duncan

The chapter was well represented on the national level with June Rosentreter Spence serving as APWA International President and Washington members serving in various capacities: Eugene Avery, Municipal Engineering, Research Foundation, and Contractor of the Year Award; Pam Bissonnette, Vice President Water Resources; Don Broadsword, Equipment Services; David Ford, Solid Waste; Jan Klippert, Public Works Historical Society; Rex Knight, Vice President Utility Location and Coordination Council; Gwenn Maxfield, Administrative Management; Roy Morse, APWA Advisory Committee; Catherine O'Donnell, Buildings and Grounds; John Ostrowski, Delegate; Fred Thompson, APWA-AGC Joint Committee; and Richard Warren, Alternate Delegate.

The chapter sponsored a rich array of training workshops and seminars around the state including: "Public Buildings and Grounds Management," held in Tukwila; "Chapter Leadership," in Bellevue; "LID/RID" in Everett; "Hazardous Waste and Public Works Professional" workshops in Yakima, Chehalis, Spokane, and Port Townsend; and "Public Works Administration in Small Communities," held in Tukwila.

Throughout the year there were a series of conferences and special events beginning with the spring conference in Bellingham in April. May was a busy month with the Chapter Leadership Luncheon held in Bellevue, the National Public Works Week Luncheon held in Everett, and the Regional Delegates Dinner held in Vancouver.

Activity continued unabated through the summer and autumn. June was dedicated to the Area Meeting East in Yakima, and the Joseph L. Thornton Golf Tournament at Lake Wilderness with the proceeds going to the scholarship fund as usual. In August the Public Works Slo Pitch Tournament was staged in Kent. The fall conference took place in Yakima in October, and early in November the traditional joint board meeting with the B. C. Chapter was held in Bellingham. In December the Area Meeting West was held in Everett.

In 1987 a number of awards went to deserving members. Public Works Leader of the Year went to Ernie Geissler; the Contractor of the Year was Inland Asphalt of Spokane; the James Robertson Award was given to Jan Klippert; Al Kimbel received the Swearingen Award; Life Memberships went to Al Coffelt and Ernie Geissler; the Asphalt Paving Association awards went to Bellingham and Yakima; and the Award of Merit was given to Lawrence Walker. In addition, eight safety awards and six student scholarships were given out. On the national level the Top Ten Award went to Don LaBelle. The Washington Chapter placed third for the President's Plaque and received a Membership Citation.

◆

AMERICAN PUBLIC WORKS ASSOCIATION
Official Program
WASHINGTON STATE CHAPTER
1987 SPRING CONFERENCE
APRIL 7 - 10, 1987
BELLINGHAM, WASHINGTON

1988

John Ostrowski
Chapter President, 1988

OFFICERS

President - John Ostrowski
Vice-President - Dick Warren
Secretary - Jack Pittis
Treasurer - Edwina Carlson

BOARD OF DIRECTORS

Don Broadsword
David Ford
Celia Strong
Terry Duncan
Fred Thompson
Dennis Covell

Nine chapter members served at the national level this year: Pam Bissonnette, Don Broadsword, Dave Ford, Jan Klippert, Rex Knight, Mary Madison, Gwenn Maxfield, Tom Odegaard and Fred Thompson.

Publications for the year included a new and updated edition of the combined *Standard Specifications for Road, Bridge and Municipal Construction.* A separate specification covering Division One was also published. A new, updated membership directory was issued. The Computer Aided Drafting (CADD) Standards Task Force developed a set of standards available to the membership on a 1.2 megabyte diskette.

The year began with a chapter-sponsored national APWA workshop, "Liability and Public Works," held in Bellevue and attended by 75 people. The LID/RID Committee held a workshop in Kennewick.

The spring conference was held in Renton in April. The program included sessions on public relations, pavement management, value engineering, landfills, ASCE standards and water quality. Luncheon guest speakers were Paul Dorpat, and State Representative Mike Patrick. In April the International Symposium on Vandalism, co-sponsored by the chapter, was held.

May brought National Public Works Week with celebrations around the state and special expositions in Snohomish County and Vancouver. The annual Public Works Week Luncheon was held at the Sea-Tac Red Lion with Slade Gorton, who would be elected Washington's U.S. Senator later in the year, as guest speaker.

In June at the eastern Washington area meeting, the state transportation plan was discussed in Wenatchee. The annual Thornton Golf Tournament at Lake Wilderness brought in more money for the scholarship fund, which now provides six scholarships. The annual slo-pitch tournament in Port Angeles hosted 22 teams.

During the October fall conference in Wenatchee, program sessions were held on liability in public works, temporary services in public works, pavement management, buildings and grounds maintenance, L.I.D.'s, and recycling. Luncheon speakers were Duane Berentson, state Secretary of Transportation and state Senator George Sellar. Safety awards and Department of Transportation awards for excellence were presented. The James Robertson Award was presented to past president Larry Southwick. The fall conference was also an opportunity for the Executive Committee and committee chairs to conduct a planning session for developing goals and objectives for the coming years, with particular emphasis on 1989. Mary Madison organized the first "Women in Public Works Luncheon" for Washington, attended by 70 people.

The "Public Works Management" seminar was held in Tukwila in December. This seminar, the premier management workshop in the National APWA Education Series, covered a wide variety of subjects in four days. The seminar was co-sponsored by the Washington Chapter and was attended by 70 people.

The major effort of the year was the work on the History of Public Works in Washington book. Jan Klippert and Dick Warren held meetings around the state to raise funds and interest in the project. Completion of the construction standards and their publication and distribution was another major project. The CADD Symbols developed by Regan Sidie's task force were adopted by the Executive Committee and presented at the National Congress in Toronto.

Bruce Wassell was selected as Public Works Leader of the Year, Pete Butkus won the Intergovernmental Relations Award, and the Contractor of the Year honor went to Silby Bridge Company and Woodworth & Company. ◆

1989

Richard E. Warren
Chapter President, 1989

OFFICERS

President - Richard E. Warren
Vice-President - Jack Pittis
Secretary - Edwina Carlson
Treasurer - Karen Brooks

BOARD OF DIRECTORS

Terry Duncan
Fred Thompson
Dennis Covell
Ervin Bader
Don Tranum
Wayne Scroggins

O ver 500 attended the chapter's spring conference, conducted jointly with the Oregon Chapter in Vancouver, Washington, exceeding attendance at all previous conferences. National President Chester Funnye and his wife and retiring Executive Director Robert Buhger and his wife were honored guests. A highlight of the conference banquet was the presentation of the chapter's Public Works Leader of the Year award to Ron Bockstrock of WSDOT. At the also well-attended fall conference in Spokane, futurist Glen Hiemistra spoke on the need for vision and strategy in planning for public works. The James Robertson Award was presented at the annual banquet to past president Phil Buswell, City of Seattle, retired.

In November a successful luncheon, organized by Mary Madison, was held at the Columbia Tower Club in Seatle with over 150 attending. Lynn Gutterman, Renton Public Works Director, gave the keynote address.

During National Public Works Week meetings, the chapter celebrated the state centennial and highlighted its sponsorship of *Building Washington,* a history of public works in the state, with presentations on ten projects important in the state's development — such as Tacoma's East 34th Street Bridge, the Monroe Street hydropower project in Spokane, and METRO's clean-up of Lake Washington. Other chapter projects during the year included a study performed jointly by the Research and Development Committee with the state Transportation Department (WDOT) on clear zone requirements, a statewide utility rate survey by the Municipal Engineers Committee, and another revision of the APWA/WDOT standards by the Construction Standards Committee. The Chapter History Committee, assisted by past presidents, completed documentation of the chapter's history to be included in the public works history.

The Stormwater Managers group held a workshop on municipal and industrial stormwater discharges that was well attended, and the Solid Waste Committee conducted a series of workshops on biomedical waste handling. The ad hoc committee on street funding and the Municipal Engineers Group convinced legislators to include the street utility concept into the state transportation bill. This concluded nine years of hard work, including that of Craig Olson and Stan Finklestein of the Association of Washington Cities, and led by Chapter President Dick Warren.

At the national level a number of chapter members were active on committees including: Pam Bissonnette, Water Resources Committee; David Ford, Solid Waste; Jan Klippert, Public Works Historical Society; Doug Mattoon, Emergency Management; Mary Madison, Administrative Management; Catherine O'Connell, Buildings and Grounds.

For 1989 the chapter was awarded the National President's Plaque symbolic of being recognized as the outstanding APWA chapter in the nation. This marked the eighth time the chapter has been so honored since the award was started in 1963 by the American Public Works Association. ◆

1990

Jack Pittis
Chapter President, 1990

OFFICERS

President - Jack Pittis
Vice-President - Edwina Carlson
Secretary - Karen Brooks
Treasurer - Dave Ford

BOARD OF DIRECTORS

Gerry Weed
Don Tranum
Duane Scroggins
Dave Mandyke
Craig Olson
Erv Bader

The general objective of the chapter for the year was to improve professional and public awareness of chapter activities and to continue the committment to serve its membership. One way this was achieved was through a chapter booth at the Redmond Earth Fair, held to commemorate the 20th anniversary of Earth Day. Susan Hall chaired the committee that developed a display for the booth, including environment-related materials from a number of agencies, a poster, and chapter T-shirts. Later in the year the committee developed a chapter brochure and poster to disseminate information about the chapter and the role of public works activities at the municipal and county level. Logo redesign by the APWA National and the Washington Chapter reflected the changing times in public works.

The spring conference was held in Bellevue in April and the fall meeting in Richland in October. At the spring meeting which focused on environmental issues, former Washington governor Dixie Lee Ray gave the keynote address. At the annual Public Works Luncheon, the Yakima Valley Transit and Seattle Water Department became the first recipients of the new chapter Award for Projects of Historical Significance.

A number of training opportunities were offered for members during the year, such as a snow and ice conference, coordinated by Doug Mattoon; a national workshop on designing and implementing recycling programs, coordinated by Edwina Carlson; and an L.I.D. workshop which included a modification of the "L.I.D./R.I.D. Procedure Manual," coordinated by Celia Strong.

The chapter also began experimenting with video taping selected conference presentations. This effort was headed by Larry Southwick and Mary Madison. In addition, the chapter leadership manual was updated by Jack Pittis and Larry Southwick, and the Specifications Committee, chaired by Bob Davis, completed a 1991 version of the Standard Specifications. Membership in the association exceeded 1,070 members in 1990. ◆

CARING FOR OUR NEIGHBORHOOD ENVIRONMENT

PUBLIC WORKS

HAZARDOUS WASTE • TRANSPORTATION/HOV/TRAFFIC CONTROL • DRINKING WATER QUALITY • RECYCLING
ENVIRONMENTAL MAINTENANCE • SEWAGE TREATMENT
SURFACE WATER QUALITY

Washington State
Chapter Spring
Conference 1990

April 4th, 5th and 6th
Bellevue, Washington

1998

Gary Wheeler
President 1998

RECENT PRESIDENTS

1992 — Karen Brooks, Seattle Solid Waste
    Division
1993 — David Ford, Public Works
    Director, Anacortes
1994 — Dennis Covell, Director of
    Engineering and Utilities, Yakima
1995 — Gwenn Maxfield, Woodinville
    Water District
1996 — Craig Olson, Association of
    Washington Cities
1997 — Jerry Copeland, Public Works
    Director, Yakima
1998 — Gary Wheeler, Skillings &
    Connolly, Inc.

THE RECENT YEARS 1992-1998

Recent years of Washington State Chapter history are abbreviated here, not because of lack of importance or activity, but more for lack of space in these few remaining pages of *Building Washington*. As the final touches and editing was done on the *Building Washington* text, the demand for space became greater. Space for Chapter history shrank proportionately as did the descriptive text.

Chapter membership continues to hold steady at about 1,000 people representing public works professionals in government, private engineering consultants, contractors, and vendors from a broad cross section of Washington state.

Throughout any one year a variety of events and activities crowd a Washington Chapter APWA member's calendar. Starting the year with a Board of Director's meeting the schedule continues on with a ski day, golf tournament supporting the Endowment Fund, regional/area professional meetings, Public Works Week recognition activities, more Board meetings, women/minorities recognition luncheon, and major conferences in Spring and Fall, several teleconferences, and other special events and area meetings.

RECENT MAJOR PROJECTS

1993 **Roy Morse**, Washington Chapter organizer and charter member, received Honorary Membership in the Public Works Historical Society.

1993 **Jerry Fay**, 1983 Chapter President, was elected Director-at-Large to serve on the American Public Works Association Board of Directors until 1999.

1994 **"An Interview with Roy Morse"** based on interviews conducted by Howard Rosen and Jan Klippert was published by the Public Works Historical Society.

1995 The Chapter sponsored an International Symposium, **Public Works and the Human Environment**, in Seattle. This major effort by the Chapter in cooperation with the University of Washington attracted more than 450 participants. **Symposium Proceedings,** including 160 papers, was published. Many national and international organizations supported and participated in the Symposium.

1996 The Chapter began a regular program sponsoring local teleconference training sites for its members through satellite broadcasts developed and coordinated by APWA national.

1997 The Chapter International Liaison Committee, Ben Yazici, Chair, sponsored a 40 member delegation from the Republic of Turkey focusing on professional/technical tours of Seattle and regional public works installations. Technical sessions and tours highlighted mutual concerns of municipal administrators including finance, transportation, mobility, land use planning, water and sewer issues, the Boeing Company, Microsoft, the Museum of Flight, Seattle Water Works, METRO Waste Water Treatment Plant, WSDOT I-90/Mercer Island Lid and bus tunnel.

1998 The Standards Committee, Dale Poussier, Chair, published the 1998 **Standard Specifications for Road, Bridge, and Municipal Construction** manual which is used throughout Washington state as guidelines for construction of municipal projects. ◆

King County Executive Ron Sims (left) receives a plaque from city mayors from the Republic of Turkey. Forty delegates from the Republic of Turkey participated in a cultural exchange program sponsored by the Washington Chapter in August 1997.

CHAPTER AWARDS

The Chapter has an extensive award program recognizing individual effort and contribution to the public works profession. Awards are granted for Contractor of the Year, an Award of Merit granted to an operational level employee, the Roy Morse Award for outstanding technical accomplishment, June Rosentreter Spence Award for furthering professional programs for women and minorities in public works, Robertson Award for outstanding service to the Chapter, Projects of Historical Significance Award, Charles Walter Nichols Award for outstanding achievement in the field of sanitation, and Donald C. Stone Award for achievement in the field of professional education.

NATIONAL AWARDS

The Chapter and contributions from outstanding individual members continue to compete well at the national level and oftentimes receive those awards and appropriate national recognition.

Washington State Chapter received the PACE, Presidential Award for Chapter Excellence, in both 1996 and 1997. This award is granted to outstanding APWA Chapters for exceptional overall programs and contribution to the profession and the community.

Top Ten Public Works Leadzer of the Year — Outstanding performance by an engineer or administrator.

    1992 - Jerry Fay   1993 - Jack Pittis
    1997 - Larry Southwick

National Meritorious Service Award — granted to a private sector member for outstanding service to the Chapter.

    1991 - Tom Gibbs   1995 - Dick Warren
    1996 - Dale Poussier   1997 - Jared Smith

Swearingen Award — for outstanding service to the Chapter.

    1991 — Jan Klippert
    1994 — Larry Southwick

National Recognition for Contractor of the Year Award

    1997 — City of Federal Way
    1997 — City of Vancouver

BUILDING WASHINGTON

SPONSORS

Roy Lehman Allen

Roy Lehman Allen, Commander, USN Civil Engineer Corps, was born April 11, 1931, in Indianapolis, Indiana. He graduated from Arsenal Technical High School in Indianapolis in 1949 and from Purdue University in 1953 with a Bachelor of Science degree in Civil Engineering. CDR. Allen's Navy career commenced as an officer candidate at New Port, Rhode Island. He then attended the Navy Civil Engineer Officer Corps School, Port Hueneme, California. His first tour was with Naval Construction Battalion Two assigned to assist in the construction of the Cubi Point Naval Air Station in Subic Bay, Phillipine Islands. His second tour was as an assistant resident officer in charge of the U.S. Navy Mine Craft Base 6th Naval District, Charleston, South Carolina.

Following Sixth Naval District tour, CDR. Allen reported as Assistant Public Works Officer at the USN Submarine Base, New London, Connecticut where he married Sally Ann Walsh and fathered son Sam Patrick. CDR. Allen's next assignment was in Yokosuka, Japan, where he had assignments as Maintenance Control Officer, Design Officer, and Construction and Maintenance Contract Administration Officer for the Public Works Department, Fleet Activities, Yokosuka, Japan. Daughters Tacie Jane and Saimi Ingree were born in Japan in 1960 and 1962.

After a tour at NAS North Island, Coronado, California, serving as Public Works Department Shops Engineer, Allen was sent to Kodiak, Alaska. His job was to oversee the earthquake restoration work for Kodiak Naval Base and surrounding communities. Son Andy Rit Allen was born in Kodiak in 1966.

Tours in Bangkok, Thailand, Adak, AK and Vietnam filled the years 1967 to 1972. In Vietnam Allen oversaw major bridge and facility construction projects. Son Bondy Roy was born in Bangkok in July 1967.

CDR Allen ended his 22-year Naval career as the Public Works Officer and ROICC for the U.S. Naval Air Station, Whidbey Island, Washington. Military citations awarded to CDR. Allen include Bronze Star, Joint Service Commendation Medal, Navy Achievement Medal, Meritorious Unit Commendation Ribbon, National Defense Service Medal with Bronze Star, Expert Rifle Medal/Expert Pistol Medal, Vietnam Service Medal with Bronze Star/Vietnam Campaign Medal with Device.

Upon retirement in 1975 he accepted appointment as the Assistant Island County Engineer and in July 1982, he was promoted to Director of Public Works and County Engineer, Island County. Many major County projects have been completed under Allen's direction including a new 50-bed jail facility, reconstruction of the Crosby Road curves, widening and reconstruction of several roads, institution of a road safety construction program, and design and construction of a new road shop maintenance facility for the North Whidbey Road District.

CDR Allen also taught firearm and hunter safety courses as an American Rifleman Association firearms instructor and a Washington State hunter safety instructor.

CDR Allen was a single parent from 1977 to 1988 and in 1989 married Nila L. (Jones) Elliott from Michigan. ◆

American Society of Civil Engineers

The Seattle section of the American Society of Civil Engineers recently celebrated its 75th year of serving the region. Founded on June 30, 1913, the section is proud to be a part of ASCE—the oldest American national engineering society.

Since its early days when members such as Gen. Hiram M. Chittenden, as head of the U. S. Army Corps of Engineers in Seattle and member of the Port Commission, pushed for the first development of Seattle's harbor, the Seattle section of ASCE has had a profound impact on public works in Washington. A prime example is the section's efforts in leading the call in the early 1980s for more public funds for infrastructure. Since creation of the Washington State Public Works Inventory Project and State Public Works Trust Fund, the section has taken an active role in developing the community infrastructure questionnaire, testifying before legislative committees, and assisting smaller communities in their local infrastructure programs.

The section has also long cherished its responsibility to speak out on specific local public works projects, such as consideration of a second Lake Washington Bridge, and bridges across Puget Sound and Hood Canal in 1957; recommended locations for I-5 through Seattle in 1957 and the cross Sound ferry terminal in 1961; and help in establishing a $38 million construction program for Seattle as part of the post World War II re-employment efforts. In 1987 the section presented to the City of Seattle its position on METRO's West Point Regional Secondary Treatment Facility expansion.

The Seattle section also affects public works in the area by promoting local projects for recognition. Projects include Seattle's Freeway Park, which received an award of merit by the National Society of Civil Engineers in the 1977 Outstanding Civil Engineering Achievement competition, and the METRO Renton ETS Outfall, awarded the Outstanding Civil Engineering Award in 1987 by the Pacific Northwest Council. An important service performed by the Seattle section of ASCE is making special technical skills of section members available to the public through technical training programs. Professional excellence is promoted through various competitions and awards, such as the "Engineer of the Year," and the Daniel W. Mead Prize for associate members.

The section has been a leader in recognizing the equal rights and abilities of minorities through such efforts as the Minority Affairs Program. The section has recommended the appointment of engineers to public offices involved in construction and engineering. The section monitors and reacts to political actions and legislation relevant to ASCE's interests and expertise.

Civil engineering students are supported and encouraged through an ASCE-Seattle-founded student chapter and the Richard Williamson Jones Memorial Award to provide direct assistance to local student civil engineers. Other assistance is given to students in the form of scholarships, fellowships and awards from the national society, made available through the local student chapter.

ASCE's objective—the advancement of the Science and Profession of Engineering—prompts it to support a variety of concerns including advancement of new engineering techniques and discoveries, and furtherance of technical research, promotion and protection of standards relating to legal registration of civil engineers.

The 1800 members of the Seattle section of ASCE are proud to be a part of the history of public works in Washington State. ◆

Alpha Engineering Group, Inc.

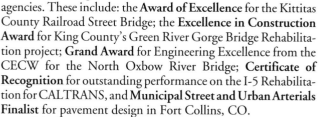

Alpha Engineering Group, Inc. was founded by Prakash Limaye, P.E. and David Lanning, P.E. in October 1981. Since that time, Alpha has expanded to 180 employees, 120 being in the Pacific Northwest, with offices in Tukwila (corporate headquarters) and Bothell, WA; Denver, CO; Phoenix, AZ and Sacramento, Pleasanton, and, most recently, Los Angeles, CA. This expansion enables Alpha to better meet Washington state's growing public works needs.

After beginning as a minority firm, Alpha "graduated" from the MBE program in 1991. Performing mainly subconsultant work at first, the firm has since gone on to provide prime consultant services on numerous projects for Washington public agencies such as: the Washington State Department of Transportation, the counties of King, Snohomish, Grays Harbor and Jefferson; the cities of Seattle, Kent, Renton, Bellevue, Everett, Bellingham, Tacoma, Port Angeles, Tukwila, Issaquah, SeaTac and Redmond.

A small portion of Alpha's significant public works projects include: the pictured I-405/N.E. 124th Street Interchange Improvements for WSDOT; the Queets River Bridge design for Jefferson County; the Southwest Grady Way Bridge Replacement for the cities of Renton and Tukwila; Acting District Engineers for the Woodinville Water and Sewer District and Acting City Engineer for the cities of Lake Stevens and Carnation.

Alpha has received numerous awards and recognition from various agencies. These include: the **Award of Excellence** for the Kittitas County Railroad Street Bridge; the **Excellence in Construction Award** for King County's Green River Gorge Bridge Rehabilitation project; **Grand Award** for Engineering Excellence from the CECW for the North Oxbow River Bridge; **Certificate of Recognition** for outstanding performance on the I-5 Rehabilitation for CALTRANS, and **Municipal Street and Urban Arterials Finalist** for pavement design in Fort Collins, CO.

Alpha's specialties include transportation engineering, including roadway design, traffic engineering, transit engineering, civil engineering, including drainage design and hydraulic analysis, structural engineering, including bridges, retaining walls and waterfront structures, electrical and mechanical engineering, environmental services including NEPA and SEPA documentation, and surveying. Alpha's hazardous materials group provides services in asbestos abatement and underground storage tank management. ◆

I-405/N.E. 124th Street Interchange

Arnold, Arnold & Associates

Arnold, Arnold & Associates was established in 1946 by Cecil C. Arnold, Consulting Engineer. Mr. Arnold had a long experience record in the design and construction of public works projects, including contributing expertise to the construction of such local landmarks as the Lacey V. Murrow, Lake Washington floating bridge and the Washington Memorial (Aurora Avenue) Bridge.

The firm's initial assignments were principally in bridge design with small cities and counties as clients. Typical early projects include the William Street Bridge, Renton, the Allentown truss bridge across the Duwamish River, Tukwila, and the Sauk River Bridge, Skagit County. Two notable bridges are the through-steel arch across the Skagit River at Concrete, Washington, and the Gorge Creek deck arch for Seattle City Light near Ross Dam.

In the 1950s the company's professional scope was expanded to include design of ferry terminals for Washington State Ferries. To date, more than 15 land/water transfer facilities have been designed. The firm was also active in civil engineering areas involving grading, paving and drainage. Among prominent projects in the 1950s were designs for runways for the U.S. Navy at Ault Field on Whidbey Island.

In the 1960s the firm designed approximately four and a half miles of the I-5 freeway and, later, approximately three and a half miles of I-90 near Issaquah.

In the 1980s the firm was involved in the completion of I-90 with responsibilities for the Rainier Avenue So. Interchange in Seattle and a section of the Seattle Access project from I-5 to Fourth Avenue So. Other projects included Whatcom County's

Gooseberry Point Ferry Terminal and the loading and mooring facilities for B.C. Steamship at Pier 69, Seattle.

In 1991, Arnold, Arnold & Associates merged with Andersen Bjornstad Kane Jacobs Inc. of Seattle. ◆

Asphalt Paving Association of Washington

The Asphalt Paving Association of Washington was formed and incorporated as a non-profit association in 1954 by a progressive group of asphalt concrete pavement material manufacturers and producers in the State of Washington. The objectives and purpose of the association were established and remain: to promote better relations between its members and public agencies, to promote high professional standards in the asphalt paving industry, to combat unfair trade practices, to encourage efficiency among contractors and contractors' associations, and to encourage sound business practices that maintain high standards for asphalt paving work. The association also provides expert counsel and advice to its members on all phases of asphalt paving construction activities. It collects, compiles and disseminates current information on new and improved methods in asphalt paving construction. It assists governments in promoting worthwhile public works projects, and helps in promoting funding for them. The association also assists architectural and engineering firms, as well as homeowners in the proper use of asphaltic pavement surfaces.

The association adopted an awards programs in the early 1960s. Three programs exist: a) the best paving projects for the preceding year on the State Highway system, both east and west of the Cascade Mountains, are determined by the WSDOT, and plaques are presented to the contractor and the state project engineers responsible; b) an awards program sponsored jointly with the Washington State Association of County Engineers; and

c) an awards program sponsored jointly with the Washington State Chapter of the American Public Works Association and the Asphalt Institute. These programs recognize superior quality work of asphalt paving on city streets and county roads. Awards are presented at the annual meeting of the Asphalt Paving Association each November.

The association holds annual asphalt concrete pavement specifications meetings with representatives of the WSDOT to review changes or problem areas in the state construction specifications.

Since its inception, the Association has maintained a cooperative relationship with the WSDOT in the area of research and development. It has been instrumental in joint funding for research projects such as the use of Drum Mixer for asphalt paving material manufacture, the use of sulfur extended liquid asphalt mixes and recycling of asphalt paving material from millings of old pavements. The results of some of these research projects have now become standard procedures within the industry.

The association has published and re-published a *Design and Specifications Manual* for asphalt concrete pavements and bases. This manual is widely used by architects and engineers in the development of design and construction of pavement in the private sector.

The association members maintain an active relationship with the National Asphalt Paving Association. In 1987 the association provided substantial financial support for the National Center for Asphalt Technology (NCAT) at Auburn University in Georgia. The primary function of NCAT is to promote and undertake education, research and information services for the asphalt paving industry. ◆

City of Auburn

Auburn's water system is continuing proof that a well engineered and well designed system can stand the test of time. Originally, Auburn's source of water was an intake on Mill Creek in Peasley Canyon. In 1884 it serviced a population of 200.

In 1907 with a population of 1500, Auburn passed a $14,000 bond issue to construct a water system utilizing springs on the plateau west of town. The springs were tapped, a reservoir built and a 10-inch wood stave line laid connecting it to the town. This spring, with a capacity of 540,000 gallons per day, is still in use.

As the town continued to grow the sources west of town had proved inadequate. Wells were dug in town but they had too high an iron content. It was time to plan ahead. A water system concept was envisioned with a large reservoir on top of the plateau just east of town. This reservoir would provide several days of reserve water with good pressure. Two sources of water were available. Rock springs near Black Diamond was a gravity source but it was 13 miles away and it had a limited supply of water. Coal Creek Springs was only three miles from the reservoir with 8 eight million gallons per day of water, but it required pumping because it was at a lower elevation than the proposed reservoir site.

Auburn's engineers researched the state of the art and concluded that the hydraulic ram provided the most economical and practical solution. Utilizing the abundance of water from Coal Creek Springs, a ram could elevate water the 154 feet to the reservoir.

In 1925 a system was set up consisting of the intake at Coal Creek Springs, a 24-inch wood stave pipe water supply line running three miles with a steel section under the White River, five rams and a three million gallon reservoir. This battery of five rams was the largest installation of this technology in the world. The rams were manufactured by Johnson Manufacturing Company of Seattle.

The rams utilized 75 percent of the water supply to boost the remaining 25 percent to the reservoir. Approximately 1.5 million gallons per day could be elevated. In 1938 the Public Works Department noted that the annual cost of operation of the facility was $357. In contrast, the annual cost of an electrical pump system for the same quantity of water would be $3,542—ten times the cost.

The principle of a hydraulic ram is to transfer the energy of moving water to elevate the water. The ram is inefficient requiring a large supply of water with a low head in order to elevate a small quantity of water. The working sequence of a ram is as follows: When a waste valve in the ram opens the water escapes and flow is started in the supply line. When this flow reaches a certain velocity the force of the current closes the waste valve and the water in the drive pipe, tending to keep in motion, forces its way through the discharge valve into an air chamber and then into the delivery pipe. When the water in the drive pipe is used up and water comes to rest, the discharge valve closes, retaining the water pumped. The waste valve again opens and the cycle is repeated. The action is continuous with the ram working as both motor and pump.

As the city continued to grow, in 1930 a pump was added to move some of the surplus water to the reservoir. With continued growth more pumps were added to utilize surplus water. By 1962 the city had expanded to the point that Auburn could not afford to waste any of the water which powered the ram. The rams were abandoned and a modern pump system was installed.

Today the heart of the Auburn water supply system at the Coal Creek Springs source consists of three miles of pipe (since upgraded from wood to concrete pipe), the pumps at the old ram site and a new five million gallon reservoir. Additional deep wells and reservoirs have been added to supplement the original water source. The number of connections has increased from 800 in 1929 to over 8,500 in 1988, but the basis of operation is still sound.

Auburn is proud of its heritage as the site of the largest battery of hydraulic rams in the world. Auburn is also proud of the ability of its Public Works staff to find a state-of-the-art economical and sensible solution to building on the historic system. ◆

Barrett Consulting Group

The staff of Barrett Consulting Group, Northwest has made considerable contribution to the development of public works in Washington State and the Pacific Northwest. Many of the senior staff have been involved in the development of public works for over thirty years.

Barrett Consulting Group, Northwest has roots in both Alaska and Washington State. The core of the engineering group were involved in numerous utility projects developed by Stevens, Thompson and Runyan during the 1960s and later under the name of STRAAM Engineers. Projects worthy of note include:
- City of Bellingham - Water Treatment Plant
- Town of LaConner - Sewage Collection System and Treatment Plant
- City of Auburn - Water System Comprehensive Plans and Water Storage Reservoirs
- City of Moses Lake - Wastewater Treatment Facility

In parallel with the Washington work, Engineering Associates of Southeast Alaska began an engineering operation in 1970 in Ketchikan, Alaska. During the next decade, the firm was principal consultant in the design and construction of major wastewater treatment facilities in southeast Alaska. Until these treatment plant projects were funded by the early EPA Programs, southeast Alaska communities discharged raw wastewater into the Pacific Ocean.

Continued growth in the southeastern Alaska market area led to continued growth of the firm. In December of 1981, the firm entered the Seattle and Pacific Northwest market area. When an office was opened in Bellevue, Washington, the name was changed to Pool Engineering, Inc. In May of 1982, the Seattle office of CRS Group Engineers, Inc., STRAAM Division, was acquired and the staff was integrated into the Bellevue office of Pool Engineering. During the 1980s, the firm was retained by Port Authorities, the City of Seattle and other Pacific Northwest municipal agencies, large and small.

In 1987, PEI announced the merger with Barrett Consulting Group. Both firms brought nearly two decades of expertise in the planning and design of water and wastewater treatment and conveyance systems to the union, greatly expanding the companies' geographical service areas. Today, Barrett Consulting Group has an outstanding record of growth, expansion of services, and reputation for providing high quality services to their clients. Approximately 250 employees now operate out of eleven locations in Washington, California, Hawaii, Guam and Mexico.

Barrett Consulting Group, Northwest employs a staff of fifty-five in their Bellevue, Federal Way and Bellingham offices in the State of Washington. The firm is recognized in the industry for its consistent use of innovative technology in the areas of water and wastewater treatment and collection systems. At Salmon Beach on the shores of the Tacoma Narrows, for instance, Barrett designed the first municipal gravity/vacuum sewer system to be

140th Street, City of Bellevue (Client—City of Bellevue).

installed west of the Mississippi. The 100-year-old community of Salmon Beach consists of homes built on pilings above tidal waters at the foot of a steep bluff. Access was so limited and costs for conventional sewers so high that the residents had never had wastewater utility service.

Barrett's successful application of a vacuum sewer system at Salmon Beach eliminated the discharge of untreated wastewater with a minimum of disruption to residents and the environment, and in effect ensured the future of the community. At the same time, the vacuum system brought residents and the City of Tacoma a considerable cost savings over traditional alternatives.

Another Barrett project that required specialized engineering expertise is the prestressed concrete tank recently completed in Bellingham. The new reservoir at Whatcom Falls Park is one of the largest cast-in-place concrete reservoirs built in Western Washington and measures in at 365 feet in diameter and 23 feet high.

Currently, Barrett Consulting Group is involved in a number of challenging projects for both public and private clients throughout the Pacific Northwest. In addition to traditional civil engineering, Barrett has branched into community planning to provide clients with a wider range of services. With the advent of the Growth Management Act (GMA), Barrett's land use planners have had their hands full. Services typically include overview of real estate and land use decisions, rather than the utility planning services normally provided by engineering consultants.

Six small cities in Snohomish County have recently employed Barrett's planning services during the GMA process, as well as other cities throughout the state like Ocean Shores and Lynden. Barrett has also provided planning services for the government of Guam, and is preparing to work with the Mexican government to develop a City planning process.

A recent addition to Barrett's disciplinary mix is Barrett Environmental Services. Barrett now offers clients a complete spectrum of civil engineering and geoenvironmental services.

Barrett's Northwest office has won the Seattle Section ASCE Outstanding Local Civil Engineering Project of the Year Award twice. First in 1985, for the Balsam Lane Pump Station. The use of a programmable controller and variable-speed pumps capable of varying frequencies resulted in an especially energy-efficient pump station. Then again in 1988 for the Perkins Lane Project, where sanitary sewer service was provided to homes in the Magnolia Bluff neighborhood of Seattle. The homes had previously been discharging 10-20,000 gallons a day of raw sewage onto the beach, as many of their private septage tank systems had failed. Barrett also received a 1992 Consulting Engineering Council of Washington (CECW) Honor Award for the Salmon Beach Vacuum Sewer Wastewater Collection System.

Barrett Consulting Group's staff is proud to be part of the long history of public works development in the Pacific Northwest. Our staff continues to be dedicated to providing the highest level of service and engineering expertise available in the Puget Sound Region. ◆

Miller Creek Secondary Treatment Plant, Burien, WA (Client— Southwest Suburban Sewer District).

R. W. Beck and Associates

In 1942, Robert W. Beck started a company to help with the acquisition of 17 Nebraska electric utility systems and the creation of new public utility districts (PUDs). The firm's first employees, in Columbus, Nebraska, were engaged primarily in unifying and integrating the organizations and rate structures of Nebraska's new PUDs. Their services also included analysis of operations, and assistance in obtaining financing to maintain and improve bond ratings in order to obtain attractive interest rates.

By 1945, the firm's services were in demand from Florida to Washington, where Seattle office staff worked on the negotiated purchase of utility properties by various public utility districts around the state. Bob Beck personally prepared the feasibility reports for these negotiations and advised the districts on many of their early operations. The firm's early assignments involved valuations, engineering and economic studies, power supply and financial planning. Organization and rate studies continue to be a strong area of service.

Some of the new PUDs, responding to the need for improved public water supply, elected to provide these services to their customers. R. W. Beck assisted Skagit, Snohomish, Clark, and Chelan County PUDs in forming and developing water supply systems.

During the '50s, the firm began branching into the hydroelectric field. Since 1953, it has completed more than 150 hydroelectric projects, involving hydroelectric development, licensing support and engineering for new and existing dams.

Venturing into the hydroelectric field also opened two additional service areas for the firm. Design of these facilities required electrical power engineering, which led to the firm's expansion into electrical design, including substations and transmission lines to deliver power to the electrical grid. The firm's hydroelectric projects frequently involved construction management services, and the firm continues to offer full capabilities in project management, inspection, claims avoidance, litigation support and other construction engineering assistance.

In 1954, Bob Beck expanded the ownership of the firm by forming a partnership with Willard Reuss, E. Weir Eaton, John Wallace, Robert Gallup, Gordon Jorgensen and Herb Westfall.

The 1960s brought R. W. Beck actively into the wastewater field. The firm was part of Metro Engineers, a consortium of engineering firms responsible for the planning, design and construction management of the vast wastewater collection and treat-

Secondary clarifier at the city of Richland's wastewater treatment plant. (Photo courtesy R.W. Beck and Assoc.)

ment system serving most cities in the greater Seattle area. This system, the first regional wastewater service in the United States, still forms the core of the Municipality of Metropolitan Seattle's wastewater system, providing service to nearly 1.5 million people.

The 1960s were a period of growth and expansion for the firm. Gordon Jorgensen was sent from Seattle to open an office in Phoenix in 1960, and in 1962 William Trommershausen opened an office in Boulder, Colo., which operated from his home for two years before moving to Denver. The Orlando office opened in 1965 and the Boston office in 1967.

Bob Beck served as the firm's managing partner until his death in 1968, and was succeeded by Herb Westfall. The firm thrived under Westfall's leadership, expanding geographically and professionally. As it grew, Westfall managed the firm carefully to maintain the quality of its services and to uphold Beck's personal philosophy of providing responsible consulting engineering services.

Under Westfall's leadership, the firm was responsible for a number of firsts.

R. W. Beck engineers designed the first elliptical arch dam in the United States for Ketchikan Public Utilities in Alaska. They designed the first SO_2 scrubbers on a power plant flue-gas emissions system to improve air quality in Key West, Florida. They also designed a

Spillway tunnel outlet at the Sultan River project. (Photo courtesy R.W. Beck and Assoc.)

R. W. Beck and Associates prepared a feasibility analysis and assisted in securing financing for adding generation units at the Rocky Reach hydroelectric facility. (Photo courtesy of R. W. Beck and Assoc.)

environmental impact statements led to the formal creation of an environmental practice. The staff of scientists carefully examines the potential impacts of proposed actions on the firm's projects. This is essential to obtaining project approval and making certain that the proposals are environmentally sound.

It is fitting for a firm that has always had its headquarters and largest office in Washington to have had an important role in developing the infrastructure of the state. From its earliest involvement in public power, R. W. Beck and Associates has grown and diversified to address the expanding needs of its clients; local and state government agencies. The firm has helped develop water supplies for Seattle, Everett, Wenatchee and Walla Walla, including the harnessing of available hydroelectric energy. In the 1970s, when Grant County was experiencing rapid industrial growth, the Grant County PUD turned to R. W. Beck to upgrade the electric transmission grid to meet the increased requirements. The firm has designed wastewater treatment plants, including a regional plant for the Yakima area and a new secondary facility for the city of Richland. In the '80s and '90s, the firm has helped create comprehensive solid waste systems such as those being developed by King, Snohomish, Pierce and Thurston counties. More recently, the firm has developed its capabilities in surface water management, and is assisting many cities and counties in western Washington with planning and management of this important environmental issue.

In 1991, one year before its 50th anniversary, R. W. Beck reorganized to better serve its clients in their increasingly demanding job of efficiently providing services to their customers. This client-based organization is centered around the firm's six service areas: water resources, solid waste management, electrical and thermal plant facilities, construction management, environmental and consulting services. This matrix management structure and approach encourages teamwork and responsiveness to the firm's clients. R. W. Beck is looking forward to its role in continuing to help its clients provide public services and operate their businesses successfully. ◆

suspension-cable pipe crossing to carry water across Washington's Skagit River when the most cost-effective river crossing location did not coincide with an existing bridge.

But the achievement of which Westfall once said he was most proud is the firm's work with joint-action electric power agencies. Over the years, the firm has teamed with attorneys, financial advisors and underwriters to help clients raise nearly $88 billion to develop power supply projects.

Westfall's vision also led the firm through a period of change and growth. Under his guidance, the firm grew to become the largest consulting engineering firm headquartered in the State of Washington. The mid '70s saw new offices open in Indianapolis, Minneapolis, Nashville and Sacramento.

In the early '80s, the firm's wastewater work, coupled with its background in planning and power plant financing, paved the way for pioneering efforts into solid waste management planning and resource recovery projects. The firm is now a recognized leader in integrated solid waste management. Solid waste management planning and facility design experience includes recycling, composting, incineration, landfilling and waste transfer.

The firm's consulting services have expanded to help clients meet the challenges of the information age and to be efficient in providing public services. This includes strong capabilities in management organization, strategic planning and information technology.

In 1987, Westfall turned the reins over to William R. Mayben, who had been R. W. Beck's executive partner since 1981. Mayben joined the firm in 1962 after graduating from the University of Colorado with a bachelor's degree in Electrical Engineering. Elected to the partnership in 1968, he helped establish several of the firm's midwestern offices, which he managed until 1980. The firm continues to thrive with Mayben's emphasis on client-focused quality and integrity, expanding the range of its services to meet its clients' growing needs.

Client requests for help with siting studies and

Water pipeline and utilidor crossing under Interstate-90 in Seattle's Rainier Valley. (Photo courtesy R. W. Beck and Assoc.)

City of Bellingham

Early settlement around Bellingham Bay began December 15, 1852, with the construction of a lumber mill at the mouth of Whatcom Creek utilizing the power available from an adjacent waterfall. The community was later named Whatcom. Within two years additional settlements were created in Fairhaven, January 1853, Bellingham, January 1853, and Sehome, June 1854.

The communities grew steadily from mid-century and in the 1880s Whatcom and Sehome incorporated, with Fairhaven following suit in 1890. In October of 1903 the collection of communities voted to consolidate into a single municipality called Bellingham which adopted its charter on July 12, 1904.

The area that has come to be known in this century as Bellingham was visited in the early days mainly from the water. Railroad service beyond the immediate area was first available in 1891 with a line north to Sumas and a connection to the Canadian Pacific's transcontinental railroad. A Great Northern Railroad connection to Everett was completed in 1892. Street cars were an important part of Bellingham's early transportation system beginning service on March 28, 1891. An extensive system of tracks was installed despite the competition between early settlements. The street car era ended December 31, 1938, as private cars and buses replaced street cars as the most popular means of conveyance. In 1972 the citizens of Bellingham voted to purchase the privately owned bus company and once again public transportation was provided by the municipality.

The Interurban, providing electric trolley service to Mount Vernon, was initiated by the Pacific Northwest Traction Company on August 31, 1912. In 1922 there was hourly service to Seattle. The trip took three hours and 50 minutes. In the fall of 1921 the Pacific Highway—Chuckanut Drive—opened, providing paved access to the south.

As early as 1870 Whatcom Creek was noted as a water supply for the citizens of the Bellingham area. A private water system from Lake Whatcom was developed by the Bellingham Bay Water Company in December 1888. This system was purchased by the city in 1892. A number of control dams were built on Lake Whatcom to impound water from the winter for use during the

Above top: City Hall 1892-1939. Currently the Whatcom Museum of History and Art. Above: Current City Hall built in 1939 by the Federal Works Agency. Below: Early road construction in Bellingham. (Photos courtesy of Whatcom Museum of History and Art, Bellingham.)

summer months. The first dam was constructed in 1911 and the current control dam was completed in 1938. The Fairhaven Water Company using Lake Padden as a supply source was begun in 1890 and remained in private hands until purchased by the city in 1926.

In the late 1950s wide fluctuations in the level of Lake Whatcom lead to the construction of a water diversion system from the Middle Fork of the Nooksack River to supplement the flow of water into Lake Whatcom. In the late 1960s a water

filtration plant was constructed at Whatcom Falls Park to serve the entire city with treated water. Lake Padden was abandoned as a source of water supply and converted into a multi-purpose park.

Sanitary sewers were recognized as necessity for urban living and first constructed to serve the York and Eureka Additions to Whatcom in 1892. Many of these sewer lines remain in service today. A sewage treatment plant was built near the mouth of Whatcom Creek in 1947. This plant was expanded several times, but was abandoned when a new, larger facility was constructed at Post Point in 1974. The Whatcom Creek treatment plant site has been converted into a park complex featuring a Maritime Heritage Center. The new Post Point plant provided primary treatment for all of Bellingham's sewage. Prior to this plant the southerly one-third of the city had no sewage treatment whatever. In 1993 the Post Point plant was upgraded to provide secondary sewage treatment.

Bellingham salutes the Washington Chapter of APWA for having the vision and dedication to create this Centennial history of Washington's Public Works. ◆

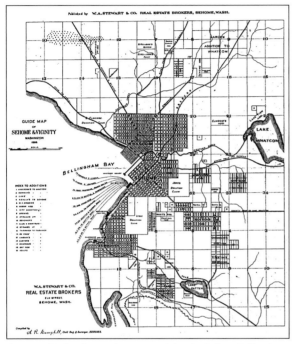

Early map of Bellingham, about 1889 (above). Below: Bellingham in the 1950s. (Courtesy of Whatcom Museum of History and Art, Bellingham.)

CITY OF BELLINGHAM

City Engineers

G. M. Gerhard, 1904-08	A. A. Edson, 1934-1935
H. W Troutman, 1908-10	J. M. Adams, 1936-37
H. Whitney, 1910-11	H. P. Dorsey, 1938
W. H. North, 1912-13, 1916-17	E. W. Gooch, 1938-48
C. Lindbery, 1914-15	Ted P. Schultz, 1949-57
C. M. Adams, 1918-23	William E. Cameron, 1957-66
J. C. Hills, 1924-33	Edwin R. Henkin, 1966-73
A. B. Culmer, 1934	John M Garner, 1973-79

Thomas L. Rosenberg, 1979 to present

Directors of Public Works

Theron L. Martin, 1973-75

John M. Garner, 1976 to present

Port of Bellingham

Established in 1920, the Port of Bellingham is the northern most port district in Washington. Spanning Whatcom County's more than 2,100 square miles. The port is two day's sail closer to foreign Pacific Rim ports than the major ports of California. Bellingham Airport has an international arrivals terminal, customs service and daily passenger service with connections to all major cities. Extension of the main runway to 6,750 ft. was completed in September 1992.

The Port of Bellingham was created by county vote and mandated by State of Washington statute to be a lead agency in economic development within its jurisdiction, Whatcom County, and to maintain safe harbors and clear terminals.

Towards its mandated goal of economic development the port is financially able to undertake property development projects such as installing infrastructure to industrial properties or utilizing creative and innovative financial tools such as Industrial Development Revenue Bonds to help businesses build and stay competitive. The port manages competitively priced retail and industrial properties—shoreline and inland—serviced by a complete intermodal system of highways, marine terminals, rail and air facilities. More than 300 tenants occupy port properties employing over 4,000 people.

The port manages a shipping terminal, harbors, docks, foreign trade zones and an export trading company. Its assets are valued above $80 million with facilities and districts including Whatcom International Shipping Terminal, Fairhaven Terminal, Bellingham International Airport, Airport Industrial Park, Sumas International Cargo Terminal, Grandview Industrial Park, Squalicum Harbor, Blaine Harbor and Foreign Trade Zones No. 129, A & B, No. 130, and No. 131. ◆

John T. Bannon

John T. Bannon served as President of Entranco Engineers from April 1, 1986 until his retirement in January 1994. Under his direction, the company has grown from a staff of sixty to one hundred twenty, with offices in Phoenix, AZ. and San Diego, CA., as well as in Bellevue.

Mr. Bannon has specialized in the planning and design of arterial streets and highways for over thirty years. He has designed and supervised more than 200 arterial and highway projects. Among the clients that have benefited from his design expertise are the cities of Auburn, Bellevue, Bremerton, Everett, Puyallup, Renton, Redmond, and Seattle. Other clients have been King, Snohomish and Kitsap Counties, the States of Alaska, Arizona and Washington and such federal agencies as the US. Navy facilities command and the US. Army Corps of Engineers.

Having been a Certified Value Engineer, he led several V.E. studies in Alaska and Washington, the most significant being a bridge vs. tunnel alternative across the Lough River on the Richardson Highway in Alaska, as well as directing the Entranco quality control program for many years. Major projects by Mr. Bannon include the Port Orchard Bypass in Kitsap County, Southcenter Blvd. in Tukwila, Urban Arterial projects in Auburn, Bremerton, Everett and Bellevue, portions of the Richardson Hwy. in Alaska, and the I-90 Corwin Detour in Seattle. ◆

William A. (Bill) Bugge

During his 14 years as Washington State's Director of Highways 1949-1963, Wiliam A. (Bill) Bugge was involved in the largest volume of highway and bridge construction projects in the history of the department at that time. He was responsible for 3,600 construction contracts and building of 4,107 miles of state highways.

As President of the American Association of State Highway Officials in 1957, he was responsible for overseeing the State Highway Departments for each U. S. state in the construction of the nation's 42,000-mile interstate system. The total system is estimated to have cost $44 billion in 1957 dollars.

He helped build Washington State's famous concrete floating bridges crossing Lake Washington and Hood Canal. He helped set up the State Highway Commission in 1951, and took over operation of Captain Peabody's Black Ball Ferry system. Over the years the Washington State Ferries system has grown to be the largest fleet of its kind in the United States.

Bugge was awarded APWA's Man of the Year Award in 1966 and Honorary Member Award in 1982. ◆

City of Bellevue

Bellevue was rural with a scattering of summer homes on the east side of Lake Washington until the opening of the historic first Lake Washington floating bridge in 1940. The area did not grow much during World War II, however, in 1946, local businessman Kemper Freeman, Sr. opened the original Bellevue Square shopping center marking the coming of what we now see as Bellevue.

New growth and development prompted incorporation in 1953, with five square miles and a population of 5,900. Bellevue became the first postwar city on the east side of Lake Washington, joining the more established cities of Redmond and Kirkland. Bellevue grew in geographic area and population with the post-war boom. It became a major residential center, a bedroom community for Seattle and Boeing workers, and later, an employment and business center in its own right.

The Public Works Department was very modest in the early days with the main activities being routine street maintenance. The implementation of several Local Improvement Districts (LID) for new facilities marked the opening of a new era. Utilities were provided by separate special purpose districts, primarily the Bellevue Sewer District and King County Water District 68.

The early 1960s saw the city begin to change as a small street bond issue passed in 1961 together with a successful LID to improve Bellevue Way (then 104th Avenue) into a major north-south arterial. It was widened from a two-lane county road to a six-lane business street with street trees and decorative street lights through the heart of downtown.

A second floating bridge between Bellevue and Seattle opened in 1963 and the entire east side of Lake Washington experienced a growth boom.

A new City Hall was built in 1964, replacing rented space in the central business district. A major bond issue was passed for more street improvements to match LID funds on a 50-50 basis. Between 1964 and 1970 most downtown streets were widened to four lanes under this program.

City leadership during this period of growth was provided by three city officials: L. Joe Miller, City Manager, J. Fred Herman, Planning Director, and Robert E. McCormick, Public Works Director. Miller was the energetic risk-taker, Herman was the visionary and McCormick was the builder.

The tallest building in 1963 was the four story Puget Power Building which they still occupy next to their new 22-story highrise. In the late 1960s the trend to taller downtown buildings continued with the erection of one thirteen-story, one nine-story and two seven-story buildings.

The city's next round of street funding came from the King County Forward Thrust bond issue in 1968 and the Urban Arterial Program, which was created by the 1967 legislature. Public Works Director McCormick was instrumental in passage of the Urban Arterial Program and was named to a seat on the Urban Arterial Board (UAB). There were some objections to his filling the "small cities" seat which was supposed to be for cities under 20,000 population. Due to a series of rapid annexations in the late 1960s, Bellevue's population had grown to over 20,000 people. McCormick retired from city service in 1968 and was succeeded by the City Engineer, Ron Kuchenreuther.

The Boeing slump of the early 1970s slowed growth to the end of the decade. The UAB continued to fund major individual projects in the city, including Bellevue-Redmond Road, NE 12th Street and 148th Avenue. These projects not only added substantial arterial capacity, but were built with a strong sense of aesthetics and sensitivity to the community. This was the beginning of the environmental consciousness of the region with Bellevue as a leader.

In 1974 the City formed the Storm and Surface Water Utility, the first of its kind in the country. Under the Department of Public Works, its role was to deal with all aspects of surface water quality and flood management. Under the management of Hector Cyre, the new utility used Public Works staff and equipment. Gradually, the utility obtained its own equipment and staff for all drainage maintenance. It developed its own comprehensive plan, codes and regulations, and took over the plan review and permit process for all private development with respect to clearing and grading, drainage systems and improvements.

This period also saw a changing organization in the public works arena. Three King County water districts and two sewer districts were taken over by the city in 1973 and formed into the Utilities Department under the directorship of John Tennant, former Manager of Water District 97. In 1978 the Utilities Department was consolidated with Public Works under J. Garth Anderson. In 1980 Hugh Warren replaced Anderson as Director. Warren oversaw the development of the City's first fully funded Capital Improvement Plan (CIP), marking a significant new phase in public works construction for the city.

This period was also marked by major growth in the central business district and other commercial areas around the city. Bellevue Square was entirely redeveloped, doubled in size and became a model for regional shopping malls.

In 1983 the Storm and Surface Water function was separated from the Department of Public Works and Utilities into a new independent department under a new director, Pam Bissonnette. She ably led the utility through its planning and implementation phases to become a national leader in surface water quality issues and management. She was subsequently awarded the Charles Walter Nichols award by APWA in 1986 in recognition of her particular achievements in this field.

Throughout the 1980s the City was actively engaged in planning for a new regional water supply including a large dam on the North Fork of the Snoqualmie River, a hydroelectric power plant near Snoqualmie Falls, a water treatment plant on the Issaquah plateau and a transmission line to south Bellevue. Initial planning was completed and a license was applied for with the Federal Energy Regulatory Commission. The license was not granted and the project was put on hold while alternative regional water supply plans were examined.

In 1986 Larry Southwick, Assistant Utilities Manager for the department was elected president of the Washington Chapter of APWA. The Chapter presented Southwick with the James Robertson Award in 1988 in recognition of his many contributions and years of active service in APWA.

In 1986 Hugh Warren left the Department of Public Works and Utilities and William Guenzler joined as the new director. Guenzler has led the department through an intensive period of political proceedings focused on the resolution of the regional traffic congestion.

As a consequence, Bellevue adopted a 12-year traffic/growth concurrency ordinance in 1989 and doubled capital spending for transportation system improvements. The City's ordinance served as a model for the subsequent state Growth Management Act, mandating a six-year traffic/growth concurrency approach, statewide.

The City of Bellevue will continue to grow in the next century and the Department of Public Works and Utilities is looking forward to the challenge to maintain its present level of public works excellence, innovation and leadership. ◆

Brown and Caldwell

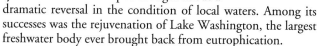

"No Swimming" signs posted on the shores of Lake Washington and Puget Sound were a common sight 30 years ago. The lake and many other bodies of water surrounding greater Seattle were seriously polluted.

Rapid population growth after World War II had created 10 cities within a 15-mile radius of downtown Seattle by 1956. Unincorporated areas were also becoming urbanized. Despite many small sewer districts, independent disposal systems, and sewage treatment plants, sewage from 43 percent of the population discharged into local waters without treatment.

The combination of raw sewage and shallow outfalls had contaminated the salt water beaches of Elliott Bay and Puget Sound. Even the treated sewage caused problems—effluent from treatment plants along the shores of Lake Washington, rich in nitrogen and phosphorus, had fertilized the lake, causing the growth of algae and leading to the lake's rapid deterioration.

Assessing the Scene—Following voter approval of a $6.25 million bond issue in 1956, the City of Seattle, King County, and the State of Washington retained a young San Francisco environmental engineering firm, Brown and Caldwell, to study the area's sewage and storm drainage problems. Thus began a long and productive relationship between the engineers and the people of Washington.

The Broad Approach—The study also opened an important chapter in the history of Washington's public works—a chapter that provides, in words from the October 2, 1967, issue of *U.S. News & World Report*, "a lesson for the whole country in how the people of Seattle and its suburbs got together to attack the area's water pollution."

The comprehensive 600-page report that Brown and Caldwell engineers produced from two years of study of the problem became the foundation for the Municipality of Metropolitan Seattle's (Metro's) unified sewerage interception, treatment and disposal system.

The study was partly responsible for the creation of Metro, the Seattle area agency that manages water and sewers. Brown and Caldwell Vice President Warren R. Uhte, a Metro Projects Manager since 1960, has pointed out that "the study showed a basic understanding of the overall environment and its issues long before the term 'ecology' became the catchword of the sixties. The recommended solution—regionalization—was a concept in advance of its times."

Intensive campaigning by citizen volunteers turned Brown and Caldwell's recommendation into a reality when voters approved the formation of Metro on September 9, 1958. Metro was created to act as a "sewage wholesaler"—the regional system would connect local systems, transport their sewage, treat it, and discharge the effluent into suitable receiving waters. To ensure that the regional approach would endure, Metro entered into 50-year standardized agreements with participants.

Success: Short and Long Term—The system that was developed brought about a dramatic reversal in the condition of local waters. Among its successes was the rejuvenation of Lake Washington, the largest freshwater body ever brought back from eutrophication.

By 1967, a year and a half ahead of schedule, the $130 million first stage of Metro's project to intercept, treat, and dispose of sewage in a 230-square-mile area in and around Seattle was completed. Design and supervision of construction were the responsibility of Metropolitan Engineers, a joint venture consisting of Brown and Caldwell—the lead firm—and Hill & Ingman (now URS Corp.), R. W. Beck and Associates, and Carey & Kramer (now Kramer, Chin & Mayo, Inc.). The cost of the completed facilities was within one percent of the cost estimated before the first contract was let.

The largest treatment plant in the system is the West Point Treatment Plant, located on a finger of land jutting into Puget Sound. The area's other major treatment facility, the Renton plant, started up in 1965 and replaced 14 local treatment plants that were discharging directly to Lake Washington. Foresight in the initial layout of the plant gave Metro room both to expand the plant to six times its original capacity and to add solids-processing facilities.

Brown and Caldwell's work on the Renton plant is a good example of the firm's "holistic approach" to resource management. At Renton, digester gas from the sludge-processing facilities is cleaned and sold to the local utility. In addition, a massive heat pumping system extracts heat from plant effluent for use in space and process heating. The heat in the effluent is also available to nearby developers for use in district heating systems.

Influence Beyond the Project—Metro tunnel work stimulated modification of the State of Washington's safety requirements for working under compressed air.

In 1961, State requirements governing work under compressed air did not reflect the extent of medical knowledge then available. Early in 1962, Metro sponsored a three-day conference on work under compressed air for representatives of the construction industry, local and state government, the health professions, and insurance carriers. An ad hoc committee including Metropolitan Engineers was established at the end of the conference with the responsibility to prepare revised regulations for work under compressed air. Bids on the Metro work were delayed for over a year while this work was completed and submitted to the legislature. The result was a set of guidelines that became a model for the rest of the country and a part of OSHA regulations. The result: no fatalities and no claims for permanent injuries on the Metro tunnel projects.

The Work Continues—Brown and Caldwell, who went to Seattle to conduct a sewage and drainage survey, has found the area impossible to leave. From 1959 to 1977, the firm headed Metropolitan Engineers, the joint venture that managed design and construction on one of the most successful regional wastewater projects in the history of the United States. Although Metropolitan Engineers was dissolved in 1978, Brown and Caldwell is still working on Metro projects. The expansion of the Renton plant to a capacity of 72 million gallons per day (mgd) in 1985, completion of the plant's solids-processing facilities in 1988, and the current expansion to a capacity of 108 mgd are but the latest examples of the continuing success of Metro's groundbreaking regional approach to wastewater management.

In 1975 a Brown and Caldwell office was opened in Seattle. Today the company is one of the major environmental consulting firms in the Pacific Northwest. ◆

Warren R. Uhte

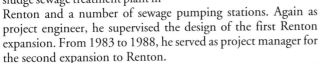

Of the original project team for the Municipality of Metropolitan Seattle's (Metro's) massive regional wastewater management project, Brown and Caldwell Vice President Warren Uhte is the only engineer still working full-time.

His first assignment in 1960 was as a project engineer, supervising the design of the activated sludge sewage treatment plant in Renton and a number of sewage pumping stations. Again as project engineer, he supervised the design of the first Renton expansion. From 1983 to 1988, he served as project manager for the second expansion to Renton.

Dick Finger, process control supervisor at Renton, has had a "good working relationship" with Brown and Caldwell for almost 20 years. He says it works because of engineers like Warren Uhte. "A lot of engineers think they have all the answers, but Warren honestly wants to know what the operators think about the plant," Finger says.

Currently, Warren is involved in ongoing studies and upgrades to the sewerage system. "The success of the Metro project is very personal to me," Warren says, "and I'm not finished yet!"

Roger Wilcox

The 184 miles of pipeline Metropolitan Engineers designed for the Metro project were kept leakproof at the joints because of the relentless determination of Brown and Caldwell's Roger Wilcox. Roger's research on rubber gaskets continued over six months, culminating in the design and production of the "Metro Gasket." Writing new standards for gaskets to fit Metro's needs, Roger met with considerable resistance from the rubber companies in his demand for a high-quality gasket. Rubber company managers felt they couldn't be competitive if forced to meet these standards; however, Roger triumphed, and the "Metro Gasket" was marketed throughout the industry.

Roger was assigned in 1960 to Metropolitan Engineers as a project engineer for design and construction on the East side interceptor. This interceptor conveys all sewage from the east side of Lake Washington to the Renton treatment plant for treatment and disposal. In 1966, Roger became chief engineer for Metropolitan Engineers in charge of the Seattle central office. From 1966 to 1977, he supervised design and construction of major facilities costing over $200 million for the Metro system. In 1981, he served as principal-in-charge of Brown and Caldwell's predesign report for the second expansion of the Renton plant.

Roger retired in 1983, after having dedicated 19 years of his career to the Metro system.

Jack Warburton

Building consensus through careful planning and negotiations has been the high point of Jack Warburton's experience with Metro.

Jack was technical manager for the initial combined sewer overflow (CSO) planning that encompassed both Seattle and the Metro system. At that time, only one Federal requirement regulated CSOs: the level of control had to be appropriate to the benefits accrued and their cost.

Seeking a consensus among all of the involved groups, Jack worked with the EPA and the State Department of Ecology's John Spencer (now Metro's Director of Water Pollution Control) to develop an acceptable level of control. He also worked with agencies to determine what costs were acceptable and who was going to pay them.

It took "many meetings with many people," says Jack, "but it was important to develop a consensus because...without it nothing would be implemented." Virtually no outside pressures of deadlines or regulations existed. Whereas now government agencies assign a "target" of control, then everyone involved had to agree on the target.

Randal Samstag, project engineer for Metro, attributes Jack's success at bringing engineers, administrators, and politicians together to a "unique quality—his ability to sense things that are troubling people, to sense conflicts. He approaches those subjects in a way that doesn't put people on the defensive."

Frank Kersnar

Frank Kersnar set up the original central office and office procedures for Metropolitan Engineers in 1960. he hired local residents to work for the joint venture—most of whom worked with him until his premature death in 1974.

Frank was gifted at implementing the innovative ideas the Metro project entailed. He did the bulk of the preliminary engineering that went into the predesign report on first-stage construction. This report, submitted to Metro on July 21, 1960, was a superior example of engineering knowledge integrated with financial planning skills.

He also displayed a phenomenal talent for grasping numbers in his responsibility for controlling costs during the first 10 years of the construction. At the end of the 10 years, the actual construction cost of $104,777,000 exceeded the original financing estimate by less than one percent.

At the dedication of the West Point Treatment Plant on July 20, 1966, speaker James R. Ellis (this acclaimed "Father of Metro") said, "Frank Kersnar typified the high skill and extra effort which professional engineers gave this project."

Photo, facing page: Clean-up of Lake Washington returned it to recreational use.

Myron D. Calkins

Myron D. Calkins was born in Tacoma, and graduated with honors in Civil Engineering from WSU. After college, he worked as a hydraulic engineer, as a Navy electronics technician during World War II, and in the bridge design office of the Washington State Highway Department. In 1948, he returned to Tacoma as design engineer with the city and in 1955 became City Engineer, where he served until becoming Director of Public Works for Kansas City, Missouri in 1964. He retired in 1986 and became Director of Public Works Emeritus.

Awards include: Honorary Member, APWA (1987); Alumni Achievement Award, WSU (1987); "Honor Man of the Year", Sigma Alpha Epsilon (1980); Edmund Friedman Professional Recognition Award, American Society of Civil Engineers (1978); Honorary Degree, Management Engineering, University of Missouri (1974); "Top Ten Public Works Leaders of the Year" (1973). He has served a variety of professional organizations, nationally and locally in both Kansas City and Washington State, including national President of APWA in 1970-71.

Presently, Calkins is an Adjunct Professor at the University of Missouri, a Diplomat of the American Academy of Environmental Engineers and Trustee Emeritus of the APWA Education Foundation. He and his wife Lenore have three children. ◆

Dennis E. Covell

Dennis E. Covell has been Director of Engineering and Utilities with the City of Yakima since 1981. He was Yakima's City Engineer for the City from 1979 to 1981. Mr. Covell is responsible for the maintenance and operation of Yakima's water, sewer and irrigation systems and management of the City's Capital Improvement program.

Mr. Covell was City Engineer for Richland from 1975 to 1979, and was employed by the Washington State Department of Highways in the Yakima District for the previous 11 years.

Mr. Covell, born in 1941 in Elmira, New York, received his B.S. in Civil Engineering from the University of Missouri. He has been a registered Professional Engineer in Washington since 1969.

While working for the Washington Department of Highways, Mr. Covell worked on Interstate Highways 82 and 90, and Walla Walla and Yakima bypasses. Projects in Richland included Wellsian Way, Water Treatment Plant upgrade, and the expansion and construction development of the Meadow Springs area. Mr. Covell has been an active member of the Washington Chapter of APWA since 1974, serving on its Board of Directors in 1988, 1989, 1991-94, and as the chapter president in 1994. He is a current member and 1989 president of the City Engineer Association of Washington. Mr. Covell and his wife Barbara have three children. ◆

Cedar River Water and Sewer District

In 1956 partners Vern Cole and William Gordon bought and started to develop 200 acres halfway between Renton and Maple Valley in an area called Maple Valley Heights. They built several streets, drilled a well, laid four-inch steel water mains and started to sell lots. After the well was condemned a new one was drilled and a 15,000 gallon wood stave storage tank was built. By 1969 population growth had exceeded the water supply. When the developer would not upgrade the water system a petition was circulated calling for the formation of a water district.

In 1960 an election was held to form the water district and three people were elected as commissioners: Arlie Parks, Lowell Stoutenberg and George Palmer. The election incorporated approximately one square mile and 75 water connections into a water district known as Cedar Mountain Water District #108 of King County. An additional 40,000 gallon tank, new pump and other improvements were installed to update the system.

In 1961 Mervin M. Minish was retained as engineer and Carl A. Jonson was retained as attorney for the district. Minish prepared the original comprehensive plan for the district and in 1966 was instrumental in annexing three square miles to the district. The next year a HUD grant was obtained and the central system was built in conjunction with a ULID assessment. This project included a City of Seattle connection, a one-half million gallon storage tank, pump station and distribution system. In 1974 Minish and his wife lost their lives in a boating accident in Idaho and Richard C. T. Li was retained as District Engineer. In 1978 a separate major system was constructed to the east of the original district in the Lake Wilderness and Maple Valley area. This system included a City of Seattle connection, a pump station and distribution system. In 1984 another major system constructed to the north of Fairwood in the valley floor area.

In 1966 Herman Sarkowsky and George Bell formed Sherwood Development Corporation and by agreement started a planned unit development around a country club and golf course known as Fairwood, which was annexed in 1967. In 1967 the system had expanded beyond a part-time activity and Bill Sutton became the first manager. In 1969 Robert M. Sloboden filled this position.

In 1985 the central area was interconnected with the east area. In 1986 Richard Li sold his business to Hugh G. Goldsmith & Associates. The company presently fulfills District Engineer functions. In 1987 the name of Water district #108 was changed to Cedar River Water and Sewer District to more closely identify with the functions and geography. By the end of 1993 the district had grown to include 4,660 water connections, 3,020 sewer connections and 3,280 street light customers. ◆

City Engineers Association of Washington

The City Engineers Association of Washington (CEAW) was formed in the fall of 1981 to establish a professional organization through which city engineers and other municipal engineering professionals could address a wide variety of issues and problems facing the state's cities. Through a cooperative effort with the Association of Cities and the motivation provided by the numerous needs of cities, CEAW has grown to over 100 members today.

Dedicated to enhancing municipal service and the quality of the urban environment by improving the proficiency of public works administrators and managers, CEAW members are licensed professionals working as city engineers and public works managers in the State of Washington. Associate members include non-licensed public works managers and consulting engineers representing small cities.

One of the goals of the organization is to strengthen the abilities of public works managers and engineers in the State of Washington. In addition, it is committed to participating in the legislative process of changing and making laws by providing expert testimony, research and reports, and providing a forum for the exchange of information between cities and public works managers. The association is dedicated to monitoring the legislative process and testifying when necessary, recommending individuals to AWC and WSDOT for appointments to various boards and committees, and conducting utility rate inventories. CEAW assisted in the development of the statewide pavement management program, and participated in the statewide road jurisdiction needs and funding study.

CEAW is a non-profit, tax-exempt professional association financed through membership dues. The organization has a semiannual membership meeting—spring and fall. The Board of Directors and members meet throughout the year in preparation for the general meetings. CEAW is proud to be a part of the history of public works in Washington. The association is committed to contribute to the excellence of public works in the future as it has in the past. ◆

CITY ENGINEERS ASSOCIATION OF WASHINGTON

Converse Consultants NW

Converse Consultants NW is a wholly owned subsidiary of the Converse Professional Group and has provided geotechnical engineering and applied earth sciences consulting services in the Pacific Northwest for close to 20 years. The Converse Professional Group has eight regional locations (Seattle, Washington; Pasadena, San Diego, San Francisco, Irvine, and San Bernardino, California; Las Vegas, Nevada; and Parsippany, New Jersey) and a combined staff of more than 400 individuals with specialized expertise in a variety of disciplines including geotechnical engineering, geophysical and geological engineering, hydrogeology, water quality studies, earthquake engineering, hazardous and solid waste assessment and management, environmental assessment, regulatory compliance, and geochemistry.

Geotechnical explorations and design recommendations are a significant element in the design of public works projects. Soil and geologic conditions encountered at a site are of primary consideration when selecting a project site and defining the most feasible and cost-effective geotechnical design solution. Although this initial stage of development is not usually visible upon completion of a project, it essentially determines the performance, safety and stability of the project. Converse has provided

Renton Effluent Transfer System.

geotechnical support on over 2,000 public works projects in the Pacific Northwest including roadways, bridges, water supply and distribution systems, surface water drainage and detention ponds, sewer lines, wastewater treatment facilities, hydroelectric projects, buildings, parks and recreational facilities. Significant projects where Converse provided geotechnical explorations, design and construction monitoring services include the Renton Effluent Transfer System; Alki Transfer/CSO Project; Renton Wastewater Treatment Plant; Interstate 90 Mercer Island roadway, bridges, tunnels and embankments; Snoqualmie Falls Hydroelectric Project; Everett Water Supply Pipeline No. 2 Rehabilitation; and the South Fork Tolt River Water Supply Line and Power Conduit.

Over the past several years, public awareness and stricter regulations have placed a greater emphasis on managing our resources to ensure a cleaner, safer environment and cleaner drinking water. Converse has been helping public and private clients evaluate and monitor soil, groundwater and sediment contamination, and remediate contaminated sites. In addition, Converse works with clients to evaluate and develop new, clean groundwater sources and protect their existing water resources. Significant projects include Snohomish and San Juan County landfill groundwater monitoring programs; landfill hydrogeologic investigations; multiple underground storage tank removals and remediation; sediment sampling and analysis, and cleanup in Elliott Bay, Duwamish estuary, and Commencement Bay; groundwater investigations and studies for numerous municipal wells including City of Yakima, Thurston County, King County; wellhead protection programs; and geotechnical and groundwater support for Environmental Impact Statements in King and other counties. ◆

CH2M Hill

Innovation that stands the test of time.
Our first office was a room over a drugstore. Our first employee were four GIs home from World War II. Today, we provide worldwide services and employ 4,000 people.

The philosophy that has earned us a reputation as one of the top-ranked engineering firms in the United States is: *Hire good people, provides superior support, and then give them the opportunity to find creative solutions.*

We put that use initially in designing wastewater treatment facilities to help clean up the polluted Willamette River in Oregon. Now we are involved in preserving the quality of Puget Sound. The work goes on.

We opened a Seattle Regional office, now located in Bellevue, in 1960, and extended our services throughout the Northwest. Our professionals work from offices in Yakima, Spokane, and Richland.

Above: Visitors reach Mount St. Helens via the new Spirit Lake Memorial Highway, Route 504, for which CH2M Hill established the alignment.

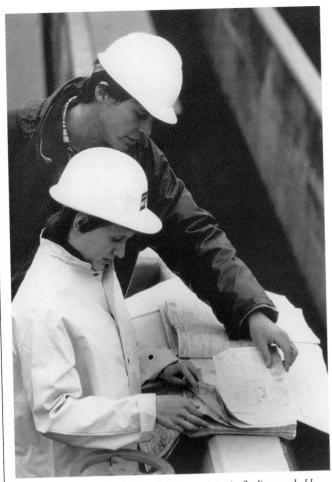

Above: People — their skills and their creativity in finding workable solutions — make CH2M Hill one of the nation's leading engineering firms.

Above right: The CH2M Hill-designed central Washington Yakima-Tieton irrigation project improves water supply, generates electricity, and extends fire protection to rural areas.

A major source of pride in our work and our commitment is that we are employee-owned — all of us have a stake in the work we do, work that stands the test of time. Although we grew to be the largest consulting firm in Washington, the fifth largest in the U.S., we have not forgotten the importance of local understanding and being part of the region we serve.

In 1989 — 29 years after opening a Washington office and 43 years after those returning GIs started it all — CH2M Hill continues to provide solutions that advance and enhance the quality of life in the Northwest. ◆

Right: CH2M Hill uses state-of-the-art equipment in project work, including the design of the control system for the Anacortes, Washington water and wastewater treatment plant.

Clark County Public Works

When the State of Washington was founded in 1889, Clarke (original spelling) County, the oldest county in the state, had already been providing government at a local level for 39 years. For Washington communities of that era, transportation was the key to development and prosperity. Clark County, situated at the confluence of the Columbia and Willamette Rivers, was a prime location to take advantage of the prominence of water travel.

But waterways were not enough. If Clark County was to grow as early settlers wanted, roads would be needed too. Hence, one of the first responsibilities of county government was to establish and maintain a sound road system. Roads, in fact, were so important to the well being of the county that in the nineteenth century every able-bodied man, with a few occupational exceptions, was required to contribute five days of labor each year to the County Engineer's efforts to build and maintain the roads that linked Clark County with the outside world.

After World War I the primary responsibility of the County Public Works Department was still roads. Instead of resident "volunteers," labor was provided by an organization very much like a union hiring hall. People with specific skills—grader operator, flagger, laborer—were employed from periods of one day to several months, depending on the type of work that was required.

By mid-century the department's work force was more permanent, but the emphasis was still on roads. In the late 1960s Clark County experienced explosive growth. The expansion period lasted almost a decade, and the department of Public Works had to keep pace. The county is once again experiencing tremendous growth. Transportation Impact Fees imposed on new development are helping to meet the growth challenge.

Although much has changed in the last 140 years, the fundamental requirement for public works has not. As Clark County has grown and developed, so has its Department of Public Works, enhancing the quality of life and meeting the needs of county residents. ◆

Top: These men are building the Etna Grade east of the mouth of Cedar Creek. Elmer Roslund is using the slip scraper to build up the road from material plowed out by Herman Spring. The man at the right was not identified. Fresno scrapers, also used in early road building, were similar to slip scrapers but were wider and had longer handles.

Bottom: Building the road from Heisson Bridge to Rock Creek necessitated moving some stubborn rock along the East Fork of the Lewis River. A crusher was set up to put the rock to good use, however. "Good Roads Day" is pictured in this photo, a time when men turned out in full force to pay their taxes by volunteering for road work. The wagon in the foreground is ready for a load of crushed rock.

Consulting Engineers Council of Washington

S ince 1955, members of the Consulting Engineers Council of Washington State have provided specialized engineering services for public works projects throughout Washington.

Consulting engineers have teamed with government to complete public works projects in an innovative, economical manner.

Awards in the National Engineering Excellence competition have provided attention and recognition for Washington State's outstanding public works projects.

Members of the council continue to seek the opportunity to team with government to accomplish quality public works projects for the benefit of the citizens of Washington state.

CONSULTING
ENGINEERS
COUNCIL OF
WASHINGTON

County Road Administration Board

The County Road Administration Board, commonly known as the CRABoard, is a unique agency comprised of county government members given a mandate to govern or regulate themselves and their peers. Created by the Legislature in 1965, the CRABoard is a state agency operating within the limits of state agency constraints, paid for funded by a portion of the counties' motor vehicle fuel tax. The agency is headed by a policy making body consisting of six county commissioners or councilpersons and three county engineers drawn from counties across the state.

The Board's primary responsibility is to assure that the road departments of all 39 counties in the state of Washington are in "reasonable compliance" with state law. To that end, the agency has developed Standards of Good Practice regulating counties in such areas as programming, management policies and maintenance management principles. The agency is able to respond to road department problems since it acts as an advocate for the 39 Washington county road departments to Congress, the State Legislature, and Washington State and Federal agencies.

The agency owes much of its success to the first Chairman of the Board, Commissioner Harry Sprinker from Pierce County. It was Chairman Sprinker's philosophy to achieve changes in the 39 counties by persuasion rather than force. The Standards of

Meeting of county officials, late 1930s.

Good Practice developed during the 27 years that the agency has been in existence still reflect that original thinking. The standards leave considerable control to the individual counties.

In recent years, the Board has assumed responsibility for administering the Rural Arterial Program (RAP) and the County Arterial Preservation Program (CAPP). The RAP program is funded by 0.58 of a cent of the state gasoline tax and provides approximately 16 million dollars per year for reconstruction of rural arterials in the state. Again, the emphasis has been on local control in that the RAP funds are prioritized in each of the five regions of the state using formulas developed by the counties in those regions. The CAPP program is funded by 0.45 cents of the state gasoline tax and provides about 13 million dollars a year for resurfacing and rehabilitation of paved county arterials. This $25 million per biennium program will be increasingly based upon a computerized pavement management program developed by CRAB. In addition, the Board has been responsible for the administration of the distribution formula for the counties portion of the motor vehicle fuel tax and with maintenance of the official statewide county road log since 1985.

In keeping with the emphasis on local control, the Board has encouraged the use of personal computers for management and engineering functions. The agency has developed database software to assist counties to manage their road networks and has distributed a major engineering design program to many of the counties. CRAB provides continual support and training for both the database and the design software programs, as well as general computer support for all of the Washington counties. ◆

Top: King County road truck, 1912. Bottom: Whitman County Engineer's Survey Crew Wagon, 1935.

Everett-Snohomish Road, Snohomish County, 1916.

The Engineers Club

On January 15, 1912, the *Seattle Post-Intelligencer* carried the following item: "Twenty-five engineers at a luncheon at the Rathskeller Saturday noon discussed the advisability of forming an Engineer's Club along social, rather than technical lines. A committee on organization was appointed. . . ." On March 8 of that year, at a luncheon at the Seattle Hotel, they elected officers and adopted a policy that "discussions of shop, religion, or politics are taboo!" Eighty-one years have passed and the club has survived—proving that, even with these constraints, engineers can find plenty to talk about.

By the end of 1914 membership had reached 139, and luncheon meetings were being held every Thursday—as they have been ever since. The club was dedicated to promoting the professional interests of all engineers, and encouraged "sustaining" memberships in engineering-related businesses. In 1916 club quarters were established in the new Arctic Club, and in 1922 they moved to the "old" College Club at Fifth and Seneca. However, the club quarters remembered fondly by most old members were those on the ninth floor of the handsome Arctic Building which the club occupied in 1925. These quarters provided a kitchen, dining room, library and poolroom where members enjoyed lunch five days a week for 43 years.

During those years engineers in the Seattle area contributed to some remarkable achievements in the area of public works: roads, bridges, tunnels, huge hydroelectric projects, electrified railroads and trolleys, ships, major public buildings, municipal water and sewer systems and the Alaska Highway. It must have been difficult not to "talk shop" at those Thursday luncheon meetings.

In 1968, faced with a substantial rent increase and desiring larger quarters, the club began a series of moves which changed its operating concept. The first move was to lease space and have lunches catered (which proved even more difficult financially than trying to maintain a club facility kitchen) and ultimately by meeting in a restaurant and contracting for office services. After trying several arrangements, the club began holding its Thursday luncheon meetings at Latitude 47° restaurant in 1976, and established a cordial relationship which continues to this day.

Like most such institutions, the club's history is full of interesting anecdotes. There was a heated debate in 1912 about whether membership should be restricted to graduate engineers or be open to, in the words written in the club's original constitution: ". . . others who may be interested in, or connected with, the engineering profession." In spite of some defections, this more liberal policy became, and remains, the club's modus operandi. In 1917 a Seattle newspaper reported that the Engineers Club "joined with affiliated Societies in the parade held by reason of the war situation." In 1920 the club was instrumental in getting the Engineer's Registration Law adopted, and in that year Herbert Hoover became an honorary member. In 1924 it had a full-time manager and was serving three meals a day; however, later that year the manager skipped town with all the club's funds.

The records for 1928 are full of correspondence between the club, its CPA and the Commissioner of Internal Revenue, as the club energetically sought tax-exempt status and a refund on "war taxes." After being rebuffed twice, victory was finally achieved through the diligence of the club's officers, and the help of a friendly congressman.

The minutes of the Executive Board meeting of September 11, 1942, illustrate the effects of wartime inflation on the price of lunches: sandwiches went from 15 cents to 20 cents, pie from 10 to 15 cents, and the "hot lunch" from 40 to 55 cents! The following year members were urged to contribute ration stamps to enable the cook to buy sugar for the club kitchen. The threat of no pies seems to have achieved the desired result.

During the 1940s the first woman was admitted to membership, although members' wives had always played an active role in social and charitable activities. Subsequently, club rosters have included several outstanding women—one of whom was recently Chair of the Board of Trustees.

Most noteworthy among the charitable efforts of the Engineers Club were the Christmas parties provided for the Washington Children's Home Society, complete with individual gifts for each child and a club member decked out as Santa. This practice began in the 1920s and was continued through the Depression years and World War II.

Since its inception the club has established a unique role among the various professional societies. It has been a meeting place for engineers of all disciplines, and, since it has had well established quarters through most of its history, it has often played host to the technical societies. At various times in the past engineers in the Seattle area have endeavored to create a true "Engineers' Center," but have been deterred by lack of funds, organization or a well-defined objective. In 1993 the opportunity to achieve such a center seems closer to realization than ever before. The Engineers Club has contributed considerable financial and human resources to this project, and continues to lend its full support.

Today the Engineers Club continues its 81-year-old tradition of the Thursday lunch program. Program topics range from technical to topical and the caliber of speakers continues to be remarkably high. Occasionally a field trip is organized, often under the auspices of a club member, to visit a place of particular interest. Evening meetings with dinner and entertainment are held several times a year, with spouses attending.

Although the focus of the club is engineering, the great affection it has engendered among its members is the result of the friendship and respect they have for one another — and their fond regard for a grand old institution. ◆

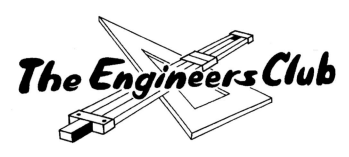

Entranco

Entranco's Beginning. In 1961, Brian Lewis and Alex Redford formed a partnership that has evolved into the company recognized today as Entranco. Founded in the Northwest, Entranco's history is linked with the growth of the Puget Sound region and Washington State over the next three decades. As the region became a force in the Pacific Rim, Entranco evolved into a multi-service engineering and environmental consulting firm dedicated to responding to public works and infrastructure challenges.

Lewis and Redford arrived in Seattle in the 1960s to evaluate the feasibility of a cross-Sound bridge from West Seattle to the Kitsap Peninsula. This historic project died one vote short of receiving funding from the State Senate. When their employer closed its Seattle office, Redford and Lewis recognized the opportunities of the growing region and formed Lewis Redford Engineers to participate in development of the expanding transportation system. Lewis left the firm in 1970 to pursue other interests. Redford became President, contributing leadership that shaped the company's first two decades.

As Lewis Redford Engineers, the company completed many feasibility studies for the Legislative Interim Committee on Highways in the 1960s. The program was a vital part of the State Department of Highway's plans to expand the Washington freeway and state route system. Entranco also provided engineering for Bellevue, Everett, Renton, and Auburn who were upgrading and expanding arterial systems because of changing traffic patterns and increasing traffic volumes. Arterial planning and design studies, traffic engineering projects, and arterial-highway design were some of the first technical strengths of the firm.

The 1970s. To complement engineering design skills, expertise was developed to take projects from start to finish, including helping cities obtain financing through grants, local improvement districts, bonds, and other funding sources. One notable effort was Entranco's work with the City of Bellevue to develop a bond issue to finance the design and construction of many arterials, including NE 8th Street.

Projects accomplished for public works and private clients in the 1970s demanded expertise in the new Entranco disciplines of environmental sciences, water and wastewater treatment, surveying, construction management, and structural engineering. Entranco was well on its way to becoming the multi-discipline, full-service consulting firm it is today. During this decade of growth and change, the name Entranco Engineers, Inc. was adopted to reflect its diversity; Entranco standing for **EN**vironmental and **TRAN**sportation **CO**nsultants.

The increasing environmental awareness of the Washington community was mirrored in the interests and concerns of Entranco staff and projects. The firm was quick to adapt to changing federal and state environmental laws and took a strong interest in environmental documentation and preserving lake water quality. By the time Washington residents were noticing that some community lakes were not as clear and inviting as in the past, Entranco had developed a first-rate lake restoration and limnological team.

A partnership approach to clients was becoming a more sophisticated element of Entranco's project management program. The firm worked closely with clients to create projects that were good neighbors, provided workable solutions, and met each client's total construction budgets.

This partnership approach was important when Entranco assisted Everett in the development of an urban arterial plan and bond issue to provide matching funds so the City could take advantage of the Urban Arterial Board funding program. Projects included miles of urban arterials through Everett including Colby Avenue. Entranco has since assisted cities and counties

Current Officers and Managers

Gary Van Wieringen, P.E., President, Washington Manager
Dale Anderson, Associate, Environmental Sciences Manager
Edward Berschinski, Associate, Construction Services Manager
Dale LeMaster, P.E., Associate, Civil Engineering Manager
Ken Oswell, P.E., Associate, Transit & Highways Manager
Ginny Hoglund-Gray, P.E., Associate, Site Development Manager
Kevin Nelson, P.E., Associate, Arizona Manager
Ben Martin, R.C.E., California Manager
Alex Redford, P.E. (Retired) Chairman, Board of Directors

with hundreds of Urban Arterial Board and Transportation Improvement Board projects.

Throughout the 1970s and 80s, Entranco participated in the widening of existing streets to increase capacity and also new alignments to enhance access to developing areas. Entranco performed transportation studies to determine capacity and access needs, identified roadway corridors, and located optimum alignments. In addition, the firm identified right-of-way acquisition needs, designed facilities, and managed construction.

The 1980s. With Entranco's assistance, many cities and counties in the state received and implemented lake rehabilitation grants from the US Environmental Protection Agency and Washington's Department of Ecology. Entranco's water quality/restoration analysis, design, and construction administration for the restoration of Wapato Lake won an award in the 1983 Consulting Engineers Council of Washington's Engineering Excellence competition and resulted in a Co-Engineer of the Year award for its project managers. Entranco devised a stormwater detention, treatment, and diversion system to treat increasingly polluted stormwater runoff to improve water quality and the environment for recreational uses, wildlife, fish, and plant life. Since then, Entranco has participated in restoration programs on over 30 Pacific Northwest lakes and reservoirs.

Entranco was responsible for assessing environmental impacts and mitigations of many landmark public construction projects including the Washington State Convention and Trade Center and Metro North Operations Bus Base in Seattle, and historic renovation projects including Union Station in Tacoma.

In 1987, Entranco enhanced its capabilities with the acquisition of Victor O. Gray & Company, a Seattle structural engineering firm noted for numerous bridges on local and state routes, and multi-level parking structures for the University of Washington. Victor O. Gray & Company's contribution in the field of historic building renovation deserves special note for renovation work on the Temple of Justice, the State Capitol Legislative Building, and Pike Place Market.

With high technology an important economic source in Washington, Entranco had the opportunity to assist private clients with state-of-the art facilities. Entranco has been proud to design transportation, site and utility improvements for Microsoft's Headquarters, a 200-acre world-class campus in Redmond. The facility was designed to accommodate the rapid changes a high technology leader like Microsoft required.

Entranco's design and construction of a ramp/flyover of I-5 at Bellis Fair Mall in Bellingham was a unique achievement, marking the first time the Washington State Department of Transportation (WSDOT) allowed a private firm to participate in construction management on the interstate highway system.

The Dawn of the 1990s. With increasing population densities, stormwater management presents major challenges to counties, cities, and developers in Washington. Entranco has demonstrated leadership in developing plans, strategies, and designs for solving stormwater problems. In 1992, Entranco completed a state-wide highway Stormwater Runoff Study for WSDOT. Once again, Entranco worked in a partnership role with multiple public agencies.

By the 1990s, Entranco developed an increasing diversity of services. Areas of specialization now encompass:
- Civil Engineering
- Transportation Planning
- Structural Engineering
- Traffic Engineering and Modeling
- Highway and Transit Planning and Design
- Environmental Services and Documentation
- Lake Restoration, Wetlands Mitigation and Design
- Surface Water Management
- Public Involvement
- Geographic Information Systems
- Construction Management and Administration
- Surveying, Computer Aided Mapping, Global Position System Surveys

Regional Growth. Entranco's capabilities, coupled with a history of public agency and private development relationships on over 2,500 projects, bridges the gap between major commercial development impacts and local agency requirements. Entranco continues to provide superior engineering and environmental services for its clients who are located in increasingly more diverse geographic locations.

In the 1980s, Entranco began looking at ways to carry the firm's philosophy of working with clients in a partnership approach into new regions. The expansion into Arizona came in 1986, with expansion into California in 1990. In 1992, Entranco began venturing forth internationally, starting with providing water quality expertise for a reservoir in Taiwan.

Many other projects than those discussed above illustrate the Company's contribution to public works in Washington State. A few are summarized in the following chronology. ◆

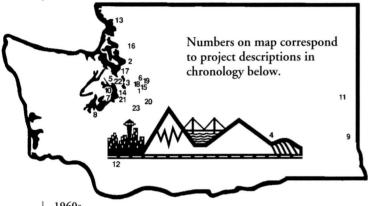

Numbers on map correspond to project descriptions in chronology below.

1960s

(1) Lake Hills Connector, Bellevue: civil and structural engineering resolution to complex transportation problem by allowing construction of a roadway through an existing major railroad trestle bridge.
(2) SR 526 from I-5 to Boeing Plant, Everett: six lane controlled access freeway providing access to Paine Field and Boeing Company.
(3) SR 520 from I-405 to Redmond: section of SR 520 linking Seattle to Redmond that featured five multi-level interchanges.

1970s

(4) Lions Park, Othello: design and construction of community park with multiple-use recreational facilities. Funded by the Interagency Committee for Outdoor Recreation.
(5) Bucklin Hill access to Silverdale, Kitsap County: connector roadway between East Bremerton and SR 3 to provide access to Trident submarine base at Bangor. Evaluated 18 alternatives and 6 different alignments. Project included award winning community involvement program.
(6) NE 12th Street, Bellevue: new four-lane roadway with overpass crossings (railroad and I-405) and pedestrian overcrossing. Bellevue received first place award from Federal Highway Administration as an outstanding example of a highway in an urban environment.
(7) Long Lake, Kitsap County: first EPA funded "Clean Lakes" project in the state. Lake restoration involved lake drawdown, dredging, aluminum sulfate treatment and various watershed best management practices. Included special features to ensure unobstructed anadromous fish passage during construction. New County park developed using dredge materials.
(8) Capitol Lake, Olympia: series of lake restoration, sediment control, environmental documentation, wetlands and non-point source pollution management projects. Involvement continues to the present.

1980s

(9) Stadium Way, Pullman: improved a major access point to Washington State University campus. Provided safety features and increased capacity.

(10) Port Orchard Bypass: involved Entranco's multi-discipline capabilities with extensive public involvement program. Developed eight alternative routes with the recommended route receiving full public support. Included a 650-foot bridge soaring 120 feet above Blackjack Creek. Won awards from the Consulting Engineer's Council of Washington and Washington Precast Concrete Industry in 1986.
(11) Bella Vista, Spokane: site planning, platting, and design of a 180-acre single family subdivision located on steep, rocky terrain. Worked with county to resolve drainage and water quality challenges.
(12) SR 504 Spirit Lake Memorial Highway, Mount St. Helen's: preliminary design for 25 miles of new highway including 10 bridges.
(13) Bellis Fair Mall/I-5/SR 539 Interchange and Arterial Street System, Bellingham: fast track interchange modifications and off-site transportation improvements for major retail center. First time WSDOT allowed private firm to participate in construction management on the interstate highway system.
(14) Construction Management Services for numerous Projects, Tukwila: construction administration, management, and documentation for projects including urban arterials, roadways, traffic signals. Services provided from 1988 to present.
(15) Microsoft Headquarters Redmond Campus: started with the largest Local Improvement District ever formed in the state—the Evergreen Highlands LID. Expansion of the site continues to the present.

1990s

(16) Stillaguamish River Bridges Replacement and Approaches NEPA EIS, Arlington, WSDOT: EIS to replace two bridges over Stillaguamish River, realignment of SR 9 and SR 530, extensive public involvement.
(17) SR 99 Improvements, Snohomish County Area, Lynnwood: began design effort for widening nearly 7 miles of highway for multi-jurisdictional facility. Construction in mid 1990s.
(18) NE 10th Street, Bellevue: an urban street along a new alignment in a developed area. Also the first concrete arterial in Bellevue.
(19) West Lake Sammamish Parkway/SR 98, Redmond: extension of Parkway to reduce traffic in downtown Redmond with new vehicle bridge and railroad bridge.
(20) Flaming Geyser Bridge, Black Diamond area, King County: cable-stayed bridge over Green River that won Honorable Mention for Northwest Regional Construction Management Project of the Year in 1992.
(21) Concourse B, C, and D Reconstruction Extension, SeaTac International Airport: civil engineering and structural engineering for reconstruction and seismic upgrading of Concourses.
(22) Seattle Center GPS Grounds Survey and Mapping, Seattle: applied new GPS and GIS technology to assist in tracking and organizing historic site information to be used for maintenance and future growth.
(23) Lake Youngs Limnological Study, Seattle Water Department: limnological and modeling expertise to protect water quality of important water reservoir.

Economic and Engineering Services, Inc.

Economic and Engineering Services, Inc. (EES) is an engineering, economics and management firm with an emphasis on planning utility systems and services for the future. EES has provided comprehensive professional engineering, planning and management services to local, state, national and international governmental and industrial clients for more than 15 years. EES works with clients to resolve policy and public service issues throughout Washington.

Today's complex utility system problems are inseparable from broader future quality of life and citizen service concerns. EES recognizes that individual projects rarely focus on a single, isolated engineering, economic or environmental issue. Therefore, EES offers consulting that considers a variety of factors to ensure development of a sound, workable solution.

The firm offers professional specialties in the following areas: rate-making, financial management, regulatory affairs, anti-trust, general management, contract negotiation, load research/management, economic forecasting, economic feasibility, government grant funding, power supply planning, utility feasibility studies, water quality evaluations, environmental engineering and water resources.

EES's staff has strong professional expertise in the planning and management of regional water and wastewater systems, and the management of public water supply watersheds. The issues of future water quality and quantity for the state's citizens are key concerns, along with the need to balance the often conflicting goals of economic development and environmental protection. These goals are carefully coordinated with corporate management goals as well as with local environmental standards and land use plans, to ensure protection of the state's water supplies.

Representative examples of the EES approach to future water resources and wastewater planning include:
- Spokane Aquifer Protection Program;
- County Ground Water Management Plans for Island, Kitsap and South King Counties;
- Coordinated Water System Plans for King County and Pierce, Kitsap, Spokane, Walla Walla, Yakima, Skagit, Whatcom, Jefferson, Clark, Grant and Pacific Counties;
- The Tacoma Pipeline 5 and Green River Diversion Projects; and
- The Sultan Hydroelectric Project, recipient of the Governor's Environmental Award of Excellence.

The company advises utilities on the most effective use of their financial resources to achieve short and long term goals. The professional staff members offer expert testimony before state and federal legislative bodies, commissions and councils. In addition, EES is an industry leader in developing cost-of-service, rate design, cash flow and financial forecasting models, as well as related specific financial information systems for electric, steam, gas, water, storm sewer and wastewater applications.

EES works with its clients to develop the best, most feasible and cost-effective solutions for utility system planning, financing, development and operations. By adding its own unique consulting expertise and experience, EES develops systems designed to meet increasingly complex environmental, economic, engineering and related requirements—now and for the next 100 years. ◆

City of Ellensburg

On June 15, 1891, the Ellensburg City Council approved a motion to purchase an electric light plant which had been built three years earlier by John A. Shoudy, the town's founder. The bond issue passed with nearly 70 percent of the vote, making the City of Ellensburg Light Department the oldest municipally owned and operated electric system in the State of Washington.

In 1891 the City Council established the Committee of Light, a governing body responsible for the care and control of the light plant. The Committee of Light left its greatest legacy when the city decided to construct and operate a power plant next to the Yakima River, two and one-half miles northwest of town. In 1911 and 1915 motions carried to make further improvements to the light plant and $170,000 was made available to support the work. The overwhelming voter support during the first couple of decades solidified the Light Department's ability to provide excellent service at a reasonable rate for several decades to come.

The light plant near the Yakima River met all of Ellensburg's electrical needs until 1925. In 1941, the Bonneville Power Administration (BPA) began supplying electrical power to the city. Today, BPA furnishes 100 percent of the city's electrical needs. The Light Department closed the Yakima River plant in 1951 because of aging equipment and cost inefficiencies.

In 1938 City Light purchased the building which is now City Hall. After World War II, innovations such as electrical space heating and hot water tanks produced a boom in service which continued into the 1970s. Added to this increased demand upon the light system was the city's 1957 purchase of Puget

Sound Power and Light facilities. This purchase added customers from six districts serviced by the private utility. In 1950 the Light Department serviced 2600 customers. Over the next 10 years, 900 accounts were added to the system. During the 1960s an additional 1500 customers were connected raising the total to 5001 by 1971.

Today the Light Department serves 5808 electrical meters. Central Washington University is the system's largest customer. The Light Department has faithfully served the people of Ellensburg for over 100 years. With hard work and continued support, it will be able to serve the city for another century to come. ◆

Jerry M. Fay

Jerry Fay is a 1966 graduate of the University of Washington in Civil Engineering and has spent most of his career in public works in the public and private sectors. After graduation Fay worked briefly at Boeing on the 747 design team, and with the City of Seattle prior to joining the firm of Munson-Nash-Futrell in 1968.

Fay became the Public Works Director for Moses Lake in 1974. In 1979 he became the Public Works Director for Clark County. In 1982 Fay assumed the additional duties of Finance Director and was promoted to County Administrator in 1984. His revision of the budget format and process in 1985 resulted in Clark County receiving the Government Finance Officers Association Award for Distinguished Budget.

During his tenure at Clark County he served as President of the Washington Association of County Engineers, Western/Puget Sound District, and Washington Chapter of APWA. He was a member of the Urban Arterial Board and County Road Administration Board, and Chairman of the Vancouver/Clark County Salvation Army Advisory Board.

In 1986 Fay joined the URS Corp. as Vice President-Director of Oregon Operations. He oversaw the establishment of a branch office in Portland and in 1987 was recognized by the Consulting Engineers Council of Oregon as the "New Principal of the Year."

Since 1988, he has been the Executive Director of the Transportation Improvement Board. In 1992 he was selected as one of the Top Ten Public Works Leaders of the Year by the American Public Works Association. Fay and his wife Cheryl have two daughters. ◆

Fujiki & Associates, Inc.

The civil engineering firm of Fujiki & Associates, Inc. was founded by Kenneth Fujiki in 1983. Donald M. Williams joined the firm in 1987 and Walter L. Cairns in 1988.

Some projects completed between 1983 and 1993 are: **Lake Stevens Sewer District**—Portions of the wastewater treatment plant, rehab. of pumping station #5 (largest in the District), U.L.I.D. #7 (8,900 LF of 24" to 8" diameter pipe, at places 30' deep). **City of Seattle**—The construction administration and inspection of the Sand Point Way Median project which consisted of 20 blocks of replacing concrete and asphalt paving and construction of a landscaped median. **METRO**—F&A was the prime consultant for the Carkeek 8th Avenue NW Interceptor Sewer Project (9,400 LF of 24" diameter pipeline and 0.7 mile of landscaped median project). **City of Snohomish**—The firm, as a prime, completed the rehab. of two pumping stations and the sewer comprehensive plan of Cemetery Creek drainage area. **City of Bellevue**—The firm completed rehab. of three pumping stations, a water control station, and one new sewage pumping station. **City of Mukilteo**—Lincoln Avenue street widening, realignment, and intersection improvements, 1989 chip seal program. **WSDOT**—The firm, as prime, produced two maintenance manuals titled "*Asphalt Seal Coats*" and "*Gravel Road Maintenance*" for the Research Department. **U.S. Navy, P-202 Indian Island, WA**—Five missile bunkers on a ten-acre site (constr. cost 4.6 million). P-303, Explosives Operation Building, (c.c. 2.4 million).

Mr. Fujiki has gone through the chairs for the Washington State APWA and served as its president in 1980. ◆

PUBLISHED SINCE 1893

Seattle Daily
Journal of Commerce
and Northwest Construction Record

| Published Daily Except Sunday | Second Class Postage paid at Seattle, Washington 98104-1482. Price 50 cents. | Vol. 93, No. 64, Wednesday, March 19, 1986 |

Public works history:

Oldest design firm first contributor

Mort Thomas, president of Gardner Engineers presenting a check to Jack Garner, president of the Washington Chapter of APWA to kick off the history project. From left to right: Dick Warren, Chapter treasurer and project leader; Jack Garner, Chapter president; Mort Thomas, Tom Fitzmorris, and Jack Locke, principals of Gardner Engineers.

EDITOR'S NOTE: The following is the first of several articles that will appear monthly in the Journal on the history of public works in Washington State. The articles are being prepared by the Washington State Chapter of the American Public Works Association in an effort to focus public attention on various aspects of public works projects and people who have made important contributions to public works.

The Washington State Chapter of the American Public Works Association has begun the preparation of a "History of Public Works in Washington State, 1889-1989." The history, released as part of the State Centennial in 1989, will record the roles of public agencies, private firms and individuals, both past and present, who have played a part in creating the public facilities that have made possible the growth and progress Washington State has experienced.

In addition to documenting for posterity an important part of the State's history, the undertaking is also planned as a fund raising event for the Chapter's Endowment Fund. Income from the Chapter Endowment Fund provides scholarships in each of the State's engineering schools to students who are pursuing careers in the public works field. In addition, the fund provides monies to enhance the performance of public works professionals in both the public and private sector.

It was especially fitting that this history project was begun with a contribution from Gardner Engineers, Inc., of Seattle, a firm recognized as the oldest, continuously operating, consulting engineering practice in the State.

Gardner Engineers was founded in 1883 by Albro Gardner, the first City Engineer for the City of Seattle. The firm has played a significant role in providing the design of public facilities in the Seattle area and throughout the State ever since.

The firm was headed by a Gardner heir until 1975 when Roy Gardner, Albro's grandson, retired. Roy passed away in 1983.

Albro Gardner, first city engineer of the City of Seattle and founder of Gardner Engineers.

Current management of the firm is Mort Thomas, president; Tom Fitzmorris, vice president, and Jack Locke, secretary-treasurer. Its offices are at 2124 Fourth Avenue, Seattle.

THE CONTRIBUTION of Gardner Engineers kicked off a fund raising drive that will continue until September 1986 or until the history project is fully subscribed. Each contributor will be allowed space in the history for a brief record of the contributor's contribution to public works. The overall history will be written by a well-known local author/historian to be announced at a later date.

All those who have been part of the public works field eligible for inclusion in the history are invited to contribute. This includes:

City and County agencies; state and Federal agencies; ports and special districts; private consulting firms to include engineers, architects, and planners; contractors; firms supplying equipment and materials; financial institutions, advisors, and consultants, including attorneys; and individuals, both active and retired, who have been involved in public works.

The history project is being directed by the Washington State Chapter of the Public Works Association. The Chapter has over 800 members in the State representing most of the agencies and firms in the public works field. Jack Garner, Public Works Director of the City of Bellingham, is the president.

The history project is being led by Richard Warren, president of Warren Consultants and Chapter treasurer, and Jan Klippert from King County Public Works (the immediate past president of the Chapter) who will be the editor of the history.

Those wishing more information or to make contributions can contact Richard Warren (441-3003) or Jan Klippert (344-7302).

John M. Garner

John M. "Jack" Garner was born in Bellingham, Washington, son of Elmer and Dorothy Garner. He grew up in Everett, Washington. Garner studied Civil Engineering at Washington State University where he received Bachelors and Masters Degrees in Civil Engineering. As a graduate student he served as a teaching assistant and developed a computer program capable of distributing the loads and analyzing the forces on a plane-frame structure of up to 100 members. This was an early application of computers to structural engineering in the time before electronic calculators, personal computers and predeveloped software.

Upon graduation Garner was employed by the City of Seattle's Engineering Management Trainee Program. This program was jointly sponsored by the American Public Works Association and the City of Seattle. Leadership for the program came from Roy W. Morse, City Engineer for Seattle.

In 1973 Garner became City Engineer for the City of Bellingham and in 1976 became the city's Director of Public Works. In Bellingham, Garner oversaw the initial construction of the Post Point Sewage Treatment Plant in 1974 and its upgrade to secondary treatment in 1994. During this same time period significant improvements were made to the water treatment and distribution systems allowing the City to meet new water quality standards and provide for community growth. Garner was instrumental in developing replacement programs for deteriorated water and sewer mains and also implemented management improvements in field operations and plant operations.

Jack Garner was responsible for many arterial improvements in the City; notably completion of a waterfront truck route along Roeder Avenue and construction of a new north-south arterial route along Woburn Street.

Jack Garner served as president of the Washington State APWA Chapter in 1986 and was the second president of the City Engineer's Association of Washington. In 1993 he was selected the Washington State APWA Chapter's Public Works Leader of the Year. He is married to Sharon Ann Kahler Garner. They have two children, Keith Stuart Garner and Margaret Jean Garner. ◆

Jack Garner receives the Washintong Chapter 1993 Public Works Leader of the Year Award.

GeoEngineers

Public works projects vary greatly in size, scope and visibility to the general population. Bridges across scenic chasms, large dams and an extensive highway system are examples of prominent public works. Equally important but far less obvious are the sewer, water supply and electrical distribution systems. Each of these projects must be designed and constructed with the public's health, safety and welfare in mind.

Started in 1980 by Jack K. Tuttle, Jon W. Koloski and Gary W. Henderson, GeoEngineers provides geotechnical and ground water engineering services to private and public clients in Washington from offices in Redmond, Spokane, Bellingham and Tacoma. The company develops practical and innovative solutions to geotechnical and geoenvironmental problems, while maintaining an ethical balance between the demands of client expectations, public welfare, environmental protection and company prosperity.

The firm is proud to have been a part of major public works projects throughout Washington State. The depth of the firm's knowledge enables it to work effectively with public agencies, keeping pace with the ever growing demand for public services.◆

Right: GeoEngineers, working with Sargent Engineers of Olympia, was retained by the State of Washington Department of Transportation to evaluate foundation design requirements for the new Summit Creek bridge in Lewis County on the southerly side of Mt. Rainier. GeoEngineers reconnaissance included rappelling down the steep rock face to map bedding and fracture zones in the exposed bedrock formation. Photo courtesy of David Krise.

Golder Associates Inc.

Golder Associates is a world wide group of consulting companies specializing in geotechnical and environmental engineering, waste management, engineering geology, and surface and groundwater hydrology. The Golder Associates group of companies has grown to a network of 46 permanent offices in the United States, Canada, Europe and Australia, employing more than 1000 engineers, scientists, geologists and technicians.

As a broadly-held, employee-owned company, the firm has a strong commitment to providing quality science and engineering consulting services integrated with a strong base of practical application and experience. These skills have enabled it to successfully complete thousands of assignments, including a diverse range of projects in Washington such as SR-504, Mount St. Helens Memorial Highway; Lake Cushman Spillway, Mason County; Upriver Dam Rehabilitation, Spokane; Kettle River Tailings Pond, Echo Bay Mining; ARCO Cherry Point Refinery, Ferndale; Polyclinic Soil Nailing Shoring Wall, Seattle; and Interstate 405/Cedar River Waterline Relocation. In addition, the firm is a major contractor associated with the environmental restoration efforts at the Hanford Reservation.

The Pacific Northwest Regional office was established in 1973 by Mr. David L. Pentz, and has grown to a staff of over 135. Principals who have served the local community include Dr. Anthony S. Burgess, Dr. R. John Byrne, Mr. Donald Caldwell, Mr. Charles W. Lockhart, Mr. Norman I. Norrish, Mr. David Cotton, Dr. William Roberds, and Mr. Ian Miller. The company is proud of its service to the citizens of Washington for the past 20 years. ◆

Golder Associates

Paul C. Hooper

Paul Hooper enjoyed more than 30 years of public service in transporation engineering, starting in 1953 with the Washington State Highway Department and ending in 1985 as County Road Engineer for King County.

Hooper grew up in Johnson, Whitman County. He graduated with a B.S. in Civil Engineering in 1953 from Washington State University. He served in the U.S. Army Corps of Engineers, and worked for two years for WSU in the Highway Research Section. In 1957-58 he attended the Bureau of Highway Traffic, Yale University, receiving a Certificate in Highway Traffic. In 1961 he joined King County as Assistant Traffic Planning Engineer. From 1963-1979 he served as the Traffic and Planning Engineer.

Over 16 years, Hooper built an organization that effectively solved county traffic problems. He developed innovative programs that were widely recognized, including School Safety Coordinating Program, School Pathway Construction Program, Traffic Data Collection and Traffic Signal Operation and Maintenance. He was instrumental in developing the King County Transportation Plan.

During Hooper's progressive tenure as King County Road Engineer, he streamlined the Road Maintenance Division and implemented a Roads Maintenance Management System. When he retired in 1985, more road and bridge construction was under contract and completed on time than ever before.

Active in the Institute of Transportation Engineers, Hooper served as an International Director from 1979-1981. A long-time member of APWA, he has served on the National Committee for the Manual on Uniform Traffic Control Devices since 1975. ◆

Hugh G. Goldsmith & Associates, Inc.

In the 35 years since its founding, Hugh G. Goldsmith & Associates, Inc. has been a major participant in the growth and history of public works in Washington. As civil engineers, planners and surveyors the firm specializes in the land development engineering infrastructure for residential housing, commercial and recreational facilities. Starting with a staff of five in 1958, the firm has grown to 55.

In the early 1960s, low interest FHA insured mortgage rates brought affordable housing within the reach of most families. This generated a high demand for the company's engineering skills. The firm was part of the pioneering effort in the designs of a new concept in 1963 — "the planned community." Goldsmith & Associates' first major project was the planning of "Fairwood," a 1,200-acre community in South King County. The company designed the public works system that included subdivision of land, design of a full water system, sanitary sewers, paved roads, curbs, sidewalks, storm sewers and site grading, and created a phasing infrastructure of public works that grew over a period of 15 years to service more than 3,000 homes and businesses.

The challenge to the Goldsmith firm was to create engineering design that met government requirements while also maintaining a level of economic feasibility, through phasing, that would help place the cost of housing within the reach of the average family. Land for roads and schools, as well as funds to design and construct these public works improvements, were the financial responsibility of the developer. When completed, these improvements were conveyed to the appropriate public works entity for control and management without requiring a heavy tax burden on the residents.

The early 1970s brought a new challenge for the Goldsmith Company as environmental policy acts necessitated a higher level of environmental analysis in the design of public works systems in land development programs. Sensitive areas such as slopes, wetlands and natural habitat areas introduced the element of preservation and added more sophistication in planning and design. This coincided with the rising market for larger, more expensive homes and provided the opportunity for the Goldsmith firm to create unique "golf club" communities, such as Sahalee Golf Club Estates, Bear Creek Country Club Estates and McCormick Woods.

In 1984 the company began designs for the "Master Planned Community" of Klahanie, north of Issaquah, which, when completed in 1995, will include over 3,200 dwelling units and nearly $50 million in public works infrastructure improvements.

During the 1960s and 1970s Federal funding was often available for major public works projects, easing the financial burden for local government and homeowners. In the 1980s such funding was no longer available, and more innovative designs were needed to control costs. In the 1960s home density in a project averaged three homes per acre. In the 1980s up to 35 percent of the project was required to be dedicated to open space, translating to a density requirement of up to six homes per acre for affordable housing. Such requirements demanded the best from consulting engineering firms. The Goldsmith firm met that challenge and continues to be a leader in land development engineering consultants. The firm looks forward to continuing partnerships with both the public works and private sector, providing engineering consulting services as our area continues to grow. ◆

Hugh G. Goldsmith & Associates, Inc.

Hart Crowser, Inc.

With a staff of 230 technical, managerial and service professionals, Hart Crowser is one of the Northwest's leading consulting firms. The company specializes in earth and environmental technologies and offers a full range of geotechnical, hydrogeologic, environmental management, remediation and construction services. The firm's clients include municipalities, industrial and commercial businesses, architectural and engineering firms, utilities, and state and federal agencies.

Headquartered in Seattle with branch offices in Tacoma, Richland, Anchorage, Portland, San Francisco, Long Beach, San Diego, Denver, Honolulu and Mexico City, Hart Crowser performs work for clients throughout the world. The firm has been ranked in the nation's top 500 design firms by *Engineering News Record* since 1987, and is consistently ranked in the top five engineering firms in Washington State by the *Puget Sound Business Journal*.

Ronald Hart, President, and John C. Crowser, P.E., Chief Executive Officer, established Hart Crowser & Associates, Inc. in 1974. From a small regional geotechnical firm, Hart Crowser has grown and expanded its services to meet changing client needs.

From the beginning, Hart Crowser developed its reputation as a growing firm that can successfully complete difficult, complex projects.

As environmental concerns multiply nationwide, clients look to Hart Crowser for help on new cleanup and regulatory issues in every sphere; from hazardous and solid waste management, remediation and construction, to siting of industrial facilities, preserving water quality,

Expansion of 76-acre container terminal at the Port of Tacoma utilized Hart Crowser's multi-disciplinary expertise in geotechnical, hydrogeologic and environmental technologies.

groundwater management and protecting archaeological resources.

Hart Crowser has responded by adding new expertise. To its base of geotechnical engineers and hydrogeologists, the company added geochemists in 1986 and remediation designers in 1987. In 1988 the company added process chemical engineers, toxicologists and remediation construction managers. In 1989, Hart Crowser formed a Laboratory Services division. In addition to full service in-house facilities, a sophisticated mobile laboratory is available. As an independent division of the firm, Laboratory Services serves the geotechnical and environmental testing needs of clients throughout the United States. The lab received accreditation from the State of Washington and the U.S. Army Corps of Engineers. Furthermore, Hart Crowser acquired Pincock, Allen & Holt, a Denver-based mining services company to assist clients involved in the mining industry.

During 20 years of operations, Hart Crowser's services have increased dramatically to reflect the changing needs of its clients, evolving environmental and regulatory issues, and important advances in earth and environmental technologies. No longer exclusively a regional geotechnical firm, Hart Crowser has grown to meet the multi-disciplinary project needs of national and international clients. ◆

The use of innovative construction procedures and foundation design earned Hart Crowser both state and national awards for engineering excellence from the American Consulting Engineers Council for the North Pacific Paper Corporation Newsprint Mill, Longview, WA.

HART CROWSER

Hammond, Collier & Wade-Livingstone Associates, Inc.

Our firm is in the process of celebrating 50 years of professional engineering service in building Washington through the Public Works industry. The General Engineering Company was founded by Ray Heath and George Hammond in 1943 with Bill Collier joining the firm shortly after World War II.

The postwar boom generated the need for experienced engineering consultants. The General Engineering Company emerged as a leader in the Puget Sound Area in providing services and developing an enviable record of successful accomplishments.

Water became a critical need in the suburban King County area, as well as other areas of the state, and General Engineering Company assisted in setting up water districts and building new systems. By 1950 the firm had been responsible for nearly $3.3 million of waterworks construction, including a major supply system on Adak Island for the U.S. Navy.

Sewerage and drainage demands parallel the need for water supply, and General Engineering completed sewage plant, pump station and collector sewer designs for Bellingham, Auburn, Sedro Woolley, Ridgefield, Bryn Mawr-Lakeridge, Rainier Vista and North Beach.

Recognizing the need for cooperation between contractors and fellow consultants, the company's principals initiated the formation of Sewer Contractors Association. In addition, Bill Collier joined locally prominent consultants Earl Sibley, Bill Shannon and Tom Sparling to form the Consulting Engineers Council of Washington — a chapter of the American Consulting Engineers Council.

Over the years the company has undergone a number of changes including location and name. The firm's office was established in Seattle's Wallingford district in the mid fifties where it remains today. Ray Heath left General Engineering to become Superintendent of the Seattle Water Department. Paul Issac acquired Heath's interest and the company name became Hammond, Collier & Issac (HCI).

During this era expanding suburban communities needed new and more LIDs, water storage, waste treatment and street improvements. Between 1950 and the late 1960s the company worked on 10 major military facilities including Fort Lewis-McChord Field, Paine Field, Ault Field, Sandpoint Naval Air Station and Northwest Air Depot, Spokane, Washington. A major accomplishment of this period is Seattle's Alki Point sewage treatment plant design.

In 1968 Larry Wade acquired Paul Issac's interest in the firm following Issac's sudden death. The company's name once again changed to become Hammond, Collier & Wade. Also in 1968, following a tour of duty with the Army Corps of Engineers in Viet Nam, Bruce Livingstone, with his father, formed The Livingstone Associates, Inc.

Following some very successful joint projects and the subsequent establishment of a close working relationship, in 1973 Hammond, Collier & Wade merged with Livingstone Associates, Inc. to form Hammond, Collier & Wade - Livingstone Associates, Inc. (HCW-L). The merger strengthened the combined firm's depth of offering water, waste water and public works engineering services.

The passage of the Clean Water Act in 1972 stimulated community efforts to upgrade wastewater treatment plants, and HCW-L worked on projects at Blaine, Brewster, Duvall, Entiat and North Bend. Other significant projects in this decade include interstate survey work on I-90, SR 509, and international survey support services for a major highway in Africa. In addition, the company was selected by the Army Corps of Engineers to monitor the status of all navigable permits in a three-state area. HCW-L developed unique water supply and storage programs for a number of metropolitan Seattle area communities including Marysville, Issaquah and Redmond.

In the 1980s the company launched an array of exciting programs, both as a member of a number of design teams and as full responsibility designers. Fred Kern joined the firm bringing his civil engineering practice with him. The firm's staff was active in a variety of professional and technical activities to further the goals of engineering professionalism. HCW-L provides extensive contributions to ASCE's continuing education effort and National committees. Contributions to APWA include assistance in preparing a new set of combined Washington Chapter and State Department of Transportation standard specifications.

Providing sound, imaginative engineering is a hallmark of Hammond, Collier & Wade - Livingstone Associates, Inc. It is a company ready to lead into the 21st century.

Corporate headquarters remain in Seattle with offices in Wenatchee and Chelan. The staff has grown to approximately 50 full-time employees and our main focus continues to be municipal public works engineering. ◆

HNTB Corporation

HNTB Corporation, as a member of the Howard Needles Tammen & Bergendoff family of companies, celebrated its 75th anniversary in 1989 as Washington State celebrated its Centennial. Founded in 1914 in Kansas City, Missouri, HNTB expanded to the Pacific Northwest in 1961, when the firm received a contract to design a section of the "new" Interstate 5 through Seattle. Upon completion of that project, the partners decided the region was viable enough to support a permanent office.

In 1974, HNTB merged with Frankfurter and Associates, a Seattle engineering firm specializing in the pulp and paper industry. HNTB then began providing engineering services to both industrial and transportation clients. In 1980 the office was moved from Seattle, to Bellevue, where it remains today. With a staff of over 120, HNTB in Bellevue is one of the firm's largest offices.

HNTB's Transportation Group has a long established tradition of excellence. One project which is cause for pride is the firm's work on the Mount Baker Ridge Tunnel as part of the monumental Interstate 90 completion work. The tunnel is the largest diameter soft bore tunnel in the world. The tunnel design earned HNTB the American Consulting Engineers Council's highest national award in 1987.

In addition to Transportation engineering services, HNTB's Bellevue office provides services in architecture, aviation, environmental engineering and industrial engineering. Locally, HNTB professionals have been involved in such diverse projects as the Bellevue Convention Center, adding private viewing boxes to the Kingdome, designing a new "Redmond Connection" pump station and pipeline for METRO to reconstructing runways and taxiways at Seattle-Tacoma International Airport. In the course of performing such diverse projects over many years, the firm has developed an extensive library of planning, architectural and engineering computer software, including many innovations by its own professionals.

Today's engineers and architects must also strive to excel as communicators. Presentations are often made to a concerned public as infrastructure projects become increasingly complex. HNTB encourages its employees to become active in the community and many donate their expertise to local boards and organizations. ◆

Top: As associated architects and engineers for the Washington State Convention and Trade Center in downtown Seattle, HNTB Corporation was responsible for facility programming and functional planning, and for civil, electrical, and security system engineering. Photo courtesy HNTB Corporation

Center: With the goal of helping in reducing traffic congestion along I-5 through Seattle, HNTB Corporation transportation engineers designed high-occupancy vehicle (HOV) lanes to carry more people in fewer vehicles. Photo courtesy HNTB Corporation

Bottom: The Bellevue Transit Center was the first facility of its type in the Metropolitan Seattle area. HNTB Corporation provided transportation planning, urban design, preliminary and final architectural and engineering design, and construction administration for this work. Photo courtesy HNTB Corporation

HDR Engineering, Inc.

H DR Engineering is proud of our achievements in public works engineering projects in Washington State. The HDR Seattle offices was opened in 1973 through the acquisition of the architectural firm Durham/Anderson/Freed. Transportation and environmental engineering departments were added and the firm remained for 15 years at DAF's original office building in the South Lake Union district. By 1988 HDR had outgrown that location and moved a much expanded company to new quarters in Bellevue, Washington. By 1992, offices in Pasco, WA, Boise, ID and Portland, OR were opened.

Since opening a Puget Sound office, HDR's transportation group has played a significant role in the completion of I-90 from the earliest project planning through completion of the famous "ramps to nowhere" and designing the Mercer Island Lid Tunnel. HDR also designed many miles of HOV (high occupancy vehicle) lanes on I-5 and I-405 to meet regional goals for transportation management. Those who travel the back roads have perhaps crossed some of our smaller bridges, including an award winner on the Snoqualmie River Road near Monroe.

In 1989 the firm Ott Engineering, Inc. became part of HDR, greatly expanding capabilities in water resources and hydropower engineering. In 1992 HDR provided relicensing and design services for Puget Power and Light's Snoqualmie Falls Hydroelectric Plant.

HDR's environmental engineers were instrumental in several major wastewater treatment plant designs for Puget Sound communities coming into compliance with the state's secondary treatment mandate to preserve the water quality of Puget Sound. HDR took a new approach to the design of treatment facilities applying lessons learned in crowded Japan. We called it the "Good Neighbor Approach" and it resulted in state of the art facilities which are free of excessive odors and aesthetically pleasing enough to blend into scenic areas.

In 1986, the staff of Culp, Wesner, Culp, a sanitary engineering firm with offices in Washington and California, joined HDR. The newly enlarged staff immediately began design of an elegant treatment plant for the City of Edmonds suitable for its location in the heart of the waterfront tourist and commercial areas. Working closely with a special citizens advisory committee and local arts commission assured that the new treatment plant would be an aesthetic, economic and environmental asset to the community. The project won a Consulting Engineers Council of Washington Award in 1992.

HDR lead a three year effort for the Municipality of Metropolitan Seattle (Metro) which laid the groundwork for a $250 million program to reduce pollution resulting from combined sewer/storm water overflows to Elliott Bay, Lake Union and the Duwamish River. The CSO Comprehensive Plan won a Consulting Engineers Council of Washington Award. In 1989 work began on modifications to Metro's Alki wastewater treatment plant, and the Alki-West Seattle and Interurban Pumping Stations. In 1991 Metro selected HDR's team to help prepare the agency's Wastewater 2020 Plus Plan, outlining regional water pollution control strategies in compliance with the Growth Management Act.

Mercer Island First Hill Lid.

Snoqualmie River Road Bridge.

Snoqualmie Falls Hydroelectric Plant.

Our public works history in Eastern Washington began in 1985 when HDR became the overall engineering management consultant to the City of Spokane and Spokane County for development of the Spokane Regional Waste-to-Energy Facility. In 1988 we began to work for the City of Yakima, preparing a sewerage master plan and designing many improvements to the Yakima Regional Wastewater Treatment Plant. Later the city engaged HDR's team to prepare a Metropolitan Comprehensive Plan outlining strategies for public works projects to keep pace with the community's vision of its future.

HDR's transportation and bridge design group prepared the plans for the Zintel Canyon 10th Avenue Bridge in Kennewick.

In 1992, HDR opened an office in Pasco. One of our first projects was to design a greatly expanded and improved secondary wastewater treatment and sewage collection system for the City of Pasco.

It has been our pleasure to help improve the quality of life in the Northwest through our efforts on many large and small public works projects. We thank our clients who have enabled us to make these contributions to history of public works in Washington State. ◆

Above: Lakota Wastewater Treatment Plant, Federal Way. Below: City of Edmonds Wastewater Treatment Plant.

Hong West & Associates, Inc.

For more than 15 years, Hong West and Associates has been providing responsive, high-quality geotechnical engineering services to clients throughout the Pacific Northwest. The firm's expertise encompasses a full spectrum of services, including:

- soil and foundation engineering
- geology
- instrumentation
- *in situ* testing
- ground water development, control and protection
- geoscientific support for waste management
- geoenvironmental services
- construction inspection
- soil and materials testing.

Established in 1978 by Sa H. Hong, PE, the company has grown steadily from a one-man operation to its current staff of 32. In 1989 Larry West joined the company, adding his expertise in ground water consulting. HWA is now respected as one of the Northwest's leading geotechnical engineering firms, and maintains offices and a fully equipped testing laboratory in Lynnwood. It also has a branch office in Portland, Oregon.

Understanding Clients' Needs— HWA's success is derived from listening carefully to clients' goals, and maintaining open lines of communication. The firm has proven its ability to respond to ever-changing conditions in the region, most notably by the addition of a geoenvironmental group, and by continuously searching for new ways to improve the quality of services. By giving responsive, personalized attention, HWA's staff makes sure that each and every project is completed to clients' satisfaction.

Varied Regional Experience—About 80 percent of Hong West and Associates' projects are devoted to public works, ranging from sewer systems, water systems, roads and bridges, solid waste management and dams. Recent examples include:

- *Seattle Brick Sewer Rehabilitation*—Geotechnical engineering services to renovate 80-year-old five- to nine-foot diameter brick sewer tunnel in Seattle, conducting core sampling, analyzing soil and reviewing earthquake history.
- *Renton Wastewater Treatment Plant*—Designed construction dewatering system for excavation, performed three-dimensional computer modeling for high ground water conditions, designed and installed recharge wells, monitored and evaluated ground water quality impact.

At the Airway Heights Prison near Spokane, Hong West & Associates' geotechnical design took into account highly variable subsurface soil factors and complex ground water conditions.

- *Boundary Dam Extensometer Installation*—To renovate crack in abutment of concrete arch dam, installed multiple-positioned extensometers (MPBX) to monitor abutment movement and analyzed a year's worth of data from intensive geological studies.
- *I-5 HOV Lane Addition*—Conducted geotechnical investigation for road widening, retaining walls and bridges to alleviate traffic congestion.
- *Port Townsend Landfill and Septage Lagoon Closure*—Hydrogeologic and geotechnical support, including installing monitoring wells at the lagoon, soil, sludge and water quality sampling, landfill slope stability and borrow source studies, and evaluation of closure alternatives evaluation. ◆

The Port of Seattle relied on off-shore test drilling by Hong West & Associates, Inc. for its Terminal 4 geotechnical and environmental investigations.

HONG WEST
& ASSOCIATES, INC.

Island County Road Department

Island County was created from Thurston County in 1853 and originally encompassed Snohomish, Skagit, Whatcom and San Juan Counties. Early transportation to the San Juan Islands was by Indian canoe. Ferry transportation gradually evolved in the twentieth century from private enterprise to a state owned system. Most of the earlier ferries were for passenger traffic. Ferries began carrying vehicles from Clinton on the south end of Whidbey Island to the mainland at Mukilteo on August 10, 1919. A ferry link between Camano Island and Whidbey Island existed from 1921 to 1935, connecting the north end of Whidbey Island with Utsalady Point on Camano Island. The Deception Pass Bridge linking Whidbey Island to Fidalgo Island was constructed in 1934 and 1935. The state started operating ferries in June 1951, and expanded service to Whidbey Island by acquiring the privately owned ferry service between Port Townsend and Keystone in the mid-1970s.

Puget Sound's maritime enterprises have long enjoyed a well deserved reputation for colorful operations. Not the least of these was that run by Puget Sound's first woman ferryboat operator, Bertie H. Olson. Coming from a Whidbey Island family of 14 children, Bertie married fisherman Agate Olson. She herself worked as a commercial fisherman on a troller off Cape Flattery. In 1921 Bertie, then the mother of three-year old twin boys, entered the ferryboat business. She was awarded the state contract for ferry service between Camano and Whidbey Islands, otherwise known as the Utsalady (Camano) - Oak Harbor (Whidbey) route. Her husband's fishing boat, "The Rainbow," was pressed into service hauling cars between the islands.

The early ferryboats and their runs, most of which had grown up from family enterprises such as the Olsons', came to an end after 50 years of service. On May 31, 1951, the Puget Sound Navigation Company, the concern that was managing the ferry system at that time, halted all of its vessels for one minute at sundown as a way of marking the end of the era. The next day, June 1, l951, the Puget Sound ferry fleet passed into ownership of the State of Washington.

In addition to water transportation between the islands, Island County engineers had the job of seeing that roads were maintained on the islands. All earlier roads in Island County were county roads. No state roads existed. Hence, State Senator Capron sponsored legislation in 1919 to return to each county all vehicle registration fees collected in the county to support road maintenance. When a gas tax was imposed by the state, legislation passed in 1923 similarly provided for the return of the gasoline tax monies to the county in which it was collected to support road work.

Following the construction of the bridge over Deception Pass in 1935, legislation was changed in 1939 so that only one-half of the gas tax revenues and registration fees were returned to Island County. As of 1989 the state owned and maintained 54 miles of state routes in Island County. Island County owns and maintains 596 additional miles of road. State routes comprise only eight percent of the total public roads in the county. ◆

Appointed County Engineers—Island County	
L. A. Wanamaker (elected)	1920 - 1924
L. A. Wanamaker (appointed)	1924 - 1943
T. C. Clark	1943 - 1952
F. W. Hamlin	1952 - 1955
George Norris	1955 - 1962
William R. Whitnall	1962 - 1963
Joseph Cecil Donnelly	1963
Richard Hulseman	1963 - 1967
Dale L. Cutler	1967
Ralph W. E. Main	1968 - 1973
Alfred Sundquist	1973 - 1974
Darrell J. Huckabay	1974
David A. Jolly	1975 - 1982
Roy L. Allen	1982 -

Island County road crew drivers and operators competing at the NAS seaplane base to represent Island County in the Washington State Association of Counties annual truck and equipment rodeo, held in Yakima in 1989. From left to right:
Sitting on equipment: Leland Mackie, Roy Hagglund, Jack Taylor (Supervisor), Randy Diefert, Sheldon Stremler
Standing: Richard Nelson, Myron Gabelein (Supervisor), Kenneth Kammenga, Steven Clark, Dennis Jennerjohn, Kurt Buchholz, Mark Greene, Marvin Koorn (Supervisor), William Holt, James Thompson (Superintendent), Roy Allen (County Engineer)
Kneeling: Bueford West, Dean Gould (Supervisor), Donald White, Michael Sullivan, Maurice Aasland, Henry Hilberdink, Lester Brager

Intermountain Corrosion Service, Inc.

Intermountain Corrosion Service, Inc. was founded in 1978 by William C. Robinson. The company's goal is to provide high quality corrosion control engineering services for owners and managers of structures where an extended useful life is cost effective. From its main Tacoma office and Alaska branch office, the firm serves clients in all of the Western states, Alaska, Canada and the Pacific Islands.

The task of retrofitting the Washington State Ferry system terminals with corrosion control equipment has provided the firm with both a professional challenge and the opportunity to enjoy the beautiful waters of Puget Sound. Over the years the company has been involved in some way with solving problems associated with nearly all of the ferries, and most of the ferry terminals.

Projects of Intermountain Corrosion Service in the Columbia Basin have been significant to corrosion control history. When Columbia River water became available for irrigation farm land was rapidly developed. Irrigators were convinced that pipe corrosion was impossible in the dry arid soils and pipe coatings were an unnecessary cost. However, the effect of water and fertilizers on the pipes makes pipe failure from corrosion commonplace. Hundreds of miles of pipelines have been replaced or retrofitted with corrosion control equipment over the past few years. ◆

Intermountain Corrosion Service, Inc.

CONSULTING ENGINEERS

Tacoma, WA

Gordon W. Johnson

Gordon Johnson has been involved in the consultant sector of public works engineering for over 30 years.

Born in Yakima, Mr. Johnson lived there until he entered the University of Washington in 1950. After graduation in 1955, with a B.S. in Civil Engineering and an Army ROTC Commission, he served two years of active duty.

From 1957 to 1972 Mr. Johnson was employed by Gray and Osborne. He was assigned major roles in the development of utility systems for the cities of Republic, Bothell, Arlington, Mukilteo, Snoqualmie and Lake Stevens. In 1972 he became a Project Director with URS/Hill, Ingman Chase and Company. Major assignments included management of facilities, plans for upgrading sewer collection systems and treatment plants in a number of cities in Washington and Alaska.

In 1981 Mr. Johnson acquired an equity position with Pool Engineering, Inc. of Ketchikan and, with others, established an office for the firm in Bellevue. In 1987 the name was changed to PEI Consultants, Inc. and in 1988 the firm was sold to Barrett Consulting Group. Subsequently, he served Mukilteo, first as Public Works Director/City Engineer and later as a contract engineer for special projects. In February, 1993 he accepted the position of Construction Engineer with Hammond, Collier & Wade-Livingstone Associates, Inc. ◆

N.G. Jacobson & Associates, Inc.

NGJ, founded in 1958 by Norman G. Jacobson, Jr., P.E. to provide civil, structural and transportation engineering services, has designed hundreds of projects and performed engineering investigations and transportation/parking studies for both the public and private sectors throughout the Pacific Northwest and Alaska.

NGJ design projects include bridges, buildings, parking structures, marine structures, structural restoration, highways and streets.

The firm's 12 design awards for projects range from the 1500-car parking structure constructed for $890 per car for the 1962 Seattle World's Fair, to the 1988 Awards for the Anchorage International Airport Parking Structure.

The Company has actively shared its expertise and knowledge in parking garage design and studies on a national level through a steady stream of design projects, papers and publications, and active participation in APWA, ASCE, ACI, ACEC, SEAW, IMPC and PCC. ◆

Photos courtesy N.G. Jacobson & Assoc.

1. *King County Automotive Center, Seattle*
2. *Seattle Hilton Hotel and 10-Story Parking Structure*
3. *Seattle Center 1500-Car Parking Structure*
4. *I-90 Seattle Access Viaduct*
5. *I-90 Seattle Access Viaduct*
6. *Valley Medical Center Parking Structure, Renton*
7. *Dockton Park Marina, Vashon Island*

Journal of Commerce

The *Seattle Daily Journal of Commerce*, which started as a "backroom" business information sheet, is today a mainstay among Northwest business publications. The *Journal*, published every day except Sunday, provides a wealth of information on government agencies, the construction and development industries and private business in general. Special weekly sections are devoted to architecture and engineering, real estate, maritime activities, the latest in construction machinery developments, the law and news from Alaska.

The business community was first introduced to the forerunner of the *Journal* in 1893. The *Bulletin*, as it was called, was a single mimeographed sheet devoted to daily reports of real estate transactions, building records and court reports obtained from the

King County Auditor's Office. Today, 100 years, later, the *Journal* still reports on these vital activities—a key reason why the paper has survived while other publications have disappeared or been swallowed up in mergers or buyouts.

Early copies and records of the *Bulletin* unfortunately were destroyed in one of Seattle's fires. It is known, however, that R. L. Davis had resigned as King County clerk to begin the paper. The paper soon expanded from a single sheet to four pages. By 1899 H. C. Piggott was the publisher. He hired Jedd P. Fuller from Denver to serve as editor of the paper now called the *Seattle Daily Bulletin*. By 1901 Piggott had sold out to Fuller. The three-column layout was expanded to six columns and with it came expanded coverage of construction activities, financial news, and daily quotations from the New York and Liverpool grain markets, as well as the New York Stock and Produce Exchange.

In 1903 the *Seattle Daily Bulletin* was bought by Col. Alden J. Blethen, publisher of the *Seattle Times*. Later, in 1907, he combined the *Bulletin* with a morning edition of the *Times*, calling it the *Seattle Morning Times & Daily Bulletin*. This combined publication did not last long. The next year it was dropped and the *Bulletin* was re-started as a separate publication.

M. F. Brown and O. J. David purchased the *Bulletin* in 1916. A little more background is in order to fully appreciate the Brown & David 1916 purchase. Early in this century a one-page construction report known as the *Daily Building Record* was being published

by W. M. Patterson. He later combined a shipping paper with his *Record* and formed the *Daily Gazette-Record*. Brown and David bought the *Gazette-Record* from Patterson in 1909. They sold the *Gazette* and changed the name of the *Record* to the *Seattle Daily Record*. The paper was published from its offices on the Grand Trunk Pier on the downtown waterfront which was destroyed by fire on July 30, 1914. What was saved of the *Record's* operation was moved to 83 Columbia Street where the *Seattle Daily Journal of Commerce* is now published.

By 1916 the *Seattle Daily Record* and the newly purchased *Daily Bulletin* were merged into one paper called the *Daily Bulletin*. That same year another paper called the *Report*, founded by Jedd Fuller, was also purchased. At this time the *Bulletin* covered construction, finance, real estate and general business. In December 1919, the paper's name was changed to the *Daily Journal of Commerce*. In 1937 M. F. Brown bought out David's interest in the paper.

During the years some colorful characters have helped to shape the editorial content of the paper, including M. W. "Milt" Bean who became managing editor in 1928 and served as editor from 1946 to 1970. Before joining the *Journal* he was a hard rock miner, mule skinner and infantryman who pursued famed Mexican bandit Pancho Villa. Bean also served in the Signal Corps during the reconstruction of San Francisco after the Great Earthquake and fire. Since Bean's departure the *Journal of Commerce* has had four editors.

Today the Brown family continues to operate the paper under the guidance of co-publishers Monte Brown, M. F. Brown's son and Monte's nephew Denis Brown. Philip Brown, son of Denis, is the managing editor. M.F. Brown's great-grandson John Elliott is the company's computer systems manager.

The paper today still concentrates on news of the construction industry, but has expanded into related fields of real estate, the design professions and law. The *Journal* remains the official publication of the city of Seattle, publishing all legal notices and bid advertisements. The official notices of most other Northwest government jurisdictions are also published, making the *Journal* a handy source for government procurement activity. The *Journal* expects to remain the most reliable source of government and business activity well into the next century. ◆

The staff of the Journal of Commerce gather for a photo commemorating the newspaper's 100th anniversary.

Kato & Warren, Inc.

Kato & Warren, Inc. was founded in 1987 by Richard M. Kato, P.E., and Richard E. Warren, P.E. Kato and Warren first met when they both were employed by Kramer, Chin & Mayo, an old line consulting engineering firm in the Seattle area. Following employment with KCM, each went his separate way and started his own practice. They came together again 1987 to pursue a mutual interest in helping government clients develop funding and management programs to implement public works projects. In 1992, the two founders were joined by Mr. Bryce Ecklein, who also worked with them at KCM. Mr. Ecklein is a recognized leader in the field of urban design and environmental impact assessment. Among the projects with which he has been associated are the planning for the high level West Seattle bridge, the Bellevue stomwater master plan and the SeaTac joint transportation study. The firm expanded to the Portland, Oregon area in 1994 with a new office managed by Dennis Robertson. In 1996, Kato & Warren acquired the northwest offices of TAMS Consultants and became a major player in transportation planning and design. As a result of this acquisition, Mr. Barry Knight joined the firm as a principal.

Mr. Warren and Mr. Kato have provided innovative approaches to funding for water, sewer, street and drainage programs for a variety of clients. They have pioneered the use of user fees for both drainage and street purposes. They have also developed innovative techniques for the funding and management of public buildings and operating facilities. Recently, they completed work on a capital facility needs study for the State Department of Transportation involving all of the highway maintenance facilities throughout the state. This included special planning for the northwest regional offices in the Seattle area.

The firm developed a strong capability in helping public agencies inform their constituent public of the need for public works programs and have developed equitable means of funding them. The firm provides services to cities, counties and other governmental agencies throughout the United States in the areas of facility planning, facility management, utilities and, in particular, urban stormwater planning, water quality and funding.

Richard E. Warren, P.E.

Mr. Warren was born in Seattle, Washington January 2, 1932. Before founding Kato & Warren in 1987 with Richard Kato, Mr. Warren operated his own firm, Warren Consultants, Inc., from 1984-87. In 1983 he resigned his post as Vice President of Kramer, Chin & Mayo of Seattle where he had worked since 1968 and took an extended sabbatical. His earlier professional experience took him to Idaho, California, Alaska and Europe.

Mr. Warren received a B.S. in Chemical Engineering from the University of Idaho in 1953, graduating with high honors. He also studied at the University of Washington and the U.S. Army's Engineering School, Ft. Belvoi, Virginia.

Mr. Warren was the originator of the concept of the Stormwater Drainage Utility approach to funding and managing urban drainage. This approach has provided a stable funding source for this critical urban service and has resulted in greatly reduced environmental damage from urban runoff. This approach is now in use across the country and Mr. Warren is called upon to assist agencies in all parts of the country in implementing such utilities. This approach led to the concept of integrated stormwater/water quality management that has become the model for EPA's National Stormwater Permitting Program (NPDES).

Mr. Warren also led the APWA Committee that developed the concept of street funding utilizing user fees and the same utility approach developed for stormwater. His work led to the passage of enabling legislation in Washington State in 1990. This approach is also achieving national interest and he has assisted many agencies in its application.

Other projects in which Mr. Warren has played a significant role include the City of Bellevue Stormwater Utility, the first in the country, West Seattle high levels bridge, the U.S. Navy's Bangor Submarine base, the Seattle Aquarium and the Tacoma Dome.

In 1982, Mr. Warren was selected Public Works Leader of the Year in Washington State. Mr. Warren was the 1989 President of the Washington Chapter of the American Public Works Association and has served the Chapter in many offices, committees, and projects including that of Co-Chairman of this History of Public Works in Washington State. Mr. Warren is a member of the Board of the National Public Works Historical Society. He is a member of several historical and professional societies.

Richard M. Kato, P.E.

Richard M. Kato was born in Seattle, Washington on July 8, 1950. He attended Cleveland High School, Whitman College and the University of Washington from which he received a B.S. in Civil Engineering in 1975.

Mr. Kato's professional experience has encompassed all facets of civil and municipal engineering. He has developed water, surface water and sanitary sewer systems feasibility and planning studies for several municipalities, special districts and ports. He has managed several utility and site development projects from the development of concepts through construction.

Because of his working knowledge of local municipalities, Mr. Kato has provided major private developers with project facilitation assistance in the areas of concept development, site selection and feasibility, interagency agreements, shared funding, zoning and permitting issues, public participation program development and negative impact mitigations.

Mr. Kato's professional work includes 1974 Project Engineer for the U.S. Forest Service in Enumclaw, Washington, road designs; 1974-79 Port of Seattle, Airport Design Group, Project Engineer Sea-Tac International Airport; 1979-84, Kramer, Chin & Mayo, Inc., Civil/Municipal Group, project management for large civil design and construction projects throughout the Puget Sound region. In 1984 Mr. Kato joined the firm of Reid, Middleton & Associates where he assumed management and project engineering responsibilities. In 1986, Mr. Kato became Manager of the Seattle branch office of Reid, Middleton. He is now a Principal with Kato & Warren, Inc.

His professional affiliations include membership in the American Society for Engineering Management, the Institute of Transportation Engineers, Consulting Engineers Council of Washington, American Public Works Association, American Water Works Association, Society of Military Engineers/Seattle Post, and American Society of Civil Engineers. ◆

The Kennewick-Pasco Intercity Bridge

Traveling between the cities of Pasco and Kennewick became a lot easier in 1978 for motorists, cyclists and pedestrians alike. In September of that year a new bridge over the Columbia River, which separates the two cities in southeastern Washington, was dedicated to the public. Known simply as the Intercity Bridge, the structure introduced a new cost effective method for constructing long span bridges, and quickly became the prototype for large bridges elsewhere in the United States and abroad.

Planning for the project began in 1970 when structural inspections indicated that the steel truss bridge was suffering from fatigue stresses in its main I-bar tension members. This, together with the unacceptably narrow roadway, mandated a new bridge.

The two city councils selected the concrete cable stayed concept after reviewing the findings of a bridge design comparative study. Each alternative bridge type was evaluated for such items as initial cost, safety, and use of local resources for construction and appearance.

The bridge is known as a "concrete cable-stayed girder bridge," which means that the girder element, over which the bridge traffic travels, is made of concrete and is suspended, i.e. stayed, from towers by cables. Although similar types of bridges had been constructed before, using steel for the girder element, the Intercity Bridge was the first in North America to use concrete.

Overall the bridge spans 2,503 feet between the levees of Lake Wallula in the backwaters of McNary Dam. The cable-stayed spans are 406.5, 981, and 406.5 feet in length, and provide needed navigation clearance for the waters flowing under it. Its 80-foot wide deck carries four lanes of traffic and two sidewalks.

Visually, the most dominate feature of the structure is the twin towers. Rising 250 feet above the river and 187 feet above the roadway deck level, these towers carry, through 144 stay cables, the weight of the entire 1,704 feet of suspended girder. The stay cables themselves are made up of between 83 and 283 individual 0.25-inch high- strength steel wires, and are socketed at each end for anchorage, and to the girder and the top of the towers. A plastic jacket around the wire bundles is filled with cement for corrosion protection. Cable diameters vary between four and seven inches.

The concrete girder was constructed in 27-foot long segments which were precast in a special plant located about two miles downstream from the bridge site. After casting and post-tensioning, the 300-ton segments were barged to the site, lifted into place, and epoxy-glued and post-tensioned against the previously installed segment, after which the stay cables supporting the segment were installed. A total of 60 such precast pieces were fabricated to make up the suspended girder section.

Construction began in 1975 and was completed in 1978 at a total cost of $30 million, which includes approach roadway construction, bridge construction, right-of-way, engineering and administrative costs. Actual bridge cost averaged just $112 per square foot. Federal Bridge Replacement Funds provided for 75 percent of the cost for the bridge. The balance was provided by local funds from the cities of Pasco and Kennewick, and Benton and Franklin Counties.

An administrative body, called the Intercity Bridge Committee, was appointed by the two city councils to handle the administrative affairs of the project. Consisting of the two city managers and a chosen citizen at large, the committee was instrumental in getting the project planned, funded and built in the record time of six years, within budget and with the full support of the people of the Tri-Cities. Responsibility for appropriation of city funds and overall policy rested with the individual city councils.

The bridge has received several national design awards. the two most notable are the Award for the National Outstanding Civil Engineering Achievement for Structural Engineering from the American Society of Civil Engineers in 1978, and the President of the United States Award for Design Excellence, bestowed upon the designers in 1985.

The engineer for the project planning, design and construction control was Arvid Grant and Associates, Inc. Peter Kiewit Sons' Co., Inc. of Vancouver, Washington, was the general contractor for construction. The chairman of the Intercity Bridge Committee, who served throughout the tenure of the project, was Mr. Ed Hendler of Pasco. The Pasco-Kennewick Intercity Bridge is a crowning achievement in transportation public works in southeastern Washington. ◆

The Kennedy Group—Consultants Inc.

In memory of
William Bispham Moore, P.E.
1911-1983

U.W., B.S.E.E., 1934
Alumnus of the Grand Coulee Dam
"School of Engineering"

Founding partner of
Livingstone and Moore, 1961,
succeeded by
Moore, Wallace and Kennedy, Inc., 1965

Senior Partner, Senior Engineer
and my friend

—*David A. Kennedy*

Black River Pump Station
Renton, WA
Owner—King County Department of Public Works
Engineer—Joint venture of Bovay Engineers and
Moore, Wallace and Kennedy, Inc.
Construction Project Engineer—David A. Kennedy
Contractor—Mottner and McCutchion, Inc.

Alan O. King, P.E.

Alan O. King was born in Omak, Washington in 1947. He received a B.S. in Civil Engineering from the University of Washington in 1970. Mr. King held positions with several firms in the 1970s: Washington State Department of Highways, Spokane; Engineering Corp. of America, Coeur d'Alene, Idaho; and Victor O. Gray & Co., Seattle. In 1977 he became Okanogan County Engineer/Director of Public Works, where he organized the county's first full service Public Works Department, one of the first in Washington. The department received a Washington State Department of Transportation award in 1983 for Outstanding Project Management as one of the first Certification Acceptance local agencies in the state.

Mr. King returned to WSDOT in 1988 and is currently serving as Systems Management Engineer. In 1992 he was appointed to a special team assembled to implement the ISTEA of 1991 and is considered one of the top experts in the State on that complex federal act.

Mr. King served as Chairman of the Washington State City and County Pavement Management System Technical Committee and as the first Research Committee Chairman of the Washington State Association of County Engineers. He served in 1986-87 as the National Association of County Engineers Research Director. He is a member of ASCE, APWA, an Honorary Member of the Washington State Association of County Engineers, and a former member or ARTBA, ITE, and the National Association of County Engineers. He has been listed in *Who's Who in the West* and in *Who's Who of Emerging Leaders of America.* Mr. King and his wife, Linda, have been married since 1969 and have two sons. ◆

Klickitat County

Klickitat County was established December 20, 1859, by the Washington Territorial Legislature. The County is split diagonally between forested mountains and rolling open ranch and farm lands. Most of the County's citizens are involved in logging or ranching; however, the single largest employer is an aluminum smelter plant. Each year we see more people living in the west end of the County and commuting to the Portland/Vancouver area for work. The population of retired people is ever increasing due to the appealing climate and lower cost of living.

Very few roads existed until about 1890; however, by the early 1920s most of the roads in use today were established. As this century progressed the population shifted from small homesteads to larger ranches and residential homes. This relocation permitted more than three hundred miles of unused county road to be vacated in the early 1980s. By 1992 most of the remaining roads are quite stable and provide good traveling which is evidenced by the fact that no school bus has been stuck in the mud in a county road for more than six years.

The County launched a bridge replacement program 15 years ago and between 1977 and 1992, 21 bridges were replaced. The Husum Bridge is scheduled for replacement in 1993 and four bridges are scheduled for replacement in 1994. It is also anticipated that the 7th Street Overpass in Lyle will be replaced by 1995. During this same 15-year period the Alderdale Road from the Columbia River to the Yakima Valley, the Centerville Highway from Lyle to Goldendale, and the Bickleton Road from Goldendale to Bickleton have been finished and hard surfaced. All of the major roads are now paved. With another few years of continued effort this County should compare with others and then be able to focus on some of the access and farm to market roads and bridges.

An equipment management program was started more than 10 years ago and now the County has a fleet of equipment to properly maintain the road system. The fleet is maintained by looking at long term costs and an effective preventive maintenance program. Nine motor graders, twelve 10-yard trucks, six five-yard trucks, five loaders and 26 pickups and numerous other pieces make up the fleet.

In early years the duties of County Engineers were limited to roads and bridges; however, changing times have brought additional responsibilities. In 1986 the County Engineer title was changed to Public Works Director/County Engineer and building inspection was added to the existing responsibilities of roads, bridges, equipment management, paths and trails, and solid waste. The Public Works Director reports directly to the Board of County Commissioners.

The County closed its landfill and contracted with Regional Disposal Company to open a new landfill to handle up to 3,000,000 tons of solid waste per year which includes the County's 10,000 tons. The Regional Disposal Company landfill has operated since 1990 and is in 1993 generating approximately $2,000,000 revenue in host fees. In addition, almost 100 jobs have been created. This has helped bring the unemployment rate to as low as 11 percent from the previous rates of over 20 percent.

Klickitat County is proud of the accomplishments and looks forward to completing several major projects in the foreseeable future. ◆

Kramer, Chin & Mayo, Inc.

For fifty years Kramer, Chin & Mayo, Inc. has provided consulting engineering services to public works clients. KCM takes great pride in the facilities it has helped provide for the people of Washington. The Tolt River Dam, Seattle's main water supply, the nationally acclaimed Seattle Aquarium, the West Seattle Bridge, the world's largest dry dock at the Bremerton Naval Shipyard, and the Metro Sewer System are among KCM's significant engineering contributions.

KCM is equally proud of the smaller public works projects for communities throughout the state that are the mainstay of the firm's work. Among these works are water systems for Friday Harbor, South Bend, Hoquiam, Olympia, Enumclaw and hundreds of other cities, towns, water districts and private clients. The firm has developed sewer systems and treatment plants in Everson, Sumas, Sultan, Monroe, Mercer Island and Shelton, Washington.

The company has also been a part of the development of streets, highways and bridges for many other communities. KCM continues to be highly innovative in the development of public works drainage projects. The company introduced the concept of drainage utilities, which are operating very successfully for a wide variety of clients. Its early work in Washington fisheries led to a thriving national and international business in the planning and design of aquaculture facilities.

As one of the largest locally owned engineering firms in the State, KCM has always committed the full resources of the firm and its members for the betterment of the community and the profession. The firm's founders James Carey and Harrison Kramer were very active with the licensing board, as well as the Consulting Engineers Council and APWA. Ark Chin, past CEO, has served as Chairman of the Board of Western Washington University, President of the Chinese Nursing Home Society, President of CECW, and on various other educational and community committees and boards.

On behalf of the contribution of the firm, KCM officers salute the APWA for its contribution to the State of Washington, and pledge to continue providing quality engineering services to their public works clients.

Kramer, Chin & Mayo, Inc. Consulting Engineers, Architects, Applied Sciences: Seattle, 1917 First Avenue, Seattle, Washington 98101-1027; and 7080 Fir Loop, Portland, Oregon 987223-8022.

Peter Kiewit Sons, Inc.

As the decade of the 1930s drew to a close war began in Europe, Peter Kiewit Sons, Inc., of Omaha, Nebraska, took the contract to build an army camp in far off Fort Lewis, Washington. The job consisted of constructing 760 barracks buildings, each to hold 64 men—a total of 48,840 GIs. All of this plus all of the streets and support utilities were to be in place in only 90 days. Hardly had the work begun than the Army more than doubled the size of the project to 1,540 buildings without increasing the contract time or unit prices. The Fort Lewis contract was for $7.5 million, the biggest job Kiewit had ever undertaken. It was winter in the Pacific Northwest and that meant rain, fog, eternal dampness and mud. The Home Office was half a continent away in Omaha, Nebraska.

As the war came to a close, Ivan Breunsbach—the man in charge of Kiewit operations in the Pacific Northwest—persuaded Mr. Kiewit that they ought to get into the highway construction business "out there." The company took Bruensbach's advice and has distinguished itself with public works projects, most notably bridges.

The Selah Canyon Bridges, twin spans carrying Interstate 82, hear Yakima, Washington, with a clear center span of 549 feet, are the longest concrete arch bridges in North America. In 1977 Kiewit completed a 2,500-foot bridge over the Columbia River connecting Pasco and Kennewick, Washington, the first cable-stayed concrete bridge in the United States and the second largest cable-stayed bridge in the world.

In the nuclear field the Washington Public Power System undertook the construction of five nuclear plants at two sites— Hanford and Satsop, Washington. Over the past 50 years Kiewit has had five major nuclear industry contracts totally more than a quarter of a billion dollars.

In Seattle Kiewit completed a four-story expansion atop the existing Harborview Hospital, one of the nation's leading burn centers, while maintaining essential 24-hour public access to the facilities.

Also in Seattle, Kiewit took over an unfinished contract and completed the city's civic jewel, the Kingdome, in time for the July 4, 1976, Bicentennial celebration. The Kingdome, situated on a 36-acre tract, is the world's largest clear-span concrete dome, and serves as the home of Seattle's professional football and baseball teams.

Another Kiewit project is the grain export terminal in Tacoma, Washington. Consisting of 48 concrete silos, a loading pier 450 feet in length, a 200 car railroad yard, car dumpers, conveyers, grain cleaners, and computerized controls to handle three million bushels of grain. The seven-inch walls of the 48 silos, each 130 feet high, were poured simultaneously in slipforms over a 10 day period in what is probably the largest multiple-silo slipform operation ever accomplished in a single lift.

In 1975 the American Public Works Association, named Peter Kiewit Sons, Inc., "Contractor of the Year." The award was given for Kiewit's construction of a four-lane Interstate Highway through a bird sanctuary near Seattle. Noise and air pollution were major concerns, and Kiewit managed to finish the project "without any negative criticism," a tribute to Kiewit's efforts in complying with all environmental requirements. Kiewit's respect for the environmental aspects of the project and its efforts to work in harmony with the community were factors in its selection as "Contractor of the Year."

Peter Kiewit Sons, Inc. salutes Washington on its Centennial and is proud to be an integral part of the public works of the Evergreen State. ◆

Kingdome construction in Seattle.

City of Kirkland

The community known as Kirkland was founded in 1888 by Peter Kirk, a British industrialist who dreamed of establishing a town and constructing a major steel mill. Kirkland was to become the "Pittsburgh of the West" Kirk successfully founded the community and built the mill. However, the Panic of the 1890s led to the collapse of the venture. The population of the community dropped from 5000 in 1892 to 600 by 1902.

In 1905, by a 60 to 49 vote, the community incorporated as the town of Kirkland and appointed Charles Daniels as the Town Marshall and Street Commissioner. Two months later, LID 1 was formed to construct a wood plank sidewalk along Market Street. This began a number of sidewalk projects which was the major public works activity for the new town.

Ollis W. Patty became Marshall and Street Commissioner in 1907 and continued to serve Kirkland for well over 30 years. A 1913 election authorized the town to install a water system and Mr. Patty was given the added title of Water Commissioner. Bonds were issued, a watershed to the south was purchased and construction of the water system progressed in varying stages over the years. Kirkland also supplied water to the neighboring town of Houghton. During the 1920s and 1930s Kirkland continued to improve streets, sidewalks and the water system, as much as limited funds permitted.

A federal grant was obtained in 1940 to construct a sewage treatment plant, and Kirkland began to provide sanitary sewer service to Kirkland and Houghton. The plant was abandoned in 1961 when Kirkland connected to the Metro system. In 1941, Kirkland acquired the remainder of the watershed now known as Watershed Park.

World War II saw major expansion of the water, sewer and street systems to support the large influx of military and civilian personnel working at the shipyards and the surrounding military facilities. Ground water quality was poor, and in 1960 the wells were abandoned when Kirkland connected to the Seattle Tolt pipeline.

In 1949, Kirkland replaced wooden water lines, installed sewer lines and graded all the streets in the northwest portion of the town. Frank "Nobby" Clark became City Engineer and served until 1966. In 1967, Arthur Knutson was appointed Director of Public Services and took over public works operations. In the mid-1960s, LID 100 was formed, allowing for construction of water, sewer and street infrastructure.

In 1968, the town of Houghton consolidated with Kirkland. In 1981, Larry Larse replaced retiring Art Knutson as Public Works Director. And in 1988, the city's population doubled to 36,000 with a major annexation. Substantial infrastructure projects were undertaken in the 1980s. The Rosehill Water District, which served portions of the city, annexed in 1988 and was assumed by the city in 1993. After Larse retired in 1989, Jim Arndt took over as Public Works Director. The city continued to grow dramatically, with the population exceeding 42,000 by 1993.

KPFF Consulting Engineers

KPFF Consulting Engineers has provided structural and civil engineering design and consulting services to architects, government agencies, developers and contractors since 1960. Headquartered in Seattle, KPFF has additional branch offices in Portland, OR and Los Angeles and San Francisco, CA. The firm's 180 professionals include 80 structural and 30 civil engineers.

KPFF's capabilities include design, development and project management services, design and preparation of plans, specifications and construction documents, and follow-on construction contract administration. Known throughout the west as structural and seismic design specialists, the firm has provided dynamic response analysis for wind and seismic loads for projects located all over the western U.S.

Structural engineering design capabilities include high-rise office buildings, housing, hotels and condominiums, industrial buildings, educational facilities, health care facilities, high-tech facilities, theaters and recreational buildings. Recent projects include the 26-story Seattle Heights Condominiums and the 55-story Washington Mutual Tower, as well as low- and mid-rise structures such as Sunset Corporate Campus, Fred Hutchinson Cancer Research Center and Port of Seattle Terminal 5 expansion.

The civil engineering staff of KPFF works on development of commercial and industrial sites, roadway improvements and transportation projects.

KPFF consultants work with the ocean transportation industry, public ports, marine developers and related government agencies. Projects include harbor planning and design for a wide range of port structures and systems. ◆

King County Department of Public Works

The Department of Public Works, created by County Home Rule Charter in 1968, is composed of four major divisions: airport, roads and engineering, solid waste, and surface water management. However, to understand the King County Department of Public Works in 1989 one must first understand its background and origins.

The Setting—Geographically King County covers 2,235 square miles. Within that area are 33 cities, fertile farmlands, vast forests, two major mountain passes, saltwater beaches and 1.5 million people, according to 1990 census figures.

The picture of King County in 1852, when it was created by the Oregon Territorial Legislature, was quite different. The county census for that year counted 170 white settlers. The first highway law passed in 1854 placed all roads under the jurisdiction of the County Commissioners. The County Commission form of government was to remain in effect until 1968 when the Home Rule Charter was passed by the voters reorganizing King County into a council/executive form of government creating the Department of Public Works.

Building the Road Network—Since the 1850s roads have been instrumental in opening the land to settlement. County surveyors, some elected and some appointed, established new roads to serve a growing community. During the years that followed, telegraph roads, mine to market roads, military roads, plat roads, logging roads, ferries and the interstate highway system were added to the developing transportation network.

By 1960, 935,000 people lived in King County. A 30 percent increase in population over 10 years exposed the need to develop plans and guidelines for growth. The Puget Sound Regional Transportation Plan provided a base for the Interstate Highway System and shaped regional growth patterns.

Population and employment continued to increase during the 1960s. Road planning and expansion of the interstate system prompted two important events. Forward Thrust, a major $333.9 million public facilities bond issue was established following voter approval. It supported construction of parks, swimming pools, citizen service centers, the Kingdome and other public buildings.

Concurrent with Forward Thrust, the Washington State Legislature created the Urban Arterial Board and increased the gasoline tax for funding road projects. During the late 1960s and early 1970s emphasis was placed on reconstruction of the existing road system. In 1965 there was one signalized intersection in the unincorporated King County road network. By 1991 there were 154 computer controlled signalized intersections, 194 bridges, and 2,474 miles of roads managed and maintained by the Roads and Engineering Division.

In the 1960s and 1970s, population and employment expanded into much of the formerly rural areas of the county. As

Illegal steel wheels on concrete road.

a result, citizen participation and environmental considerations became a part of the design process for all road projects. A King County Design Commission was created to review all projects, and the County Council created the Environmental Development Commission—a citizen review committee created to review the environmental impacts of growth in the county.

According to estimates, King County's population is anticipated to grow to 2.1 million people by the year 2020. King County Transportation Plans, updated annually, reflect how the transportation system supports land use patterns projected for the county and identifies road projects which are needed to accommodate expected traffic increases. In 1991 a system was started to charge developers an impact fee proportionate to the additional traffic that would be generated by proposed development. Other local option revenues for road, high occupancy vehicle and transit improvements are being studied. Increasing emphasis is also being given to the needs of non-motorized users of the transportation system, including pedestrians bicyclists and equestrians.

Contributing to Aviation—King County International Airport (Boeing Field)—Charlie Hamilton, barnstormer, stunt flyer and all around daredevil, drew a crowd of 20,000 to the Meadows Race Track in 1910 to see his patent dive (now known as "a stall"). It was the first manned heavier-than-air flight in the Northwest. Years later, the Meadows Race Track would become a part of Boeing Field. In 1986 it became the site of the Museum of Flight, the largest aviation museum on the West Coast.

The Bogue Plan, published in 1911, visualized an industrial/commercial complex in the Duwamish Valley. By 1922 the dredging, filling and straightening of the Duwamish Waterway was completed. That effort raised the tide flats eight feet and provided level ground for a cinder airstrip later known as Boeing Field. Across the Duwamish River was Boeing Company Plant 1—affectionately known as the "Red Barn." It was home for the fledgling enterprise that would one day become the world leader in commercial aviation. King County acquired these properties for its airport, and official dedication ceremonies took place July 26, 1928, with 50,000 attending the festivities.

DEDICATION OF BOEING FIELD ADMINISTRATION BUILDING AND DEPOT ... A

During World War II, Boeing Field's runways were paved and lengthened. The post war years brought peace and renewed energy to the King County area. In 1951, the main runway was extended to 10,000 feet to accommodate the region's leap into the Jet Age with the Boeing 707-80 making its maiden flight to Boeing Field in 1954. The region would never be the same again. Today the economic impact of Boeing Field on the local economy is more than one-half billion dollars annually.

Controlling Flooding, Surface Water and Water Quality— During the 1930s flood control projects in King County were staffed by over 200 employees, many funded by the Federal Works Progress Administration (WPA). During World War II, however, WPA workers were gradually withdrawn until the flood control services faded away.

A major storm in 1959 devastated bridges, roads and homes throughout the county, causing several million dollars damage. Considerable portions of the levees on the Green River in South King County were lost. The county's Flood Control Division and the River Improvement Fund were established that year to help prevent the recurrence of such major damage.

Rapid population growth and urbanization in the county during the 1960s and 1970s replaced hundreds of acres of natural vegetation with hard, impervious surfaces. This decreased the land's natural ability to absorb rainfall, dramatically increasing urban runoff and the damage from storm water flooding and erosion.

To draw greater government and public attention to the growing severity of urban runoff problems and to improve maintenance of streams, ditches and drainage systems, the county reorganized the Flood Control Division into the Hydraulics Division in the late 1960s and early 1970s. The new division continued to provide river maintenance and flood control services.

Discussions about a countywide service charge to address surface water needs began in 1974, when the need for a comprehensive drainage and basin planning program was identified as a priority for the Juanita Creek and May Creek Basins. In 1980 these discussions prompted the County Council to initiate a feasibility study for expanding and financing a surface water program. There was also interest in changing the division's name to reflect current concerns. Shortly thereafter, the Hydraulics Division became known as the Surface Water Management Division.

In 1984 a study identified 280 capital improvement projects with a price tag of over $60 million. A Citizens' Advisory Committee then prioritized the projects. These efforts would set the stage for a greatly expanded surface water management and basin planning program.

Numerous public meetings and surveys were conducted throughout 1984 and 1985. A major storm on January 18, 1986, caused extensive flooding and property damage countywide. The following May, the County Executive and Council approved the establishment of a new surface water program supported by service charges program to be implemented on January 1, 1987. As a result of the 1986 Ordinance, the Surface Water Management Division was able to provide basin planning, design and construction of capital improvement projects, enhancement and preservation of wetlands and streams, maintenance of facilities, water quality monitoring and public education. The goals of this comprehensive program included enhanced flood and erosion controls, improved water quality, and preservation of fish habitat and other natural resources.

Disposing of Solid Waste—Prior to the 1950s, King County provided solid waste disposal services through a system of open dumps located throughout the county. In the late 1950s, King County established the Department of Sanitary Operations which later became the county's Solid Waste Division, and began replacing the open dumps with a regional transfer system. By 1967, one of the nations's first regional transfer and landfill facilities at 1st Avenue Northeast and Northeast 165th Street had been constructed and placed into operation.

In 1974 a more comprehensive solid waste plan was still needed to manage the County's waste. King County, the City of Seattle, and METRO participated in the preparation of an expanded plan which recommended that incineration with energy recovery be the future alternative for solid waste disposal in King County. The plan also recommended improvements to the county's system of transfer stations and landfills.

By 1982, the Solid Waste Division had completed construction of a new transfer station at Bow Lake, installed automated scale systems at all transfer stations, constructed a leachate collection system at Cedar Hills, and constructed a five mile forcemain to transmit leachate to the METRO interception and treatment system. The division had also become self-sustaining through a weight-based user fee system.

Also in 1982, the Puget Sound Council of Governments completed an updated study of the 1974 plan. It focused on additional landfill upgrades, and eventual closure of the county's four rural landfills. While incineration with energy recovery was still recommended, recycling also emerged as a significant component of the region's solid waste disposal system.

Through the 1980s, the Solid Waste Division continued to make improvements to its landfills. This work included the installation of composite liners, active landfill gas collection, and other state-of-the-art capital and operating improvements.

In 1987, a goal to achieve 65 percent waste reduction and recycling by the year 2000 was adopted by county officials. Incineration was dropped as a recommended disposal method, thus signalling a desire to achieve volume reduction through conservation-oriented methods.

In recent years, updates of the county's Comprehensive Solid Waste Management Plan have continued. The plan adopted by all participating municipalities and approved by the Department of Ecology, will make recycling an integral part of King County's solid waste management system. This vision is founded upon a disposal system that is designed, constructed and operated with a commitment to environmental quality and control. ◆

Top: Norman Bridge, two miles north of North Bend.
Bottom: Green River Valley.

Kitsap County

Kitsap County's unique geographic isolation has contributed to its socioeconomic history almost as much as the influence of the United States military. Surrounded by water, the Kitsap Peninsula falls short of island status by a two-mile stretch of land near Allyn in Mason County. Taking advantage of the natural water transportation routes and sheltered harbors, five mill towns were founded during Kitsap's Territorial period, 1857-1889.

Early roads followed Indian trails and early County Commissioners appointed road surveyors to suggest approval and eventual transformation of the trails into road districts. All residents were taxed for road improvements, but taxpayers could work off the tax at $2.50 per day. Road District No. 1 connected Port Gamble and Port Madison bays. The earliest public building was an abandoned blockhouse which was partially converted for use by county officials and located on the wharf at Port Madison, then the county seat.

Kitsap became a Third Class county on January 1, 1941, which permitted a number of improvements in the operation of the county's business including employment of a County Engi-

Port Orchard bypass bridge

neer on a full-time basis. In 1991 the County Engineer, Randy W. Casteel, P.E., also held the title of Director of Public Works.

Before the appointment of a County Engineer, commissioners were totally responsible for support and maintenance of a county hospital, construction and maintenance of roads, and licensing saloons and billiard tables, among other activities. The earliest County Engineer's responsibilities included the county hospital, sustenance of paupers, the development of the airport, and construction of its first 600-foot runway, as well as duties associated with roads. The county constructed an airplane hangar in 1938 and realized a monthly income of $150 for rental space for 13 private, commercial and Navy planes.

In 1941, when the County Engineer was first employed on a full-time basis, Kitsap had 717 miles of road, 70 paved. Today there are 1,015 miles of road, nearly all paved. Kitsap County's Public Works Department has five key areas of responsibility as defined by the three elected commissioners: 1) equipment maintenance, repair and replacement, or ERRF; 2) engineering, including design, development and plat approval; 3) operations or road maintenance and construction; 4) wastewater/solid waste utility; and 5) accounting. The annual budget in 1989 was $25 million. ◆

Above left: Finishing around wing wall—Gorst Creek Arch Culvert.
Left: Starting Brownsville Bridge project.
Below: Completed Brownsville Bridge.

Jan P. Klippert

Jan Klippert was born in Rochester, New York. In 1958 he received the Bachelor of Arts degree with emphasis in history from the University of Rochester. He moved to Seattle in 1959. Since that time, he has been an advocate for community awareness and citizen involvement in governmental projects and programs. Mr. Klippert has written for community newspapers, has been a community activist, and has provided staff support to a variety of commissions, committees, and organizations whose voices have shaped the changes that affected many communities.

In the early 1960s, while employed by the City of Seattle Mayor's Office, Mr. Klippert worked with the Seattle Arts Commission and Seattle Urban Renewal Enterprises. Later he was Director of the Seattle Neighborhood Youth Corps.

During the late 1960s, while working as Mayor's Assistant in the City of Renton, Mr. Klippert served as liaison between the city and the consulting firm Johnston-Campenalla during the building of the Renton City Hall.

In 1971 Mr. Klippert founded the community relations function for the King County Department of Public Works. He became a publicist for the department emphasizing the need for community awareness of public works projects and programs. Road projects were funded by Forward Thrust and the Urban Arterial Board encouraged expansion and improvement of the county road system. Community residents expressed concern for a voice in shaping community road networks. Mr. Klippert provided the link.

Making provision for citizen education and awareness of planned works projects has become a regular part of the project design and construction process. Also the environmental review processes have become institutionalized in response to general public requirements for project coordination, analysis and citizen involvement in reviewing project goals and design.

The Department of Public Works has expanded the community relations function to integrate community awareness, public meetings and citizen advisory committees in its regular annual work program requiring those activities as an integral part of doing business.

Throughout his more than 30 years of public service he has been active in the community, including the Washington Trails Association, Volunteers for Outdoor Washington, Haller Lake Improvement Club and the Haller Lake United Methodist Church.

During 1993 he helped the Public Works Historical Society with publication of interviews with Roy Morse. Also, the foundation was laid for a 1995 International Symposium in Public Works to be held in Seattle.

Mr. Klippert has served as a director of the Seattle Engineers Club and trustee of the national Public Works Historical Society. In 1992 he received the Swearingen Award from the American Public Works Association International for outstanding service to the association at the chapter level. ◆

City of Lacey

The City of Lacey is known for its progressive and positive approach to growth. In a span of 20 years it has advanced from a slow-paced farming community to a focal point of growth within Thurston County. Incorporated in 1966, Lacey grew from a few hundred to a 1992 population of over 22,500.

In the late 1800s the community was known as Woodland. The existence of another Woodland post office led to the town's 1891 name change to Lacey, in recognition of O. C. DeLacey, a local attorney and land developer. Lacey was a community of family farms and dirt roads, some dating back to the 1850s. Tourists visited local lake resorts, dance halls and sulky horse racing. A Benedictine school, known today as St. Martin's College, opened its doors in 1894, and established its own water and hydropower system by utilizing nearby Woodland Creek.

The 20th-century growth in population has required continuous expansion of the public works in the community. The first public water system was established by L. C. Huntamer. Using his plow and shovel, Huntamer connected many neighbors to his deep wells. By the mid-1960s more than 3,000 customers were served by Huntamer's water system. The City of Lacey purchased Huntamer's system in 1967, acquiring over 20 miles of pipeline. Today the system has 16 wells, five reservoirs, three satellite water systems, over 200 miles of waterline and a metered "interconnection" with the City of Olympia. Currently, maximum water demand rate stands at over 14 million gallons per day, serving over 10,000 customers.

Over the years, improvement activities include 17 LIDs/ULIDs, six Federal Aid street improvements, eight Railroad Protection and Safety System projects, six bond issues, and 19 UAB/TIB projects from the Transportation Improvement Board. In 1987 Lacey received Washington's first Public Works Trust Fund Award.

In November 1976 the Cities of Lacey, Olympia and Tumwater, and Thurston County joined in an intergovernmental agreement for a wastewater facilities management plan called LOTT. Planning ensued for wastewater collection, treatment and disposal facilities for urban Thurston County. Lott's first phase was completed in the late 1970s, and the jurisdictions negotiated a plant upgrade agreement in 1989, which is nearing completion in 1993.

Old Highway 99, now know as Pacific Avenue, became the site of the community's first traffic signal in 1966. In the 1970s, with the help of state and federal funds, the community enjoyed the construction of sidewalks, curbs, gutter and street lights. Storm water drainage was addressed in the mid-1980s through implementation of a storm water utility charge to property owners.

John Moran became Lacey's first Public Works Director in 1971. Others who have served in the position include: John Swift, 1972; Ralph Klei, 1973; Norman Krueger, 1974-76; Don Hertzog, 1976-80; Doug Zenor, 1980-82; Jim Robertson, 1983, Rich Cobb, 1984-1992, and Brian Barnett, 1993. ◆

City of Lacey Public Works Department, 1988.

Lakehaven Utility District

The history of Federal Way Water and Sewer is a history of orderly transition. The district that began as numerous small systems serving isolated early day communities is today a united utility providing water and sewer service to a large, urban area under provisions of the state statutes governing special service districts.

Through a number of successful mergers and consolidations beginning in the 1940s, the district developed and grew. By the early 1990s the district encompassed 35 square miles and provided water and/or sewer service to over 100,000 customers. To serve its customers, the district taps groundwater sources with an elaborate well net system and is a leader in environmental protection issues related to sewage treatment. The district is one of the first major sewer utilities on Puget Sound to provide secondary treatment of all sewage flowing through its facilities.

It all started in the early 1940s when the Steel Lake Water Company was formed to serve an area in the vicinity of Steel Lake. Not long after, King County Water District 64 was formed and took over ownership and operation of the Steel Lake Water Company system. This system was gradually expanded, assuming operation of the North Lake Cooperative system and continuing until it extended to most of what is now the northern part of the present district.

To the south, the Lake Center Water Cooperative was also being formed in the mid-1940s to serve a wide area in the southern part of the present district. In 1958, King County Water District 100 was formed and took over ownership and operation of the Lake Center Water Cooperative system. The system was gradually expanded until it brought together most of what is now the southern part of the district from the Pierce County line north to abut the expanding Water District 64. As a result of a public vote by residents of Districts 64 and 100, the two districts were officially combined on November 30, 1971, forming King County Water District 124. The district continued to grow, incorporating the Ellenwood Water Company, and creating what is now the primary water supplier to the greater Federal Way community.

The other half of Federal Way Water and Sewer history is the development of the sewer utility. Federal Way and the surrounding communities of Star Lake, Redondo, Buenna and Lakota are relatively old in terms of years; however, they remained rural and isolated until the 1950s. Beginning in the mid-1950s Federal Way began experiencing the rapid growth that has continued to the present day. The citizens of Federal Way recognized and accepted the responsibility for development, authorizing the formation of Lakehaven Sewer District, a municipal corporation of King County, Washington, in a special election on January 31, l956.

In 1962, construction of the initial sewage collection facilities began in the Federal Way business area as well as around Steel Lake. In the succeeding years various extensions to this system have occurred in response to growth. Pocketed communities that developed away from the gravity interceptors were tied to the system using pump stations and force mains. Secondary treatment of sewage is provided at both the Redondo and Lakota Wastewater Treatment Plants.

In the early 1970s, King County Water District 124, Lakehaven Sewer District, and King County Fire Protection District 39 initiated planning for a joint administrative facilities site. In 1973, the three Districts purchased the current site on First Avenue So., near So. 316th Street. The administration offices of the districts were occupied in 1978.

In 1985, King County Water District 124 and the Lakehaven Sewer District merged and changed their name to form the Federal Way Water and Sewer District. Water District 56, formed in February, 1939, is the oldest district in the area, and the latest to seek merger with Federal Way Water and Sewer. A portion of the original areas of Redondo Beach and Buenna had previously been served by a private water company owned by Weston Betts, a pioneer in the Redondo community. The original water system was constructed by the Works Progress Administration (WPA) from materials purchased by the water district. In the years since formation, the water district gradually annexed additional areas along and in close proximity to Puget Sound, expanding until it incorporated most of the shorelines of Poverty Bay. In 1987, the Federal Way Water and Sewer District and Water District 56 merged.

The merging of these various cooperatives, companies and districts had, by the early 1990s, resulted in a district serving approximately 24,000 water services, 20,000 sewer services, and 13,000 street lighting services. The outcome is a utility that spans the greater Federal Way area and is committed to serving customers and the future with the greatest economy and efficiency. ◆

A 45,000 gallon elevated tank, erected in 1941 near 22nd Avenue South and South 308th Street, was pulled down in August 1957. By this time Water District 64 had completed a 500,000 gallon standpipe on South 312th Street and a similar 250,000 gallon facility in Auburn Heights Park. In 1990, the district is served by 12 reservoirs. Photo courtesy Federal Way Water and Sewer District.

City of Longview

Looking down upon the confluence of the Columbia and Cowlitz Rivers in the late 1910s, R. A. Long decided that here was the place to erect his city. Considered by many to be the first formally planned city west of the Mississippi River, Longview required the development of an extensive water control system. Over 15 miles of dikes were built surrounding the site to protect it from flood waters. A system of storm sewers and ditches was necessary to control a high level of ground water. Long, the president of the Long-Bell Lumber Company was determined that the new city would provide a home for the workers for his nearby lumber mills, thus encouraging a stable and contented work force. Long wanted his city to be much more than the typical mill towns on Puget Sound.

Once Longview was established, Long immediately set to work developing water and sewer systems with over 60 miles of pipe and 50 miles of sewers. Paved streets and alleys were constructed. Interested in advanced technology, Long used a number of modern innovations in completing his public works projects including dredges, on-site mobile concrete mixers and "new" hexagonal shaped, underwater cured concrete street panels. Of all of these early public works, Longview's water system is most unique.

Longview's water system progressed from its beginnings as a private developer project to a private utility and finally was placed under public ownership. The Long-Bell Corporation used public financing to pay for the new town's public works. In 1922 bonds were sold to finance improvements and an assessment was placed against each parcel of property benefiting from the improvements. In 1923 Long-Bell created the Longview Public Service Company to operate the electrical power, water and bus systems. ◆

Above and below: Early city reservoirs constructed of lumber.

Below: Hexagonal paved street.

Metro Seattle

The Municipality of Metropolitan Seattle (Metro) is a special-purpose government founded by citizens in 1958 to clean up Lake Washington and Elliott Bay water pollution problems. In 1972 Metro also assumed responsibility for providing public transportation in the Seattle-King County region. Today Metro is an agency with more than 4,000 employees. Its primary mission is to provide efficient wastewater treatment and public transportation for more than 1.5 million citizens.

Metro is governed by the 45-member Metropolitan Council with elected representatives from the governments of King County, Seattle, various smaller cities and sewer districts, and appointed representatives from unincorporated areas.

James R. Ellis, Seattle attorney, led the citizens' movement to create Metro. Ellis helped draft the legislation enabling the formation of municipal corporations or metropolitan governments to address regional problems like water pollution control and areawide planning. After Metro's formation, C. Carey Donworth became the Metro Council's first chairman in 1958 and Harold E. Miller the agency's first executive director in 1959.

Metro's development reflects the growth of the Seattle-King County region. As the population of the Puget Sound region has expanded, Metro has sought to provide more effective safeguards for water quality and ways to increase the effectiveness of public transit.

Water Quality—During the 1950s numerous small treatment plants could not adequately clean sewage coming from the growing number of homes in the Seattle-King County area. Sewage from these plants was discharged directly into Lake Washington, and raw sewage was discharged into Elliott Bay. The sewage fouled the water and caused swimming beaches to close during the summer months.

Soon after Metro was established in 1958, the Metro Council approved a 10 year water pollution control plan, which called for construction of new sewage treatment plants to replace 28 smaller, inefficient plants. By eliminating sewage discharged into Lake Washington and raw sewage discharged into Puget Sound, Metro produced dramatic results. In Lake Washington water that once was so dirty that one could see only two and one-half feet down is now clear enough to see through 20 feet. Swimming beaches opened, and people once again enjoyed water activities. Metro received worldwide recognition for its water pollution control efforts.

In July 1962, Metro took over operation of all treatment plants, major trunk sewers and pump stations within its boundaries. Under the comprehensive plan, Metro began building four wastewater treatment plants at Renton, West Point, Carkeek Park and Richmond Beach. Metro also took over operation of the City of Seattle's new sewage plant at Alki beach. In addition, Metro began building large interceptor sewer lines around Lake Washington, on the Duwamish River and along the city's waterfront.

Seattle Park Board President Waldo J. Dahl burning the sign that had kept people out of the water until Carkeek treatment plant opened in 1962.

The Metro system today includes four treatment plants serving a 680-square mile area. The system contains 255 miles of sewer pipeline, enough to stretch from Seattle to Port-

Top: The Renton Treatment Plant's expansion was completed in 1985.

Center: The West Point Treatment Plant is the largest treatment facility in the Pacific Northwest.

Bottom: Metro's Environmental Laboratory monitors and analyzes water quality data.

land. In 1985 Metro began a new program to upgrade its wastewater treatment system to secondary treatment. Metro and the City of Seattle are also developing plans to reduce greatly the combined sewer overflows into area waters. Metro hopes to achieve a 75 percent reduction in overflows during a 20 year period to meet new state Department of Ecology requirements. In 1986 Metro opened its new Environmental Laboratory to monitor and analyze environmental data for use in its regional comprehensive water quality plans.

Transit—Seattle-King County voters authorized a Metro operated countywide public transit system on September 19, 1972. In 1972 the Metro Council adopted a voter-approved comprehensive public transportation plan. The plan called for expanding and improving service to connect suburban and City of Seattle routes into one system. It also called for replacing the old and obsolete trolleys and

The Bellevue Transit Center, opened in 1985, is helping to meet growing transportation demand east of Lake Washington

buses, setting up a network of park-and-ride lots, passenger shelters, freeway express stations and high-capacity vehicle lanes for buses, vanpools and carpools. Metro began transit service in Seattle and King County on January 1, 1973.

During the next 20 years, Metro built new operating and maintenance bases, erected more than 1,250 passenger shelters, installed route information signs and expanded service throughout the region. Metro and the state Department of Transportation also built a system of 83 park-and-ride lots, enabling riders to park their cars outside major activity centers and board buses to their destinations. The first park-and-ride lots were opened in Auburn and Kent in 1977.

In 1978 Metro put into service high-capacity articulated buses. In addition, Metro worked with the DOT and local governments to develop a 66-mile network of high-occupancy vehicle lanes for buses, vanpools and carpools along freeways, arterials and highways. The bus is still the backbone of Metro's transportation system. The agency's fleet now includes 530 standard diesel buses, 351 articulated diesels, 109 standard trolley buses, 46 articulated trolleys and 236 articulated dual-power buses. Together these buses travel almost 38 million miles a year, service 247 routes and cover more than 4,800 route-miles.

In April 1978 the Metro Council adopted a transportation policy for elderly and disabled citizens, equipping buses with wheelchair lifts to make them fully accessible to all riders. In 1992 Metro had more than 970 lift-equipped buses operating on 569 routes.

Finally, Metro replaced an aging overhead trolley system and bought new trolley buses to run on the refurbished line. The rehabilitated trolley system, which began operating in 1980, now has 55 street miles of two-way overhead trolley wire. In 1986 Metro assumed ownership of Seattle's Waterfront Streetcar line along Elliott Bay. An extension to the system in 1990 connects the waterfront, Pioneer Square, the International District, Kingdome and Metro's downtown Seattle transit tunnel.

To meet the region's growing transportation demand, Metro has also built a network of transit centers to provide better service throughout King County. Transit centers provide convenient places for riders to transfer between buses. In 1985 Metro opened the first two centers—the Bellevue Transit Center and Aurora Village Transit Center in north King County. Metro's newest transit center opened in 1992 near the Northgate Shopping Mall.

Despite growth in travel demands outside downtown Seattle, the downtown area remains the region's most important activity center. That is why Metro and the U.S. government invested about $426 million in the Downtown Seattle Transit Project.

During rush hours, traffic clogs downtown Seattle as buses passing through the central business district are reduced to speeds averaging five miles per hour. With more than 80 percent of Metro's bus routes traveling through downtown Seattle daily, those slowdowns affected the general quality of bus service by making schedules unreliable.

To help remedy that problem, Metro built a 1.3-mile bus tunnel under Third Avenue and Pine Street. Five passenger stations, each designed to reflect the architecture of its neighborhood, serve the tunnel.

The tunnel, which opened in September 1990, moves people through downtown Seattle at speeds up to 30 miles per hour. That helps buses stay on schedule throughout Metro's service area, improving the efficiency and attractiveness of Metro bus service.

Beyond 1990, Metro and transit agencies in Pierce and Snohomish Counties are looking at ways to alleviate congestion in the region's major corridors and integrate transportation solutions for each corridor and downtown Seattle. ◆

Tunnel construction crew dismantling steel and wood tunnel liners at the Pioneer Square station.

Macaulay & Associates, Ltd.

Macaulay & Associates, Ltd. is a real estate appraisal firm established in Everett in 1962 and incorporated in 1969. Since 1975 the firm has prepared numerous special benefit/proportionate assessment studies for cities, counties and sewer districts ranging from the City of Blaine to Spokane County, and from Jefferson County to the City of Kennewick. Other clients include Pierce County, Metro and Seattle, Spokane, Redmond, Everett and Ocean Shores.

Charles R. Macaulay, MAI, President of Macaulay & Associates, Ltd. Photo courtesy of Marchand's.

The firm's studies involve recommending the LID/ULID boundaries and feasibility of projects, as well as an assessment to each ownership that is in proportion to the special benefit derived from the LID/ULID project. The firm is often retained as a consultant to establish the foundation for special benefits, explain theory and techniques of measuring special benefits, and present assessment recommendations at hearings. LID/ULID projects have involved street system improvements, sewer and water service, and problems which are challenging from a real estate valuation perspective such as landslides. The company's founder and staff have enjoyed working with many friends affiliated with firms providing engineering, bond counsel, financial and other expertise, as well as municipality staffs. ◆

Montgomery Watson

Montgomery Watson, established in 1945, has become one of the largest firms in the U.S. specializing in environmental engineering. The firm has a staff of over 2,300 engineers, scientists and technicians located in offices throughout the United States and overseas. Montgomery Watson has been active in the Pacific Northwest for over 15 years, with offices in Bellevue, Tacoma, Richland, Portland and Boise.

To support its basic engineering capability the firm provides in-house mechanical, structural, electrical, environmental, architectural, geological and chemical engineering services, as well as construction management, operation and maintenance services. Field support includes surveying and construction supervision. The firm has a very strong aquaculture and aquarium planning and design division. It has an EPA-approved water quality laboratory, a complete interactive computer network, and a computer-aided design system.

Montgomery Watson has completed several major projects for the Seattle Water Department, notably, the 32-million gallon Eastside Reservoir in Bellevue. The award-winning facility is the world's largest buried prestressed concrete water storage reservoir. Other Seattle Water Department projects include water quality studies, water treatment process pilot plant investigations and water treatment plant siting studies.

Montgomery Watson was retained by Pacific Power and Light Company to design a new trout hatchery for the Merwin Dam recreation complex. Merwin Dam, on the Lewis River, is a 60-year-old gravity arch dam. The hatchery will be the first to utilize disinfection by ozonation for control of pathogens as an original project component. ◆

Paul Eugene Meyer

Paul Eugene Meyer was born in Quincy, Illinois in 1900. He served in World War I immediately after high school. Following the war, he earned his B.S. degree in Engineering from the University of Washington in 1923, and began work in Grays Harbor County for the Hobi Timber company.

During the Depression when work in the woods came to a standstill, Meyer was hired by the federal government to serve as Civilian Engineer Supervisor for Camp Elma in the Civilian Conservation Corps, where he spearheaded many public works that stand today in the Olympic National Park. Using native materials, he designed a gigantic timber structure that served as Camp Elma's recreation hall and community center. Other projects included the Girl Scout Camp at Lost Lake and a ranger station atop a giant fir in the middle of rugged terrain.

As the economy improved, Paul Meyer was hired by the Weyerhaeuser Company to implement the northwest's first successful Clemens Tree Farm near Satsop—a pioneering operation which set the pattern for logged-off land reclamation.

Meyer spent World War II as Principal Civilian Engineer in the Army Engineer's office in Fort Lewis. He became the principal engineer at the McChord Field Office where he participated in implementing the base system for the Northwest. During this period he served as a Military Engineer Leader, and as President of the Puget Sound Chapter of the ASCE.

When he retired, his life of public service continued. A memorable contribution was to Pacific Lutheran University's rowing crews. He built docks, acquired boats, oars, and shellhouses, and coached. Since his death, the "M" cup used by the crew teams symbolizes the excellence he worked for in life. ◆

Mukilteo Water District

Mukilteo Water District is one of the oldest water Districts in the State of Washington. The District was established in 1920 by a vote of the people. Mukilteo is a picturesque community overlooking Puget Sound at Elliot Point and was the first county seat for Snohomish County.

The first water construction project for the District was in 1922 with the construction of a reservoir, pump station and 49,280 feet of main with a cost of $52,000. Today the District serves a rapidly expanding area in Snohomish County. The District provides service to 5,317 water accounts and 1510 sewer accounts. ◆

William Chester Morse

Born in 1874 in Evanston, Illinois, Chester Morse's first connection with the future public works of Seattle came when he homesteaded on the eastern shores of Cedar Lake, about 1892. This lake was to become the source of Seattle's water supply in 1901. In 1956 the lake was renamed Chester Morse Lake honoring his years of positive stewardship of the city's water resources.

Starting in 1908, as hydraulic engineer, Morse had complete charge of the regrading work that built the Rainier Avenue connection via Dearborn Street, the 12th Avenue steel bridge over Dearborn Street, and several hundred acres of the industrial south end tide flats which were filled to final grades.

After service in the United States and France during World War I, Chester Morse, as Chief Engineer for Puget Sound Bridge and Dredging Company, built the Rainier Avenue trunk sewer between 1919 and 1921. Another major project was the University of Washington stadium which was finished in 1920, exactly six months from date of start. Next Morse started the W. C. Morse Company, which designed and supervised construction of the Port Angles, La Conner, Bainbridge Island Country Club and Broadmoor water systems.

Appointed Seattle City Engineer in 1927, he was responsible for the design of the Diablo Dam on the Skagit River. He earlier served on the three member Engineer Consulting Board retained by the city to report on the hydro-electric power potential of the Skagit River. Their report has served as the continuing guideline for Seattle City Light's development of the Skagit as its primary source of electric energy.

In 1932 Governor Clarence D. Martin appointed Morse to the three member Columbia Basin Commission charged with reviewing the Bureau of Reclamation plans for construction of the Grand Coulee Dam, power house and the Columbia Basin irrigation project.

As Chairman of the Board of Public Works and Superintendent of Water for Seattle from 1938 until his death in 1949, he supervised construction of the Diablo Dam on the Skagit and negotiated the Cedar River Logging Agreement. This agreement enabled the city to acquire title to all privately owned timber lands in the watershed as those lands were logged off and to acquire Forest Service lands by exchange of City-purchased acreage outside the Watershed. These were major steps towards the eventual ownership and control of the entire watershed by the City of Seattle.

Chester Morse's dedication of talent, time, energy and creativity to fulfilling some of the area's major public works needs during his lifetime has left a valuable legacy for generations to come.

Roy W. Morse

A University of Washington Civil Engineering graduate, Roy W. Morse's start in public works was appraising water systems in cities and towns in Washington, Oregon and California.

Recruited by the Boeing Company in 1938 Morse worked as Administrative Engineer for 10 years. He resigned to accept the appointment of Seattle City Superintendent of Water, following his father William Chester Morse in that role. While Superintendent of Water from 1949 to 1955, major water transmission facilities to serve Seatac Airport and the Bellevue-Kirkland-Mercer Island areas were built. He instigated the land acquisition and development of the Tolt River water supply.

During 1955 to 1957, as Director of the Technical Staff for the Secretary of the Interior, he served on President Eisenhower's Committee on Water Resources which published the National Water Resources Policy Report in 1957.

Mayor Clinton appointed Morse City Engineer and Chairman of the Board of Public Works in 1957, the year when the difficult integration of Interstate 5 into Seattle's unusual pattern of sharply graded streets started. The narrow waist of Seattle's downtown presented challenges which were compounded by the opening of Seattle's World's Fair in 1962.

Major projects of the Board of Public Works completed during Morse's 14 years as Chairman included: generator units in the Ross Dam powerhouse on the Skagit, the Boundary Dam, powerhouse and transmission lines in Pend Oreille County; construction of the Opera House, the Coliseum, the Monorail and other permanent buildings for the 1962 World's Fair, the Tolt River Dam, reservoirs and water supply transmission lines, built to serve North Seattle, completed in 1961.

Morse has received a number of honors over his long and productive career including President and Honorary Membership of the National American Public Works Association, Director and President of the Washington chapter of APWA, ASCE Fellow, AWWA Life Member and the Fuller Awardee, ASCE Civil Government Awardee, and Honorary Member, Public Works Historical Society. ◆

Right: Chester Morse Lake.

Keith (Pat) Nevins

Pat Nevins began his career by earning degrees in math and civil engineering in Kansas while working for the Kansas State Highway Commission. In 1960 he went to work for John W. Smith Consulting Engineer and Associates.

In 1963 Mr. Nevins came to Washington, as Walla Walla's Assistant City Engineer. He became Director of Public Works and City Engineer for Moses Lake in 1965, and held the same position in Auburn from 1969 to 1985. Since 1985 Mr. Nevins has been the City Supervisor for Oak Harbor.

Mr. Nevins has served on the Board of Washington APWA and progressed through the chairs to become President in 1976. He also served as President of the Institute for Administrative Management for National APWA. Awards include the James Robertson Award (1981) and Public Works Leader of the Year (1982). He has served on the Island County Economic Development Council, on the Urban Arterial Board, on the Greater Oak Harbor Chamber of Commerce Board, and on the River Basin Coordinating Committee for King County. He is also a member of Washington Society of Professional Engineers National Society of Professional Engineers, and the American Society of Civil Engineers.

Mr. Nevins has written and lectured widely, and taught college level public works classes. ◆

John Ostrowski

In 1989 John Ostrowski was serving as the Vancouver Public Works Director and Past President of the Washington Chapter of APWA. He has worked for the Washington State Department of Transportation, the cities of Olympia and Vancouver, and Clark County.

Born in Milwaukee, Wisconsin, Mr. Ostrowski received a Bachelor of Civil Engineering degree from Marquette University in 1968. Upon graduation he went to work for the Washington State Highway Department where he worked on a variety of projects in the Seattle area. He worked for the City of Olympia from 1973 until 1978 with responsibility for design and construction of city streets, and the water and sewer Capital Improvement Program.

During his brief three years with Clark County as Assistant Public Works Director (1978-1981), he guided the preparation of a new Solid Waste Plan and a Master Sewer Plan, as well as establishing the joint city/county storm drainage utility in the Burnt Bridge Creek basin.

Since 1981 Mr. Ostrowski has been Public Works Director for the City of Vancouver. During that time, Vancouver's Water and Sewer system have been expanded and utilities have been put on a sound financial basis. The city street system has also undergone dramatic improvements.

In addition to APWA activities, Mr. Ostrowski is a past president of the City Engineers Association. He also served as co-chair of the Road Jurisdiction Committee, a task force established by the State Legislature to make recommendations on statewide roadway needs and revenue sources. Mr. Ostrowski and his wife Caroline have a son, Eric, and daughter, Angela. ◆

Oak Harbor

Until the 1950s Oak Harbor was a small farming community located on the northern portion of Whidbey Island. The town provided drinking water for its residents from three drilled wells. Storage was provided by a 125,000 gallon water tank in the middle of town. The U. S. Navy founded the Sea Plane Base nearby in the early 1940s. The base purchased its water from Anacortes via a Navy installed 10-inch transmission line from Fidalgo Island.

With the Navy base growing during the 1950s, things started to change in Oak Harbor. In 1954 the city drilled another well yielding 500 gallons per minute. In 1955 a new water reservoir was built on 850 Avenue East, with a storage capacity of 250,000 gallons, and sodium fluoride was added to the city water supply. During the 1960s four new wells were drilled, a 450,000-gallon reservoir was built on the west side of Oak Harbor.

At the beginning of the 1970s NAS Whidbey Island's water supply was determined to be insufficient. A plan was developed

to bring water from Fidalgo Island, approximately 15 miles away, to the air station via a 24-inch water transmission line. The project was undertaken as a Navy/city partnership, and the 24-inch main was installed parallel to the existing 10-inch line. Next the city built a pump station on the air base and connected

the city's distribution system to the new transmission line.

By this time, regulations on water quality were more stringent, and several of the city's wells contained excessive amounts of iron or hydrogen sulphate. With the availability of the new water supply, the city made a decision to abandon these wells and utilize the new supply.

In the 1970s the city built another storage tank on the west side of the city with a capacity of 2,000,000 gallons. A program was also instituted to replace older and undersized mains throughout Oak Harbor. In 1985 the city retained the firm of PEI Consultants to update the city's water Comprehensive Plan and prepare a model for computer use.

Oak Harbor constructed its first sewer system during the 1940s consisting of a piping network and septic tank on Pioneer Way. The effluent of this septic tank was discharged through a chlorination chamber into Oak Harbor Bay. This sewer system was a combined network of sanitary and storm sewers. In 1956 the first primary treatment plant was completed on 70 SW Street. After several overhauls and updates this plant was converted to a secondary plant (bio-filters) in 1978.

As Oak Harbor grew, this plant became overloaded. In 1987 the city negotiated with the Navy for use of the sewage lagoons on the seaplane base with the stipulation that the city would treat the wastewater from government properties. URS Consultants drafted plans to pump wastewater from the Oak Harbor plant to the lagoons on the base to alleviate the overload. The lagoons are now updated to accept the pumped wastewater. It is estimated the city has adequate wastewater treatment capacity to the year 2015. ◆

Pacific Northwest Section
American Water Works Association

In 1927 a small group of men interested in water issues met in the Portland Hotel, Portland, Oregon, and started the Pacific Northwest Section of the American Water Works Association (AWWA). A constitution was drawn up, bylaws established, and the first officers elected: Chairman, W. A. Kunig, Tacoma; Vice chairman, Ben S. Morrow, Portland; Directors Alex Lindsay, Spokane, and L. Murray Grant, Seattle; and Secretary-Treasurer, Kenneth Shibley, Seattle. Meeting in Portland with these first officers were Carl McClain from Eugene, Oregon, and Fred Sharkey from Wenatchee.

There were 90 participants registered for the first Section meeting held in Seattle during the spring of 1928. Presided over by Mr. Kunig, the conference program included discussions on a variety of topics: "Water Resources in the State of Washington,"

"Chlorination of Water Supplies in the Pacific Northwest," "Should the Water Superintendent Favor Consulting Service?" "Underground Water Resources in the Vicinity of Tacoma," "Legal Phases of Financing Municipal Water Systems in the State of Washington," "Design and Construction of a Three Million Gallon Covered Concrete Reservoir," and "Relation of Fire Service Protection to Growing Concentrations of Property Values." Sixty years later these topics are still relevant.

The Pacific Northwest Section—AWWA has grown with the region and currently has over 2,500 members led by a six-member Board of Trustees and four officers. The section has 35 active committees addressing such diverse concerns as water resource management, education, safety, and cross connection control. The officers and trustees are elected by the membership and the committees are appointed by the section chair. The members actively participate on committees and in the American Water Works Association national leadership. ◆

Pacific Water Works Supply

Pacific Water Works Supply, Washington's oldest waterworks supplier and destined to become the leading distributor of waterworks products in the Pacific Northwest, was founded in 1917 in Seattle's Arcade Building.

H. I. Miller started Pacific Water Works Supply (PWWS) as a sole proprietorship, selling various waterworks materials ranging from water meters to wood stave pipe. His work force consisted of one and one-half people, himself, "HI" as he was known, and a half-day office assistant. The office and warehouse in the old Arcade Building was a cozy 150-square feet, which was shared with a doll hospital.

By 1925 the business needed more space and the company moved to the Port of Seattle at the Atlantic St. dock: 1200-square feet and five employees. Also in 1925, C. J. Murray joined HI Miller, and the two eventually became partners. In 1940, again outgrowing their facilities, a move was made to 2900 First Avenue So.

In 1946, after almost 30 years of piloting the company, HI Miller decided to retire. He sold his interest in the company to his son, John H. L. Miller, who formed a partnership with C.J. Murray. In 1948 Miller and Murray opened the first branch/distribution yard of the company on Porter St. in Portland, OR. That branch, like the original Seattle location, soon outgrew its space and moved to Macadam St. Since 1976 the Portland branch has been located on McEwan St. in Lake Oswego.

John Miller became president in 1961, the year PWWS incorporated. He opened Pacific Water Work's main distribution center in Tacoma on 10 acres of land near the Port of Tacoma, 1691 Lincoln Ave. That distribution yard is the single

largest water works center in the U.S., and is dedicated to large stock inventories and quick-reacting delivery procedures. Over the past 10 years, with continued economic growth in the Pacific Northwest and continued successful operations at the Seattle, Portland, and Tacoma yards, Pacific Water Works Supply has established new branch/distribution yards in Woodinville, WA 1980; Pasco, WA 1985; Boise, ID 1988; Vancouver and Bellingham, WA 1991; Medford, OR, 1992; and Olympia, WA 1993. 1993 will also mark the relocation of the Seattle headquarters and the main distribution center in Tacoma. They will be combined into a major facility in Puyallup, WA. The Seattle warehouse will remain.

In June 1986, 40 years after he took over the leadership of the company from his father, John Miller retired as President of Pacific Water Works. He was succeeded by William A. "Bill" Davis, formerly vice-president of operations since 1980, and one of the driving forces in the success and expansion of the company in the 1980s. ◆

In 1940, in front of their new facility at 2900 First Avenue So., Seattle, are the Pacific Water Works founders and first employees. From left to right: Jerry Angie, Josephine Van Augustine, C. J. Murray, H. I. Miller, founder, Barbara Potter and John H. L. Miller. The dog is "Prince" of the night basement patrol. Photo courtesy Pacific Water Works Supply.

Pierce County

On December 22, 1852, the Oregon Territorial Legislature split Thurston County into Thurston and Pierce Counties. Pierce County was named for the newly elected President of the United States, Franklin Pierce. The county seat was first established in the Town of Steilacoom, and in 1880 it was relocated to Tacoma. John M. Chapman was the first County Surveyor, and the Pierce County Road Department was administered by the county surveyor from 1859 until 1907. In 1907 the department administration was changed to the County Engineer. Adolph Funke was the first County Engineer.

A major force in the early 1900s was the White family. David H. White was the County Surveyor from 1890 until 1893 and the County Engineer from 1914 until 1919. His son, Ernest A. White, was the County Engineer from 1919 until 1923 and again from 1939 until 1941. Ernest's son, Clint White, worked in various capacities from 1950 until 1974. Along with public surveying records, Pierce County was able to acquire the private survey records of David H. White from his estate after Mr. White, in his mid-90s, reportedly "died at his transit."

In 1918 Miss Verona M. Morgan became the first woman superintendent for a concrete highway contract in Pierce County. Miss Morgan, then 19 years old, acted as General Manager for the construction of Pacific Highway, from Tacoma to Camp Lewis. This was during the first World War.

William R. Thornton, P.E., was the first County Engineer in Pierce County to hold the title of Public Works Director, a position established in 1970. Mr. Thornton has the longest tenure of any Pierce County Engineer, serving for 14 years. Mr. Thornton was instrumental in forming sanitary sewer ULID 73-1, one of the largest sewer projects in the state. During Mr. Thornton's tenure as Public Works Director, many projects were

Above: Pierce County Survey Team Circa 1918

Below: Pierce County loader and truck, May 2, 1917.
(Photos courtesy of Pierce County Public Works)

Anderson Island Ferry Landing—Waiting facility and Park 'N Ride. Courtesy Pierce County Public Works.

completed including numerous road and bridge projects, major river improvement projects, purchase of the ferryboat "Steilacoom" of Pierce County, and construction of a new equipment maintenance facility.

Frederick L. Anderson, P.E., became Public Works Director/County Engineer in 1983 and led Public Works through the transition to the charter form of county government. Three years later he was named the Urban County Engineer of Washington State, and went on to receive the prestigious National Urban County Engineer Award in 1986. In a major restructuring of county government, Pierce County Executive Joe Stortini appointed Mr. Anderson Executive Director of Operations in 1987.

In 1990, the responsibilities of Public Works Director and County Engineer were separated, and John O. Trent, P.E. was appointed Public Works Director after having served as Assistant Public Works Director and County Engineer since 1986. Mr. Trent has been instrumental in development of the first community-based Transportation Plan, provided coordination with growth management planning, and implemented the Surface Water Management Plan.

Mr. Thomas G. Ballard, P.E. was appointed County Engineer in 1990 having previously served as Traffic Engineer. Mr. Ballard oversees all road and bridge engineering and maintenance functions and is responsible for 1835 miles of county roads, 161 bridges, over 100 traffic signals, 50,000 signs and the county ferry operation.

Pierce County Public Works currently is responsible for the following functions: roads, surface water, survey, equipment rental, river improvement, and administrative services. ◆

Left to right: W. R. Thornton, P.E., John O. Trent, P.E., and Frederick L. Anderson, P.E., Pierce County Public Works Directors (Courtesy Pierce County Public Works)

Parsons Brinckerhoff

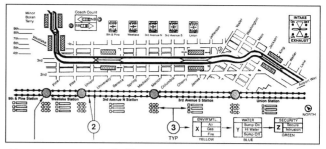

Parsons Brinckerhoff Quade & Douglas, Inc. has made major contributions to the public works of Puget Sound. Among those of which the company is the most proud are the West Seattle Freeway Bridge Replacement, Hood Canal Bridge Replacement, and the Downtown Seattle Transit Project. ◆

Below: For the City of Seattle, Parsons Brinckerhoff, in joint venture, provided engineering and design services for a replacement bridge for the northern bascule bridge of the West Seattle Freeway which was severely damaged in 1978 by a ship collision. The high level six lane main bridge span carries the freeway across the west waterway of the Duwamish River providing 140 feet of vertical clearance for marine traffic. Photo courtesy Parsons Brinckerhoff.

Above: Parsons Brinckerhoff has provided design and engineering services for Seattle's innovative bus-subway system—the first U. S. transit system to utilize dual-propulsion electric and diesel buses. The system includes a 1.3 mile tunnel under downtown Seattle and five transit stations—three underground and two above ground. Photo courtesy Parsons Brinckerhoff.

Below: For the Washington State Department of Transportation, Parsons Brinckerhoff, in joint venture, designed a replacement for the western half of the 1.5 mile Hood Canal Bridge—the world's only floating bridge that spans a tidal waterway—after its westerly half was destroyed by a violent storm in February 1979. The bridge is a key transportation link between Seattle, Washington and the Kitsap and Olympic Peninsulas. Photo courtesy Parsons Brinckerhoff.

Jack N. Pittis

Mr. Pittis is currently the Director of Public Works for the City of Port Angeles, where he is responsible for streets, water, sewer, solid waste, equipment services, engineering and building permits.

Mr. Pittis was the City Engineer for the City of Mount Vernon 1976-80, where he designed and managed the downtown improvement project, new city maintenance shops and revisions to the city's comprehensive land use plan, zoning code and subdivision ordinances. Prior to Mount Vernon, Mr. Pittis worked as project engineer for the City of Seattle designing sanitary sewers and storm drains, as well as in the development of the initial critical path scheduling system used by the Engineering Department.

Mr. Pittis received a B.S. in Civil Engineering from Washington State University in 1969, where he was active in the student chapter of the American Society of Civil Engineers. Mr. Pittis credits his interest in Civil Engineering to his father, Bill, who was a Civil Engineer for the Corps of Engineers.

Other interests include APWA, where he served as the 1990 President of the Washington State Chapter. He is a charter member and past President of the City Engineer's Association of Washington, was appointed to the Urban Arterial Board and the Transportation Improvement Board, and is actively involved in the Association of Washington Cities. ◆

Port Angeles

Shortly after its incorporation, the municipality of Port Angeles, Washington, created Local Improvement Districts (LIDs) for the purpose of accomplishing major public works projects needed by the expanding town. The first LID in Port Angeles was established in December 1890, under the direction of City Engineer W. H. Aubury, for the purpose of improving Front Street—filling, grading and building sidewalks on both sides of the roadway. The city's early public works projects were contracted out to a number of local companies including P. A. Construction and Concrete Company, George Mangano, Owens Bros., Angeles Gravel & Supply, and Western Utilities.

The 1960s marked Port Angeles undertaking its biggest public works projects to date. LID 198 was created in the southern portion of the city. Most of this land had been annexed early in the decade and needed extensive public works including streets, alleys, curbs and sidewalks, and water and sewer lines. In 1967 construction of the wastewater collection and treatment system was begun under the direction of John Warder, Director of Public Works and Ken Rodocker, Plant Superintendent. Teeples & Thatcher Contractors, Inc. were the project general contractors, Harold Kaeser Construction Company was the general contractor for the interceptor sewers, and McCray Marine

Street project, 1914. Front St., looking west. Planking street after filling.

Company general contractor for the outfall. The project cost $2.4 million.

The 1970s was marked by many new projects under the direction of David Flodstrom, Director of Public Works. One of the most significant projects was developing a new water source for the city. A lawsuit between the city and the Washington Department of Social and Health Services prompted the City to shift from Morse Creek to the Elwha River for its water source. Financial support from Washington Futures Referendum 27 and the Economic Development Administration permitted the project to be completed by July 1978, at a total cost of $3.3 million.

With a combination of grants from the federal and state development funds, citizens' bond issues and contributions from other public and private agencies, Civic Field and a waterfront park were developed. At a total cost of a little over $1 million the city-owned athletic field was renovated and a new stadium constructed. The municipal pier and waterfront park cost $2.5 million and provides fishing, public moorage, public beach access, rest rooms and a public meeting place.

The most recent project to date is the construction of the new City Hall, under the city's Master Plan which includes beautifying the area with adjoining parks and recreation facilities. This project was realized under the direction of Jack N. Pittis, Director of Public Works and cost $2.8 million. ◆

City of Pullman

Early settlers had populated Whitman County by the mid-1860s. By 1881 the present townsite of Pullman had been platted and named. Pullman was incorporated in April 1888, when the population was approximately 300. To fulfill the need for a public water supply the city leaders drilled a well in 1884. Their efforts were rewarded with an artesian well yielding sweet pure water. By 1892, the young municipality had developed a public water distribution system.

By 1912 a new system of cast iron and steel pipe had replaced the original construction. Throughout the 20th century an ongoing program of systematic replacement and extension of the original distribution system has been followed as new wells and reservoirs have been constructed to keep pace with the growth of the city. Points of major expansion were in 1935, Sunny Hill Reservoir and Well No. 1; 1947-51, Pioneer Tank No. 2, Landis Reservoir; 1957-59, Pioneer Reservoir No. 4, Sunnyside Standpipe No. 5, Military Hill Standpipe No. 6; 1968-72, High School Standpipe No. 7 and North Campus Heights Standpipe No. 8.

Treatment of wastewater has a similar history in Pullman. The City of Pullman assumed responsibility for maintaining community health and sanitation in the early 1900s with the construction of a large septic tank and drainfield north of town along Guy Street, adjacent to the south fork of the Palouse River.

Population in the early 1920s was approximately 5,700. As the town and college developed in the 1920s the sewage flows increased until in 1922 the city contracted with C. H. Green Consultants of Spokane to design a new treatment facility.

The Imhoff tanks and outfall sewer project was completed in 1925, at a cost of $53,773. The cost was shared by the City of Pullman (50.166 percent) and Washington State University (49.834 percent).

The next wastewater treatment improvement occurred in the late 1940s and was brought on by post World War II growth. In 1948, Joe Lundberg Construction Company was contracted to build a new trickling filter secondary treatment plant at the current plant site. It was completed in 1949 at a cost of approximately $250,000.

By 1964 the total population for the City of Pullman and WSU was 15,600. The wastewater treatment system was no longer adequate. In May of 1964 a bid from SCEVA Construction Company of Spokane for $432,000 was accepted for modifying the plant by additional aeration, thickening, new headworks, digestor mixing, chlorination facilities and a new control building and laboratory. The city and WSU shared the cost of the project—60 percent City of Pullman, and 40 percent WSU. A federal grant was obtained to underwrite $160,000 of the cost.

Further improvements were made to the treatment plant in response to the 1972 Federal Water Pollution Control Act. A master facilities plan was adopted in 1977. Construction began in 1983 under the direction of City Engineer Jim Hudak. Completed two years later by Humphery Construction Company of Woodinville, the new facility cost $6.7 million. The cost sharing agreement was similar to the 1925 agreement with the city covering 54.6 percent and WSU 45.4 percent.

For over 60 years the City of Pullman and Washington State University have amicably shared the cost of providing high quality public utilities. This cordial relationship is expected to continue as the needs of the community change. ◆

Preston Thorgrimson Shidler Gates & Ellis

Jim Ellis, Partner

In 1985, 90-year-old Frank Preston joined a group from the law firm of Preston, Thorgrimson, Ellis and Holman, as it was then known, on an exciting tour of the unfinished Columbia Seafirst Center. The group rode up the side of the building in a "cage" to the 75th floor which had no walls and was edged only with a small cable. Mr. Preston walked boldly to the very edge and proceeded to give an impromptu geographical history of the firm in Seattle. Urging the party toward the edge, he pointed to all of the office locations in the history of the firm: the Pioneer Building, 1912, the Northern Life Tower, 1929, the IBM Building, 1964. Mr. Preston was incredibly excited about the view and obviously proud of where the firm had been and where it was going. Unfortunately, Mr. Frank Preston died that May and did not move to the Columbia Seafirst Center with the firm in September 1985.

Preston Thorgrimson Shidler Gates & Ellis is the oldest continuously practicing law firm in the City of Seattle. Harold Preston, Frank Preston's father, began it all in 1883. In 1890 the first partnership was formed and the firm was known as McBride, Preston, Carr and Preston. The partners were Harold Preston, his younger brother Clarence, their brother-in-law, E. M. Carr and Henry McBride, the former Governor of the State of Washington. The firm had two locations at this time, one in the Pioneer Building at First Avenue and James Street, the other in Mount Vernon.

In 1891 McBride left the firm and the name changed to Preston, Carr and Preston; and in 1894, when Gilman became a partner, the name was changed to Preston, Carr and Gilman. Carr moved to Alaska as U. S. Commissioner in Fairbanks, and Clarence Preston retired, leaving Harold Preston to practice alone until 1912.

In 1912 Harold Preston formed a partnership with O. B. Thorgrimson and opened new offices at 605 Lowman Building. Leander T. Turner became a partner in 1917; the name became Preston, Thorgrimson and Turner, and the office was moved to larger quarters at 911 Lowman Building.

In 1929 the office was moved to the twentieth floor of the newly opened Northern Life Tower. In this same year Frank Preston, Harold Preston's son, became a partner and principal trial lawyer of the firm, and Charles Horowitz joined the firm as an associate. He and Albert E. Stephan became partners in the firm in 1934, and the name changed to Preston, Thorgrimson, Turner, Horowitz and Stephan. Charles Horowitz remained with the firm for 40 years until 1969, when he became a member of the newly formed Court of Appeals, Division 1, in Seattle. He remained a Judge of that court until he was elected to the State Supreme Court in 1975. Justice Horowitz served as counsel with the firm and was its chief historian until his death in March 1989. Justice Horowitz recalled that during the 1929 stock market crash and Great Depression, legal services were traded for fresh fruit, which was shared with the staff.

In 1941 billing rates went from pounds of fruit per hour to $7.50 per hour. That same year Stephan left the firm and the name was changed to Preston, Thorgrimson, Horowitz and Turner. The retirement of Turner in 1948 changed the name to Preston, Thorgrimson and Horowitz.

Variations of the firm name since 1958 are Preston, Thorgrimson, Horowitz, Starin, Ellis & Holman (1969 to 1972); Preston, Thorgrimson, Ellis Holman & Fletcher (1972 to 1979); Preston, Thorgrimson, Ellis and Holman (1979 to 1989); and Preston Thorgrimson Shidler Gates & Ellis (1990-present)..

The firm's present name is the result of what is perhaps the biggest change it has undergone, the merger with the firm of Shidler McBroom Gates & Lucas, which became effective January 1, 1990. The merger with Shidler strengthened the firm's corporate and environmental/land use practices and made the firm Seattle's fourth largest. In addition, the merger gave the firm a presence on the rapidly growing East side with the Bellevue office. The firm had opened other branch offices in the 70s and 80s: Washington, D.C. (1973), Anchorage (1979), Spokane (1981), Portland (1982), Tacoma (1989), and Coeur d'Alene (1992).

The firm has truly expanded since its early days in the Pioneer Building and a branch office in Mount Vernon. It progressed to a modest sized Seattle firm specializing in municipal finance and has now developed into a dynamic Northwest enterprise serving a wide array of both regional and national public sector clients. The firm's clients now include not only a large number of municipalities and other governmental entities, but an even larger number of private sector clients engaged in a broad range of commercial endeavors including real estate, broadcasting, banking, international trade, transportation, timber, energy, health care and high technology.

In all, 240 attorneys and 400 staff worked in the firm's seven offices in 1992. The entire staff continues to be committed to the highest degree of professionalism in the representation of its clients and is committed to the maintenance of an informal, flexible and congenial atmosphere. ◆

A "rite of passage" for new partners was to climb Mt. Rainier in the yearly partners' climbing retreat.

City of Redmond

The days of poling barges down the Sammamish River and carting goods along the river trails were over by the time Redmond was incorporated in 1912. Good roads were needed by this growing commercial hub of the Sammamish Valley. With a source of revenue created by incorporation, the community leaders immediately turned to public works projects. In the first year a total of $300 was, in fact, allocated for maintaining the city's five streets. Cleveland and Leary Streets, having curbs and gutters, were clearly defined but most were rough and built for a specific need. For example, the Corduroy Road which had logs placed across the roadway at water level to support the heavy timbers being hauled to the Sammamish Slough.

From this simple beginning, the contemporary City Street Department maintains 111 miles of roadway within the city's fourteen square miles. Puget Sound Traction, Light and Power Company, later Puget Power, proposed a trolley system in 1913. This system was not be built. However in 1913 the company was granted permission to maintain poles for electrical wires and the sale of electric current.

Vying with roads was the need for a reliable water supply for a town surrounded by water and built over a shallow aquifer. A series of ordinances created the first town water supply from Perrigo's Springs west of Avondale Road. The system included two acres and a 180,000 gallon reservoir behind Dam No. 1. Water was brought to town through an eight-inch wooden water main. Its iron replacement was used until 1959. All told the original system cost $13,000.

Individual residential water meters were installed in 1925 at $2.25 each. This was at a time when major metropolitan areas like New York were still on master meters. Some of these meters can still be found in the old section of Redmond. Today, the utility is replacing mechanical meters with "touch-read" computer-compatible meters.

Redmond has had supplementary water sources since 1926 when S. J. Humes engineered two small dams on Seidel Creek. Beginning in 1951 a series of five wells were constructed. Four of them remain in service in 1989 and provide approximately 50 percent of the water carried to Redmond's population. The rest of the supply comes through interties and agreements with Seattle and Bellevue, including the multi-million dollar Tolt River pipeline. Concealing water storage tanks within the city has presented a design challenge, met in one case by burying a four million gallon tank and placing a tennis court on top of it.

Over the decades occasional droughts have created water shortages. In 1916 stiff fines were levied against citizens engaged in unauthorized watering, and tolling the fire bell halted all outside water use. In contrast, citizens responded to the 1987

drought and to 1992's cutailments with voluntary cutbacks.

Municipal sewers first proposed in 1939 became a reality in 1955, when the city began operating its own treatment plant that dumped into a lagoon. METRO and Redmond agreed to abandon the lagoon in 1965 in favor of using the existing Lake Hills Sewer District disposal plant. The lagoon site was redeveloped into the Luke McRedmond Landing Park. Today, as part of METRO, Redmond enjoys sewer rates in the lowest twenty-five percent of municipal sewer rates.

The low, wet geography of the valley often meant flooding during winter and summer storms. The 100 year storm that hit the area in January 1986, provided the final push to create a Public Works Division to develop and coordinate miles of storm drain ditch and pipe needed to control flooding.

In the days of Old Redmond city services, including machine maintenance and inspections, were housed in the Fire Station at NE 79 Street. As the need for more space arose, Lester Jones, the building inspector, designed additions to Town Hall. Along with the usual municipal activities, Redmond has operated the 2.14 acre Community Cemetery since 1969. All of these operations are under the direction of the Public Works Director.

Some of Redmond's early municipal administrators were colorful and resourceful. F. A. Reil undoubtedly wins the prize for holding municipal positions. From 1913 to 1919 he served as Mayor. In the following years he progressively worked his way through the positions of Water Collector, Deputy Marshall, Police Judge, Water Superintendent, and Superintendent of Streets. A Town Engineer was hired at ten dollars a day in 1925 to estimate costs for sidewalk improvements on Leary Way. However, it was not until 1956, that the office of Town Engineer was created.

Since 1970 a variety of major public works projects have modified the face of Redmond. Two significant projects helped promote the commercial growth of the city and helped ease the immediate access problems across the Sammamish Slough. First, the NE 85 Street Bridge was constructed across the slough to the Willows Industrial Area. Second, the railroad bridge was raised to allow bigger trucks to pass under. Recent activities, including the five million dollar Avondale project, improved traffic north and south along the valley from Highway 520.

In the late 1980s the citizens approved $12 million to fund a Municipal Campus Project which provides the community with a senior center, a new public safety building to house finance and police operations, and renovations to City Hall. The buildings share a new landscaped common green. After seventy-five years of public works activity Redmond continues to work to provide its citizens with a safe, healthy and attractive place to live. ◆

City of Richland

The City of Richland sprang from humble roots during the late 1800s and early 1900s with a handful of people who scratched a living from the soil. The area was primarily a farming and ranching community lying along the banks of the Columbia River. With the advent of World War II and the "Manhattan Project," the history of Richland, southeastern Washington, and the world, was to be significantly changed forever.

On November 18, 1942, the E. I. DuPont de Nemours & Company, Inc., and the Manhattan District of the U. S. Army Corp of Engineers agreed to tackle the construction of the Hanford Engineer Works (a nuclear plant) on the 600 square mile, 400,000 acre parcel of semi-arid desert in Benton County. On February 23, 1943, the U. S. District Court in Spokane ordered possession by the Federal Government (a form of condemnation) of all land commonly known as Richland, Hanford and White Bluffs.

On March 20, 1943, with a population base of 240 people, the design for a new Richland was begun by DuPont, who was the prime government contractor. The new city design and layout included housing, streets, utilities, schools and commercial facilities. By the end of 1945, 4,000 homes were completed.

During the construction phase of both the plant called "Hanford Engineer Works," and the new City of Richland, approximately 51,000 people were employed, and lived and

Goethals Drive — Mansfield Street

"Old" Richland Shops complex shows three warehouses in the foreground; maintenance shop (hangar building), tire storage building, and fertilizer storage building are visible behind warehouses.

worked in the vicinity of Richland, Hanford and White Bluffs. The original owners of the farmland were removed. Because of the high security required, the only people allowed to live in Richland were those working for the U. S. government, the prime contractor, or one of the private businesses that operated within the city. The maintenance of utilities, streets, commercial facilities and residences was done by DuPont, who was also the landlord. There was no municipal government in Richland until December 10, 1958, when Richland became a first-class city in the State of Washington with a population of 22,790. Until that time, Richland literally was a company, i.e. Federal government, town.

Aerial photo of new Richland Shops-Warehouse complex completed in January 1998 at a cost of $15 million. Located west of Yakima River (left) and north of I-182 in Richland.

CITY OF
RICHLAND

On June 12, 1957, the residential and commercial properties were offered for sale by the Atomic Energy Commission. The Commission had also set aside funds for the new city. These funds were to be used for a hospital, street improvements, city hall, water meters, fire station and library. They also covered replacement of water and sewer lines, and the equipment necessary to maintain them.

During the latter part of 1957 and early 1958, the new city assumed the ownership and maintenance of all the public utilities, electrical, water, sewer and refuse, under the leadership of a newly elected City Council, City Manager and his staff. On September 5, 1963, a new water treatment plant and pumping facilities went into operation at a cost of $2,115,000. Richland's largest building, the Federal Building, was dedicated by Senator Warren Magnuson.

From 1958 to the present, many of the streets have been refurbished with curbs, gutters and sidewalks. Most vacant land within the original city limits has been improved with new commercial and residential development. The original incorporated area of Richland in 1958 was 10 square miles and today it encompasses approximately 35 square miles.

Many old World War II water and sewer mains and streets have been and continue to be replaced utilizing the LID financing mechanism. A new sewer treatment plant was put into operation in 1986 at a cost of $33 million. Parks, which occupy approximately 25 percent of the incorporated area, have been improved with playfields, and athletic and recreational facilities for the enjoyment of all residents. Shopping centers within the city limits have been developed and many new commercial facilities, such as hotels, motels, banks, retail stores, office space, a modern hospital and new churches have been built.

Richland, which started as a small farming community of 240 people in 1943, has risen to a first class city of approximately 13,500 residences and a population of 33,550 today. ◆

Sahlberg Equipment, Inc.

Armed with 14 years of experience in construction equipment sales, a desire to succeed and his son at his side, A.J. Sahlberg Sr.'s two-man operation was destined to flourish. In less than 40 years the firm has grown to include four locations and 70 employees, and is one of the most respected construction equipment dealerships in the country.

It's 1950, the economy is booming and A. J. (Jack Sr.) Sahlberg, Sr. and his son A. J., Jr. (Jack Jr.) have just moved from Portland to Seattle. For the past 14 years Jack Sr. had been working for a construction equipment dealership and was well respected in the industry. Once back in Seattle he was approached by a construction equipment manufacturing company to take on their line. Jack Sr. took the opportunity to start his own company.

The country was busy building interstates, state and county roads. Sahlberg Equipment, Inc. was busy selling rock crushing equipment, pug mills and asphalt paving equipment to help complete these roads. The majority of Sahlberg's business revolved around the state, counties, municipalities and contractors. This was because Sahlberg sold only the best equipment available at competitive prices and serviced on a timely basis, everything it sold.

In the mid-1960s the Safety Supply Division was created, offering traffic safety, vehicle lighting, light equipment and construction supplies to states and municipalities. Heavy construction and safety salesmen were assigned to meet the specific needs of various governments.

Sahlberg Equipment covered the entire state of Washington for most of the lines it distributed. As the company grew, so did the need for a full service branch in eastern Washington. In 1967 the Spokane branch was opened. New road construction was nearing completion in the late 1960s. Maintenance, rehabilitation and repair were now the main focus of counties and municipalities, and Sahlberg answered their need by expanding its line to include street sweepers, sewer maintenance equipment, brooms, snow plows, mowers, utility graders and rollers.

In 1970 Jack Sahlberg, Jr. opened the third full service branch in Anchorage. Having grown up in the business, John and

June 10, 1968; left to right Rex Russell, A.J. Sahlberg Sr., Paul Madnis, John Randall, Joe Ralph, Tom Horswell.

Bob Sahlberg, Jack Jr.'s sons, took an active part in the company beginning in the mid-1970s. Starting on the ground level and working in every aspect of the business, John and Bob were being groomed to continue the company name and uphold it's reputation. With three generations actively involved in Sahlberg Equipment, John and Bob were able to learn from and consult with their father and grandfather. With over 40 years of experience to draw from, the younger Sahlbergs could have had no finer training.

Sahlberg Equipment was experiencing tremendous growth in the eighties due to an on-going commitment to professionalism, quality equipment, follow up and service coupled with a strong Northwest economy. In 1987 Sahlberg Equipment saw a changing of the guard, as Jack Sahlberg Sr. passed away in December of that year. He was active in the day-to-day operation of the company up to one year before his death at age 91.

In 1988 John and Bob ventured into a new state, opening another full service branch in Portland, Oregon. Active in the Washington Chapter of the American Public Works Association since the mid-fifties, Sahlberg Equipment boasts three members, Jack, John and Bob. To stay informed about the government needs, Sahlberg Equipment always has representation at the National American Public Works Association Conferences.

In 1992, Sahlberg Equipment, Inc. moved to their new headquarters in Kent Washington, giving them better parts and service facilities for many years to come.

Armed with 42 years of experience in the construction equipment industry and an outstanding reputation, Sahlberg Equipment is looking forward to serving Washington State, its counties and cities for the next 100 years. Sahlberg Equipment, Inc. salutes Washington State's Centennial. ◆

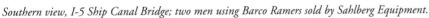

Southern view, I-5 Ship Canal Bridge; two men using Barco Ramers sold by Sahlberg Equipment.

SAHLBERG EQUIPMENT INCORPORATED
SEATTLE • SPOKANE • ANCHORAGE • PORTLAND

Sammamish Plateau Water and Sewer District

Sammamish Plateau Water and Sewer District, established in 1948, was the 82nd water district formed in King County. It was created to improve water quality and reduce seasonal fluctuations in the area's shallow wells. The driving force behind the formation of the District was a poultry farmer named Oscar Freed, who was elected as one of the District's first commissioners and served until his retirement in 1978.

The District grew very slowly during its first 20 years, reaching 200 customers in 1969. Significant subdivision activity began that year with the platting of Pine Lake Highlands, followed by Pine Lake Heights. The subdivisions resulted in the District's first sewer. A six-inch diameter sewer line was constructed by a developer diagonally across Lake Sammamish State Park, and up the hill to the subdivision. It was built without benefit of District review, approval or inspection. When the developer asked the District to assume ownership of the facility, it declined. Since the developer could not build homes without District ownership, he sued, and the District was forced into the sewer business. It owned a utility it knew little about and which was constructed using questionable standards. The sewer failed many times until it was replaced in 1984.

A period of very rapid growth occurred in 1977-78, followed by another beginning in 1983. Today the District encompasses about 24 square miles, with over 165 miles of water lines and over 50 miles of sewer pipelines. In 1987, the District name was changed to Sammamish Plateau Water and Sewer District. Located in an area subject to significant growth and development, its continued growth and expansion is anticipated. ◆

Duane Scroggins

Duane Scroggins is a native of Springfield, Oregon, and a graduate of Oregon State University. He is a past Chapter President of the Oregon Chapter, APWA. He began his municipal public works career in San Leandro, California, where he was Senior Engineer. After 10 years, Scroggins and his family returned to Oregon. For four years he was Public Works Director of Roseburg, and then Medford for seven years.

After five years of private practice in Roseburg, he accepted appointment as Public Works Director in Walla Walla in 1983. His first task was to replace the City's 15 mile water transmission line from the City's Mill Creek Watershed to distribution reservoirs. He facilitated a power sale contract and provided for installation of a two megawatt hydroelectric facility that will provide revenue to repay bonds. Other tasks include the first TIB Project in Washington, advanced wastewater treatment plant and regional landfill facilities.

Duane has been active in the APWA in three states, is a fellow in the ASCE and member of the AWWA and WPCF as well as registered professional engineer in the states of Washington, Oregon, California and Alaska. He resides in Walla Walla with his wife, Dot, two daughters Darla and Darinda, and son David. ◆

Walter W. Saxton

Walter W. Saxton received his Bachelor of Civil Engineering from the University of Washington in 1944 and later did graduate study in hydraulics under a fellowship in Sanitary Engineering at the University. Following graduation he served in World War II as a Civil Engineer officer in the Navy.

For 10 years Saxton worked for the Pollution Control Commission, rising to the position of Chief Engineer. In 1959 he became an Associate in the firm of Stevens & Thompson. He was project engineer for the first Green Lake Rehabilitation Program (1961-1962).

In 1962 Saxton joined John P. Esvelt, a Spokane structural engineer to form the partnership of Esvelt & Saxton. During the ensuing 10 years the municipal engineering discipline under Saxton completed more than 400 projects, including both municipal and industrial facilities in wastewater collection, treatment and disposal, water supply and storage, and storm drainage systems for clients in eastern Washington, northern Idaho and western Montana. Saxton served as Project Director for the development of a Master Plan for separation of storm drainage from the sanitary sewers for the City of Spokane.

The partnership dissolved in 1972 due to John Esvelt's ill health. Saxton reorganized the municipal engineering part of the firm as Saxton & Kennedy, Inc. This firm later merged with two other Washington firms to form Futrell-Redford-Saxton, Inc., a subsidiary of Envirodyne International. After nearly three years in the Middle East, Saxton terminated his relationship with Envirodyne in 1977, and joined the staff of CH2M HILL as Project Manager in St. Louis with subsequent assignments in Milwaukee, Alexandria (Egypt), and Calgary (Alberta, Canada).

Wearying of the gypsy life of a project manager, Saxton left CH2M HILL to settle in Seattle, taking a consulting position with the Washington Municipal Research & Services Corporation. For three and a half years he was available to all 266 incorporated cities in the state, providing advice and counsel on municipal infrastructure problems. He spent his last year before retiring in 1988 as Instructor in Engineering in the Technical Education Division of South Seattle Community College.

Saxton is a past President and Life Member of the Pacific Northwest Pollution Control Association, and in 1975 received the Water Pollution Control Federation's Bedell Award for meritorious service. He is a Fellow and Life Member of the American Society of Civil Engineers, a Life Member of the American Waterworks Association, and Life Member of the American Academy of Environmental Engineers. He has been a member of the Washington Chapter of APWA since 1963, becoming a Life Member in 1989. ◆

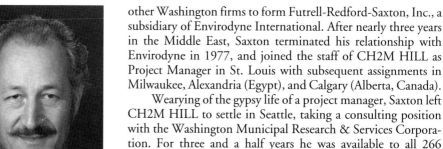

COMPREHENSIVE STUDY FOR GRANT COUNTY WASHINGTON 1965

ESVELT & SAXTON AND REISNER ASSOCIATES
CONSULTING ENGINEERS & PLANNERS
SPOKANE & SEATTLE, WASHINGTON

June Rosentreter Spence

June Rosentreter Spence has functioned as the Manager of the Administrative Division/ Public Works Contract Officer for the City of Vancouver. Combining public works experience with an interest in the problems of municipal management, she could be described as a "Renaissance Woman" in the public works profession.

Ms. Spence has been in the center of a series of sweeping changes that have taken place in Vancouver's Public Works Department. Her own contributions to that change have been recognized not only in Vancouver but also by her peers in the profession. She was the first woman to serve as President of the Washington Chapter of APWA, as well as the first woman to serve on the APWA Executive Board as Region IX Director, and in 1986 was elected to the top office in the organization, President of National APWA.

Ms. Spence's early achievements in Vancouver's Public Works Department grew out of a concern that engineers were spending valuable time performing tasks that could be handled more cost-effectively by the staff. In 1972, she set up a word processing system—the city's first experiment in office automation—to speed up the processing of construction specifications and contracts. She also established a records management system which eliminated much of the duplication in files.

Building on these successes, Ms. Spence consolidated many of the previously separate elements of contract administration. Under this program, the engineering staff prepared specifications and monitored construction progress, while Ms. Spence's staff handled the various legal and administrative requirements of approximately five million dollars in public works contracts each year.

Impressed with the savings that had taken place in the Public Works Department, in 1977 the City Manager directed that these services be available city wide through the creation of the Administrative Division. Working under the motto "We can do anything!" Ms. Spence's team took on central services, established centralized dictation and word processing (with satellite word processing stations in other departments), as well as contract administration and other support services targeted to public works. Ms. Spence also served as coordinator for handicapped requirements and minority business enterprise liaison officer. She was instrumental in establishing a one-stop citizen service center in the City Hall lobby.

Ms. Spence's varied interests are reflected in the broad scope of her activities. She served on the Disaster Preparedness Committee dealing specifically with the Mount St. Helens eruption, and chaired the Solid Waste and Program Committees of APWA's Washington Chapter.

Her excellent work has won her numerous awards over the years. In 1978 she received the Washington Chapter APWA distinguished James Robertson Award in recognition of outstanding service in the field of public works. In 1990, the Washington Chapter instituted an annual June Rosentreter Spence award to be given the man or woman who has done the most during the past year to reorganize, promote, encourage and support women and minorities' involvement in public works. ◆

San Juan County

San Juan County did not become part of the United States until 1872, 19 years after Washington Territory was established. San Juan County is one of the most unique of all the counties in Washington. Washington State Ferries serve the four main islands as roads to the rest of the world. It is necessary to use airplanes, private boats or the State Ferry System for transporting materials or personnel to the area from the mainland, or even between the islands within the county.

The county has three District Road Foremen; George Lindem based on San Juan Island; Jerry Todd based on Orcas Island; and Harold Ogden based on Lopez Island. Each of these men is in charge of his own district, as was his predecessor. Because of the water distances between districts, in emergency situations such as power failure these foremen may be out of contact with the main office on nearby San Juan Island for hours.

The roads in the county began as wagon roads for transporting goods to market. Slowly they evolved to what they are today. Many still do not have adequate ballast and pavement. Up until the late 1950s rock used in the county road system was hauled by wagon up from the island

beaches. It was not until the 1980s that the road department was able to purchase gravel from a local gravel pit on San Juan Island. Gravel from the San Juan Island pit was transported to other islands by barge at night so that it could be unloaded without conflicting with the ferry schedule. The delivery of a barge load of gravel brought together the road crews from all of the islands who worked all night unloading the barge into five yard trucks at whichever island needed the rock. Not long ago road patching material was all blade mixed with one of the loaders. In 1989 the practice was to purchase patching materials from a mainland firm and have it shipped out to the island by ferry.

Among the major projects accomplished in San Juan County was making 20 to 30 foot rock cuts along a 60 to 100 foot vertical rock shoulder on San Juan Island and a similar project in Deer Harbor on Orcas Island. San Juan County has been very fortunate to have dedicated, loyal people working in its Public Works Department. ◆

City of Seattle

Seattle City Light

Seattle City Light is among the largest municipally owned electric utilities in the United States. Formed in 1910, the Washington Utility has evolved into a complex and far-flung entity that owns six hydroelectric plants and part of a coal-fired steam-electric plant. It has developed other hydroelectric generating resources too, such as the Grand Coulee Project Hydroelectric Authority in Central Washington and the Lucky Peak Hydroelectric Project in Idaho. The utility also maintains 649 miles of high voltage transmission lines and more than 3,300 miles of distribution lines, as well as a sophisticated communications capability to control and monitor its system operations.

From a modern perspective, it is difficult to believe how precarious the utility's existence was in the early part of the 20th century. The history and legends surrounding Seattle City Light's origins and public works construction are filled with tales of derring-do. It is a proud story that still inspires the utility today.

Seattle entered the electric power business out of a need for reliable and inexpensive municipal street lighting. At the beginning of the century, private companies sold electric service for 20 cents per kilowatt hour. Only the very rich could afford electric lighting. After the city started providing electric service to Seattle homes in 1905, it charged a maximum of 8.5 cents per kilowatt hour. This utility has continued to provide reliable electric service to its customers at the lowest rates of any major American city.

Almost from the very beginning, it was apparent that hydroelectric generation would be the resource of choice. In 1905, the first plant was established at Cedar Falls, 37 miles east of Seattle. Then came a series of other projects along the Skagit River in Whatcom County: Newhalem in 1921, Gorge in 1924, Diablo in 1929, and Ross in 1952. Boundary Dam was built on the Pend Oreille River in northeastern Washington in 1967. The next generation addition was in 1988 at Lucky Peak, Idaho. This dam is owned by area irrigation districts.

Currently, the Utility is back at Cedar Falls developing a 15 megawatt capacity plant using the Seattle Water Department's storage dam on the South Fork of the Tolt River. This project is expected to be in operation by the end of 1995. City Light also is replacing turbine runners, generators and transformers at several of its older sites to improve efficiency and gain more energy from existing plants.

Throughout its history, Seattle City Light has worked to bring sufficient, reliable and economical supplies of electrical power to its service area in an environmentally responsible way. To do so has required the talent, skill and determination of several generations of employees, contractors and suppliers. Seattle City Light joins with the rest of the engineering and construction community to salute 100 years of public works for public progress in Washington State.

Seattle Water Department

One hundred years ago, the City of Seattle envisioned a publicly owned water system to serve 100,000 people. That number was quickly surpassed and today the water system serves over 1.2 million people.

Seattle's water supply was first developed by private companies and individuals using Lake Washington, deep wells and springs as sources. The first spring-fed tank and V-shaped flumes were constructed in 1854 by Henry Yesler to bring water to his mill and neighbors along the waterfront. Water supplies were stretched as Seattle's population burgeoned from 1,100 to 42,800 between 1870 and 1890.

In 1888 Seattle's Mayor Robert Moran and the Common Council called for an election to decide if Seattle would control

Past Mayor Gordon S. Clinton (left) and Robert E. Brown, City Light resident engineer on the high Gorge Dam project.

its own water system. The Cedar River was suggested as a future source. While plans were developing the existing water system proved unequal to the demands of the June, 1889 Great Seattle Fire that destroyed the city's waterfront business district. Shortly after the fire on July 8, the electorate voted to operate and build its own water supply system by a margin of 1,875 to 51. Privately owned water supply systems totaling 2,414 services for 11,700 people were purchased and improved to handle the rapidly increasing population.

The decision to develop a water resource in the Cascade Mountains reflects great foresight because the system could be designed to operate by gravity, not by relying on expensive

Workers encircle wood stave pipe with metal tension bands on Cedar River Pipeline No. 1, circa 1900. Photo by Andres Wilse courtesy of Seattle Water Department.

pumping facilities. City Engineer R. H. Thomson and Water Department Superintendent L. B. Youngs, were instrumental in keeping the vision alive for several years through many upheavals in city government. Delays were caused by rapid population growth and extensive repairs needed after the 1889 fire. A financial crisis, called the Panic of 1893, followed by a scarcity of money and numerous legal problems arising from bonding technicalities contributed to the delay.

On December 1, 1895, the community approved issuing $1,250,000 in bonds to build the Cedar River water source. Following two years of intensive survey and engineering work, construction began in 1897 on several parts of the new system. Volunteer Park and Lincoln Park reservoirs and Queen Anne Standpipe No. 1 were erected to store water for distribution in the city. A diversion dam, seven miles of steel pipe, and 22 miles of wood stave pipe completed the connection from the Cedar River to the existing reservoir and distribution system in Seattle.

In January 1901, the new pipeline with a capacity of 23.5 million gallons per day delivered water from the new intake on the Cedar River at Landsburg to serve 80,600 people to the reservoirs built earlier. The new system served 80,600 people. As the population grew over the next half century, three more pipelines were constructed to deliver Cedar River water and 21 reservoirs, standpipes and tanks were added to the distribution storage system. For the next 63 years, the Cedar River supplied all the water for Seattle and its regional customers.

Over 30 years ago, planners looked to the Tolt River when a growing population required more water, especially in northern and eastern King County. Construction began on the new supply system in 1959, and in 1964 the first water from the South Fork of the Tolt River began serving a regional population of 824,000. From the impoundment at the Tolt Regulating Basin east of Carnation, the pipeline runs 24 miles westward, interconnecting with the Tolt eastside supply line west of the Sammamish River and the northern reaches of Seattle's distribution system at the Lake Forest Park Reservoir.

Highline Well Field is the first new source of supply since the Tolt development. Two wells were put into service in late 1987, with a third installed in 1990.

Today the Seattle Water Department supplies water to more than 1.2 million people in a service area that includes 29 wholesale water customers, encompassing nearly 450 square miles in King and southwestern Snohomish counties.

Seattle Water's vision for the 21st century includes a number of innovative plans. A key element in water planning is to continue an aggressive conservation program, in keeping with the conservation ethic of the region. By the 1990s, water began to be viewed as a precious, finite resource that could not be wasted. Water also began to acquire a more prominent profile as a factor in the economic and environmental vitality of the region. Exploration for potential new sources of water supply also continues, as Seattle Water increasingly takes on responsibility for the regional scope of water.

The vision is alive, generating the future out of the Seattle Water Department's commitment to provide an adequate supply of high quality drinking water at the lowest economic and environmental cost.

Seattle Engineering Department

Although the area presently called the City of Seattle was settled around 1852 and incorporated as a municipality in 1865, the position of City Engineer was not formally created until 1890. Leadership in public works was sorely needed because Seattle's distinctive topography presented major obstacles to conventional urban development. The key geographic problems centered around the seven hills that define the city's contours and

Present and former city engineers: Left to right: Paul A. Wiatrak, Roy W. Morse, Robert J. Gulino, William E. Parker, and Ralph W. Finke.

Puget Sound tidelands.

The area's problems were tackled with imagination and energy by a series of able public works engineers who served the city over the years. Late twentieth century Engineering Department projects involved replacing or renovating earlier work.

Around the turn of the century R. H. Thomson served one of his three separate terms as City Engineer. Thomson, a giant in the building of Seattle, created and managed many important

Construction of the seawall along Railroad Avenue (now Alaskan Way) began in the early 1930s and maintenance continues today (lower right). Lower left: Seawall construction along Beach Drive.

and impressive projects, none more so than the first Denny Regrade. Denny Hill restricted the city's growth from the downtown district to the north; the hill was too steep to allow the construction of usable streets. In a monumental sluicing operation, over six million cubic yards of earth were removed, carried by flume and tunnel into the harbor. The partial leveling of Denny Hill surpassed any such undertaking previously attempted. After the Denny Regrade the Engineering Department took on other regrades, including a second effort at Denny Hill, to establish grades and contours that enabled the department to build a transportation system connecting different parts of the city.

Improved transportation was also furthered through bridge construction. In 1989 the Engineering Department was maintaining more than 180 bridges in the city to cross and connect Seattle's hills, waterways and ravines. Six of these are bascule bridges, built in a flurry of activity in the first decades of the twentieth century. These bridges are now being rehabilitated after providing half a century and more of service. One of the largest projects in Engineering Department history, the high level West Seattle Bridge—one mile long and 160 feet high—was completed in 1984 to improve access to West Seattle, previously provided by a bascule bridge.

Board of Public Works August 12, 1970. Front row left to right: Everett G. Henry, Exec. Secretary; Roy W. Morse, City Engineer; and Kenneth M. Lowthian, Supt. of Water; Back row left to right: Hans A. Thompson, Supt. Parks and Recreation; John M. Nelson, Supt. of Light; and Lester Gillis, Supt. of Buildings.

To define Seattle's harbor lines and make better use of the harbor front downtown, the Engineering Department has fought water, worms and weather by building seawalls at various locations around the city. In the early 1930s the city built a 6,100 foot seawall along what was then called Railroad Avenue, now Alaskan Way. It used the then novel design of precast concrete slabs with sheet piling cutoff beneath. The Engineering Department has since maintained the seawall, along with others built at Alki and Seaview Avenues and Beach Drive. In 1988 major reconstruction has been accomplished on the seawalls along Alaskan Way and Beach Drive, making Seattle's shorelines more attractive and usable.

As Seattle has grown through increased population and land annexation, the responsibilities of the Engineering Department have changed and grown. In 1988 the department comprised seven divisions to serve the citizens of Seattle with strong public works and maintenance programs and innovative projects.

Public Works Milestones of the 1980s

High level West Seattle Bridge - The largest capital improvement project in the Engineering Department's history, altogether the project required $150 million from various fund sources.

Street Tree Program - The Engineering Department has contributed to the greening of Seattle by planting more than 22,000 trees since 1970.

Downtown Signal Improvements - A master computer, in the process of being installed in Transportation Services Headquarters in 1989, will control all signals in the Central Business District.

New Drainage and Wastewater Utility - To implement the combined sewer overflow program, the sewer outreach program, and other improvements, the Engineering Department created a new division.

Curbside Recycling - The solid waste utility gives citizens an opportunity to recycle waste paper, metal, glass, some plastics and newspaper conveniently at their homes.

The 1990s saw major changes in the Engineering Department—organization and financial.

The Washington State Legislature, recognizing the needs of local jurisdictions for additional revenues to support local transportation systems, authorized cities to establish a street utility and impose charges for the use of the streets.

Department staff successfully met the challenge of preparing a proposal for establishing a street utility for Mayor Norman B. Rice and City Council members. It was instituted on January 1, 1993.

In preparation for a new utility, the department was reorganized to simplify accounting and budgeting. Additionally, a more decentralized structure was adopted which gave divisions autonomy for their operation while imposing responsibility for efficiency and productivity.

Environmental concerns drove the Solid Waste Utility's recycling program which expanded to include apartment recycling. The South Transfer Station's Household Hazardous Waste (HHW) facility was enlarged and a new shed was built at the Haller Lake maintenance shops.

The low-level West Seattle Swing Bridge—a first of its kind in the world—was opened for traffic. This structure received national, regional and local awards for its innovative design and use of materials.

The Engineering Department's motto: "Pride at Work," characterizes the energy, attitude and accomplishments of the nearly 1,000 employees of the department in 1989. The department's history is rich and colorful. The department is dedicated to maintaining its tradition of serving Seattle in the future and keeping it Washington's greatest urban center.

City of Seattle Department of Parks and Recreation

The history of the City of Seattle's Parks and Recreation Department is marked by tireless efforts by the Board of Park Commissioners and City Park Superintendents to create parks and recreational areas in the steadily growing municipality.

For the first thirty years after incorporation, little attention was given to the setting aside of land for parks. However, the

1880s and 1890s witnessed vigorous efforts to assure that the city would have a treasure of parks. In 1884 the first Park Commissioners Board argued strongly for the acquisition of public park lands. Successful in their efforts the first city park, Denny Park, was developed on the site of an old city cemetery. In creating the park two hundred graves were transferred to Lakeview Cemetery. In 1890 the City Engineer George F. Cotterill developed a twenty-five mile system of bike trails which became the basis for Seattle's scenic boulevard system. Seeing the need for planning, E. O. Schwargl, City Park Superintendent/ Engineer/Landscape Architect, proposed the first comprehensive plan for Seattle's parks and parkways.

Green Lake Park, January 4, 1913, a photo by Frank Nowell, dredging of the lake.

In 1902, E. F. Blaine, Park Board President and the "Father of the Seattle Park System," put the park system on a firm business-like foundation and ensured its future. One of his first moves was to hire the Olmsted brothers of Brookline, Massachusetts, to develop a comprehensive plan of parks and playgrounds. This work was spurred by the upcoming 1909 Alaska-Yukon-Pacific Exposition. Blaine's next move was to free the Park Board from City Hall—a position it maintained until 1967.

In the first twenty years of this century forty percent of the land in the city's current park system was acquired. In 1906 the first park bond was passed providing funding for the Olmsted Plan which was actualized in 1909 with the construction of Volunteer Park, installation of children's swings at Denny Park, the construction of tennis courts at Broadway Field, and several parks in the newly annexed municipalities of Ballard, West Seattle and Columbia City.

Between 1910 and 1924 many goals were realized including the opening of several community recreation centers, construction of Queen Anne Boulevard, development of Green Lake as a recreation area, building golf courses and lighting playgrounds.

The Great Depression was a boon to the expansion of the Seattle park system. Federal and state work programs provided millions of dollars worth of improvements to the park system including trails and shoreline work at Seward, Lincoln, Carkeek, O. O. Denny and Woodland Parks. In addition, Woodland Park Zoo, Washington Park Arboretum, Camp Long, Green Lake, and many others were the focus of development projects.

Since the middle of the twentieth century long term planning has accompanied the expansion of the park system during an extended period of population growth. In the 1960s much needed funds came from a $4.5 million bond issue for playfields. Forward Thrust bonds provided $65 million over a twelve year period for major park improvements and the creation of new parks, such as Gas Works

Park on Lake Union, Discovery Park on the campus of old Fort Lawton, the Burke-Gilman Trail, and the Seattle Aquarium.

In the 1980s Seattle 1-2-3 bond issues provided $28 million for renovation of Seattle's park system including play areas for children, tennis court resurfacing, sea wall construction and building new community centers. The plan included partial restoration of Lake Washington Boulevard and Interlaken Boulevard to enhance the city's most historic Olmsted Park/Boulevard. As we near the midpoint of the 1990s, the Department has completed a COMPLAN, a functional plan setting forth the policies, mission and actions to achieve short-term and long-term goals along with the functional activity plans and neighborhood new directions to serve as resources for community planning. The Department is also cooperating with the City Department of Planning in the development of the Seattle Comprehensive Plan.◆

Below left: Pioneer Square—totem raising prior to unveiling on October 18, 1899. Below top: Broadway playfield and wading pool (photo by Webster and Stevens). Below lower: Leschi Park, dock and boat scene (photo by Webster and Stevens).

Skagit County

Skagit County has undertaken and realized many public works projects over the years that have improved the lives of those living in the county. Because the county has many miles of sea coast, as well as numerous rivers, bridges are a major public works focus. Skagit County is proud of its well designed—beautiful and functional—bridges that allow for safe and convenient travel. ◆

1a—The LaConner Bridge, built in 1915, crossed the Swinomish Channel connecting the town of LaConner and the Swinomish Indian Reservation. The swing span allowed vessel travel through the Swinomish Channel.

1b—The LaConner Bridge was replaced in 1957 with the construction of the steel arch Rainbow Bridge. Photo Courtesy of Skagit County Public Works Dept.

2a—The North Fork Bridge over the Skagit River was built in 1912 and connected Fir Island with the Skagit Flats west of Mount Vernon. The swing span allowed vessel travel up the Skagit from Skagit Bay. Photo Courtesy of Skagit County Public Works Dept.

2b—The North Fork Bridge was replaced with a high clearance steel girder span in 1959. Photo Courtesy of Skagit County Public Works Dept.

3a—The South Fork Bridge of the Skagit River was built in 1914 and connected the town of Conway to Fir Island. The swing span allowed vessel travel up the Skagit River from Skagit Bay. Photo Courtesy of Skagit County Public Works Dept.

3b—The South Fork Bridge was replaced in 1972 with a multispan concrete structure. The north fork of the Skagit River was still available for larger vessels. Photo Courtesy of Skagit County Public Works Dept.

Snohomish County

The history of the engineering or public works operations in Snohomish County can be broken down into three primary periods of development—the coming of the automobile, the era of getting out of the mud, and the period of modernization.

When the automobile appeared on the scene it was quickly apparent that a network of roads and bridges had to be developed to serve communities that heretofore had been served only by trails or water access routes. New roadways and bridges were constructed to all parts of the county, opening up new opportunities for farming, logging, rural living and recreation. Engineering accomplishments during this period expressed new ideas in structural design, roadway geometrics and pavement development. Snohomish County was among the first to pave some of its primary roadways with concrete.

"Getting the county out of the mud" summarizes the focus of the second period for Snohomish County's public works engineers. This period is marked by an aggressive asphalt paving program. The county was divided into three road districts, each district headed by a County Commissioner, who ran his own road program and road crews like a private construction company. For a period of time Snohomish County may have been one of the largest asphalt paving contractors in the area with each of the three commissioners running their own asphalt plants, paving machines, and all the supporting trucks, equipment and manpower. While this program subjected the county to much criticism from the private contracting community, it did accomplish the goal of eliminating many miles of gravel and dirt roadways. Citizen acceptance was very high as almost everyone was served by a hard surface roadway that eliminated the problems of dirt and dust.

By the second decade of this century the county rapidly changed from a forest products and agriculture supported society to a metropolitan residential community with a rapidly developing "high tech" industry corridor.

In 1979 there were substantial changes in the form of government with the three commissioners being replaced by five County Council members, representing individual districts, and an elected County Executive.

During this last period the County Department of Public Works grew rapidly providing new services heretofore not provided by county government. These include an aggressive and progressive solid waste disposal program, and ordinances and review procedures to deal with the traffic impacts of growth. In addition the county has a surface water program to deal with wetlands protection, stream inventories and the creation of a surface water utility to pay for

Above: Laying concrete on Everett Snohomish Highway, 1916. Photo by A.J. Cook.
Below: Snohomish County Road Maintenance Fleet, circa 1912.

Laying concrete on Everett Snohomish Highway, 1916. Photo by A.J. Cook.

ongoing maintenance and operation of facilities to mitigate stormwater runoff impacts.

In the 1990s, the Department is heavily involved in activities related to Washington's Growth Management Act, ISTEA, and major transportation funding initiatives for a Regional Transit Project. Snohomish County is happy to be a part of a proud tradition of public works excellence in Washington for over 100 years. ◆

The photos below are of Bridge #111 over the North Fork of the Stillaguamish River (251st Avenue NE) in two eras. Top: 1916, bottom: 1988.

Public Works Director/County Engineers

1910 - 1912	J. S. Birney
1913 - 1918	Hans J. Mumm, Jr.
1919 - 1922	S. G. Tegtmeier
1923 - 1934	Ross D. Alverson
1935 - 1944	Clarence Hickey
1945 - 1948	Roy Crane
1949 - 1966	Earl Barnwell
1967 - 1976	Harry D. Martin
1976 - 1992	Gerald E. Weed
1992 - present	Peter E. Hahn, Public Works Director
	Jack Bilsborough, County Road Engineer

Soil Sampling Service, Inc.

Gerald T. Sweeney and Oliver E. Erdman founded Soil Sampling Service, Inc. in 1964 to provide creative solutions to drilling problems. From the two partners as the sole employees, the company has grown into a leading drilling contractor serving civil, environmental, geotechnical and mining clients.

Soil Sampling Service got its start with the construction of Interstates 5 and 90 in Washington state. The projects called for massive earth cuts that created severe slope stability problems. Sweeney and Erdman saw this problem as an opportunity to refine and prove their new Aardvark® Drilling Machine and Method.

This technology was a revolutionary way to install elongated rods in unstable earth formations by drilling horizontal, vertical and angle holes from a tractor-mounted rig. Patented in 1968, the Aardvark Drill and Method installed thousands of feet of horizontal drains on the two interstates. The I-5 Tukwilla interchange alone had more than 80,000 linear feet of horizontal drains installed by Soil Sampling Service.

Since then, Aardvarks have been used to install horizontal drain systems in almost every type of formation in North America and many around the Pacific Rim. Soil Sampling Service's clients have grown to include highway departments across the U.S. and Canada and federal agencies such as the U.S. Army Corps of Engineers and the U.S. Bureau of Reclamation. Corporate clients have included CH2M Hill, Dames & Moore, Ebasco Ser-vices, Geo Engineers, Harding Lawson, Kiewit Pacific, Parametrix, Shannon & Wilson and Sweet Edwards/Emcon, to name a few.

Public works projects have ranged from earthquake evaluation in the Aleutian Islands to stabilizing mass transit tunnels in Seattle, Los Angeles and Vancouver, B.C.; from test drilling programs for nuclear facilities in eastern Washington to slope stabilization for highways, dams and bridges throughout the United States. Soil Sampling Service also is heavily involved in groundwater monitoring work.

As part of the Aardvark Method, Sweeney and Erdman developed slotted plastic pipe for use as non-corrosive, clog-resistant drains. To manufacture this PVC pipe, they formed Hydrophilic Industries, Inc. in 1966. And to make the new drilling equipment they kept inventing, they started Tigre Tierra Inc. in 1972 to manufacture their Aardvark drilling rig and other specialized tooling. In 1985, the two manufacturing firms were merged into one company, Aardvark Corporation. Parallel joint ventures in drilling and manufacturing also were established in Canada.

Today, Soil Sampling Service and Aardvark Corporation employ almost 100 people at their 10-acre headquarters near Puyallup. Oliver Erdman, the company's first president, retired in 1984 and sold his share of the companies to partner Gerald Sweeney. A Tacoma native, Sweeney received his master's degree in geology from the University of Idaho and now serves as Soil Sampling Service's and Aardvark's president. ◆

Larry Southwick

Larry Southwick, born in Leavenworth, Washington, received a BSCE from Seattle University in 1964. He has worked at the City of Bellevue Department of Public Works and Utilities in several capacities from 1973 to the present including City Engineer, Utility Manager and Acting Director. He started as a contract Project Engineer for the Bellevue 148th Avenue Improvement Project beginning in 1973. This project gained attention as an environmentally and community sensitive boulevard. Up to 35 houses were acquired and relocated to allow sufficient right-of-way and extensive landscaping to buffer the project in residential neighborhoods. Over two miles of tall acoustical walls were built to reduce the noise impact of the traffic which reaches up to 30,000 vehicles per day. The real key to success was a strong team effort between the staff and affected citizens along the arterial working together throughout the five years of the project.

Since he joined the Washington Chapter of APWA in 1975, Mr. Southwick has served in many capacities including: President 1987, Vice President 1986, Secretary 1985, Treasurer 1984, Director 1980-81. He was Program Committee Chair for many years and served on the Awards, Program, Public Awareness, International and Council for Equal Opportunity committees. He is currently the Chapter delegate. ◆

Celia "Cee" Strong

Celia "Cee" Strong is the Downtown Development Coordinator for the City of Everett. Under her administration the city was acknowledged as having the most effective Local Improvement District financing program in the area, averaging in excess of $10 million of capital improvement financing annually.

In 1964 Ms. Strong completed a program for the gifted and able at Southern Oregon College. A Department of Transportation Fellowship award in 1977 allowed her to pursue her interests in traffic engineering. In a career of diverse challenges, she has administered major capital construction projects, public works permits and environmental reviews; has served as assistant real property manager; done land surveying, analyzed torpedo tests, and performed research and written evaluations for a comprehensive revision of Everett's employment position descriptions. In addition, Ms. Strong is an accomplished commercial artist and photographer.

Ms. Strong co-authored the *Washington State LID-RID Procedure Manual* and *Everett Developers Guide and Standard Specifications for Developers*. She frequently lectures and organizes workshops on project financing, public relations and communications, and has served on countless boards and committees. Most recently she was appointed Commissioner to the City of Seattle Indian Services Commission. An active member of APWA, she currently serves as chair to the Capital Improvement Funding Subcommittee and is a past member of the Board of Directors. At the 1986 International APWA Conference, she presented a Special Assessment Financing Session. In her spare time she is an avid Gilbert and Sullivan fan. ◆

City of Spokane

The City of Spokane Falls' incorporation on November 29, 1881 was enacted by the Legislative Assembly of the Territory of Washington. Spokane is the second oldest city in Washington. The act empowered the newly formed government to erect water works to provide fire and domestic service, to provide for the construction of streets, alleys, sidewalks and crosswalks and to provide sewers, gutters, water courses and underground drainage. This act was amended in 1883 to expand and better define the powers of the city of Spokane Falls. Included in this amendment was the legislation to finance and staff public facilities. In addition, municipal officers, including a Council and a Superintendent of Streets were to be elected. Revisions made in 1886 broadened the definition of the city's responsibilities in the area of public works. The office of City Surveyor was established, presumably to better control subdivision activity.

Spokane's transition from a small town of 500 in 1881, to a city of 23,602 inhabitants in 1890, can be greatly attributed to the coming of the Northern Pacific Railroad (NPR) in 1881. In fact, one of the earliest established streets, Sprague Avenue, was named in honor of General J. W. Sprague, General Superintendent of the NPR, Western Division. Sprague Avenue, anchored on the west at Cedar Street, ran east to Dishman, where it intersected with the Mullan Trail Road.

The first bridge was constructed across the Spokane River in 1881. The bridge was located at the foot of Howard Street and crossed the south river channel to Havermale Island. It was constructed of timber at a cost of $5,475. The north river channel at Howard was spanned in 1888. Within the next few years five more timber bridges were constructed across the Spokane River. Most notable were the Monroe Street and Post Street bridges. The Monroe Street Bridge was constructed to accommodate a north-south cable car route.

The year 1881 brought the first water surveyor to the city. A private company was organized to supply Spokane's growing demand for water. In 1883 the city purchased the water system, which was financed through the sale of local utility revenue bonds. Spokane was in the forefront nationally in using this financial mechanism. Both wood stave and cast iron pipe were used in the construction of the system.

Between 1890 and 1900, the population grew from 9,922 to 36,948. Near the beginning of this eventful decade, Spokane was devastated by the Great Fire of 1889. On Sunday, August 4, 1889, a fire swept through the central business district destroying 32 blocks. Although destructive in nature, the fire generated a major redesign effort in the core area and corresponding growth. After the fire the name Spokane Falls was shortened to Spokane, presumably to accommodate the telegraph operators.

It was during the reconstruction of the city that the first sewer lines were built. Much of the area from the base of South Hill to the river, falling between Cedar and Division Streets, received sewer service at this time. The sewer lines were typically combined or were designed to accommodate both sanitary sewage and storm water runoff. The sewer lines of this half square-mile area discharged to the Spokane River.

The increasing population growth aroused concern regarding the condition of the streets. These concerns were well founded during the fall and spring when the mud formed by wagon traffic reached depths of four to eight inches. Crosswalks had been constructed to facilitate pedestrian traffic, but offered little relief to this recurring problem. Monroe, Lincoln, Post, Wall, Howard and Stevens Streets were surfaced in the late 1890s. These streets and much of the remaining central business district streets were surfaced with asphalt over a cement concrete underlayment . A portion of Riverside between Monroe and Stevens Streets was surfaced with stone blocks presumably for aesthetic reasons.

The 1890s brought a resurgence in bridge building activity. This was in part the result of the spring floods of 1894, which carried away the bridges located at Olive Avenue and Natatorium Park. New bridges were placed at Mission Avenue, Monroe Street, Post Street and Division Street. All the new structures were of steel construction, which at the time was deemed to be a safer construction material than timber. New steel spans were also completed at Olive and Washington Streets in 1902.

It has been recorded that an incident involving a circus parade in 1907 initiated the replacement of the Monroe Street Bridge. During a Ringling Brother's parade, in August of that year, the Circus' line of elephants refused to cross the bridge. Apparently the elephants sensed the rickety condition of the bridge which had both weight and speed restrictions at that time. Street car traffic had previously been diverted to a new bridge at nearby Post Street.

As a result of this incident city engineers planned and designed the third Monroe Street Bridge. This concrete arched bridge cost nearly one-half million dollars. The bridge is distinguished for having the largest single monolithic arch in the United States in 1912—281 feet long, 135 feet high and 71 feet wide. A similar bridge was built across Hangman Creek at the Sunset Highway crossing also in 1912. In 1989 the system included 37 bridges 20 of which are major structures. All but one of the major bridges is of cement concrete construction.

Growth of the city created a greater demand upon the city's water system and sewer systems. Plans were developed to not only construct a new pump station but also provide the power to drive the pumps. It was during the excavation for the new Upriver Pump Station, in the late 1890s and early 1900s, that the Spokane/Rathdrum Prairie Aquifer was detected. Wells were constructed between 1907 and 1910, and the city's water supply source was converted from river or surface water to groundwater.

City public works systems; streets, sewers and water, grew along with the population. Additional water supply wells were constructed through to 1960 in response to increases in demand. The system currently is supported by 10 well stations, one of which will support an 80 million gallons-per-day flow demand.

As the water system expanded, so too did the sewage collection system. City policy throughout its history required the systematic expansion of the sewer system in response to the increase in population from 150,477 in 1930 to 171,562 in 1950. Like other U. S. cities, post World War II Spokane was forced to reconsider its current method of sewage disposal. Sewer system expansion had increasingly burdened the ecological system of the Spokane River.

In 1946, with financing from a local bond issue, construction of an interceptor system and treatment facility was undertaken. This work continued from 1948 to 1958. The interceptor

Monroe Street Bridge — 1910–1912

September 1910 — Construction underway on the East and West arches of the South Approach.

Scaffolding in place for the East Side River arch. (Taken from the North Bank, looking toward the East.)

April 1911 — Construction underway on the East side of the main river arch.

January 1912 — Completed structure representing the largest single monolithic arch in the United States.

system was designed to carry normal dry weather flows and some storm flows from the combined sewer system. Approximately 40 sewer trunk systems were intercepted, of these 35 were combined sewer systems. The treatment plant was again upgraded in the 1970s for capacity and to provide advanced treatment capability, at a cost of $55 million. Its current rated capacity is set at 44 million gallons per day.

In order to alleviate damage to the river's ecological systems, Spokane undertook an extensive combined sewage overflow reduction program during the 1980s. Approximately 120 miles of separate storm sewers were constructed, reducing by over 85 percent the annual overflow volume at a cost of $40 million. The Spokane Treatment Plant has been designated as a regional plant. As a result, efforts are underway to provide the entire Spokane metropolitan area with collection sewers and conveyance capacity to the regional plant. In addition, major trunk lines are being extended west to the Spokane Plains area to support existing and future industrial development.

In 1974 the City of Spokane hosted a World Exposition. At that time Spokane was the smallest city on record ever to host such an event. A coalition of business and local government interests assisted in financing the redevelopment of the riverfront area lying between Monroe and Division Streets as the Fair site. The result of Expo '74 has been a much needed rejuvenation of the central business district. Similar to the reconstruction following the Great Fire of 1889, the core area has been transformed into an attractive and viable business center. The Expo '74 effort transformed an area that was rundown and heavily commercialized area into a beautiful regional park attracting visitors from all over the world. Numerous pedestrian bridges allow walkers to cross the river to enjoy the park on both banks. Undoubtedly, Spokane's founding father, James Nettle Glover, would have greatly appreciated the restoration of this riverfront area, which prompted him to settle in the area in the first place. ◆

Spokane County

Spokane is an area of much natural beauty with abundant resources. Early settlers were attracted to the area's forests, lakes, mountains, minerals, fertile soil, and, of course, the river. As the river ran on an east-west direction, it divided the area into sections north and south of the river, which were split again and again by five major drainage ways radiating from the river. Because of its location the river became a major travel route as well as a source of power, provider of food and a physical barrier.

Early transportation was primitive, but as the settlers' needs and the economy changed, so changed their mode of travel. Transportation was crucial to give freedom to the settlers' spirit of adventure and opportunity. The development of roads, bridges and railroads allowed people to move and to trade. Indian trails evolved into wagon roads and dugout canoes were replaced by ferries.

The first "public works" project in the county was a ferry built and operated by Antoine Plante. Plante's ferry was the first that could carry wagons across the river. He ran his ferry from 1852 to 1864 at the site of the present Spokane County Plante Ferry Park in the Spokane Valley. Plante had competition from other ferry operators, but his was a more sturdy ferry and people were willing to pay up to four dollars to have their wagons and goods safely conveyed across the river. Most early public works projects were built and operated by private citizens as businesses.

The Mullan Road, the first major road that traversed what is now Spokane County, was a road of national significance built with federal funds. The wagon road, little more than a trail by today's standards, was built primarily as a military road so troops could quickly come to the aid of settlers during times of Indian unrest. Other forces of equal importance led to the construction of the road including the need for a northern route to the Pacific Ocean, the desire for better trade markets and a nationwide interest in the Northwest Territory.

Construction of the road began in 1859 by Captain John Mullan at Fort Benton on the Missouri River and extended 624 miles west to Fort Walla Walla. The Mullan Road was completed August 1, 1862, at a cost of $230,000, nearly $400 per mile. This cost seems insignificant when compared to the "millions per mile" cost of today's interstate highways. The Mullan Road helped open up the West and was heavily used. In Spokane County the Mullan Road brought pioneers west along the river, then south through the Valley, Moran Prairie and the Palouse Country.

The Washington and Idaho Centennial trail, dedicated in 1992, once again transports people at the same pace as when they traveled the historic Mullan Road. The trail accommodates bicyclists, pedestrians and equestrians, and makes provision for the disabled. It follows the Spokane River from Spokane to Coeur d'Alene, Idaho, thus following the same route and putting back in service a section of the old Mullan Road.

In 1864 the Spokane Bridge, the first timber bridge, was built near the Washington-Idaho border. This bridge replaced the ferry for travelers on the Mullan Road. The Spokane Bridge washed out four times, but was rebuilt and remained in operation until 1951. For many years the Spokane Bridge was the only bridge across the Spokane River between the Idaho border and the City of Spokane. It was rebuilt in 1911 by Spokane County, this time with steel trusses. This important bridge refused to die when it was torn down. Rather than being scrapped the trusses were broken down and salvageable sections were used in construction of Sullivan Road over the Spokane International Railway. The main trusses were sold to Chelan County for one of their bridges. The concrete bridge that replaced the old steel truss has since been by passed by the I-90 Freeway bridge which crosses into Idaho only a short distance upstream from where the first Spokane Bridge was built.

Spokane County was also crisscrossed with railroads. In 1881 the Northern Pacific Railroad line reached Spokane. Others soon followed and in the heyday of railroading five lines crossed through the county: the Great Northern; the Northern Pacific; the Chicago, Milwaukee-St. Paul and Pacific; the Oregon Washington Railroad and Navigation; and the Spokane International. All these lines were a boon to trade. In 1912 while the city was replacing steel bridges with concrete, three railway companies, as if to contradict the city's project, combined their efforts to build steel bridges for the railroad tracks. The local spectators were impressed with the technical skill they saw as the "modern" bridges went up, fitting neatly together and carrying the great loads of the trains. Most of these railroad bridges came down in 1973 to clear the site for Spokane's World's Fair, Expo '74.

Settlers built their own travel networks until population growth made it necessary for a central entity to take over the responsibility and coordination of these and other systems. Thus, after several unsuccessful attempts, the Spokane County government was finally established in 1879. From 1880 to 1906 the County Surveyor was in charge of the roads. In 1906 an engineer was required for the position. The combined job of county surveyor and county engineer was an elected office until 1937, when a change in state law required that a county engineer be appointed.

With the incorporation of Spokane Falls in 1881, the town gained the means for raising funds for public works projects. The first such project was the Howard Street Bridge. It was built of planks and crossed the river to Washington Street. At that time the nearest bridge was still the Spokane Bridge located 18 miles east of town at the Idaho border.

Within five years five bridges were built across the Spokane River thus allowing the city to expand north. But these timber structures were dangerous. Eventually, several collapsed because of overloads and flooding resulting in loss of life. Soon steel trusses and concrete replaced wood. By 1915 there were 29 bridges spanning the Spokane River within the city. Plans for the renovation of the city's major bridges (Division, Lincoln/Monroe and Maple) were in place in 1992.

As the local and state governments took over managing the roadways, a county arterial system was introduced. In June 1927 the Board of County Commissioners passed a resolution requiring stop signs to be placed at all road approaches to state highways. These original county arterials were the Spokane Bridge, Palouse and Trent highways. The state highways included Inland Empire 3, Sunset 2, Central Washington 11, and Pend Oreille 6. In 1931 the county added eight roads to the "stop-sign arterial" system. These arterials served all four geographical areas radiating from the urban core.

The transportation system of Spokane County that began as a series of Indian and trader trails has grown into the largest county road system in Washington State—a total of 2947 miles. This is equivalent to the overland distance from Spokane to Key West, Florida. The Spokane County Engineers Office oversees the construction and maintenance of this diverse network of urban and rural roads. As the road system has grown, so has the scope of the County Engineers Office. Now a division of Public Works, the County Engineers are responsible for stormwater management, aquifer protection (208), transportation planning, traffic safety, CARTA, Commute Trip Reduction, Geographic Information Systems, and air quality mitigation projects. ◆

Southwest Suburban Sewer District

Southwest Suburban Sewer District (SWSSD) is responsible for the collection, transportation, processing and disposal of public sewage and wastewater. The SWSSD Service Area lies Southwest of Seattle and generally includes White Center, Burien and Normandy Park.

As Seattle grew, so did its surrounding areas. Forested hills became barren slopes dotted with homesteads. White Center and Burien began as independent suburban communities, growing slowly and predictably. When World War II broke out two large housing developments were constructed near White Center for military personnel and employees, and the population leaped dramatically. The federal government made an attempt to build a sewer system for the developments, but all it really did was remove the wastes from one area to dump them, essentially untreated, in another.

The first sewer district, White Center, was formed following the war under the guidance of commissioners Arthur E. Mullen, H. R. Land and Harold Moore, who functioned as manager. The service area steadily grew and soon extended well beyond White Center. In December 1949, the name was officially changed to Southwest Suburban Sewer District. In spite of this, however, most of the area residents were still using septic tanks.

By the early 1950s the effect of decades of casual dumping of wastes was beginning to haunt the residents. Hicks Lake, now Lake Garrett, and Lake Burien were both closed to the public. Seahurst Beach, long a favorite swimming spot on Puget Sound, was also declared unsafe as a result of human pollution.

On September 24, 1953, the first commissioners of what is now the SWSSD authorized the construction of new facilities on Salmon Creek. In 1957 the old system was replaced with a new primary treatment process at the Salmon Creek Plant. By 1963 a second primary treatment facility on Miller Creek was under construction. In 1964 the two plants were treating over four million gallons of sewage a day.

In 1985, in response to deteriorating water quality in Puget Sound and a mandate by the EPA, SWSSD began the planning and construction of secondary treatment facilities at both the Miller Creek and Salmon Creek sites. The scope of the project made it the single most ambitious undertaking SWSSD had faced since its inception.

After due consideration, the community consultants and government representatives agreed that a Utility Local Improvement District (ULID) was the best approach. Hence ULID 55,

Participating in the Official Ground Breaking ceremony held on March 14, 1986 for SWSSD's new secondary treatment plant (from left): Bob Royer, Consultant; Steve Sandelius, General Manager; Beth Williams, Citizens Advisory Committee Chair; Tim Harrigan, ST Engineering; Dale Cap, Superintendent; Bruce McKnight, Commissioner; Craig Chambers, PEI, Inc.; Dick Seibert, Commissioner; Keith Harris, City of Normandy Park; Dick Barnes, State Representative; Eleanor Lee, State Senator; Dixie Scott, CCA, Inc.; Steve Ragsdale, E.P.A.; Janice Kelly, D.O.E.; Carl Nadler, Citizens Advisory Committee member; John Stetson, D.O.E. (Commissioner Bert Lysen unable to attend).

the largest ULID in the history of the State of Washington, was formed. This was an opportunity for the community to decide for itself how it wanted to take care of its wastes. The tireless efforts of the Citizen's Advisory Committee were instrumental in the selection of the technology and method of funding the construction.

The technology selected is known as "rotating biological contactors" and is a superior method removing a much higher percentage of the metals and toxics in sewage than does primary treatment alone. Financing was handled through forming the ULID and assessing each property owner a fixed amount. Rather than raise property taxes and sewer rates, people could pay their assessments over a 15 or 20 year period, or elect to pay off the assessment in full at any time.

Once the initial assessment role was completed, an extensive public education effort was undertaken. Public notices of the project were posted and four public hearings were held. There was ample opportunity for the community to question the proposed action. Each hearing was attended by 250 to 300 people. The ULID regularly published a newsletter and ULID Activity Notice that were sent out with area utility bills

The formation of ULID 55 and its assessments involved extensive financial planning. Total project costs amounted to $29.8 million. Major funds came from the State Department of Ecology. The State Public Works Trust Fund, provided a low interest loan and the ULID raised a substantial portion of the funds. Areas receiving service, but lying outside of the SWSSD, contributed their share of the cost of secondary treatment.

Construction of secondary treatment facilities at the Miller Creek plant were completed in February 1988. The Salmon Creek facility was completed in the spring of 1989.

The situation in Puget Sound has reversed from a century ago. Today there are more people than natural resources. The Salmon and Miller Creek plants treat over eight million gallons of sewage every 24 hours—twice the volume treated 20 years ago. The people served by SWSSD have achieved a new secondary sewage treatment process they can afford. And most of all, residents have an increased awareness of their responsibilities, individually and as a community, to safeguard our dwindling natural resources. The district's goal is to protect our water quality and the delicate balance that is our Puget Sound Basin, today and for generations yet to come. ◆

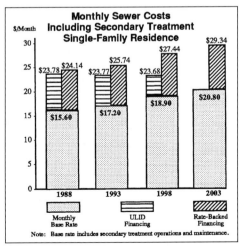

Monthly Sewer Costs Including Secondary Treatment Single-Family Residence

$/Month

Year	Monthly Base Rate	ULID Financing	Rate-Backed Financing
1988	$15.60	$23.78	$24.14
1993	$17.20	$23.77	$25.74
1998	$18.90	$23.68	$27.44
2003	$20.80		$29.34

Note: Base rate includes secondary treatment operations and maintenance.

This comparison of financing alternatives convinced SWSSD officials and the citizens advisory committee to proceed with the largest utility local improvement district (ULID) in the history of Washington State.

Sverdrup Corporation

Sverdrup

In the mid-1960s Washington State public works officials were planning the development of what would eventually be one of the most sophisticated transportation systems in the United States. Sverdrup's expertise as a leader in transportation technology helped realize these plans. The firm's Bellevue office was opened to perform freeway route location studies on segments of I-5 and I-90. This marked the beginning of a series of transportation projects that involved hundreds of miles of roads, highways, bridges, tunnels, and port and marine facilities.

Sverdrup's capabilities grew through the 1970s and services were extended to the private sector, including industry and commercial development. Eventually the office staff grew to more than 100. In addition to engineering and design experts, the firm has a specialized team of fish and wildlife experts.

Sverdrup's contributions to the rich history of public works in the State of Washington have included many significant projects of which the company is proud. In 1941 Professor John Parcel, one of the two founders of the Sverdrup Corp., served on the consulting review board for redesigning the Tacoma Narrows Bridge. Sverdrup's Bellevue office has participated in the planning and design of nearly every interstate highway in Washington. In the late 1960s the firm was the lead designer for the Puyallup Freeway System, which included 16 miles of four-lane freeway, eight major interchanges and 27 bridges in Pierce County.

Sverdrup designed several segments of I-90 west of Snoqualmie Pass in the late 1960s.

The I-205 Columbia River Bridge at Portland, Oregon, winner of the 1983 Grand Conceptor Award from the American Consulting Engineers Council.

Sverdrup's design for the I-205 bridge over the Columbia River connecting Vancouver, Washington, and Portland, Oregon, helped advance bridge construction technology in the United States. Recognition of the bridge's unique design was overwhelming: an *Engineering New Record* cover story called it "the first in a new generation of large-scale, segmental bridges in the U.S." The American Consulting Engineers Council gave Sverdrup the 1983 Grand Conceptor Award for the project.

Sverdrup was responsible for complete mechanical and electrical design of the I-90, Mount Baker Ridge and First Hill LID tunnels, including control and operating systems, ventilation, lighting, power distribution, television surveillance, emergency telephone, radio broadcast and air quality monitoring. One of Sverdrup's most notable achievements on this assignment, however, was design of the largest foam-deluge fire detec-

tion and sprinkler system in the world—a total of 140 separate 150-foot long ceiling arrays containing a total of 11,439 sprinkler heads—covering the tunnels portal-to-portal and wall-to-wall. Sverdrup's tunnel expertise was also utilized on the City of Seattle's downtown Metro bus tunnel project, where the firm's engineering specialists identified significant design and construction cost savings.

Sverdrup has served major ports in western Washington throughout the past several decades. Important renovation and improvement projects for the Ports of Seattle, Tacoma and Bellingham have helped reaffirm Puget Sound as the "Gateway to Alaska and the Pacific Rim." Sverdrup designed the Alaska Ferry Terminal located at the Port of Bellingham, as well as other ferry loading facilities throughout the region. Other marine related projects include the Elliott Bay Marina in Seattle, one of the largest privately-owned facilities of its kind in the United States.

The citizens of Washington are very lucky because of the dedication and commitment of those public works engineers and planners who have come before us. Without their foresight, we would not have today fine public works systems. The people of Sverdrup are dedicated to contribute to the future of the state and its projects of progress. ◆

Sverdrup has been instrumental in the design and development of terminal facilities for Washington State ferries. Above: The Alaska ferry Columbia *arrives for its inaugural docking into the new Sverdrup designed berthing facilities in Bellingham, Washington.*

Streeter/Dermanis & Associates Architects, AIA

Streeter/Dermanis & Associates is an association of architects combining diverse talents and experience to provide a wide range of architectural services. Established in 1967 as Mel Streeter & Associates. It became Streeter/Dermanis and Associates when Paul Dermanis joined the firm in 1973.

The company is of a size that allows for the direct involvement of a principal and project manager in all phases of project development. Quality control at every level of project and production management is carefully planned and implemented within the firm's organizational framework. This process guarantees that each project receives the firm's focused attention and the benefit of accrued expertise.

Project experience encompasses new construction and renovation, a wealth of public as well as private development projects, and capital improvement programs of all sizes. Recent projects include educational facilities, corporate headquarters and office buildings, correctional facilities, medical laboratories, bridges and parking structures. The firm has provided architectural design services on numerous public utilities projects proving its ability to unite rigorous aesthetic design principles with the basis of functional design. Awards for design excellence include the Federal Aviation Administration Regional Headquarters Building in Seattle and Department of The Navy Administration Building in Bangor, Washington.

The firm offers a full range of architectural services from planning, programming and feasibility studies, through site and building design and construction. The firm serves both as general project coordinator and as a specialist on planning and feasibility

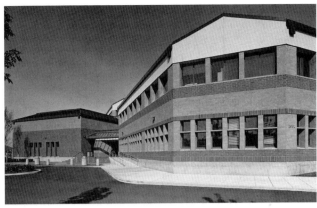

Fleet Support Headquarters/Administration Building at Everett Naval Station for a Nimitz-class aircraft carrier and associated support vessels.

studies. No matter how large or small the role, close attention is given to all aspects of the project, including functional, financial, environmental, aesthetic and community considerations.

Streeter/Dermanis & Associates projects include a wide variety of buildings. A representative sample is included here: F.A.A. Regional Headquarters, Boeing Field; Trident Administration Building, Bangor; Auburn City Hall; Lacey Library; Renton and Northeast District Courts; Washington Mutual Savings Bank, Ballard Branch; Washington Employee Credit Union; High Point Community Center, Seattle; Whidbey Island Arts and Crafts Hobby Shop; Bellevue Racquet Club; McChord Air Force Base Gymnasium; Patterson Hall renovation, University of Washington; and the Seattle Urban League's building alterations. ◆

Techstaff, Inc.

In October of 1980 Jan Kennedy opened the doors of Techstaff, Inc., a temporary help service specializing in support staff for the engineering, architecture, construction management, environmental and computer industries. By 1987 sales had reached $2.3 million and the thriving Seattle firm was listed on *Inc.* magazines "500 Fastest Growing Companies," list for 1987. In April 1994, Techstaff, Inc. was purchased from Jan Kennedy by Mary Irvine and ECA. Techstaff, Inc. is a woman-owned business, and uses the name CSR Tech Services outside of Washington State.

Techstaff works closely with a variety of technically skilled people ranging from P.E. engineers to drafting support, who are ready upon short notice to work for a period of days, weeks or months, according to the employer's needs. In an average week over 75 people are assigned to projects in the Northwest.

Techstaff, Inc.'s services consulting engineers and high tech companies involved in public works projects from feasibility through design and construction. These major projects include King County's Harborview Hospital Expansion, Metro's Westpoint Capital Project, the Seattle access to Interstate 90, the downtown transit tunnel, West Seattle Bridge, the Seattle Convention Center, Sea-Tac airport expansion and the Mount Baker Tunnel. ◆

City of Tacoma

Geography, that now little studied grammar school topic, seems to have a particular and recurring tie to Tacoma and its closely watched destiny. The Northern Pacific Railroad, second of the transcontinental railroads to cross the country, selected the insignificant little hamlet of Tacoma, platted in 1863, for its western terminus in 1873. This decision by the Northern Pacific hastened the town's growth to city status. Tacoma rivaled Seattle as an urban center through the 1880s. With the crash of 1893 real estate values plummeted, the Northern Pacific went bankrupt, and a third of the city's population decamped. The Northern Pacific fell into the hands of James J. Hill who controlled the Great Northern Railway. Hill is viewed as a great villain in Tacoma history for his expressed preference for Seattle.

The Northern Pacific continued to dominate the city until merchants and shippers broke the railroad's monopoly rates about 1909, and began to have a more direct influence on city politics and decision making. The most important local industries revolved around forest products, with Tacoma milling more lumber annually during the first third of this century than anywhere else in the U.S. Copper smelting and coal mining added to the industrial base which was, in turn, supported by the city's low electric rates. Tacoma's vast hydroelectric dams, generating plants and delivery lines, started in 1893, were the first municipally owned power system in the country.

Tacoma's industrial base was one of the most concentrated on the West Coast, and as a result the city's politics and social attitudes had a strong blue collar influence. Both Roosevelts carried Tacoma heavily, and from 1932 until 1972 it was a Democratic bastion.

The city's other great economic factor has been its strategic north Pacific position in terms of national defense. Camp Lewis, later Fort Lewis, established in 1917, and McChord Air Force Base made the Defense Department the area's single largest employer in 1941 and it has remained so since. The two World Wars stimulated a boom in ship building. Tacoma today is again benefiting from its geography as the Port of Tacoma grows in capacity and strengthens the city's ties to other port cities in the Pacific Rim.

Balanced against the desire to control and exploit the land and sea, there is also an appreciation of scenic beauty. The Olympic Mountains, the Cascade Range and Mount Rainier are seen from the optimum perspective from Tacoma. Similarly, the steep banks arising from Commencement Bay below the city continue to be Tacoma's foremost scenic asset. ◆

This is the first dump truck purchased by the Tacoma Public Works Department in 1915. Commissioner Charles D. Atkins is at the wheel.

Engineers learned how NOT to build a suspension bridge with the dramatic failure of the Tacoma Narrows Bridge on November 7, 1940.

Entries from *The Diary of the Commissioner of Public Works, City of Tacoma, 1897-98*

Wednesday, July 7, 1897
This office was opened for business at 8 o'clock a.m. Notice of the discharge of John Sheridan, light inspector, on account of reduction of force, was sent to Civil Service Commission. A requisition was made on Civil Service Commission for one Rodman for City Engineers department. There being no names on the eligible list for rodman, F.A. Keasal was temporarily appointed and the Commission was asked to confirm the same. Other routine business was transacted during the day, and at 5 o'clock p.m. the office was closed.

Approved:	T.E. Doherty	W.S. Burt
	Commissioner	Act Clerk

Tacoma, Thursday, April 7, 1889
This office was opened for business at 8 o'clock a.m. Communication was sent [to] the City Council requesting authority to purchase a horse for use of the Commissioner of Public Works at cost from $50 to $75. Other routine business was transacted during the day and at 5 o'clock p.m. the office was closed.

Approved:	T.E. Doherty	S.T. Armstrong
	Commissioner	Clerk

Tacoma, Thursday, May 19th, 1889
This office was opened for business at 8 o'clock a.m. A communication was addressed to the City Council directing attention to the inadequacy of finances for performing the current and necessary street work in the ordinary manner and recommending the purchase of a road scraper, capable of performing the work of 25 men or more, at a cost of $275 or $300. Other business of a routine character was transacted and at 5 o'clock p.m. the office was closed.

Approved:	W. E. Hacker	S.T. Armstrong
	Commissioner	Clerk

1—Following the start of construction in July 1981, the Dome's 530 foot perimeter had taken shape by February 1982.

2—Like a giant erector set, the dome roof is assembled in concentric fashion toward its peak at 152 feet above floor level.

3—In April 1982, workers begin to cover the laminated beam roof structure with tongue and groove decking.

4—Fully enclosed by August of 1982, finishing touches including the Dome's distinctive diamond roof pattern, were completed in time for the grand opening in April 1983.

Below: Tacoma Public Works received national attention in 1961 for having constructed the first publicly-owned moving sidewalks in the country.

Mortimer H. Thomas, P.E.

Mort Thomas, a Tacoma native, graduated in 1954 from the University of Michigan with a Bachelor's degree in civil engineering. After serving in the Army he joined the Seattle consulting firm of Gardner and Hitchings in 1957. Projects included extensive site, drainage, and utility design for northwest military facilities. Mort became an associate with Roy Gardner and Associates in 1962. During the 1960s the firm was involved in utility design for suburban King County.

A major task was the changing of the western Bellevue area water supply to the City of Seattle Water Department's new east side supply line. Projects included transmission lines, four reservoirs and four pump stations. The firm also worked on several parks improvement projects for the City of Seattle.

In 1969, Gardner Engineers was incorporated under four principals. Mort served as vice president until 1972 when he became president. During the 1970s, Gardner Engineers expanded its capabilities in transportation engineering and industrial development. Street and highway design projects were carried out for Seattle, Renton, Auburn, Redmond, Poulsbo, King County, Snohomish County and Grays Harbor County. Industrial development clients included Burlington Northern Railroad, the Koll Company and Amax.

In the 1980s, Gardner Engineers work included highway projects for the Washington State Department of Highways. In 1987 the firm was reincorporated as Gardner Consultants with a new ownership. Mort served as vice president and principal engineer for two years. He left Gardner Consultants in 1989 and after a brief period with OTT-HDR he joined KCM in July 1990 and manages the Quality Assurance Program. ◆

Fred A. Thompson, P.E.

During his tenure with the City of Tacoma Public Works Department, Fred Thompson advanced from a Special Projects Engineer, to City Engineer, to Director of Public Works. The Public Works Department has an annual budget of $120 million with over 700 employees.

A number of major projects have been completed under Mr. Thompson's direction including the Tacoma Dome and the Tacoma Spur, I-705 project. This project has been in progress for 30 years and in the 1990s the East/West Road connecting the Spur to northeast Tacoma will be completed.

Mr. Thompson has directed the Tacoma Union Station Project, one of the foremost historic renovation projects in Tacoma. The renovation work developed the interior of and the adjacent property as a home for the Federal District Court. The project was completed in 1992.

Mr. Thompson served on the state's Transportation Improvement Board and American Public Works Association Board. He is also a past President of the Structural Engineers Association of Washington. He has served as an Army Reserve Colonel with the Corps of Engineers. Mr. Thompson has received the American Public Works Association, Washington Chapter, Public Works Leader of the Year Award, 1985. ◆

The TRANSPO Group, Inc.

Since our beginning in 1975, The TRANSPO Group has been a regional leader in providing quality transportation planning and traffic engineering to both private and public sector clients. Our services are designed to respond to emerging trends in transportation such as demand management planning, transit and HOV facility planning, and comprehensive transportation plan preparation to comply with the Growth Management Act. We provide services in the areas of transportation impact analyses, traffic signal and control systems design, parking studies, and traffic operations analyses. ◆

TRANSPORTATION SYSTEMS PLANNING
City of Des Moines Comprehensive Transportation Plan
City of SeaTac Comprehensive Transportation Plan
City of Kirkland Transportation Policy Plan
City of Marysville Comprehensive Transportation Plan
Enumclaw Central Area Traffic Study
Long-Range Plan for the Washington State Ferry System
Bellevue Long-Range Transportation System Plan

TRAFFIC DESIGN SERVICES
Park Ave. N and Garden Ave. N Road Improvements - Renton
I-90 Seattle Access Traffic Signalization - Seattle
NE 120th Street Pedestrian Signal - Kirkland
SR 202/228th Avenue NE - King County
Andover Park W/Baker Boulevard - Tukwila

PARKING
Kingdome
Seattle Center
Shilshole Bay Marina
Children's Hospital Medical Center
North Seattle Community College
Washington State University - Vancouver Campus

TRANSPORTATION IMPACT ANALYSIS
Residential Subdivisions
Urban High Rise Offices
Shopping Centers
Mixed-Use Projects
Master Plan Developments
Educational Institutions
Solid Waste Transfer Stations/Landfills

TRANSPORTATION DEMAND MANAGEMENT
PSCOG TDM Plan for Vision 2020
King County TDM Cost Effectiveness Analysis
University Center
Security Pacific Plaza
Washington Natural Gas
Sunset Property
Overlake Hospital Medical Center
Providence Medical Center
North Seattle Community College

TRANSIT AND HOV FACILITY PLANNING
SR 99 HOV Lane Alternatives Study
I-5 North HOV Lanes
Washington State Ferries Planning
High Capacity Transit Element of the Regional Trans. Plan
Northgate Transit Center and Park-and-Ride
Metro Park-and-Ride Locations and Prioritization Study
Neighborhood Transit Centers Program

THE NORTHWEST TRANSPORTATION SPECIALISTS
The TRANSPO Group, Inc.
14335 NE 24th Street, Suite 201
Bellevue, Washington 98007
(206) 641-3881

Thurston County

Olympia, as the state capital and before that the territorial hub, has always drawn active, politically-minded people to Thurston County. The history of the building of the county's roads and bridges reflects those organizational minds. They acted with incredible speed, given the size of the territory they were dealing with, to section, subdivide and create a network of roads in the county. The first 50 years of the *County Road Book* reads like a narrative to an ongoing Monopoly game. Starting at a place known as the Willamette Stone, west of Portland, the early surveyors proceeded up what is called the Willamette Meridian to a place just north of Olympia. Surveys which branched off of the meridian were first conducted in the Olympia area. The surveyors superimposed a grid of six miles square townships.

Thurston County was established in 1852 to "include land west of the Cascade Mountains and north of the Cowlitz Divide." The vast country was named after Samuel R. Thurston, Oregon Territory's delegate to Congress. Four years later Washington Territory was etched out of Oregon Territory and Thurston was broken into four counties: Snohomish, Pierce, King and Thurston. However, the need for roads stimulated a flurry of immediate road building activity. The first meeting of the Thurston County Board of Commissioners on July 5, 1852, saw Commissioners Arthur A. Denny and David Shelton divide the county into five precincts: Skagit, Port Townsend, Duwamps, Steilacoom and Olympia. David Chambers, of Chambers Prairie fame, was designated supervisor of the Olympia district. On that same day recorded business reflects the establishment of school districts and the granting of grocery licenses to William Coulter and Emma Sylvester.

Two months later, on September 6, the commissioners met again, this time to divide the county into four road districts. In those days public works were truly of the public. The commissioners ordered that all "portion of hands" residing in any of the given districts "are hereby allotted to work on the road." The routes built by these "hands," drafted to construct roads, most often followed horse-drawn carts or the feet of the Native Americans who had long since worn the paths of least resistance through the brush.

On December 8, 1952, the first road petition was put forth to the commissioners by John M. Chapman, Thomas A. Chapman and others "praying for the establishment of a county road running from the town of Seattle on Dewamps [sic] Bay to Steilacoom City." This was granted. S. Moses also presented "a petition from John Edgar and others praying for the establishment of a county road from the Yelm Prairie to McAllister's landing—on McAllister's Creek." This was allowed. The commissioners then appointed viewers to "view-out" and mark the two roads. The viewers trekked back into Olympia four months later, on April 4, 1853, to give their reports. They stated that they had marked out the Yelm Prairie Road "that commences at the point known as the Five Oaks, commencing at the most northerly oak. The road goes over hard ground the entire route and with very little work can be made an excellent road."

Road district supervisors also had a chance to report on their "volunteer" laborers: "On this day comes David L. Chambers, Road Supervisor and makes the following report. That the hands allotted to his district have faithfully performed their duties as required by law by working their full-time on said Road District for the year ending April 1, 1853."

Road districts proliferated over the years, until there were seemingly more districts than roads in them. At one time the districts numbered as high as 44, at which point they began using the alphabet as well. Districts were subdivided, added to, or taken over, as needs or politics changed.

References to a County Engineer appear sometime in 1907, and perhaps he had something to do with a consolidation into eight main road districts. The first County Engineer's name that can be verified from record is Theodore Young. Young apparently was the first of a line of able public works leaders that have shaped Thurston County's roads for the past century. ◆

Thurston County Public Works

County Engineers

T. D. Young	1910	Leo L. Coulter	1948-57
Fred Brown	1911-12	Arthur Ward	1958
W. H. Yeager, Jr.	1913-19	Ronald W. Wilder	1959-61
Fred Brown	1920	S. D. Betzing	1962-73
Frank Weir	1921-23	Murray Walker	1973-75
Neil R. McKay	1923-31	Tom Fitzmorris	1975-77
W. F. Dillaway	1931-32	Alva Williams, Jr.	1978-87
Neil R. McKay	1933-37	Gerald M. Hendricks	1988
Clarence B. Shain	1938-42	Jacob Armstrong	1988-present
W. H. Yeager, Jr.	1942-48		

Public Works Directors

Daniel F. Durig   1988-1993

Joe Cavin, Carl Parkhurst, John Dotson, Dewey Elliott, Dale Montgomery, Dave Clark, Jim McDougall, Konrad Muench, Ed Oliphant, and Will Garner have been with the Roads and Equipment Management Division for a combined total of 237 years.

Glenn Thompson (right), an Engineering Technician with the County for 10 years and a resident of Thurston County since the 1920s, rescued this plaque from the old Independence bridge, before it was demolished and a new one built in 1975.

Transportation Planning & Engineering, Inc.

Transportation Planning & Engineering, Inc. (T P & E) was founded in April 1968. Victor H. Bishop, P.E., was named president of the firm in April 1969. Bishop, a graduate of the Traffic and Transportation Engineering Master of Science program at the University of Washington in 1966, developed the 17 employee firm into a leader in traffic engineering in the State of Washington.

T P & E has retained the original goal of providing quality services in the specialized area of traffic engineering. The success and reputation of T P & E among its peers is testimony to this approach.

Victor H. Bishop, P.E., President

T P & E's first project in 1968 was a comprehensive traffic safety program for the City of Bellingham using National Highway Traffic Safety Administration Section 402 funds. This was Washington State's first traffic safety grant for a local agency. It stimulated 12 safety projects undertaken by T P & E for local agencies statewide. One element of this effort was the development of the Model Traffic Ordinance by Victor Bishop through the Municipal Research and Services Center of Washington. This ordinance, embodied in state law as RCW 46.90 in 1975, is widely used by the cities and counties of Washington.

Another early project by T P & E was the traffic engineering analysis of the Seattle Center area. This detailed analysis resulted in operating Mercer Street one way from the Seattle Center to Interstate 5, beginning in 1968. The Westlake Avenue N./Ninth Avenue N. and Queen Anne Avenue N./First Avenue N. one way couplets were implemented at the same time. This traffic operation, affectionately known as the "Mercer Mess," has withstood the test of time. Untold numbers of studies for traffic changes, freeway construction and park proposals to "fix" the "Mercer Mess" have been brought forward, only to be discarded in favor of T P & E's traffic engineering solution.

A project of the 1980s was the planning, design and implementation of the coordinated traffic signal system in the Lakewood/University Place area of Pierce County. Sixty-five independent traffic signals were interconnected with modern computer control, communication cable and signal timing plans to enhance the traffic flow on the arterial streets south of Tacoma. This project, led by David H. Enger, P.E., Vice President of T P & E, is an excellent example of the application of traffic engineering techniques to enhance the quality of life of Washington citizens.

In 1986, Mr. Bishop was presented the Outstanding Service Award by the Washington State Section of the Institute of Transportation Engineers.

Victor Bishop and David Enger are proud of the more than 125 traffic signals designed under their direction that are in operation around the State of Washington. T P & E continues to provide quality traffic engineering services to public agencies and the private development industry of the northwest. ◆

Transstate Paving Company

Transstate Paving Company started in business in the Tri-Cities in January 1983. The company, owned by Albert E. DeAtley, is licensed, bonded and insured. In December of 1982 Transstate bought the L.W. Vail Company, a long standing company located in the Tri-Cities area.

Transstate conducts $10-12 million dollars of gross business per annum. It has three permanent asphalt processing plants located in Richland, Pasco, and Walla Walla, and one portable plant which can be located at a project site as needed. In total, they produce 200,000 to 220,000 tons of hot mix annually. The company also owns and operates all the equipment necessary to provide a wide range of road construction services including excavation, surfacing, drainage, concrete curb and gutter as well as hot mix paving.

Transstate Paving was named "Contractor of the Year" by the Public Works Association for 1985 and 1986. The company is a division of Superior Asphalt and Concrete Company of Yakima, Washington which has been in business for more than 50 years. Mr. DeAtley chaired the National Asphalt Paving Association, NAPA, in 1994 and he has testified before the United States House Subcommittee on Surface Transportation. In addition to his involvement in resolving industry issues, Mr. DeAtley has been spokesman in the industry supporting research for improving hot mix asphalt pavement. His involvement with the National Center for Asphalt Technology, NCAT, helped establish a Professor Training Program and a research scholarship program. Two scholarships from this program have been presented to civil engineering students at Louisiana State University and similar scholarships are available to students participating in similar programs in other universities.

The Transstate President, Brian Sims, is also 1994 President of the Washington State Asphalt Paving Association. Mr. Sims has been instrumental in the promotion and operation of a cooperative Joint Industry/Washington State Department of Transportation Task Force and also a Joint Training Program.

Transstate Paving Company is proud of its many projects especially those which include all phases of road building. An example of this work is the Adams County Line project that consisted of an asphalt concrete overlay to include excavation for the slope flattening, latex modified concrete overlay of the existing bridge deck, drainage system renovation, permanent signing, guard rail installation, seeding and fertilizing.

The City of Richland Leslie Road Reconstruction is another significant project in the Tri-Cities region. The project consisted of construction of a city street from the raw land to the final details including excavation, embankment, placing sanitary sewer lines, storm sewers, concrete retaining walls, concrete curb, gutter, and sidewalks, placing crushed rock and asphalt concrete pavement, illumination system, seeding and fertilizing, and roadway paint striping. The project won the APWA "Contractor of the Year Award" for 1986. The Richland, Keene Road project won the same award for 1985. ◆

Transportation Improvement Board (Urban Arterial Board)

The Urban Arterial Board (UAB) was established by the Washington State Legislature in 1967 to reduce congestion on Washington urban arterial roads and streets. In June of 1988, the UAB was replaced by a new Transportation Improvement Board (TIB) that took on an expanded role.

In its more than 25 years in existence, the TIB (UAB) has funded over 1400 projects and provided over $900 million in grant funds. The highlights are summarized here:

1967 - The legislature authorized a new program of financial assistance to urban area cities and counties with population above 5,000 and increased the state tax on motor vehicle fuels by one and one-half cents per gallon. Five-eighths of one cent tax per gallon was devoted to the Urban Arterial Program. To accelerate the development of urban arterials, the legislature authorized the issuance of up to $200 million in bonds to be supported by revenue generated from the five-eighths of one cent tax per gallon on motor vehicle fuels.

1971 - The board changed the project matching ratio on all projects to not less than ten percent.

1977 - The legislature extended the eligibility for program participation to cities with less than 5,000 population. In addition, the legislature authorized a Series II $60 million bond program with $45 million allocated for statewide distribution and $15 million direct funding to rural incorporated cities. To generate more funding, the legislature enacted a variable fuel tax which changed the UAB funding to 7.12 percent of the fuel tax revenue.

1981 - The legislature authorized a Series III $100 million bond program with $84 million allocated for statewide distribution and $16 million direct funding to rural incorporated cities. The board was not able to implement the program because of insufficient fuel tax revenue to finance the bond debt payments.

1983 - The legislature increased the fuel tax to eighteen cents per gallon with the UAB receiving an additional one-third of one cent of the new fuel tax to enable the board to implement the Series III bond program.

1985 - The board changed the project matching ratio to not less than 20 percent for federal urban areas, but left the matching ratio at not less than 10 percent for rural incorporated cities.

1987 - The legislature enacted a law that requires a Value Engineering Study on all projects where the total project cost exceeds one million dollars or any other project where the UAB determines a study is necessary.

1988 - The legislature replaced the Urban Arterial Board with the new fifteen-member Transportation Improvement Board (TIB) and created the Transportation Improvement Account (TIA). The legislation provides that the new board will administer the Urban Arterial Trust Fund Program and will develop policies and procedures for implementing the TIA program. ◆

Transportation Improvement Board. Left to right: Annette McGee, James Toohey, Irving Reed, Darlene McHenry, Fred Thompson, Fred Anderson, Bill Hordan, George Benson, Ernest Geissler, Jack Pittis, Brian Corcoran, Dennis Skeate, John McBride, and M.J. Hrdlicka. Not shown - Robert Schuster.

N.E. Northgate Way in Seattle, looking east before construction.

Same view as above after construction.

Town of Cusick – First Street looking north before construction.

Same view as left after construction.

U. S. Army Corps of Engineers

Washington is rich in water. Rain from harsh Pacific storms and snowmelt from high mountain peaks feed an extensive system of lakes, river and harbors. It is this valuable resource that provides the historical connection between the State of Washington and the U. S. Army of Corps Engineers.

Although the Corps' beginning is rooted in the military service building forts and mapping out new territory during Revolutionary War days, the Corps took on another challenging engineering role in 1824 which would later greatly influence the growth of Washington.

Construction of the Lake Washington Ship Canal locks at the narrows of Salmon Bay viewed from the Great Northern Railroad Company bridge, July 9, 1815.

Hiram M. Chittenden

Entrance to filling culvert in the upper end of the south wall of the large lock, March 18, 1914.

James B. Cavanaugh

The motor launch Orcas is raised to the upper level of the small lock, July 25, 1916.

As hearty pioneers were moving westward, Congress passed the General Survey Act of 1824 and other laws which gave the Corps the responsibility of improving navigation of the country's rivers and harbors. From snagging logs to clearing sandbars in the Northwest, the Corps deepened and maintained these waterways to allow supplies and news from the outside world to reach small settlements like Fort Vancouver, Aberdeen and Port Townsend.

One of the Corps' earliest efforts in improving navigation in Washington began in the mid-1800s with removing rocks and snags on the Snake River between what is now Pasco, Washington, and Lewiston, Idaho. This allowed sternwheelers to travel the river carrying gold from Idaho mines to help finance the Civil War effort.

Throughout the 1800s, the Corps continued to explore this state's rivers for other possible transportation routes. In the autumn of 1882, Lt. Thomas W. Symons traveled up the Upper Columbia River "for the Corps [to] make an examination of the Columbia River, to determine its navigability and the advisability of putting steamboats on it to be used in the transportation of troops, stores, supplies, etc." Traveling in the small wooden boat *Witchwater*, Symon's expedition brought back never before seen maps and descriptions of Little Dalles, Kettle Falls and Grand Rapids. Later, his reports were used to improve and open up this stretch of the upper Columbia.

From the Columbia River to Grays Harbor and inland to the waters of Puget Sound, the Corps continued to improve navigation into the next century. Jetties were built along the mouth of the Columbia and at Grays Harbor to protect these main arteries of transportation from storms that pounded the coast.

As a result of great effort on the part of Major Hiram M. Chittenden in 1911 Corps' engineers began work on the construction of the Hiram M. Chittenden Locks in Ballard.

Under the direction of Major James B. Cavanaugh, District Engineer, it would take five years to complete the project with over 300 laborers being paid $2 a day to build the small and large locks. Completed in 1916 the large lock measured 825 feet long and 80 feet wide and the small lock was 150 by 28 feet. By the end of the year, over 7,500 vessels had used the locks.

Out on the coast, the Corps made passage over the treacherous Columbia River bar safer when it dredged a channel in the 1920s. Today the Corps still maintains 480 miles of the winding Columbia-Snake Inland Waterway connecting the Pacific Ocean to the inland cities of Clarkston, Washington and Lewiston, Idaho.

Completed in 1916, the Hiram M. Chittenden Locks provided water access from Puget Sound to Lake Union and Lake Washington.

Recognizing the hydropower potential of the Columbia in 1931 the Corps of Engineers submitted the 308 Report. This concise document served as the basic plan for Columbia River hydroelectric development over the next 50 years.

Under this plan, the first federal dam—the Bonneville Lock and Dam, named after an Army captain who had explored the Columbia River Basin over 100 years earlier—was built on the Columbia. Bonneville Dam took over five years to complete at a cost of $83 million. At the peak of construction, the total work force averaged about 3,000, with skilled workers earning a minimum hourly wage of $1.20, and unskilled workers earning 50 cents.

In the years following the construction of Bonneville Lock and Dam, the Corps of Engineers built eight other hydropower dams including The Dalles, John Day, McNary and Chief Joseph on the Columbia River and Ice Harbor, Little Goose, Lower Monumental and Lower Granite on the Snake River.

While electricity is produced from Northwest rains and snowmelts that feed its many rivers, rain and melting snow also produce devastating floods in many Northwestern communities, like those in the Skagit Valley or in Palouse country in Eastern Washington.

Three hundred fifty miles of Corps levees help protect areas across this state from troublesome river flooding, and in western Washington three dams are used for flood control on the Wynoochee, Green and White Rivers.

As Washington moves into its second century, the U. S. Army Corps of Engineers will continue its long historical tradition of helping to manage this state's valuable water resources in the areas of navigation, hydropower and flood control so Washington will continue to grow and prosper. ◆

U.S. Army Corps of Engineers famous snagboat W.T. Preston.

U.S. Army Corps of Engineers snagboat patrols Puget Sound for hazards such as partially submerged logs.

For over 50 years the Army Corps of Engineers has been involved in dam construction. Above top: Mud Mountain Dam under construction on the White River in 1941 for flood control. Above middle: Wynoochee River flood control dam. Above bottom: Chief Joseph Dam, hydropower.

URS Consultants, Inc.

Introduction to URS Consultants, Inc.

In 1991, the northwest operations of URS Consultants, Inc., (URS) celebrated its 100th anniversary—making it one of the oldest consulting engineering businesses in the Pacific Northwest.

The company, which originally provided surveying services, now specializes in engineering of wastewater collection and treatment; water supply, distribution, and treatment systems; roads and highways; marinas and ports; industrial and energy systems; and hazardous and toxic waste remediation. Other services include environmental studies and construction engineering services.

Over the years, URS has been responsible for the design of many of Washington state's major infrastructure improvements. Among the more notable projects are the predesign and final design of the Renton Effluent Transfer System, design services for utilities relocation and storm drainage facilities as part of the Downtown Seattle Transit Project, design of the Fred G. Redmon Bridge near Yakima, Washington, and final design of three I-90 westbound lanes and two center roadway lanes on Mercer Island. More recently, URS was hired by the Municipality of Metropolitan Seattle (Metro) to design the University Regulator Combined Sewer Overflow (CSO) Control Project to intercept storm flows from the Densmore Drain area.

URS was also involved in many of the state's early environmental projects and the company maintains an in-house staff specializing in environmental impact services.

Many of URS' projects have produced award-winning designs. For example, URS received the Engineering Excellence Award of the Consulting Engineers Council, the Grand Award of the Washington Aggregates and Concrete Association, and the Prestressed Concrete Institute Award. URS has also received an Award of Excellence from the Consulting Engineers Council.

History of the Company

URS' current offices, located at 1100 Olive Way in Seattle, house survey field books dating back to 1891. URS was originally named Stixrude and Naston, Land Surveyors, after its founders. Faint pencil entries in one of the survey books show that Stixrude and Naston helped survey sections of the University of Washington campus in the early 1890s.

The company's founders remained only during its early formative years, and both left shortly after the turn of the century. I. Curtiss Parker—a major contributor to the company's early growth—joined in 1905. In 1921, W. R. Hill joined the company. The company was known as Parker & Hill from 1921 to 1949.

When Allen E. Hill, W. R. Hill's son, and Gordon G. Ingman became partners in 1949 and 1951, respectively, the firm was renamed Parker, Hill & Ingman. W. R. Hill retired in 1951; Parker retired in 1955. William J. Chase became a partner in 1960. The company's name was changed to Hill, Ingman, Chase & Co. to reflect the new partnership, and it was officially incorporated later that year.

In 1968, Chase became president of the company and Hill, Ingman, Chase & Co. became a wholly owned subsidiary of URS Systems Group based in San Francisco, California.

Chase directed the growth, development, and service capabilities of URS' northwest operations until 1981. The company name was changed to URS Engineers in 1981, then changed again in 1987 to URS Consultants, Inc. After Chase retired, Walter L. Berschauer was promoted from senior vice president to the head of the Seattle office. After Berschauer retired in 1988, the company management was transferred to the URS corporate

The first prestressed concrete water reservoir in the Pacific Northwest was built in Ephrata, WA and held 1 million gallons of water.

office. John Butts, Vice President of Northwest Operations, currently manages the Seattle, Anchorage, and Portland offices.

Contributions to Washington History

In 1971, the *Seattle Daily Journal of Commerce* published an article celebrating the company's 80th anniversary and referred to it as "a pioneer engineering firm." Although URS has provided engineering consulting and land surveying services in Washington state throughout the last 100 years, the company's primary contributions began in the mid-part of this century. In the 1940s, Americans began a mass exodus from cities and farms to the new "suburbs." I. Curtiss Parker recognized the need for sewer and water system regulations to guide development. His efforts led to the enactment of the state's first sewer district laws and the beginning of a cooperative relationship between the company and the state's burgeoning sewer districts.

In addition to the company founders, a number of individuals have played key roles in URS and Washington state history. Chester J. Woods played a key role in the company from 1947 to 1987. He received both the Harry S. Swearingen and James S. Robertson awards for public service from the American Public Works Association (APWA) Washington chapter. Walter G. Ramsay worked for URS for more than 30 years. He was involved in a number of the original water supply, wastewater, urban drainage, and transportation projects for the City of Kent.

In addition to providing consulting services, URS has helped to advance techniques and methods in design and construction. Some of URS' contributions are described below.

URS improved the quality of gravity sewer system construction through the introduction of rubber sewer gaskets and by development of air pressure testing for pipe leaks.

URS was instrumental in the development of specifications and tests for concrete pipe.

URS was the first company to use a hydraulic grit eductor to replace the more costly mechanical methods of removing sand and gravel from wastewater treatment facilities.

URS introduced the first prestressed concrete water reservoir in the Pacific Northwest (located in Ephrata).

URS introduced an innovative floating breakwater system for the Port of Poulsbo.

Looking Toward the Future

URS is now one of the largest publicly held professional services organizations in the country and is ranked by *Engineering News Record* in the top 10 percent of consulting engineering firms based on gross revenue. Revenues and backlog have more than doubled since 1984, and new offices and major service capabilities in the hazardous/toxic waste remediation area have been developed. ◆

Utilities Underground Location Center

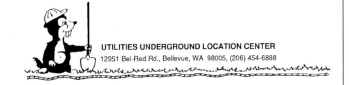

UTILITIES UNDERGROUND LOCATION CENTER
12951 Bel-Red Rd., Bellevue, WA 98005, (206) 454-6888

In 1978 five sponsoring utilities established the Utilities Underground Location Center (UULC). The intent was to establish a One-Call Utility Notification System for excavators in King County. In the past decade this original goal has expanded to include several states and dozens of counties. The founding sponsors of UULC are: Pacific Northwest Bell (US West), Puget Sound Power & Light, Washington Natural Gas, King County Department of Public Works and Seattle City Light.

The Center is managed by an Operating Committee composed of representatives from each sponsor. The committee, which meets monthly, is responsible for budgeting; overseeing Center contractors; establishing operating policies and procedures for the UULC; and setting rates for UULC participants.

Since 1978 UULC has become the largest and most efficient One-Call Notification System serving the north western States. Its growth has come from increased membership, expansion of the geographical service area and volume of location requests. In 1978 the founding five sponsors confined their geographical area to King County and dealt with 17,430 requests. In 1992 the geographic area included six states—Washington, Oregon, Idaho, Montana, North Dakota and Wyoming—with 389 utilities. The total requests for that year were 212,800.

During its first 12 years the UULC has become nationally recognized for its large and broad based membership and its determination to lead the industry by providing a cost effective One-Call Notification System. The organization has been active is helping set standards in Washington and helped pass a very progressive "dig safely" law in Washington. Since its passage this statute has become a model for several other states. ◆

Founders of the Utilities Underground Location Center

Jerry Cronin
Washington Natural Gas

Carl (Andy) Anderson
Puget Sound Power & Light

Vic Sparling
King County Dept. of Public Works

Ron Browne
Pacific Northwest Bell

Harry Lewing
Seattle City Light

Tim Hogan
Washington Natural Gas (Legal Counsel)

Jerry Henry
Puget Sound Power & Light Manager

Tom Odegaard
Asplundh Tree Expert Co.

William M. (Bill) Valentine, P.E.

Bill Valentine's career in the public and private works sector has spanned four decades. In 1956 he founded Valentine, Fisher & Tomlinson, Consulting Engineers and served as president of the firm until his retirement in 1980. The small firm grew to a staff of 58 by 1979. One of the best-known undertakings of this firm was the design and construction of the mechanical and electrical features for the International Fountain at the Seattle Center constructed for the 1962 World's Fair.

The fountain's theme, "sculpture with water," had never been attempted before on so large a scale. Valentine, Fisher & Tomlinson working with the Seattle Fireboat "Alki" to determine visual impact of the water patterns—created by the fire hoses during the trials—made decisions as to water quantity, operating pressure, size and shape of individual water streams, angle and throw. The fountain control panel operates 217 control valves and 256 colored lights, choreographed to match prearranged musical programs. This challenge was complicated by an extremely short time schedule. Keeping water pressure constant while flow rates changed, and automatically adjusting to wind velocity were also major problems resolved under Valentine's direction as project engineer.

Mr. Valentine has contributed technical articles in engineering trade magazines, and he has served in many professional organizations throughout his career, including WSPE, CECW,

International Fountain, Seattle Center, Seattle, WA. Structural Engineer, Al Kelly; local architects: John Phillips, Harry Rich; fountain concept: Japanese Architects.

SAME. He is also a member of ASHRAE, American Association for the Advancement of Science, New York Academy of Science, and the Seattle Engineers Club.

Mr. Valentine has been active in civic groups, including Seattle Round Table, MIBC, Mercer Island Board of Appeals, Moose and Elks. In retirement, he is involved in Video Stores, Inc., video productions. ◆

Val Vue Sewer District

The Val Vue Sewer District is the oldest of the sewer districts in the State of Washington. It was formed in February 1941, following a favorable vote of the people of the area to incorporate and to pass general obligation bonds.

The district first served a large housing development and businesses along Pacific Highway South. As the area developed there were numerous annexations. The merger with the inoperative McMicken Heights Sewer District further enlarged the district.

The present boundaries of the district extend on both sides of Pacific Highway South from the Seattle city limits on the north, to Sea-Tac Airport on the south, and west to include Riverton Heights, and east to include Riverton, McMicken Heights and part of Tukwila to Interstate-5.

The district presently services 3,600 accounts within an area of 1,800 acres. The district operates a sanitary sewerage collection system comprised of 55 miles of sewer line with pipes ranging in size from six inches to 24 inches, 1,500 manholes and 12 pump stations. The original part of the district system was built in 1946 and consisted of two miles of six-inch and eight-inch pipe and a spirogester-type treatment facility which discharged its effluent into the Duwamish River. In 1956 a new primary treatment plant was built to replace the original treatment facility and to provide capacity for the expanding district. This plant operated until 1966 when the State Highway Department condemned the treatment plant to make way for SR 599 freeway. Since 1966 the district has contracted with Metro for treatment of its sewerage.

One of the very early resolutions, adopted in April of 1946, stated: a) the County Engineer would be the operating agent; b) $90 a lot would be charged to all individuals who wished to connect; c) the monthly maintenance charges would be $1.75 per month to be collected annually. The district presently charges $3.75 for collection and maintenance. The METRO charge of $9.70 for treatment brings the total monthly charge to $13.45.

Over the years the district has been well served by many dedicated commissioners. William F. Fairbanks was elected to the Val Vue Board shortly after the formation of the district and served for more than a decade. The commissioners in 1989 were Betty Lunz, Blaine W. Butters and Michael J. West. Ms. Lunz was elected in 1965 and has served continuously for 24 years. She was the first woman in the State of Washington to be elected Sewer District Commissioner. Mr. Butters has been a commissioner for 18 years and Mr. West has served for six years.

In the past 20 years the district has tripled the area served. Connections have increased from 900 to 3,600. The office grew from one person in the 1960s to a full service staff in the 1980s. In June of 1973, Terry J. Matelich was employed as the first district manager and has served for 16 years. In 1975 the district constructed a modern facility located at 14816 Military Road South with offices, a conference room for public meetings and a shop area for maintenance equipment.

By 1989 a staff of six, working with current technology and equipment, ensure the health and safety of the ratepayers of the district. The goal of protecting the environment and maintaining the health and safety of the public is one to which the Board of Commissioners and the employees of the Val Vue Sewer District are totally committed. ◆

Val Vue district office located at 14816 Military Road South, Seattle, Washington.

District staff include (left to right): Steven Fletcher, Barbara Stensland, Bryan Lampshire, Donna Gleason, Terry Matelich, and Mark Parsons.

Val Vue Sewer District Commissioners: Michael J. West, Betty Lunz, and Blaine W. Butters.

City of Vancouver

Candy L. Arata • Arnold A. Armstrong • Charles Avery • Jerry Max Bacon • Hurman Bain • Keith Ballard • John Bean • Terry Ray Berdinner • Larry Bergstrom • Edward R. Birch • Thomas D. Boyer • Timothy John Brace • Bonnie S. Bremer • Mary Jo Briggs • Eric L. Brown • Richard Brown • Terry Bryant • Cathryn Burke • Richard Butterfield • John A. Cain • Robert A. Combs • William Combs • Elizabeth M. Cook • Marilyn Correll • Betsy Dahlstrom • Jerry H. Davies • Debi Joyce Davis • Vikki Lee Davis • Dave Mark Dunbar • Patrick G. Easley • Curtis H. Ebel • Paul Thomas Edgerton • Victor R. Ehrlich •

TRADITION

INTERSTATE BRIDGE:
Completion of the Interstate Bridge in 1917 dramatically changed travel patterns and opened new markets and growth opportunities for Vancouver.

Robert Arthur Eichhorst • Emil Fercho • Ronald Fredin • Cevin Fritz • Steven P. Furno • Russell W. Glaser • Lynda M. Goad • LeRoy Goodwin • Annette M. Griffy • Laurence Gruber •

Michael Hale • Joan Marie Hall • Maurice Leroy Han • Ralph Scott Hancock • James Christopher Harmon • Laura Harper • Brian Harte • David M. Hays • Jan L. Hedges • Edward J. Heidt • Richard J. Hoffman • George Horner • Charles Howard • Donald A. Jackman • Frederick Bernhard Jackson • Leroy Johnson • Steve R. Kennedy • Norman B. Kramm • Gunther Krannich • Dan L. Kunze • Fred Langer • Donald Rex Lawry • David Lee Lengvenis • Paul L. Lester • Ralph L. Lieser • John Lowry • Lawrence Margicin • Charles Craig Marler • Lewis D. Marler • Rick Myron Masser • Kim Evan McBride • Terry D. McClure • Richard G. McNett • Donald Monfort • Kevin Lee Morgan • Brian

PUBLIC WATER SUPPLY:
Throughout its history, Vancouver's growth has depended on abundant supplies of clean water. The municipally-owned water system has guaranteed this quality since 1937.

Ronald Moss • Dennis C. Murphy • Dale E. Netherda, Jr. • Dale Netherda • A. J. Olson • Bonita J. Oslund • John Ostrowski • Stephen Ouellette • Patricia Jean Owen • Denny J. O'Neil • William K. Parke • Lanny Parson • Cindy L. Peterson • Dean A. Pfaender • Gary Pierce • Robert Pine • Karen Gail Ratliff • Thomas W. Ray • John Edward Repman • Dale Richardson • Charles Riddle • Thayer K. Rorabaugh • Keith Clyde Ross • John N. Rundquist • Loren Russell • Thomas R. Sadler • Gary D. Salmi • James A. Sedell • Janell Sessions • Donald L. Skaggs • Barbara Jane Smith • Terry Smith • Marce Sorenson • Robert P. Spencer • Calvin Stair • Francis Story • Steven A. Syverson • Robert Tabor • Kenneth Thomas • Jim Thomson • Wayne Timmins • Eric M. Torgerson • Janice L. Totten • Allen Roger Trenda • Tracy L. Tuntland • Nora B. (Jacki) Unger • Alice Van Kirk

FORT VANCOUVER:
The first major Public Works Project in Vancouver was the fort, established in 1826 on the site where the reconstructed fort stands today.

• Virginia Ellen Vincent • John M. Walter • David Wannamaker • Frank T. Wilson • Jodie Ann Wyrick • Candy L. Arata • Arnold A. Armstrong • Charles Avery • Jerry Max Bacon • Hurman Bain • Keith Ballard • John Bean • Terry Ray Berdinner • Larry Bergstrom • Edward R. Birch • Thomas D. Boyer • Timothy John Brace • Bonnie S. Bremer • Mary Jo Briggs • Eric L. Brown • Richard Brown • Terry Bryant • Cathryn Burke • Richard Butterfield • John A. Cain • Robert A. Combs • William Combs • Elizabeth M. Cook • Marilyn Correll • Betsy Dahlstrom • Jerry H. Davies • Debi Joyce Davis • Vikki Lee Davis • Dave Mark Dunbar • Patrick G. Easley • Curtis H. Ebel • Paul Thomas Edgerton • Victor R. Ehrlich • Robert Arthur Eichhorst • Emil Fercho • Ronald Fredin • Cevin Fritz • Steven P. Furno • Russell W. Glaser • Lynda M. Goad • LeRoy Goodwin • Annette M. Griffy • Laurence Gruber • Michael Hale • Joan Marie Hall • Maurice Leroy Han • Ralph Scott Hancock • James Christopher Harmon • Laura Harper • Brian Harte • David M. Hays • Jan L. Hedges • Edward J. Heidt • Richard J. Hoffman • George Horner • Charles Howard • Donald A. Jackman • Frederick Bernhard Jackson • Leroy Johnson • Steve R. Kennedy • Norman B. Kramm • Gunther Krannich • Dan L. Kunze • Fred Langer • Donald Rex

BUILT BY PEOPLE

Lawry • David Lee Lengvenis • Paul L. Lester • Ralph L. Lieser • John Lowry • Lawrence Margicin • Charles Craig Marler • Lewis D. Marler •
Rick Myron Masser • Kim Evan McBride • Terry D. McClure • Richard G. McNett • Donald Monfort • Kevin Lee Morgan • Brian Ronald Moss • Dennis C. Murphy • Dale E. Netherda, Jr. • Dale Netherda • A. J. Olson • Bonita J. Oslund • John Ostrowski • Stephen Ouellette • Patricia Jean Owen • Denny J. O'Neil • William K. Parke • Lanny Parson • Cindy L. Peterson • Dean A. Pfaender • Gary Pierce • Robert Pine • Karen Gail Ratliff • Thomas W. Ray • John Edward Repman • Dale Richardson • Charles Riddle • Thayer K. Rorabaugh • Keith Clyde Ross • John N. Rundquist • Loren Russell • Thomas R. Sadler • Gary D. Salmi • James A. Sedell • Janell Sessions • Donald L. Skaggs • Barbara Jane Smith • Terry Smith • Marce Sorenson • Robert P. Spencer • Calvin Stair • Francis Story • Steven A. Syverson • Robert Tabor • Kenneth Thomas • Jim Thomson • Wayne Timmins • Eric M. Torgerson • Janice L. Totten • Allen Roger Trenda • Tracy L. Tuntland • Nora B. (Jacki) Unger • Alice Van Kirk • Virginia Ellen Vincent • John M. Walter • David Wannamaker • Frank T. Wilson • Jodie Ann Wyrick • Candy L. Arata • Arnold A. Armstrong • Charles Avery • Jerry Max Bacon • Hurman Bain • Keith Ballard • John Bean • Terry Ray Berdinner • Larry Bergstrom • Edward R. Birch • Thomas D. Boyer • Timothy John Brace • Bonnie S. Bremer • Mary Jo Briggs • Eric L. Brown • Richard Brown • Terry Bryant • Cathryn Burke • Richard Butterfield • John A. Cain • Robert A. Combs • William Combs • Elizabeth M. Cook • Marilyn Correll • Betsy Dahlstrom • Jerry H. Davies • Debi Joyce Davis • Vikki Lee Davis • Dave Mark Dunbar • Patrick G. Easley • Curtis H. Ebel • Paul Thomas Edgerton • Victor R. Ehrlich • Robert Arthur Eichhorst • Emil Fercho • Ronald Fredin • Cevin Fritz • Steven P. Furno • Russell W. Glaser • Lynda M. Goad • LeRoy Goodwin • Annette M. Griffy • Laurence Gruber • Michael Hale • Joan Marie Hall • Maurice Leroy Han • Ralph Scott Hancock • James Christopher Harmon • Laura Harper • Brian Harte • David M. Hays • Jan L. Hedges • Edward J. Heidt • Richard J. Hoffman • George Horner • Charles Howard • Donald A. Jackman • Frederick Bernhard Jackson • Leroy Johnson • Steve R. Kennedy • Norman B. Kramm • Gunther Krannich • Dan L. Kunze • Fred Langer • Donald Rex Lawry • David Lee Lengvenis • Paul L. Lester • Ralph L. Lieser • John Lowry • Lawrence Margicin • Charles Craig Marler • Lewis D. Marler • Rick Myron Masser • Kim Evan McBride • Terry D. McClure • Richard G. McNett • Donald Monfort • Kevin Lee Morgan • Brian Ronald Moss • Dennis C. Murphy • Dale E.

OFFICERS ROW ENTRANCE:
The new traffic circle at the entrance to historic Officers Row is a symbol of the combination of new, modern facilities with the traditions of the past.

KAISER SHIPYARDS:
Many shipyard workers such as these contributed to the economic growth of Vancouver during World War II. The demand they created for public facilities started a postwar Public Works boom that continues today.

Netherda, Jr. • Dale Netherda • A. J. Olson • Bonita J. Oslund • John Ostrowski • Stephen Ouellette • Patricia Jean Owen • Denny J. O'Neil • William K. Parke • Lanny Parson • Cindy L. Peterson • Dean A. Pfaender • Gary Pierce • Robert Pine • Karen Gail Ratliff • Thomas W. Ray • John Edward Repman • Dale Richardson • Charles Riddle • Thayer K. Rorabaugh • Keith Clyde Ross • John N. Rundquist • Loren Russell • Thomas R. Sadler • Gary D. Salmi • James A. Sedell • Janell Sessions • Donald L. Skaggs • Barbara Jane Smith • Terry Smith • Marce Sorenson • Robert P. Spencer • Calvin Stair • Francis Story • Steven A. Syverson • Robert Tabor • Kenneth Thomas • Jim Thomson • Wayne Timmins • Eric M. Torgerson • Janice

VANCOUVER   WASHINGTON

Walker and Associates

The Walker Company was founded by George F. Walker in 1953, a time when private industry was able to take advantage of mapping technology refined during World War II. Originally called North Pacific Mapping Service, the company name was changed in 1956 to Walker & Whiteford, Inc. and in 1967 to Walker & Associates, Inc.

In addition to aerial mapping and surveying, services include photographic prints and murals for presentation as well as translucent mylars for project planning. Aerial film archives include a large collection of historical photography. In 1967 the company acquired the assets of Pacific Aerial Survey, which was the original aerial photographic firm in the Northwest. As a result the aerial negative file at Walker & Associates dates back to 1936 and contains over 400,000 frames.

The original concept of Walker & Associates, Inc. has not changed over the years. It was and still is dedicated to providing a complete aerial mapping service to other professionals, including government agencies, municipalities and industrial clients.

Walker & Associates, Inc., has played a role in the development and planning of a great number of Washington public works projects. As a photogrammetric mapping company, its services are required before design can begin on power lines, sewers, freeways, dams and other types of construction. Some representative public works projects include: transportation, public power, wastewater, landfills and municipal planning.

The company is proud of its public works achievements over the years:

1957 - Walker & Whiteford, Inc. mapped the lower Queen Anne area for the Century 21 Exposition.

1962 - Adapted a Cessna 180 to high altitude capabilities.

1967 - Initiated major surveying and mapping projects for Spokane County and other municipalities for the purpose of city wide planning.

1974 - King County Department of Public Works selected Walker & Associates for small scale topographic mapping of south King County for a flood mitigation study.

1980 - Walker & Associates moved from the downtown Seattle to a new building carefully designed to facilitate each step of the mapping process.

1984 - The company made the shift from analog to digital map making capabilities.

1989 - George F. Walker, prior to his passing, began negotiating the purchase of Walker & Associates, Inc. by the Sheboygan, Wisconsin based Aero-Metric Engineering, Inc. (AME). When negotiations were complete, we became one of six offices covering the continental United States. This affiliation greatly enhances our resources and technical services. These include surveying, topographic, and planimetric mapping, photo lab services and digital orthography.

1990 - Walker & Associates moved to a new and larger location. These new facilities include a full service color and black and white photo lab. ◆

City of Walla Walla

As one of the oldest communities in Washington, Walla Walla was an established fur trading center beginning in 1810. Fort Walla Walla was established in 1818. The Whitman Mission was opened in 1837, and was the scene of a massacre in 1847. "New" Fort Walla Walla was constructed in 1856 where today's central business district is located. Washington State's first constitution was signed at the Walla Walla Constitutional Convention in 1878, 11 years before statehood.

Walla Walla public works history begins with construction of military forts. The John Mullan Road was built in 1861 running 624 miles to Fort Benton, Montana. The gold rush of 1861-67 created a boom town. At this time Walla Walla was the largest city in Washington.

The first railroad in Washington was constructed in 1874. The nationally known "rawhide" railroad ran from Walla Walla to Wallula on the Columbia River. Rails were four-by-six timbers with "strap iron" strips tied to the top with rawhide, hence the name. Transportation systems began with game trails, and progressed to wagon roads, railroads, street cars, modern streets and finally, freeways. The first street paving project was Main and Alder Streets in 1904. In the 1920s many streets were paved with "Warrenite," a natural asphalt product.

The unique and naturally pure water supply system is the centerpiece of Walla Walla's public works. The city purchased the water system from the Walla Walla Water Company in 1899. At that time the municipal water supply was drawn from Mill Creek near the heart of downtown. The city extended a pipeline in 1907 along Mill Creek 12 miles east near the Oregon border where an intake was constructed in Mill Creek. In 1922 the pipeline was extended another four and one half miles to the edge of a 22,000 acre protected watershed at the headwaters of Mill Creek.

In 1983 the city began $20 million public work replacing the old pipeline and converting the natural water energy of water falling 1,140 feet to electrical energy and selling the electric energy. Portions of the new pipeline were placed in service in 1986 and the power plant began generating December 1988.

Walla Walla also leads the state in water pollution control. The city constructed one of the first secondary treatment facilities in Washington in 1928. A 700 acre spray irrigation facility designed to make multiple use of cannery waste water was completed in 1972. In 1983 the city completed an advance wastewater treatment facility for domestic waste.

Original coal oil street light lamps installed in 1874 were converted to gas in 1881 and later to modern day high pressure sodium lights. Public transportation was provided by horse drawn street cars in 1884, progressing to electric trolleys at the end of the century and to buses in 1926. Today the city has a modern transit system.

The Corps of Engineers has been headquartered in Walla Walla since the floods of 1931. A major project involved lining the portion of Mill Creek that runs through the heart of Walla Walla with concrete. Flood control projects concluded with a dam and flood storage reservoir in 1941. ◆

Washington State Association of County Engineers and Public Works Directors

The Washington State Association of County Engineers (WSACE) is one of the oldest of public officials' organizations in the State of Washington. The WSACE was organized at a meeting held in North Yakima in 1906. King County Engineer, A.L. Valentine, was elected as its first President when the group held its second meeting in Bellingham in 1907.

Not much is known about the activities of the organization during its early years, because all of its official records were destroyed when the Ferry County Courthouse burned to the ground in 1935.

Following the courthouse disaster there was a concerted effort, over a period of several years, by officers and members of the Association to reconstruct the organization's records as accurately as possible. The result of that effort was the compilation of a "Family Bible" which contains a reasonably good record of all of the Association's annual meeting since 1915. The volume of history is now in the custody of the County Road Administration Board in Olympia.

The organization's first constitution was adopted at a meeting in Chehalis in January 1915, during the presidency of Roy Thompson of Pierce County. Among the participants was Island County's Burwell Bantz, who went on to become Director of Highways. The first set of bylaws, also adopted at the 1915 meeting, established annual dues of $1. Minutes of the annual meetings held during the 1920s reveal that at each session there was spirited discussion of two key issues: a) the need for a law requiring that county engineers be licensed; and b) that highway construction contracts be let on a unit bid rather than a lump sum basis.

The reconstructed minutes of the 1926 meeting in Longview make reference to the President of the newly formed Public Works Contractor's Association, who assured the group that the contractors had organized not to fight public officials, but to assist them by eliminating wasteful construction methods.

At the Walla Walla meeting in 1929 and Vancouver meeting in 1930, Governor Rowland A. Chartley and Highway Director Samuel J. Humes were distinguished guests. Among other things, the group adopted a resolution favoring the addition of one cent to the state gas tax, provided that all of the money be returned to counties for maintenance and construction of roads and bridges.

At the Spokane meeting in 1935 there was heated discussion regarding a recently passed law limiting the expenditure for day labor work on any one project to $5,000. In addition, there was considerable conversation about the need for a uniform cost accounting system. During the early and mid-1930s the topic of debate was the idea of both maintenance and construction of county roads being put under the jurisdiction of the county engineer, who was typically only in charge of construction at that time.

It was during these years that some of the legendary greats of county engineering became active including J. Swain of Asotin; Charley Derako of Clark; Cub Winnett of Columbia; John Kirkwood of Grays Harbor; and O.E. Brashers of Yakima.

Also at the 1935 meeting the engineers were urged to support an initiative petition which would provide for a three member County Board of Commissioners consisting of the Sheriff, Treasurer and County Engineer. Each office was for six years.

In the 1930s the Association became involved with the issue of engineers' pay. At the 1938 meeting the Engineer's Salary Committee recommended that no licensed professional engineer working under bond should be asked to work for less than $200 a month. In 1938 a resolution was passed noting that in certain counties commissioners were paid a per diem wage, a method of compensation which was not found conducive to good business practice. The state legislature was requested to pass legislation providing that all county commissioners were compensated with a yearly salary.

Entering the 1940s new faces appeared in leadership position such as Walt Winters in Douglas (later in King), Harold Blanton in Franklin, Cecil Kinder Garfield (later in Benton and Clark), Bill Bugge in Jefferson (later Director of Highways), S. Pattison in Kitsap, Augie Hanson in Klickitat (later in Wahkiakum), Jim Dodson in Grant and Don West in Chelan. During these years the position of County Engineer was an excellent training background for higher office in that almost every Director of Highways through the mid-1960s came out of the ranks of county engineers.

Today, the Association has over 150 members with representative from 38 of Washington's 39 counties. Current committees include Past President's Committee; Executive Committee; Professional Development; Salary Survey; Technical Programs; Communications; Membership; Finance & Resources; Telecommunications; Legislative & Law Review; and Emergency Services. In 1996, the Association hired a part-time consultant to develop an Officer's Manual, a membership directory and organize the Associations files.

As the Association approaches a new millennium the primary goal of the assembled county engineers has been to serve their respective constituencies in as professional and economic a manner as possible. The organization itself offers a forum for the members whereby they may be afforded opportunities to enhance leadership effectiveness, promote professional development, build professional relationships, and to advocate stewardship of the environment and infrastructure with which they have been entrusted. The record clearly shows that they have been and continue to be dedicated public servants. The responsibilities of the WSACE members are increasing, as the duties become more varied in a county government structure that is becoming increasingly more complex.

Washington State Department of Transportation

Before the Department of Highways (DOH) was created by the Washington State Legislature in 1905 people traveled by foot, canoe or horseback. People moved from place to place on foot paths and narrow wagon roads built mostly with volunteer labor provided by the farmers and businessmen who benefited most from such improvements. In 1889 when Washington State was officially declared a state, volunteer labor road improvement had been well established.

In 1893 the state legislature sought wagon road construction over a North Cascades route. A sum of money was earmarked to construct a road designated as "between the Nooksack River in Whatcom County . . . to Marblemount and on to Marcus near Kettle Falls." This route is today's modern, picturesque, environmentally sound SR 20, which was completed and opened to full traffic use in September 1972—79 years after the first legislative action.

When DOH was created in 1905 under the leadership of J. M. Snow, the first Highway Commissioner, there were 1,081 miles of state roads, with 124 miles in "improved" condition. Today travelers enjoy a modern, sophisticated transportation network that includes 7,000 miles of state highways, 3,500 bridges and 16 emergency airfields. Seven hundred sixty-four of these miles are complex, multi-laned interstate freeways. In addition, the system includes the largest ferry fleet in the nation, with 25 vessels carrying 23 million passengers a year. Moreover, a public transportation system exists that allows users to reach most major cities by bus or rail transit within the Evergreen State.

Early 1900s . Practical travel via horsepower, often in gumbo mud. (Credit: WSDOT photo)

State Road #1, Kent-Des Moines Road to Seattle in 1930s. Full crew is laying concrete pavement. (Credit: WSDOT photo)

Seattle's early transportation modes...looking north from Third and Spring Streets, early 1900s (after 1907, since Denny Hotel is gone). (Credit: Seattle Historical Society)

By 1910 the first automobiles caused complex problems and led to a search for hard surface materials for road building. The 1911 Permanent Highway Act gave more control over road construction to the state. A variety of paving materials were used including macadam oil paving, Warrenite paving and wooden planks. Concrete paving was first used in 1912 on a section of highway near Chehalis in Lewis County.

Washington State's Motor Vehicle Fund was created in 1919 with funds dedicated to highway related projects. By 1920 citizens owned 186,827 motor vehicles. In 1921 DOH gained complete control of highway maintenance on the state highway system, and a one cent per gallon gas tax began to pay for construction and maintenance of the system. The tax was later raised to three cents and five cents per gallon and the speed limit was raised from 30 mph to 40 mph.

Steam shovels were first used in 1922 to keep snowbound Snoqualmie Pass open through the winter. And, in 1927 oil was first used to prevent dust on highways.

The permanent post of Director of Highways was established in 1933, with Lacey V. Murrow named as Director. The following year the department began using aerial photography, radio communications and truck weighing stations. The Washington Toll Bridge Authority was established in 1937. In 1940, the first Lake Washington concrete floating bridge was opened to traffic across Lake Washington between Seattle and Mercer Island. The First Tacoma Narrows suspension bridge, nicknamed "Galloping Gertie," collapsed in high winds four months after it was opened to traffic.

The Federal Aid Highway Act, providing for a national system of interstate highways, was enacted in 1944. In 1956 the U.S. Congress passed the legislation that created the 42,000 mile nationwide Interstate and Defense Highway System.

In 1963 a corridor hearing was held concerning expansion of Interstate 90 between Seattle, Mercer Island and South Bellevue. As a result of the hearing the second concrete floating bridge, the Evergreen Point Bridge, was built between Seattle and Kirkland. Today completion work continues on the $1.4 billion I-90 Project. Massive improvements were completed in 1993, including the longest soft soil bore tunnel in the United States, multi-laned floating bridges across Lake Washington, and lids near Mount Baker Ridge and Mercer Island.

In 1965 a management survey created seven major divisions within DOH. In that year a grant was received to build four new super-ferry vessels. In 1970 the DOH moved into its new home on Olympia's east campus where it remains today. The Department of Transportation (created in 1977) sees continuing challenges ahead in the next century as Washington grows. ◆

Early DOH cable ferry vessel used to carry people, animals, and vehicles across the Columbia River in early 1900s. (Credit: WSDOT photo)

Early 1900s. Old Steam shovel used to excavate soils and rocks in early road-building era…on Tanwax Hill Pierce Conty. (Credit: WSDOT photo)

State Road #1, November 3, 1930, Seattle South. Equipment breaking up existing highway paving with a 5,500 lb. cast iron ball. Old pavement removed, replaced with cement concrete pavement. (Credit: WSDOT photo)

Lacey Murrow Concrete Floating Bridge project (old U.S. 10 route, now I-90) in Seattle. "Gasless" handling of concrete in tunnel paving (June 19, 1940). Use of gasoline-powered trucks with carbon monoxide fumes was a big concern deep inside the bridge approach tunnels. (Credit: WSDOT photo)

Washington State Good Roads and Transportation Association

"The oldest, continually active membership organization concerned with highways in the world—since 1899."

The above description summarizes the essence of the Washington State Good Roads and Transportation Association (WSGRTA). The organization has a long history of dynamic leadership and accomplishments in realizing its goal of assuring that Washington has good roads. A look back at its founding at the end of the nineteenth century by a handful of determined men reveals the vision and organizational skills that have always been present in the group's membership.

More than 100 important men had been invited by Samuel Hill to attend that September 14, 1899, meeting in Spokane which Hill had called to discuss forming an association to promote good roads for the new State of Washington. Fourteen men answered Hill's call and founded the organization that quickly became a potent factor in Washington affairs.

The "Old Guard," as the original 14 founders came to be affectionately known, were drawn together by the mutual agreement that the chaotic road situation in the state needed to be straightened out. In the early years of this century owners of horseless carriages were fair game for every city councilman, county judge and state legislator who needed someone to tax. Conflicting laws often made it necessary for motorists to stop at city limits or county lines and purchase special licenses in order to proceed. At ferry landings, gas tanks had to be emptied to prevent fires aboard the boat. Because the racket caused by cars often frightened farm animals, some farmers plowed deep ruts cross the road in front of their farms to discourage cars.

The first issue tackled by the feisty Good Roads Association was the problem of who was to plan, build and pay for highways. At the turn of the century most of this work was done by county commissioners who generally worked independently without an overall regional plan. Hence, often one county's fine roadway would abruptly revert to a cow path at the county line.

In 1909 the Association proposed that there be "centralized state control" of highway affairs overseen by a commission form of administration. Instantly county commissioners throughout the state were up in arms. Farmers, business owners and bankers declared that the association wanted to ruin the state. After two years of heated controversy, in 1911 the Association endorsed the idea in a five-to-one vote. This action made Washington the first state in the Union to adopt a centralized statewide authority to build highways. It was not until 1913 that the State Legislature agreed to fund the highway plan and $2 million, a princely sum in those days, was dedicated to building Washington's road system.

Aside from the "Old Guard," who remained devoted to the goal of good roads throughout their lives, one other name dominates the association's records in the first half of the century—Douglas A. Shelor. For years Shelor managed the Automobile Club of Washington. People still talk about Shelor throughout the state and many Seattle officials have memories of his work. Shelor's devotion was indefatigable. He attended every session of the State Legislature as an observer for both the Auto Club and WSGRA, and personally saw that important road legislation was not "side tracked" on its way through the legislative process.

The history of the Association is intermingled with the history of the state's two automobile clubs—the Auto Club of Washington (now AAA Washington), headquartered in Seattle, and the Inland Auto Association, headquartered in Spokane. Many officers and employees of the motor clubs have served the association. Most notable of these is Frank W. Guilbert, former manager of the Inland Auto Association, and his son David C. Guilbert. Both of these men served long terms as President of WSGRA and carved lasting niches for themselves in the annals of highway progress with long hours of effective lobbying in Olympia serving the interests of good roads. Another name high on the list of Association leaders is Clinton S. Reynolds of Tacoma. Reynolds was President in 1941 and a long term veteran of the legislative process.

The accomplishments resulting from the Association's dedicated lobbyists in Olympia are too many to list here. To a greater or lesser degree the Association has been involved in every gain that has been made in Washington's highway and street system. Two of the most important decisions affecting the ongoing maintenance of good roads are the anti-diversion amendment to the State Constitution which guarantees that money taken from motorists in the form of taxes will be spent exclusively for highway purposes. The Association was also instrumental in the appointment of the bi-partisan Highway Commission to administer the affairs of highways of this state. It is largely because of the non-political nature of the Highway Transportation Commission that Washington has enjoyed a continuity and smoothness in its highway program that is the envy of many other states.

Today WSGRTA continues its work of helping Washington have the best possible roads through the efforts of Good Roads members and member organizations. The way that the organization works has changed little over the years. Only the faces and issues are different. In keeping with Washington's growth and the widening scope of its transportation problems, more people and organizations are involved today than earlier.

The WSGRTA is a low-budget, non-profit delegate member group made up of member organizations including chambers of commerce, local improvement clubs, local road associations, auto clubs and professional groups interested in highways.

Since all highway, road and street projects must be legislated, it is inevitable that the Association's main efforts are channeled towards legislative influence. Since legislation follows the desire of public opinion in our democracy, the Association performs a dual role. It provides the opportunity to sound out and amass public thinking on highway policies and programs. This can be translated into legislative action. The WSGRTA rarely lends its name to projects of strictly local interest, but based on its policies as adopted by the convention is vociferous in support of area and statewide highway matters. The challenge is just as great today as it was back in 1899 to provide a state wide "sounding board" of public opinion on transportation matters and public leadership for sound management of this integral part of the state's economy.

◆

The "Old Guard"

Samuel Hill, *Seattle*	J. J. Donovan, *Bellingham*
John P. Hartman, *Seattle*	W. A. Bollinger, *Methow*
Judge C.H. Hanford, *Seattle*	A. L. Rogers, *Waterville*
R. H. Thomson, *Seattle*	W. W. Perrigo, *Redmond*
Claude Ramsey, *Seattle*	Eli Rocky, *South Bend*
Frank Terrace, *Orillia*	Lee Monohan, *Renton*
R. I. Cline, *Bellingham*	W. H. Parry, *Richmond Beach*

Washington State Water/Wastewater Association

This association was formed in 1961 in response to Washington State statute RCW, Titles 56 and 57. Locally elected water and sewer district commissioners formed the first non-profit corporation to improve the organization and operations of water/wastewater special purpose districts. The association membership and its governing board of elected directors established a tradition of supporting responsible local government. The initial bylaws stated the organizational purpose would be achieved through education, communication and the promotion of legislation to help water and wastewater districts provide the best possible service to rate payers. This mission has remained constant throughout the association's 32 year history.

Just as the legislature perceived the need for an association to represent the public served by special purpose water and sewer districts, legislative mandates have added emphasis to each aspect of the association's mission. During the 1960s locally elected district commissioners met regularly, offering one another professional support and developing ways to improve rate payer services.

The decade of the 1970s was one of growth for service areas under one operational management. The RCW titles were changed substantially in 1969 and 1971. Permissive language was added to enable mergers between water districts and sewer districts. Districts also could provide street lighting. Throughout the state, consolidation of districts was mutual and cooperative, and was based upon a shared commitment to provide better, less expensive service for the rate payer. Despite major changes in Titles 56 and 57, most legislative action taken during the early 1970s was reactive and the association did not initiate legislation.

However, with the changes in the enabling statutes, districts became larger and more numerous. Management issues became more complex. The association board recognized the need to become more proactive and to strengthen the organization's legislative and communication programs.

The decade of the 1980s was a period of rapid growth for the association. Associate memberships became an effective way for business and professionals working with water and sewer districts to support the industry trade association. This membership category grew from fewer than 20 to more than 90 in 1988. District memberships also continued to increase steadily. In 1986 the association reorganized as a newly named non-profit corporation to include water, sewer and combined water/wastewater special purpose districts in its responsibilities. With the advent of mandatory certification requirements the WSW/WA formally developed its educational mission. The traditional annual meeting became a three day annual conference. Professional growth workshops are also offered on a regular basis throughout the year.

Another characteristic of the 1980s is greater district involvement in legislative issues. The non-partisan nature of water/wastewater districts continues to contribute to bipartisan support of the membership's prioritized legislative agendas. The mission of the association is dynamic and seeks to anticipate membership needs, just as the members seek to respond to their rate payers. The WSW/WA is prepared for the "decade of water ahead," as one legislator has identified the 1990s, and looks forward to another century of clean water for the citizens of Washington. ◆

Washington State Public Works Trust Fund

The Washington State Public Works Trust Fund established by legislative action in 1985, provides low interest loans and technical assistance to eligible local governments in Washington State. The Trust Fund program is the result of a three year development process which began in 1983 with a public works inventory developed to assess the scale and character of critical public works needs in the state.

The trust fund is managed by a 13-member Public Works Board composed of representatives from local governments, the engineering, construction, labor, and financial communities. Staff support for loan, policy development and technical assistance functions is provided through the Public Works Unit of the Washington State Department of Community Development.

Projects including bridges, roads, domestic water, sanitary sewer and storm sewer systems are eligible for funding and financing may be provided to cities, counties and special purpose districts. Applicants must have a long-term plan for financing their public works needs. Loans are presently offered only for the purpose of repair, replacement, rehabilitation, reconstruction or improvement of existing eligible public works systems in order to meet current standards. Since 1985 interest rates on Trust Fund loans have varied between one percent and three percent with the term of loans limited to the useful life of the public works improvements financed.

At the direction of the Public Works Board, proposals for public works projects are solicited annually by the Public Works Unit of the Washington State Department of Community Development. Since substantially more Trust Fund dollars are requested than are available, local jurisdictions must compete for the available funds. The Public Works Board annually submits a prioritized list of those projects recommended to receive low interest financing to the state legislature. The legislature reviews the list and indicates its approval through the passage of an appropriation from the Public Works Assistance Account to cover the cost of the proposed loans.

While several key features make the Public Works Trust Fund Program unique, of special importance is the clear focus on local efforts to manage public works systems—where critical management, planning and financial decisions must occur on a regular basis. The Trust Fund's appeal is not that it represents a new source of funds to replace existing grant programs, but rather that it is a new way for local governments to plan public works improvements and schedule the costs. ◆

Public Works Board Charter Members 1985-1989	
Chair	
Robert C. Anderson, *Exec. Vice-Pres.*	Washington Bankers Assoc.
Paul Blanchard, *President*	East Wenatchee Water Board
Denis Coburn, *Manager*	Clark County PUD - Water
Joe Gavinski, *City Manager*	City of Moses Lake
Don Gonzales, *President*	Northwest Boring
John Horsley, *Commissioner*	Kitsap County
Don LaBelle, *Public Works Dir.*	King County
Doreen Marchione, *Mayor*	City of Redmond
Allan F. Osberg, *President*	Osberg Construction
Sydell Polin, *Manager*	Ronald Sewer District
Jim Salatino, *Council Member*	Pierce County
Mel Tanasse, *Mayor*	City of Moxee
William Wright, *Vice-President*	Century West Engineering

Watson Asphalt Paving Company, Inc.

Watson Asphalt Paving Company of Redmond, Washington, was founded in the early 1950s by Ross Watson. The company concentrated on small residential and commercial asphalt paving projects.

In 1964 Mr. Herb Schroeder and his two eldest sons, Bob and Cliff, purchased the company, which consisted of two single axle five yard dump trucks, a small roller, grader and a pickup truck. An important part of the business was Mr. Watson's reputation for quality asphalt work.

With new ownership the company steadily grew and expanded, undertaking larger paving projects. In 1967 the Schroeder's purchased their first asphalt production plant. This enabled the company to undertake the paving of city streets, county roads and state highways. In the early 1970s the two younger Schroeders, Peter and Steve, joined the firm on a full-time basis.

In the following years the Watson Asphalt Company added asphalt plants and related equipment, and expanded its operations to include general road construction. The company has completed numerous projects throughout the states of Washington and Oregon, including the asphalt paving of various portions of the Interstate Freeways.

The company under the management of the four Schroeder brothers, their father having retired in 1978, remains committed to the asphalt paving business and strives to continue performing quality work. ◆

Annually, Watson Asphalt paves 50 to 100 miles of roadway throughout the Puget Sound Basin. Paving includes streets, roads and highways new construction, overlay, and the newer plane-pave-recycle resurfacing of older roads. Photo by Bob Britain, DOT.

Richard E. (Dick) Wolff

Dick Wolff's professional career began in 1933 after receiving a Civil Engineering degree from the University of Wisconsin. His first work assignment, which continued until 1940, was with the USDA Soil Conservation Service designing erosion control features in rural Wisconsin.

At the conclusion of this work, Mr. Wolff accepted a job with the Army Corps of Engineers in Seattle as head of the Reports and Surveys Branch of the Alaska Railway project. Under his direction a rail route was surveyed throughout the British Columbia coast range from Prince George to Nome. He coordinated much of the supply work. With the decision made to build an Alaskan highway in lieu of the railroad, he finished service with the Corps on Amchitka Island in the Aleutians.

After World War II, Mr. Wolff established a consulting engineering practice specializing in water and sewer projects. Dick designed the elevated tank prominent on the east hill at Renton, and standpipes and covered reservoirs at Alderwood Manor, Mukilteo, Auburn and Issaquah. His last project was the reconstruction of the Kaanapali to Lahaina railroad on the island of Maui.

Mr. Wolff retired in 1971 and passed away March 26, 1976. He is survived by his wife Lois and a son and daughter. ◆

Woodworth & Company, Inc.

Originally located at 113-1/2 A Street, Tacoma, the company, in 1929, bought property on City Waterway— where its main office and plant were built in 1936. Woodworth and his son J. Alden became stockholders on January 28, 1936; a few months later, on May 7, the firm became Woodworth & Cornell. Harold Woodworth was named President of the firm in 1940, which became Woodworth & Company, Inc., the following year. J. Alden succeeded his father as President in 1952, and his son, John A. assumed the post in 1973. Jeff Woodworth, John's son, is currently vice president and manager of the estimating department.

A major project during World War II was paving shelter areas for U. S. Army aircraft. In 1942 the firm built wartime housing in Lincoln Heights.

Contracting to demolish the remains of the collapsed Tacoma Narrows Bridge in 1948, Woodworth also constructed the center and end piers and anchors, as well as asphalt paving the new Narrows span.

Crushed and screened rock are provided at both Woodworth's gravel pits and any variety of hot-mix asphalt is available from asphalt plants located at both sites.

The building construction division assists in engineering, designing and erecting structures of all types. The road construction division has brought Woodworth recognition as a leader in highway construction. The company was named APWA's Contractor of the Year in 1991 for projects under $2 million.

The firm, which has provided four generations of community leaders, now looks to the future. ◆

Whitman County

Through the years, the Whitman County Public Works Department has expanded services from primarily maintaining roads and bridges to meeting the demands of Administration, Solid Waste Management, Land-use Planning, and Building Code enforcement. In order to meet these demands the department has applied innovative solutions to the challenges faced by the county.

Design and Administration

In 1969 the County was noted as one of the first in the United States to receive federal and state grants to build a bridge with pre-stressed concrete. At 149.9 feet the bridge, in Elberton, Wa., was the longest single span pre-stressed concrete bridge of its time. The project totaled $51,900 and was coordinated by former County Commissioner Ed Curtis and John McInerny, County Engineer.

John McInerny continued as County Engineer until January 1974, when he retired from Whitman County after 16 years of service with the Department of Roads and Public Works. McInerny's retirement marked a new approach to project management and administration within the Public Works Department. The Engineer position was changed to Public Works Director. The new position was to have an emphasis on administration of the overall department.

Gene Sampley was the first person to hold the new administrative position. He was noted for attracting state and federal funding for replacement and repair of the county's 252 bridges and nearly 2,000 miles of roads.

In 1978 Marvin Carroll became Public Works Director. Carroll secured funds from the Washington State Rural Arterial Program and was also instrumental in attaining Whitman County's early participation in a maintenance management program. The program allowed more efficient scheduling of the road crews and also produced a more accurate measure of each crew's effectiveness.

During Carroll's tenure the construction of "state-of-the-art," pre-stressed concrete bridges continued. A 155 foot single span, prestressed concrete bridge was constructed in West Elberton and now stands as the longest bridge using this technology in Washington. The record holding bridge was dedicated to former commissioner Ed Curtis, in recognition of his promotion of what is now referred to as the "super construction bridge."

Carroll's exemplary career with Whitman County was brought to an untimely end in April of 1989 when he succumbed to a cancer related illness. Lon R. Pedersen was asked to take over the position.

Pedersen used the experience and knowledge gained from working with the previous Public Works leaders to successfully make the transition from a support to leadership role. Once the transition was complete, he began the complicated process of hiring the specialists needed to handle increasingly stringent regulations, while maintaining a cohesive department. In October of 1991 all of the various aspects of Public Works which had offices in various County buildings were consolidated in 9,400 square feet of newly remodeled office space on the second floor of the Whitman County Public Service Building.

Solid Waste Management

In the early 1970s, as a result of pressure brought by the national Environmental Movement, local jurisdictions were required to adhere to minimum functional standards for managing solid waste. In 1971 the Neil Klemgard Solid Waste Plan was adopted as one of the first solid waste plans in Washington to be accepted by the Department of Ecology (DOE). Based on the recommendations of the Klemgard Plan, the county utilized a matching grant from DOE for the purchase of land and construction of a new solid waste facility. The engineering staff designed the building, managed the construction, and in August 1975, the first "bale fill" solid waste facility in the Western United States was open for business.

The facility crushed the waste into bales and laid them like building blocks into the ground. The bales helped to stabilize the Palouse area's clay textured soil. The capacity of the landfill enabled the county to consolidate the waste previously sent to 15 town or numerous roadside dumps into one sanitary facility. The landfill was both financially and operationally efficient and was known as a model facility.

Currently the landfill is being scheduled for closure in mid-1993. The future will see an increased emphasis on recycling, with the landfill facility being used for that purpose.

Land Use Planning

In 1988 the County Commission hired a Director of Planning as a division of the Public Works Department through the Planning Enabling Act. The division administers the county's Comprehensive Plan and land use regulations. The Comprehensive Plan and the Zoning Ordinance, adopted in the late 1970s, has effectively preserved farmland and discouraged urban sprawl. Since many of the requirements of the 1990 and 1991 Growth Management Act were met by the existing Comprehensive Plan and Zoning Ordinance, Whitman County became a model for other Washington Counties working toward GMA compliance.

Building Code Enforcement

The Whitman County Building Department works closely with the Planning division to insure that development within the county not only meets the zoning ordinance, but also meets the state building code requirements. Currently, one full-time and one part-time employee are working to insure that development in the County meets the requirements of the Uniform Building, Mechanical, Fire and Plumbing Codes. In addition, the recently adopted Washington State Energy Code and Barrier Free access code are also enforced.

Although the role of Whitman County Public Works has expanded, the same innovative spirit which led to the completion of award winning projects continues today. ◆

Above top: The Whitman County Solid Waste Treatment Facility was opened in August 1975. It was the first "bale fill" solid waste unit built in the western United States. Above lower: Recycling became in integral part of the solid waste system in 1979 with the manual separation of material at the Whitman County site.

City of Yakima

CITY OF YAKIMA

Public works have always been important to Yakima. The city began as a public works project in 1885, shortly after the Northern Pacific Railroad announced its intention to buy land and expand into what is now Union Gap—then called Yakima. Property owners had met and raised prices to levels the railroad felt were unacceptable. The Northern Pacific Railroad decided that a new town was the answer. The railroad purchased land a few miles to the north and platted a town site, which it named North Yakima.

The railroad ensured the new town's growth by offering to pay relocation expenses for any Yakima business that moved to North Yakima. The offer was widely accepted and many buildings made the slow trip north on log rollers. One interesting episode of note was the moving of the Guilland House. Its tenants, not wanting to be inconvenienced, continued to occupy the hotel during the entire trip. Some years later, the original town of Yakima changed its name to Union Gap; North Yakima then became known as simply "Yakima."

The new town was patterned after Salt Lake City with wide, spacious streets and generous right-of-way. The town's first streets were paved with brick, which was used until the early 1950s, and open concrete gutters ran along the sidewalks in the downtown area.

Agriculture in the area had led to the establishment of irrigation ditches long before Yakima was created, and the new town used water from the ditches for both crop production and domestic consumption. In a short time, however, the population had increased to the point where it was no longer safe to use ditch water for domestic purposes. A separate domestic water system was built and operated by the Northwest Light and Power Company which was later part of the Pacific Power & Light Company (PP&L). Water diverted to the power plant was used to generate electricity, some of which, in turn pumped domestic water into the town.

In 1926 residents passed a bond issue that enabled Yakima to develop water supply and distribution facilities, and accompanying water rights. PP & L continued to provide electricity at this time. A water treatment plant was later built on the Naches River near Oak Flats. This plant served until the late 1960s when a new plant, capable of meeting Yakima's projected needs through the year 2000, was built at the site. Further development of irrigation systems has come through Local Improvement Districts.

Public health concerns led to two major projects in the 1930s, when the city built both a refuse incinerator and a waste water treatment plant. Rapid growth rendered the incinerator and a second waste burning facility inadequate. In the 1960s the city switched to a landfill operation for refuse disposal. Yakima currently utilizes the regional landfill system developed by Yakima County in the 1970s.

The wastewater treatment plant was modernized in 1955 to provide separate industrial and domestic treatment, and then again in 1965, when secondary treatment filters were added. During the 1970s Yakima accepted the responsibility for regional wastewater treatment. Extensive plant modification began in 1978, and resulted in a totally renovated primary treatment facility and a new secondary treatment plant.

Transportation has been vital to Yakima's development. In 1907 a trolley system began operation, and tracks were added on many of the principal arterials and along major roads to neighboring communities. The streetcars were run by a subsidiary of the Union Pacific Railroad and remained in operation until 1947, when they were replaced by buses. Since 1966 the city has operated the bus system, which today is known as Yakima Transit. Yakima celebrated America's Bicentennial in 1976 by re-inaugurating trolley service. The Yakima Interurban Lines Association, a volunteer non-profit organization, operates two trolleys purchased from the Collective Transports Society of Oporto, Portugal. They run from May through September on the Yakima-Selah line. In 1989 two original Yakima streetcars were returned to service in Yakima from a museum where they had lain dormant for many years.

The construction of railways and highways throughout this century has given Yakima world wide access to both markets and products, and the Yakima Air Terminal has added air transport. The Yakima Air Terminal began as a dirt strip in 1928 which was greatly expanded by the end of the 1930s. Subsequent expansions have given it the capacity to serve cities throughout the region and have led to further growth in the area.

One of Yakima's most pleasant features is its city park and recreation system. The city's first park was built in the mid-1890s, and several others followed in the subsequent years. The Metropolitan Park District was formed in 1942 to provide long range perspective to park development and operation. Under the district's guidance, park acreage and recreation programs grew rapidly. The Park District was dissolved in 1968 and the city has managed Yakima's parks and recreation programs since that time. In 1989 there were 365 acres of parks in the city's 13 square miles and recreation programs serve a wide variety of interests for people of the area.

The story of public works in Yakima is the story of Yakima itself. The public works of yesterday have made possible the Yakima of today; the public works of tomorrow will lead Yakima into the future. ◆

Tieton Drive during and after repaving.

A Thank You to Our Sponsors

The publication of **Building Washington** was made possible through the generous contributions of many individuals and corporate sponsors:

Jess Abed
Roy Allen
Alpha Engineers, Inc.
American Society of Civil Engineers
American Water Works Association
  Pacific Northwest Section
Arnold, Arnold & Associates
Asphalt Paving Association
City of Auburn
John Bannon
Barrett Consulting Group
Gail Bartley
R.W. Beck & Associates
Fred Becker
City of Bellevue
City of Bellingham
Port of Bellingham
Pam Bissonnette
Brad Blegen
Gary Bourne
Don Broadsword
Karen Brooks
Brown and Caldwell
William A. Bugge
Myron Calkins
Ed Cameron
Cedar River Water and Sewer District
CH2M-Hill
City Engineers Association of
  Washington
Clark County Public Works
Consulting Engineers Council of
  Washington
Converse Consultants, Northwest
County Road Administration Board
Dennis Covell
Clark Douglas
Terry Duncan
Duncan Industries
Economic and Engineering Services
City of Ellensburg
The Engineers Club
Entranco Engineers
Jerry Fay
Federal Way Water and Sewer District
Fujiki and Associates
Gardner Consultants
John Garner
GeoEngineers, Inc.
Golder Associates
Hugh G. Goldsmith & Associates
Hammond, Collier & Wade-Livingston
  Associates, Inc.
Frank Hansche
Hart & Crowser, Inc.
HDR Engineering, Inc.
Hong West & Associates, Inc.
Paul Hooper
Howard, Needles, Tammen &

Bergendoff, Inc.
Dave Hudson
Intermountain Corrosion Services, Inc.
Island County Road Department
N.G. Jacobson and Associates
Gordon Johnson
Seattle Daily Journal of Commerce
Alan King
Richard Kato
Kato & Warren,Inc.
The Kennedy Group Consultants, Inc
City of Kennewick
Peter Kiewit Sons, Inc.
King County
City of Kirkland
Kitsap County
Klickitat County Road Department
Jan Klippert
KPFF Consulting Engineers
KCM, Inc.
City of Lacey
Richard Lofgren
City of Longview
Macaulay & Associates, Ltd.
Mike Mariano
Gwenn Maxfield
Martha Meyer
Terence Monaghan
Roy Morse
Municipality of Metropolitan Seattle
James H. Montgomery Consulting
  Engineers
Mukilteo Water District
Pat Nevins
City of Oak Harbor
Craig Olson
Carol Osborne
John Ostrowski
Pacific Water Works Supply Company
Parsons, Brinkerhoff, Quade & Douglas,
  Inc.
City of Pasco
Roy Peterson
Pierce County
Jack Pittis
Port Angeles
Dale Poussier
Preston, Thorgrimson, Shidler, Gates,
  & Ellis
City of Pullman
City of Redmond
Lloud Reitz
City of Richland
June Rosentreter
Rosewater Engineering, Inc.
Sahlberg Equipment, Inc.
Sammamish Plateau Water and Sewer
  District
San Juan County

Roy Sawhill
Walter Saxton
Duane Scroggins
City of Seattle
Shannon & Wilson, Inc.
Skagit County Public Works
Snohomish County
Soil Sampling Service, Inc.
Southwest Suburban Sewer District
Larry Southwick
Lee Spahr
June Rosentreter Spence
City of Spokane
Spokane County
Streeter/Dermanis & Associates
Celia Strong
Sverdrup Corporation
City of Tacoma
Techstaff, Inc.
Al Theal
Mort Thomas
Fred Thompson
W.R. Tracy
The Transpo Group, Inc.
Thurston County
TP&E, Inc.
Transtate Paving Company
Utilities Underground Location Center
U.S. Army Corps of Engineers
United Technical Services Corporation
U.R.S. Consultants
William Valentine
Val Vue Sewer District
City of Vancouver
Walker and Associates
City of Walla Walla
Charles Hugh Warren
Richard Warren
Washington State Association of
  County Engineers and Public Works
  Directors
Washington State Association of Water/
  Wastewater Districts
Washington State Department of
  Transportation
Washington State Good Roads and
  Transportation Association
Washington State Public Works Trust
  Fund
Washington State Transportation
  Improvement Board
Larry Waters
Watson Asphalt Paving Company
Whitman County Public Works
Fritz Wolff
Suzi Wong-Swint
Woodworth & Company
City of Yakima